Biology

**Its Principles and
Implications**

A Series of Books
in Biology

Garrett Hardin

UNIVERSITY OF CALIFORNIA, SANTA BARBARA

Biology

Its Principles
and
Implications

SECOND EDITION

Drawings by Evan L. Gillespie
Portraits by Howard Warshaw

 W. H. Freeman and Company

SAN FRANCISCO AND LONDON

(C2)

Preface

With the beginning of the second half of the twentieth century two publications turned biology in new directions. The first of these has frequently been singled out for notice: Watson and Crick's two-page paper, "Molecular structure of nucleic acids," which appeared in 1953. In the complex endeavor we call science it is always somewhat unfair to identify any one contribution as crucial; but if a single publication may be said to have announced the coming of age of molecular biology, it is this one.

In 1962 a contribution of an utterly different sort was made by Rachel Carson, with the publication of her book, *Silent Spring*. Watson and Crick's work dealt with the ultramicroscopic organization of living matter; the scale of Miss Carson's was global. The assertions of the molecular biologists were made with great precision; those of *Silent Spring* were more general, more qualified, and more controversial. Miss Carson's work has been both praised and criticized; but whatever its merits, I think it is clear by now that this impassioned work has redirected the attention of biologists to their civic responsibilities. Every plucking at the web of life produces multiple effects, in which the distinction between "principal effect" and "side effects" is merely a reflection of our desires. It is the function of ecology to furnish an intellectual framework on which may be displayed the consequences of human interference in the world of nature. On rare occasions—much rarer than we would like to think—we can alter natural arrangements in a way that favors the ends of man. The deliberate human interventions that produce some obvious good effects (amply advertised by financially interested parties) invariably generate also numerous subtle bad effects (the knowledge of which is routinely—though perhaps subconsciously—suppressed). It was the merit of *Silent Spring* that it forced biologists to institute a policy of total ecological accounting.

These, then, are the two principal influences that have affected the revision of this text. The first influence is most evident in Part I, where I have tried to present a fair and understandable picture of the molecular approach to problems of metabolism and heredity. In writing this section I have had my eye less on the embryonic specialist in molecular biology than I have on the future well-educated citizen whose need to know the difference between U-235 and U-238 is almost equalled by the necessity that he understand the functioning of messenger RNA. The concepts of molecular biology, at first sight difficult, actually simplify some of the great problems of biology. The scientific progress predictable from the application of these concepts during the next few years makes it imperative that all students learn this new vocabulary.

That important progress will soon be made along ecological lines is, I think, equally predictable; but the problems are quite different. In ecology, we often only rediscover what has been known to a few men (but contradicted by many others!) for decades or even centuries. The century-old writings of Thoreau have more truth and wisdom in them than the most contemporary advertising copy (faint praise, in truth!). But why do we have to *re*discover this wisdom? Surely it is in part because the old wisdom consists of rather isolated insights that are not set into a unifying conceptual framework. Such a framework is desperately needed to increase the intellectual half-life of ecological truths and diminish the effectiveness of counterattacks by vested interests. The conceptual framework available in the published literature is far from complete; I have therefore presumed to add to it and reorganize it in Part II, using the language of cybernetics to make simple sense of the problems of ecology and evolution. I have even gone so far as to coin a few new terms that seemed to be needed. Excreting neologisms is something of a disease among ecologists; I only hope my performance is not as ridiculous as that of the classical ecologist who assembled the word "geotome" to stand for "spade." My readers must judge.

With the unifying concepts of ecology and molecular biology biologists are now equipped to resurvey all of traditional biology, making it simpler and more of a piece. I have done something of this sort in the last three Parts, though no one is more aware than I of the incompleteness of my work. It takes a long time and the cooperation of many people to redigest old truths with new intellectual enzymes. In times of intellectual revolution like ours the writing of an elementary textbook is an on-going process in which each edition is only a milestone, not a terminus. In the preparation of future editions I hope that I shall continue to be the grateful recipient of critical suggestions from my readers, as I have in the past.

It is one of the sad facts of life that the author of a textbook who thanks all the people who have helped him to develop his ideas gives adequate acknowledgment to none: there are so many names that the individual contributor is lost in the crowd. In order that at least some may be suitably thanked let me say that the present edition owes much to the criticisms of previous editions of my biology textbooks by J. Cushing, G. DuShane, R. Emerson, C. A. Lawson, R. Lewis, J. W. McMenamin, and R. D. Owen. Above all, I want to thank Michael Starks, who read literally every word of the 1961 edition, working all the problems and submitting the whole to a minute and regenerative criticism. In the preparation of the present edition, various chapters have benefited by the searching criticisms of Donald Kennedy, Eduardo Orias, William Purves, and James Walters. To these, and my many other unnamed but also valuable critics, I extend my grateful thanks.

GARRETT HARDIN

Santa Barbara
November, 1965

Contents

Part V Heredity

In Memory of My Parents

Life at the Cellular Level

In the study of the intermediate processes of metabolism we have to deal, not with complex substances which elude ordinary chemical methods but with simple substances undergoing comprehensible reactions.

FREDERIC GOWLAND HOPKINS

1

The Ways of Science

1. Control and Understanding

Man is a curious animal. To survive, he tries to master the environment in which he lives. The psychiatrist Jules Masserman has remarked that we try to control our universe in only three ways. "First we can try to control material things, and so reassert our technical mastery of the physical universe. Second, we can collaborate with our fellow human beings and so establish collaborative friendships. Or, third, we can resort to a transcendent system of beliefs, whether we call it science or philosophy or metaphysics or theology, and so find order and security in an otherwise chaotic universe." The second way we must all follow, even in the pursuit of science, for we are inescapably social animals; but there is nothing characteristically scientific about it so we need not discuss it further here. The first way corresponds roughly to the path we call technology, which gives us externally oriented control, control in the ordinary sense. This is different from the inner-directed control sought by the third path, which includes science in the strictest sense, sometimes called "pure" science; this kind of control is perhaps better called understanding. The impulse to understand runs deep in man's being. "Man, by his nature, wants to know," said Aristotle twenty-three hundred years ago. In spite of millions of apparently contrary instances of phlegmatic or fearful nonquestioning

adults, we still think Aristotle was right about man's fundamental nature. Man *does* want to understand. Man is a curious animal.

Control and understanding. In many occupations men can be quite successful if almost all their activity is directed toward control, with little thought of understanding. Not so in science, where the attempt to discover that which was not known before is seldom successful unless it is guided by a sincere desire to understand. The "practical" men whose strongest desire is for control need not fear that efforts directed at understanding will result in waste of time and money; the history of science shows clearly that out of deep understanding comes control of a magnitude unobtainable by those who seek it directly. This truism has not always been recognized by the men-of-the-world who control the purse-strings. Speaking of Einstein's theories and his fundamental equation $E = mc^2$, the influential London *Times* once condescendingly remarked: "It is agreed that the new conception will make little difference to the practical world." That was in 1919. Twenty-six years later, on the sixth of August, 1945, an atomic bomb was exploded above Hiroshima, putting an end to talk of the impracticality of pure science. As the mathematician Warren Weaver has remarked, we have learned that "an important characteristic of science is its incapacity to be impractical."

Our concern here is with the science we call

biology. Being human, we desire the control that knowledge of many technical details will give us; but we must also try to get an understanding of the theory underlying the facts. One of the best arguments for studying biology was given by Darwin's friend T. H. Huxley in this famous passage written a century ago:

Suppose it were perfectly certain that the life and fortune of every one of us would, one day or other, depend upon his winning or losing a game of chess. Don't you think that we should all consider it to be a primary duty to learn at least the names and the moves of the pieces; to have a notion of a gambit, and a keen eye for all the means of giving and getting out of check? Do you not think that we should look with a disapprobation amounting to scorn upon the father who allowed his son, or the state which allowed its members, to grow up without knowing a pawn from a knight?

Yet it is a very plain and elementary truth, that the life, the fortune, and the happiness of every one of us, and, more or less, of those who are connected with us, do depend upon our knowing something of the rules of a game infinitely more difficult and complicated than chess. It is a game which has been played for untold ages, every man and woman of us being one of the two players in a game of his or her own. The chessboard is the world, the pieces are the phenomena of the universe, the rules of the game are what we call the laws of Nature. The player on the other side is hidden from us. We know that his play is always fair, just, and patient. But also we know, to our cost, that he never overlooks a mistake, or makes the smallest allowance for ignorance. To the man who plays well, the highest stakes are paid, with that sort of overflowing generosity with which the strong shows delight in strength. And one who plays ill is checkmated—without haste, but without remorse.

2. What Is Biology?

Two hundred years ago a book with the title *Biology* could not have been written, for it was not until 1802 that the word (in its French form, *biologie*) was coined, by two men independently, Treviranus and Lamarck (of whom we will hear more subsequently). The new word

was derived from the Greek roots *bios,* meaning life, and *logos,* meaning word, thought, speech, or discourse—by extension, a body of knowledge or a science. The analysis of this word into its roots is here exhibited not to display the linguistic erudition of the present author—for he has none—but to help that rare and delightful person, the attentive student. The terms of our science are numbered in the thousands, which, taken separately, surely constitute a strain on anyone's memory. But in the making of the more important words, a few score of Latin and Greek words have been used over and over; *bios,* for example, appears also in the words *bio*chemistry, *bio*luminescence, anti*bio*tic, and sym*bio*sis, to mention only a few. It is, therefore, economical of effort to learn such roots (even though we know nothing more of Latin or Greek); from them, we can often deduce the meaning of new words. In this textbook, the majority of the scientific terms will be etymologically* analyzed, to make the student's path easier. When such an analysis is omitted, it is usually for a good reason. (For example, explaining how the microscopic green plant *Platydorina* got its name would take half a page, and would yield more amusement than light, for the man who christened it was simply befuddled. But most scientific names have good reasons.)

It may seem strange that the word "biology" is less than two centuries old—surely living things have been studied longer than that? Yes; but for the most part the earlier studies were of plants or of animals *as such*—rather than of the characteristics that are common to both groups of living things. It is only in comparatively recent times that men have spent much time studying what is common to both plants and animals—the laws of heredity and cell physiology, for instance. There are other aspects of biology which are, by their nature, peculiar to one group of organisms or the other; plant anatomy, for example, is so different from the anatomy of vertebrate animals that little would be gained by lumping the two studies together

---

* 1-1. "Etymology" is not to be confused with "entomology." What's the difference?

under the heading of, say, "the biology of structure." Plant anatomy is best considered as a branch of *plant biology* (botany), vertebrate anatomy as a branch of *animal biology* (zoology), while the study of heredity (genetics) is a part of *general biology*—the biology that is not restricted to one kingdom. All three kinds of biology are treated in this text.

3. What Is Science?

Since biology is the science of life, it might be supposed that we could get a better idea of its scope by defining "science" and "life." This is an interesting supposition. Let's see where it leads to, taking up the term "science" first. Consider the following definitions:

"Science is ordered knowledge of natural phenomena and of the relations between them." (William Cecil Dampier, 1867–1952, a historian of science.)

"Science is the search for the reasons of things." (Havelock Ellis, 1859–1939, a psychologist and physician, best known for his studies in the psychology of sex.)

"Science is, I believe, nothing but *trained and organized common sense,* differing from the latter only as a veteran may differ from a raw recruit: and its methods differ from those of common sense only so far as the guardsman's cut and thrust differ from the manner in which a savage wields his club." (T. H. Huxley, 1825–1895, an English biologist.)

"Science is knowledge, not of things, but of their relations." (Henri Poincaré, 1854–1912, a French mathematician.)

"Natural science is the attempt to understand nature by means of exact concepts." (Georg Friedrich Bernhard Riemann, 1826–1866, a German mathematician whose novel ideas helped to pave the way for Einstein.)

"Science is the process which makes knowledge." (Charles Singer, 1876–1960, a historian of medicine.)

"Science is an attempt to systematize our knowledge of the circumstances in which recognitions occur." (Alfred North Whitehead, 1861–1947, a logician and philosopher.)

No two of these definitions are alike, but comparison reveals that they can be separated into two groups—namely, those (see Dampier and Poincaré) that, in effect, define science as *organized knowledge,* and those (see Ellis, Riemann, Singer, and Whitehead) that define science as a *process* that leads to organized knowledge.* The first would make science a static thing; the second, a dynamic one. More important, the former implies that scientific activity is primarily *conservative,* that is, involved in the conservation of knowledge already obtained; whereas the latter depicts science as a *progressive,* or dynamic, activity. Which view is correct?

Both are correct. Science has both conservative and progressive aspects. In some fields of science, the former predominate; in others the latter. Within the broad field of biology, consider first the subject of gross human anatomy, the science that deals with such human structures as are visible to the naked eye. Because it is extremely unlikely that there are still unknown muscles and bones to be discovered in the human body, anatomists do not search for them. Anatomy can therefore be satisfactorily described as a static science, the practitioners of which are concerned primarily with the conservation and transmission of knowledge.

In contrast, consider the subject of biochemistry, the chemistry of living activities. In this field, what remains to be discovered exceeds by many times that which has thus far been learned. It is probably fair to say that biochemists, as a group, are more involved in investigative activities than they are in conservative ones. A definition of science framed by a biochemist would probably emphasize the dynamic aspects.

Anatomy and biochemistry were selected merely to illustrate the extremes in the nature of science; other sciences are more of a mixture. Differences among the sciences are determined by age and maturity. Human anatomy had its

---

* 1-2. How would you classify Huxley's definition?

real beginning in the work of Vesalius, in Italy, in the sixteenth century; after four centuries of rapid development, it is a mature, well-rounded body of knowledge with little more to be discovered. Biochemistry, however, began in earnest only a century ago and is still in its vigorously growing childhood. It will, no doubt, mature even as anatomy has.

In the preceding discussion the words "conservative" and "progressive" have been used—words that may (because of political associations) be charged with emotion for many readers. It must be emphasized that, as here used, there is no implication of approval or disapproval of either. Neither aspect should be said to be more important than the other. Most of us, imbued with the feeling that this is not the best of all possible worlds and that improvement is desirable, can easily see the desirability of seeking more knowledge. Those who feel that the conservative aspects of science need justification should ask themselves this question: What would happen to the practice of medicine during one generation if that old, conservative science of anatomy were omitted from the training of medical men? The answer should be obvious. Moreover, even in the youngest, most dynamic science, continued progress is made possible only by the conservation of knowledge and the transmission of it to each new generation of investigators. Lack of such conservative activity would produce either anarchy or endless, nonprogressive repetition of elementary discoveries.

Methods of conserving science need no explicit discussion—they are much the same as the methods of conserving any other body of knowledge. It is the methods by which new scientific facts are discovered that interest us most. We suspect that the methodology of science is somehow connected with the fact that science is progressive and accumulative. Our science is superior to that of the ancient Athenians, or third-century Christians, and of the Zuni Indians of our own time; but can the same be said for our ethics and morality, our art works, and our way of life? If so, it is not obvious. Oscillations may be more common than progress in many nonscientific fields. The human importance of ethics and the arts makes us yearn to make them as undeniably progressive as the sciences. Can the scientific method be extended to them; and, if so, would it produce the result we desire?

Opinions differ on this matter. We must recognize at the outset that what we might call the "substrate" of scientific activity differs from that of art and ethics. Scientists deal with material, *sensible things*—things that one can touch, feel, smell or apprehend by some other *sense*. This does not preclude the postulation of an entity of which one can have no *direct* sensations—the electron, for instance. But the concept of the electron does include the idea that it will, under certain circumstances, lead to certain pointer-readings on scientific instruments, which can be sensed. By contrast, consider the concept of a soul; in the very act of defining it, it is made clear that it cannot be apprehended by the senses. By science, as ordinarily defined, we cannot study such an entity; nor, indeed, assert that it does not exist. Beauty and justice similarly are concepts not amenable to scientific study.

Science deals only with phenomena that, directly or indirectly, can be sensed. In determining the truth about such phenomena, the senses are the ultimate authority. No scientific truth is accepted as such merely because some human authority, however great, has pronounced it. For a fact to be true, it must be verifiable by all who use their senses to check it—this is the *attitude* of all scientists. This sounds eminently reasonable, but it is not always easy to adhere to this attitude. Not easy, but essential. We can perhaps best appreciate some of the difficulties of the practice of science by considering at length a particular recorded instance.

Our example comes from the laboratory of George W. Corner, an American embryologist. The published account* includes some rather fancy terms—"progestational proliferation," "estrogen," and the like—the meaning of which

---

* *The Hormones in Human Reproduction*. Princeton, N.J.: Princeton University Press (1947), pp. 118–119. By permission of the author and publisher.

we do not need to know at this time. Our present concern is only with the human investigator and his tribulations.

Willard Allen and I had a queer experience with our first extracts, from which we learned something important, so that the story is not only amusing but useful. The beginning of this tale is that when we started we followed . . . a hint from the work of Edmund Herrmann, who had obviously produced progestational proliferation in a few of his experiments without knowing it. He had used very young rabbits, roughly 8 weeks old. They react more readily than adults to the estrogen which was the chief ingredient of his extracts. Since we wanted to follow his methods closely at first, we used infant rabbits too, and with them our first successes were obtained. In the spring of 1929 we were all ready to report the first steps in print. The paper was being written, when it occurred to me that our directions for extracting the hormone ought to be tried out by a none-too-good chemist, just to make sure they were foolproof. We did not want others to think our work could not be repeated, just because our directions were not clear. It was agreed that I was a bad enough chemist for the test: if I could make the extract all by myself, then anybody could. So Allen went on his vacation and I went back to our extractors and vacuum stills. In a week I had a batch ready; to my horror it was ineffectual. I made another batch; it, too, was worthless. I suppressed the paper and telegraphed for Allen. We decided that I needed a vacation and that we would look for the trouble in the fall. In September I made another batch with Allen watching every step, but not touching the apparatus. It was no good. What could be wrong? Since my laboratory was sunnier than his, perhaps my hormone was being spoiled by sunlight. I had a room blacked out and made a batch in the dark. That failed. Then we remembered that Allen, being a better chemist than I, usually got his extracts freer of superfluous grease and therefore had to mix them with corn oil (Mazola) so that he could inject them. Mine were greasy enough to inject without added oil. Perhaps the corn oil protected his hormones somehow while mine spoiled. We checked that idea—another two weeks gone—and that was not the answer. Then in desperation we made a batch together, side by side and almost hand in hand, each watching the other. We divided it into two lots and

tested it separately—Allen's worked; mine did not! Eureka, my trouble was in the testing, not in the cookery.

The explanation will seem so silly that I almost hesitate to admit what it was. The fact is that rabbits do not respond well to progesterone until they are about 8 weeks old and weigh about 800 grams. We did not know this, and our rabbits ranged from 600 to 1,200 grams. When we went to the cages to inject them, Willard Allen's idea of what constitutes a nice rabbit led him to choose the larger ones, while I must have had a subconscious preference for the infants. My extracts had been as good as his all the while, but my rabbits were insensitive. It is staggering to think how often the success or failure of research may hang upon such an unimaginable contingency.

This passage is rich in implications. Let us begin by noting the origin of the work—in "a hint" from the work of another man who had "obviously produced" a certain phenomenon "without knowing it." This is one of several ways in which an investigation may begin—in the thoughtful study of the published work of others. There is a continuity in scientific work; science is like a relay race. Even the work of genius has its origins in the discoveries of others. Isaac Newton, acknowledging particularly his indebtedness to Robert Hooke, once remarked: "If I have seen further it is by standing on the shoulders of giants." It is because all scientists are keenly aware of this truth that they are somewhat impatient of the popular interest in giving credit to the man who happens to stand on the top of the pile. The reality of the situation also helps explain how it is that a genuine scientist can find satisfaction in doing work for which he may never receive public acclaim. There is a quiet satisfaction in knowing that one has furnished solid shoulders for others to stand upon.

Movies and novels all too often picture the scientist as a lone wolf—a view that is far from the truth. Science is a social activity; not social in the sense that it is carried on by mobs, but social in that the individual scientist, however much he may be alone in the laboratory, is always acutely aware of the subtle presence of his peers who await what he has to say with critically keen interest. Whatever science is, it is a public thing. A fact is not a fact until it has been published; it is not accepted into the general body of scientific knowledge until others have repeated the essential experiments and observations. A fact must satisfy the **criterion of repeatability.** Notice how this criterion influenced Corner's actions. Notice the crisis that arose when he was unable to repeat the work of his colleague Allen. What had happened? Why the difference? Who was wrong?

The character of a discipline is most evident in the way it deals with conflict. In this regard, science shows a maturity that is well worth emulation in other fields of human action. Faced with a difference, a scientist does not declare war, issue a challenge for a duel, indulge in polemics, ignore his opponent, or yield to authority. Rather, he takes the hardest road of all, but the only road that in the long run can lead to satisfaction. He seeks the truth.

This is easy to say, but hard to do. In the writing of a scientific report (called a "paper"), the experimenter tries to record *all the significant detail,* so that others may repeat his work—but the joker lies hidden in the word *significant.* One cannot possibly report *all* that one does in performing even the simplest act*—so, in reporting, one necessarily selects (however unconsciously) only those details that one is aware of and believes may be significant. G. W. Corner, seeking new significant differences, thought first of his possible personal incompetence ("with Allen watching every step"), then of sunlight, and then of contaminating oils. Then he thought of what we call the "personal equation" in scientific research: ". . . we made a batch together, side by side and almost hand in hand," he says, hoping that if there should be some subtle, unrecognized difference in the way the two of them manipulated the apparatus, it would in this way be discovered. Thus Allen

and Corner made a single batch which they then each *tested* separately, thus discovering that the significant differences lay in the testing, not the making.

If, in re-creating this experience in your own mind, you do not feel the nervous tension of it, you have missed half of the meaning of the life of science. Corner was confronted with a baffling puzzle. It would have been so comforting to have resorted to the refuge of authority ("Herrmann says so"), or to hide behind an appearance of modesty ("I'm just a poor chemist"). Obedience and humility may be virtues in other situations, but in the ordeal of the scientist they may be only defense mechanisms, in the bad sense. Only an undiluted love of the truth above all else is praiseworthy. Love of the truth is more than a mere intellectual quality; it is something else, something we try vaguely to describe by the word "character." How important character is in scientific work has been attested to by the Nobel prizewinner J. J. Thomson, who remarked: "In the course of experience of many generations of students, I have known far more to fail from lack of grit and perseverance than from the want of what is commonly called cleverness." Thomson should know: six other Nobel laureates in physics came out of his laboratory, not to mention a legion of other very competent scientists. The fact that towering intelligence is not absolutely essential for good scientific work strengthens the will of those of us—necessarily in the majority—whose intellectual abilities are little better than ordinary. The endeavor of science has rewards for earnest men of many grades of ability. This is part of the strength of science.

There is yet one more moral to be extracted from Corner's account before we go on to other matters. We have already pointed out that the experimenter might have adopted an "either-or" attitude, saying "Either I am right or he is right"; and one position might have been supported by a brilliant rhetorical attack, the other by a display of humility worthy of Uriah Heep. The one would have been as wrong as the other. By rejecting the either-or approach, by searching out the truth instead, Corner discovered a

---

* 1-3. If you don't believe this, write down *now* what you believe to be *all* your actions in performing a habitual act—for instance, putting on your shoes in the morning. Then check your description at the next opportunity. Better still, have an impartial observer check your actions against your description.

completely unforeseen new fact: that sensitivity to the hormone develops only at a certain age. An "emergent" discovery of this sort is a common reward for those who love the truth above both arrogance and humility. When we contrast science with those fields of endeavor in which there seems to be little progress, we notice that in the latter the men involved often love intellectual "security" and ultimatums more than truth.*

4. What Is Life?

Biology, we agree, is the science of life—but what is "life"? M. F. X. Bichat, an eighteenth-century anatomist, said that "Life is that which resists death." Does this definition satisfy us? Hardly, because we recognize it as a disguised **tautology.** A tautology is a circular definition: "A is A." Of course, seldom does anyone state a definition that is openly, shamelessly tautological; the circularity is usually only implicit. "A is B," one may say, implying that B is A also. Bichat defined life by introducing the term "death." And what is death? That which has not life, one suspects.

Progress in any intellectual inquiry depends on one's ability to ask the right question. Experience has shown that "What is life?" is not the right question—it is too difficult to answer at the present time. Asking it often provokes an answering storm of plausible verbiage, high in abstraction and low in meaning. It is better if we ask, "What do we mean when we say something is living?" This is a question man has asked for tens of thousands of years: not explicitly, perhaps, but certainly implicitly—he has had to in order to survive. It was literally a matter of vital importance for him to be able to tell whether the object before him was alive or not—whether it was a possible enemy, a possible meal, or merely part of the nonliving landscape.† How did primitive man distinguish the living from the nonliving? And how do we do so now?

Undoubtedly the most frequently used indicator of life is **movement.** Not everything that moves is alive, but if it moves you had better first act as if it is alive, saving your scholarly analysis for later. Our nervous systems have this action-assumption built into them. "Life," said the novelist Samuel Butler, "is the art of drawing sufficient conclusions from insufficient premises." We are descended from a long line of animals who inferred life from movement, and survived to think about the matter further. It is the moving object that catches the eye and focuses the attention of the whole body upon it. Motion that is erratic or "spontaneous" (that is, unpredictable) holds our attention longer than uniform or cyclical motion. It is noteworthy that prehistoric man painted accurate representations of animals on the ceiling of the cave of Altamira thousands of years before plants were first depicted.

Next to motion, **uniformity of size and shape** is undoubtedly the most primitive criterion of living things. Stones in the road are very variable in size and shape: field mice are much less so. In seizing upon uniformity as an indication of life it is as though the observer unconsciously constructed some sort of probability argument that connected improbably uniform objects with life. The uniformity of manufactured objects is no contrary example, of course, for these have been made by living organisms. When we observe very uniform objects that have been formed by exclusively nonbiological means we are genuinely surprised.

Remarkably, living objects are capable of changing their size without changing their shape significantly: this they do by **growth.** Among higher animals, growth involves complex processes of *ingestion* (taking in) of food, *digestion* of it (breaking it up chemically into smaller particles), and *assimilation* of the small particles—that is, turning them into large particles again, particles that are now chemically different from the food particles. There is only a loose relationship between the kind of raw material ingested and the resulting product. It does not take

---

* 1-4. For example?

† 1-5. If we grant that there can be such things as implicit questions, was man the first animal to ask, "Is it alive?"

a very good chemist to tell a dog biscuit from a dog. The nature of the final product is significantly determined by the ingesting organism. A dachshund and a St. Bernard puppy may always be fed from the same box of dogfood, but they do not, as a result, come to resemble each other. Each grows true to its (not the food's) type.

Responsiveness is also a notable characteristic of living things. Speak to a dog, and his ears erect as he turns toward you. Put a plant near a window, and the plant, as it grows, bends toward the source of light. In both situations, the first action is called a **stimulus** (Latin, meaning goad; pl. **stimuli**), and the resultant reaction of the organism is called a **response.** The most obvious stimuli come from the outside, but internal stimuli are also known; for instance, sensations in a man's midregion may impel him to hasten to his doctor's office. In general, *the stimulus furnishes only a small fraction of the energy involved in bringing about the response.* For example, the scarcely audible ticking coming from a package may stimulate an apprehensive postal clerk to turn and run at championship speed. Clearly, the ticking sound does not furnish enough energy for his sprint. Chemical reactions in the man's body furnish this energy: the tiny sounds act only as a stimulus in releasing the energetic response.

No characteristic sets living things more apart from nonliving than the power of **reproduction.** But although only living things reproduce, an object need not necessarily possess the ability to reproduce to be called living. Most ants, for instance, are completely sterile, but we nevertheless call them alive.

Connected with the phenomena of reproduction is another one which the geneticist H. J. Muller has put forward as a fundamental characteristic of life—**evolvability.** Mice reproduce mice and rats reproduce rats—but only over a short period, as geologists reckon time. In the long run, over millions of years, species do not remain constant but evolve into other species. Even in a short period of time a species may change slightly but significantly in response to the environment, as when DDT-susceptible mosquitoes evolve into DDT-resistant mosquitoes after a few years of exposure to the insecticide. It is hard to imagine how life could long persist without the ability to evolve to meet changing conditions.

Organisms require energy for their activities, not only for movement and response, but also for growth and reproduction. Where does this energy come from? From food—that is, from chemical compounds that are rich in energy. Some organisms (green plants) can make their own food, using light as an energy source; others (animals) cannot. Everything that the organism does, it does by means of scores of biochemical reactions, that is, chemical reactions taking place inside the organism. The entire complex of these reactions we call by the collective name **metabolism.**

5. Mechanism versus Vitalism

It is the belief of most professional biologists that *every activity of a living organism is the result of understandable physical and chemical processes.* This statement gives in a nutshell the attitude of the **mechanists**—the people who believe that all living phenomena have a mechanistic explanation. Since the adjective "every" in the italicized statement carries us beyond the limits of present verifiability it is clear that there is room for a contrary view. Some people think that there are aspects of the activities of living organisms which can never be explained in terms of physics and chemistry, and that to explain these aspects we must invoke a mysterious force which has been called an *entelechy* or an *élan vital.* It is such a "vital force" that permits a living organism to do those marvelous things that living organisms can do and which no physical-chemical machine of man's devising can come near doing. Those who maintain this position are called **vitalists.** Who's right—mechanist or vitalist?

In the strictest sense, we cannot say. The vitalist may always find fault with the mechanistic position until the last link in the mechanist's proof is forged. The vitalist may even maintain that his is a more humble position; he does not assert that which he cannot prove. Opposed to this argument the mechanist has two points to make. *First,* to explain living phenomena by terms like entelechy or *élan vital* is not to explain them at all, but is merely to give ignorance a name. As Julian Huxley has pointed out, saying that an amoeba is moved by its *élan vital* is about like saying a locomotive is moved by its *élan locomotif.* We would not permit an engineer to get away with the latter explanation—why should we permit a biologist to get away with the former? *Second,* the mechanist's position should not be regarded as a law or a theory, but as a mode of procedure. It is an admirable **working hypothesis** to assume that living phenomena are at bottom physical and chemical phenomena, for such a hypothesis is *fruitful.* It leads us to perform experiments whose results provide a greater understanding of life (even when these results contradict our expectations). History shows us that the vitalist position is a sterile one: men who have adopted it have usually ceased to discover new facts. The mechanist position, whether it is ultimately proved right or wrong, has been and will continue to be productive of new discoveries. Indeed, if vitalism is ultimately proved to be true, it is the mechanist who will prove it so.

Movement, uniformity, growth, responsiveness, reproduction, metabolism and evolvability —all these are characteristics of living organisms. Do they suffice to construct a definition by which we can distinguish a living thing from a nonliving one? Probably not. Some of these characteristics are admirably imitated by nonliving systems—responsiveness, for example, which man has built into hundreds of such self-adjusting systems as thermostatically controlled rooms and electric-eye door openers. On the other hand, metabolism, which is most characteristic of living systems, cannot yet be precisely defined, and so any attempt to define life in terms of metabolism borders on the tautological.

No unexceptionable definition of life can yet be given. This might seem like a serious defect of biology to those who think that we must define our terms before we can go forward; yet biologists have not found it so. True, it is hard to decide whether or nor to say that a virus is alive, but most of the time biologists have no difficulty in agreeing on which objects are living, and hence proper objects for their study. "It is harder to discover the elements than to develop the science," said Whitehead; and biology is no exception. The "elementary" problem of the nature of life itself will undoubtedly be among the last to be solved, but in the meantime, research will go on, using concepts that are only partly clear. As more facts are learned, the elementary concepts will be sharpened and thus, by successive approximations, we will (we believe) come closer to the truth. To do so will undoubtedly require a great deal more work, but this is no cause for complaint. We remember what Sigmund Freud replied when asked what he considered the ultimate aims of a normal life: *"Arbeiten und lieben."* Science is one means of fulfilling half the prescription.

Suggestions to the Student

You will have noticed that the flow of exposition in the text is interrupted from time to time by an asterisk (*) leading to a question or challenge in the footnotes. This is an unconventional way to write a book and it may have disturbed you. If so, splendid! The intercalation was intended to disturb you. *Science is not a spectator sport;* it can be understood only by those who make an effort. In reading any scientific work, your mind should be constantly buzzing around the subject, so to speak. The interruptions of the text by challenging footnotes are designed to help you develop the habit of reading science as science should be read— slowly, meditatively, critically.

Additional questions will be found at the end of each chapter. Some of these are straightforward factual questions requiring simple answers. Others involve disputed points and require an intelligent discussion. Still others require you to integrate knowledge from more than one chapter in the text; or, indeed, from sources outside the text that should be known to "the average student." Only if you can give good answers to the majority of these questions should you assume that you have understood the chapter.

A word about the Readings. These have been selected not as the most authoritative or exhaustive of the subject, but as the most likely to interest you at your present stage of intellectual development. Some of them are spirited enough to make good reading in vacation time. (Regard this as a suggestion.)

One other point: If you will read question 1-24 below, you will see that it suggests that you write extensively in the blank spaces of this book. Such a suggestion may surprise you. You may have been "conditioned" against "defacing" books. But this is *your* book and you should use it in whatever way will best further your learning and remembering. Perhaps it will

help you to know how Charles Darwin treated his books. As his son Francis wrote:

For books he had no respect, but merely considered them as tools to be worked with. . . . He would cut a heavy book in half, to make it more convenient to hold. . . . Pamphlets were often treated even more severely than books, for he would tear out, for the sake of saving room, all the passages except the one that interested him. The consequence of all this was, that his library was not ornamental, but was striking from being so evidently a working collection of books.

Perhaps you don't care to go as far as tearing up this textbook for convenience in handling, but you should never hesitate to write critical comments in the margins, add corrections derived from lectures or readings, or to do anything else that will make this text more useful to you. In the act of writing in it, you will learn; and that is what is important.

Questions and Problems

[A double dagger (‡) before the number means that the problem is answered in the section *Answers to Problems* which appears near the end of the book.]

1-6. Make a list of the **boldface** terms in Chapter 1. Book closed, try to write out a definition or description of each. Compare your work with the text or the Glossary at the back of the book.

‡1-7. Dr. Masserman, in the quotation given in §1 uses the word "reassert." Why did he not merely say "assert"? What general idea from psychoanalytic literature is involved in this choice?

1-8. One biologist has defined life as the "sum total of all phenomena common to all living things." Critically evaluate this definition.

1-9. In tabular form, list the merits and defects of the various characteristics of life given in the text, considered individually.

‡1-10. Of all the characteristics of life, which one is most important to the technique of a hunter stalking game?

1-11. What characteristic of life, and of the reactions of living organisms, is involved in the efficacy of flashing signs?

1-12. From a biological point of view, discuss the morality of permitting flashing advertising signs along the sides of a busy highway.

1-13. Suppose that someone insisted that the flame of a candle is alive. Using the characteristics of life given, try to present a convincing argument that it is not.

‡1-14. Peanut-fed hogs yield a bacon that not only tastes of peanuts but is unusually limp. In what respects is this somewhat surprising?

1-15. Suppose you read in a book that is universally regarded as the greatest authority on insects that all houseflies have four pairs of legs, and suppose you could never find more than three pairs of legs on a housefly. Would you deny the authority of the book or of your senses?

1-16. René Descartes (1596–1650), in introducing his ideas of physiology, wrote: "I shall try to explain our whole bodily machinery in such a way, that it will be no more necessary for us to suppose that the soul produces such movements as are not voluntary, than it is to think that there is in a clock a soul which causes it to show the hours." Are these the words of a mechanist or a vitalist?

‡1-17. A perfect crime may be defined as a crime that is so well executed that not even the occurrence of a crime is suspected. In this sense, how many "perfect murders" are committed annually in the United States? How could you determine the answer to this question?

1-18. How would you define a miracle? As defined, can the reality of a miracle be proved or disproved scientifically?

1-19. In a semiquantitative way, contrast the relationship of *ability* to *rewards received* in (a) the sciences, and (b) the arts. Of what importance is the difference (1) to the individual, and (2) to society?

1-20. What are polemics? What role should they play in scientific controversy?

‡1-21. At one time, the Académie des Sciences of Paris acted as conservators of *plis cachetes* —sealed letters in which a member could announce a new discovery, with a certified date on the envelope, the envelope to be opened only when and if the member desired. This practice is generally viewed askance by modern scientists. Why?

1-22. David Riesman, in *The Lonely Crowd,* divides men into three categories: tradition-directed ("What would my ancestors have done?"), inner-directed ("What does my conscience tell me to do?"), and other-directed ("What are the other fellows doing?"). Recognizing that these are only broad generalizations, into which category would you say scientists fit best?

‡1-23. In the last paragraph of the text of this chapter the word "elementary" was put in quotation marks. Why?

1-24. Give a definition of science, making it as complete and meaningful as you can at the present time. Write it inside the back cover of this book, *initial it, and date it.* At the end of the course, review your definition to see in what respects you would then want to amend it.

1-25. What is the English meaning of Freud's advice given at the end of the chapter? (If you don't know German, get the help of a colleague who does. Science is a social activity.)

Readings

The spirit of science is admirably conveyed by these brief books: *The Excitement of Science* by John Rader Platt, *The Common Sense of Science* by Jacob Bronowski, and *Science, Faith and Society* by Michael Polanyi. Darwin's *Autobiography* gives a wonderful picture of the mind and character of a great investigator. Excellent case studies in scientific method are to be found in Cohen's *Science, Servant of Man.* Perhaps even more enlightening are the case studies of pseudoscience to be found in Martin Gardner's *Fads and Fallacies in the Name of Science.*

The physicist E. Schrödinger has written a stimulating little book, *What Is Life?* It is difficult in places, but it can be read with profit even if it is not all perfectly understood.

The complete bibliographic citation for these and all other Readings will be found in the Bibliography, near the end of this volume.

Scientific American Offprints | The *Scientific American* Offprints listed below and after the other Readings in this book are available from your bookstore or from W. H. Freeman and Company, 660 Market Street, San Francisco 4, California, and Warner House, 48 Upper Thames Street, London, E. C. 4. Please order by the number preceding the author's name.

437. Lewis M. Terman: *Are Scientists Different?*

450. Solomon E. Asch: *Opinions and Social Pressure*

453. Bernard & Judith Mausner: *A Study of the Anti-Scientific Attitude*

2

Cells and
Cell Division

6. The Cell: A Conceptual Unit of Biology

One aim of science is to paint a complete picture of the world as revealed to us by our senses. The history of the various sciences shows us that before we can do this we must, in our minds, take the world apart, to see what the pieces are. That is to say, we must first resort to **analysis** (Gr. *lysis* = a loosening + *ana* = up: a loosening up of a complex). Eventually we hope to reach the stage of **synthesis** (Gr. *syn* = with, together + *tithenai* = to place: putting the parts together to make a whole again). But synthesis has to come later; analysis is first.

In the process of analysis, scientists discover or invent certain conceptual units out of which the whole seems to be constructed. In physics the units are atoms and their various constituents—electrons, protons, and so on. In biology we have the **cell,** a microscopic, or almost microscopic, unit of which all common living organisms are composed. The human body is composed of about one hundred million million,* that is, about 10^{14}, cells.

That a large living body is really made up of smaller living units is not always readily apparent. In general, it is harder to verify the cellular construction of animals than it is that of plants; for this reason, much of the early

---

* 2-1. How do you suppose this number was determined? How accurate do you suppose it is?

progress toward the cell theory was made by botanists, their generalizations being later verified by zoologists. Each cell of a plant is usually surrounded by a relatively thick wall of dead material (called a **cell wall**), which makes the limits of the cells easy to see. Animal cells do not have cell walls.

There are thousands of different kinds of cells. A few of these are shown in Figure 2-1. Facing such variety, how then can we speak of "the" cell—what do cells have in common? The minimum elements of a cell are a delicate **cell membrane,** which forms the outer boundary of the cell within which there is a clear, viscid material called the **cytoplasm;** floating in the cytoplasm are a number of bodies, among the most important of which is the **nucleus.** These are almost invariably elements of cells; if one of them is lacking we use the word "cell" with reluctance. For example, the red blood "cell" (Fig. 2-1) of most mammals lacks a nucleus; for this reason, it is often called a red blood *corpuscle* instead.*

---

* A red blood corpuscle is the last developmental stage of a nucleated cell which becomes a corpuscle by the degeneration of its nucleus. In amphibians and birds, the developmental process does not go so far, and the mature cells have nuclei; in most mammals they do not, and are called "cells" in quotation marks. But *camel* red blood cells do have nuclei. . . . That's the way with the living world—its variety often plays havoc with the biologist's simplest generalizations. Nevertheless, generalizations are useful, as hooks to hang the exceptions on, if nothing else.

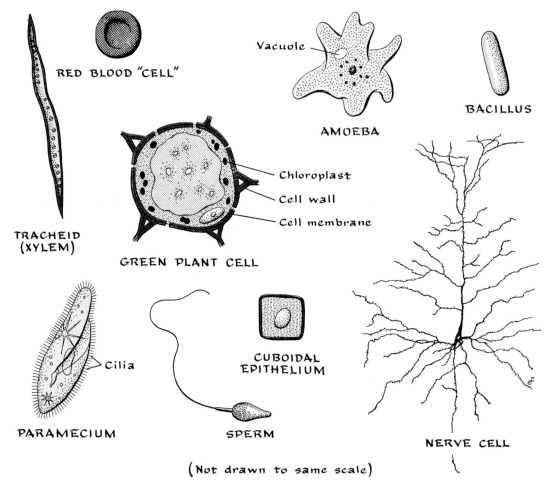

RED BLOOD "CELL"

Vacuole

AMOEBA

BACILLUS

Chloroplast

Cell wall

Cell membrane

TRACHEID
(XYLEM)

GREEN PLANT CELL

Cilia

CUBOIDAL
EPITHELIUM

PARAMECIUM

SPERM

NERVE CELL

(Not drawn to same scale)

Fig. 2-1. *A small sample of the great variety of plant and animal cells.*

7. Who Founded the Cell Theory?

Biology textbooks traditionally state that "the cell theory was founded in 1839 by Schleiden and Schwann." This is one of those half-truths that survive chiefly because of the school examination-system, for which the statement's definiteness and clarity are so well suited. But its virtues are also its defects: it does not give a proper picture of the way in which great scientific generalizations usually come to birth. It will be worthwhile to examine the origins of the cell theory before discussing its present meaning.

The story begins with Robert Hooke (1635–1703), a talented English scientist and architect who was employed by the Royal Society (the oldest scientific society still existing) to prepare three or four "considerable experiments" for demonstration to the members each week. This was no inconsiderable burden (which he bore for forty years) and it is understandable that Hooke laid hands on every scientific instrument known in his day to help him in his demonstrations. The compound microscope had been invented about the year 1600, but had been little used. Hooke found that he could entertain the Society members week after week with its revelations, and in 1665 he published many of these in a book entitled *Micrographia*. In it he tells how, wondering what gave cork its resilience, he took a "penknife sharpened as keen as a razor" and cut off a thin slice of the cork. Examining this under the microscope he found that it was "all perforated and porous, much like a honeycombe . . . in that these pores, or cells, were not very deep, but consisted of a great many boxes." He had found the reason for the cork's resilience; had he discovered cells as well? True, he used the word "cell," but when we look closely at his statement we realize that he conceived the cell as a cubicle or little room, with no conception of contents within the cell walls. Indeed, in dead cork, there are no living contents. Later, looking at similar slices of living plant tissues Hooke remarked that the cells were "filled with juices." But he had no conception that these "juices" were structured and alive. Hooke contributed little more than the word "cell" to the cell theory.

The first one to see cells as living units was a contemporary of Hooke's, the Dutch amateur scientist, Antony van Leeuwenhoek (1632–1723), a draper by trade. The microscope that Hooke used was what is called the "compound microscope," and consists of two (or more) lenses mounted in a tube. Because the theory of optics was in its infancy, the compound microscope of the seventeenth century produced miserable images that suffered badly from **spherical aberration** (straight lines appearing curved) and **chromatic aberration** (producing colored fringes around objects). After first experimenting with compound microscopes, Leeuwenhoek abandoned them for the "simple microscope," which contains just a single magnifying lens. By using a tiny glass lens with a high curvature he could get magnifications in excess of 200 power. One of Leeuwenhoek's microscopes is shown in Figure 2-2. Looking at this simple instrument we are struck by the fact that what Leeuwenhoek saw could have been seen by anyone else (given suitable motivation!) many centuries earlier, for magnifying lenses are mentioned by Seneca, a Roman contemporary of Jesus'; and they may have been known before this.

Leeuwenhoek saw many different species of protozoa, algae, and bacteria, which he described and pictured in letters written to the Royal Society. But though he saw these unicellular organisms—"saw" them in a simple physiological sense—he did not see them conceptually as cells. Nor indeed was there any reason why he should. The idea of *uni*cellular organisms is a by-product of the general cell theory; were there only unicelluar organisms no one would conceive of a cell theory.

Little progress was made toward a cell theory until the nineteenth century, at which time a

Fig. 2-2. *The construction of Leeuwenhoek's microscope. The eye was applied close to the lens on one side, while the object was mounted on the screw-point on the opposite side of the lens. (From W. W. Umbreit,* Modern Microbiology, *W. H. Freeman and Company, San Francisco and London, 1962.)*

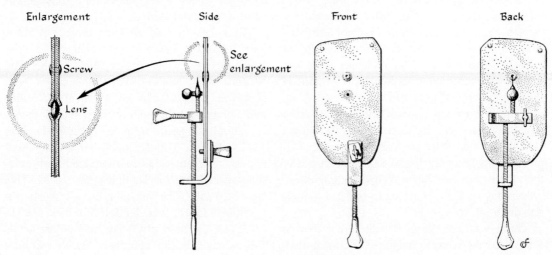

Enlargement   Side   Front   Back

Screw
See enlargement
Lens

series of statements made by several men showed dawning recognition of the cellular nature of organisms. Consider the following statements:

1809. J. B. de Lamarck: "No body can possess life if its containing parts are not a cellular tissue."

1809. B. de Mirbel: "Plants are made up of cells, all parts of which are in continuity and form one and the same membranous tissue."

1824. H. J. Dutrochet: "All the organic tissues of animals are actually globular cells of exceeding smallness, which appear to be united only by a simple adhesive force; thus all tissues, all animal organs, are actually only a cellular tissue variously modified."

1826. J. P. F. Turpin: (Subtitle of a book) "Observations on the origin and primitive formation of cellular tissue, on each of the vesicles composing such tissue, considered as so many distinct individuals having their particular vital centers for life and reproduction, and destined to agglomerate to form the compound individual of every plant which consists of more than one vesicle."

The progress toward a cell theory shown in these statements is impressive; particularly in the last quotation, if we merely substitute the word "cell" for the word "vesicle." All these statements were made before 1839. What, then, did Schleiden and Schwann contribute? Careful examination of the historical evidence indicates that their principal contribution was publicity. Schleiden was particularly adept at gaining the attention of his colleagues. By energetic and repeated statements he convinced the scientific world that the cell theory—as he was the first to call it—was true, and that he and Schwann were its discoverers. As Edwin G. Conklin said: "I once heard a distinguished physiologist [Jacques Loeb] say pessimistically that there are two ways to gain recognition, either brag or fight. It seems to me that Schleiden did both."

There was one thing beside publicity that Schleiden and Schwann might have contributed,

something that had almost entirely escaped their predecessors, and this was an understanding of how cells reproduced. But in this they failed, and in a rather interesting manner. Schleiden thought his greatest contribution to the cell theory was his discovery of the method of cell reproduction. According to him, cell reproduction begins with the appearance of some sort of nuclei of crystallization inside a cell; these nuclei grow and grow until new cells are formed completely within the old cell; then the old cell bursts, releasing the new ones.

How did he come to make so monumental an error? Partly because he seized upon one of the few instances in the living world where something of this sort takes place, namely the development of the embryo sac of flowers. If he had checked his generalization in other situations it would have broken down. Indeed, at least three different men before him had correctly described cell division in algae.

There may have been another factor that contributed to his error. In general, when confronted with a new situation we tend to see it in terms of old ideas. It is very hard to see something new. Schleiden, viewing the problem of cell multiplication, may have unconsciously tried to harmonize it with what we know of the reproduction of mammals, where new individuals begin as specks of matter within the mother, specks which grow and ultimately break out. Cell reproduction in Schleiden's view was the consequence of a sort of cell pregnancy. His error is understandable.

His colleague had an even more erroneous view. Schwann believed that cells could arise from specks of material residing in the fluid *between* cells. Nothing like this has ever been observed. Between the two of them, Schleiden and Schwann held up progress in cell theory for about ten years until Wilhelm Hofmeister (1824–1877), a music publisher and amateur scientist, presented his own meticulous observations of cell division by living plant cells. That was in 1849. The meaning of his work was verbalized in 1859 by Rudolf Virchow (1821–1902), a German physician and politician, in the coinage of the aphorism *Omnis cellula e cellula*—all cells come from cells. The truth of this statement still stands unchallenged.

Who discovered the cell theory, and when? It is clear that credit must be divided amongst a number of scientists whose labors extended over at least half a century, from 1809 to 1859. Historical truth does not always produce a neat, simple statement easily adapted to mechanical examinations.

8. Are There "Crucial Experiments?"

The practitioners of science, like all artists and artisans, are largely unconscious of the logical foundations of their procedures. As science has developed, philosophers of science have appeared, and these have tried to analyse and describe "the scientific method." Their labors have not been wholly successful. One of their less happy conceptions has been that of the *experimentum crucis*—the critical experiment without which the proof of a theory is supposed to be unsatisfactory. As this idea developed during the nineteenth century it implied that really good scientists would not accept or work with a theory until the *experimentum crucis* had been carried out. How inaccurately this describes the behavior of scientists is easily seen in the later developments of the cell theory.

If cells are the unit of structure and function of multicellular organisms then it should be possible to isolate a single cell from an organism and have it grow into a multicellular organism, or at least into a colony of (poorly organized) cells—this surely is a necessary implication of the cell theory. Surely the experiment described is a true *experimentum crucis* and must have occurred to a number of biologists of the last century. However, the possibility of testing it did not develop until 1907 when Ross G. Harrison (1870–1959) of Yale University succeeded in keeping salamander cells continuously alive outside the body of a salamander, thus establishing the technique of **cell culture.** (We use here the term favored by Philip R. White, a leading worker in this field; the older term is *tissue culture*.) Following

Harrison's work hundreds of different kinds of cells have been established in cell culture, but curiously the idea of critically testing the cell theory by establishing a culture *from a single cell* seems to have occurred to few cell culturists. There are considerable technical difficulties of course: it is not easy to isolate a single microscopic cell, and if the culture medium is less than optimal a single cell is less likely to survive than is a cluster of cells. It was not until 1948 that the *experimentum crucis* was first carried out by K. K. Sanford, W. R. Early, and G. D. Likely, using an animal cell. In 1954, W. H. Muir, A. C. Hildebrandt, and A. J. Riker established a similar culture using a plant cell. Their reports were scarcely noticed by the scientific community. Clearly the *experimentum crucis* sometimes plays only a minor role in the scientific process.*

9. The Size of Cells

How big is a cell? How can we measure a microscopic object? Measurement is fundamentally a comparison of two things in a quantitative way. Antony van Leeuwenhoek compared his "little animals" with such common objects as a human hair and the eye of a louse. Lice no longer being normal denizens of the household, let us see what we can do with a hair. On the inside of the human cheek there are cells called **epithelial cells.** With the blunt end of a toothpick, some of these can be scraped off and mounted in a drop of water on a microscope slide. Before putting the cover slip on, add a single human hair. If properly arranged, hair and cells will appear in the same field of view (Fig. 2-3). By comparison, we find that the greatest width of an epithelial cell is about half that of the hair.

But it won't do to say that an epithelial cell is "half a hair wide." We need a standard measure (hairs vary) and one that is widely ac-

---

* 2-2. Should it? In your opinion, would science progress more rapidly and less often stand in need of revision, if scientists were more rigorous in their methods?

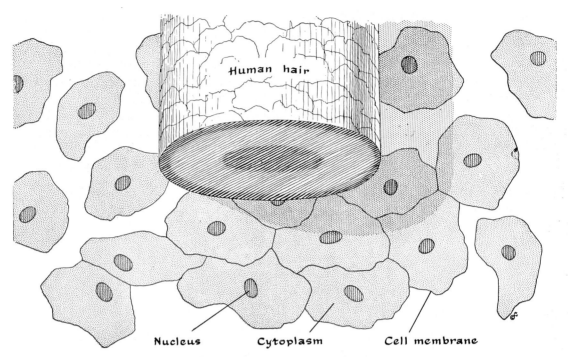

Fig. 2-3. *Comparative size of human cheek epithelial cells and a human hair, which is about 100 microns wide.*

cepted. For this we use the metric system (Fig. 2-4), a system that is the only standard in most civilized countries (the United Kingdom and the United States are exceptions); it is universally used by scientists. With a little patience it

Fig. 2-4. *Comparison of English and metric scales.*

is possible to place a hair and a transparent ruler under the microscope so that the hair is parallel to the marks of the ruler. When this is done, it will be seen that the hair is about 1/10 of a millimeter in width, from which it follows that the width of a human-cheek epithelial cell is about 1/20 of a millimeter.

Because fractions are awkward to deal with, a smaller subunit of the metric system has been devised: the **micron.** By definition, **1,000 microns = 1 millimeter.** The micron is symbolized

by μ, the Greek letter "mu." The width of an ordinary human hair is about 100μ; the width of a typical epithelial cell is about $\frac{1}{2} \times 100\mu$, or 50μ. If precisely ruled grids are not available for microscopic measurements, a human hair will serve as a rough-and-ready means of measuring.

Cells vary greatly in size. Among the protozoa, cells of *Spirostomum* may measure more than a thousand microns in length; at the other extreme, certain soil protozoa collectively called "monads" may be only two or three microns long. Some bacterial cells are considerably less than a single micron in their greatest dimension. But what of it? Does size matter? And if so, why? To answer these questions we must call upon some basic geometrical ideas.

10. The Scale Effect

During the Second World War the possibility of developing an atomic bomb was presented to the British government. After some debate

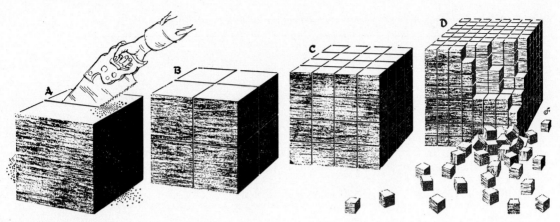

Fig. 2-5. *The ratio of surface to volume is greater for small bodies than it is for large bodies of the same shape.*

a project was set up by Prime Minister Winston Churchill, in a directive that began with these grudging words: "Although personally I am quite content with the existing explosives . . ." That so well educated and so wise a man could have so poorly understood the enormous difference between existing explosives and the proposed one may seem incredible, but we must realize how small a role quantitative thinking played in a classical education of the sort Churchill received. Perhaps no single thought pattern distinguishes the scientist quite so clearly from the nonscientist as his habit of putting questions into quantitative form before seeking answers. This does not mean that the scientist makes a fetish of exactness. Sometimes he measures or counts things very precisely; but often he is content with the crudest of estimates. He does, however, try to get an idea of the order of magnitude of things.

In science, measurements are often expressed in **exponential** fashion. For instance, the weight of a man may be given as 7×10^4 grams; of a hen's egg as 6×10^1 g; or of a cell as 1×10^{-9} g. Rules for handling exponents are explained in Appendix 5. From the habit of dealing with quantities expressed in exponential form there has developed the practise of identifying the **order of magnitude** with the exponent of the base 10. For example, if the cost of an airplane is estimated at $500,000, but in fact costs $4,000,000, the actual cost is said to exceed the estimate by one order of magnitude. (4×10^6 is almost 10^1 times 5×10^5.)* Many of the important decision-making situations of the world are ones in which we are quite happy if our estimates are reliable to within one order of magnitude.

The mere relative size of two things, *i.e.,* the size of one relative to the other, is often sufficient to dictate a decision. The increase in size of a cell or an organism or a population may have far-reaching effects. Consider two towns: one of 10,000 people, the other of 100,-000. Does the latter differ from the former only in having ten times as many people? Not at all. It has many characteristics that are almost completely lacking in the smaller town; and vice versa. A change of scale may bring with it quantitative differences so great as to be qualitative. Precisely why (in the example of towns), it would be hard to say—hard, at least, for a biologist to say. But analogous changes accompany a change in the scale of biological things. Here, fortunately, we can explain with some precision why a shift in scale matters. The reason is rooted in mathematics.

Consider a cube. A cube of a certain size will have a certain volume and a certain surface. Suppose we cut the cube into smaller pieces and separate the pieces. From Figure 2-5 it is evi-

---

* 2-3. Give an order of magnitude comparison of the following paired figures: (A = 27; B = 3,472); (C = 0.03; D = 42); (E = 847; F = 1,024).

TABLE 2-1 *Relation Between Surface and Volume of Cubes of Various Dimensions.*

LENGTH OF EDGE OF CUBE, CM	SURFACE OF CUBE, CM²	VOLUME OF CUBE, CM³	SURFACE: VOLUME RATIO
1	6	1	6 to 1
2	24	8	3 to 1
3	54	27	2 to 1
4	96	64	1.5 to 1
5	150	125	1.2 to 1
6	216	216	1 to 1
7	294	343	0.86 to 1
10	600	1,000	0.6 to 1
100	60,000	1,000,000	0.06 to 1

dent that the new, smaller cubes (in *D*) have, in the aggregate, more surface than the original cube (in *A*), though the total volume must be the same. Or to put it another way, each of the small cubes in *D* has more surface per volume than does the single large cube in *A*.

In exact, quantitative terms, how is the surface:volume ratio changed by change in size? To see, let's start with a cube with a 1 centimeter edge and calculate its surface and volume as we increase it to a cube of 2 cm, 3 cm, and so on. From the figures assembled in Table 2-1, we see how the surface:volume ratio *decreases* with increase in size. It can be shown that this is true for an object of any constant shape— cube, sphere, ellipsoid, or whatever.* The exact values of the surface:volume ratio are different for different shapes; but for each object, the surface increases as the square (1, 4, 9, 16, 25, . . .) of the basic dimension, whereas the volume increases as the cube (1, 8, 27, 64, 125, . . .). Consequently, *the surface:volume ratio of any solid body of constant shape decreases as the size increases.* This principle is called the **scale effect.**

The scale effect can be demonstrated more generally by resorting to **dimensional analysis.** Consider a body of any shape whatsoever. We may represent its surface by the formula:

$$S = Cx^2, \qquad (1)$$

where *x* stands for some basic dimension of the body (*e.g.,* the radius of a sphere, or the edge of a cube), and *S* stands for the surface. *C* stands for a constant which will vary from one shape to another; for a cube it is 6, for a sphere it is 4π. *C* is a constant that does not change as the body increases in size, whereas the variable (dimension) *x* does. We say that "the surface has the dimensions of x^2," not bothering to mention the relatively less important constant.

The volume of a body is given by this formula:

$$V = C'x^3, \qquad (2)$$

in which the constant is represented by C' ("C prime") to indicate that this constant is (in general) different from the preceding constant. "The volume has the dimensions of x^3."

Now consider the surface:volume ratio:

$$\frac{S}{V} = \frac{Cx^2}{C'x^3} = K \cdot \frac{1}{x}. \qquad (3)$$

Since C/C' is one constant divided by another, the result is a new constant, which we represent by K; it will, of course, vary from one geometrical shape to another.* "The surface:volume ratio has the dimensions of x^{-1}." The graph of this ratio is shown in Figure 2-6. Note

---

* 2-4. Construct a table like Table 2-1, but with a sphere as the body, with the radius varying from 1 cm to 100 cm. See Appendix 6 for formulas for surface and volume of sphere.

* 2-5. Give the value of K for (a) a cube; and (b) a sphere.

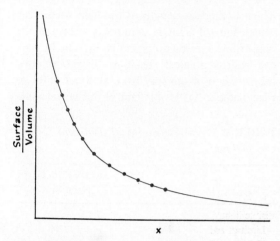

Fig. 2-6. *Showing how the surface : volume ratio decreases as a body of constant shape (any shape) increases in size.*

that as x increases, S/V becomes smaller and smaller.

The significance of the scale effect in biology was apparently first pointed out by Rudolf Leuckart (1822–1898) in the middle of the last century. Imagine a free-living cell of, say, cuboidal shape (Fig. 2-7). Living requires me-

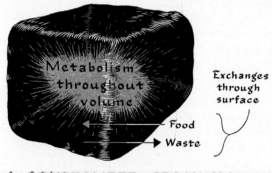

A GENERALIZED ORGANISM

Fig. 2-7. *Why size matters to a living organism.*

tabolism, which takes place throughout the volume of the cell. For these reactions to continue, the organism must be able to carry on exchanges with the environment, taking in food and giving off wastes—both through the surface. *Metabolic needs are proportional to the volume; exchanges are proportional to the surface.* When a cell of constant shape increases in

size, its needs increase faster than its ability to carry on exchanges with the environment. In this we have the most general reason for a limitation to the size of cell. If a free-living cell were to become indefinitely large, its metabolic rate would become vanishingly small until it could hardly be said to live at all. By dividing periodically, a cell keeps its surface:volume ratio within fixed bounds, and so its rate of living, or metabolic rate, is kept relatively constant.

But what about a multicellular organism? Its cells, when it divides, do not separate and present many new surfaces to the environment. True, but in its construction a multicellular organism shows innumerable details the adaptive significance of which is explained by the scale effect. Consider, for example, the organism most familiar to us—namely, man. It is well known that his intestine is much longer than his body; this great length serves to increase the amount of surface available for the movement of nutrient molecules through the intestinal wall into the body. Moreover, the intestinal surface is further increased by millions of microscopic convolutions. Modifications of similar significance are to be found in the lung surfaces available for exchanges of oxygen and carbon dioxide between organism and environment. In plants we find analogous modifications of surfaces. Generally, the modifications are on a microscopic scale and not at all obvious to the casual glance. The *effective* shape of a multicellular organism is seldom what it at first appears to be. Its structural complications are always at least in part necessitated by mathematical principles, of which the surface:volume ratio is the most all-pervasive in its influence.

11. The Development of the Microscope

In the development of a science, ideas and techniques are mutually independent, mutually stimulating. **Cytology,** the science of cells (Gr. *kytos* = a vessel: now used to indicate a cell), began shortly after microscopes were invented and progressed as microscopes improved. The

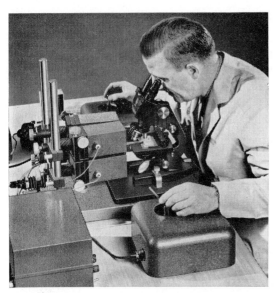

Fig. 2-8. *A modern optical microscope being used with a micromanipulator, which may be used to probe the interior of a cell. (Courtesy American Optical Co.)*

which is the wavelength of the light used. The wavelength of light is commonly measured in Ångstrom units (see Appendix 3). The human eye has its greatest sensitivity in the yellow-green region of the spectrum, at about 5500 Å (see Table 2-2). Using light of this wavelength

TABLE 2-2   *Wavelengths of Different Colors of Light.*

COLOR	λ = WAVE LENGTH (IN ÅNGSTROMS)
Visible light	
Limit of red	7200
Yellow	5800
Region of maximum sensitivity	
of eye	5500
Green	5000
Blue	4500
Limit of violet	4000
Ultra violet	
Limit of transparency of glass	3500
Limit of transparency of quartz	1800

first compound microscope appears to have been invented by Zacharias Jansen in 1590, but (as previously noted) compound microscopes suffered badly from optical aberrations for a long time. It was not until the nineteenth century that men learned how to correct the chromatic aberration by combining lenses made of different kinds of glass. Microscopes improved rapidly, and the question arose, could they be indefinitely improved? Ernst Abbé (1840–1905) gave a definite answer to this question in 1878, showing that there are theoretical limits to the optical microscope. What are these limits?

Our first impulse is to ask, what is the maximum magnification possible? But this is the wrong question, for any image produced can always be magnified further by simple magnifying lenses. There comes a time when further magnifying reveals no further detail—merely a fuzzier (though larger) image. What we want to know is how far apart must two points be if a microscope is to "resolve" them into two points rather than confuse them in one blurred image. The **resolving power** of an optical instrument is determined by several factors, one of

the best compound microscope has its limit of resolution at about 0.2μ. With light of half this wavelength, it is possible to resolve points only half as far apart, i.e., 0.1μ. However, such light is in the ultraviolet part of the spectrum and cannot be observed with the human eye; one must project the image on a fluorescent screen or on photographic film. Moreover, glass does not transmit UV light (see Table 2-2), so quartz lenses must be employed. Although UV microscopes have more than twice the resolving power of ordinary light microscopes, the expense and inconvenience of using them is seldom justified.

A great burgeoning of microscopical research in the nineteenth century was made possible by improvements not only in microscopes but also in auxiliary apparatuses and techniques. The more powerful the microscope, the more essential that the specimen looked at be thin. Hooke sliced his piece of cork with a knife held in his hand, but there are limits to how thin one can make slices in this way. For very thin slices of controllable thickness we now use the **microtome,** a sort of glorified meat-slicer. Also developed during the nineteenth century were a host of techniques for **fixing and staining** tissues, so that one kind of tissue or structure could be distinguished from another. The word "fixing" refers to techniques for killing cells with a minimum of distortion. Most studies of cells and tissues are made with fixed, stained, and often sliced material, which always raises a question as to whether the structures seen under the 'scope are natural or are **artifacts** produced by the preparative procedure. Many questions of this sort were definitively settled when the **phase microscope** was developed in the twentieth century. The theory of this instrument is a little complicated, but what it does is easy to understand. Imagine a piece of clear glass immersed in a swimming pool: how would you see it? Plainly it would be difficult, and this example presents a common problem of ordinary microscopy—how to see a transparent object suspended in a transparent medium of the same color. However, equally transparent substances may diminish to different degrees the velocity of light passing through them. The **refractive index** of a substance is a measure of its effect in slowing the transmission of light. The phase microscope transforms subtle differences in refractive index into easily visible contrasts in intensity, permitting us to see colorless objects in the living, undisturbed cell, thus settling many old arguments about possible artifacts in fixed and stained material.

A new era in cytology was ushered in when the electron microscope was developed. The work of the physicist Louis de Broglie in 1924 indicated that one can meaningfully speak of the wavelength of a beam of electrons; as compared with light, it is very short and should therefore make a high degree of resolution possible if only one could construct a microscope capable of using electron beams in place of light rays. Building on the work of several men, Max Knoll and Ernst Ruska developed the first electron microscope in 1931. Although it was rapidly improved until it was more powerful than the light microscope by two orders of magnitude, the new instrument was a

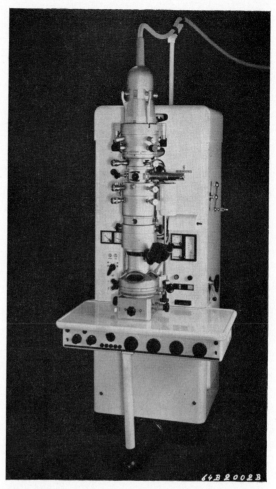

Fig. 2-9. *An electron microscope. (Courtesy Siemens America, Inc.)*

disappointment to biologists until after the Second World War. Like the optical microscope before it, it did not reach its full usefulness until various auxiliary tools and techniques were developed. We can see why these were required if we understand the construction and use of the instrument.

An external view of an electron microscope is shown in Figure 2-9: this is not very informative. A diagrammatic cutaway view is seen in Figure 2-10; an "exploded" view of an inverted optical microscope is arranged alongside to show the functional similarity of the parts. Note, however, this significant difference: the electron microscope is connected to a vacuum pump. Electrons are absorbed by every

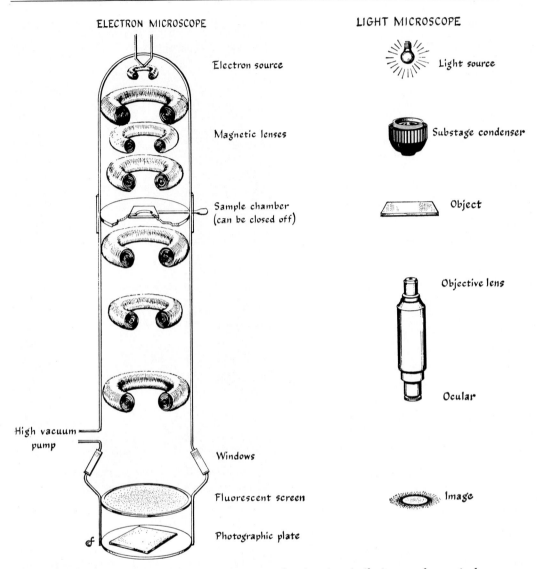

Fig. 2-10. *Diagram of the electron microscope showing its similarity to the optical microscope. For ready comparison of parts, the optical microscope has been turned upside down and then presented in "exploded" view.*

kind of matter, including air; hence the specimen to be examined must be placed in a high vacuum. To stay alive, cells must contain water. This is not possible in a vacuum, therefore the electron microscope is used only for examining dead material. Moreover, the absorption of electrons by the specimen to be examined creates another problem: the need for ultrathin sections. The standard microtome routinely slices tissues to 10μ thickness, and with some

care to 2μ. For electron microscopy the technique of sectioning had to be modified. New, harder embedding materials were found for holding the specimen rigidly; new methods of gearing the microtome were developed; and diamond wedges were introduced as cutting tools. With these improvements it is now possible to make slices 100 Å thick.* Put in other

* 2-6. This is thinner than the old method by what order of magnitude?

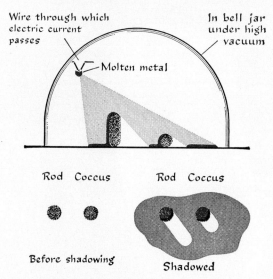

Fig. 2-11. *Shadowing technique for electron microscopy. A rod and a coccus standing on end would look alike in an electron micrograph; but by shadowing, the difference between them is made evident.*

terms, such slices are about 100 atoms thick. The resolving power of the best 'scopes is about 4 Å.

One other invention was required before the new instrument reached its full usefulness. The ordinary **electron micrograph** (picture taken with an electron microscope) is essentially a shadow picture; it fails to reveal many differences in shape. An ingenious device was created in 1944 by Robley C. Williams (who at that time was an astronomer) and R. W. G. Wyckoff. The device is shown in Figure 2-11. The objects to be revealed are put under a bell jar which is evacuated. Using an electric current, a metal (commonly gold) is heated and evaporated from a source at one side. As the metal molecules disperse throughout the chamber they condense on surfaces. Any objects in the way, such as bacteria, will interfere with the deposition of the metal, producing a **metal shadowing** which reveals the shape of the objects that cause the shadowing. A particularly fine example of such shadowing is shown in Figure 2-12, which shows two bacteria plus bacterial virus particles adhering to one of them.

The heads of these virus particles are only 650 Å thick.

12. The Pedagogic Cell

In the first orientation of the student into the wonders of cell structure it is customary to present a picture of a "typical cell." Cells vary greatly in size and shape, and they do not all contain the same structures. Nevertheless, most known cell structures are included in a diagram of the "typical cell," accompanied by a text which says that the "typical cell" does not exist —hence the quotation marks. This is rather an odd use of the word "typical."

But diagrams of this sort have a utility. Since what they depict does not have any real existence outside the classroom it might be better to call the object depicted the *pedagogic cell*, from the Greek word for teaching (Gr. *paidos* = boy + *agogos* = leading). Such a cell (see Fig. 2-13) is useful for learning the names and location of the parts of the cell. No pedagogic harm will ensue provided one remembers the shortcomings of the diagram, which are principally the following. Not all of the parts shown will be seen in every cell examined; the relative sizes of the various parts is not always correct; and the detail shown mixes the information obtained from different procedures, e.g., electron microscopy and optical microscopy.

Moreover, some common cell structures are omitted from our version of the pedagogic cell, for instance *chloroplasts*. These green bodies by which plant cells carry on *photosynthesis* will be discussed later when that topic is taken up. Besides its chloroplasts, a plant cell is characterized by the presence of a cell wall, which is not (strictly speaking) part of the cell at all, but a nonliving secretion formed outside the living cell. Wood is composed of almost nothing but compressed cell walls surrounding spaces in which cells once lived. Animal cells may also produce an external secretion (*e.g.,* bone or cartilage), but such a secretion is more

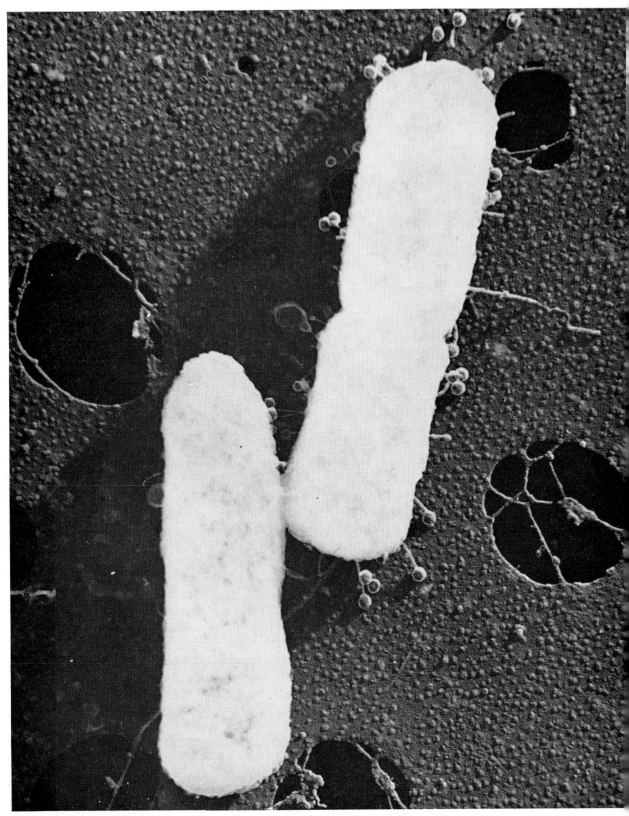

Fig. 2-12. *A shadowed electron micrograph of two bacterial cells fixed at the moment of sexual fusion. One cell is of a virus-resistant strain, the other is virus-susceptible. (From Anderson, Wollman, and Jacob,* Ann. Inst. Pasteur *(1957)* **93:***450.)*

variable in extent and not so definitely assignable to one cell or another; it is called *interstitial substance,* that is, the substance of the interstices between cells.

The structures shown in Figure 2-13 will be discussed one by one. For each, the basic structure and function will be briefly treated; more extensive discussion of some of the structures will be found elsewhere.

The **cell membrane** (plasma membrane) marks the outer limit of the cell. It varies in thickness, but typically is 100 Å to 200 Å thick. The electron microscope has revealed that there are sometimes pores of about 50 Å diameter in the membrane, so the separation of inside and outside the cell is not absolute; the pores may not be constant in position. Exchanges of substances with the environment are controlled by complex biochemical processes in the membrane; the ability of the membrane to control exchanges is lost when the cell dies. The entrance of material through pores in the membrane is poorly understood. Within the cell membrane are the cytoplasm and the nucleus. The **organelles** (cell-organs) of the cytoplasm will be described next.

Pinocytic vesicles play a role in bringing some substances into some cells. As shown in the figure, an invagination of the cell membrane forms small pockets of material, which then break off as individual balloons of fluid or **vacuoles.** In the single-celled animal *Amoeba* (see Fig. 2-1 again), proteins in the environment stimulate this process of **pinocytosis.** This process was first observed, in living amoebas, by W. H. Lewis in 1931.

The **endoplasmic reticulum** is a complex network of spaces bounded by double membranes. A characteristic view of the reticulum in an actively secreting cell is shown in the electron micrograph of a thin section of a cell in Figure 2-14. The reticulum is a set of interconnected long narrow canals which may be regarded as much elongated vacuoles, hence the alternative name, the *cytoplasmic vacuolar system.* All cells so far examined possess this system, developed to a greater or lesser degree, with the single exception of mature mammalian erythro-

cytes or red blood cells.* The reticulum is often seen to have openings to the exterior through the cell membrane, and to the lumen of the double nuclear membrane; the pinocytic vesicles may empty their contents into the reticulum. The reticulum is also connected to the **Golgi body** (named after its discoverer), the functions of which are still to be completely elucidated.

For some years after its discovery by K. R. Porter, A. Claude, and E. F. Fullman in 1945 there was some question as to the reality of the endoplasmic reticulum, some workers suggesting that it was but an artifact produced by the fixing and drying process required for electron microscopy. This doubt was laid to rest when the reticulum was observed in living cells examined under the phase microscope. Various functions have been suggested for the reticulum. It is responsible for synthesizing the nuclear membrane, and possibly other membranes as well. Its immense surface ideally fits it to be a site of enzymatic reactions, which can be segregated to one or another portion of it. The openings of the reticulum to nucleus, Golgi body, and exterior, as well as its wide distribution throughout the cytoplasm, suggest that it serves to conduct material from one part of the cell to another.

The reticulum occurs in two forms, *rough* and *smooth.* The rough form (illustrated in the pedagogic cell and in Fig. 2-14) has attached to its membranes minute bodies called **ribosomes;** the smooth form lacks them. Cells that are active in carrying out protein synthesis have an abundance of the rough form; the smooth form characterizes cells that are active synthesizers of fatty substances (steroids). From this (and other evidence) it is deduced that ribosomes are involved in protein synthesis. Ribosomes also occur in the cytoplasm not attached to the endoplasmic reticulum. Their function will be discussed further in Chapter 4.

Some cells are motile because they possess many **cilia** (sing., L. *cilium,* an eyelash), small hairlike projections from the surface which, by rhythmic beating, propel the cell through a liquid medium, or move fluid past a stationary

---

* 2-7. Is this a genuine exception? Explain.

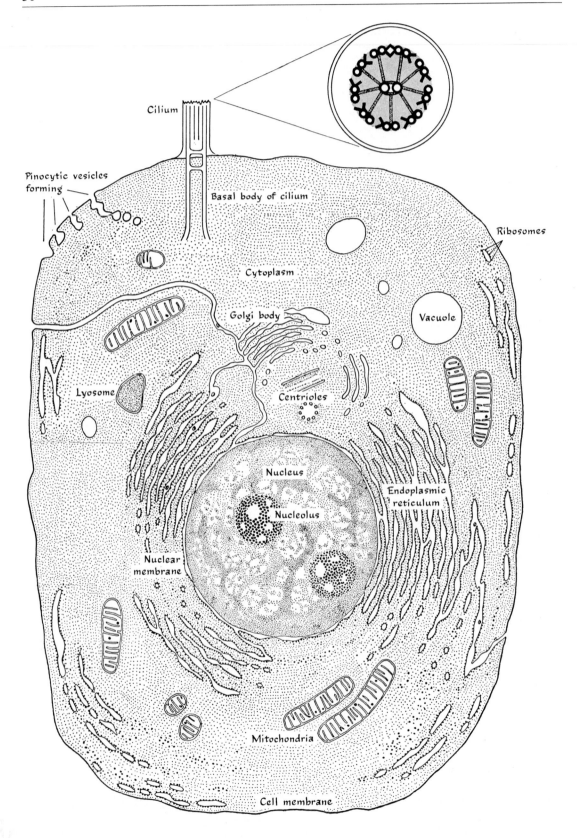

Cilium

Pinocytic vesicles forming

Basal body of cilium

Ribosomes

Cytoplasm

Golgi body

Vacuole

Lyosome

Centrioles

Nucleus

Nucleolus

Endoplasmic reticulum

Nuclear membrane

Mitochondria

Cell membrane

cell. Only the base of a single cilium is shown in the diagram. If the cell has only one or a few such movable whips, the word **flagellum** (L., whip; pl. *flagella*) is applied to each such organelle. Flagella are usually longer than cilia. In cross-section, both cilia and flagella show a most remarkable structure, as was discovered by I. Manton, B. Clarke, A. D. Greenwood, and E. A. Flint in 1952: *always* the cross-section shows a "9 + 2" structure (see upper right-hand corner of Fig. 2-13), with 9 filaments in the periphery, and 2 in the center. The peripheral filaments may be double (as shown) or triple in some species, but the 9 + 2 structure is found in all animal and plant cilia and flagella. (The flagellum of a bacterial cell, however, consists of only a single filament.) The "tails" of spermatozoa are constructed on the 9 + 2 plan. Why this number and arrangement rather than some other? The answer is unknown.

Mitochondria (sing. *mitochondrion*) are small bodies—typically 0.5μ by 2μ—in ceaseless motion in living cells, moving about actively, breaking up into short rods and granules, and re-forming into filaments. They were discovered in 1894 by R. Altmann and given some fifty different names before the name used here became stabilized. In the optical microscope they can be seen best by **dark-field illumination,** that is, by being illuminated from the side against a black background (like particles of dust in a beam of light, seen from the side, in a dark room). Some cells have several thousand mitochondria per cell. They can be collected in quantity by grinding up liver cells and subjecting the **homogenate** to centrifugation at $200,000\ g$ (200,000 times the force of gravity). The heavier mitochondria settle to the bottom of the centrifuge tube in relative purity. Using this material in experiments it can be shown that many important energy-releasing chemical

reactions are brought about by the mitochondria, which are often called the "power houses" of the cell. Their function is discussed further in Chapter 4.

Lysosomes (Gr. *lysis,* a loosening, hence destruction + *soma,* body) contain enzymes capable of destroying other cellular constituents; when the cell is injured the release of these enzymes results in the **autolysis** (self-destruction) of the cell. Presumably the normal function of the enzymes is not cell-destruction; the enzymes are kept safely isolated from the rest of the cell by incorporation in the lysosomes.

The **centrioles,** usually two per cell, each consist of a sheaf of nine filaments, one centriole being arranged at right angles to the other. Each filament is usually triple. There is some observational evidence that the **basal body** (also called *kinetosome*) of a cilium is derived from a centriole. Centrioles play a role in cell division, to be discussed presently.

13. The Nucleus

With the **nucleus** (L. kernel) we come to one of the most important structures. That this structure is present in almost all cells was first pointed out by the English botanist Robert Brown (1773–1858) in 1831. That the nucleus is a uniquely important part of the cell has been shown by innumerable experiments, of which we consider two types.

The single-celled animal *Amoeba* is large enough to submit to microsurgery. If the nucleus is removed from an amoeba, the cell continues to move for a time, and it may even divide once or twice; but it will not multiply indefinitely, nor will such *enucleated* cells (cells without nuclei) live long. Does this show that the nucleus is necessary for continuous life and reproduction? *Not at all.* The results might have

Fig. 2-13. *An idealized cell, showing most of the more important structures. Only the base of a single cilium is shown; the whole hairlike structure may be as long as the cell. One centriole is shown in longitudinal section, the other in cross-section. The dots lining the endoplasmic reticulum are ribosomes. (Modified from "The Living Cell," by Jean Brachet. Copyright © 1961 by Scientific American, Inc. All rights reserved.)*

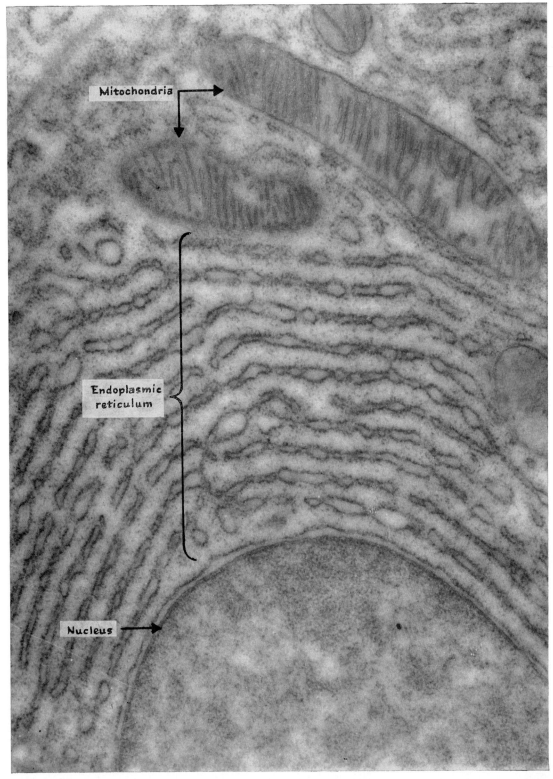

Fig. 2-14. *Fine structure of a cell, as revealed by an electron micrograph, at a magnification of approximately 40,000. An exocrine pancreatic cell. (Courtesy George E. Palade.)*

been caused by the operation itself. To check on this point, workers have divided amoebas in half; when this is done, only the nucleus-bearing half multiplies and lives indefinitely. As an even more convincing experiment, after bisection, the half bearing the nucleus may be enucleated and its nucleus inserted into the other half; the half that finally gets the nucleus is the one that survives indefinitely. In this experiment we speak of the enucleated cells as the **experimental** group, the nucleus-bearing cells as the **controls.** From the controls we learn the consequences of all the incidental operations involved, except enucleation itself, the consequence of which is revealed by the experimental group. This is the sort of thing a biologist means when he speaks of a **controlled experiment.**

The development of biological generalizations depends to a marked degree on finding just the right plant or animal to carry out the most revealing experiments. One of the neatest experiments showing the importance of the nucleus was carried out by the German biologist J. Hämmerling using the marine alga *Acetabularia,* a single-celled plant that may be as tall as 5 centimeters. Such a large cell makes experimentation easy. One species of this plant, *Acetabularia mediterranea,* has a mushroomlike cap (see Fig. 2-15*A*); another species, *A. crenulata,* has one with "fingers" on it. In each species, the nucleus is in the base. If the cap is cut off, the stem of a plant regenerates a new cap of the proper sort for its species. How does it "know" enough to develop the right kind of

Fig. 2-15. *The role of the nucleus, as shown by experiments with* Acetabularia. *From B it appears that a decapitated plant develops a new cap like the old one. Note in C that the regenerated head is true to the nucleus-type, even when the intervening cytoplasm is from another species.*

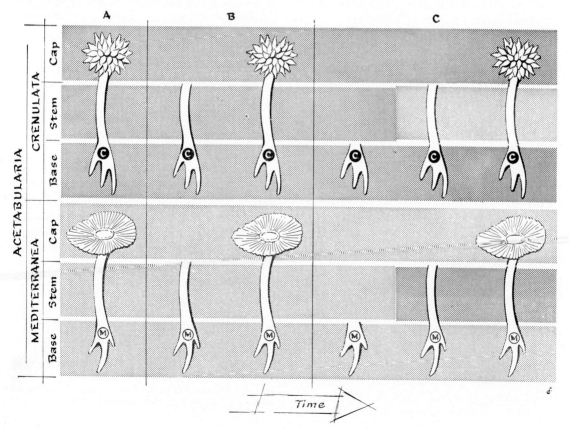

cap? The following ingenious experiments of Hämmerling indicate that this "information" is in the nucleus.

The cap and stem were removed from species *C*, and then a new stem from species *M* was grafted on (Fig. 2-15*B*). When a new cap developed, it was a *C*-cap, like the distant *C*-base with its *C*-nucleus, rather than like the contiguous *M*-stem, which has no nucleus of its own type. The **reciprocal experiment** (Fig. 2-15*C*) yielded results of like sense. From this work it appears probable that the "information" about development comes from the nucleus.

14. The Transmission of Information in Cell Division

Virchow's aphorism *Omnis cellula e cellula* implies that cells are potentially immortal. It is scarcely reasonable to demand a rigorous testing of this implication, since an infinity of time is hard to come by. A satisfactorily close approximation to it was, however, carried out at the Rockefeller Institute in New York City, by a group of workers under the direction of Alexis Carrel. In January, 1912, some "fibroblast cells" were taken from a living embryonic chicken heart and put in sterile (germ-free) nutrient solution in a number of glass vessels. In these, the cells lived and multiplied. From time to time they were given new food; periodically, the excess of cells produced by cell multiplication was removed and discarded. The cell cultures were maintained continuously until 1939, when the experiment was terminated for reasons having nothing to do with science. For 27 years these cells flourished without signs of senescence, though the chick from which they were taken would have (had it been saved) grown old and probably died in less than ten years. There seems little reason to doubt that cells are potentially immortal. This is true of all the different kinds of cells of the body—which raises another problem: If all the cells are potentially immortal and ageless, why does the whole body grow old and die? This is still a great mystery.

The Rockefeller experiment merits examina-

tion from another point of view. We need to see the quantitative aspects of cell multiplication and understand their bearing on the question of "information" and its transmission from generation to generation.

Suppose one of the cell cultures had been started with but a single cell in 1912. Under the experimental conditions used, the cells divided once every two days. At this rate, one cell would produce 2^{10} or 1,024 descendants in 20 days. For simplicity in further calculations, let's call this 1,000, or 10^3. Every 20 days, then, the cells (if unhindered) increase a thousandfold. In 40 days there would be $10^3 \times 10^3$, or 10^6 cells; in 60 days, $(10^3)^3$, or 10^9, cells. In our calculations, for every unit of 20 days we increase by 1 the power of *x*, the exponent *outside* the parentheses in the expression $(10^3)^x$. In 27 years there are 493 units of 20 days each. The time of the experiment was actually a bit more than 27 years, so for simplicity in calculating, let's assume 500 units; that is, $x = 500$. At the end of this period, our cell would have produced $(10^3)^{500}$ descendant cells, or 10^{1500}. How large a number is 10^{1500}? *

The number 10^{1500} is immensely large. Perhaps the most meaningful comparison to make with it is the estimate of the number of electrons in the universe. According to accepted physical theory, the number of electrons in the entire universe does not exceed 10^{90}. . . . It is safe to say that 10^{1500} is a large number.

We see now why it was essential that the Rockefeller workers periodically threw away part of their cell culture, carrying only a small fraction of the cells through succeeding generations. Had they not done so, the Institute, the nation, soon the world,† and eventually the entire universe would have been nothing but chick-heart cells (had they been able to maintain this rate of reproduction).

---

* If you have had difficulty in following the calculations, work through the review of exponential numbers given in Appendix 5 at the end of the book.

† 2-8. How soon? Assume each cell has a weight of 10^{-9} grams, and calculate how many days would be required for one cell to produce a mass of cells equal to the earth in weight. (See Appendix 4 for the weight of the earth.)

There is another aspect of the situation that needs to be pointed out. Consider this question: *If* all cells had been saved, a single cell in the last cell generation would, on the average, have contained what fraction of the material present in the first cell? If we *assume* (contrary to fact) that material that once becomes part of the cell material never leaves it but is subdivided and passed on from cell to cell, then the material in the original cell would be divided among 10^{1500} cells at the end of 27 years. This means that, on the average, each cell would contain only 10^{-1500} of the material present in the original cell. It follows that it is highly probable that a given cell in the twenty-seventh year would contain not so much as a single atom of matter that was present in the original cell. All of its atoms would, with a high degree of probability, have joined its cellular substance within the last year.

In reasoning thus, we have assumed that all the cells were kept—which is not true. But a little thought will show that exactly the same conclusion is reached when we allow for the fact that only a few of the cells were kept. The "dilution factor" of 10^{-1500} is the same.

Except by the rarest and most insignificant chance, not a single atom in a cell of the twenty-seventh year would be one that traced its origin to the first cell. Yet the cells at the end of these approximately 500 generations are still the same kind of cells* as in the beginning. *The maintenance of such constancy clearly depends on "information"* which must not only be transmitted from generation to generation, but must —because of the dilution factor—be reproduced periodically. Information, which is a nonmaterial concept, must always have a material basis. (For instance, the information in this paragraph is "borne" by the pattern of ink on paper.) What material substance is there in cells that shows a constant pattern and that is reproduced from one generation to another? Our first answer: chromosomes.

---

* There is a minor qualification to be made. For the first few weeks, cells in culture may change slightly as they adapt to the artificial cultural conditions, which are never quite the same as conditions in a living body. After that, the cells stay the same.

15. Chromosomes: The Information Bearers

Not long after Robert Brown first called attention to the nucleus as a constant feature of cells, various other workers, beginning with Hugo von Mohl in 1835, observed that the nucleus has in it threadlike bodies. Their name, **chromosomes** (Gr. *chroma* = color + *soma* = body), which was not coined until a half-century after their discovery, implies that they are colored, which they are not. In the living cell they are colorless, nearly transparent, and scarcely distinguishable from the rest of the cell. However, since certain dyes are selectively taken up by them (leaving the rest of the cell comparatively colorless), they are called chromosomes, or colored bodies.

Unfortunately, most chromosomes are too small to permit being seen in much detail using the optical microscope. Electron microscopy has also proved a disappointment up to the present time, apparently for lack of suitable preparative methods. The most interesting pictures we have of chromosomes are the product of a rather special case. Among the flies (insect order of Diptera) certain cells, notably cells of the salivary glands of the maggot stage, produce giant chromosomes, as was first noted by E. G. Balbiani in 1881. In the vinegar-fly *Drosophila melanogaster* the chromosome called the "X chromosome" is, in a salivary-gland cell, some 400μ long, whereas this chromosome in normal body cells is only a little more than 1μ in length. Giant chromosomes are also correspondingly thicker; each consists of hundreds of strands produced by repeated divisions, the products remaining together in a bundle. Though discovered in 1881, the significance of giant chromosomes was not appreciated until half a century later when they were rediscovered and it was pointed out that the sequence of identifiable bands (see Fig. 2-16) corresponds to the sequence of genetic factors determined by breeding tests; of this, more in Part V.

Chromosomes, even when of the ordinary rather than the giant form, are distinguishable, one from another. In most of the cells of higher plants and animals, there are two of each dis-

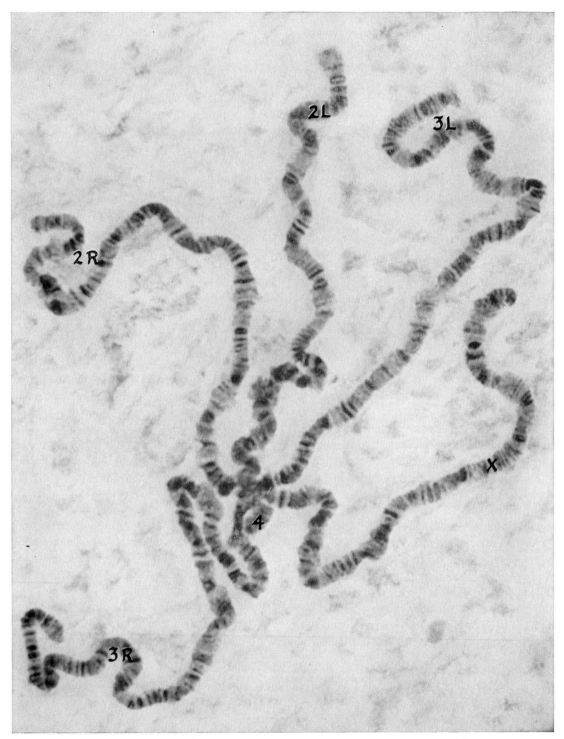

Fig. 2-16. *Salivary-gland chromosomes of* Drosophila melanogaster. *The colored symbols identify the chromosomes by number and left (L) or right (R) arms; X is the X chromosome. (Courtesy Berwind P. Kaufmann.)*

tinguishable kind of chromosome; such cells are **diploid** (Gr. *diploos* = double). The number of chromosomes varies from species to species; in humans it is 46, in house mice 40, in corn 20, in the vinegar fly 8. The number seems to be the same in most of the ordinary, or **somatic** (body), cells of an organism. The cells that take part in sexual reproduction, the **gametes** (sperms and eggs), are different, containing as they do exactly *one* of each kind of chromosome, the **haploid** number (Gr. *haploos* = single).* The haploid numbers of chromosomes in several species are given in Appendix 9.

That all the somatic cells of an individual should have the same kinds and the same number of chromosomes is most remarkable, and suggests two things: (1) that in each cycle, from cell division to cell division, there must be a duplication of each chromosome; and (2) that the duplicates are separated in cell division, each "daughter" chromosome going to one or the other of the two daughter cells. Thus each daughter cell receives exactly the same number and the same kind of chromosomes as were present in the original cell; this kind of cell division is called **equational division.** It is also called **mitosis.**†

In Figure 2-17, mitotic cell division is represented by a series of diagrams. The cell involved is a hypothetical one with two pairs of chromosomes, which are shown more clearly than they would appear in real life. To make it easier to follow the process, the two different kinds of chromosomes are represented by different colors. It must be recognized that the process of cell division is a continuous one, that it does not occur in a series of phases, but that we give names to various stages of the process in order to talk about the facts more easily. As you read, try to connect the pictured phase-stages by the necessary intermediate steps, mak-

ing the whole into a smoothly unrolling cinematographic record in your mind.

Most of the time the cell is in **interphase** (sometimes called the *metabolic stage*). In the nucleus can be seen a densely staining **nucleolus.** Also visible is a tangled mass of exceedingly fine threads that are stainable with chromosomal dyes; but only under exceptional circumstances can the chromosomes be seen as such. Various evidence indicates that chromosomes maintain their integrity throughout interphase, but are long and thin and individually unrecognizable. Note the **centriole,** which plays an important role in cell division in all animals and some plants.

As the time of cell division approaches, the previously thin elongated chromosomes "condense" into shorter ones; this evidently occurs as a result of the coiling of each thread to make a shorter, thicker, coiled entity. As the chromosomes become clearly visible we speak of the cell as being in **early prophase.** Only one part of each chromosome appears to be single at this stage: this is the **centromere.** The rest of each chromosome consists of *two* intertwining threads called **chromatids.** The chromatids are identical, region for region. The centriole has by this time divided to form two centrioles which are drawing away from each other. (Each centriole is actually a double structure, but is seen as single under the optical microscope.)

As mitosis proceeds each chromosome continues to become shorter and thicker, and the **nucleolus** starts to fade from view. (Is it destroyed? Or does it merely become invisible? We don't know.) Some cells have two or more nucleoli. By **late prophase** the spindle is visible. This is a set of visible **spindle fibers** arranged in the shape of two cones placed mouth to mouth. It is formed, outside the nucleus, with the two sets of centrioles serving as poles, the whole constituting the **mitotic apparatus** of the cell. The nuclear membrane now dissolves, leaving the chromosomes floating in the cytoplasm, where they soon become oriented on the mitotic apparatus.

By the **metaphase** stage the chromosomes have come to lie in the equatorial plane, or

---

* 2-9. How diploid cells can give rise to haploid cells we will see later. Can you see *why* the gametes are haploid, that is, why in terms of adaptive significance? (What would happen if gametes were diploid?)

† Best pronounced with a short *i*, as if spelled *mittosis*, to distinguish it from meiosis (pronounced as if spelled *myosis*), which will be described later.

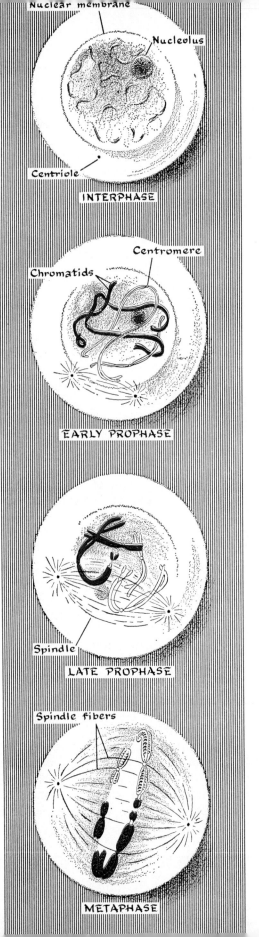

Nuclear membrane

Nucleolus

Centriole

INTERPHASE

Centromere

Chromatids

EARLY PROPHASE

Spindle

LATE PROPHASE

Spindle fibers

METAPHASE

metaphase plate, of the spindle. Each centromere is attached to two **spindle fibers,** one for each pole of the spindle. The centromere still appears single, though all the rest of the chromosome is clearly double. Metaphase is the most favorable stage for examining the chromosomes because they are now at their maximum degree of contraction.

With the division of each centromere into two, **anaphase** begins. The sister centromeres are pulled in opposite directions by the spindle fibers, thus beginning the separation (in **early anaphase**) of the sister chromatids—which, from this time onward, should be called *chromosomes*—and thus insuring that each daughter-cell-to-be receives the same complement of chromosomal material.

By **late anaphase** one set of chromosomes has been drawn to each pole of the spindle. The nuclear material, one may say, has been divided; now it is the turn for the cytoplasm to be divided. In animal cells a constriction begins to form across the equator. In plant cells, which are rigid, the division is brought about by the formation of a wall across the middle.

The last phase, **telophase,** sees a reversal of the processes of prophase. A nucleolus appears (*re*appears?) in each cell, always attached to the same region of the same pair of chromosomes. A nuclear membrane begins to form in each cell. The chromosomes become more elongated and less distinct, ultimately fading from view.

Cell division is complete with the formation of two new cells in the interphase stage. Except for their smaller size, the two daughter cells are indistinguishable from the parental cell. They have the same hereditary material (the same chromosomes) and the same metabolic capabilities. During the succeeding metabolic stage each cell grows in size; and its chromosomes marvellously succeed in reproducing themselves to form the identical chromatids required for the next cell division.

It should hardly be necessary to state that mitosis is a most remarkable process. Mechanistically minded biologists—that is to say, all active investigators—are committed to a pro-

Fig. 2-17. *Mitosis, beginning.*

gram of explaining biological phenomena by physical and chemical laws. But what laws explain the "dance of the chromosomes" during mitotic division? We are indeed very far from knowing.

Perhaps even more remarkable, and certainly more basic in importance, is the duplication of chromosomal material during interphase. That this must happen is clear from the fact that the amount of chromosomal substance is always the same at the prophase stage of each cell in an indefinite series of descendant cells; yet the actual act of duplication is not visible. We have, nevertheless, by indirect means, learned a great deal in recent years about the duplication of the information-bearing material of the cell. We will return to this topic in Chapter 5.

16. Textbooks and Scientific Evidence

The process of cell division has just been presented by means of a series of diagrams. Why were photographs not used? Most people regard a photograph as something closer to reality than a diagram; it seems more "objective," more convincing. When we use diagrams (as we often do in textbooks), a few words of explanation are in order. In what way is a diagram better, or preferable?

To begin with, facts can be simplified in a diagram. Instead of showing 40 chromosomes (a common number in mammalian cells, for example), we can restrict ourselves to 4 chromosomes. We can also eliminate visible detail that is irrelevant to the process in question. Since perhaps no single view seen under the microscope shows all that we want to show, we can combine the best of them into a single composite. We can eliminate aspects peculiar to particular species and show only features common to many species.

A photograph has other disadvantages. Since the camera has a limited depth of focus, even in a photograph of a thin microtome section some structures may be out of focus. The contrast between dark and light parts of the final photograph may be too great or not great

Fig. 2-17. *Mitosis, concluded.*

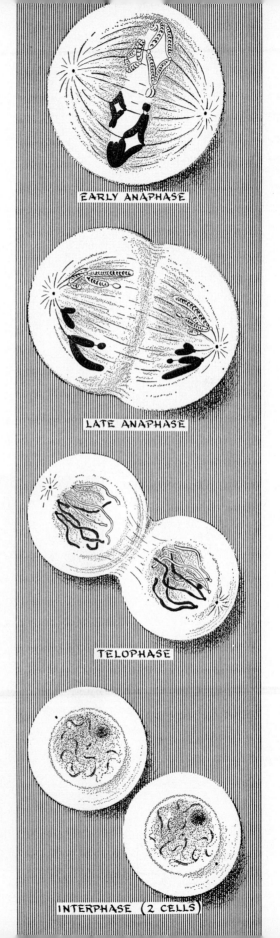

EARLY ANAPHASE

LATE ANAPHASE

TELOPHASE

INTERPHASE (2 CELLS)

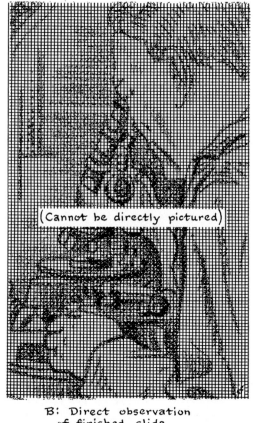

A: The entire procedure

B: Direct observation of finished slide

(Not presented because of the great expense)

C: Photograph (An original print)

D: Half-tone of photograph

E: Drawing

F: Diagram

enough; in a diagram we can make it what we will. A photograph in a book shows structure that is not as "sharp" as the image seen in a microscope because loss of detail takes place at four stages: (1) in making the photomicrograph, for no film is lacking in "graininess"; (2) in making the "halftone" engraving from the photograph; (3) in making the printing plate from the engraving; and (4) in printing, that is, in transferring the image from the printing plate to the paper. The "screen" (dots by which shading or tone is shown) of a halftone engraving may be easily seen by examining Figure 2-18D with a magnifying lens.

Figure 2-18 is designed as a case study in the presentation of scientific evidence. The particular problem is this: By what means do chromosomes become shorter and thicker as they approach metaphase? After fixing, staining, and slicing cells (A), an investigator looks at slides of cells in many stages of cell division (B). From this study he concludes that the shortening of a chromatid is brought about by a coiling of a thread, which was originally long and thin, into a helix. He can clearly see such helices. How does he report this to others so as to convince them? He would like to include in his publication a direct photographic print, but it is too expensive to "tip in" a print into the journal (C indicates the omission). So a halftone is made for printing. But since the turns of the helices are near the resolving power of the 'scope, the losses in making first the photograph and then the halftone are so great that the published result is not very satisfactory (D). To remedy this, the investigator makes a drawing (E) from the original slide, depicting what he sees as exactly as he can. A photographic reproduction may suffer loss of detail; yet it is more "objective" than a drawing, which is clearer. Which should he include in his report? This is the dilemma that faces a scientist when he reports what he has seen. It is particularly critical in the field of cytology, where new investigations make increasing demands on the resolving power of the instruments. Faced with this problem, cytologists have worked out a sort of compromise: they usually document the announcement of a new discovery with *both* photographs and drawings.

It sometimes happens that a cytologist's colleagues doubt the correctness of the conclusions reached. How does such a doubter check on the work? If he is not satisfied with the drawing and the halftone (E and D), he asks first to see an original print (C). If this does not satisfy him, he next asks to examine the original microscope slide (which a careful researcher will have kept, labeled with the coordinates of the significant region, as determined using a microscope with a calibrated mechanical stage). If, even after looking at the slide (B), the doubter still doubts—perhaps because he suspects the structures were produced by overly drastic fixing and staining procedures—there is nothing left for him to do but repeat the whole operation (A) so that the criterion of repeatability may be met.

And how much of all this appears in a textbook? Only a simple diagram (F), which gives no hint of the sweat that went into the making of it.

Fig. 2-18. *Levels of evidence underlying the statement that "the shortening of a chromatid during mitosis comes about when the chromatid is thrown into a helix (as diagrammed in* F)*."*

Questions and Problems

[A double dagger (‡) before the number means that the problem is answered in the section *Answers to Problems* which appears near the end of the book.]

2-10. Make a list of the **boldface** terms in this chapter. Write out a definition or description of each. Compare your work with the text.

2-11. It is a curious property of the memory that it is easier to remember more than less. Discoveries that are connected with names become humanized and more memorable. You should make a practise of noting the names of the principal, or earliest, contributors to a field. As a beginning, write out a brief description of the contributions of the following men mentioned in this chapter, giving the date of each: Abbé, de Broglie, R. Brown, Hämmerling, Harrison, Hofmeister, Hooke, Leeuwenhoek, Schleiden and Schwann, Virchow.

2-12. Define *drawing* and *diagram* so as to distinguish between them.

2-13. What do we mean when we say that a certain structure is "selectively stained" by a certain dye?

‡2-14. In what sense may something that is inside the vacuole be said to be outside the cell?

‡2-15. In the early days, Carrel made a number of attempts to culture epithelial cells from chick embryo, without success. Because of operational difficulties, he started each culture with a mixture of both epithelial cells and fibroblasts. After a few weeks he found he had a culture of fibroblast cells only. Later a worker named Fischer succeeded in starting a culture of epithelial cells only; this could be maintained indefinitely. It was then observed that the time required for doubling was 2 days with fibroblasts, but 3 days with epithelial cells. Assuming no other factors (such as tissue antagonism), how do you explain Carrel's failure?

2-16. Suppose fibroblasts divided every 2.00 days, and another type of cell every 2.01 days. What would happen to the mixed cell culture?

2-17. Some experimenters have succeeded in examining living bacterial cells with the electron microscope by enclosing wet bacteria in envelopes of water-impermeable plastic. Their electron micrographs have not been very revealing. Why not?

‡2-18. Was the electron microscope required for the discovery of pinocytosis? Show how you arrive at your answer.

2-19. Using Appendix 10, give the diploid chromosome number of the following species: rice, onion, guppy, mouse, horse, man.

2-20. In Figure 2-19 are shown halftones of several stages of mitosis in a wild peony, as photographed by M. S. Walters and S. W. Brown. They are *not* ordered the same way as the diagram in Figure 2-17. Underneath each picture write the name of the stage.

2-21. There is an order in the pictures in Figure 2-19. What is it?

‡2-22. What is the chromosome number of the species shown in Figure 2-19?

2-23. "Other things being equal," a cell 20μ in length will have a metabolic rate (metabolism per unit mass) of *what,* as compared with a cell of the same proportions that has a length of 10μ? Assume that metabolism is limited in both cases by diffusion of food through the membrane.

‡2-24. A microscopist measures some cells of *Paramecium,* a protozoan. He finds that one of these cells is about 1¾ times as long as a human hair is wide, but that the hair is about 2½ times as wide as the protozoan. What are the approximate dimensions of the protozoan, in microns?

‡2-25. The higher the microscopic magnification, the smaller the volume that can be examined (with the same care) in a given period of time. Suppose that a certain volume of material requires 1 hour to be thoroughly examined with the highest power of an optical microscope. How much time will be required to examine it with the same care using the electron microscope?

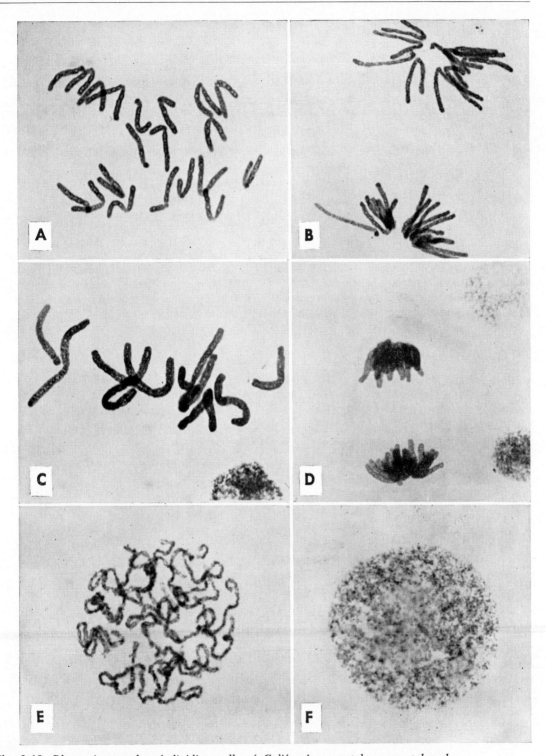

Fig. 2-19. *Photomicrographs of dividing cells of Californian coastal peony, taken by M. S. Walters and S. W. Brown. (From Srb, Owen, and Edgar,* General Genetics, *2nd ed., W. H. Freeman and Company, San Francisco, 1965.) Can you arrange the stages in the correct sequence?*

2-26. What is a "reciprocal experiment"? Illustrate, using the following example. In studying the inheritance of albinism, an albino male is crossed with a normal female. What would the reciprocal experiment be?

2-27. What is a "controlled experiment"? How does the biologist's use of the word "control" differ from everyday usage?

2-28. Describe a controlled experiment set up to test this hypothesis: "Students who drink coffee and study late the night before an examination will get higher grades than those who drink no coffee and go to bed early."

Readings

For a comprehensive statement of the cell theory and its history, see the studies of John R. Baker. Some of the original papers are reprinted in Hall's *A Source Book in Animal Biology*. For magnificent drawings and photographs of cell division, see McLeish and Snoad. Illuminating comments on drawing as a technique of discovery are found in Elias' essay. Methods, some of them quite simple, for culturing cells may be found in Philip R. White's manual.

Scientific American Offprints

76. Arthur K. Solomon: *Pores in the Cell Membrane*

79. Peter Satir: *Cilia*

90. Jean Brachet: *The Living Cell*

93. Daniel Mazia: *How Cells Divide*

96. Heinz Holter: *How Things Get Into Cells*

3

The Physical
Bounds of Life

17. The Molecular Picture of Matter

The boundaries between the sciences are man-made. They are matters of convenience, dictated by the reality that no one can do or know everything. Scientists, by voluntarily limiting themselves to such restricted fields as botany or zoology, chemistry or physics, increase their productivity. But the walls they erect between their fields must not be too high, and must have, here and there, holes for looking through them, or stiles by which to climb over them. It is particularly important that the walls separating biology from chemistry and physics be full of gaps, for history has shown how often a biologist has found an answer to one of his problems by looking beyond the property line into an adjacent field. As a matter of fact, physical scientists have also benefited by such violations of professional property rights. Not infrequently a biologist makes an observation that requires a physicist or a chemist to enlarge *his* theories.

Such an event occurred in 1828 when the botanist Robert Brown—who later discovered the nuclei of cells—reported some curious observations made with the microscope. Looking at some pollen grains suspended in water, Brown was struck by the fact that these grains showed continuous movement of a rather pointless, dancing sort, without consistent direction. Was this motion attributable to the life of the pollen grain? No; for dead pollen grains moved just as vigorously. Perhaps the motion was due to the particular chemical constitution of living or once-living matter? Again, no; for various mineral particles of approximately the same size showed the same type of movement. In fact, Brown could demonstrate only two factors that influenced the amount of movement: the size of the particles, and the temperature of the water—the smaller the particles, or the higher the temperature, the more vigorous the movement.

When this discovery was first reported, the time was not ripe for an explanation of **Brownian movement.** It was not until approximately fifty years later that physicists could explain the biologist's observations, as follows. The very small bodies that we see under the microscope move because they are jostled about by much smaller particles that are invisible even with the highest power of the optical microscope. These still smaller, invisible particles are called **molecules.** In the pages to follow, we will try to convey a picture of these molecules as envisaged by physical scientists. Many words will be used, but the reader who wishes to understand biology must go beyond the words and produce in his own mind dynamic pictures. We strongly commend this statement of the great biologist William Harvey: "Those who, reading the words of authors, do not form sensible images of the things referred to, obtain no true ideas, but conceive false imaginations and inane phantasms." Probably the majority of the "boners" written in science examinations are contributed by students who have no mental picture of the events and processes they are discussing. The student who, in the first instance, creates a mental picture of what he reads thereby establishes a framework to which can be attached a large number of ideas and concepts. Ideas that are thus *structured* can more easily be remembered than those that are not.

Picture, if you will, a world made up entirely of submicroscopic particles called molecules, with much space between them. Inside the molecules themselves there is further structure, but for the moment we will think of molecules as a sort of structureless ping-pong balls. Molecules are continuously in motion. When two molecules collide, they rebound from each other vigorously, for *molecules are perfectly elastic.* At the molecular level there is no such thing as friction or frictional losses of energy; therefore, the motion of molecules continues without end. Molecular motion is random motion: at any moment in time, a molecule at any particular place in space is as likely to be moving in one direction as it is in another. All matter is made up of moving particles, but the type and extent of movement depend on the condition of the matter. In gases, the molecules show almost no attraction for each other; as a result, a gas completely fills the space made available to it. In liquids, the molecules show more attraction for each other; as a result, a liquid does not fill all of any space made available to it, but rather flows into it until the height of the liquid is the same in all parts of the containing vessel. In solids, on the other hand, the molecules are strongly attracted to each other, each one being confined to a relatively small submicroscopic volume within which the molecule moves rapidly back and forth; consequently, a solid retains its shape, indifferent to a larger volume made available to it.

How big are molecules? They are very small indeed. Perhaps we can best get an idea of their size by comparing molecules with visible objects. Recall that a human hair is about 100μ in diameter. A single bacterial cell, which is about the smallest living thing that can be studied with a microscope, may be a cylinder 1μ long by 0.5μ in diameter; that is, its length is about 1/100 the width of a human hair (Fig. 3-1). Such a tiny cell is made up of approxi-

Fig. 3-1. *Approximate comparative sizes of a human hair, a bacterial cell, and a molecule.*

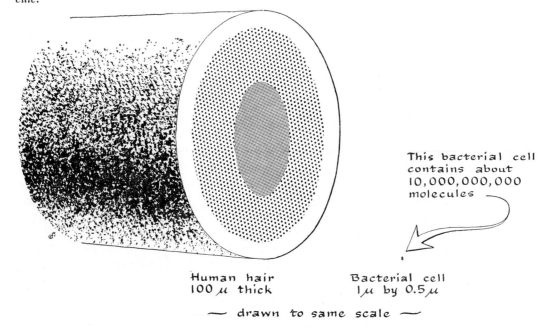

This bacterial cell contains about 10,000,000,000 molecules

Human hair 100 μ thick

Bacterial cell 1 μ by 0.5 μ

— drawn to same scale —

mately 10^{10} molecules. Molecules vary greatly in size; some of the largest (millions of times the mass of the smallest) can be studied with the electron microscope, but the smallest of them—by far the great majority—are too small to be detected even with this instrument. The evidence for their existence is indirect.

18. Kinetic Energy and Temperature

Bacteria, like the much larger pollen grains, exhibit Brownian movement. But since a bacterial cell is so large that it contains 10 billion molecules, it must be subject to the bombardment of millions of molecules. How does it happen, then, that the bacterial cell "jitters" visibly under the microscope? If the movements of molecules are at random, should not the bombardment of so many millions of molecules against a bacterial cell average themselves out, thus causing no net change in position of the microscopic cell? In answering this question, we must begin with the fact that the bacterial cell *does* move in a Brownian fashion. If molecules are as small as we say (and there is no doubt of this), Brownian movement indicates tremendous molecular velocities. As one would expect from the picture we have developed, not all molecules at any given instant are moving at the same speed. In fact, the range of speed is very great, but under ordinary conditions an average figure for the speed of molecules is about ⅓ of a mile per second. With such great velocity it is possible for even a tiny molecule to move a relatively huge bacterial cell. Most of the Brownian movements are not due to single molecular impacts, but rather to the momentary lack of balance in the force of the molecular bombardment on opposite sides of the cell. Since molecules are capable of performing such **work** as moving bacterial cells, we say that molecules possess **energy.** They possess this energy by virtue of their movement; we therefore call it **kinetic energy** (Gr. *kineo* = move; the same root is found in "cinema"— short for "cinematograph").

Robert Brown observed that a particle moves

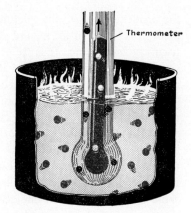

Fig. 3-2. *Temperature is a measure of molecular motion.*

faster and changes its direction more frequently when suspended in hot water than when in cold. Why is this? The most reasonable explanation is that at high temperatures the invisible molecules move more rapidly than they do at lower. In fact, *temperature is a measure of the kinetic energy of molecules.* With this statement in mind, let us re-examine the well-known fact that the mercury rises when a thermometer is put in hotter surroundings, and see how this fact may be interpreted in terms of the molecular picture of matter. Figure 3-2 is designed to help us in this visualization. When the bulb of a cool mercury thermometer is immersed in a pan of hot water, the rapidly moving molecules of the water impart some of their kinetic energy to the molecules of the glass of the thermometer; as these glass molecules gain in kinetic energy, they impart some of their energy in turn to the molecules of the mercury enclosed by the glass tube. *When molecules move faster, they hit harder against each other, thus increasing the average distance between themselves.* Or, looking at the situation macroscopically, we say that when a substance is heated, it expands. We can see now why the mercury in the thermometer rises as the surrounding temperature increases. It is because the average kinetic energy of the mercury molecules is increased.

In the preceding exposition, use was made of a picture printed on paper—namely, Figure 3-2. At the risk of being obvious, we must point out the inadequacies of the picture. In the first place, it is static. In the second place, it is quantitatively misleading. It is quite clear that the size of the molecules depicted is far from correct. Furthermore, the representation of the glass of the thermometer as some sort of material (glass?) within which are embedded molecules (glass molecules?) is incorrect also. There is no material that *contains* molecules; on the contrary, all material *is* molecules. But it is easy to appreciate the difficulty faced by an artist grappling with the molecular concept of matter. The student who wishes to understand science must mentally transcend the limitations of any medium of the graphic arts. The diagrams printed in science books are only aids to the visualization of reality, not reality itself.

19. Probability and the Movement of Molecules

Among the great changes in thought in the past three centuries have been a gradual decline in the belief that the world is demonstrably governed by necessity and absolute certainty and an increase in the tendency to look at problems of the most diverse sorts as ones that are best understood as probability situations. The molecular theory of matter involves probability in the most intimate way. This has already been implied by our use of the word "random" in speaking of the motion of molecules. We want now to see some of the consequences of random motion, and how they are related to the size of things.

Picture a tiny box divided into two equal rooms: one colored, one black (Fig. 3-3). Between them is a door that is gas tight. We suppose, to begin with, that the door is closed and all the molecules (exactly 12) are in the colored room, none in the black (Fig. 3-3A). What will happen, however, if we open the door? The first molecule to reach the opening will pass into the black room and continue moving until it strikes a wall and rebounds. Subsequently, other molecules will move from colored room to black room, each molecule continuing in a straight line until it bumps into other gas molecules or into the wall. Very soon a census would reveal the same number of molecules in both rooms (see Fig. 3-3B). Once this situation is reached, it will be maintained indefinitely unless outside forces interfere.

How does it happen that the numbers of molecules in the two rooms soon become equal and remain equal? It surely does not imply any intelligence on the part of the molecules. We can most easily see what it is that makes the two numbers equal if we first *assume* that they are equal and ask what it is that keeps the numbers equal.

Assume that the situation diagrammed in Figure 3-3B has been reached, with 6 molecules in each room. All of these molecules are in continuous motion. All directions of movement are equally probable. The probability of some molecule moving from the colored room to the black room is exactly equal to the probability of some other molecule moving from the black to the colored room—a fact indicated in Figure 3-3C by two equal, oppositely pointing arrows. Therefore, it is most probable that the number of molecules will remain the same in the two rooms.

The argument can be put another way. Suppose, by some chance, the molecules moved differentially until there were 8 molecules in the colored room and only four in the black (Fig. 3-3D). The motion of the molecules is of a random sort. Any particular molecule is as likely to be moving in a specified direction as is any other molecule. That is, the probability that a *particular* molecule in the colored room will be moving toward the right is exactly the same as the probability that another *particular* molecule in the black will be moving toward the left. *But there are twice as many molecules in the colored room as there are in the black.* Therefore, the probability that *some* (unspecified) molecule will move from colored to black is twice as great as the probability that *some* (unspecified) molecule will move from black to colored. The colored-to-black movement will remain more probable than the opposite movement until the number of molecules in the two

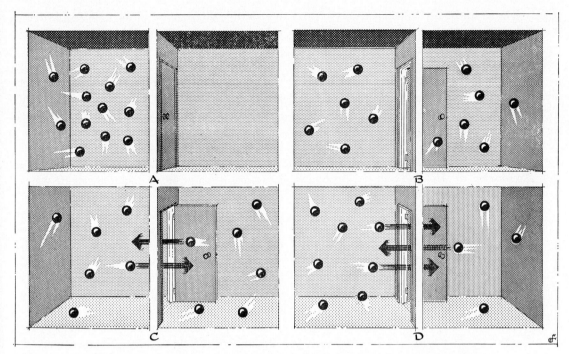

Fig. 3-3. *When a door is opened between two compartments, the number of molecules in one becomes approximately equal to the number in the other* (B). *When this state has been reached, it will tend to continue because the probability of a molecule moving from left to right is the same as the probability of one moving from right to left, as indicated by the equal arrows in* C. *Should the number of molecules in the left compartment be twice as great the the number in the right compartment* (D), *the probability of a movement from left to right would be twice that of a movement from right to left, as indicated by the arrows. Hence, the inequality of the two compartments would eventually be eliminated. The argument is stated in terms of a few molecules, whereas even a small volume (say that of a thimble) contains many millions of molecules.*

rooms is equal. From this time on, a movement $\longrightarrow$ will be as probable as one $\longleftarrow$; therefore, the number of molecules in the two rooms will remain the same.

The critical reader will notice in this discussion the following unexpressed assumption: Of a number of possible events that have different probabilities of occurrence, the most probable one will happen. Is this true? Are we justified in making this assumption?

Everyone knows that sometimes the less probable event happens. To take a common example: A player *sometimes* wins money from a slot machine—*but only rarely.* The odds of a slot machine are arranged in favor of the ma-

chine and its owner. If a customer plays the machine only a few times, he may come out winner. If he plays it a great many times, he is almost certain to lose; that is, the probability of his winning becomes very small. Looking at the problem from the other side, we may say that the owner, since he is in effect playing a great many games with the odds in his favor, is almost certain to win. Where large numbers are involved, we may, *as a practical matter,* disregard the possibility of the less probable event happening.*

Let us return to the molecules in the two rooms. It is apparent that, by chance, the mole-

* 3-1. Does the owner of a gambling house gamble?

cules might be unequally distributed to the two rooms, but the probability of a *significantly* unequal distribution will *decrease* as the number of molecules *increases*. By the laws of probability, the probability that *all* the molecules will be in one room (either room) with the opposite room empty can be calculated. The calculations for a few simple cases are shown in Table 3-1.

TABLE 3-1 *The Probability of an Unequal Distribution of Molecules in a Two-Room Box at a Given Instant.*

NUMBER OF MOLECULES	ALL MOLECULES ARE IN:	
	EITHER ROOM	BLACK ROOM
2	1/2	
4	1/8	
6	1/32	
8	1/128	
10	1/512	
12	1/2,048	

With only 2 molecules, there is a 50-50 chance that both will be together, but with as few as 12 molecules, the probability that all the molecules will be together is less than 1 in 2,000. In other words, if we made an observation every half-hour of the setup pictured in Figure 3-3*B*, only about once every 42 days would we expect to find all the molecules in one room.† Less extreme inequalities in molecular distribution would, of course, be more probable.

Ordinarily, how many molecules are we dealing with? Suppose the two "rooms" each had a volume of only one pint and contained air at ordinary temperature and pressure. In this case, the number of molecules would be about 2.5×10^{22}. From the trend of the figures in Table 3-1, it is clear that the probability of all the molecules being in one room is so ridiculously small that we can ignore it. Indeed, the probability that the number of molecules in one room would exceed the number in the other by as much as 0.001 percent is very, very small. In a setup of this sort, no one has ever found a

measurable discrepancy in the number of molecules in connecting chambers. Our measuring devices are too crude.

Another point may be made here. Earlier it was stated that an ordinary bacterial cell is made up of about 10^{10} molecules. This may seem like a great many. But it is close to the minimum number present in any organized living being that exhibits all the characteristics of living things as described in §4. Most of the molecules of an ordinary bacterial cell are water molecules. The molecules of specific kinds of proteins, substances known to be essential in living things, make up only a small fraction of the total number of molecules. There is probably a minimum number of molecules needed in an organized living being. This minimum is undoubtedly connected with the probability matters we have been discussing. Life—whatever it is—depends on the regular, reliable performance of certain functions. These functions are linked with the behavior (including the movement) of molecules, and will be carried out dependably only if a relatively large number of molecules are involved. An organism composed of too few molecules would be too much at the mercy of the so-called Laws of Chance to be reasonably sure of survival.

20. The Slowness of Diffusion

A bit of dye is placed in the bottom of a tall tube of water (Fig. 3-4). After a time, color is visible at some distance up from the bottom, showing that the dye is slowly moving through the liquid. As weeks go by, the edge of visible color slowly creeps upward. Ultimately, the dye will be almost uniformly distributed throughout the tube, though it may be years before this is true. The intermixing of the molecules of dye and water is brought about by the process of **diffusion,** which involves the continuous molecular motion of both substances.

There is something paradoxical about diffusion that needs explaining. The speed of molecules is very great—for instance, "methylene blue" molecules travel at approximately 100

---

† 3-2. What is the probability that all the molecules will be *in a specified room* (say, the black one) at a given instant? Fill in the last column of Table 3-1.

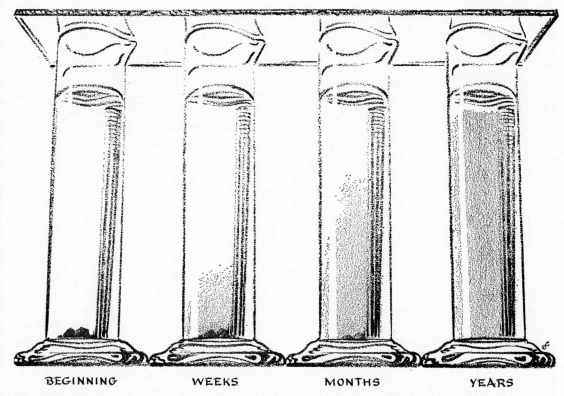

BEGINNING   WEEKS   MONTHS   YEARS

Fig. 3-4. *The macroscopically visible diffusion of dye through water as the result of the continuous, random motions of invisible molecules of dyestuff and water.*

meters per second, or more than 200 miles per hour—and yet diffusion is very slow. How come? Because molecules bump into each other. A molecule that travels 200 mph will not go even a millionth of a millionth of a mile before it will bump into another molecule and have its direction of motion altered, perhaps even reversed. Each molecule is jostled by others millions of times per second. Appreciable diffusion over a distance of inches necessarily takes months or even years.

21. Diffusion, the Scale Effect, and the Variety of Living Forms

The slowness of diffusion creates a problem that all living things must meet: how to carry out exchanges with the environment at a fast enough rate to permit life to go on. Many ways in which this problem is met will be seen as we survey the plants and animals later, but by way of preview we can list the principal ways here.

1. Small size is an answer to the problem posed by diffusion. Recall (§10) that as an organism of constant shape increases in size, its surface increases as the square; its volume, as the cube of some basic dimension. Since metabolic needs are proportional to volume, and diffusion is proportional to surface, it follows that a smaller organism will be able to supply its needs by diffusion better than a larger one. Bacteria are so small that their quite high metabolic rates are made possible by diffusion alone.

2. A low metabolic rate is an answer, of a sort, to the problem—an acceptance (so to speak) of the consequence of the scale effect. In part, all large organisms give this answer. The metabolic rate of an elephant (rate of chemical reactions per gram of tissue) is lower than that of a mouse.

3. A change in shape may alter the surface:

volume relationships. Many large seaweeds have very flat, thin *fronds* ("leaves") with a great amount of surface available for exchanges with the environment.

4. Motion of the organism with respect to the environment increases the rate of exchange between the two. Such motion may be brought about in three ways: (a) By the organism being attached in a region of environmental motion. The intertidal zone of the ocean is a region of great movement of water. Many organisms—for example, seaweeds and barnacles—by attaching to rocks in intertidal zones, take advantage of the rapid movement of the environment. (b) By the organism being attached and forcing the environment through itself. A sponge, for example, is essentially a pump with two holes in it; it moves a tremendous quantity of the environment through itself in the course of a day. (c) By the movement of the organism through the environment. The movement may be simply at random, as it apparently is with some bacteria; or away from regions of unfavorable environment (some protozoa); or directed by sense or-

gans toward favorable environmental stimuli. In its highest development this last type of reaction is found among vertebrate predators hunting their prey. At this level the problem of food procurement has progressed far beyond the level of simple molecular diffusion with which we began this discussion (though even here, there are problems of diffusion once the food is in the intestinal tract of the predator).

22. Osmosis

If a fresh cabbage leaf is placed in a strong solution of sugar or salt, it soon wilts. Quantitative study shows that the weight of the cabbage leaf is decreased by this treatment. Why? What has the leaf lost, and why?

To develop the principles needed to answer these questions, let's consider a quite different setup (Fig. 3-5*A*). The large opening of a thistle tube is covered with a *membrane* of dead pig's bladder, and the bowl of the thistle tube is filled with a strong sugar solution. The in-

Fig. 3-5. *Osmosis. Experimental observations shown in* A *and* B; *theoretical explanation indicated in* C. *The D-P membrane holds back sugar molecules while permitting free movement of water molecules; probability principles therefore insure a* net *movement of water molecules from the more watery solution to the less watery.*

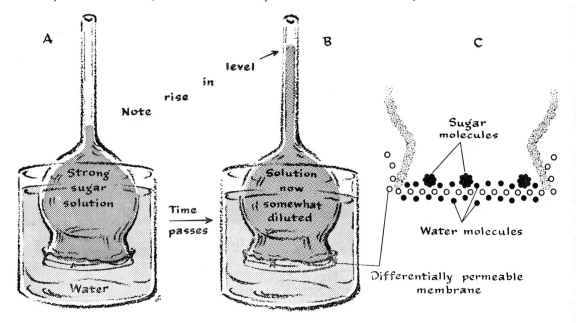

verted tube is immersed in a beaker of water. In a half-hour (Fig. 3-5*B*), the level of the solution inside the thistle tube rises perceptibly. This rise indicates that water has passed through the membrane; quantitative chemical analysis shows that the sugar solution within the thistle tube is now less concentrated.

How are these results explained? In terms of the molecular theory of matter developed previously. From the experiment it appears that water molecules are permitted to pass through the membrane more readily than sugar molecules. Because such a membrane is not equally permeable to all kinds of molecules, we call it a **differentially permeable membrane** or, for brevity, a **D-P membrane** (sometimes called a "semipermeable membrane"). For simplicity in developing the theory of such a membrane, we will first assume that the membrane is completely *impermeable* to sugar molecules and freely permeable to water molecules.

Consider now the molecular situation as it must be on the two sides of the D-P membrane. The membrane itself is made of molecules, as shown in Figure 3-5*C*, with spaces between them through which water molecules can pass, but not sugar molecules. At the outset of the experiment, there are more water molecules (per unit area of the membrane) beneath than above the membrane. Consequently, by the principles of probability developed previously (§19), the net movement of water molecules will be upward—from the beaker into the thistle tube. Sugar molecules are found only above the membrane. If the membrane were permeable to sugar molecules, we would expect the net movement of sugar molecules to be downward, through the membrane. But the membrane (by hypothesis) is impermeable to sugar molecules; hence this transfer cannot take place. As a result, the over-all effect is a net movement of water molecules into the thistle tube; consequently, the level of fluid in the thistle tube rises. Such a differential movement of molecules through a differentially permeable membrane is called **osmosis.**

Will the process of osmosis in the thistle-tube setup ever come to an end? It will be noted that, as the level of the fluid rises, the weight of the solution inside the thistle tube pressing against the D-P membrane increases, and the hydrostatic (fluid) pressure in the thistle tube becomes greater than that in the surrounding vessel. That is, as a result of osmosis, hydrostatic pressure develops. Ultimately, the hydrostatic pressure pressing downward against the membrane stops the net movement of water molecules into the thistle tube from the outside. The stronger the initial concentration of sugar inside the thistle tube, the greater the hydrostatic pressure required to bring the process of osmosis to a halt.

Solutions can, in fact, be characterized quantitatively in terms of the hydrostatic pressure they are capable of producing by osmosis. However, to make meaningful measurements, we need to modify slightly the experimental apparatus. It is clear that the process of osmosis results in a dilution of the sugar solution inside the thistle tube and a consequent diminution of its osmotic effect as the experiment proceeds. We can measure the potential ability of a solution to support the weight of a column of water by using a setup essentially like that shown in Figure 3-6. The column of fluid inside the thistle tube is covered by a tight-fitting piston on which can be placed weights of varying size. By adding weights to the piston until the process of osmosis is just stopped, we can determine the weight-supporting ability of a solution subjected to osmosis, that is, the **osmotic potential** of the solution. A strong sugar solution has a higher osmotic potential than does a weak one. Two solutions that have the same osmotic potential (though they may contain different substances) are said to be **isosmotic** (Gr. *isos* = equal + *osmos* = pushing).

In developing the theory of osmosis, we made the assumption that the D-P membrane was permeable only to molecules of the *solvent* (water), being completely impermeable to molecules of the *solute* (sugar). Such a stringent assumption is not necessary. Many a D-P membrane permits movement of solute molecules also. If, however, solute molecules move through the membrane less rapidly than do sol-

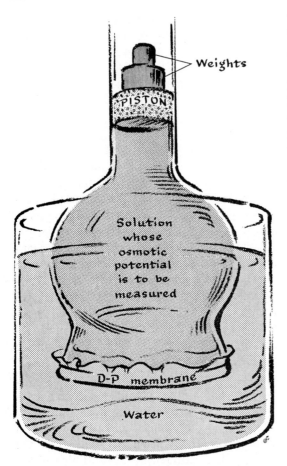

Fig. 3-6. *How the osmotic potential of a solution might be measured. (In practice, a less direct method is used to apply weight or pressure to the solution.)*

vent molecules, the solution will still have an osmotic potential; though measurement of this potential must be made rapidly, before there is an appreciable movement of solute molecules through the membrane.

23. Osmotic Phenomena and the Life of Cells

Now what about the cabbage leaf placed in brine (§22)? Can we explain its behavior? The results can be explained in terms of osmosis. In the cabbage leaf the membrane of every cell of the leaf acts as a differentially permeable mem-

brane, as do the membranes of all living cells. The living stuff inside a cabbage cell is a rather dilute solution of various chemical substances. When the cell is exposed to a solution with a high concentration of solute—that is, with a high osmotic potential—the net movement of water through the D-P membrane of the cell is from the cell outward. As all the cells lose water, the cabbage leaf becomes limp.

Since all cells are surrounded by a differentially permeable membrane, all cells are confronted with problems raised by osmosis. Some cells, such as those of many species of bacteria, are capable of surviving exposure to solutions of widely different osmotic potential; whereas others, such as those of the higher plants and animals, cannot survive exposure to a solution that is far from being isosmotic. With a multicellular plant or animal we may, in fact, speak of two environments: (1) the environment in the ordinary sense, that part of the world that is completely outside the organism; and (2) the **internal environment,** the internal fluids that bathe the cells. Many of the problems of the physiology of multicellular organisms revolve around the maintenance of the isosmotic character of the internal environment.

A solution that is not isosmotic with respect to a given cell is said to be **hypotonic** (Gr. *hypo* = under + *tonos* = tension) if it has a lower osmotic potential than the cell, or **hypertonic** if its osmotic potential is higher.* If the tonicity of a solution is too far from that which is normal for the cell, life becomes impossible; but within limits, a cell can survive exposure to nonisosmotic solutions. It does so by two different sorts of adjustments:

1. The cell may be "realistic" and undergo a change in the concentration of chemicals in its cytoplasm until the cytoplasm is nearer to being isosmotic with the environment. The water content of one common species of bacteria, *Escherichia coli,* can vary from 60 to 80 percent, depending on the osmotic potential of the fluid around it.

---

* 3-3. Will a cell shrink or swell when it is immersed in a hypotonic solution?

2. The cell may "resist" * the osmotic effect of the environment. All cells possess, to a greater or lesser extent, an ability to maintain inside the cell membrane an osmotic potential different from the potential outside.

Not only can cells control their total osmotic potential, but they can also accumulate fairly high concentrations of some substances that are present in dilute solution around them. As a striking example of such ability, consider certain seaweeds that accumulate iodine from the sea water until its concentration reaches that of one or more parts per hundred inside the plant, although the concentration of this element in sea water is only about five parts per hundred million.

Whenever a cell maintains its volume unchanged in an environment that is not isosmotic, or whenever a cell accumulates a substance, it brings about what we would regard as an improbable situation, according to the molecular concept of matter just developed. It is as though the situation shown in *C* of Figure 3-3 changed to the situation in *D*. How can a cell bring about such a change? We cannot give a general answer to this query, but there is no doubt that the ability to produce and maintain such improbable situations is characteristic of living cells. Only so long as a cell is alive and actively metabolizing can it produce and maintain differences on the two sides of its membrane. Biologists use the term **active transport** to indicate the movement of substances across a cell membrane in a direction contrary to that which the concentration gradient would cause if the system were nonliving. Active transport requires *work*, in the physical sense; *energy* is expended to carry out this work. Food is the source of this energy. A cell that is seriously starved can no longer carry out active transport; the chemical differences between inside and outside rapidly become less and the cell dies. In this particular context we see the importance of energy in the maintenance of life. We must now review in a more general way what scientists have discovered about energy and its relation to life.

* 3-4. Why the quotation marks around this word?

24. The Laws of Thermodynamics

Among the many fundamental discoveries of the nineteenth century the first two laws of thermodynamics are preeminent. These laws are concerned with energy, with what we can and cannot accomplish with it. The **First Law of Thermodynamics** asserts the principle of the **Conservation of Energy:** *Energy can be neither created nor destroyed.* An objection can be raised to this crude statement of the principle by those who know about radioactivity, but for the moment we will ignore the objections and accept the statement of the principle as it was given before 1903. (A more sophisticated treatment of the problem is deferred to the next section.)

That energy is in general conserved has been known in a dim way since antiquity. The conservation of energy is implicit in the laws of levers. A gymnast of 70 kilograms dropping 2 meters to one end of a teeter-board can catapult another gymnast of the same weight to about the same height. If the other gymnast is lighter he will be propelled higher; if heavier, not so high. In countless practical situations, over many centuries, men must have made decisions that presupposed the truth of the First Law. As science became more conscious of its foundations in the nineteenth century the question as to the truth of this principle was explicitly raised. There were a number of interesting practical situations in which it was not obvious that energy was conserved. Consider, for instance, water poised at the top of a waterfall: it has potential energy by virtue of its position. A moment later, the water tumbles into the pool below. What happens to the positional energy it formerly possessed? Some of it has been converted into the sound-energy associated with the roar of the falls, but surely not much. What has happened to the rest?

It was this problem that James Joule (1818–1889) attacked in midcentury, using, however, some laboratory apparatus that was a bit more convenient than a waterfall. By the most careful experiments he showed that mechanical agitation of water increases its temperature.

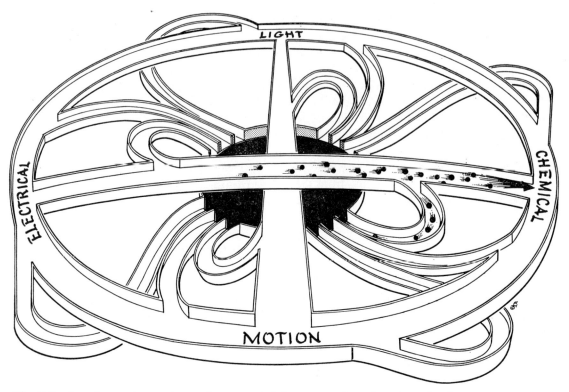

Fig. 3-7. *Any form of energy can be converted into any other, but there is always "leakage" to heat energy.*

The effect is slight: to raise the temperature of one pound of water one Fahrenheit degree it takes 778 foot-pounds of energy (the amount of energy in one B.T.U.—British Thermal Unit). To verify this you might, say, drop a piece of iron weighing 77.8 pounds ten feet into a pan containing a pint of water—the temperature of which should rise 1°F. (This is a hopelessly sloppy experiment; but you get the idea.)

The work of a great number of clever experimentalists established the doctrine that any form of energy can be converted into any other, without loss or gain. Motion to heat; motion to electricity; electricity to light, and so on.* Figure 3-7 shows a visual metaphor of the idea of the interconvertibility of the various forms of energy. The ball bearings represent energy; by tilting the apparatus, energy may be converted from one modality to another. The picture also

brings in another important idea. Note the off-ramps leading to the "heat sink;" it is a fact that every conversion of energy from one form to another always produces a certain amount of heat. Once in this sink the energy is lost to the other modalities. The *ultimate* result of all energy changes is the complete "degradation" of energy to heat.

It is because degradation is so easy to bring about that we commonly measure any form of energy by converting it into heat, which can then be measured in Calories. One Calorie—capital C—is the amount of heat required to raise the temperature of one kilogram of water 1° Celsius* (starting at 14.5°C). Figure 3-8 shows the kind of apparatus used to determine

---

* 3-5. Give examples of these conversions: (a) light to motion, (b) motion to light, (c) chemical to electrical, and (d) light to chemical.

* Formerly known as "Centigrade." An international conference on weights and measures, in 1948 and again in 1960, gave well-reasoned arguments for abandoning the term Centigrade in favor of the term Celsius, from the name of Anders Celsius, a Swedish astronomer who first described this thermometric scale in 1742. (See H. F. Stimson, 1962. *Science,* **136**:254.)

the caloric value of any substance. A sample of the substance must first be completely dried, then weighed and put into a pan inside the calorimeter. The vessel is closed and filled with oxygen under pressure. When the sample is ignited by remote control the heat it produces in burning raises the temperature of the inner water jacket. By measuring this change one determines the number of Calories released.

It is impossible to stop the degradation of energy. *In any conversion of energy from one form to another, there is always a decrease in the amount of useful energy.* This is one way of expressing the **Second Law of Thermodynamics,** a law first explicitly stated in 1850 by the German physicist Rudolf Clausius (1822–1888). To see why loss of useful energy is inevitable we reintroduce our model of the two interconnected rooms, only this time we shall have the two rooms differ not in the number of molecules within them, but in the speed (energy content) of the molecules (Fig. 3-9*W*). Initially the

molecules in the left room are moving (on the average) more slowly than the molecules in the right room. As time passes, what will happen? The laws of probability tell us that, unless only a very few molecules are involved, the difference in kinetic energy of the molecules in the two rooms will soon vanish as the molecules exchange sides or hit each other about in a random fashion (Fig. 3-9*X*). The kinetic energy of the molecules in the two rooms will soon be equal.

Of course, like anything that is merely most probable, this state would not *have* to be reached. In 1871, the English physicist James Clerk Maxwell (1831–1879) pointed out that

. . . if we conceive a being whose faculties are so sharpened that he can follow every molecule in its course, such a being, whose attributes are still as essentially finite as our own, would be able to do what is at present impossible to us. For we have seen that the molecules in a vessel

Fig. 3-8. *A bomb calorimeter for determining the heat content of a dry sample of, for example, a foodstuff.*

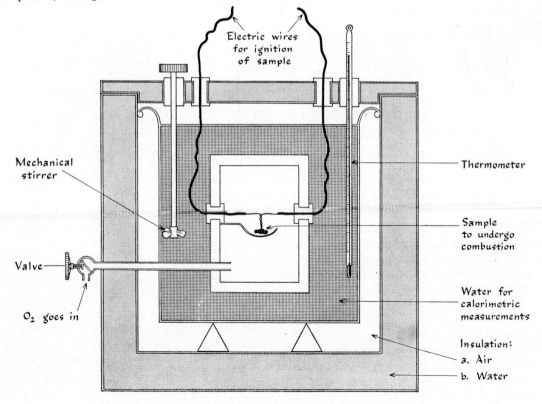

Electric wires
for ignition
of sample

Mechanical
stirrer

Thermometer

Sample
to undergo
combustion

Valve

Water for
calorimetric
measurements

O_2 goes in

Insulation:
a. Air
b. Water

II LAW OF THERMODYNAMICS

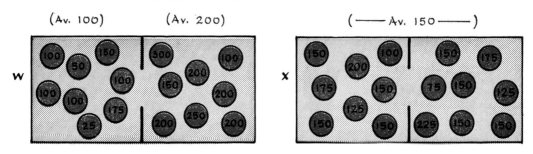

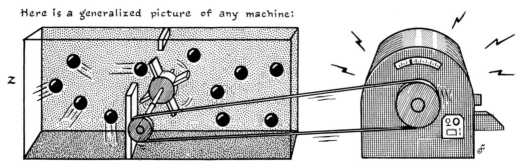

It is the difference in energy levels that we utilize to drive our machines

Fig. 3-9. *Probability principles involved in the driving of machines.*

full of air at uniform temperature are moving with velocities by no means uniform, though the mean velocity of any great number of them, arbitrarily selected, is almost exactly uniform [Fig. 3-9X]. Now let us suppose that such a vessel is divided into two portions, A and B, by a division in which there is a small hole, and that a being [Fig. 3-9Y], who can see the individual molecules, opens and closes this hole, so as to allow only the swifter molecules to pass from A to B, and only the slower ones from B to A. He will thus, without expenditure of work, raise the temperature of B and lower

that of A, in contradiction to the second law of thermodynamics.

But Maxwell did not think it possible for anything analogous to his little "being" (now known as **Maxwell's Demon**) to exist. That is, Maxwell suspected that it would be impossible to devise any sort of physical apparatus that could act as a demonic valve on the molecular level. This suspicion was confirmed in 1929 by theoretical studies of the Hungarian physicist Leo Szilard (1898–1964).

Let us see now what it is that any machine—and in this sense, a living organism is a machine—really does. Figure 3-9Z shows an idealized machine, which we will suppose to run without friction in the ordinary sense. What drives the machine? *The difference in the energy* of the molecules of the two rooms. Since the machine is, by hypothesis, "frictionless," can it run forever? No. *It must stop when, by the operation of the laws of probability, the difference in energy levels disappears.* Notice that it is not energy, but *difference* in energy levels that we use to drive our machines. It is this difference that we call "useful energy." "Friction"—in the broadest sense—is as unavoidable as probability. This fundamental relation between the Second Law and the laws of probability was first made clear in 1877 by the German physicist Ludwig Boltzmann (1844–1906).

The Second Law may be stated in yet another way, from a slightly different point of view. Compare the two rooms in Figure 3-9W and X. In what respect is X different from W? One way of verbalizing the difference is to say that there is more *chaos* in X; or we may say that there is more order in W, more disorder in X. Physicists make this point by using the word **entropy,** a word coined by Clausius to indicate (roughly) the *amount of disorder* in a system. Using this term, we may say that in any isolated system *entropy always tends to increase toward a maximum.* This is another way of stating the Second Law.

However we state it, the Second Law asserts that a machine can be kept going only by being continuously supplied with **"negative entropy,"** that is with a difference in energy levels which it may exploit. An organism is a kind of machine. The negative entropy it lives on is the food it takes in, which becomes degraded to the high-entropy products carbon dioxide and water.

25. Radioactivity and Conservation Laws

We must refine our idea of the conservation of energy in the light of the facts of radioactivity. The story is briefly told. In 1895, Wilhelm Roentgen discovered X-rays, noting that these rays could penetrate opaque matter and could make other substances become phosphorescent, that is, make them glow in the dark. A. H. Becquerel became interested in the latter phenomenon and turned X-rays on many substances including uranium compounds. Irradiated uranium was phosphorescent; but so also was unirradiated uranium, as Becquerel discovered in 1896. This was puzzling: the light given off in phosphorescence is a form of energy: where does it come from? Previous to this time, chemical phosphorescence had been known; this is the light given off during certain chemical reactions. Such phosphorescence can be altered in extent by changing the temperature (which changes the rate of the reaction) or by adding chemicals that interfere with the reaction. But the phosphorescence of uranium is indifferent to temperature and chemical interference. Most puzzling.

In 1903, Pierre Curie and A. Laborde studied a similar substance, radium, and showed that a chunk of it is always hotter than its surroundings. Since it inevitably loses heat to the environment, this means that it must constantly generate heat. Yet the first measurements failed to show any loss of substance. Did this mean that heat and light were being created out of nothing? Would the First Law have to be abandoned?

Very refined measurements proved that the generation of light and heat by radioactive substances is accompanied by a loss of weight. But the amount of energy produced is tremendously large compared with the energy yielded by chemical reactions. For instance, 1 gram of a mixture of carbon and oxygen, burning to form carbon dioxide, yields 2.2 Calories of heat. In contrast, a gram of the radioactive element radon in the process of becoming converted to radium-D yields almost exactly a million times as much energy. If we collect all the end products of this reaction (radium-D, and alpha and beta particles) we find that they weigh only 0.9999 gm. That is, one ten-thousandth of the weight has been converted to energy. The quantitative equivalence of mass and energy was given in 1905 by Albert Einstein (1879–1955) in his famous equation, $E = mc^2$. The letter E stands for energy, m for mass, and c is the velocity of light. By this equation the two separate principles—the conservation of matter and the conservation of energy—are united into a single conservation law. For "everyday" physical phenomena we continue to deal with the conservation of mass and of energy separately; when dealing with radioactive substances and the transmutation of elements we must use the unified law. But in either case, the world obeys conservation laws.

26. Impotence Principles

From the ancient Greeks, science has received two great gifts:

1. The idea that the world can be understood. We can see this attitude especially well expressed in the Hippocratic writing on *The Sacred Disease,* that is, on epilepsy, which was believed to be caused by the gods and hence beyond human understanding and control.

As for this disease called divine, surely it too has its nature and causes whence it originates, just like other diseases, and is curable by means comparable to their cure. It arises—like other diseases —from things which enter and quit the body, such as cold, the sun and the winds, things which are ever changing and never at rest. Such things are divine or not—as you will, for the distinction matters not—and there is no need to make such division anywhere in nature, for all are alike divine or all are alike human. All have their antecedent causes which can be found by those who seek them.

This attitude, probably rare in Greek times, permeates all of modern science. With respect to that which is not yet understood, the belief that it can be understood is always a form of faith. It is the near universality of this faith among modern scientists that has made scientific inquiry so productive.

2. The Greeks also gave us a second idea, the idea that there are limits to what we can do. By

a most simple and beautiful proof Euclid showed that the square root of two could never be expressed as a simple fraction, or as a terminating decimal. $\sqrt{2} = 1.4142 \ldots$ and it goes on forever, without repeating. The idea that an exact answer is impossible shocked Euclid's contemporaries profoundly and there are people today who are unwilling to accept such a limitation to human knowledge. Even in the twentieth century books have been written purporting to show that the circle can be squared and the angle trisected, using compass and straight-edge alone.

The idea that there are limits to the possible has not penetrated the consciousness of Western man very deeply, partly because science has been so fantastically successful in developing unforeseen methods of control. Think of the airplane, of radio and television, and of electronic "brains." Yet slowly, beneath the surface of a thousand surprising inventions, there has developed an underpinning of principles that state the limits of the possible—**impotence principles** the English physicist Edmund Whittaker has called them. The Law of the Conservation of Matter is one; the Laws of Thermodynamics are others. These latter assert, to take an everyday example, that perpetual-motion machines are impossible. Science fiction thrives on dreams of omnipotence. The Patent Office refuses even to look at applications for patents on perpetual-motion machines.

Many common people, converts to a sort of religion of Science, are emotionally repelled by impotence principles. They see them as discouraging, pessimistic inhibitions of action and progress. Scientists see them otherwise. Only if some things are impossible can other things be. A conservation principle asserts (to put the matter most generally) something of this sort:

$$A + B = C + D.$$

For example, with respect to substances it asserts that the weight of materials before a reaction must exactly equal the weight after. Matter is conserved. If the results of an experiment fail to show an equality of the two sides of the equation, we go back to the laboratory and look again. In this way, the noble gases were discovered. Indeed, it would be hard to point to an important discovery in quantitative science that did not involve the discipline of the conservation laws. Science fiction writers and the worshippers of Science may "solve" their problems with dreams of Superman, Buck Rogers, or omnipotent Martians; the practitioners of science must construct their theories within the framework of impotence principles. The willingness so to do springs from a sort of moral cleanliness unknown to believers in Santa Claus.

27. On the Nature of Scientific Revolutions

Critics of science often point with scorn to the impermanence of supposedly permanent principles. How, they ask, can one place emotional reliance in an intellectual structure whose foundations are constantly shifting? Yesterday, we thought the Conservation of Energy was a foundation stone of science. Then we found the exception of the radioactive elements and replaced our old foundation stone with a new one engraved $E = mc^2$. How do we know that this is permanent? Maybe tomorrow we will discover a Santa Claus and throw out all conservation principles?

By its nature, such an argument is unanswerable. All we can do, each of us, is decide how we are to proceed with the next day's work.

The attitude of scientists has been admirably set forth by the physical chemist G. N. Lewis (1875–1946):

The scientist is a practical man and his are practical aims. He does not seek the *ultimate* but the *proximate*. He does not speak of the last analysis but rather of the next approximation. His are not those beautiful structures so delicately designed that a single flaw may cause the collapse of the whole. The scientist builds slowly and with a gross but solid kind of masonry. If dissatisfied with any of his work, even if it be near the very foundations, he can replace that part without damage to the remainder. On the whole, he is satisfied with his work, for while science may never be wholly right it certainly is never wholly wrong; and it seems to be improving from decade to decade.

Lewis states the scientist's position in terms of the metaphor used by critics of science, a metaphor which evokes the image of a *structure* that has *foundations*. It is a vivid metaphor, but from Lewis' discussion and from the history just given of the conservation principles it is apparent that there is something wrong with the metaphor. A house is seriously weakened if its foundations are disturbed; the "structure" of science, though momentarily disturbed, emerges stronger from the ordeal. Stronger, and in many important respects, unchanged. The discovery of radioactivity altered our view of the conservation of energy, but did not wholly destroy it. The *spirit* in which we view the world is still much the same.

Questions and Problems

3-6. Make a list of the **boldface** terms in the text of this chapter. Write out a definition or description of each. Compare your work with the text.

3-7. Write out a brief description of the contributions of the following men, giving the approximate date of each: R. Brown, Joule, Clausius,

Maxwell, Boltzmann, Roentgen, Curie, Einstein.

3-8. Bacterial cells are so small that all of them exhibit Brownian movement. Some bacteria are motile. In observing a bacterial cell under the microscope, by what criteria would you decide if the movement it showed was only

Brownian or was in part due to its own motility? Show by drawings the sort of path you would expect an immotile cell to take, and the sort a motile one might take.

‡3-9. Ice floats in water. Which are farther apart (on the average), the molecules in ice or the molecules in water?

‡3-10. Referring to the experiment diagrammed in Figure 3-2, what happens to the average kinetic energy of the water molecules when a cool thermometer is put into warm water? By such a procedure, then, does one determine the true temperature of the water? Explain.

3-11. Consider the requirements of two clumps of algae ("green-water slime") living on the hulls of two boats. One of the boats is a ferry plying from one bank of a fresh-water stream to the other. The other boat makes a daily trip from a town that is 50 feet above sea level to the ocean bay at the mouth of the river. If the cytoplasm within the algal cells at all times has a constant osmotic potential approximately equal to that of the fresh water, and if the two algal clumps flourish equally well, which clump has the greater need for foodstuffs or other source of energy? Explain.

‡3-12. Immotile seaweeds range in size from microscopic species to giants weighing dozens of pounds. Some seaweeds are found attached to the rocks or bottom near the coast. Some are free-floating in the ocean. With almost no exceptions, the large forms are coastal forms, not free-floating. Can you give a general theoretical reason for this fact?

3-13. Consider the setup of Figure 3-5A. Compare (or contrast) the short-term results, using the following alternative assumptions: (a) The D-P membrane is completely impermeable to the solute molecules. (b) The D-P membrane permits solute molecules to pass through, but more slowly than the solvent molecules.

‡3-14. Regarding the setup of Figure 3-5A, compare (or contrast) the results obtained in the long run on assumptions (a) and (b) above.

3-15. In the setup of Figure 3-5A, does gravity influence the long-term results obtained if the D-P membrane is completely impermeable to solute molecules?

‡3-16. Most of the iodine in our bodies is found in the cells of the thyroid gland. All of the cells of our bodies get their foodstuffs (including iodine) from the blood that circulates throughout the body. The concentration of iodine in the blood stream is very low, much lower than it is in the thyroid cells. In general terms, how do the thyroid cells manage to accumulate iodine?

3-17. Distinguish between a gas, a liquid, and a solid in terms of the molecular theory of matter.

3-18. In which of the three states of matter is molasses in June? In January?

‡3-19. Physicists regard window glass as a sort of transparent molasses in a very cold January. Is glass a liquid or a solid?

3-20. What bearing does the answer to the preceding question have on the use of common words in science?

‡3-21. To help us conceive the immense number of molecules, Lord Kelvin calculated that if one should pour a glass of "labeled" water into the ocean, stir thoroughly, and then dip a glassful of water out of the mixture, one would find 100 of the original molecules in the second glass of water. Assume Kelvin's figures are correct. A gram-mole of water (18 grams) contains approximately 6×10^{23} molecules (Avogadro's number). Assume the glass holds 300 grams of water. (a) How many molecules are there in a glass of water? (b) How many glassfuls of water are there in the ocean?

3-22. Another way of conceiving the number of molecules in a glass of water: Assume that everyone in the world does nothing but count out molecules; that there are 3×10^9 people; that each one counts at the rate of one molecule per second all day, all night long; that the glass contains 300 grams of water. A year consists of about 3.16×10^7 seconds. How many years will it take the entire population of the world to count all the molecules in a glass of water?

‡3-23. If one of the Hippocratic physicians were to return to life and take part in biological research, would he be a vitalist or a mechanist?

‡3-24. How does the small-c calorie differ from the Calorie used in this text?

3-25. In some climates heat is the last thing we want when we eat food. Yet food value is always reckoned in Calories. Why?

3-26. A physicist's wife frequently refers to her three-year-old son as "Entropy's Little Helper." Why?

3-27. Norman St. John-Stevas has written: "The law's view that the contract of marriage creates a permanent status and is not dissoluble by mutual consent, is founded on Christian principles. 'It has got there,' as Sir Patrick Devlin points out, 'because it is Christian, but it remains there because it is built into the house in which we live and could not be removed without bringing it down.' "

What is the metaphor used here? Do scientists use the same metaphor when speaking of science? If so, with the same implications or not? Explain.

3-28. Surveying various fields of human knowledge and belief, what would you say is the relation between the relative reliability of the various fields and the relative inalterability of their recognized foundations?

Readings

In his *What Is Life?* Schrodinger discusses the problem of the relative sizes of living things and physical particles. One of the earliest clear statements that matter is best conceived in terms of particles is to be found in *On the Nature of Things* by Lucretius (95–55 B.C.), particularly in Book I; the student should notice the evidence Lucretius marshals in support of his theory. For a sensitive exposition of an impotence principle (the Pythagorean Theorem) see Hardy's *A Mathematician's Apology*.

Scientific American Offprints

96. Heinz Holter. *How Things Get Into Cells*

262. Arthur M. Buswell and Worth H. Rodebush. *Water*

4

From Lavoisier to Molecular Biology

---

28. Is Life a Flame?

"Life is like a fire," says an old Arab proverb: "it begins in smoke and ends in ashes." An ancient sage of China made a similar remark: "Man's life is like a candle in the wind." To the eye of the poet there are many similarities between life and a flame. The common man must have been aware of these for centuries before Antoine Lavoisier (1743–1794) gave the analogy deeper meaning.

Toward the end of the eighteenth century the work of a number of men, principally Joseph Priestley (1733–1804) and Lavoisier, revealed the framework of the chemical events involved in both burning and respiration. It was possible to write similar equations for the over-all results of the two processes:

Combustion: Organic material $+ O_2 \longrightarrow$
$$CO_2 + H_2O + \varepsilon. \quad (1)$$

Respiration: Organic material $+ O_2 \longrightarrow$
$$CO_2 + H_2O + \varepsilon. \quad (2)$$

The ε in the above equations stands for energy. By failing to distinguish between different kinds of energy we emphasize the similarity of the two processes at the risk of obscuring important differences. In combustion the energy we are interested in is heat, whereas the usefulness of respiration does not usually lie in the heat produced but in other energetic actions: moving, fighting, seeking a mate, and even thinking (though the energy involved in the last is so small as to be almost undemonstrable). Heat is usually regarded as a by-product of respiration.*

The thinking of 19th century physicists focused on the interconvertibility of the various forms of energy and the importance of demonstrating the conservation laws. Biologists, following the fashion, set out to show that energy was conserved also in organisms. This was not easy. Lavoisier had shown how heat production by a living organism could be approximately measured (see Fig. 4-1), but there were experimental difficulties. For instance, the evaporation of water from the lungs of the animal in Lavoisier's apparatus introduces an appreciable error.† In 1824 the Paris Academy offered a prize for the best essay on the origin of animal heat. The contest was won by a man who claimed that only 90 percent of this heat originated from respiration. Such apparent nonconservation, of course, opened a wide door to vitalist speculations, which were not slow in appearing. It was not until 1894 that Max Rubner (1854–1932) removed the support for such speculations by showing that, within the limits of experimental error, conservation laws are completely observed by living organisms. His study, carried out with dogs, necessitated

---

* 4-1. In what instance may it be considered the principal product?

† 4-2. In what direction? Explain.

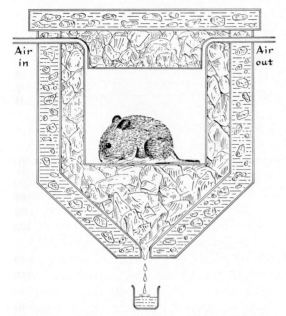

Fig. 4-1. *Lavoisier's calorimeter. The outer jacket is an "adiabatic jacket"; the mixture of ice and water prevents heat flow to and from the inner jacket. The heat from the animal melts the ice in the inner jacket. From the amount of water collected heat production can be calculated. (It takes 80 Calories to melt 1 kilogram of ice.)*

(among other refinements) the collection and calorimetric combustion of the urine and feces. Since Rubner's experiments there has been no reason to think that energy is either created or destroyed by a living organism; an organism merely converts one form of energy to another.

Demonstrating that conservation laws apply to living as well as to nonliving phenomena was a great and important accomplishment. But the practical necessity of establishing this fact through the use of the techniques of calorimetry had unfortunate effects on the unconscious mental set of many biologists: it tended to make them take too seriously the superficial similarity of the equations of combustion and respiration, and to think of a living organism as merely some sort of heat engine. The operation of a man-made heat engine such as an automobile motor may be symbolized thus:

$$Fuel + O_2 \longrightarrow CO_2 + H_2O$$
$$+ \text{ Heat (which produces motion).} \quad (3)$$

Is not the operation of a living machine adequately represented by a similar equation?

$$Food + O_2 \longrightarrow CO_2 + H_2O$$
$$+ \text{ Heat (which produces motion, etc.).} \quad (4)$$

Is not "life" some sort of flame which drives the machinery of the organism?

That a living organism cannot possibly be a heat engine becomes clear when we consider the basic characteristics of such engines. Figure 4-2 shows, in the most generalized possible way, the nature of a heat engine. For such a machine to run, there must be a **source** which has a higher temperature than the **sink**. Thermodynamic theory indicates that the maximum possible efficiency of such a system is given by the following formula:

$$\text{Efficiency} = \frac{T_2 - T_1}{T_2}.$$

where: T_2 = temperature of the source;
        T_1 = temperature of the sink.

Both temperatures are given in degrees on the Kelvin scale (273 degrees + the Celsius degrees). The greater the difference in temperature between source and sink, the greater the efficiency.

How efficient is an organism, considered as a machine? Man is a convenient animal to use for this study. Performing sustained muscular work, he achieves an efficiency of about 20 percent; that is, 20 percent of the energy in the food he eats is converted into foot-pounds of work. *If* he is a heat-engine, what must be the

Fig. 4-2. *The generalized idea of a machine. Negentropy at the source is degraded to maximum entropy in the sink, in the process, the machine is set in motion.*

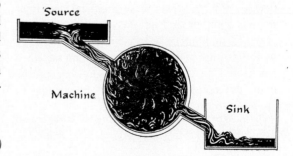

temperature-difference of his "source" and "sink"? With the sink at room temperature (293°K), we have:

$$\text{Efficiency} = 0.2 = \frac{T_2 - 293}{T_2}.$$

Solving for T_2:

$$T_2 = 366° \text{ Kelvin}$$
$$= 93° \text{ Celsius.}$$

In other words, for man (or any other organism) to operate as a heat engine with 20 percent efficiency, some part of the body (the thermodynamic *source*) would have to be at a temperature almost as high as the boiling point of water. No such hot spot occurs; the temperature differential of different parts of the body at room temperature is seldom as great as two degrees Celsius.*

It is clear, then, that an organism is not a heat engine. Any comparison of a living body to an internal combustion engine or of life to the flame of a candle must be regarded as no more than an analogy.

29. The Chemical Approach to Life

Developing concurrently with thermodynamics and accelerating rapidly toward the end of the nineteenth century was another approach to the study of living organisms, the chemical approach. In such studies, energy occupied a secondary position; emphasis was on the step by step, molecule by molecule, atom by atom changes that take place during the complex of processes we indicate by the words "respiration" or "metabolism." The difficulties of this work were (and are) enormous. The picture that has emerged from these chemical investigations is complex and not easy to master; but it is worth making the effort for it is surely one of the glories of our civilization that we have penetrated so deeply into the mystery of the living process. Fortunately it is not necessary to

become a chemist to see the general outlines of the biochemical picture of life. The following sections present some of the elementary ideas needed to see this picture.

30. Atoms

There are millions of different kinds of chemical substances in the world. Each pure substance (by definition) is made up of only one kind of molecule. The molecules are composed of atoms. How many different kinds of atoms are there? The answer depends on just what one means by "different kinds."

The first man to bring order out of chaos in surveying the world of atoms was the Russian Dmitri I. Mendelyeev, who, into the years 1869–1871, arranged the **elements** (as the different kinds of atoms are called) into a "periodic table" that grouped them according to their chemical properties. A modern descendant of Mendelyeev's table is to be found in Appendix 1. In Mendelyeev's system there were places for 92 elements, of which the last was uranium. During the Second World War (1939–1945), elements "beyond" uranium, called "transuranium elements," were found. These are unstable and do not occur in nature; they are made in the laboratory by the use of cyclotrons and other high-energy accelerators. The transuranium elements are of no importance in biology, except as they (and other elements produced by atomic bombs and such) are destructive of life. All the elements, both natural and artificial, known to date number just over one hundred.

But in a sense this is not all the kinds of atoms. With the discovery of a new kind of neon by J. J. Thomson in 1913, it was realized that not all atoms that properly bear the same name are exactly the same. There are, for example, six different kinds of oxygen, which we symbolize as O^{14}, O^{15}, O^{16}, O^{17}, O^{18}, and O^{19}. What do we mean by "different"; and why do we call them by the same name? We call them all "oxygen" because they all enter into the same kind of chemical reactions; they are chemically indistinguishable. They are different in

---

* 4-3. What is the maximum possible efficiency of a heat engine operating with that temperature difference?

weight, O^{17} being $\frac{1}{16}$ heavier than O^{16}, and O^{18} being $\frac{2}{16}$ heavier.

Different kinds of the same element are called **isotopes** (Gr. *isos* = equal + *topos* = place) of one another.* All known elements have at least two isotopes.

31. Radioactive Isotopes and Their Use in Research

The history of science shows that it is almost impossible to give a name to any object or phenomenon that will not eventually prove to be, in some sense, inappropriate. Consider the word "atom": it comes from the Greek roots *tomos,* meaning a slice or cut, and *a,* meaning not. Anything called an atom should be noncuttable, nonsplittable—in a word, stable. Yet, as every literate man now knows, many kinds of atoms are unstable. Uranium-238 (U^{238}), for example, breaks down to form a number of other elements, one after another, producing ultimately a stable form of lead, Pb^{206} (the "Pb" is for L. *plumbum*). During the course of this breakdown, two kinds of small particles are thrown off:

alpha particles (α-particles or α-rays), which are helium atoms stripped of their outer electrons; these particles come off moving at high speed.
beta particles (β-particles or β-rays), which are electrons moving at high speed.

In addition, a radioactive element may give off **gamma rays** (γ-rays), a form of electromagnetic radiation, as light and heat are also, but radiation of much shorter wavelength and invisible to the human eye. Gamma rays are identical with the rays from an X-ray tube operated at high voltage.

High-energy radiation has destructive effects on living cells. Such effects on the somatic tissues of the body are in part reparable (as is

somatic damage generally); in the affected region, undamaged cells reproduce, their daughter cells replacing the damaged cells. Cells differ in their sensitivity to high-energy radiation. Use is made of this fact in treating cancerous growths. Cancer cells are usually more sensitive to radiation than are the normal cells around them. By carefully controlling the exposure of a cancerous part of the body to high-energy radiation, it is often possible to kill cancer cells while leaving normal cells alive (though somewhat damaged). Reproductive cells also are very sensitive to radiation damage, which, with them, includes the type of change we call "mutation," that is, change in the hereditary characteristics. But discussion of all such matters must wait until later.

At the moment, we are concerned with another aspect of isotopes: their usefulness in solving questions in biology. Isotopes, recall, are chemically identical, but can be physically distinguished. Nonradioactive isotopes must be identified by their different weights: heavy hydrogen, H^2 (sometimes called **deuterium**), and heavy oxygen, O^{18}, must be so identified. Radioactive isotopes reveal themselves in the act of disintegrating. We have no sense organs that can perceive the radiations given off, but we can detect them either with such instruments as a Geiger counter, or with photographic film. The latter method is often quite simple to carry out. If a potted plant is irrigated with water containing radioactive phosphorus, within a few hours this phosphorus may be demonstrated in a leaf by clamping the leaf against a piece of photographic film for a while. (The film is not, of course, exposed to light.) When the film is developed in the usual way, the presence and distribution of the radioactive element is apparent. The resulting record is called an **autoradiograph.**

Routes followed in the transport and circulation of substances in plants and animals are often difficult to figure out. Radioactive isotopes have made the problem much easier. The first **tracer experiments,** carried out by the Hungarian physicist George de Hevesy in 1923, had (according to legend) a homely beginning some

---

* 4-4. The term "isotope" was invented by Frederic Soddy (1913). What sense do you make of its etymology?

years earlier when de Hevesy was a needy student living in a boarding house. Young de Hevesy suspected that the scraps left on the boarders' plates of one day were used to make up the goulash that was served the next. To test his hypothesis, de Hevesy surreptitiously added some radioactive particles to the food scraps on his plate. When the inevitable goulash appeared the next day he quietly set aside a sample which he later took to the laboratory for testing. It was radioactive.

Some time later de Hevesy carried out an experiment of somewhat wider scientific significance. He immersed the roots of bean plants in solutions of radioactive lead and showed that it was possible to follow the ascent of the solute up the stem of the plant by making very local measurements of radioactivity. Interesting though this experiment was as a first example of tracer work, it was not very significant because lead is not an element normally involved in fluid transport in plants. More significant work is possible now that we have available isotopes of the elements normally involved in metabolism and transport (carbon, phosphorus, etc.). The quantities of radioactive materials needed for tracer experiments are extremely minute, and the consequent damage to cells is virtually nil. We can therefore assume that the path taken by radioactive isotopes is identical with that followed by stable isotopes of the same element.

32. Organic Molecules:
Problems of Synthesis

The science that deals with the way in which atoms are joined to form molecules is called **chemistry.** In this field the common word "substance" is given a special meaning: to a chemist, a **substance** is some material that consists of one kind of molecule only. Water (if pure) is a substance (H_2O) as are table salt (NaCl) and table sugar ($C_{12}H_{22}O_{11}$). The **molecular formula** of a substance is indicated by a shorthand that shows both the kinds and the numbers of atoms present in each molecule. As indicated

above, each molecule of water has two atoms of hydrogen and one of oxygen; each molecule of table salt has one atom each of sodium (L. *natrium*) and chlorine. The chemical abbreviations may be found in Appendix 1.* If material consists of more than one substance, it is called a **mixture.** Most of the materials we deal with in this world, from soil to plum pudding, are mixtures.

Although there are only about a hundred different kinds of atoms in the world, the number of different substances that can be formed from them is practically limitless. A substance that consists of more than one kind of atom is called a **compound.** Atmospheric oxygen (O_2) is *not* a compound; water (H_2O) is. Each compound is composed of (*1*) *particular kinds of atoms that* (*2*) *are present in fixed and definite proportions and that* (*3*) *are bound one atom to another in specified ways.* We can illustrate these three points by examples.

1. *With respect to kinds of atoms:* A molecule of H_2S has almost the same weight as one of H_2O. But these are quite distinct substances (compounds). The former is called hydrogen sulfide, and is a noticeable component of the bouquet of rotten eggs. H_2O is water and is odorless.

2. *With respect to proportions of atoms:* The substances H_2O and H_2O_2 both contain hydrogen and oxygen atoms, but in different proportions. The former is, of course, water; the latter is called hydrogen peroxide and is a strong antiseptic and bleaching agent.

3. *With respect to molecular structure:* A molecule of methyl ether, a poisonous substance used as a refrigerant, has in it two atoms of carbon, six of hydrogen, and one of oxygen (C_2H_6O). A molecule of ethyl alcohol, the well-known intoxicant, has the same atoms in the same proportions. But methyl ether and alcohol are distinctly different substances. The properties of a substance are the properties of its molecules. Since methyl ether and alcohol have markedly different properties, an ether molecule and an alcohol molecule must be different.

---

* 4-5. Give, in words, the composition of a molecule of table sugar.

Chemists tell us that the two substances have these structures:

H   H   H H
| | | |
H—C—O—C—H   H—C—C—O—H.
| | | |
H   H   H H

methyl ether   ethyl alcohol

In the above **structural formulas,** the lines between the letters (atoms) indicate the presence of forces that tend to hold the atoms near one another. These attractive forces are called **chemical bonds.**

Chemistry is divided into two branches: **organic chemistry** and **inorganic chemistry.** Originally, the distinction between these two divisions was based on the origin of the substances studied: Organic chemistry was concerned with substances that were obtained from organisms; inorganic chemistry was concerned with all others. It was for a long time supposed that man would never be able to synthesize an organic substance from an inorganic one. But in the early part of the nineteenth century, as chemists succeeded in transforming organic substances into one another, various influential chemists (notably Liebig, Berzelius, and Wöhler) came to suspect and then to assert that the original distinction between the two fields would ultimately be destroyed. So confident were they that when the first synthesis of an organic compound from inorganic substances was finally achieved by Adolph Kolbe in 1845, the event passed almost unnoticed.* In fact, many organic chemistry texts even today give the credit to the wrong man (Wöhler) and the wrong time (1828).

Chemists are now able to synthesize many thousands of organic compounds from inorganic substances, so the original meaning of "organic" is gone. The distinction between the two great fields of chemistry is now this:

Organic chemistry is the chemistry of the carbon-containing compounds.

Inorganic chemistry is the chemistry of all compounds that do not contain carbon.

---

* 4-6. What event in the history of the cell theory does this remind you of?

A few substances are studied in both fields— CO_2 (carbon dioxide), for example. Since this substance may readily be made from the elements carbon and oxygen, when a chemist succeeds in making an organic compound using only CO_2 as a source of carbon, we say that he has achieved a **total synthesis,** or a **synthesis from the elements.**

33. Ions and Ionization

Physicists and chemists have ways, indirect but reliable, of determining the number of molecules in a quantity of matter. From the theory of osmosis developed in §22 and §23, it would appear that equal numbers of molecules of two different soluble substances should exert the same osmotic potential against a differentially permeable membrane. Often this expectation is realized. A liter of aqueous solution containing "one gram molecular weight" (180 g) of the organic chemical glucose ($C_6H_{12}O_6$) exerts the same osmotic potential as a liter containing a gram molecular weight (342 g) of sucrose ($C_{12}H_{22}O_{11}$). Both solutions have the same number of molecules of the solute. However, a liter of salt solution with one gram molecular weight (58.5 g) of the inorganic substance sodium chloride (NaCl) exerts much more osmotic potential than the number of molecules would lead us to expect. Exceptions such as this (which are numerous) were first pointed out, and explained, by the Dutch chemist J. H. van't Hoff in 1886. The osmotic potential of a dilute solution of NaCl is, in fact, almost *twice* the expected value, calculated from the number of molecules present. In other words, such a substance has almost twice as many osmotically active particles as it has molecules. The substances sodium nitrate ($NaNO_3$) and magnesium sulfate ($MgSO_4$) behave in a similar fashion.

How can this be? Have the molecules broken up into their elements? No; for the element sodium reacts violently with water, and we see no such reaction; chloride is a gas, and we see no gas; sodium nitrate should give three elemental particles, rather than two; and so on. Rather, the story is this: Each of the substances mentioned splits into two electrically charged particles that are neither molecules nor atoms. These particles are called **ions** (from a Greek word meaning *to go* or *to come*). NaCl ionizes into a positively charged sodium ion, Na^+, and a negatively charged chlorine ion, Cl^-; $NaNO_3$ yields Na^+ and $(NO_3)^-$; $MgSO_4$ yields Mg^{++} and $(SO_4)^{--}$. When an ionized substance is dissolved in water, its ions **dissociate** to yield separately mobile particles, capable of acting osmotically. Some substances ionize to yield more than two ions per molecule, and have the corresponding osmotic effect (for example, $Na_2SO_4 \longrightarrow Na^+ + Na^+ + (SO_4)^{--}$).

A brief explanation of the origin of the charges will be given. Every atom consists of a central core, or **atomic nucleus**, surrounded by one or more minute particles called **electrons**. Each electron constitutes a negative charge of 1. The atomic nucleus is positively charged. The nucleus of an atom has a positive charge exactly equal to the total negative charge of the swarm of electrons around it, and so the net charge is zero. If one of the electrons is *removed* from the outer swarm, the atomic remainder becomes a **positive ion.**

A high degree of ionization is very common among inorganic, or noncarbon-containing, compounds. On the other hand, organic compounds, *for the most part,* are ionized weakly, or not at all. Consequently, most organic molecules act osmotically like so many single particles.

34. Acids and Bases

We will first look into the chemical nature of acids and bases in the inorganic realm. **Acids** taste sour. Common inorganic acids are HCl (hydrochloric acid), HNO_3 (nitric acid), H_2SO_4 (sulfuric acid), and H_3PO_4 (phosphoric acid). It will be noted that the only element common to all of these is hydrogen. These substances dissociate as follows:

$$HCl \rightleftharpoons H^+ + Cl^-,$$
$$HNO_3 \rightleftharpoons H^+ + NO_3^-,$$
$$H_2SO_4 \rightleftharpoons H^+ + HSO_4^-,$$
$$H_3PO_4 \rightleftharpoons H^+ + H_2PO_4^-.$$

It is the hydrogen ion that gives these substances their acidic properties, one of which is their sour taste. The acidic properties of the substances depend on their ability to dissociate to form H^+ ions. The more readily a molecule produces H^+ ions, the more strongly acid it is.

An inorganic **base** is a substance that can produce the hydroxyl ion, OH^-. NaOH (sodium hydroxide) and KOH (potassium hydroxide) are bases:

$$NaOH \rightleftharpoons Na^+ + OH^-;$$
$$KOH \rightleftharpoons K^+ + OH^-.$$

A substance that can produce OH^- ions is said to be basic, or *alkaline.*

When solutions of an acid and a base are mixed, the H^+ and the OH^- ions combine to form the weakly dissociated HOH, water (H_2O). If the proper proportions of acid and base are used, the resulting solution is neither acidic nor basic, but is **neutral.** H_2O is neutral.

As an example of such a reaction, we may consider

$$NaOH + HCl \longrightarrow HOH + NaCl, \quad (5)$$

which would be better written

$$Na^+ + OH^- + H^+ + Cl^- \longrightarrow$$
$$HOH + Na^+ + Cl^-. \quad (6)$$

Any inorganic substance that can ionize to produce $+$ and $-$ ions, neither of which is a hydrogen or a hydroxide ion, is called a **salt.** NaCl, for instance, is a salt. Other salts are KCl, $NaNO_3$, and Na_3PO_4.

Equation 6 may be generalized thus:

$$a \ base + an \ acid \longrightarrow water + a \ salt. \quad (7)$$

In the organic realm some additional chemical groups confer acid or basic properties. For example, $-COO^-$ and $-NH_2$ are common basic groups, and $-NH_3^+$ is acid. In general, organic substances dissociate into ions only slightly, and so most organic acids and bases are only weakly so. A common organic acid is acetic acid, which dissociates thus:

$$CH_3COOH \rightleftharpoons CH_3COO^- + H^+.$$
(acetic acid) $\rightleftharpoons$ (acetate ion) + (hydrogen ion)
(8)

35. Some Compounds of Biological Importance

Thousands of organic compounds are to be found in living things. Fortunately they can be grouped into several large classes of substances; the first useful categorization of these was offered by William Prout in 1827, who spoke of "the albuminous, the oily, and the saccharine" substances—or, as we would now say, proteins, fats, and carbohydrates. We will briefly consider the chemical composition and importance of these, and other, substances.

CARBOHYDRATES. The name implies that carbon has been hydrated—that is, has had water compounded with it. From a strictly quantitative standpoint there is something to be said for this: glucose, $C_6H_{12}O_6$, can be rewritten $(CH_2O)_6$. The 1:2:1 ratio of C:H:O in this compound *approximately* obtains in sucrose, $C_{12}H_{22}O_{11}$; in lactose and maltose, also $C_{12}H_{22}O_{11}$; and in raffinose, $C_{18}H_{32}O_{16}$. Glucose is called a "monosaccharide" and sucrose a "disaccharide." These substances are interconvertible by reactions that add (**hydrolysis**) or remove (**condensation**) a molecule of water, thus:

$$C_{12}H_{22}O_{11} + H_2O \xrightarrow{\text{(hydrolysis)}} 2C_6H_{12}O_6; \quad (9)$$
$$C_{12}H_{22}O_{11} + H_2O \xleftarrow{\text{(condensation)}} 2C_6H_{12}O_6. \quad (10)$$

The process of condensation can be performed repeatedly to produce polysaccharides (etymologically, "many sugars"). Glycogen, or "animal starch," is a polysaccharide that serves for the chemical storage of energy in animal livers and muscles. The true starches serve the same function in plants; they result from the condensation of many simple sugars. Still more condensed molecules are the celluloses, insoluble compounds that are important constituents of the cell wall of plants.

The process of digestion (as in the intestinal tract of a mammal) depends upon the hydrolysis of various compounds including the carbohydrates. As a general rule, the larger the carbohydrate molecule, the more difficult it is to digest. Starches are more difficult to digest than disaccharides and trisaccharides. Celluloses are still more difficult; most animals cannot digest them, and among those that can (e.g., cows), cellulose digestion takes many hours.

FATS. As an example of a fat, we may take stearin, the molecular formula of which is $C_{57}H_{110}O_6$. It is important to notice that *there is a much smaller proportion of oxygen in a fat molecule* than there is in a carbohydrate molecule. Fats are used by both plants and animals as a means of storing energy; they are more efficient energy-storers than are starches. That is, the amount of energy stored per pound of storage product is greater in fat than in starch, partly because the fat does not include much of the oxygen needed for its respiration, which may readily be picked up from the surrounding atmosphere.

AMINO ACIDS. Amino acids include one element not found in either fats or carbohydrates—namely, nitrogen (N). The simplest amino acid is glycine, NH_2CH_2COOH. The NH_2 group is called an *amino group,* and the COOH group is called a *carboxyl group,* and contributes acid characteristics to the molecule. Every amino acid possesses both of these groups.

The number of conceivable different kinds of amino acids is tremendous; but only 20 different kinds are used in the construction of proteins (discussed below). The names of these 20 primary amino acids are given in Table 4-1, together with their conventional abbreviations. Their chemical constitutions are given in Appendix 7, which should be looked at now: notice the similarity in structure of the various amino acids. As a consequence of this similarity many of the ordinary methods of chemical puri-

TABLE 4-1   *The Common Names of the 20 Primary Amino Acids, Together with Their Conventional Abbreviations*

ABBR.	NAME	ABBR.	NAME
Ala	*alanine*	Leu	*leucine*
Arg	*arginine*	Lys	*lysine*
Asn	*asparagine*	Met	*methionine*
Asp	*aspartic acid*	Phe	*phenylalanine*
Cys	*cysteine*	Pro	*proline*
Glu	*glutamic acid*	Ser	*serine*
Gln	*glutamine*	Thr	*threonine*
Gly	*glycine*	Try	*tryptophan*
His	*histidine*	Tyr	*tyrosine*
Ilu	*isoleucine*	Val	*valine*

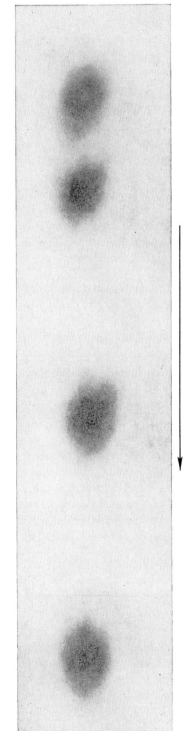

Mixture of amino acids put on here — X

Glycine

Alanine

Valine

Leucine

fication are insufficiently powerful to separate mixtures of amino acids.

The analysis of the amino acid content of proteins has been aided immensely by the development of **paper chromatography.** This technique is based on a phenomenon everyone must have observed at some time or other. If you let a large drop of ink fall on a piece of blotting paper you may observe that the ring that develops is not uniform; there may be an inner circle that is darker than the outer, with a rather sharp boundary. Most ordinary writing inks have two (or more) pigments. Spreading out through blotting paper the various pigments are differentially absorbed. If you should cause them to pass through enough paper by constantly feeding fresh solvent into the center you could separate the pigments.

Paper chromatography depends on the differential solubility of substances in the components of a solvent mixture, and on their differential adsorption on paper. A mixture of amino acids can be placed at one edge of a strip of paper (at X in Fig. 4-3) and the material "driven" through the paper by the continuous application of solvents at the edge. The solutes

Fig. 4-3. *Paper chromatography. Solvent applied to upper edge of paper "drives" the amino acids through the paper, which separates them. Subsequently, reagents are applied to the paper to color the amino acids.*

will travel at different speeds, and so can be separated. A technique for separating substances by adsorption was first worked out in 1897 by the American petroleum chemist D. T. Day, using columns of granular adsorbents rather than paper; this technique was later applied to the separation of plant pigments by the Russian Mikhail Tswett, in 1906. Many elegant applications of paper chromatography were developed in the 1950's by the English chemists A. J. P. Martin and R. L. M. Synge. By using a succession of solvents, various components can be separated; if the substances are colorless (as amino acids are) their position can be revealed subsequently by treatment with suitable color-producing reagents.

Except for the simplest amino acid, glycine, each amino acid occurs in two different forms called **stereoisomers:** there is a "left-handed form," or *l*-amino acid (*l* for L. *laevo* = left); and a "right-handed form," or *d*-amino acid (*d* for L. *dextro* = right). The meaning of this distinction can be seen by comparing the two forms of the amino acid alanine, shown in Figure 4-4 and Figure 4-5. If you fold one of the pages so as to bring the two molecules side by side, you will notice that, although the atoms are put together in the same order in both molecules, it is not possible to superimpose one molecule on top of the other, atom for atom. However, if you use a small hand mirror and hold one of the pages at such an angle that you can bring the mirror-image of one alongside the direct picture of the other, you will see that these two views are such that one could be superimposed on the other.* The *d*- and *l*-forms are mirror-images of each other.

What of it? In a way, nothing of it. In the chemical laboratory these two are the same, the properties of one are the properties of the other (except that they rotate polarized light differently). When the chemist synthesizes any of the amino acids he always synthesizes a mixture

of exactly equal proportions of the *d*- and the *l*-forms; he is unable to synthesize one alone. *But:* within the laboratory of living bodies it is quite otherwise. The *d*-forms of amino acids are rare; they occur in some naturally produced compounds, but never in proteins. *Proteins contain l-amino acids only.* An organism may be able to use both forms for energy, but it can use only one for growth. This is most significant. Chemically, one should be as suitable as the other, but evidently the whole machinery of the living cell is standardized on a "left-hand" pattern of amino acids. (Sugars and other carbohydrates, which play a different role in the cell, are of the *d*-form.) It is as though we were dealing with a machine with exchangeable parts, but with all nuts, bolts, and other threaded parts with a left-hand thread. A priori, it might not matter whether the threads were left- or right-handed, but once one system was adopted, parts with the opposite threading would be useless. So it is with living matter; it can repair itself and grow new living matter only with laevo-amino acids. The fact that all organisms are built on the *l*-system of amino acids argues strongly for a single origin of life on earth.

Proteins. Proteins are composed of amino acids, united through C-N-C linkages called **peptide bonds.** The bulding blocks of proteins are often referred to as "amino acid **residues.**" This curious phraseology is the result of the technique of investigation. In analyzing a protein its peptide bonds are broken, leaving the investigator with a "residue" of amino acids. "Amino acid units" would be a better term for these constituents. A molecule with many amino acid units in it is called a **polypeptide.** A large polypeptide is called a protein. There is no sharp distinction between these terms.

Twenty amino acids are shared by almost all organisms, but many of the proteins of each species are found in no other species. There are, therefore, millions of different kinds of proteins. How can so few amino acids be used to produce so many different proteins? It is simple. Think of the twenty different amino acids as the different letters of the alphabet (exclusive

---

* Alternatively, you can verify this by holding the two pages together in the normal way and shining light through them: one image will then be superimposable on the other.

of *u, v, w, x, y* and *z,* say); think of the proteins as words, but very long words—generally with several hundred letters each. The number of possible different words (proteins) should be astronomically large; and so it is. We are only beginning to find out the ways in which the amino acids (letters) are put together.

The first protein to be completely known was *insulin,* a substance produced by the pancreas and required for normal functioning of cell membranes in mammals. This protein is the simplest known, but it is by no means simple, as the formula in Figure 4-6 shows. It contains 51 amino acid units put together in a very particular way. Many men spent many years in deducing this formula. A Nobel prize was awarded in 1958 to the principal investigator who brought this work to completion, Frederick Sanger of Cambridge University. The insulins of a number of different species have been

Fig. 4-4. l-*alanine.*

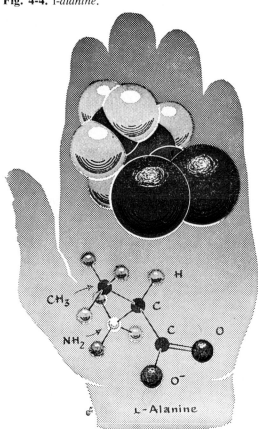

L-Alanine

analyzed. Their structures are almost identical, but they vary slightly in the amino acids found at certain specified positions. Table 4-2 lists these variations; the numbers correspond to the numbered positions given in Figure 4-6. The two different analyses given for the rat may indicate a hereditary difference within the species.

36. Catalysts and Enzymes

The nineteenth century was a time of great advance for the mechanistic view of biology. The chemist Louis Pasteur (1822–1895) played an important role in advancing the chemical view of life. He viewed the living cell as a sort of factory for carrying out chemical reactions. One of the reactions to which he gave much of his attention was that of alcoholic fermentation by yeast:

$$C_6H_{12}O_6 \longrightarrow 2CO_2 + 2C_2H_5OH$$

(sugar $\longrightarrow$ carbon dioxide   *(11)*

+ ethyl alcohol).

By Pasteur's time it was already known that the characteristic reactions of living organisms could often be demonstrated using the secretions of living cells, that is, substances that cells had exuded to the outside. The Italian Lazzaro Spallanzani (1729–1799) had, in 1765, shown that gastric (stomach) juice could dissolve meat. In the language of the day, the active substance produced by the stomach was called a "ferment." To Pasteur and his contemporaries it appeared that yeast cells must produce a similar ferment, for which the name *enzyme* (Gr. *en* = in + *zyme* = yeast) was proposed by W. Kühne in 1878.

That there was such an enzyme in yeast was only an article of faith for a long time, because neither Pasteur nor any other student of alcoholic fermentation could demonstrate any fermenting power in cell-free exudates of yeast cells. Not until after Pasteur's death did the demonstration occur, and then only by accident. Eduard Buchner (1860–1917), aided by his brother, was engaged in studying the therapeutic value of various tissue extracts. For some reason he decided to include yeast cells in his survey. Grinding up tiny yeast cells is quite a chore, however, and in order not to have to do this every day Buchner tried to preserve his yeast juice. Since he intended to use it therapeutically, poisonous preservatives like formaldehyde were out of the question. Taking an idea from housewives, he decided to preserve it with an excess of sugar. The results were spectacular: the yeast juice frothed the moment the sugar was added. This was the sort of occasion that Pasteur had in mind when he said: "In the realm of observation, chance favors only the prepared mind." It would have been easy to overlook the frothing of the sugared yeast juice as no more than an amusing phenomenon. Buchner, however, knew of the puzzle of the nondemonstrable yeast enzyme and immediately saw the significance of what he had observed: he had seen alcoholic fermentation taking place outside of cells. He had proved the existence of Kuhne's hypothetical *enzyme* by forcibly taking it out of yeast cells. Buchner called this enzyme *zymase,* using the suffix **-ase** which conventionally indicates an enzyme. Buchner assumed that only a single enzyme was involved in alcoholic fermentation; we now know that there are about a dozen. Nevertheless Buchner deserved the Nobel prize that he was awarded in 1907.

What is an enzyme? To answer this we must first introduce the idea of a **catalyst,** a concept crystallized by the chemist J. J. Berzelius in 1835. The substance hydrogen peroxide spontaneously decomposes to form water and oxygen, thus:

$$2H_2O_2 \longrightarrow 2H_2O + O_2. \qquad (12)$$

The reaction takes place very slowly at ordinary temperatures; many days may be required for it to go even halfway to completion. If, however, one introduces a tiny mass of finely divided platinum into the solution—as little as 1 atom of platinum per *billion* molecules of hydrogen peroxide will suffice—the reaction then proceeds very rapidly, and can be represented thus:

$$2H_2O_2 \xrightarrow{(Pt)} 2H_2O + O_2. \qquad (13)$$

The platinum atom undoubtedly forms an association with the peroxide molecule, but it is only a temporary one; as oxygen splits off of the peroxide, the platinum is freed to take part in another such reaction. We indicate the fact that the platinum is not used up in the reaction by writing the symbol *Pt* above the arrow, rather than as one of the reactants. In choosing the name *catalysis* (Gr. *cata* = downward + *lysis,* loosening) for such reactions, Berzelius was influenced by the fact that the first catalytic reactions studied by him were ones in which large molecules were broken down to smaller ones. Catalytic reactions in which small molecules are combined to form large ones were later discovered, but the name catalysis, however inappropriate etymologically, is used for both types of reactions.

Fig. 4-5. d-*alanine.*

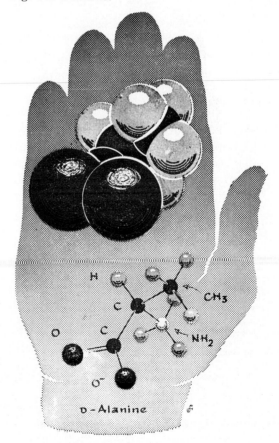

D-Alanine

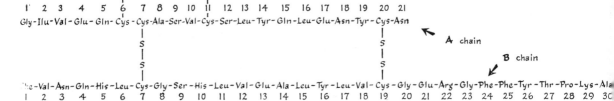

Fig. 4-6. *The structure of beef insulin, as worked out by Sanger and co-workers.*

At the same time that the general concept of catalysis was developing, various men were working toward the concept of biological catalysis. It soon became clear that the characteristic reactions of living systems were catalyzed by specific proteins, which are now called enzymes. *All enzymes are proteins.* More than 700 enzymes are known. All enzymes are formed only within living cells, and most of them do not normally escape from the cell. There are a number of other properties of enzymes that should be noted:

1. Enzymes are readily inactivated by moderate heat. A temperature considerably lower than that of boiling water (100°C) will alter an enzyme irreversibly so that it can no longer act as a catalyst. The altered molecule may still be a protein, but it will not be an enzyme.

TABLE 4-2 *Variations in the Amino Acid Sequence of Insulins from Various Species of Mammals. (Source: F. G. Young, 1962, Proc. Roy. Soc. (B) 137:2.)*

Here we see one reason why there is an upper temperature limit for life.

2. Enzymes are sensitive to changes in acidity. Some enzymes work best in acid solutions, others in alkaline, others at the neutral point. An enzyme that works in acid surroundings will be inactive under alkaline conditions, and vice versa.

3. Each enzyme is specific with respect to the type of action it brings about. Although there are hundreds of different enzymes, there are only a few dozen types of enzyme actions, the principal ones of which are listed in Table 4-3. Except for the oldest known enzymes (e.g., pepsin, trypsin), enzymes are *usually* named by adding *-ase* to a stem that indicates its type of action, thus: pyruvic decarboxylase and pyruvic oxidase, for enzymes which remove (respectively) CO_2 and H from pyruvic acid.

4. With respect to the raw material (**substrate**) it works on, an enzyme is usually very specific. Hydrolyzing enzymes often work upon many different related compounds; but most other enzymes work on only one, or a few, substrates. In this limitation we see the reason for the multiplicity of cellular enzymes.

The obvious importance of enzymes in the living cell has motivated a vast amount of research. In 1926, James B. Sumner (1887–1955) first succeeded in purifying and crystallizing an enzyme, namely urease, which hydrolyzes urea to ammonia and carbon dioxide. Because of a covert vitalistic attitude toward biochemistry at that time, Sumner's discovery was not believed for several years. At the present time more than 100 different enzymes have been crystallized. The analysis of the structure of enzymes is even more difficult; only a few

MAMMAL	POSITION						
	A CHAIN				B CHAIN		
	4	8	9	10	3	29	30
Beef	Glu	Ala	Ser	Val	Asn	Lys	Ala
Sheep	Glu	Ala	Gly	Val	Asn	Lys	Ala
Horse	Glu	Thr	Gly	Ilu	Asn	Lys	Ala
Sei whale	Glu	Ala	Ser	Thr	Asn	Lys	Ala
Pig	Glu	Thr	Ser	Ilu	Asn	Lys	Ala
Sperm whale	Glu	Thr	Ser	Ilu	Asn	Lys	Ala
Dog	Glu	Thr	Ser	Ilu	Asn	Lys	Ala
Human	Glu	Thr	Ser	Ilu	Asn	Lys	Thr
Rabbit	Glu	Thr	Ser	Ilu	Asn	Lys	Ser
Rat 1	Asp	Thr	Ser	Ilu	Lys	Lys	Ser
Rat 2	Asp	Thr	Ser	Ilu	Lys	Met	Ser

TABLE 4-3 *Some of the Principal Types of Chemical Reactions Catalyzed by Enzymes.*

NAME OF REACTION	MEANING	NAME OF CONTRARY REACTION
Oxidation	*a.* addition of oxygen	Reduction
	b. removal of hydrogen	
	c. removal of electron	
Hydrogenation	addition of hydrogen	Dehydrogenation
Phosphorylation	addition of PO_4	Dephosphorylation
Hydrolysis	splitting of molecule as result of addition of H_2O	Condensation
Carboxylation	addition of CO_2, increasing length of carbon chain	Decarboxylation
Methylation	addition of CH_3	Demethylation
Amination	addition of NH_2	Deamination

are known at present, the first to be worked out being ribonuclease, which was deduced principally by C. H. W. Hirs, W. H. Stein, and S. Moore in 1960.

37. How an Enzyme Acts

One of the remarkable things about enzymes is their enormous size with respect to the molecules they work on. The smallest enzyme has a molecular weight of about 10,000 (that is, it is roughly 10,000 times as heavy as a hydrogen atom); the largest enzymes have molecular weights in the millions. The molecular weight of the substrates of enzymes is usually in the hundreds. This discrepancy in size is all the more striking in the light of the fact that, with few exceptions, *each enzyme molecule has only one active site,* that is, one place at which the substrate molecule temporarily associates until the enzymatic action is performed.

Symbolically, the course of enzyme action can be represented thus:

$$E + S \longrightarrow ES \longrightarrow P + E. \qquad (14)$$

That is, the enzyme (E) and the substrate (S) form a temporary association (ES) which decomposes to yield the product or products (P) plus the unaltered enzyme molecule which is now free to combine with another substrate molecule. The complete cycle from E to ES

and back to E again is called a "turnover"; the number of molecules of substrate an enzyme is capable of "treating" in each minute is called the **turnover number** of the enzyme. By everyday human standards, turnover numbers seem very high. Catalase, the enzyme that brings about the breakdown of hydrogen peroxide to water and oxygen, has a turnover number of about 2×10^8. This is exceptionally great. A more typical turnover number is 2×10^4.

The great protein chemist Emil Fischer (1852–1919) was the first to try to picture the nature of enzyme action (1894). He pictured the enzyme molecule as having a particular configuration of atoms at the active site which acted as a template for a complementary arrangement of the substrate molecule. This model of enzyme action has been generally accepted down to the present time, with significant modifications introduced in 1958 by D. E. Koshland, Jr. Koshland's model pictures some of the free "arms" of the enzyme molecule as moving (by purely atomic-molecular forces), and being capable of surrounding the substrate molecule (Fig. 4-7). Only if the substrate molecule is of the correct size and shape will the catalytic groups (X and Y) of the enzyme molecule be able to come into close proximity with the critical region of the substrate molecule thus bringing about its decomposition. It takes only a little imagination to see how this same model can be developed to account for the phe-

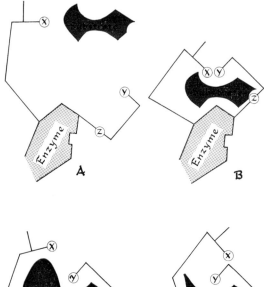

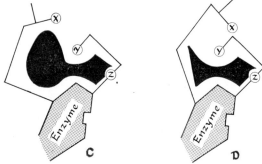

Fig. 4-7. *Koshland's flexible active site model of enzyme action. With the correct substrate (A and B) the catalytic groups X and Y come into close proximity with the critical region of the substrate, resulting in catalytic reaction. But if the substrate is wrong in size or shape (C and D) the catalytic groups do not align properly and no reaction takes place. (After D. E. Koshland, Jr.,* Science *(1963)* **142:***1539.)*

nomenon of "enzyme poisoning." A molecule that closely resembles a proper substrate but which is incapable of being attacked by an enzyme may form an irreversible association with the active site of an enzyme molecule, thus blocking its access to proper substrate molecules. Just as it takes only a little bit of enzyme to do a lot of metabolic work, so also it takes only a little bit of an enzyme-poison to have a devastating effect on a living organism. Many of the "nerve gases" so feared as agents of chemical warfare are in this category.

38. ATP—The Coin of the Metabolic Realm

Glycogen is a polysaccharide that often serves as a storage product in the cell. It can be made from glucose—but not directly. We see why not when we examine the energy relations of these two substances:

$$\text{glucose} + \varepsilon \longrightarrow \text{glycogen}. \qquad (15)$$

Where is the energy to come from? We have already seen that a cell cannot be a heat engine, so ε cannot stand for heat (*i.e.,* a temperature differential between source and sink). Some other source must be found. In the cell, this source is a chemical source. The cell uses the chemical energy found in a substance called "ATP" to "drive" the synthesis indicated in equation (15). What is ATP?

Figure 4-8 shows the chemistry of a number of substances important in cell metabolism. The only two we are interested in at the moment are the two longest compounds of the set, *ADP* and *ATP;* the full names for these substances are given in the figure. For our present purposes we need note only that the difference between ADP and ATP is a phosphate group connected by an **"energy rich bond,"** indicated by a squiggly line, thus: $\sim \mathbf{P}$. This relation holds between the two compounds:

$$\text{ATP} \longrightarrow \text{ADP} + \text{phosphate}$$
$$+ \text{ 12 Calories.} \quad (16)$$

By converting ATP to ADP the cell can obtain energy which it can use to drive other reactions. The energy from reaction (16) would be useless, of course, if it were in the form of heat. What the cell must do is keep the energy in the form of the energy rich phosphate bond, transferring this bond—phosphate and all—to another compound.

Returning to our original problem, the cell makes glycogen not directly, but by first making a higher-energy carbohydrate, glucose-6-phosphate, in the following manner:

$$\text{glucose} + \text{ATP} \longrightarrow \text{glucose-6-PO}_4$$
$$+ \text{ ADP} + \varepsilon. \quad (17)$$

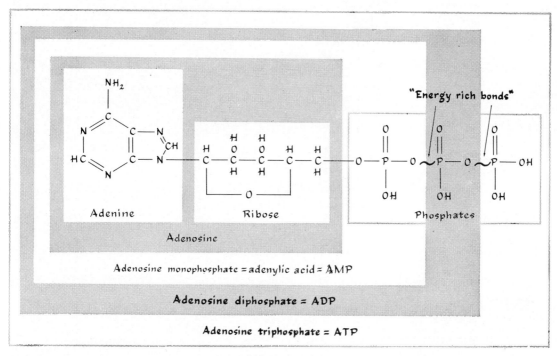

Fig. 4-8. *The chemistry of ADP, ATP and some related compounds that are also important in cell metabolism.*

This reaction can proceed because (unlike reaction 15) it releases energy rather than requires it, and so it does not violate the Second Law. Part of the energy resulting from the ATP→ADP change is incorporated into glucose-6-PO₄, and part appears as the waste ε. The further conversion of glucose-6-PO₄ to glycogen, through a series of steps, takes place because it also is a "downhill" process from high energy glucose-6-PO₄ to the relatively lower energy substance glycogen.

Speaking teleologically, i.e., in terms of "goals," the cell's ever-present problem is to find a way to pay for chemical reactions that require energy. In reaction after reaction it does so by using the energy resident in the terminal high energy phosphate bond of ATP. It is instructive to see the way this substance appears repeatedly in the series of reactions involved in the fermentation of glucose (sugar) to ethanol (ethyl alcohol). This process is shown in Figure 4-9. You should refer constantly to this figure as you read the following paragraphs.

As in the synthesis of glycogen, the first step is the conversion of glucose to the compound of higher energy content, glucose-6-phosphate; ATP "pays" for this reaction, becoming degraded to ADP. Two reactions later, another molecule of ATP is used to pay for another reaction, following which the di-phosphate 6-carbon compound is split to form two monophosphate 3-carbon compounds. We will follow the degradation of only one of these.

First an inorganic phosphate group is incorporated into the 3-carbon chain, being converted to a high-energy phosphate group. Such a change in energy level must be paid for, which it is by a partial oxidation of the 3-C compound. (Oxidations yield energy.) The result is a di-phosphate 3-carbon compound. In succeeding degradative steps, two molecules of ATP are split off; then a molecule of CO_2; and the process ends with the formation of a molecule of ethyl alcohol.

But this is the result of the degradation of only one branch of the process; *two* 3-C com-

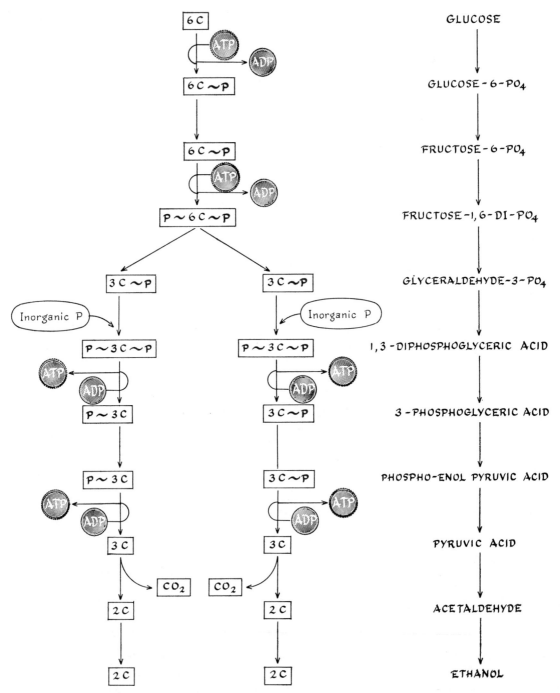

Fig. 4-9. *The sequence of enzymatic steps in alcoholic fermentation. Note the way the "coinage" of ATP is used as a medium of exchange in passing energy from one compound to another.*

pounds are degraded to produce a total of two molecules of carbon dioxide, two molecules of ethanol and—most important—*four* molecules of high-energy ATP. This is two more than we began with. The net gain of two ATP's is like money in the bank—the metabolic bank. These ATP's can be used not only for initiating the splitting of other molecules of glucose, but also for driving a myriad other energy-requiring metabolic reactions of the cell. *ATP is the medium of energy exchange of the cell.* Like coins, ATP molecules can be passed around, can be accumulated, and can be spent.

Two more important points should be noted. First of all, contrast the implications of Figure 4-9 with the implicit view of Eduard Buchner. In creating the unitary term "zymase" Buchner implied this sort of explanation for alcoholic fermentation:

$$C_6H_{12}O_6 \xrightarrow{\text{(zymase)}} 2CO_2 + 2C_2H_5OH + \varepsilon. \quad (18)$$

But each of the downward pointing arrows in Figure 4-9 stands for a reaction that has its own enzyme (and Fig. 4-9 is not quite the whole truth!) so we can see that Buchner's "zymase" has multiplied into a host of enzymes. Such multiplication of entities is a common result of progress in science. What we first think of as a single entity usually turns out, on closer view, to be subdivisible into many.

Our second point concerns energy. Notice how far we have come since the days when biologists more or less unconsciously thought in terms of heat-engines. In such terms, the over-all metabolic sense of alcoholic fermentation is adequately represented by equation (18), the energy (ε) appearing at the end of the equation being used presumably, in some mysterious way, to drive the engines of the cell. In the light of the information incorporated in Figure 4-9, however, we can better represent the over-all sense of alcoholic fermentation thus:

$$C_6H_{12}O_6 + 2\,ATP$$
$$\longrightarrow 2CO_2 + 2C_2H_5OH + 4\,ATP + \varepsilon. \quad (19)$$

The important energetic consequence of the degradation of sugar to alcohol is the net gain of 2 ATP's. The remaining energy (ε), appearing as heat, is simply an unavoidable, wasteful consequence of the Second Law of Thermodynamics.

39. An Alternate Coin—NAD

Let's return to the alcoholic fermentation scheme (Fig. 4-9) once more. Just after the phosphorylated *hexose* (6-carbon sugar) is split into two phosphorylated *trioses,* an inorganic phosphorus molecule furnishes another phosphorus to each sugar molecule. High energy groups are indicated by color in the figure. How is the low-energy phosphate (black) raised to high energy phosphate (color) in this transformation?

The reaction in question is shown in detail in Figure 4-10. The 3-C compound is glyceraldehyde-3-phosphate. The inorganic P is present in the form of phosphoric acid (H_3PO_4); the phosphorus is bound in a low-energy form in this compound. In the reaction shown, a high-energy phosphate bond (—C—O—P—) is formed. How is this paid for? By oxidation. Oxidation, recall (Table 4-3) does not always mean the addition of oxygen to a compound; it may mean the removal of hydrogen. It is this second type of oxidation that is involved here. Glyceraldehyde-3-phosphate becomes oxidized; for this to happen, something else has to become reduced—that is, has to act as a hydrogen-acceptor. This something else is *NAD,* or *nicotinamide-adenine-dinucleotide,* to give it its

Fig. 4-10. *How NAD acts as a source of energy and as a hydrogen-acceptor in the cell.*

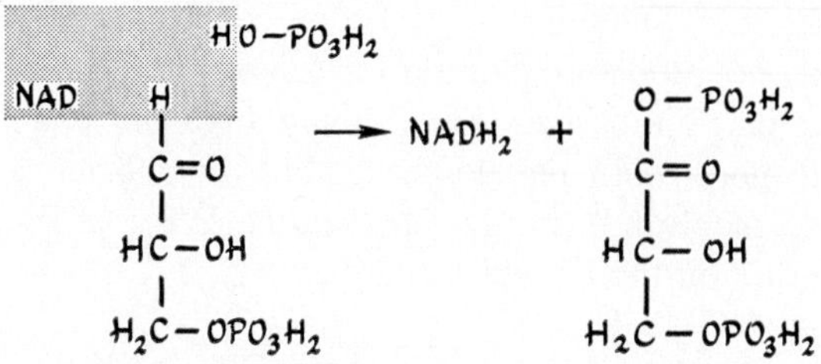

or, more briefly:

$$P \sim C{-}H + HP + NAD \longrightarrow P \sim C \sim P + NADH_2$$

full name.* In becoming reduced, the NAD yields energy which forms the second high energy phosphate bond of the product shown on the right—1,3-diphosphoglyceric acid.

More briefly the sense of this reaction is shown in the bottom half of Figure 4-10. A low-energy phosphate bond (black) is converted to a high-energy phosphate bond (color) at the expense of high-energy NAD (color) which is reduced to lower energy $NADH_2$ (black). ($NADH_2$ is read either "$NADH_2$" or "reduced NAD.")

Like ATP, NAD acts as an energy currency; by means of it, energy can be passed from one part of the cell to another, can be accumulated, and can be spent. NAD also acts as an agent for hydrogen-transport, moving hydrogen from one compound to another.

40. From Protoplasm to Comprehensibility

As the pioneer cytologists of the nineteenth century looked ever more closely at living tissues, they became aware that not everything they saw was alive. Cell walls of plants certainly were not, nor were the contents of a vacuole. How, then, were biologists to speak of the living portions of cells, as distinct from the nonliving? Hugo von Mohl solved this problem in 1846 by referring to the living stuff as "Schleim" or "Protoplasma." He solved one problem, but he created another, for before long the word *protoplasm* took on powers far beyond that of mere identification. It came to stand for some supposed living substance which was to be found in all cells; which was always the same; and which was (as one textbook put it) the "life stuff." But no one could ever give an operational definition for this supposed material. The *processes* of living organisms are demonstrable and definable; but the *substance* "protoplasm" is only a reification. It is like the grin† on the Cheshire cat.

_____

* This energy-transporter is called DPN in the older literature.

† 4-7. Remember Lewis Carroll's treatment of this? Explain the comparison.

That the word "protoplasm" acted as a genuine impediment to progress in the understanding of living processes we know from the words of the biochemist Frederick Gowland Hopkins (1861–1947), a Nobel laureate who, more than any other single man, created the biochemical framework within which modern biology sets its discoveries. When Hopkins was a young man the chemistry of living things was widely regarded as hopeless: *Tierchemie ist nur Schmierchemie* was a popular saying among chemists. One distinguished organic chemist, informed of Hopkins' ambition to study the chemistry of living processes, advised him: "The chemistry of the living? That is the chemistry of protoplasm: that is super-chemistry. Seek, my young friend, for other ambitions." As Hopkins remarked toward the end of his life, such an attitude was "almost as inhibitory to productive chemical thought and study as any of the claims of vitalism."

Hopkins succeeded brilliantly in his ambition because he broke the large problem up into bite-size pieces. He did not try to understand in one fell swoop, metabolism, from beginning to end; instead, he contented himself with understanding, one at a time, some of the intermediate stages. As he stated his program in 1913:

My main thesis will be that in the study of the intermediate processes of metabolism we have to deal, not with complex substances which elude ordinary chemical methods but with simple substances undergoing comprehensible reactions. By simple substances I mean such as are of easily ascertainable structure and of a molecular weight within a range to which the organic chemist is well accustomed. I intend also to emphasise the fact that it is not alone with the separation and identification of products from the animal that our present studies deal; but with their reactions in the body; with the dynamic side of biological phenomena.

Simple substances undergoing comprehensible reactions—this is the article of faith that has produced marvels of discovery. As biochemists have delved deeper into the mysteries of life, some of the substances have turned out to be not so simple, but it was success in discovering the simpler ones that put them in a position to understand the more complex. In asserting his faith in the comprehensibility of biochemical reactions, Hopkins (and all who followed in his footsteps) reasserted the ancient Greek article of faith that the world is comprehensible.

The word "protoplasm" is still used somewhat as a casual finger-pointing word, but as a reified concept it has virtually disappeared from scientific circles. In place of the rather static concept it implied, we have a much more dynamic concept of living systems. That living processes are complex should already be clear from the discussion of the cascade of reactions involved in alcoholic fermentation, but it is time to correct the over-simplifications of even that complex picture. The most serious erroneous implication of Figure 4-9 lies in the arrows: they go only one way, implying that the chemical reactions go in only one direction. This is not true.

Any chemical reaction can be represented by an equation of this sort:

$$A + B \rightleftarrows C + D, \qquad (20)$$

where the arrows indicate that the reaction goes in both directions. If we begin with only substances A and B, they will interact to produce C and D, which will increase in quantity until the contrary reaction ($\leftarrow$) exactly equals the first reaction ($\rightarrow$) considered. Arrows of equal length, as shown above, imply that the reaction goes only 50 percent of the way to completion; after that, there is an equilibrium between the two counteracting reactions and there is no *net* change, though both reactions continue to go on. If the equilibrium point is something other than 50 percent, we indicate this by using arrows of different lengths. For example, a reaction that goes 90 percent "toward the right" we might indicate thus:

$$G + H \xrightarrow{\quad\longleftarrow\quad} J + K. \qquad (21)$$

What the equilibrium point is, is a matter of chemistry only, and has nothing to do with life.

The equilibrium point is the same in both organism and test tube. What, then, is the role of enzymes? *An enzyme speeds up the reactions, but does not alter the equilibrium point.* Then it would seem that a cell would soon be just a mess of counteracting reactions that "don't get anywhere." Yet, as we know, the reactions do get somewhere. How can this be?

There are many answers to this question, which lies at the heart of cellular biochemistry. Let us examine only one. If, in equation (*20*), one of the products (say D) is a gas, then the reaction will proceed steadily to the right. The gas, by bubbling off, removes itself from the reactive system, thus interfering with the reverse reaction, thus preventing the establishment of an equilibrium. Instead of an equilibrium, there will be a **steady state,** that is, a *steady rate* of production of products (so long as the supply of reactants holds out). Such a reaction will be observed in Figure 4-9, near the bottom, where pyruvic acid produces acetaldehyde and CO_2—which bubbles off.

If we amend Figure 4-9 to include the fact that enzymatic reactions can go both ways we get a metabolic scheme like that shown in Figure 4-11. In this figure there is no doubt more than you want to know about metabolism, but a few general impressions are worth underlining. Note that each of the reactions shown is catalyzed by a specific enzyme (in color). Note that almost every step is chemically a *small* one—e.g., the addition of a phosphate group, or the loss of two hydrogen atoms (". . . simple substances undergoing comprehensible reactions"). Note that the same reactions occur over and over again, in different parts of the metabolic scheme: addition or removal of phosphate, or hydrogen, or water, or carbon dioxide.

That which is shown in Figure 4-11 is only a tiny fraction of what takes place in metabolism all of the time. Less than two dozen enzymes are indicated in the picture. We know that there are hundreds of different kinds of enzymes in the cell and maybe thousands. These enzymes are, in a sense, competing with each other for different common reagents—ATP,

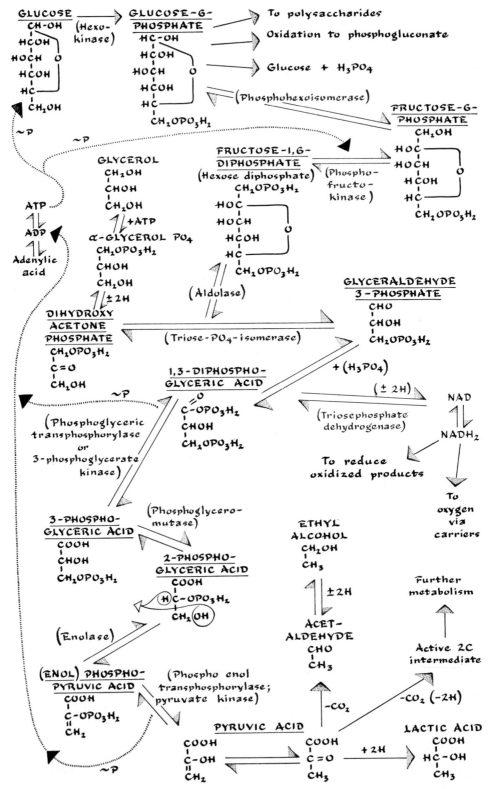

Fig. 4-11. *A small fraction of the metabolic reactions taking place in a living cell. The more important enzymes are indicated in color.*

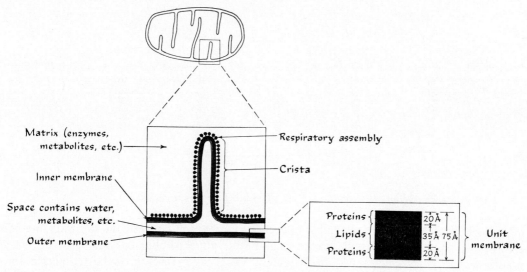

Fig. 4-12. *The ultrastructure of a mitochondrion, diagrammatically shown. There is some evidence that the matrix is not structureless as shown, but has filaments in it. Note the enzyme molecules attached to the crests (cristae). (From Newcomb, Gerloff, and Whittingham,* Plants in Perspective, *W. H. Freeman and Company, San Francisco and London, 1964.)*

NAD, etc. How can there be an ordered progression of reactions under those circumstances? The answer lies partly in the fact that chemical competition is, to a large extent, prevented by the structure of the cell. We have seen previously, in studying the cell in Chapter 2, that on the finest observable scale of the electron microscope the cell is rich in structure—*fine structure,* it is called. (Look again at Fig. 2-14.) The fine structure of a particularly important organelle, the mitochondrion, is shown in Figure 4-12. It has been known since the work of Otto Warburg in the 1920's that most of the important oxidative reactions of the cell take place in the fraction that was later identified as the mitochondrial fraction. It is here that the energy-releasing reactions we have been talking about take place. The elaborate internal sculpturing of a mitochondrion can hardly be without significance in the functioning of this organelle. It is suspected (and there is some evidence for the belief) that enzyme molecules are attached to the internal **crests** (see Fig. 4-12); and that the pattern in which they are there attached is not random, but bears some relation to the sequence of metabolic steps. If so the cell, on a

molecular scale, bears more than an analogical resemblance to the assembly line of a factory. When we have learned to draw a picture of the arrangement of these molecules and atoms of the cell's machinery we will have discovered the **ultrastructure** of the cell. Integrating the knowledge of this ultrastructure with the facts of biochemistry is the goal of **molecular biology.**

41. Endproduct Inhibition: A Negative Feedback

One competent biochemist has estimated that there are between 1,000 and 10,000 different kinds of enzymes inside a cell. The wide limits of this estimate reveal the extent to which it is a "guesstimate;" nevertheless, the order of magnitude may be right. In any case, there is a very large number of kinds of enzymes within a cell. It is extremely unlikely that any two enzymes have the same turnover number. From this it would follow that, unless there is some regulatory control of the actions of enzymes, the passage of time would create a great imbalance in enzyme endproducts (unless by some

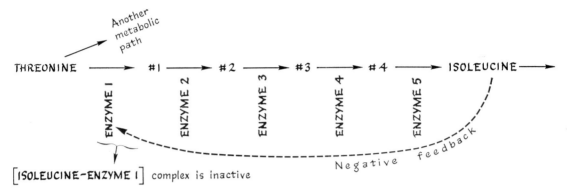

Fig. 4-13. *Endproduct inhibition as a method of control by negative feedback.*

improbable chance the turnover number of each enzyme was precisely proportional to the quantitative need for its products). Moreover, under different conditions, with different supplies of foodstuffs, the comparative needs for different enzyme actions would change. How can the cell adjust to different environmental demands?

There are several mechanisms for the regulation of enzyme action, of which only one will be discussed here, namely the method of **endproduct inhibition.** This can be illustrated by the metabolic path leading from the amino acid threonine to the amino acid isoleucine. As shown in Figure 4-13, there are a number of chemical steps involved, each one catalyzed by a specific enzyme. (For simplicity both the enzymes and the intermediate substances are indicated merely by numbers.) What happens if the cell is faced with a surplus of isoleucine molecules, as it is if (for instance) it is furnished isoleucine in its diet? In this case, the further synthesis of isoleucine promptly stops. It can be shown that it is the first enzymatic process in the link that is brought to a standstill. What happens, apparently, is that the endproduct isoleucine combines with enzyme 1 in an enzyme-endproduct complex, thus preventing the normal substrate-enzyme complex from

forming; consequently the substrate threonine is not attacked by enzyme 1. The enzyme-endproduct reaction is fairly specific for the particular product. The product (isoleucine) which is quite a different shape from the substrate molecule (threonine) does *not* combine at the enzymic site reserved for the substrate, but it does somehow interfere with the usual substrate-enzyme combination. If and when the endproduct starts disappearing from the cell (perhaps because the diet no longer includes it), the enzyme-endproduct complexes break up freeing the enzyme molecules which can then combine with the substrate and set the normal train of enzymatic changes in motion again, ultimately producing more endproduct. Such a system adjusts itself rapidly to the changing needs of the cell.

Because the endproduct goes back into the system that produced it, the word feedback is used. Because the effect of this feedback is to *diminish* the process in question we speak of **negative feedback.** Negative feedback is a dynamic way of producing stability in spite of changing circumstances. We will see many other examples of negative feedback as we continue with the study of biology.

Questions and Problems

4-8. Make a list of the **boldface** terms in the text of this chapter. Write out a definition and description of each. Compare your work with the text.

4-9. Write out a brief description of the contributions of the following men, giving the approximate date of each: Berzelius, Buchner, Hopkins, Lavoisier, Pasteur, Rubner, Sanger.

‡4-10. The over-all efficiency in the process of producing ATP molecules by the process of completely oxidizing glucose to CO_2 and H_2O is about 55 percent. If the cell were a heat-engine, what temperature differential would it have to maintain to achieve this efficiency? Give the answer in both Celsius and Fahrenheit degrees.

4-11. Given that a heat engine operates with a 100°C temperature differential between source and sink, what will be the maximum possible efficiency if the temperature of the sink is: (a) 300°K; (b) 100°K?

‡4-12. When, as recounted in Section 28, a French scientist said that only 90 percent of the body's heat was produced by the chemical process of respiration, another Frenchman (François Magendie) opined that the remaining 10 percent was produced by the friction of the blood flowing in the blood vessels. What fundamental criticism of this explanation can one give?

4-13. In discussing the setup illustrated in Figure 3-3, it was stated that even after the two rooms contain the same concentration of molecules, the exchange of molecules between the two rooms continues. How do we know? Suppose that only CO_2 gas is used in such an experiment. How could the postulated exchange be demonstrated?

‡4-14. An investigator of earthworms wishes to follow the wanderings of a worm beneath the surface of the soil without disturbing the soil. Can you suggest, in general terms, a technique whereby he may do this?

4-15. A cytologist wishes to know whether the phosphorus taken up by cells is distributed uniformly or is concentrated in spots within the cell. There is a radioactive isotope of phosphorus. How could this isotope be used to solve the problem?

4-16. How can we justify stating all forms of energy in terms of Calories, when a Calorie is a unit of heat energy only?

4-17. What is the difference between H_2 and H^2?

‡4-18. In the first chapter of Lewis Carroll's *Through the Looking Glass,* Alice speaks thus to her kitten: "How would you like to live in Looking-glass House, Kitty? I wonder if they'd give you milk in there? Perhaps Looking-glass milk isn't good to drink . . ." Is it?

4-19. Suppose you took trips to four other planets and found living organisms on all of them. Suppose that chemical analyses showed that:

a. Mars organisms contain *l*-amino acids only.
b. Venus organisms contain *d*-amino acids only.
c. Some Jupiter organisms contain *d*-amino acids only; others contain *l*-amino acids only.
d. All Saturn organisms contain both *d*- and *l*-amino acids.

Has life on each of these planets had a separate origin from earthly life? Discuss.

‡4-20. Platinum gauze is used as a catalyst for the oxidation of ammonia. After several weeks of use, the amount of Pt is unaltered (as verified gravimetrically), but the surface of the metal is visibly roughened. What does this fact indicate about the nature of catalysis?

4-21. Why use gauze for such a reaction as the one just described? Why not just a chunk of metal?

4-22. What etymological criticism can be made of the word "catalysis"? Why don't we use its etymological opposite, "analysis"?

4-23. Each of the following substances is a carbohydrate, an amino acid, or a fatty compound. Identify the class of each:
(a) $CH_2 \cdot NH_2 \cdot COOH$
(b) $C_{12}H_{22}O_{11}$
(c) $(C_6H_{10}O_5)_x$
(d) $C_{20}H_{29}OH$
(e) $C_3H_5O_3(NH_2)$
(f) $C_{18}H_{32}O_{16}$
(g) $CH_3 \cdot (CH_2)_{16} \cdot COOH$

4-24. A certain number of molecules of substance A, dissolved in one liter of water, have an osmotic potential of X. The same number of molecules of substance B, dissolved in one liter of water, have an osmotic potential of 1.98 X. You are told that one of these substances is organic, the other inorganic. In all probability, which is which? Give your reasoning.

‡4-25. Raffinose is what kind of a saccharide? How could it be derived from sugars of the constitions $C_6H_{12}O_6$?

‡4-26. Using only the basic twenty different amino acids how many different:

a. dipeptides are conceivable? (Remember: glycine-leucine is not the same as leucine-glycine.)

b. tripeptides are conceivable?

‡4-27. Apparently a basic length of polypeptides produced by living cells contains about 150 amino acid residues. Assume a straight chain polypeptide of this length. *Approximately* how many different molecules are possible? (See Appendix 5 for a method of making such approximations.)

4-28. Biologists suspect that every kind of plant or animal possesses at least one kind of protein molecules that is to be found in no other kind of organism. Is this assumption a tenable one in the light of the estimate that there are perhaps two million different kinds of plants and animals now living? Explain.

4-29. Give an etymological analysis of "zymase."

‡4-30. The enzyme glutamic dehydrogenase has a turnover number of 3×10^4. How many molecules of glutamic acid can one molecule of this enzyme alter in one day?

4-31. How long would it take for one molecule of catalase to decompose one gram-mole of hydrogen peroxide? (Turnover number of catalase in §37; number of molecules per gram-mole is 6×10^{23}.) Give the answer in years.

‡4-32. Soluble mercury compounds combine with proteins to form insoluble mercury-protein complexes. Why are such mercury compounds poisonous?

4-33. Two tracer experiments are carried out:

a. In the first, an organism is fed water made with O^{18}, to follow the movement of water.

b. In the second, an organism is fed sugar made with C^{14}, to follow the movement of sugar.

A critic objects to these experiments on the grounds that normal physiology is interfered with by isotopes—that when an isotope disintegrates, it damages a cell and interferes with its physiology. Is this a valid objection?

‡4-34. What is a triose?

4-35. If the structure of a cell is destroyed (as by ultrasonic vibrations) the cell dies almost immediately. Give a general chemical explanation.

‡4-36. If anything may properly be said to be made of protoplasm, which of the following may be said to be made of it: nucleus, plasma membrane, vacuolar contents, vacuole membrane, cell wall, cytoplasm?

4-37. Are the elements that make up "protoplasm" distributed at random throughout the Periodic Table? (See Appendix 1.)

4-38. Discuss these statements about "protoplasm," culled from biology textbooks:

a. Protoplasm has been aptly called life stuff, for life cannot exist without it.

b. The material inside the alga is nothing less than "protoplasm," the essential living substance.

c. Protoplasm is the physical basis of life, the common substance shared by all forms of life —the substance in which all reactions of a living body have their origin.

d. Purkinje was the first to make use of the term *protoplasm* for living matter, but the term was not in general use until Max Schulze, about 1861, demonstrated that the sarcode of animal cells and the protoplasm of plant cells were one and the same thing.

e. The living material contained within the walls of these cells is termed "protoplasm." All life is composed of this substance. It *is* life!

f. Cat protoplasm and dog protoplasm are not alike; protoplasm of the corn leaf differs from the protoplasm of the oak leaf; indeed the protoplasm in different parts of the same organism differs to some extent. . . . For example, the protoplasm of a liver cell is different from that of a muscle. Yet, in spite of this, the fundamental nature of all kinds of protoplasm is the same.

Readings

For a general background in inorganic chemistry, consult Pauling's *College Chemistry*. Read's *A Direct Entry to Organic Chemistry* gives a brief introduction to the chemistry of the carbon compounds, with numerous sidelights. The nature of the work of the organic chemist is discussed in Chapter 15 of Cohen's *Science, Servant of Man*. Chapter 7 of Conant's *Science and Common Sense* sketches in broad outline the early development of chemical concepts. Chapter 7 of Borek's *The*

Atoms Within Us is a splendid account of the logical path followed in deducing the structure of proteins; it is better than a detective story. For an excellent introduction to molecular biology, see Lehninger's *Bioenergetics*.

Life, as we know it, could develop only in a world possessed of rather particular chemical characteristics; this point is the thesis of Henderson's *The Fitness of the Environment*. For its antithesis, see Haldane's essay, *Possible Worlds*.

Scientific American Offprints

36. Philip Siekevitz. *Powerhouse of the Cell*

42. E. O. P. Thompson. *The Insulin Molecule*

69. Albert L. Lehninger. *Energy Transformation in the Cell*

121. John C. Kendrew. *The Three-Dimensional Structure of a Protein Molecule*

5   Coding the Mechanism

42. What Makes Enzymes?

The work of the cell is performed by enzymes. An enzyme molecule, being a true catalyst, can be used over and over to process millions of substrate molecules. No catalyst, however, lasts forever. Industrial catalysts become "poisoned" by impurities and have to be "regenerated" (treated to remove the poisoning agent). Enzymes too can become poisoned, or "denatured" (converted to a catalytically inactive form of protein); moreover they can be digested —for proteins are, after all, a kind of food. Denaturation and digestion within the cell may be rare accidents, but accidents happen. Plainly, if a cell is to continue to have its needed supply of enzymes, either enzymes must be capable of self-reproduction—*but they are not*—or there must be something else that synthesizes enzymes.

The necessity of this "something else" becomes even more apparent when we think of the significance of cell division. Since one cell gives rise successively to 2, 4, 8, 16, *et cetera,* it is clear that there must be a similar multiplication of whatever it is that produces enzymes —this is the logical point that was made in a less specific way in §14. This "something else" must not only produce enzymes (either directly, or through a chain of reactions), but it must also *re*produce itself. Historically, knowledge of the reproduction of chromosomes developed

synchronously with knowledge of the properties of enzymes around the turn of the twentieth century; this synchrony caused a number of speculative minds to suggest that there must be some sort of chemical compound in the chromosomes that was capable of reproducing itself and equally capable of bringing about the production of enzymes. What kind of chemical compound was it in the chromosomes that had this remarkable property?

For a long time it was supposed that the self-reproducing producer of enzymes must be a protein of some sort. This was a reasonable supposition. The chemist Berzelius had coined the name protein from a Greek root meaning "of the first rank." Proteins were known to be indispensable for life, and the rich complexity of their structure made plausible the hypothesis that proteins were the carriers of the tremendous amount of hereditary information that is passed on from parent to offspring. The hypothesis was, however, wrong. The correction of this error took a full generation.

In 1928 Fred Griffith performed some experiments with the bacteria that cause pneumonia, with puzzling results. These bacteria (at that time called *Pneumococcus*) occur in two different phases, *rough* and *smooth,* symbolized by the letters *R* and *S* respectively. The smooth is the normal, virulent kind (i.e., the kind capable of causing disease); it is so named because colonies of these cells growing on a plate of nutrient jelly or agar are smooth and shiny. The individual cells are surrounded by a mucilaginous capsule. Under prolonged cultivation outside the animal body, the capsules may be lost; the cells then are bunched close together into a colony that appears rough to the eye. The cells from a rough colony are non-virulent, or at any rate greatly attenuated in their virulence.

In addition to the smooth-rough variation, *Pneumococcus* shows another kind of hereditary variation. The chemical composition of the capsule of the cells varies. The various *types* are given Roman numerals. Each kind of *Pneumococcus* is therefore indicated by both a letter and a numeral, e.g., S-IV, meaning smooth phase of type four. *Each kind breeds true;* but since the R-phases lack capsules, the type determination must be based on their hereditary origin—on the type of capsule the strain had many generations back, before the capsule was lost in culture.

With this background we are ready for Griffith's experiments. In summary, they fall into four groups.

A. Living R-II injected into a mouse. Mouse survives. No living bacteria recoverable from mouse.
B. Living S-III injected into a mouse. Mouse dies. Living S-III recovered from mouse.
C. Dead S-III injected into a mouse. Mouse survives. No living bacteria recovered from mouse.
D. Living R-II plus dead S-III injected into a mouse. Mouse dies, and *living* S-III can be recovered from it.*

How can we explain the results given in D? Logically, we might assert that in the presence of R-II cells the S-III cells, like Lazarus, arose from the dead, but we hesitate thus to fly in the face of all other biological experience. A more reasonable hypothesis is that some sub-stance from the dead S-III cells passes into the R-II cells and changes some of them to type III. This is a hereditary change, for the new type III cells breed true to type. That this is the correct explanation was shown by J. L. Alloway in 1932, who demonstrated that a sterile filtrate of S-III added to living R-II cells in culture converts some of these cells (and their descendants) to S-III.

What is present in this cell-free filtrate derived from the dead S-III cells that can cause a permanent hereditary change in the living R-II cells? What is the "transforming principle," as it was called? In 1944 this question was answered by O. T. Avery, C. M. MacLeod, and M. McCarty, working at the Rockefeller Institute. By meticulous chemical purification they showed that the transforming principle was a type of chemical compound now known as *deoxyribosenucleic acid* or *DNA,* for short.* It is not protein. The revolutionary implications of their finding were only cautiously hinted at in Avery, MacLeod, and McCarty's conclusion: "If the results of the present study on the chemical nature of the transforming principle are confirmed, then nucleic acids must be regarded as possessing biological specificity the chemical basis of which is as yet undetermined."

Within less than ten years, the chemical basis of that specificity was determined. But before we learn of this discovery we must go back a half century to the discovery of a remarkable class of biological entities, the viruses, which have proved most useful in the investigation of the molecular basis of heredity.

43. The Discovery of Viruses

Nothing is harder to assimilate into an intellectual framework than phenomena which require the creation of new categories of thought. A

---

* 5-1. The best way to make sense of a complex of experimental protocols like this is to convert them into a table. Please do so before proceeding.

5-2. If the table were presented to you ready-made in the text, would it be as valuable for learning as the table you make yourself?

---

* In their original paper, Avery, MacLeod, and McCarty used the word desoxyribosenucleic acid. This spelling is now being generally abandoned. In addition to the form given in the text, "deoxyribonucleic acid" is sometimes used.

pertinent example is found in the viruses, entities which could be understood only after a thorough reexamination of ancient ideas of life, of individuality and of information. We will mark the principal milestones in the long road of the discovery of viruses.

It is often said that the Russian D. Iwanowski discovered the first virus in 1892. If this is true, it is true only in a limited sense. Iwanowski was studying a transmissible disease of tobacco plants, a disease which caused the leaves to become a mosaic of healthy and diseased areas. The agent of this disease is now called **tobacco mosaic virus** or **TMV** for short. Iwanowski was unable to see the causative entity, but he showed that if he used fine filters that were capable of holding back visible bacteria, the filtrates of diseased leaves could infect healthy leaves. Iwanowski supposed that there really

were bacteria in the filtrates, but that they were unusually small and hence both invisible and filterable (filter-passing).

In 1898, a great Dutch microbiologist, M. W. Beijerinck (1851–1931), added new dimensions to the puzzle when he observed that TMV: (a) could diffuse through agar gel; and (b) could be precipitated by alcohol without losing its potency. Neither of these properties are found in ordinary living organisms so Beijerinck concluded that TMV was not an organism, though it was alive; it was, he supposed, some sort of infective substance—a "contagium vivum fluidum," he called it. In 1913 he said: "The existence of these contagia proves that the concept of life is not inseparably linked up with that of structure." As we see the matter now, he could hardly have been more wrong. The elaborate fine structure of cells, as revealed

Fig. 5-1. *The elongated balloonlike structure is an empty cell wall of a bacterium,* Escherichia coli. *The small structures attached to it are individual viruses called "T2 phage." (From E. Kellenberger and W. Arber, 1955.)*

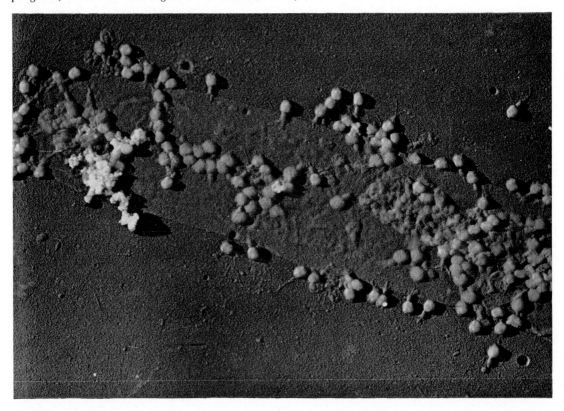

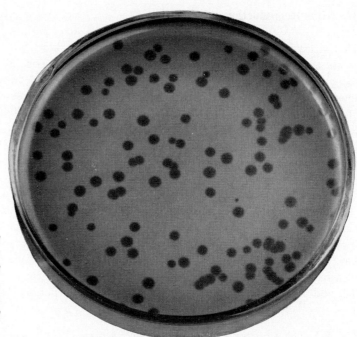

Fig. 5-2. *Nutrient agar in a petri dish covered all over with a "lawn" of* E. coli *bacteria. Each cleared area is where one phage particle landed, multiplied intracellularly for several cycles, and destroyed millions of bacterial cells.*

to us by the electron microscope, we now regard as a necessity for the harmonious coexistence of the many competing enzymes of a living system. Nevertheless, Beijerinck did a real service in calling the attention of biologists to viruses as a genuinely new biological category.

Particularly interesting among the viruses are the ones which infect bacterial cells (see Fig. 5-1). The world's attention was first called to these in 1915 by F. W. Twort (1877–1950), who found that a large population of bacteria could be almost completely destroyed overnight by these agents acting *in vitro*, i.e., in a test tube or other vessel outside the body. The number of virus particles capable of infecting bacteria can be determined by dilution procedures. Diluted material can be spread out on a Petri plate already inoculated with bacteria. As the bacteria multiply into a "lawn," each spot where a virus particle has landed becomes a cleared area in the lawn where the bacterial cells have been lysed by the many particles descended from the original virus particle (see Fig. 5-2). Each cleared area is called a **plaque** (from Middle Dutch, *placke,* a piece or patch).

For a number of years it was hoped that this lytic ability of the bacterial viruses would also be useful *in vivo** as a therapeutic agent against bacterial infections, but this hope was never realized, for reasons that are still not understood. The idea did, however, serve as a theme of Sinclair Lewis' novel *Arrowsmith.*

Two years after Twort's publication, Felix d'Hérelle (1873–1949) published similar observations which he had made independently in studies carried out over a number of years. D'Hérelle gave a name to the bacterial viruses: **bacteriophage** (Gr. *phago,* to eat), now usually shortened to **phage.** More important, d'Hérelle defined viruses in general as *particulate, invisible, self-reproducing, filterable entities that are obligate intracellular parasites.* With only quantitative qualifications this definition has stood the test of time. Now that the electron microscope has been invented, viruses are no longer invisible. In size they range from 16 mμ to 300 mμ.† As for the filterability, that depends on the fineness of the filters used.

* 5-3. What is the etymology of *in vitro* and *in vivo*?

† 5-4. J. B. Buist in 1887 reported that he had seen the "spores" of the cowpox organism. Electron microscopy shows the dimensions of the cowpox virus to be 210 × 260 mμ. Should we credit Buist with the discovery of viruses?

44. Virus Reproduction

That viruses are obligate intracellular parasites is still an essential element of the definition of these entities. Twort never accepted this and spent most of the last thirty-five years of his life vainly trying to culture viruses in nonliving medium. Many bacteria that had initially required living cells for their growth were eventually cultured in very complex nonliving media. Why should we not eventually expect to do the same with viruses?

The answer to this question was not achieved easily; it required a thorough knowledge of the life history of a virus. Different kinds of viruses have different life cycles; we will examine that of a bacteriophage of the "T-even" types (T2, T4, and T6) which infect *E. coli* bacteria. An electron micrograph of one of these phage particles is shown on the left of Figure 5-3; on the right is shown the structure as deduced from many studies. When phage particles were first seen in electron micrographs, the elongated portion was immediately dubbed the "tail" since it reminded observors of the tail of a tadpole or the flagellum of a flagellated protozoan. The tail is not, however, a propulsive organ. Its function is quite different. The phage is nonmotile. When, by Brownian motion, it is brought into contact with a bacterium, if the bacterial cell is of the correct type, the tail fibers adsorb onto the bacterial surface, attaching the phage tail first and head outward (Fig. 5-4). Then what happens? We cannot follow the course of events directly because the electron microscope does not permit observation of aqueous systems. We

Fig. 5-3. *The structure of a T-even phage particle.* Left: *Electron micrograph of a single particle.* Right: *The structure deduced from many studies.* (*Based on E. Kellenberger, 1962; from Gunther S. Stent,* Molecular Biology of Bacterial Viruses, *W. H. Freeman and Company, San Francisco and London, 1963.*)

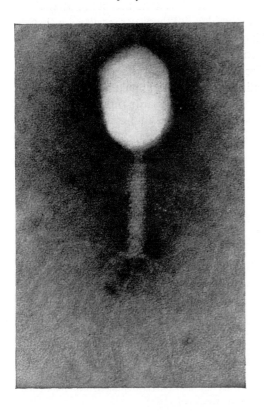
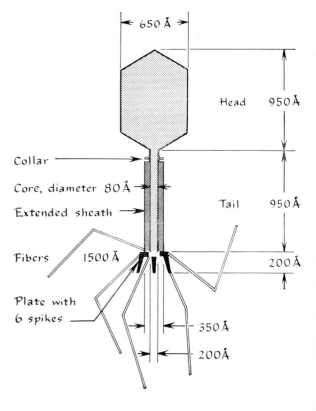

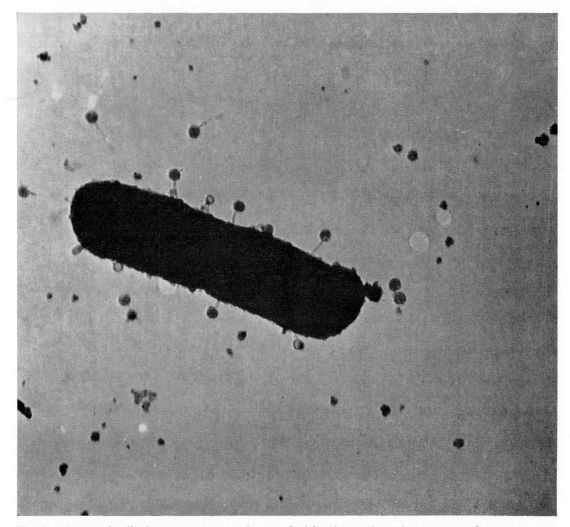

Fig. 5-4. *Bacterial cell, showing virus particles attached by their tails.* (*Photomicrograph by T. F. Anderson; from Gunther S. Stent,* Molecular Biology of Bacterial Viruses, *W. H. Freeman and Company, San Francisco and London, 1963.*)

must deduce what happens from experiments.

Using the plaque method of assay, we can determine the number of infective particles as a function of time in the life cycle of the phage. The result is a growth curve that is markedly different from any ever observed before; it is shown by the black curve in Figure 5-5. Notice that for more than 20 minutes the number of virus particles, *as determined by the plaque method,* is absolutely constant. Then abruptly it starts rising, and within less than 10 minutes has increased to the "final yield," given in the

graph as 100 percent, which typically means about 50 phage particle per infected bacterial cell.* In other words, as far as this assay method goes, the number of phage particles is apparently constant for a long time, and then abruptly jumps to about 50. The only reason the steeply rising part of the black curve is not vertical is because the bacteria-virus complexes are not completely in phase. When a bacterium is full of virus particles, the cell lyses, releasing

---

* 5-5. What is remarkable about the scale of the ordinate in this curve? Why is such a scale used?

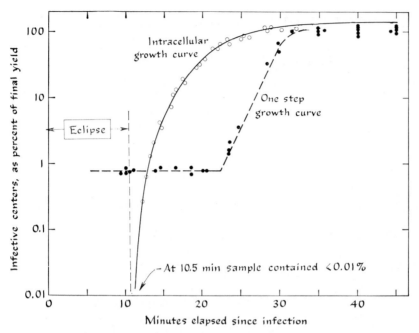

Fig. 5-5. *The growth curve of a bacteriophage, as assayed by the usual method (black curve); and by lysing the bacterial cells from the outside (color). (Data of A. H. Doermann, 1952; from Gunther S. Stent,* Molecular Biology of Bacterial Viruses, *W. H. Freeman and Company, San Francisco and London, 1963.)*

the virus particles which can then be assayed by the plaque method; not all bacterial cells lyse at the same instant.

Figure 5-6 shows a series of electron micrographs taken at different periods of the life cycle.* If one more stage were shown, it would be of a lysed (ruptured) bacterial cell with the new virus particles escaping from it into the medium. If new, uninfected bacterial cells are available to these phage particles, they will infect them in turn and start another cycle of phage growth.†

The newly produced phage particles are not normally assayable until the cell lyses, at which time a full complement of particles has been produced. Suppose, however, that one forcibly breaks open the cell before this time, by some other lytic agent applied from the outside (chlo-

roform will serve)—what then? Return to Figure 5-5; the results are shown in the colored curve. As one would expect from the electron microscopical studies (which were, historically, carried out later) the number of phage particles per cell shows a smooth increase rather than an abrupt increase. Still more remarkable: there is a period of time (about 10 minutes under the conditions of this experiment) during which *no phage particles whatever can be demonstrated* in the gruel of lysed infected bacterial cells. This period is called the **eclipse.** It is essential to point out that the lysing agent has no effect on demonstrably competent phage particles.

These phenomena are most remarkable. If we call a bacteriophage "living," then we end up with some such statement as this: a living phage particle infects a bacterial cell, following which (for ten minutes) the phage is dead; then it becomes alive again and multiplies. If the word "living" is to be used, the statement above corresponds with the facts. But facts so remarkable as these, so at variance with ordinary ex-

---

* 5-6. Are these pictures all of the same bacterial cell? How do you know?

† 5-7. Draw the growth curve of a bacteriophage through 70 minutes time, given an initial ratio of bacterial cells to phage particles of 10,000 to 1. Label and scale the coordinate axes.

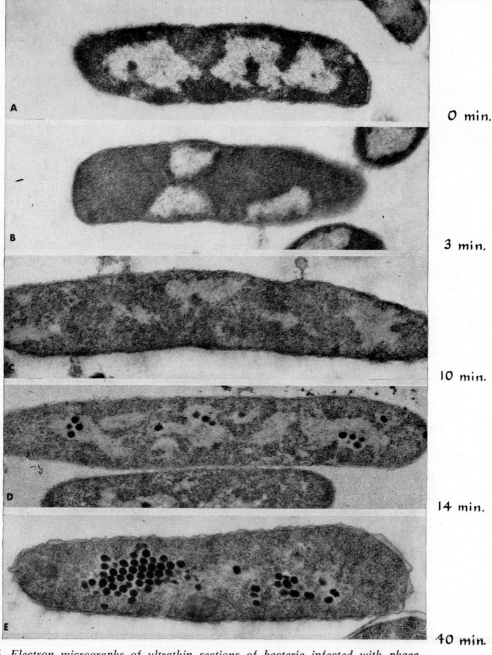

0 min.

3 min.

10 min.

14 min.

40 min.

Fig. 5-6. *Electron micrographs of ultrathin sections of bacteria infected with phage.
(A) At the moment of infection; the normal bacterial nuclei are visible as electron-
transparent areas. (B) Two to four minutes after infection; the nuclei have changed
their form and migrated towards the cell wall. (C) Ten minutes after infection; the
nuclei have disappeared; vacuoles filled with fibrillar material (phage DNA) have made
their appearance. (D) Fourteen minutes after infection; the first condensates of phage
DNA have been formed. (E) Forty minutes after infection; many condensates and
structurally intact phage heads are present. (Micrograph by E. Kellenberger; from
"Viruses and Genes," by F. Jacob and E. L. Wollman. Copyright © 1961 by Scientific
American, Inc. All rights reserved.)*

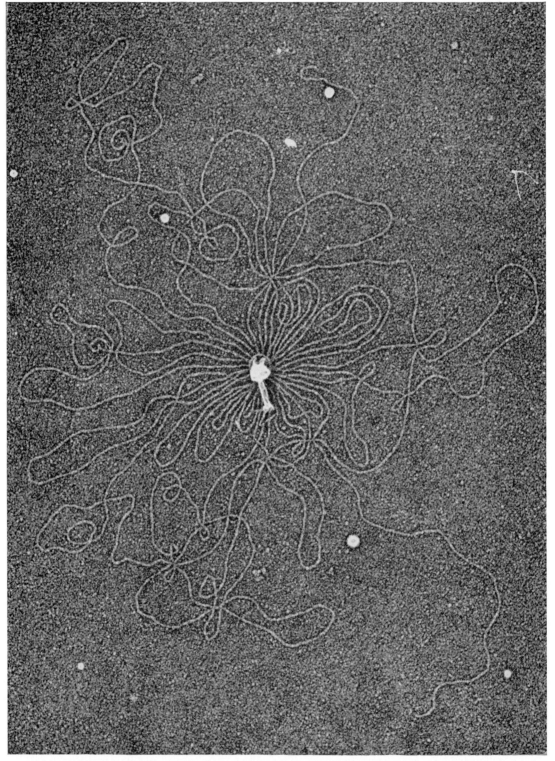

Fig. 5-7. *Electron micrograph of osmotically shocked phage particle, showing the DNA outside the "ghost" of the phage. Approximate magnification: 80,000×. (From A. K. Kleinschmidt, D. Lang, D. Jacherts, and R. K. Zahn, 1962.)*

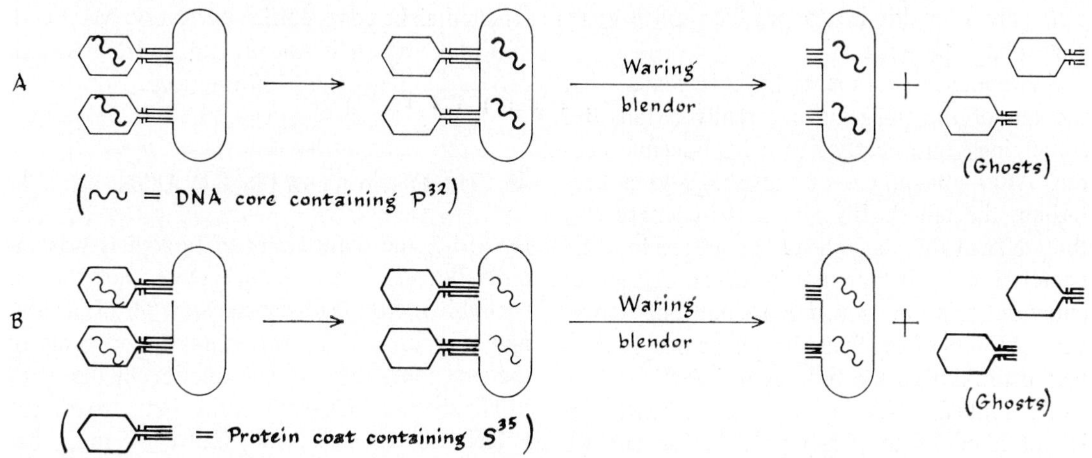

$\left(\sim\!\!\!\!\sim \ = \ DNA \ core \ containing \ P^{32} \right)$

$\left(\hexagon\!\!=\!\! \ = \ Protein \ coat \ containing \ S^{35} \right)$

Fig. 5-8. *How Hershey and Chase showed that only the DNA core of the bacteriophage is injected into the bacterial cell. Color indicates radioactive material.*

perience, make us wonder if the word "living" is justified in these circumstances. Perhaps viruses are not alive: after all, they have no metabolism of their own (though the metabolism of cell-plus-virus is different from metabolism of cell-alone). On the other hand, viruses do multiply—that seems to justify calling them alive. What are we to say?

During the 1930's a considerable literature was written on the subject, "Are the viruses alive?" It was interesting, but did not seem to get us very far with our work. Enlightenment came through more experiments, and through emphasis on other categories of thought—on "information," rather than "life," for example. Among the most important experiments were those reported by A. D. Hershey and Martha Chase in 1952. It had been previously found that phage particles are susceptible to "osmotic shock": by placing them in strong salt solution for several minutes and then diluting this as nearly instantaneously as possible, the contents of the head of the phage are released into the medium, leaving behind the empty husk or "coat" of the phage, which appears as a "ghost" in electronmicrographs.* The ghosts can be separated from the solution. Chemical analysis shows that the ghosts are protein, and the solution contains DNA. This means that the coat

of a phage particle is protein, and the contents are DNA. An electron micrograph of an osmotically shocked bacteriophage is shown in Figure 5-7. Note that the DNA is a single long filament.* All this long fiber was originally packed into the head of the phage.

To follow the protein and DNA in the process of infection, Hershey and Chase did two sorts of experiments. In one, the virus was grown for a number of cycles in a medium that contained phosphorus-32, which is radioactive. Phosphorus, as we shall see subsequently, is an essential part of the substance DNA, but not of protein. With P³² incorporated into its DNA, phage particles were allowed to infect bacteria (*A* of Fig. 5-8). The infected bacteria were then put in a Waring blendor which agitated the phage coats off the cells. Phage coats and bacterial cells were separated, and most of the radioactivity was found in the bacterial fraction.

In a complementary experiment, phage was grown in the presence of radioactive sulfur-35, which was incorporated into the protein but not into the DNA (see *B* of Fig. 5-8). After infection and agitation, most of the radioactivity was found in the viral coat fraction. These two experiments together indicate that in viral infection of bacteria, *only the DNA enters the*

---

* 5-8. Give a detailed explanation of the evident mechanism involved in osmotic shock.

* 5-9. Find the two ends of the DNA fiber.

5-10. The length of the *head only* is 950 Å. How long is the DNA fiber?

cell; here it multiplies to produce more complete phage particles.

Subsequent experiments have indicated that the tail of the phage is not really a tail, but something more nearly like a hypodermic needle. After attachment of the phage to a bacterium, the tail sheath contracts in length and the DNA of the phage head is squirted into the bacterial cell. It apparently takes energy to carry out this injection, for a small but significant amount of ATP in the phage tail is converted to ADP in the process of infection.

The naked DNA injected into a bacterium is not a complete phage particle for (as we have seen) if the cell is ruptured just after infection it yields no competent phage particles. During the eclipse period of the phage life cycle the phage DNA causes the synthesis of (*a*) replicates of itself, and (*b*) the coat parts (heads, tails and other less conspicuous components). The eclipse ends as (*c*) the first coats and DNA filaments are assembled into competent phage particles at about 10.5 minutes after the original infection.*

If the DNA injected into the bacterial cell is not an organism—and it certainly is not—then what is it? Simply this: it is **information.** It is a quantity of information that can, in the complex brew of the host cell, bring about the synthesis of its own duplicate. It can also cause the synthesis of other materials—the coats of heads and tails—and the assemblage of all these parts into complete phage particles. All these syntheses are brought about at the expense of the normal syntheses of the host body. The virus *subverts* the machinery of the host to its own end. The word "subversion" is often used in a pretty sloppy way; here, in virus infection, the word is justly used.

The viral DNA contains all the information needed for the construction of a complete phage unit. The DNA is the hereditary material. The results of Hershey and Chase corroborate, in a singularly elegant manner, the conclusion

reached eight years earlier by Avery, MacLeod, and McCarty. It is not protein, but DNA, that carries the hereditary information.

45. The Discovery of Nucleic Acids

By 1952, the community of biologists was rapidly becoming aware that DNA was the essential hereditary substance. Most of this awareness was created by the many experiments of the preceding decade, culminating in the work of Hershey and Chase. But the first work on the nucleic acids dates back almost a century before this. Nucleic acids were discovered and first characterized in 1868 by a German chemist, Friedrich Miescher (1844–1895). Miescher was interested in the chemical composition of cell nuclei. He first used as a source of material the pus cells obtained from discarded bandages; later he changed to a somewhat pleasanter source, salmon sperm. He found that he could obtain nuclei in a high degree of purity by treating cells with proteolytic enzymes— which fact by itself should make one doubt if nuclei are predominantly protein. From these nuclei Miescher isolated, and characterized in chemical terms, what we now call the class of nucleic acids.

The times, however, were dominated by what, in retrospect, we might call the Protein Doctrine. G. J. Mulder, the chemist who, at Berzelius' suggestion, had first used the name "protein," said of this class of compounds: "There is present in plants and animals a substance which is . . . without doubt the most important of all known substances in living matter, and without it, life would be impossible on our planet. This material has been named protein." The *over*emphasis of statements like this acted as blinders to biological vision. To biologists of the time, proteins seemed all-important, while nucleic acids were a merely somewhat puzzling by-product of life. Not even the discovery by Robert Feulgen in 1924 of a specific stain for DNA altered the unconscious attitude of most biologists. The **Feulgen stain**

---

* 5-11. Make a diagram of the life cycle of phage, from one infection to another, showing the DNA at all stages.

came to be recognized as a definitive stain for nuclei, but there was no general realization of the significance of equating a nucleic acid stain with a nuclear stain.

In understanding the way in which science progresses, errors are often as enlightening as successes. One of the most famous errors in the story of the nucleic acids was that committed in the first analysis of the tobacco mosaic virus. Crystals of TMV were first obtained by Wendell M. Stanley in 1935, an accomplishment which immediately excited a great deal of attention and ultimately gained him the Nobel prize. To some bystanders, his accomplishment seemed like a crystallization of life itself. Stanley, more cautious, made no such claim but reported his chemical analysis of TMV crystals: they were, he said, pure protein. Two years later this important error was corrected by Frederick Bawden and N. W. Pirie who found nucleic acid in TMV. Repeating his analysis, Stanley admitted that his critics were right: *6 percent* of TMV is nucleic acid. This amount is much too great to have been missed by such excellent chemists as Stanley and his co-workers. Why was it missed? To this day, no satisfactory explanation has been given. On a verbal level, we can only speak vaguely of what the poet Goethe called the *Zeitgeist*—the spirit of the times. "We see only what we know," said Goethe; and most of the time, this is certainly true. For decades, biologists saw only proteins in the underbrush of heredity. But the nucleic acids were there all the time.*

46. Information: Coding, Replication, and Reading

The experiments described in this chapter and Chapter 2 indicate that cell nuclei, and more specifically, the nucleic acids, contain the in-

---

* The nucleic acid of TMV and a number of other viruses happens to be ribosenucleic acid (RNA) rather than DNA; this is a minor difference, the significance of which is not understood. We will learn more about RNA in the next chapter.

formation that is needed to bring into being cell after cell, in indefinite series. Before we see how this information is contained in the nucleic acids, and how it is read out, it would be well if we looked at information problems from a quite general point of view.

Perhaps the most important idea in information theory is that *information is nonmaterial.* The word STOP conveys information—a command, in this case, with an implied warning. The information just transmitted from author to reader was conveyed by a pattern of ink on paper—both material substances. However, it is not the ink or the paper that is important, but the *pattern*—which is nonmaterial. Being nonmaterial, it is theoretically independent of size. The information conveyed by the three signs STOP—STOP—STOP is precisely the same. Size is of no theoretical importance; it has practical importance, of course. A sign wrapped around the earth would be difficult to see; so would one only 20 Ångstroms long. And one smaller than the dimensions of an atom—well, what material would one use for the pattern? But this is purely a secondary matter. Information is fundamentally nonmaterial.

A second important general idea about information is connected with the meaning of the word "pattern." Whatever a pattern is, it is a *nonrandom* arrangement of parts, an improbable arrangement. I can spatter ink from a vibrating brush held three feet from a piece of paper, but the resultant random arrangement of spots, though interesting in an aesthetic sense (to some people) will convey no information. There is only a vanishingly small probability that the ink will arrange itself in a pattern that says STOP.

With these general points in mind, we can distinguish three practical problems in information handling:

1. Coding
2. Replication
3. Reading the code

Coding. The Morse code will serve as an example of one system of coding. It includes three symbols: dot, dash, and space (time lapse). The last named element is most often called a "comma" in current information theory: a comma serves to tell where the code for one coded element (letter) ends and another begins. For example, STOP coded into International Morse is:

$$\cdots \quad - \quad - - - \quad \cdot - - \cdot$$
$$\text{S} \qquad \text{T} \qquad \text{O} \qquad \text{P}$$

If this were written without spaces (commas) it would be

$$\cdots - - - - \cdot - - \cdot$$

Which might be read out as:

$$\cdots - \quad - - - \quad \cdot - \quad - \cdot$$
$$\text{V} \qquad \text{O} \qquad \text{A} \qquad \text{N}$$

the meaning of which is most unclear. Clearly, commas have their use in coding. Does the code of heredity include commas? We will see in the next chapter.

Replication. If there is need for more than one copy of a coded message, or for multiplication of it (as there certainly is of any biological message) how is the replication of it achieved? One way to replicate is by going through a cycle of decoding and encoding. For example, the tape recording of a piece of music has the message encoded in a pattern of magnetized particles on the tape. If we play the tape (that is, if we **decode** it) in the presence of another tape recorder we can record (**encode**) a replicate message on a second tape. It is possible to carry out such a decoding-encoding cycle in indefinite series, obtaining an indefinite number of copies. If there is no error in the physical processes, the last message of the series will be exactly like the first. But in the real world there is always error, and the errors are themselves reproduced and hence they are cumulative. The last member of a long series will be significantly different from the first.

In many mechanical processes, **templates** are used for replication. A cookie cutter is a template for cutting cookies. Most templates are negative templates. Such is a cookie cutter: where there is space in the cutter, there is solid (cookie dough) in the thing made. A rubber stamp might be regarded as a positive template:

the solid areas of the stamp produce solidly inked areas on the paper.*

Reading the code. The coded message is never an end in itself, but is always for the sake of something else. It must be decoded, of course; but something more is involved. When a tape recording is played, a pattern of magnetism in space is decoded into a pattern of sound waves in time, but this decoding (really, *trans*coding from one system to another) is not all that we mean by "reading the code." The sound waves have other, more complex effects on the person who hears them. "Reading the code"—discovering the meaning of it, is a complex and only partially understood phenomenon. The code of heredity must also be "read," i.e., converted into cell structure and function, and multicellular structure and function. This aspect of the hereditary code will be taken up in the next chapter.

Why code information anyway? In a way, this is the wrong question to ask, for we have no choice. All the information that comes into us is coded somehow, in the brain; though what the system of coding and read-out is, is still largely a mystery. All information is coded: but why transcode it onto notebooks, punched cards and the like? Most of the answers are well-known, but a brief review is not out of place. In deliberately coding information into systems outside the human brain we seek, in varying degrees, to achieve the following:

To minimize mutability. "The palest ink is better than the strongest memory," says an old Chinese proverb. It is an interesting exercise in imagination to picture what would happen to the modern world if that oldest of artificial coding systems, writing (and all its successors, printing, etc.), disappeared suddenly without a trace.

To minimize space. The blueprint of a house occupies much less space than the house itself; a microfilm of the blueprint occupies still less space and is more easily transportable.

---

* 5-12. An ordinary photographic negative is what sort of template?

5-13. What sort of template is a sheet of ordinary Polaroid film when used to print a duplicate of itself?

To minimize ambiguity. "How do I know what I think until I hear myself say it?" asked the old woman. Many (all?) systems of coding have their areas of ambiguity. Since these areas in different systems will not, in general, be completely congruent, the act of transcoding a message purges it of some of its ambiguity. This principle is a fundamental tenet of the "logical positivists" in philosophy who insist that translatability (from one language to another) is a necessary characteristic of any philosophical argument that is to be regarded as having sense.*

To maximize speed. It is well known that the information stored in the memory banks of modern computing machines can be handled with speeds far greater than that possible in the human brain.

To maximize accessibility. A properly designed memory system of a modern "electronic brain" permits drawing information out in an almost infinite number of permutations of combinations of categories. For example, one could ask of the records in the Census in Washington, "What is the number of U.S. males between the ages of 30 and 33 who are married, have two children, and own their own homes?" and receive the answer in a matter of minutes.

The art of information storage and retrieval —beyond that found in the printing of books and establishment of libraries—is almost wholly a development of the twentieth century. It has firm roots, however, in the eighteenth century. It was in that century that the music box was developed, with its various systems, of deriving musical tones from patterns of holes in, or tabs on, metal plates. More impressive were various elaborately programmed moving dolls and manikins, built for the delight of the very wealthy. Curiously, scarcely anyone saw the possible practical significance of this technology, which was developed for play and amusement. About the only significant practical application was the "Jacquard loom," invented by M. Falcon in 1728. In this machine, perforated cards instruct the loom, telling it what thread to use when. Such punched cards opened up possibilities far beyond rug-making, but this was not realized for more than a century and a half. In 1890, H. Hollerith of the U.S. Bureau of the Census used punched cards to classify census data, and a new world was opened up in the handling of information in human affairs.

47. The Code of DNA

With this background in general coding theory and practice we are now in a position to look at the hereditary code. How is the information needed for function and structure coded in the cell? Not in the form of tiny punched cards, of course, but in the linear sequence of a small number of different chemical compounds. The DNA filament shown in Figure 5-7 is made up of a linear sequence of chemical compounds that determines the "message" of the DNA.

There is more than one kind of nucleic acid. A nucleic acid includes many units of the chemical "bases" shown in Figure 5-9; these are divided into two categories, the *purines* and the *pyrimidines.* Of the purines the two principal kinds found in nucleic acids are: **adenine** and **guanine.** Of the pyrimidines the three best known are shown in Figure 5-9; for the moment we will consider only **thymine** and **cytosine.*** A DNA filament is made up, however, not of these four units as such, but of larger units called nucleotides: a **nucleotide** consists of one base (purine or pyrimidine), one sugar (deoxyribose in DNA), and one phosphate group. For a given kind of nucleic acid, the phosphate and sugar groups are the same in all its nucleotides; only the bases of the nucleotides vary, so it is the sequence of bases that determine the information of the DNA. The number of nucleotides per filament of DNA varies from species to species. A whole DNA unit is sometimes spoken of as a "molecule," but it seems somewhat preferable to call it a **macromolecule,** thus calling attention to the fact that it is an assemblage of units we ordinarily call molecules

---

* 5-14. What about poetry?

* Hydroxymethyl cytosine replaces cytosine in the DNA of the T-even phages. Uracil replaces thymine in RNA, which will be discussed in the next chapter.

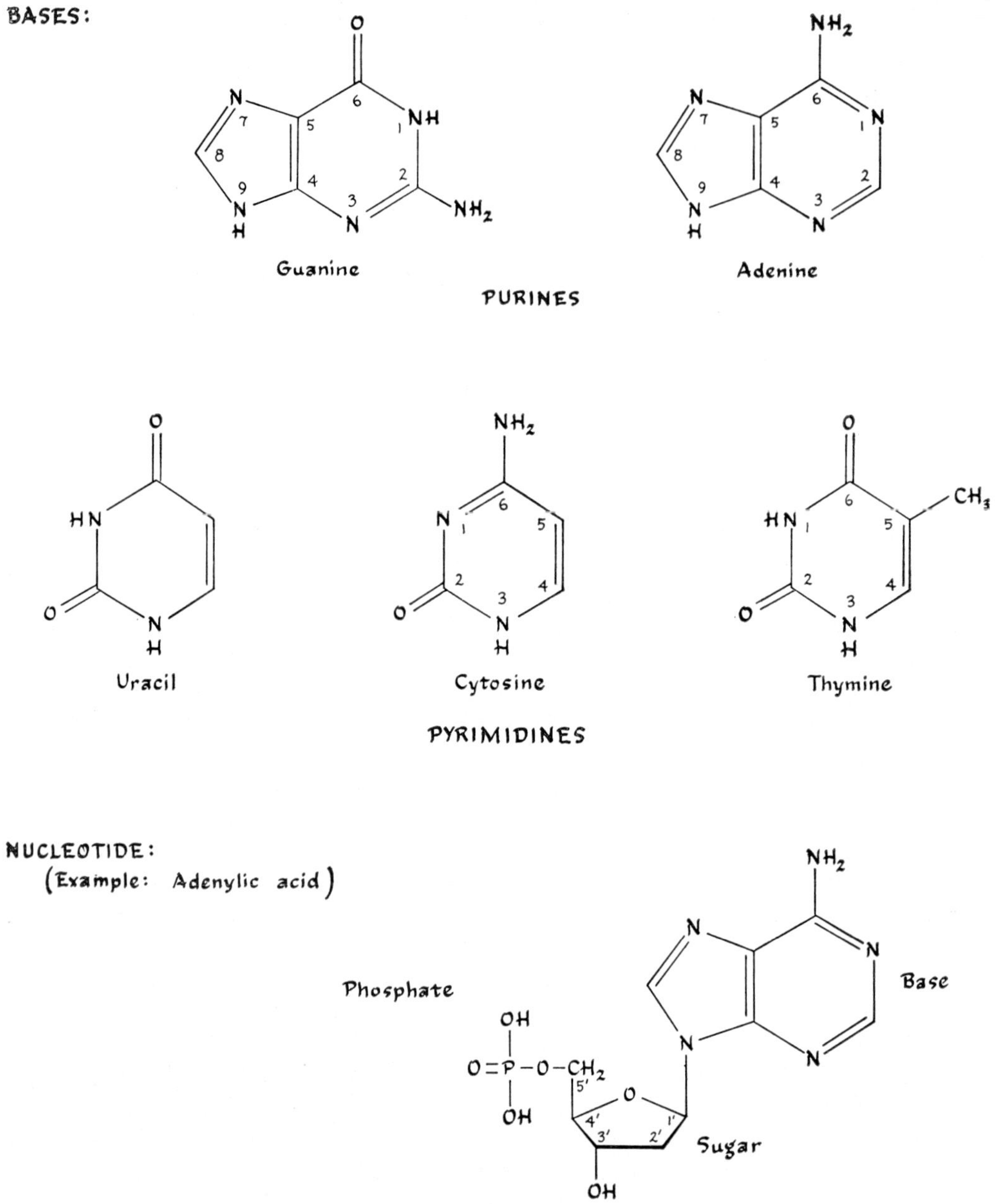

BASES:

Guanine   Adenine

PURINES

Uracil   Cytosine   Thymine

PYRIMIDINES

NUCLEOTIDE:
(Example: Adenylic acid)

Phosphate   Base

Sugar

Fig. 5-9. *The chemical structure of the units of a nucleic acid.*

—the nucleotides and their still smaller molecular constituents, as indicated in Figure 5-9. (Proteins also are macromolecules, with amino acids as constituent molecules.)

Because only the bases vary in the nucleotides, we will hereafter refer to the various nucleotides by the initial letters of their base members only, namely: G, A, T and C, for guanine,

adenine, thymine and cytosine respectively. These compounds are the "letters" of the genetic code. How are these letters arranged in the DNA macromolecule? The quantity of any one of the four letters in DNA is "arbitrary," that is, it follows no apparent rule. It will be constant for a given species, but there is no way one can predict in advance what this quantity will be. However, in 1950, Erwin Chargaff discovered a most remarkable uniformity, namely that in every species of DNA, *the quantity of A always equals the quantity of T;* and *the quantity of G always equals the quantity of C.* "Quantity" here means the number of molecules. It was immediately recognized that such an invariant relation must be of great significance. It was natural to suppose that A and T are always and necessarily linked together, and similarly for G and C. But how are they linked together, and what is the over-all structure of DNA?

The problem was solved at Cambridge, England in 1953 by an English physicist, F. H. C. Crick and a visiting American biologist, James D. Watson. Their work rested very heavily on X-ray studies previously carried out at King's College, London, by M. H. F. Wilkins and his collaborators, especially Rosalind Franklin. The elucidation of the structure of DNA in 1953 marks a true watershed in biology. For this work the Nobel Prize was awarded to Watson, Crick, and Wilkins in 1962 (Miss Franklin was dead by this time and hence not eligible for the prize).

The basic idea of the **Watson-Crick** model is that of *two* long chains of nucleotides wound helically around each other. These are represented in Figure 5-10, where one helix is shown in darker color than the other so the eye can easily follow them. Each helix is like a "spiral staircase"—which should really be called a *helical* staircase. (A watch spring is a spiral.*) It will be noted that the (colored) atoms of the two helices are connected by black crosshatched atoms. To see how these connections are made, examine Figure 5-11, which represents "in plan" (to use an architectural term) two different levels of a DNA macro-

---

* 5-15. State explicitly the difference between spiral and helix here implied.

Fig. 5-10. *A portion of a DNA unit. In order that they may be distinguished, one of the two helically wound chains of deoxyribose phosphate is shown darker than the other. The purine-pyrimidine linkages between the helices are cross-hatched.*

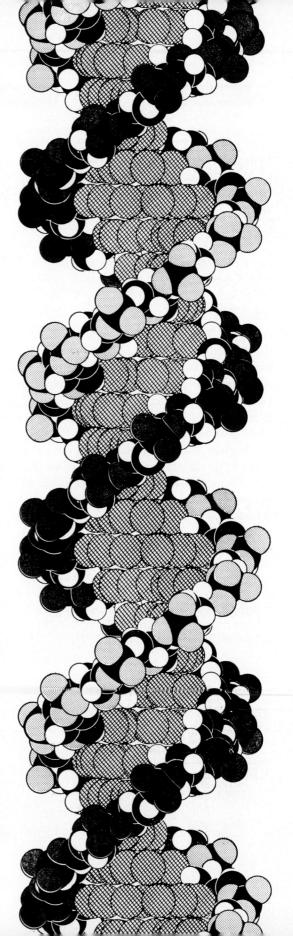

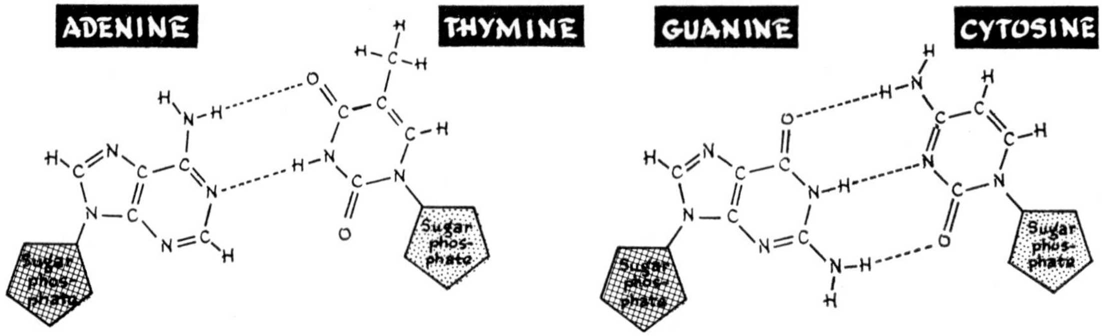

| ADENINE | THYMINE | GUANINE | CYTOSINE |

Fig. 5-11. *Schematic cross-section of a DNA unit. As in Fig. 5-10, the deoxyribose-phosphate (sugar-phosphate) chain is in color, the purine-pyrimidine linkage in black. Note that only two types of linkage are possible. In the next figure these will be abbreviated A-T and G-C.*

molecule. That is, a plane is taken at right angles to the long axis of the DNA and projected onto the page. The same color-key is used. Each such plane includes two nucleotides. (A nucleotide is a complex of a base and a sugar-phosphate compound.) The sugar-phosphate portion of each nucleotide is the helical backbone of the macromolecule (in color); the bases form the cross-connections between the two helices. **Always a pyrimidine is linked to a purine.** The only possible linkages are between the bases A and T; and the bases G and C. If

we know that one helix has an A at a particular level, the other helix must have a T at the same level; similarly for G and C.

A—T

Base Pairing Rule

G—C

Since the sequence of bases attached to one helix completely determines the sequence of the other, each helix is the **complement** of the other. Complementary nucleotides are linked by weak **hydrogen bonds,** indicated in Figure 5-11 by dotted lines. Being weak, these bonds are easily broken, as we will see in the next section.

The bases occurring at any level are subject to the restriction of the Base Pairing Rule given above. The sequence of bases at different levels is, however, "arbitrary," that is, free to vary. A possible sequence is shown in Figure 5-12, in which a short segment (four nucleotide pairs) of the DNA is shown. In preparing this diagram, each helix has been (so to speak) stretched out flat so that the linkages can easily be presented in two dimensions. According to the Watson-Crick theory the linear sequence of nucleotides is constant for a given species (except for minor hereditary variations within the species), and it is the actual linear sequence of nucleotides that encodes the genetic message. The length of the DNA macromolecule varies from species to species. The most studied of the T-even phages, the T2 phage, has 4.3×10^5 nucleotide pairs; its host, the bacterium *E.*

Fig. 5-12. *How the two sugar-phosphate helics are linked. It is believed that the sequence of bases— A, C, T, and G—is the genetic code to which the cell responds. Given the sequence in one sugar-phosphate helix, the sequence in the other is absolutely determined by the restriction that A cross-links with T, and C cross-links with G.*

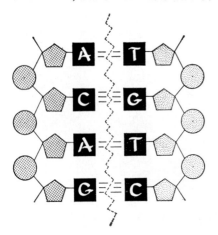

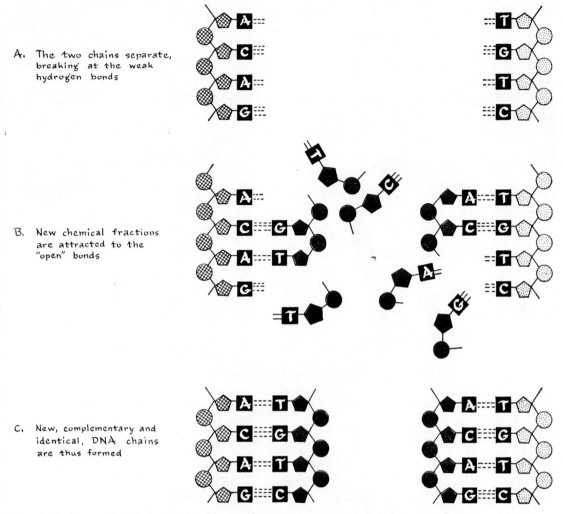

A. The two chains separate, breaking at the weak hydrogen bonds

B. New chemical fractions are attracted to the "open" bonds

C. New, complementary and identical, DNA chains are thus formed

Fig. 5-13. *How a double helix of DNA can break into two, each half bringing about a synthesis of its missing half, according to current hypothetical notions.*

coli, has 3×10^7 nucleotide pairs; man has 1×10^{10} nucleotide pairs in each of his reproductive cells (eggs or sperms). This objective evidence corroborates our traditional belief that man is a more complex organism than a bacterium or a virus. It takes a longer coded message to produce a man than is needed for a virus.

48. Reproducing the Coded Message

Accurate reproduction of organisms or cells necessarily requires accurate reproduction of the coded information under which they operate. The Watson-Crick model of DNA has, for the first time, given us an intellectually acceptable picture of how a coded structure may be replicated in living organisms.

Because the two DNA chains are complementary to each other and because of the Base Pairing Rule, reproduction of the double helix can take place *if* the two single helices can be separated from each other in the presence of a supply of the nucleotides needed to make up new DNA chains. Figure 5-13, in which the processes are represented in a flat plane, shows how this replication process can be conceived.

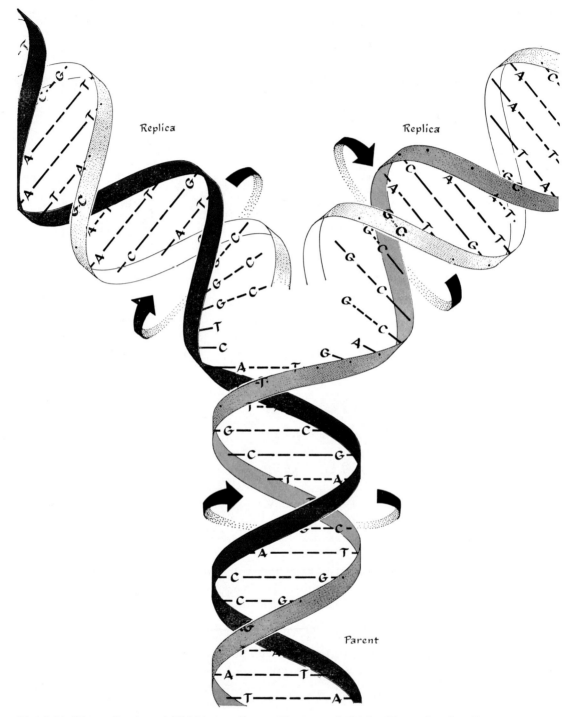

Fig. 5-14. *The replication of DNA, according to Watson and Crick. (From Gunther S. Stent,* Molecular Biology of Bacterial Viruses, *W. H. Freeman and Company, San Francisco and London, 1963.)*

First (in *A*) the two chains (helices) separate, along the line of the weak hydrogen bonds. This leaves bonds at the ends of each purine or pyrimidine base that are "unsatisfied." The process takes place inside a cell where there is a large supply of many substances, including the nucleotides needed to form new DNA chains. These are attracted to the unsatisfied hydrogen bonds (Fig. 5-13); attaching themselves thereto according to the Base Pairing Rule, they form a new complementary chain attached to each old one (Fig. 5-13). Thus, from one double helix DNA, we get two identi-

cal double helices. Each contains an intact half of the original helix.

In telling this story, we have glossed over a point that is still felt to be a difficult one: How do the two helices separate? The distortion of the facts created by our imaginary unwinding of the double helix so as to flatten out each chain into a plane figure permitted us to escape being impressed by this difficulty. Get two ordinary steel springs of open structure and of the same size; "thread" one of them into the other. Then try to get them apart. They have no bonds between them, but they can be separated only

Fig. 5-15. *The conservative and semi-conservative theories of DNA replication compared in their consequences. The material of the "original" macromolecule is shown in gray; newly synthesized material in color. (From Gunther S. Stent,* Molecular Biology of Bacterial Viruses, *W. H. Freeman and Company, San Francisco and London, 1963.)*

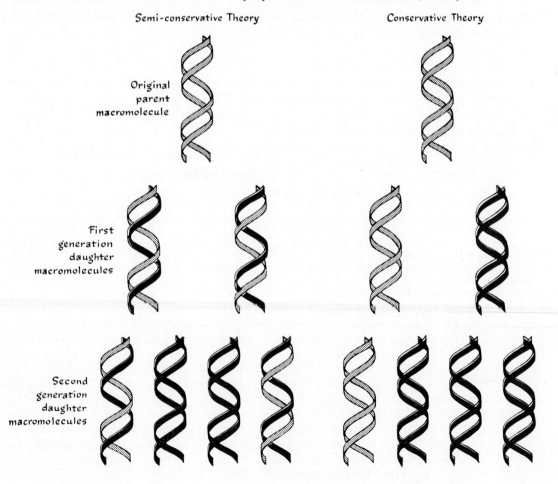

by unthreading them, turn after turn. Is this the way two unbonded DNA helices separate (Fig. 5-14), making thousands of turns?* We don't know. The present evidence indicates that separation of the helices and their replication take place concurrently in time and space, as indicated in Figure 5-14; if so, at no time is there a free, single helix.

The method of replication indicated in Figure 5-14 is not the only one we can conceive of. One might postulate, on the contrary, that the double helix of DNA remained intact and catalyzed the formation of another double helix made entirely from new nucleotides. The difference between this theory and the preceding one is shown in Figure 5-15. Replication taking place according to the last described theory has been described as a *conservative* process, since all the material in a DNA filament is conserved intact. The other type of replication is called a *semi-conservative* process since half the material is distributed between each of the "daughter" molecules. Note that the two theories lead to different predictions; they should, therefore, be testable. For example, in the second generation, the semiconservative model leads to a prediction of two filaments like those of the first generation and two new ones, with none like the original filaments; the conservative model

predicts that one and only one filament in each generation will be like the original.

The two models were tested by M. Meselson and F. W. Stahl in 1958. The test involved labeling DNA with N^{15} by growing *E. coli* cells for many generations in a medium containing this heavy nitrogen instead of the normal N^{14}. N^{15} is not radioactive, so it has to be detected by gravimetric means, that is by a technique that depends on the slightly heavier weight of compounds containing the N^{15} as compared with N^{14} compounds. The difference is so slight that it takes a centrifuge of great power (ca. 100,000 g.) to separate N^{15}-containing compounds from ones made up with N^{14}.

The results are shown in Figure 5-16.* Compare these results step by step with Figure 5-15. Note that when the bacterial cells are transferred to N^{14}, after 1 generation the DNA is homogeneous in weight and halfway between what it would be if it were all N^{15} or all N^{14}. We can call this DNA "hybrid DNA." After 2 generations the DNA is equally divided between hybrid DNA and light DNA. Clearly Meselson and Stahl's results corroborate the semi-conservative theory of DNA replication.

49. The Biological Miniaturization of Information

In designing new computers, engineers constantly seek to use less and less material for

---

* 5-16. Examine Figure 5-10 carefully. (*a*) How many nucleotide pairs are there in the space taken for a helix to make one complete revolution of the long axis? (*b*) If human DNA were in the form of one long filament, how many turns would there be in it from one end to the other? (*c*) If human DNA were equally divided among the 23 different chromosomes in each egg or sperm, how many complete turns of the DNA would there be per chromosome?

* 5-17. Before you read further, read the legend of Figure 5-16 and add an arrow to the figure to indicate which way gravity was acting while the samples were in the ultracentrifuge. That is, the arrow should point "down," with respect to gravity.

Fig. 5-16. *Demonstration of the semi-conservative replication of DNA. Column A: Ultraviolet absorption photographs of an ultracentrifuge vessel, in which DNA macromolecules are banded in a density gradient established in a concentrated cesium chloride solution. Each frame represents the bands formed by DNA extracted from a culture initially grown in N^{15} and then grown in N^{14}-labeled medium for the number of generations indicated. The density of the cesium chloride solution increases toward the right, regions of equal density occupying the same position on the x-axis in each photograph. Column B: Densitometer tracings of the photographs in A. The height of the curve is proportional to the concentration of DNA. The relative content of the two isotopes is indicated by the position of its band compared with the reference frame given at the bottom. (From Meselson and Stahl, 1958.)*

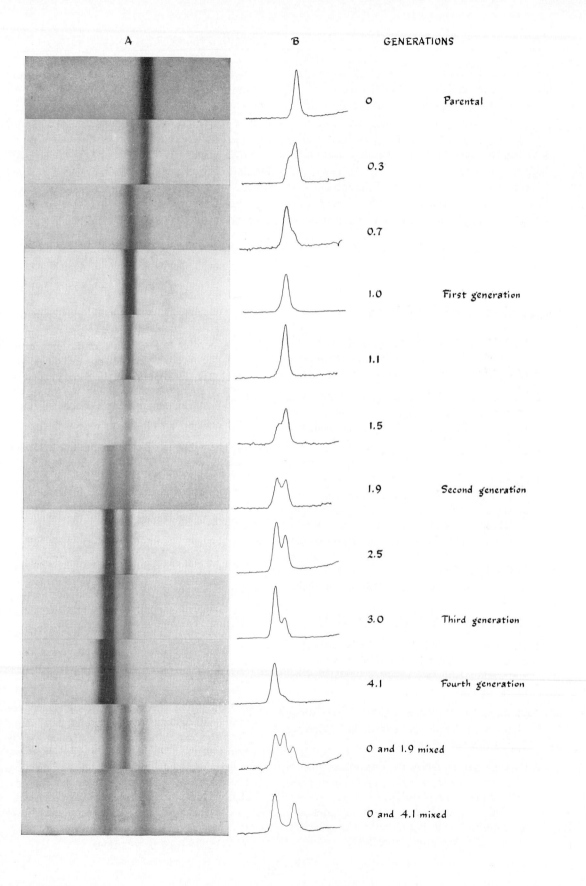

	A	B	GENERATIONS
			0 Parental
			0.3
			0.7
			1.0 First generation
			1.1
			1.5
			1.9 Second generation
			2.5
			3.0 Third generation
			4.1 Fourth generation
			0 and 1.9 mixed
			0 and 4.1 mixed

the coding of information. Progress has led first to what was called the "miniaturization" of components and later to "microminiaturization." But the very best the engineer can do is still a long way from what nature has already accomplished, as the following facts and calculations will show.

A human zygote contains all the information that is needed to produce an adult human being—a pretty complex and wonderful bit of machinery however you look at it. This information is coded into the DNA of the egg. The DNA of a fertilized human egg weighs 6 picograms. After consulting Appendix 3 to figure out what a picogram is, answer this question:

5-18. What was the weight of the coded matter that carried the information needed to produce all the present world's population of *Homo sapiens*? Compare this weight with that of an ordinary postage stamp (about 60 milligrams).

Questions and Problems

5-19. Make a list of the **boldface** terms in this chapter. Write out a definition or description of each. Compare your work with the text.

5-20. Write out a brief description of the work of the following men, with the approximate date of each: Griffith; Avery, MacLeod, and McCarty; d'Hérelle; Hershey and Chase; Miescher; Watson and Crick.

‡5-21. In the 1952 edition of this textbook these two statements were made: "Genes are constituents of the chromosomes of the cells;" and "A chromosome may be regarded as a sort of giant protein molecule, or as an organized collection of proteins." Criticize these statements in the light of (*a*) knowledge available at the time of writing and (*b*) knowledge available now.

5-22. For what is the Feulgen stain used?

5-23. How many symbols are there in the written code for English? Give the minimum number, and various alternate answers, explaining the bases for making them.

5-24. Is spoken English a code? If so, for what? How do we decode and encode in it? Can we bypass this coding process?

‡5-25. Considering DNA as a template, does a DNA macromolecule act as a positive or negative template in replication?

5-26. Enlarge Figure 5-15 so it includes also generations 3 and 4, and compare predictions with results shown in Figure 5-16.

‡5-27. According to the Population Reference Bureau, the total number of human beings who have ever lived is 7.7×10^{10}. Expressed in postage stamps, what was the weight of the coded information that produced all these people?

‡5-28. The number of cells in the adult human body is about 10^{14}. Assuming all cells have the same quantity of DNA (which is almost true) what is the weight of DNA in the human body? Express it in both metric and English systems.

5-29. Westerners often speak disparagingly of the fact that the Chinese invented gunpowder but used it only for pleasure (fireworks), not seeing that it had a "practical" use (killing people). Cite a comparable, though less conspicuous, example in the Western world.

‡5-30. Is information, like matter and energy, conserved? Does the answer have any practical significance?

5-31. The physicist J. Robert Oppenheimer once said: "All history teaches us that these questions that we think the pressing ones will be transmuted before they are answered, that they will be replaced by others, and that the very process of discovery will shatter the concepts that we today use to describe our puzzlement."

Use the history of our concept of viruses to illustrate this point. An adequate answer will require a fairly long essay.

Readings

The papers of Avery, MacLeod, and McCarty (1944) and Watson and Crick are reprinted in Peters' *Classic Papers in Genetics*. Ruth Moore, in *The Coil of Life*, has given a good popular history of the development of knowledge of DNA; her book is full of anecdotes and photographs. Stanley and Valens' book, *Viruses and the Nature of Life* is a well-illustrated account of these organisms, their importance and the techniques for studying them. For a professional account rich in intellectual excitement, see Gunther Stent's excellent *Molecular Biology of Bacterial Viruses*, from which I have borrowed heavily in preparing this chapter.

Scientific American Offprints

9. Heinz Fraenkel-Conrat. *Rebuilding a Virus*

40. Gunther S. Stent. *The Multiplication of Bacterial Viruses*

54. F. H. C. Crick, *Nucleic Acids*

89. François Jacob and Elie L. Wollman. *Viruses and Genes*

6 Reading the Code

50. Ribosenucleic Acid

In 1651 William Harvey, puzzling over the mystery of the development of a highly structured embryo (foetus) from an egg that appears to be almost without structure, said: "There is no part of the foetus actually in the egg, but yet all the parts of it are in it potentially." This potentiality we now conceive as residing in the linear sequence of nucleotides in the DNA of the cell nucleus. But how is this coded potentiality translated into actual structure and function? The process is by no means completely understood, but we think we know the basic elements of the mechanism.

Translation of DNA into metabolic meaning involves a transcribing of the DNA message into the code of a closely related class of macromolecules, RNA, or ribosenucleic acid. As indicated by its name, the sugar in this substance is ribose (instead of the deoxyribose of DNA). Where DNA consists of two strands, RNA is a single strand. The length of a free segment of RNA is much less: typically it ranges from 250Å to 1μ, instead of 1μ to 2 cm characteristic of DNA. The bases of which RNA is most commonly composed are A, C, G, and U—adenine, cytosine, guanine and uracil. Note the U (uracil) in RNA in place of the thymine (T) of DNA.*

---
* 6-1. Make a table showing the differences between DNA and RNA.

DNA is almost entirely confined to the nuclei of cells. As recounted in §48, isotope studies show that the actual material of a DNA strand is conserved indefinitely. This lack of metabolic turnover is just what we would expect in a system designed to preserve information. RNA, by contrast, is found in both nucleus and cytoplasm; it is formed in the nucleus and passes out into the cytoplasm, there to function for awhile before being destroyed and replaced by fresh RNA from the nucleus. The ribosomes (see Fig. 2-13) are especially rich in RNA. They are the site of protein synthesis. There is an immense variety of proteins, of course, and the information needed to determine which protein is to be synthesized is carried to the ribosomes by RNA. Let's see how this information passes from DNA to RNA, and from RNA to protein.

51. Transcribing and Translating the Message of the DNA

We have seen (§47, §48) how DNA is duplicated, each single strand bringing about the synthesis of its complement. By way of review, this process is diagrammatically shown in the top half of Figure 6-1, in which the original strands of DNA are indicated in black, while the new strands are in color. Each new com-

DUPLICATION

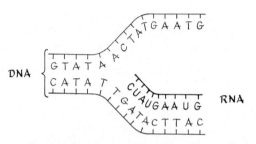

TRANSCRIPTION

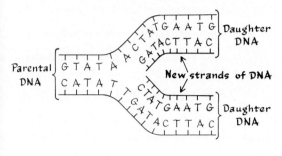

Fig. 6-1. *Comparison of the duplication of DNA with the synthesis of a single strand of RNA, which is coded by one strand of DNA. This is a diagram showing the logical relations; the actual spatial arrangement may be more complex.*

plete DNA macromolecule consists, of course, of one original and one new strand.

RNA is synthesized in a similar fashion, but there are a number of differences. For one thing, RNA has U (uracil) instead of T (thymine); this leads to the following difference between **duplication** (of DNA strand to its complementary DNA strand) and **transcription** (of DNA strand to RNA):

Duplication Rule (*DNA to DNA*)	**Transcription Rule** (*DNA to RNA*)
C ⟶ G	C ⟶ G
G ⟶ C	G ⟶ C
T ⟶ A	T ⟶ A
A ⟶ T	A ⟶ U

The synthesis of a representative RNA strand, following the transcribing rule, is diagrammatically shown in the bottom half of Figure 6-1. It will be noted that only one strand of

DNA is used in the transcription process. A priori it might seem just as reasonable to expect both strands of DNA to bring about the synthesis of RNA strands, but the best evidence available at present indicates that only one strand is transcribed.*

The RNA that is synthesized differs from the DNA not only in being single instead of double, but also in being in shorter chains. There are several functionally different kinds of RNA; for the moment we will focus on the kind called **mRNA,** which is an abbreviation for **message RNA** (or *messenger RNA* or *translatable RNA*). The various names suggest that mRNA has a message to be translated: translated into what? And how?

Recall that the most important agents in the cell are enzymes, and that enzymes are proteins. A protein is made up of one or more polypeptide chains, that is, chains of amino acids. Only 20 different amino acids are used in the construction of these polypeptides. The information that specifies which amino acid is used at each place in a polypeptide chain is carried by the mRNA. But RNA has only 4 different kinds of nucleotides (G, C, T and U)—how can these code for 20 different amino acids?

The theoretical physicist George Gamow was apparently the first one to ask this question, in

TABLE 6-1

NO. OF NUCLEOTIDES IN "WORD"	NO. OF DIFFERENT "WORDS" POSSIBLE	ENUMERATION OF THE "WORDS"
1	4	G, C, A, U
2	$4 \times 4 = 16$	GG, GC, GA, GU
		CG, CC, CA, CU
		AG, AC, AA, AU
		UG, UC, UA, UU
3	4^3	(Prob. 6-3)

1954. The answer is easy, of course (see Table 6-1). Notice that the table is incomplete: enu-

---

* 6-2. If both strands of DNA were transcribed, what would be the logical relation between the two RNA's produced?

merate the 64 triplets needed to fill in the lower right-hand corner.* It is clear that two-letter "words" are not enough to specify 20 different amino acids, whereas three-letter words are more than enough. Assuming that "Nature" is governed by a sort of principle of parsimony,* Gamow suggested that the words of the RNA that are translated into amino acids are three-letter words, that is, nucleotides taken three at a time. The truth of this hypothesis was first verified by F. H. C. Crick, L. Barnett, S. Brenner, and R. J. Watts-Tobin in 1961. Further details were worked out by many people, particularly Marshall Nirenberg and his collaborators at the National Institutes of Health in Bethesda, Md., and a group led by Severo Ochoa at New York University. It is now clear that the "word" of the genetic language is a **nucleotide triplet,** also called a **codon.**

Triplet coding makes 64 different "words" possible, but only 20 different amino acids are produced by this coding mechanism. Why? Is there some profound chemical reason for this restraint? We don't know. Since only 20 triplets should be needed for the specification of these amino acids that should leave $64 - 20 = 44$ "wasted words"—what of them? Most, we know, are not wasted, but are, in fact, alternative methods of coding. A code in which such synonymy occurs is called a **degenerate code.** The degeneracy of the nucleotide code is apparent in Table 6-2. When more than one triplet is available for coding a given amino acid, how does the cell "decide" which one to use? That is, are there different cellular conditions that make now one, now another, code word more advantageous to the cell in some sense? This question will no doubt be difficult to answer.*

In §46 the question was raised as to whether the genetic code included a comma (like the "space" in the Morse code). It has been estab-

lished that there is no comma. A sequence of amino acids in a polypeptide, for example:

$$\text{lysine—phenylalanine—serine—valine} \quad (1)$$

might be coded by this sequence of nucleotide triplets:

$$\text{AAAUUUUCUGUG,} \quad (2)$$

which (though there really are no commas or spaces) we will spread out for better visibility thus:

$$\text{AAA—UUU—UCU—GUG.} \quad (3)$$

This sequence in the mRNA must, by the Transcription Rule, have been produced by the following sequence in the DNA:

$$\text{TTT—AAA—AGA—CAC.} \quad (4)$$

Tracer studies show that DNA is very stable; yet it can be altered by high-energy radiation and various chemicals. What happens when it is altered? The answer depends on the kind of alteration. One possibility is that one nucleotide in the DNA is altered to another one. Suppose (in our example) that the third thymine from the left in (4) is replaced by guanine, indicated by the colored G in (5). The consequences will be as follows:

DNA: TTG—AAA—AGA—CAC;   (5)
mRNA: AAC—UUU—UCU—GUG;   (6)
polypeptide: asparagine—phenylalanine
                      —serine—valine.   (7)

By comparing (7) with (1) we see that only the first amino acid in the chain is changed. What effect this will have on the organism we cannot say a priori. It may, *so far as we can tell,* do no more than produce the sort of species-specific differences exhibited previously in the structure of insulin (look again at Table 4-2); or it may produce a molecule that is demonstrably pathological, as are some of the abnormal hemoglobins we shall consider subsequently (§55).

Another type of change that can take place in the DNA is one in which an additional nucleotide is inserted in the chain. Suppose a single G (guanine) were to be inserted between

---

* 6-4. If the "words" were 4 nucleotides long, how many different permutations would there be? (Don't enumerate them!)

* 6-5. Meeting?

* 6-6. Looking over Table 6-2, what uniform degeneracies are visible throughout the system? How do these reduce the number of entities codable?

TABLE 6-2   *The RNA Codons (Nucleotide Triplets) for the Amino Acids. Codon in Black, Trans-*
lation in Color. Sequences Indicated by Nonsense* *May Be Readable When They Are Internal*
Codons, But Not When Terminal. UAA and UAG May Function As Full Stops. (Source: M.
Nirenberg et al, 1965. Proc. Nat. Acad. Sci., **53:***1161–1168.)*

UUU UUC	Phe	UCU UCC	Ser	UGU UGC	Cys	UAU UAC	Tyr
UUA UUG	Leu	UCA UCG	Ser	UGA UGG	Nonsense* or Try	UAA UAG	Nonsense
CUU CUC	Leu or Nonsense*	CCU CCC	Pro	CGU CGC	Arg	CAU CAC	His
CUA CUG	Leu	CCA CCG	Pro	CGA CGG	Arg	CAA CAG	Gln
AUU AUC	Ilu	ACU ACC	Thr	AGU AGC	Ser	AAU AAC	Asn
AUA AUG	Met	ACA ACG	Thr	AGA AGG	Arg or Nonsense*	AAA AAG	Lys
GUU GUC	Val	GCU GCC	Ala	GGU GGC	Gly	GAU GAC	Asp
GUA GUG	Val	GCA GCG	Ala	GGA GGG	Gly	GAA GAG	Glu

the first and second triplets of (*4*), as shown by the colored letter in (*8*). Since the DNA chain is always read from one end, triplet by triplet, the new DNA and its derivative macromolecules would be:

DNA:

TTT—GAA—AAG—ACA—C . . .   (*8*)

mRNA:

AAA—CUU—UUC—UGU—G . . .   (*9*)

polypeptide:

lysine—leucine—phenylalanine—

cystine—? (*10*)

Not only was the amino acid derived from the directly affected triplet changed, but so were those "to the right" of it, as is seen when (*10*) is compared with (*1*). In general, we would expect most, but not necessarily all, of the amino acids to the right to be changed.*

In the two examples given above the change

in the DNA resulted in **missense:** the changed triplets "made sense," they coded (through the mRNA) for some amino acids, but these were the *wrong* amino acids. A change in DNA may, however, produce a triplet which has no translation, for instance the DNA triplet *ATC* would transcribe as mRNA triplet *UAG* which—according to Table 6-2—has no translation into an amino acid. A triplet which has no translation is said to be **nonsense.** The chain of amino acids into which mRNA is translated will be brought to an end by a nonsense codon.

Such, in brief, is the way in which the words of the DNA code appear to be translated into the words of amino acids. Details of the theory may not be entirely correct, but in this scheme we have a fine working hypothesis for which there is much evidence, a hypothesis which should be correctible. Before continuing with the exposition the student is advised to work Problems 6-13 through 6-18 at the end of the chapter to make sure he understands the system of translation.

_____

* 6-7. Why "not necessarily all"? Answer with an explanatory example.

52. "One Gene—One Polypeptide"

Several facts and assumptions that may not have been completely explicit in the preceding discussion should be stated:

1. There is a *polarity* to both DNA and RNA in the transcribing and translating processes; that is, there is a beginning and an end of the message being "read," a part that is read out first and a part that is read out last. This assumption is supported by experimental evidence.

2. There is *collinearity* in the ordering of the elements of DNA, DNA-derived mRNA, and mRNA-derived polypeptide. The meaning of collinearity is easily seen in the similar ordering of units (codons or amino acids) in equations (5) (6) and (7) above.

3. Because of degeneracy, there is some *loss of information* in the process of translation of mRNA to a polypeptide.

4. There is no loss of information in the process of transcription from DNA to RNA.

5. In the translation of mRNA to polypeptide, a long chain of RNA codons may be broken up into shorter chains of corresponding amino acids, the breaks being created by nonsense codons which function as "full stops." As of 1965, it was not certain what codons could serve as normal full stops, but experiments of Sidney Brenner and others indicate that, at least under certain conditions, UAA and UAG are full stops.

The polypeptides that are best known at the present time have a length of about 150 amino acid units. Since the codon for each amino acid is a triplet of nucleotides, this means that the length of the corresponding mRNA segment must be about 450 nucleotides. In some cases this may be the length of the discrete mRNA entity; in others, several 450 nucleotide units in a single mRNA entity may be separated from each other by full stops. Either way, such a unit of 450 nucleotides in the RNA code must have its collinear equivalent of 450 nucleotides

in the DNA from which it was transcribed. Such a segment in the DNA corresponds to what is meant by the word "gene," a genetical concept that was developed prior to Watson and Crick on the basis of a quite different analytical approach. As we learn more, we may find considerable variation in the size of genes, here taken to be about 450 nucleotides; but for a first approach it will not hurt if we ignore this possible variation. In summary, a DNA segment about 450 nucleotides in length is transcribed into an mRNA segment of the same length which moves into the cytoplasm and is there translated into a polypeptide of about 150 amino acid units. Briefly stated:

one gene ⟶ one polypeptide.

This is the working hypothesis on which genetic research is proceeding.

There is a necessary relation between the code of the gene and the composition of the resultant polypeptide, *barring accidents*. An abnormal polypeptide will result if an error occurs either in the duplication of DNA to DNA, or in the transcription of DNA to RNA. An error in transcription is relatively less important, because it occurs only in a particular cell, at a particular time, and its effects are limited by the functionally short period of activity of the resultant erroneous segment of mRNA. In fact, there are great experimental difficulties in the way of proving the existence of transcription errors. Errors in duplication—**copy errors,** they are called—have enduring effects because the new "erroneous" DNA is just as permanent* and is duplicated just as faithfully as the old, "correct" DNA.

Various sorts of copy errors are conceivable. In the act of duplication one purine may accidentally be substituted for another—A for G, or the reverse; or one pyrimidine for another pyrimidine. Such a change is called a **transition.** If the substitution is of a pyrimidine for a purine, or the reverse (T for G; or G for C, for example), the change is called **transversion.** Whatever the substitution, the result (after

---

* 6-8. Is this adjective used here in an absolute or a relative sense?

transcription to RNA and translation to a polypeptide) may be either missence or nonsense. Another type of change involves the dropping of a nucleotide from the DNA chain—this is called a **deletion.** Some of the conceivable copy errors are listed in Figure 6-2, together with their analogues in typography.

Substitution
(producing missense)

> away, and already the doomsday warnings are arriving, the foreboding accounts of a Russian horde that will come sweeping out of the East like Attila and his Nuns.
> —*Red Smith in the Boston Globe.*

Substitution
(producing nonsense)

> Sitting in the middle of the bed, being wheeled across London by three attentive young men, Nancy falls in love with the conveyance. Need I say what the outcome is?
> kfln. shrd shrd cmfw cmfw cm
> —*New York News.*

Deletion

> "I can speak just as good nglish as you," Gorbulove corrected in a merry voice.
> —*Seattle Times.*

Insertion

> "I have no fears that Mr. Khrushchev can contaminate the American people," he said. "We can take in stride the best brainwashington he can offer."—*Hartford Courant.*

Inversion

> He charged the bus door opened into a snowbank, causing him to slip as he stepped out and fall beneath the bus, which ran over him.
> —*St. Paul Pioneer Press.*

Fig. 6-2. *The names of various kinds of mutations (in color), and their analogues in the realm of typographical errors (in black). Gleaned mostly by Seymour Benzer from the pages of* The New Yorker. (The Harvey Lectures, *Ser. 56, p. 3, 1960-61.)*

Any change in the sequence of nucleotides of the DNA is called a **mutation;** the process that produces it is also called "mutation." The altered gene is called a **mutant gene** or **mutant allele;** the new genetic type of individual is called a **mutant.** The mutant or the mutant allele are often contrasted with the **wild type,** i.e., the "normal" type of individual or allele from which the mutant mutated.

Because there is degeneracy in the RNA code that is translated into the amino acid chain, information is lost. This means that many changes at the level of the gene must be undetectable. This deduction from theory is necessarily unverifiable at the polypeptide level; perhaps we may some day verify it in a more direct way.

A mutation may also be undetectible at the polypeptide level because it produces a DNA chain that is incapable of self-duplication. Since a cell needs all the information coded in its DNA,* failure of part of the DNA to replicate will be lethal. The cell will not produce descendants; such a mutant gene we call a **lethal** mutant.

The effect of lethal mutations can be detected in populations of cells by a diminution in the number of living cells, or of cells that can reproduce. If all the DNA of a cell is required for normal functioning, and if the probability of a lethal mutation is approximately the same for each nucleotide, then the probability of *at least one* lethal mutation in *some* region of the DNA should increase with an increase in the amount of DNA per cell. Since a cell can only be killed once, the more DNA it has, the easier it should be to kill it with an agent that alters DNA. Table 6-3 shows that this is so. The DNA-altering agent is high energy radiation, the intensity of which is measured in "rads." The third column of the table gives the number of rads required to kill 37 percent of the cells. (The theoretical reasons for selecting this figure need not be gone into here; the essential point is that all species are compared with respect to

---

* For the moment we put aside qualifications required for diploid cells. These do not significantly alter the principle.

TABLE 6-3   *Nucleotide Content and Radiosensitivity of Various Cells and Viruses. (From Data Assembled by H. S. Kaplan and L. E. Moses, 1964,* Science, **145**:*23.)*

ENTITY	NUCLEOTIDES PER INFECTIVE UNIT OR CELL	LETHAL DOSE (D_{37} IN RAD)
Group A_1: RNA viruses		
Phage R17	3.0×10^3	8.4×10^5
Tobacco ringspot virus	5.0×10^3	4.6×10^5
Tomato bushy stunt virus	5.0×10^3	4.5×10^5
Tobacco mosaic virus	$6.5-7.2 \times 10^3$	2.0×10^5
Rous sarcoma virus	$3.2-4.0 \times 10^4$	$1.6-2.0 \times 10^5$
Newcastle disease virus	1.1×10^5	4.6×10^4
Group A_2: DNA viruses (single-stranded)		
Phage ϕX174	5.5×10^3	3.8×10^5
Phage S13	6.0×10^3	$2.3-2.5 \times 10^5$
Group B: DNA viruses (double-stranded)		
Shope papilloma virus	4.7×10^4	4.4×10^5
Phage BM	8.3×10^4	1.9×10^5
Phage T7	$1.2-1.6 \times 10^5$	1.35×10^5
Phage T1	1.3×10^5	1.7×10^5
Phage P22	1.3×10^5	1.25×10^5
Phage λ	2.3×10^5	1.0×10^5
Adenovirus, type V	2.2×10^5	7.0×10^4
Phages T2, T4	4.3×10^5	$5.0-5.2 \times 10^4$
Vaccinia virus	5.2×10^5	$4-10 \times 10^4$
Group C: haploid microorganisms		
Escherichia coli, strain B	$2.3-3.0 \times 10^7$	2.0×10^3
Bacterium aertrycke	2.4×10^7	4.0×10^3
Micrococcus pyogenes aureus	2.8×10^7	4.0×10^3
Haemophilus influenzae	4.0×10^7	3.6×10^3
Saccharomyces cerevisiae	4.0×10^7	$2.8-3.7 \times 10^3$
Group D: diploid cells		
Diplococcus pneumoniae	4×10^7	1.3×10^4
Escherichia coli, strain P-6	$8-9 \times 10^7$	8.5×10^3
Saccharomyces cerevisiae	$8-9 \times 10^7$	$7-13 \times 10^3$
Chicken embryo cells	5×10^9	$2.7-3.2 \times 10^2$
Mouse (bone marrow, in vivo)	1.3×10^{10}	1.1×10^2
Guinea pig	1.7×10^{10}	1.0×10^2
Human (fibroblasts)	2.1×10^{10}	$0.5-1.0 \times 10^2$

the same degree of damage.) Notice that as the number of nucleotides increases (second column), the susceptibility to radiation damage also increases (third column). Put another way: the greater the genetic information possessed by an organism, the greater its complexity *and* the greater its vulnerability. The positive association of complexity and vulnerability is not, of course, confined to the field of genetics.

53. The Translating Mechanism

From the preceding discussion it might be inferred that the mRNA automatically translates itself into a polypeptide, given an adequate supply of amino acids. This is not true. There is quite a bit of molecular machinery involved in reading the message on the mRNA; the principal elements of this machinery will be described here.

In the cytoplasm there occurs another kind of RNA which is abbreviated **sRNA** and which will here be called **transfer RNA** (rather than either of its synonyms *soluble RNA* or *adaptor RNA*). The function of each particle of transfer RNA is to pick up a specific amino acid at one of its ends and then (as directed by mRNA) bring this amino acid into line with other amino acids and thus synthesize a polypeptide.

The hypothetical structure of an sRNA molecule is shown in Figure 6-3. Note that the single strand of about 70 nucleotides is actually folded back on itself to make a double helix (of only one strand) reminiscent of DNA. The bulk of this structure (the **body**) is species-specific, i.e., it varies from one species of organism to another.

A specific amino acid can be picked up at the **attachment site:** this action requires ATP and a particular enzyme. An sRNA which has picked up an amino acid is said to be "loaded." The chemical configuration of the attachment site seems to be the same for all kinds of amino acids; there must, however, be some chemical differences somewhere in the sRNA to differentiate the 20 different kinds of sRNA with respect to the kinds of amino acids they pick up.

The other end of the sRNA is the **recognition site,** which is thought to consist of a nucleotide triplet that is complementary to one or another codon of the mRNA. The recognition site is not species specific, since the mRNA code is apparently universal among all species.

We are now ready to see how loaded sRNA's are brought together on the mRNA to construct a polypeptide. Involved in this meeting is one other kind of RNA, namely RNA in the form of ribosomes. Study Figure 6-4 carefully. The ribosome may be aptly analogized to an automatic machine tool, with the mRNA acting as

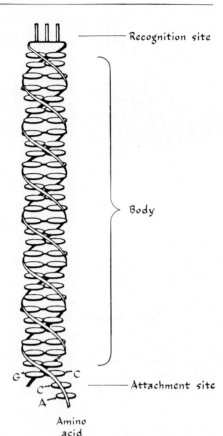

Fig. 6-3. *Structure of transfer RNA (sRNA), as proposed by G. Zubay, 1963. A single polynucleotide chain forms a higher order structure with itself by weak hydrogen bonding between different regions of the chain. Note similarity to double helix of DNA. The recognition site (here diagrammed as a sort of electrical plug) consists of a trinucleotide complementary to an mRNA coding triplet. Capital letters stand for nucleotides. The sRNA molecule is about 100 Å long and 20 Å wide.*

its coded tape. As the tape is read by the ribosome, triplet by triplet, the proper sRNA is picked up. The amino acids at the attachment sites are attached to each other with peptide bonds. The informational sequence of the mRNA is precisely reproduced in the sequence of amino acids in the polypeptide. As the sRNA's are unloaded and the mRNA's are "read" they become freed from the ribosome and can go through the cycle again. The act of

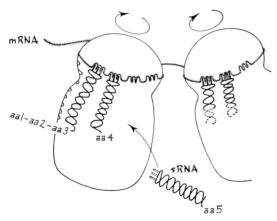

Fig. 6-4. *A diagrammatic representation of the way in which the transfer RNA (sRNA) molecules attach to the mRNA at the site of the ribosomes, thus bringing about the synthesis of the polypeptide chain, by successive additions of amino acids. The information of the mRNA (color) is translated into the information of the polypeptide (also in color). (After Philip E. Hartman and Sigmund R. Suskind,* Gene Action, *© Prentice-Hall, 1965. Reprinted by permission of Prentice-Hall, Inc., Englewood Cliffs, N.J.)*

polypeptide synthesis requires about 0.6 second for the addition of each amino acid to the growing polypeptide chain.

54. The Regulation of Gene Action

The cell is a fantastically complicated system in which thousands of enzymes are at work, each at its own rate, producing interrelated series of products, competing with each other, and yet somehow producing relative stability. It will surely be a long time before we have a complete picture of this dynamic, changeable system. At present, we can sketch only a few tentative lines on the theoretical canvas. One of these was limned in §41, which described the way in which an endproduct inactivated an early enzyme in a metabolic sequence. It might be well to review that story before reading the present example of another cellular mechanism used in regulating metabolism.

The bacterial species *E. coli* can synthesize

tryptophan by virtue of the enzyme *tryptophan-synthetase.* If this amino acid is added to the nutrient medium the bacteria immediately stop synthesizing the amino acid, as can be shown by tracer studies.* If we stop adding tryptophan to the medium, as soon as the external supply is exhausted the bacterial cells again synthesize the amino acid from its chemical precursors. So far the results seem to fall into the pattern of endproduct inhibition previously described in connection with the synthesis of isoleucine.

However, if we continue the external supply of tryptophan for many cell generations we discover a new phenomenon. When we then stop the external supply, the exhaustion of the tryptophan is followed by a long **lag period** during which there is scarcely any multiplication of cells. At the first of this lag period almost no tryptophan is being synthesized because the cells possess *few or no molecules of the enzyme tryptophan-synthetase.* As enzyme molecules reappear, the synthesis picks up speed, and presently conditions are back to normal.

In this situation we see that the endproduct exerts its effect by interfering with the *synthesis* of the enzyme (rather than merely with its activity, as in the case of isoleucine). Since the synthesis of enzymes is a genetic function this must mean that tryptophan exerts its effect on the DNA-RNA system in some way. How is this possible? To explain this we will present the genetic model originated by Nobel prize-winners Francois Jacob and Jacques Monod of the Pasteur Institute in Paris. There is a large speculative element in this model, but it is at least proving useful as a working hypothesis.

To begin with, the concept of a gene is enlarged. In Figure 6-5 the entity called **structural gene** corresponds to what we have hitherto called a *gene;* it is a portion of the DNA which codes a segment of mRNA which codes a polypeptide. (Such a structural gene is also called a **cistron.**) Sometimes an mRNA filament codes for more than one polypeptide; this fact is indicated in the figure by several structural genes

---

* 6-9. Describe in more detail an experiment of the kind here too briefly mentioned.

combined into one **operon.** The operon also includes, at its "starting" end, a segment of DNA which is called an **operator,** or *operator gene.* Think of this as a switch. In our example (tryptophan synthesis), in the absence of tryptophan the switch is "open"; i.e., the operon is coding the mRNA and the mRNA is coding the polypeptide(s) needed for tryptophan-synthetase.

Before we follow the consequences of adding tryptophan we need to augment the model by one more hypothetical entity, a **regulator gene.** In general, the regulator gene need not have a close spatial connection to the operon to which it is functionally related. The regulator gene produces a regulator substance (R in the figure), the chemical nature of which is in dispute. This substance (R, in Fig. 6-5) has the ability to combine with the endproduct (EP), which is tryptophan in our example. $R + EP \rightarrow R_{EP}$, which acts as a **repressor** for the operon, probably by combining with and blocking the action of, the operator, as shown in Figure 6-5. Thus is the operon repressed.

With a slight modification, the Jacob-Monod model is capable of explaining another type of experimental observation that seems to be the exact opposite of the above. There is a class of carbohydrates called β-galactosides which can serve as food for *E. coli.* Bacteria grown in the absence of this substrate show only traces of the enzyme β-galactosidase. When β-galactosides are added to the medium, the requisite enzyme presently appears and the substrate is attacked. In the Jacob-Monod model this may be represented as shown in Figure 6-6. Without substrate (A) it is normal for the regulator gene to produce a repressor substance (REP) which combines with the operator to prevent the action of the operon. In other words, the "switch" is normally closed. If, however, the substrate (S) is added, it combines with REP to form REPS, which does not interfere with the operator, thus leaving the "switch" open. The entire phenomenon is called **induction;** the substrate (galactoside) *induces* its specific enzyme (galactosidase), through de-repression.

The evidence for the Jacob-Monod model is notably indirect, but reasonably consistent. The model has been warmly welcomed, particularly by students of embryology who are constantly confronted with puzzling instances of enzymatic "switches" being turned off and on at different stages of the life cycles, and being set differently in different tissues. (All cells, we think, have the same genes—but why do only the thyroid cells secrete the thyroid hormone?) Some such scheme as this is needed to explain the puzzling relations of potentiality and actuality with which William Harvey grappled.

Fig. 6-5. *The Jacob-Monod model for explaining the repression of enzyme formation by the presence of the endproduct.*

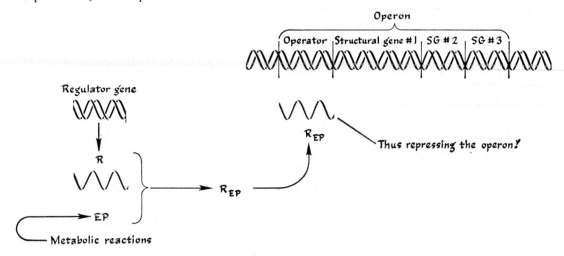

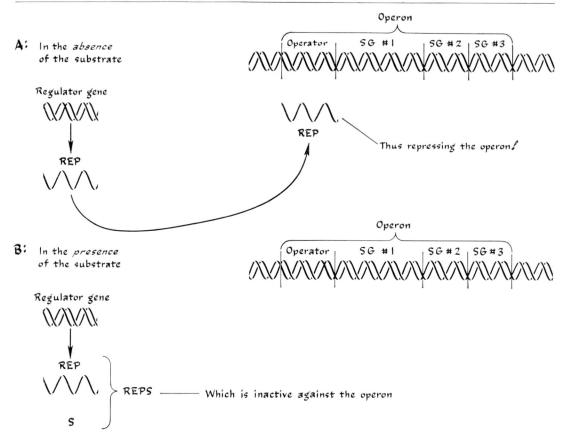

Fig. 6-6. *Induction explained as de-repression in the Jacob-Monod model.*

55. Chemistry into Morphology

The appearance of a completed polypeptide is not the end of the DNA-induced effect on the cell and the organism. Typically, two or more polypeptides join together to form a protein molecule. Some kinds of proteins are, of course, enzymes; others are "structural proteins" and become parts of cell membranes, etc. In the formation of proteins various levels of structuring are distinguishable.

The **primary structure** of the protein is the detailed arrangement of its atoms in the polypeptide chains described above. In the text, this structure has been indicated in only a crude way by writing a sequence of the names of the amino acids, as in *(10)* on p. 117. To represent the primary structure more completely one should replace the words with the structural formulas (Appendix 7), joining the amino acid

units by peptide bonds (§35). However, the structure so indicated seldom represents the facts in nature, for the amino acid chain is generally distorted into a **secondary structure.**

A common pattern of secondary structure is the *alpha helix* discovered in the 1950's by Linus Pauling and co-workers. In this structure (Fig. 6-7), weak hydrogen bonds are formed between atoms connected to different "levels" of the polypeptide chain. Thus the chain is held in a helical form.

Structures of still higher degrees are possible. To illustrate these, we examine the anatomy of the tobacco mosaic virus as revealed in some much magnified models constructed under the direction of Wendell M. Stanley. TMV is a highly ordered structure made of both protein and RNA units. In the first view (Fig. 6-8) we see, in the center of the model, a coil made of coated wire. This coil represents an alpha helix.

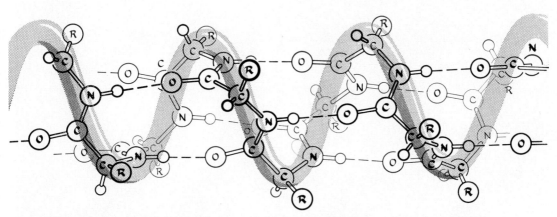

Fig. 6-7. *Secondary structure involved in a protein. The primary structure of a poly-peptide chain is shown in detail at the top, and in standard abbreviations in the middle line. At bottom: a polypeptide chain is thrown into a secondary helix (in color) held together by additional chemical bridges.*

This helix is gathered together in separate bunches, of which one is visible as a helix while the others are merely indicated in the model by the visual shorthand of the large jellybean-like structures seen on all sides of the wire. The model would be more accurate if each of these large jellybeans were replaced by the coil of wire for which it stands—but more difficult to handle and more difficult to make. The important point is this: the organization of the secondary structure of the alpha helix into a *larger* unit constitutes the **tertiary structure** of the pro-

tein. But this is not the end of the story either.

In Figure 6-9, at lesser magnification, we see the jellybeans (polypeptides of tertiary structure) being organized into a **quaternary structure.** In the case of TMV the quaternary structure involves also a ribosenucleic acid chain (represented by the piece of thin tubing in the model); but such an additional type of molecule is not a necessary part of quaternary structure. A later stage in the construction of the model of this macromolecule is shown in Figure 6-10, with the completed model of TMV shown in

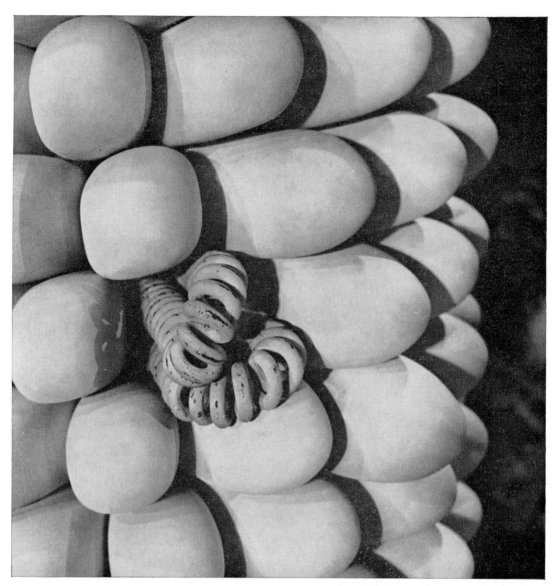

Fig. 6-8. *The colored portion of the preceding figure is here represented by the coiled, coated wire near the center of the photograph. This is a model of tobacco mosaic virus (TMV), showing how the secondary structure of an alpha helix is arranged into a tertiary structure. Each "jellybean" is such a tertiary structure. (From W. M. Stanley and E. G. Valens,* Viruses and the Nature of Life, *E. P. Dutton & Co., 1961.)*

Figure 6-11. Figure 6-12 is an electron micrograph of the virus itself. The structure indicated in the model is not actually visible, but has been deduced from chemical and X-ray studies made over many years' time.

One of the amazing features of the higher orders of protein structure is that they arise spontaneously, given a supply of the primary in-gredients. The primary structure of the polypeptide is determined by enzymes and genes. Enzymes produce the amino acids, and DNA-derived RNA assembles the amino acids into polypeptides. The sequence of amino acids is derived, through RNA, from DNA. But once the polypeptide is formed it undergoes further organization into secondary and higher order

Fig. 6-9. *Model of tertiary structures being combined into the quaternary structure of TMV. (From W. M. Stanley and E. G. Valens,* Viruses and the Nature of Life, *E. P. Dutton & Co., 1961.)*

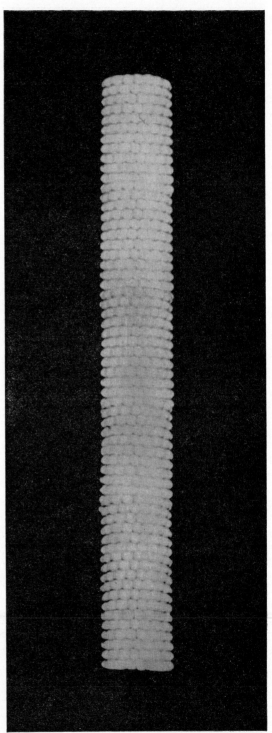

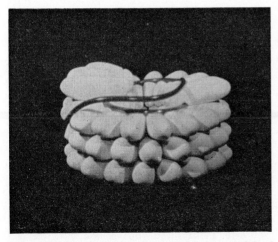

Fig. 6-10. *Further development of the model of TMV shown in the preceding figure. (From W. M. Stanley and E. G. Valens,* Viruses and the Nature of Life, *E. P. Dutton & Co., 1961.)*

Fig. 6-11. *Model of a long segment of TMV. (From W. M. Stanley and E. G. Valens,* Viruses and the Nature of Life, *E. P. Dutton & Co., 1961.)*

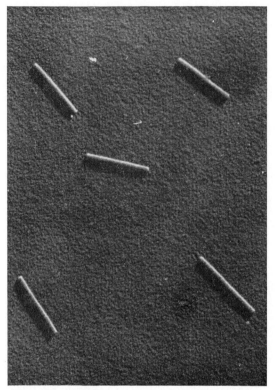

Fig. 6-12. *An electronmicrograph of TMV. (Courtesy R. C. Williams, Virus Laboratory, University of California, Berkeley.)*

structures spontaneously, without the need of detailed instructions from the DNA. The positions of its various "unsatisfied" chemical bonds determines what new connections will be made. The formation of these connections may sometimes be facilitated by enzymes of rather generalized action, but secondary, tertiary, and higher order structures are implicit in the primary structure of the polypeptides.

Can differences in the structure of enzymes and other proteins produce differences in the form of an organism? In the study of the genetic origins of individual differences it is easiest to see how biochemical differences can result from differences in the chemical products of the genetic material. For an illustrative example consider *albinism,* which is the result of a lack of *melanins,* a class of dark pigments. To produce melanins a specific enzyme acting on the substrate tyrosine must be present. The normal

course of events can be characterized by the following sequence:

$$\text{normal gene} \longrightarrow \text{enzyme (tyrosinase)}$$
$$\text{tyrosinase} \longrightarrow \text{pigment (melanin).} \quad (11)$$

In albinism, the mutant gene fails to produce active tyrosinase, hence there is a lack of melanin. This is easy enough to understand.

But will the same explanatory scheme suffice to deal with hereditary differences in **morphology** (Gr. *morphe,* form)? Can differences in form and structure be traced back to the level of enzymes? At first sight this may seem too much to hope for; but, in principle, it is generally believed that the framework of (*11*) is applicable to all problems of development. Admittedly, this is no more than a working hypothesis for we are a long way from giving an enzymatic explanation of most of morphology. But the detailed study of examples such as the nucleic acid coding of TMV gives biologists hope. After all, molecules have *their* morphology too, even though it is at an invisible level. The hierarchical assemblage of invisibly structured entities *can* produce visible structure, as the example of TMV shows. It is not unreasonable to hope some day to achieve a molecular explanation of such visible hereditary differences as no sweat glands, extra toes, and hairs on the next-to-last joint of the fingers.*

56. A Cascade of Consequences

Repeatedly, the advance of a science has shown that profound consequences can follow from causes that might by themselves appear to be trivial. A single example from molecular genetics will serve to illustrate this point.

Red blood cells can carry a considerable load of oxygen by virtue of the compound **hemoglobin.** The normal adult hemoglobin, symbolized as *HbA,* consists of four polypeptide chains plus four *heme* groups. Each heme group con-

---

* 6-10. Perhaps you don't believe there are individual differences of this sort? Using a good light, examine the fingers of several of your friends. The difference is hereditary. The adaptive significance is unimaginable.

sists of a protoporphyrin molecule with an iron atom which is responsible for the ability of the molecule to form an easily reversible combination with O_2. The polypeptides are of two sorts, called alpha and beta. In summary:

$$\left.\begin{array}{l} \alpha \text{ polypeptide} + \text{heme} \\ \alpha \text{ polypeptide} + \text{heme} \\ \beta \text{ polypeptide} + \text{heme} \\ \beta \text{ polypeptide} + \text{heme} \end{array}\right\} = \text{hemoglobin A.}$$

Hemoglobin is a protein of quaternary structure with a molecular weight of about 67,000. *The exact structural formulas of α polypeptide and β polypeptide are known, atom for atom.* The α chain consists of 140 amino acids; the β chain has 146. The composition of the two chains is shown in Figure 6-13, which is arranged to show the similarities of the two.

What would happen if one amino acid in one of the polypeptides were replaced by a different one? No general *a priori* answer can be given. At some loci such a substitution may have only trivial consequences, at others profound. For example, in Hemoglobin-Zürich, the histidine at position 63 of the β chain is replaced by arginine, but the consequences for the individual are negligable. On the other hand, if the glutamic acid of position 6 of the β chain is replaced by valine, life itself is endangered.

Hemoglobin in which valine is found at the number 6 position of otherwise normal β polypeptide is called **sickle cell hemoglobin** or **HbS.** The reason for the name will be explained shortly. What is the genetic origin of HbS? Because of the degeneracy of the triplet code we cannot give a unique answer, but only a possible one. The sequence of events leading to the appearance of the different amino acids in number 6 position in the two different polypeptide chains *might* be this:

Kind of Hb	DNA	mRNA	Amino acid	
HbA:	GTT	CAA	Glu	*(12)*
HbS:	CAT	GUA	Val	*(13)*

Assuming this is true, the change (transversion) in only two nucleotides of the DNA is all that

is needed for the consequences now to be described.

HbS is called sickle-cell hemoglobin because it causes the red blood cells that contain it to be distorted, some of them appearing sickle-shaped (see Fig. 6-14). The distortion is particularly notable in venous blood, which is low in oxygen. Evidently the change in the primary structure of the β chain results in a difference in the quaternary structure and in the way in which hemoglobin molecules associate with each other, which thus affects the structure of the erythrocyte itself. An erythrocyte is normally the shape of a filled-in doughnut, 7μ in its greatest diameter and hence easily visible in the optical microscope. In sickle cells we have a clear case of an understandable chemical change producing a morphological effect.

This is only the beginning of the story. HbS is not as efficient an oxygen-carrier as HbA. If a person has a mixture of the two genes involved (normal gene plus sickle-cell gene) he is not seriously affected. But if he has only the sickle-cell gene, all his hemoglobin is HbS and he then suffers from a form of anemia called **sickle-cell anemia** or *sicklemia*. The consequences of this are serious. The primary consequences of the sickling phenomenon might be said to be increased fragility of the red blood cells, increased clumping of them and stagnation of them in the spleen. From those consequences many secondary results proceed, as shown in Figure 6-15, which is by no means the whole story: weakness, poor physical development, kidney involvement and rheumatism. The miserable life is usually brought to an end before adulthood by heart failure, brain stroke, or kidney failure. All because of the change in two nucleotides in the DNA.

One is reminded of the old bromide of the Elizabethan poet George Herbert: "For the want of a nail the shoe is lost, for want of a shoe the horse is lost, for want of a horse, the rider is lost." It would be equally true (though less memorable) if one were to recast this saying, beginning: "For the want of the codon for glutamic acid in number 6 position of the β polypeptide of human hemoglobin . . ."

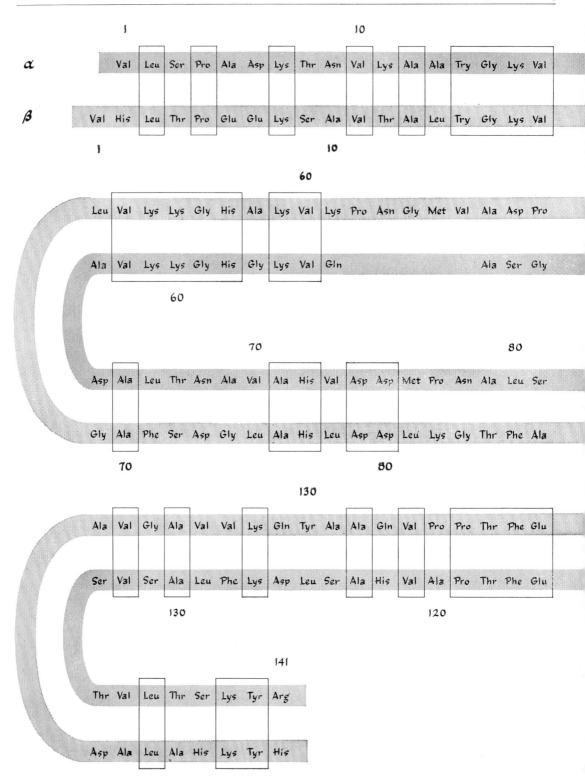

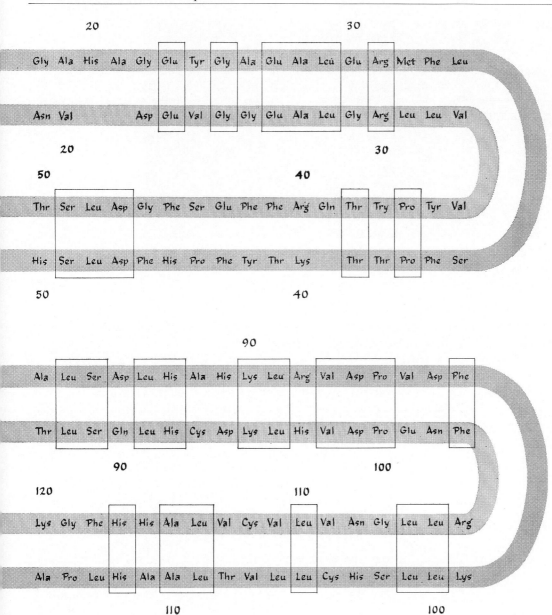

Fig. 6-13. *Alpha polypeptide and beta polypeptide chains from normal human hemoglobin A laid out so that their homologous sequences of amino acids are apparent. This method of display produces fictitious gaps in the chains.*

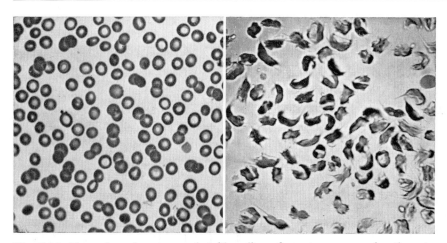

Fig. 6-14. *Normal erythrocytes and sickle-cell erythrocytes, seen under the microscope. (Photos by C. L. Conley; from C. Stern,* Principles of Human Genetics, *2nd ed., W. H. Freeman and Company, San Francisco and London, 1960.)*

Fig. 6-15. *The cascade of consequences connected with sickle-cell anemia. "Cause" and "final effects" in color; intermediate effects of the causal sequence in black.*

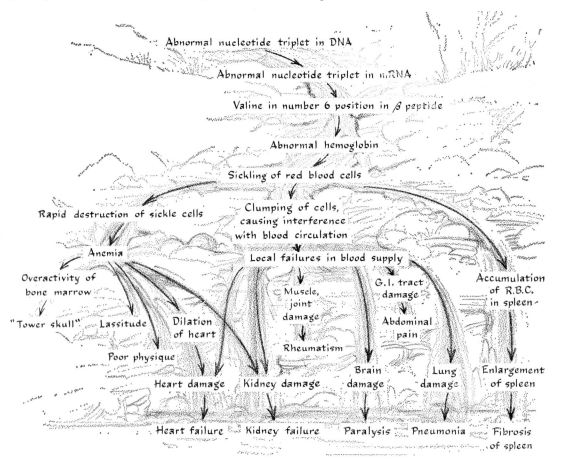

Questions and Problems

6-11. Make a list of the **boldface** terms in this chapter. Write out a definition, description or explanation of each. Compare your work with the text.

6-12. Write a brief description of the contributions of the following men: Nirenberg and Ochoa, Jacob and Monod.

‡6-13. (a) Using Table 6-2 as a guide, give one possible coding for an mRNA segment that could produce the first six amino acids of β hemoglobin. (b) Give the corresponding DNA segment.

‡6-14. How many different answers are possible for part (a) of 6-13?

‡6-15. If you knew the nucleotide sequence for the first six DNA codons of a polypeptide, how many different polypeptides could be derived from it?

‡6-16. Give the mRNA sequence that will be transcribed from this DNA sequence:

   GCCAGGGGGATGTATTCA.

‡6-17. Give the amino acid sequence into which the mRNA produced by the DNA above is translated.

‡6-18. Suppose the second cytosine from the left is deleted from the DNA segment given in Prob. 6-16: what will be the amino acid sequence produced by the mutant?

‡6-19. How would the amino acid sequence be altered by an inversion of a segment of the DNA 30 nucleotide pairs in length? Explain by example(s).

‡6-20. *If we assume* that the nucleotide content of a cell is a true measure of the complexity of different species, what is the relative complexity of the following species: chicken, *E. coli* (use lower figure), guinea pig, human, mouse? Assign the least complex organism a value of unity, and state the others in terms of it.

6-21. On the assumption used in Prob. 6-20, by what order of magnitude is a man more complex than a bacterium?

‡6-22. On the assumption used in Prob. 6-20, by what order of magnitude is a human more complex than Phage T7?

6-23. If man is so ill-advised as to unleash tremendous quantities of radioactive material into the atmosphere as a result of which most species perish, what kinds of species would most probably survive? State evidence and reasoning.

6-24. For a score of years, genetics was governed by the "one gene-one enzyme hypothesis" which was implicit in a paper published by G. W. Beadle and E. L. Tatum in 1941. What argument can you see for preferring the "one gene-one polypeptide hypothesis" presented here?

6-25. The text spoke of *transcribing* DNA to mRNA, but of *translating* mRNA to polypeptide. What issues of taste are involved?

‡6-26. If you can speak Spanish fluently try to explain to a monolingual Spaniard what a "spelling bee" is; you will find you have some difficulty. Account for the difficulty, using the terminology of coding theory.

6-27. In the legend to Figure 6-15, why are quotation marks used for the words "cause" and "final effects"?

Readings

Boyer's *Papers on Human Genetics* has a fine collection of classic contributions to our knowledge of the sickle-cell trait, in Part III, Section Two. Hartman and Suskind's *Gene Action* is a good introduction to the advanced aspects of genetic translation. Srb, Owen, and Edgar's *General Genetics* integrates classical genetics with the modern approach through nucleic acid function.

Scientific American Offprints

121. John C. Kendrew. *The Three-Dimensional Structure of a Protein Molecule*

171. Alick Isaacs. *Polyribosomes*

183. S. Spiegelman. *Hybrid Nucleic Acids*

196. M. F. Perutz. *The Hemoglobin Molecule*

1008. J.-P. Changeux. *The Control of Biochemical Reactions*

7

Reproduction: Life Cycles and Meiosis

57. The Idea of a Life Cycle

The chromosomes of a cell are, with careful study, distinguishable, one from another. It was pointed out in §15 that some cells (e.g., gametes) have only one of each of the kinds of chromosome that occur in the species; such a *set* of chromosomes is called a **genome.** A gamete has one genome, symbolized by *N;* the genomic numbers of a variety of species are given in Appendix 9. Each ordinary body cell has two genomes, a fact indicated by the symbol *2N.* Gametes are said to be haploid; body cells are diploid.

In terms of the genetic content of the cells the life of a man can be reduced to the life cycle shown in Figure 7-1. In this figure we introduce a convention which will be followed in all our diagrams of life cycles. Haploid cells are in color; diploid cells are in black. Life, in our experience, never begins; but we may say that the life of a new individual begins when two haploid gametes (an egg and a sperm) unite, forming a fertilized egg or **zygote,** which is diploid. The zygote, by successive mitoses (§14), produces the approximately 10^{14} cells* that constitute the adult body; almost all of

these cells are diploid. Why the qualification "almost all"? Because the adult body also produces some haploid cells—gametes—by a process of reduction division which will be studied in the next section. The haploid cells are found in the gamete-producing organs (**testes** in the male, **ovaries** in the female) and in the associated passages. In a human, sperm cells are produced by the billions; egg cells only by the thousands, of which no more than a few hundred ever become fully mature.

The diploid cells from which the sperms or eggs come are not just any cells, but are specialized cells which can be recognized for what they are long before sexual maturity—in fact, long before birth. If such cells are destroyed, they will not be replaced. There is, then, during most of the lifetime of an individual (during all but the first few weeks of prenatal life), a separation of cells into two sorts which, following August Weismann (1834–1914), we call the **germ cells** (gametes, and the cells that give rise to gametes) and the **somatic cells** (all the other cells of the body; Gr. *soma* = body).

A significant characteristic of the life cycle is the expendability (in the military sense) of the somatic cells. In every generation some 10^{14} somatic cells die, and this is natural. The germ cells are potentially immortal, though (in fact) the spark of life is passed on to the next generation by only one germ cell from each individual

---

* 7-1. According to the diagram, it takes only about 50 mitotic divisions to produce 10^{14} cells. Prove the truth of this statement, and replace the "about 50" by a more precise figure.

SIMPLIFIED LIFE CYCLE OF MAN

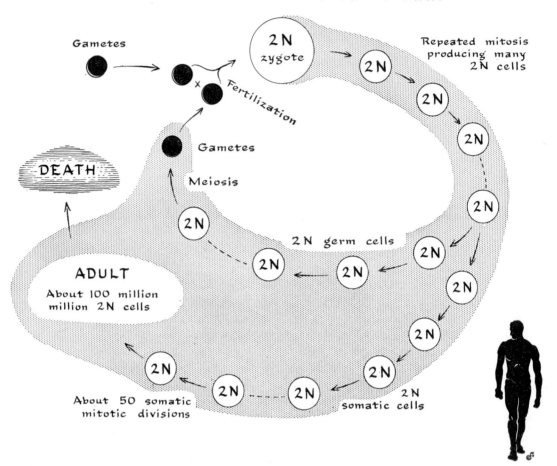

Fig. 7-1. *Human existence reduced to its biological essentials. Haploid cells in color, diploid in black.*

(on the average)—that is, 1 cell out of a bit more* than 10^{14}. The wastage of cells is noteworthy. From a certain point of view we might say that the principal function of some 10^{14} somatic cells is but to create conditions suitable to the maintenance of life in one germ cell. In the words of the nineteenth-century novelist Samuel Butler: "A hen is only an egg's way of making another egg."

The life cycle diagrammed in Figure 7-1, though labeled as that of man, will do (with only minor modifications) for any other of the higher animals. Among the higher plants the situation is a little different. As suggested in

Figure 7-2*A,* the separation of the germ line from the somatic line occurs rather late in the life cycle; one cannot, for example, recognize the pollen-to-be in a seed. In fact, germinal tissue is not usually irreplaceable in a higher plant. The response of a zinnia to having its flowers chopped off is to produce more flowers, in contrast to a guinea pig, say, where the effect of early castration (removal of testes) is permanent. There are also other differences in the flower life cycle, but consideration of these will be postponed. For the present, we are interested in the similarities in the nuclear phases of the life cycles of higher animals and higher plants.

There is more variety among life cycles in

---

* 7-2. Why "a bit more"?

the plants than there is in the animals. For a very different cycle, study Figure 7-2B. *Chlamydomonas* is a single-celled green plant belonging to the group called "algae." In sexual reproduction, these cells produce the usual diploid zygote. However, the *zygote is the only diploid cell in the life cycle.* When it divides, it does so by meiosis, producing haploid cells. After a variable number of mitotic divisions, two haploid cells, of opposite sex, may fuse to form once more a diploid zygote. The nuclear changes shown in the diagram indicate the simi-

larity of this life cycle to that of higher plants and animals. It is clear, also, that this life cycle is different from the others in that there is no separation of germinal and somatic lines of cells. Also, there is no natural death.

The life cycles of *Chlamydomonas* and a flowering plant are at two extremes of a gamut. As we will see later, the relative duration of haploid and diploid phases takes on almost all possible values in one group of organisms or another. Whatever its particularities, *the life cycle of every sexually reproducing species always*

Fig. 7-2. *Contrasting life cycles of two kinds of plants. Haploid cells in color, diploid in black. The life cycle of man more nearly resembles which of these?*

A. SIMPLIFIED LIFE CYCLE OF A HIGHER PLANT

B. SIMPLIFIED LIFE CYCLE OF A SIMPLE PLANT (CHLAMYDOMONAS)

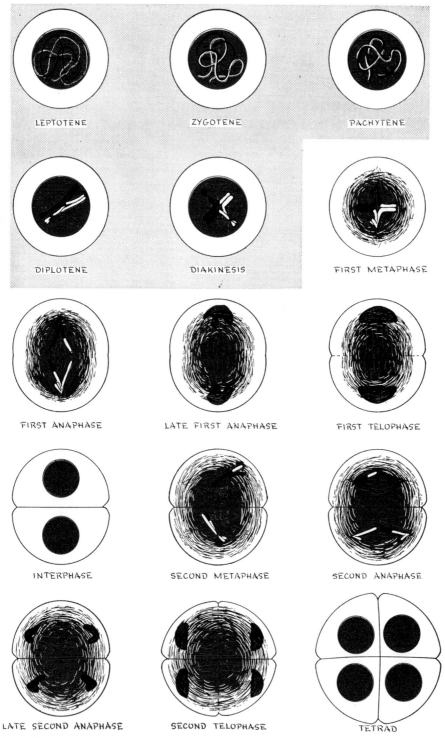

Fig. 7-3. *Stages in meiosis. For clarity only one maternal (white) and one paternal (black) chromosomes are represented. The stages included in the shaded area are subdivisions of the prophase. (After McLeish and Snoad,* Looking at Chromosomes, *Macmillan and Co., London, 1959, by permission of authors and publisher.)*

involves two complementary processes: fertilization and reduction division.

58. Meiosis

If mitosis were the only kind of cell division, the pattern of the life cycle would create a curious problem. In the act of fertilization the number of genomes per cell is increased from one to two; at the next period of fertilization the number of genomes would go from two to four; then from four to eight, and so on. Such doubling is prevented by the intercalation in the life cycle of a reduction division, or **meiosis** (Gr. *meion* = less). (The word is best pronounced with a long ī sound, as if spelled *my*osis, to distinguish it from mitosis, pronounced with a short ĭ.)

In Figure 7-3 are diagrammed the principal stages of meiosis. For simplicity, we show only one pair of chromosomes. Because the prophase of meiosis is so significantly different from the prophase of mitosis, it is subdivided further into the stages indicated in the shaded area at the top. In the prophase of both types of division, one can see that each chromosome is duplicated lengthwise into two constituent chromatids. But whereas each chromosome of a homologous pair of chromosomes is independent in mitosis, this is not true in meiosis; in meiosis, homologous chromosomes approach each other and come to lie side by side—a situation called "pairing" or **synapsis** (Gr. *conjunction*). This is seen first in the zygotene stage in our diagram. (Note: The fact that two centromeres are shown here indicates that these threads are two chromosomes, not just two chromatids.) The synapsis of chromosomes is very precise, each locus of one chromosome lying opposite the (same) locus of the homologous chromosome. What forces bring about this precision is still a great mystery. In our diagram, the chromosome that came from the maternal parent in the *preceding generation* is shown as white; the chromosome from the paternal parent is black.

Then, just as in mitosis, each chromosome consists of two chromatids. But notice, in the diplotene stage, that the four chromatids are not shown as two black and two white; instead, there are one black, one white, and two that are mixtures. How can this be? It is because there has been **crossing-over** between two of the chromatids, an exchange of homologous portions between synapsed chromatids. Such crossing-over is not exceptional; it is the rule. Every pair of chromosomes probably undergoes at least one crossing-over in the meioic process (we have shown only one). The genetic consequences of this we will consider shortly, but first let us follow the meiotic process to its conclusion.

As in mitosis, meiotic prophase is followed by metaphase, anaphase, and telophase, culminating in an interphase. Then the process of division starts all over again, but this time *without any further multiplication of chromosomal material.* The centromeres, which have gone to the poles undivided in the first division, divide during the second, the products going to different poles. Because the chromosomal material undergoes *one* duplication and *two* divisions, the end result of meiosis is to produce cells that have only *half* the amount of chromosomal material the beginning cell had.

Now we are ready to see the genetic consequences of meiosis. A chromosome is made up of many different genes, arranged single file along its length, as shown in *G* of Figure 7-4. For simplicity, we assume that we are dealing with an animal species in which the haploid number is 1; and we represent the chromosome contributed by the male as black and its homologue from the female as white. Fertilization produces a zygote (*B*) containing both these chromosomes. The many mitoses that take place during the subsequent developmental process (*C, D*) produce cells that are alike in that both chromosomes are still discrete, separate entities, as they were when they were brought together in fertilization. But during meiosis, these homologous chromosomes may exchange homologous parts (*E*), thus producing (*G*) some haploid cells that contain com-

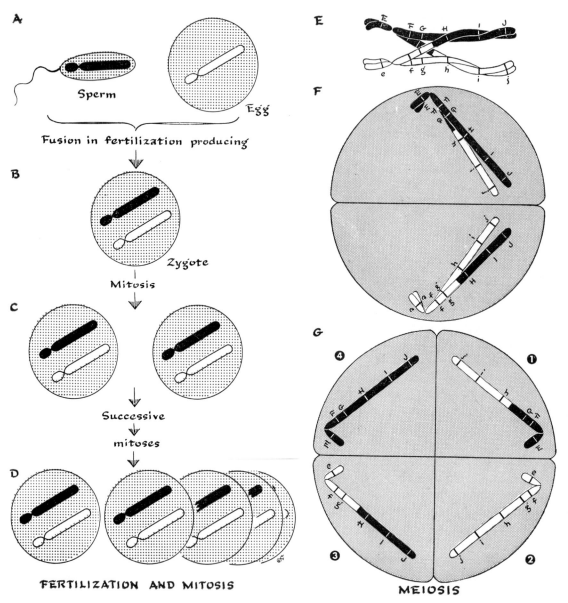

FERTILIZATION AND MITOSIS   MEIOSIS

Fig. 7-4. (*A, B*) *How fusion of gametes may bring together chromosomes that are genetically different; and* (E, F, G) *how during meiosis later the genetic complements of homologous chromosomes may be exchanged and reassorted.* (*In part, after McLeish and Snoad,* Looking at Chromosomes, *Macmillan and Co., London, 1959, by permission of authors and publisher.*)

binations of genes (cells 1 and 3 in *G*) never found in the parental gametes, as well as other combinations of genes (cells 2 and 4) that are like those of the parental gametes.

What if a species has more than one pair of chromosomes? Then **recombination of genes** can take place not only by crossing-over between homologous chromosomes (as we have just seen), but also by reassortment of non-homologous chromosomes. Some of the possibilities are shown in Figure 7-5, which represents the results of meiosis as it would occur in

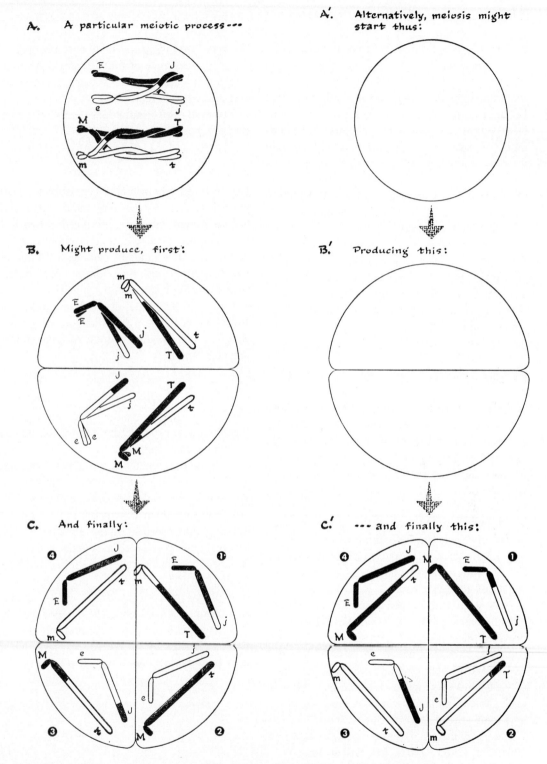

Fig. 7-5. *How reassortment of genes is brought about by meiosis. (After McLeish and Snoad,* Looking at Chromosomes, *Macmillan and Co., London, 1959, by permission of authors and publisher.) Problem: How were the results shown in C′ produced by meiosis? Complete the diagram by filling in A′ and B′ properly.*

a species with two pairs of chromosomes. Again, the chromosomes coming from the paternal parent are represented as solid, those from the maternal in outline only. In crossing-over and in the assortment of crossover products, non-homologous chromosomes behave independently. Sometimes a haploid cell will contain crossover products of both chromosomes (1 and 3 in *C*), or a crossover product for one chromosome and a noncrossover for the other (all the cells in *C'*). Even when the haploid cells are all noncrossover types, they may be types that were found in neither parent (2 and 4 in *C*). As the number of genes in which the parents differ increases, the chance of producing any gamete exactly like one of the gametes that was combined to produce the parent, becomes smaller and smaller.

59. Sex: Generator of Variety

Suppose that we had a diploid organism whose genetic formula, or **genotype,** was *AABB*. By meiosis, such an organism could produce only one kind of gamete, *AB*. Suppose, further, that we had another organism of the same species with genotype *aabb,* by which we mean that the alleles it has at the *a*-locus and the *b*-locus are different from those of the first-mentioned organism. Such an individual would produce only *ab* gametes. If these two different gametes should unite, they would produce a diploid zygote of genotype *AaBb*.

Now what will happen when an *AaBb* individual comes to produce gametes? From the previous discussion of meiosis, the following principles should be clear:

1. Each gamete contains *one, and only one,* of each kind of gene (pair of alleles). That is, each gamete has some sort of A-gene (*A* or *a*), and some sort of B-gene; but only one of each. (That is, gametes of these types are *not* possible: *Aa, AaB, AABB, BB,* and so on.)

2. The meiotic process makes all possible combinations (within the above-mentioned restriction) of all the genes available in the germ line, regardless of whether or not the genes are

"linked," that is, in the same chromosome. The relative abundance of the different types will be affected by linkage, but we are not now concerned with this fact.

From an *AaBb* individual the following gametes are possible:

AB	*aB*
Ab	*ab*

Notice that by hybridizing (crossbreeding) two pure varieties *AABB* and *aabb* (also called **homozygotes**), we have produced a hybrid, or **heterozygote** (*AaBb*), that is capable of producing two new kinds of gametes (*Ab* and *aB*) which neither of the homozygous parental strains could produce.

Carrying this type of analysis to the next stage, we see that a heterozygote of genotype *AaBbCc* will produce a total of eight different gametes—namely,

ABC	*AbC*	*aBC*	*abC*
ABc	*Abc*	*aBc*	*abc*

Of these, only two are the same as the gametes that united to produce the hybrid, the other six (8 minus 2) being new.

How many gametes could a heterozygote of genotype *AaBbCcDd* produce? The answer is 16, which we could discover either by laboriously writing them down; or, more neatly, by noticing that however many gametes a 3-gene heterozygote produces, a 4-gene heterozygote will produce this number multiplied by 2—for adding the *Dd* combination means that each of the "old" gametes (say *AbC*) can be split into two groups (*AbCD* and *AbCd*). For each new heterozygous set of genes, we multiply the number of gametes by 2. We can express this fact in a brief table:

Number of Heterozygous Sets of Genes	Number of Different Kinds of Gametes
1	2
2	$2 \times 2 = 2^2$
3	$2 \times 2 \times 2 = 2^3$
4	2^4
.	.
.	.
.	.
.	.
n	2^n

The exponent n does not have to be very large for 2^n to be quite large indeed. Suppose a human being were heterozygous for only 10 pairs of genes: he could then produce 2^{10}, or 1,024, different gametes. If he were heterozygous for 20 pairs of genes, he could produce 2^{20}, or 1,048,576, different gametes. Probably no human being is so pure as to be heterozygous for as few as 20 genes. It is small wonder, then, that offspring never look exactly like their parents. Even if the environment were constant (which it is not), we would not expect them to.

Actually, we have not really been speaking of offspring but of gametes. A heterozygote of n pairs of genes produces 2^n different gametes; if two such heterozygotes marry, they will produce 3^n different zygotes,* which is an even larger number. Some of these genotypically different zygotes may be **phenotypically** alike; that is, they may look alike. For example, consider albinism in humans. The gene for albinism is symbolized by c, its normal allele by C. The homozygous type cc is albino; CC is normal; and the heterozygote, Cc, is also normal in its phenotype. In such a case we say the allele C is **dominant** to c; or c is **recessive** to C. (It is a convention to use a capital letter for the dominant allele.) Not all gene pairs exhibit dominance, but when they do, three genotypes produce only two phenotypes.

In general, then, we can say that two individuals who are heterozygous for the same n pairs of genes will be capable of producing between 2^n and 3^n phenotypically different offspring, depending on the extent to which dominance does, or does not, prevail among the genes involved. Even at the lower limit, it is clear that sex (meiosis + fertilization) is able to produce an immense amount of variety in the living world.

60. Mutation: Originator of Variety

Yet there is a sense in which the variety-generating capacities of sex are limited. Whenever

---

* You should be able to demonstrate this by an argument that exactly parallels the argument for gametes given above.

two different pure strains are hybridized, the number of different offspring that may appear in the second and subsequent generations is immense, but finite. The number of combinations of genes sexual reproduction may bring into being is limited by the number of gene loci for which alternative alleles are available. If a population possesses two alleles for each of 20 loci, only 3^{20} different genotypes are possible. To transcend this limit, more alleles must come into existence. The process that brings this about is called mutation.

Mutation is a rare event. Suppose we had a pure strain of albino rabbits, cc. Mating only among their own kind, all their offspring would be albinos—except for about one out of every million which would be colored because a c allele would have "spontaneously" mutated to C. (Exactly what color this mutant would be would depend on what other genes it had. These other genes affecting color are able to do so only when there is a color to affect, that is, only in non-albino genotypes.)

For our example we have considered a mutation from a recessive gene to a dominant one; such a mutant is easiest to detect. But in wild populations, most of the "natural" alleles are dominant to any new mutants that appear; put another way, *most new mutations are recessive*. Because of this, they are not readily detected, since they first appear in heterozygotes. Only when two mutant genes of the same sort happen to get together in the same individual do we notice anything unusual. The appearance of an odd-looking organism in a wild population usually does not indicate a recent mutation, but rather a *recent recombination* of mutants that originated a long time in the past.

Recent concern with the dangers of atomic radiation has called attention to another characteristic of mutations—namely, *most new mutations are bad*. Why? The answer is easy to see if we recall our picture of heredity as a process of passing information on from one generation to another. The form and function of a living organism are produced by a hereditary message which—in the case of a mammalian genome—consists of about 10^{10} nucleotides. The sequence of these nucleotides has been determined by a long process of evolution (to be considered in Part II). The living organism is a highly organized system of enzyme reactions. What is the probability that a random alteration in the sequence of nucleotides will result in a new polypeptide that will make the mutant organism superior to the standard type? We cannot give a quantitatively defensible answer, but we can suggest an analogically useful alternative question. Take the printed version of the play *Julius Caesar*. Suppose we change, at random, one of the letters in the text to some other letter. What is the probability that the change will improve the sense of the play?

Is it really so strange that new mutations should almost always be bad?

Questions and Problems

7-3. Make a list of the **boldface** terms in this chapter and write a brief description of each. Compare your work with the text.

7-4. What was August Weismann's contribution to our conception of the life cycle?

7-5. If you wanted to study the phenomenon of genetic dominance, which organism would be a more favorable object of study—*Nasturtium* or *Chlamydomonas*?

7-6. In what cells of the body of a man does meiosis take place? Of a woman?

7-7. In what cells of a daisy does meiosis take place?

7-8. Complete the following table:

tation, how would you represent the haploid cells?

‡7-10. Suppose that the members of one homologous pair of chromosomes (i.e., the A's or the B's) in the organism described in the preceding question can be distinguished microscopically—a fact that we can indicate by writing the chromosomal constitution of a diploid cell as A_1A_2BB. As a result of meiosis, such a diploid cell could produce how many *distinguishable* kinds of haploid cells? Diagram the course of meiosis in such an organism, labeling the chromosomes and showing what the meiotic products will be.

‡7-11. Suppose we can distinguish the members of

ORGANISM	NUMBER OF CHROMOSOMES IN HAPLOID CELLS	NUMBER OF CHROMOSOMES IN DIPLOID CELLS	NUMBER OF PAIRS OF CHROMOSOMES IN DIPLOID CELLS
Ascaris megalocephala (parasitic roundworm)	1	2	
Drosophila melanogaster (vinegar fly)		8	4
Onion	8		
Pea			7
Domestic cat			19
Man	23		
Crayfish (one species)		200	

‡7-9. Consider an organism that has two pairs of chromosomes in its diploid cells. Let us represent the state of a diploid cell by writing *AABB*, in which *A* stands for one kind of chromosome, *B* for the other. Using this no-

both pairs of chromosomes of the organism described in question 7-10. In this case, we indicate the chromosomal constitution of a diploid cell by writing $A_1A_2B_1B_2$. In meiosis, how the members of one pair of chromosomes are distributed to the haploid cells has no influence on the distribution of the members of other chromosome pairs. In this organism, how many different kinds of haploid cells can be produced? What are they?

7-12. When does life begin?

7-13. The present population of the world is about 3.5×10^9 people. Assume that all people, regardless of age, have the same number of somatic cells. What is the present world population of human somatic cells?

7-14. We do not know the explanation of dominance. Most new mutant genes are recessive to their normal genes ("alleles"). In the ornamental plant "Four O'Clock," however, a cross of pure red by pure white yields a heterozygote that is pink. Can you *suggest* models that will account for dominance, and the lack of it?

7-15. Assuming that the same morphology and function can be produced by either haploid or diploid genomes, what advantage can you see in the diploid state?

Readings

McLeish and Snoad's little book has beautiful photographs of cells in meiosis. For general discussions of genetics and mutation, see Srb, Owen, and Edgar; or Stern.

II Equilibria, Ecology, and Evolution

W.

Nothing is easier than to admit in words the truth of the universal struggle for life, or more difficult—at least I have found it so—than constantly to bear this conclusion in mind.

CHARLES DARWIN

8

Cybernetic Systems

61. How Organize Complexity?

The mathematician Warren Weaver has defined biology as "the science of organized complexity." Such a definition may not be very enlightening to one who is utterly ignorant of biology, but to biologists it seems rather appropriate. All living activities are based on what is aptly called the metabolic maelstrom, a complex of literally thousands of processes going on simultaneously within the narrow confines of a cell, processes which conflict and compete with each other but which are nonetheless organized in such a way that they act together—*cooperatively* we might say, except that the word may imply too much—producing an end result that is harmonious with life. How is such organization achieved? What is the basis of *any* organization?

Two methods of organization are easily distinguishable: 1. Organization by rigid unification; 2. Organization by feedback control.

The first type of organization is the kind seen in most of our older machines. Take an automobile engine for example. The piston moves the piston rod, the piston rod moves the crankshaft and the crankshaft turns the drive shaft. There is a rigidity in this organization in the sense that given a certain amount of movement of the piston, a certain amount of movement of the drive shaft necessarily and inevitably follows. (The fact that there is a gear box inter-

vening, with a choice of gears, does not alter the logic of the machine.) Such a machine is deterministic to a high degree.

In the biological realm an example of rigid organization is found in the genetic mechanism. The hereditary message is reproduced when the DNA is duplicated according to the precise specification of the Base Pairing Rule (§47), a rule which allows for no uncertainties or errors. Errors do occur, of course, though only rarely; when they occur, they are not corrected for but instead lead to a new type of message ("mutant") which is itself rigidly reproduced. The mechanism for dealing with the threat of continual degradation of the genetic message is the subject of Chapter 10. For the moment we need note only that a rigidly organized system, like the genetic mechanism, has no *intrinsic* way of correcting for errors.

By contrast, a feedback control system can correct for errors. As an example of such a system we can take an endproduct inhibition system of the cell (§41). In this, the amount of product produced by a given enzyme molecule is not *rigidly* determined by its turnover number, for a molecule of enzyme may (at a particular moment) be estopped from activity by a molecule of endproduct. When, because of some "error," the number of endproduct molecules rises above normal (as it would if additional molecules were suddenly supplied from the outside), the excess supply quenches the activity of the enzyme, and thus the error is corrected for. A system that is organized by feedback controls is far more flexible and less vulnerable to damage than is a rigid one. Let us see, in detail, what is meant by feedback, both in man-made machines and in living systems.

62. How a Thermostat Works

Perhaps the best known feedback control is the **thermostat,** invented in 1830 by Andrew Ure (1778–1856). A modern form of a thermostat is shown diagrammatically in Figure 8-1. Use is made of a bimetallic strip, a strip of two metals that have different coefficients of expansion. As the temperature rises, the black T in the diagram is moved upward; as the temperature falls, T moves downward. When T touches S an electrical circuit is completed turning on the fur-

nace. This raises the temperature and ultimately breaks the contact between T and S, thus turning off the furnace, allowing the temperature to fall, etc. The result of this mechanism is shown in the bottom half of Figure 8-1: the temperature of the room fluctuates about the **set point.** The set point is, in general, movable.

Notice that an *increase* in temperature causes the mechanism to *diminish* the heat coming in; a *decrease* in temperature causes an *augmentation* of the heat supplied. This negative relation of the impressed change with the response change, shown in Figure 8-2, is the reason for using the phrase **negative feedback** to describe this sort of action. The mechanism, we say, is **error-actuated;** an error in the temperature of room actuates the mechanism to correct it. Named teleologically, negative feedback is sometimes called **corrective feedback.**

The opposite kind of feedback would result if we (unwisely) inserted a reversing relay in

Fig. 8-1. *Diagrammatic representation of a thermostat. Contact T is moved upward by heat, down by cold. When T touches S, an electrical circuit is completed which turns on the furnace. When the contact between T and S is broken, the furnace is turned off. The Set Point is movable.*

MECHANISM:

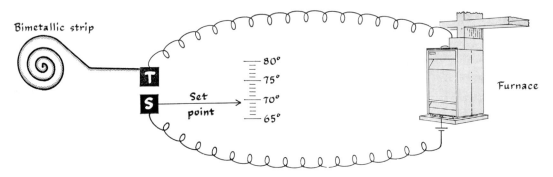

RESULT:

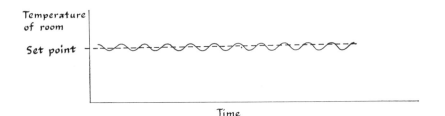

Fig. 8-2. *Why we use the phrase "negative feed-back."*

the circuit so that breaking the contact between T and S resulted in turning the furnace *on*. In this case, the sign of the response change (+) would be the same as the sign of the impressed change (+), and the temperature would go up and up. Errors would *not* be corrected for, therefore such **positive feedback** is sometimes called **runaway feedback.** It is particularly important to notice that *a system that includes only positive feedback cannot be stable.*

Few corrective feedback systems were invented before Ure's thermostat. One of the most important early examples was the speed governor which James Watt (1736–1819) de-

veloped for his steam engine in 1787.* Like every negative feedback device this governor allowed fluctuations in the speed, centering about the set point. In some machines, under some operating conditions, the fluctuations were disturbingly wide. A secure theoretical basis on which to design satisfactory governors was created in 1868 by James Clerk Maxwell. Gradually, more and more automatic controls were developed, a process that was much accelerated by the demands of World War II. At this time the theory was much further advanced by Norbert Wiener (1895–1964) who, in 1948, coined the word **cybernetics,** taken from a Greek root for steersman (of a boat), from which word the Latin word for governor (*gubernator*) is derived. Cybernetics is defined as *the science of communication and control in complex systems.* The systems may be either living or dead; the principles are quite general.

In the analysis of cybernetic control it often helps to visualize the operations as a cybernetic diagram of the sort shown in Figure 8-3, in which thermostatic control is the example. The dotted arrows indicate a random or impressed change on the system. The solid arrows indicate a necessary change brought about by the system itself. The boxes give some (though usually not all) of the links in the causal sequence. All cy-

---

* 8-1. Why should anyone want to develop such control devices anyway?

Fig. 8-3. *The cybernetic diagram of thermostatic control.*

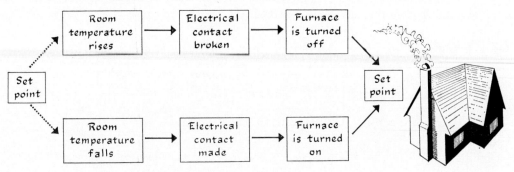

SYMBOLISM:
   Broken arrow (•••••••▶) indicates hypothetical, or random, impressed change.
   Solid arrow (——▶) indicates necessary, response change.

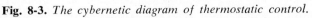

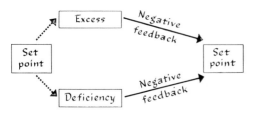

Fig. 8-4. *The generalized cybernetic diagram for a negative or corrective feedback system.*

bernetic diagrams of particular negative feedback systems (of which Figure 8-3 is an example) can be subsumed under the general diagram illustrated in Figure 8-4.

63. Endotherms

Organisms consist of cells, and each cell is a highly organized system of thousands of different kinds of enzymes. Each enzymatic reaction has its own *temperature coefficient*. One reaction may speed up by a factor of two when the temperature rises 10°C, whereas another may increase by a factor of 2.5, a third by 1.8, and so on. A change in temperature therefore threatens to create imbalances in metabolism; how is this threat met? In part, no doubt, by negative feedbacks within the cell (of the sorts discussed in §41 and §54)—by endproduct inhibition, for example. But feedback mechanisms may themselves have a variety of temperature coefficients. We know all too little of the details of cellular adjustment to varying temperatures, but it is certainly clear that any organism stands

to gain if it can keep the temperature of its cells near their optimum temperature, whatever that may be. There is, in a word, an advantage to being a **homotherm,** that is, an organism with a (relatively) uniform temperature (*homo* is a corruption of Gr. *homoios,* like, resembling; Gr. *thermos,* heat). The advantage of homothermy in a competitive world no doubt helps to account for the rise of the mammals and birds to a dominant position during the last hundred million years.

How does a mammal keep its internal temperature nearly constant? Several devices are used; in Figure 8-5 only the negative feedback of sweating is considered. Suppose the room becomes suddenly hotter, and consequently an increase in body temperature is *impressed* on man from the outside (as indicated by upper broken arrow). The increased body temperature stimulates a temperature-regulating center in the brain, which sends messages to the sweat glands causing them to produce more sweat; with the evaporation of more sweat, more heat is lost from the body, and the body temperature therefore falls toward the normal. (All these changes that take place in *response* to the departure from the equilibrium point are indicated by the upper series of solid arrows in the diagram.)

If the temperature should fall (lower broken arrow), a corresponding series of response changes with an opposite effect will be brought into play. Sweating will decrease, and the body temperature will rise (lower series of solid arrows).

Fig. 8-5. *The cybernetic system that controls body temperature in a mammal.*

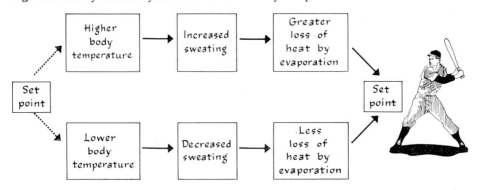

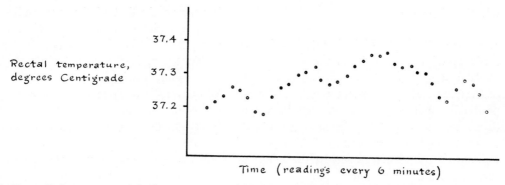

Rectal temperature, degrees Centigrade

37.4

37.3

37.2

Time (readings every 6 minutes)

Fig. 8-6. *Normal fluctuation of body temperature. (Rectal temperature is somewhat higher than oral.) Data of F. G. Benedict and E. P. Slack, 1911.)*

Like any feedback mechanism this one produces not an absolutely constant temperature but one which fluctuates within limits, as is shown by the record graphed in Figure 8-6. The readings shown there were taken rectally and are somewhat higher than the oral temperature of man, the set point of which is nearer 37.0°C. The set points for some other species of mammals and birds are given in Appendix 10.* What inner details of mechanism account for the differences in the setting of "normal" for different species is quite unknown. Certain conditions can alter the set point for awhile even within a given individual. For example, a microbial infection may cause a fever, that is, a high temperature which sometimes may fluctuate considerably, but at other times equilibrates fairly closely around a new, higher set point.

Whatever the temperature of a mammal or a bird, it is obvious that most of the time most of the heat used by the animal to achieve homothermy is generated internally, by metabolism. The dissipation of heat to the outside is encouraged or impeded by various physiological mechanisms (sweating, flushing, shivering, etc.). Because the physiological mechanism is designed to control internally derived heat, such organisms are called **endotherms.**

The temperature-control mechanism is only one of many such equilibrating devices in the animal body. Other devices maintain constancy in the amount of water in the tissues, in the amount of sugar in the blood, and in the concentrations of various salts. The physiologist Walter B. Cannon (1871–1945), for many years at Harvard, studied such systems in detail and gave them a name: **homeostatic systems.** Mammals are preeminently animals that maintain themselves in a condition of **homeostasis** (Gr. *homoios* = like + *stasis* = standing). As used here the terms "homeostatic system" and "cybernetic system" are substantially synonymous, if by the latter is understood to be a negative feedback system. There really is no need for the two terms, but since both are well entrenched we will use both.

Although Wiener coined the word "cybernetic" in 1948, and Cannon the word "homeostatic" in 1928, the idea is older than the terminology (as is often the case). The French physiologist Claude Bernard (1813–1878), in an essay published in the last year of his life, clearly delineated the idea of homeostasis, calling attention particularly to the significance of the chemical constancy of the circulating fluids of the mammalian body, the blood and the lymph. Since these are the only fluids with which most of the cells of the body ever come in contact, they constitute the environment of the cells. Bernard called them the *internal environment,* saying: *The constancy of the internal environment is the necessary condition of the free life.*

---

* 8-2. Is there any consistent difference between birds and mammals? What is it? How reliable is the generalization?

8-3. What is the normal temperature of a pigeon, in Fahrenheit degrees?

64. Ectotherms

A recurrent failure of biologists derives from a tendency to make broad generalizations based on laboratory work alone, unchecked by field observations. The same point may be put more positively: many opportunities for important discoveries lie in wait for the investigator who uses both the laboratory and the field approach. For an illustrative case, consider the temperature of a lizard.

For a long time it was customary to say that a lizard was a "cold-blooded" animal, explaining (if pressed) that its blood is not necessarily cold, but is merely a fraction of a degree warmer than the temperature of the surrounding air, whatever that is.* This statement was based on laboratory experience. When, however, a number of biologists, notably R. B. Cowles, carried their observations into the field they found that the body temperature of a lizard during most of its "working day" is surprisingly constant, at about the same value as mammalian temperature, though the air temperature may be twenty degrees less. How does a lizard achieve this degree of constancy? By behavioral means, as observation showed.

The elements of body temperature control by a lizard are diagrammed in Figure 8-7. At the start of the day the body temperature of a lizard

---

* 8-4. Why not exactly the same temperature?

8-5. From the conceptual model here implied, would the temperature of a large lizard differ more or less from that of the environment than would the temperature of a small lizard? Why?

is very nearly that of the surrounding air; he soon remedies this. He lies stretched out in full sunlight until his body temperature rises to within his optimal range, 36°–42°C; then he sets about his business of catching insects. Whenever his body temperature is too high he moves into the shade; when too low, he moves back into the sun or onto a well-heated rock. By this behavioral feedback he controls his body temperature. The system works pretty well, though not quite as well as the physiological feedback system of a mammal. For one thing, there may at times be a conflict between the demands of temperature regulation and those of food-catching. Such a conflict gives particular meaning to Bernard's aphorism, "The constancy of the internal environment is the necessary condition of the free life."

Because its body temperature is largely determined by external sources of heat, organisms like a lizard are called **ectotherms.** Most of the animals of the world are ectotherms; only a fraction of these can achieve the degree of homothermy of a lizard. In general, control of body temperature by an ectotherm is possible only to land forms; water dwellers (e.g., fish) have to make do with a body temperature that is little different from that of the water around them. Put another way, an ectotherm uses a mosaic of environmental temperature differences to synthesize the homothermal condition for itself.

It is interesting to compare the appearance of an ectothermic reptile and an endothermic

---

Fig. 8-7. *The cybernetics of body temperature control by a lizard.*

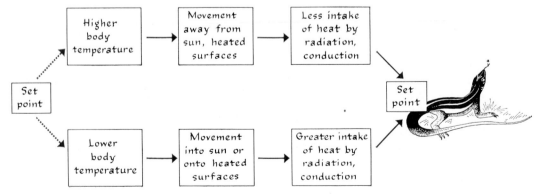

Fig. 8-8. (A) *A snail-eating Caiman lizard,* Dracaena guianensis. (B) *Young fennec foxes of the Sahara desert,* Fennecus zerda. (A, *from C. J. & O. B. Goin,* Introduction to Herpetology, *W. H. Freeman and Company, San Francisco and London, 1962.* B, *courtesy Zoological Society of Philadelphia.)*

mammal, bearing in mind the body-environment heat exchange problem. A mere inspection of the animals in Figure 8-8 suggests that the hairy coat of a mammal acts as a buffer against the environment; by contrast, the surface of a lizard is so constructed as to make exchanges of heat with the environment readily possible.

65. Heterothermy

The species that becomes homothermous achieves freedom—but at a price. The price

may sometimes be too great. The seasons put a particular stress on animals in temperate or arctic zones. In the winter time not only is there a greater temperature differential between environment and homotherm, but the food supply is often less abundant, for a variety of reasons. Under such circumstances it would be advantageous if the homotherm could turn off his thermostat, or at least set it to a lower reading. Some "warm-blooded" animals can, in fact, do this: we call the process **hibernation.**

Careful studies made in the twentieth century

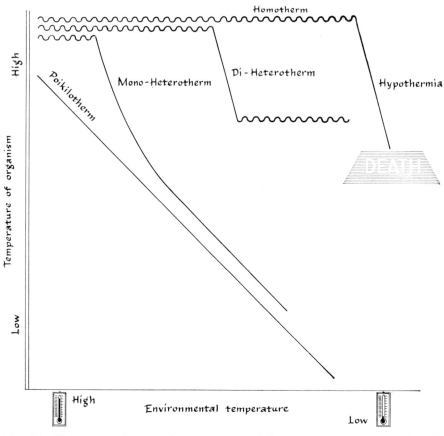

Fig. 8-9. *The principal ways of reacting to a falling temperature. Note that the environmental temperature* decreases *going from left to right.*

have shown that there is more than one kind of hibernation. As a background for studying the various temperature patterns note first, in Figure 8-9, the temperature pattern of a homotherm. The graph is organized in an unusual way: the environmental temperature is high *at the left,* low at the right. As the environmental temperature falls (going from left to right) the body temperature of a homotherm remains constant until a critical temperature is reached, which is between 17° and 22°C for an unclothed man. When the temperature falls below this, man's thermostat abruptly fails and his temperature falls, death ensuing in the neighborhood of 13°C. Subnormal temperatures above the death point produce a condition of **hypothermia;** metabolism proceeds at a slow pace and the individual is unconscious. In cer-

tain medical procedures hypothermia is used as an anaesthetic in preference to chemicals.

Contrasting with the homotherms, note the reaction of most ectotherms to falling temperature. Most ectotherms, unlike lizards, are unable to maintain a reasonably constant temperature; their body temperature is almost the same as the environmental temperature. Organisms in this functional class are called **poikilotherms** (Gr. *poikilos,* variegated, various). A lizard in the laboratory, with no access to sunlight or heated surfaces, is a strict poikilotherm; so are fishes and most insects. As shown in Figure 8-9, the temperature curve of a poikilotherm is simply a straight line, falling with the fall in temperature of the environment.

What about a hibernator? Two general patterns are known. The first, the "classical" pattern, is found among mammals in the European hedgehog and the dormouse, and among birds in swifts and the Western poor-will. In this pattern, the body temperature is always under thermostatic control, but there are two alternative set points, one for winter, one for summer. An animal with this pattern we can call a **di-heterotherm,** the *di* to indicate two, and *hetero* to indicate other or different. In the summer, the di-heterotherm has his thermostat set to the higher reading (see Fig. 8-9). At the approach of winter, stimulated by the falling temperature (and possibly other clues) the animal's thermostat is abruptly set to the lower reading, typically about 18°C. The heart rate, breathing rate, and metabolic rate are greatly lowered and the animal goes into a deep sleep. In this unconscious condition the animal is very vulnerable to attack; in preparation for its changed condition the hibernator finds or makes a secluded place to hide in. During the winter, hibernation is interrupted from time to time. Stimulated perhaps by some internal "clock," the set point is rapidly moved upward to the upper setting, the animal comes out of its nest or den to look around, perhaps finds a bit of food, then returns to its hiding place and re-hibernates. Finally, some fine spring day, it stays out.

Bats follow a different pattern. A bat does not turn his thermostat down; he simply turns it off. Such an animal we call a **mono-hetero-therm;** as shown in Figure 8-9, there is only one set point; when the thermostat is turned off, the body temperature simply becomes very nearly that of the environment. This does not mean that it falls indefinitely (as one might infer from the graph), for the environment itself (a cave for bats) may have a very steady temperature.

Such are the two general patterns of hibernation. The details vary greatly from one species to another. In principle, hibernation is not altogether different from sleep. In sleep, man's thermostat is set about half a degree below the daytime set point. The hibernation of bears is intermediate between sleep and the classical

hibernation of hedgehogs; the two set points for a black bear are 38° and about 34°C. At the lower temperature the bear is torpid, but by no means completely "out," as a hedgehog is at 18°C. This fact in the life of a bear was ascertained by Ray Hock who entered the den of a bear to take its rectal temperature, an act of no small courage as it seems to other biologists, whatever might be the thoughts of the bear on the subject.

One of the functions of science is the classification of knowledge, and the coinage of terms is one way of classifying. Properly pursued, the activity is defensible; but it is amusing how often "Nature" mocks man's best efforts. The word "hibernation" seems quite apt, since it is derived from the Latin word *hibernus* which means winter. Hibernation tides an animal over hard times. What, then, should one say of a comparable inactive stage into which some desert animals enter at the height of the summer, going into seclusion in deep and cool holes? For this type of process a separate term has been invented, namely **estivation,** derived from the L. *aestus,* summer. One might argue that a separate term is not needed: the season is different, but the teleology is the same.

Recently, another stimulus to torpor has been found. Hummingbirds can be classed as mono-heterotherms, but the torpid periods occur not once a year, but once a day. Every night a hummingbird turns off its thermostat; before daybreak, it turns it on again. A separate term might have been invented for this phenomenon, but with unusual restraint, and reckless of the consequences of verbal inconsistency, biologists speak of the "diurnal hibernation" of the hummingbird.*

The reason for diurnal hibernation follows directly from the scale effect. Small homotherms in a cool environment must have a higher metabolic rate than large homotherms, because heat loss is proportional to surface. Hummingbirds are *very* small homotherms—you could mail eight of them for only one five-cent stamp. Such a small organism must take in food almost con-

---

* 8-6. *If* a separate term is desirable, can you suggest one?

tinuously to pay the price of homothermy. Hummingbirds, however, can see only in the daylight and have a poor sense of smell: hence the necessity of hibernation each night. In Figure 8-10, notice how a shrew, a mammal of the same size as a hummingbird, maintains a fairly steady metabolic rate throughout the 24 hours by virtue of its ability to find food at all times. An accounting of the energy budget of an Anna hummingbird showed that only 7.6 Calories were required for a normal 24-hour period, whereas if the bird had not hibernated at night it would have required 10.3 Calories, an increase of 36 percent. For a homotherm the size of a hummingbird, living near the limit of what is possible, such a saving is of vital significance.

66. The Homeostatic Plateau

There are limits to the capability of every homeostatic system. Consider the thermostat of the human body. If the temperature of the surrounding air lies between 17° and 32°C the body's thermostat works very well. But if (with a relative humidity of 100 percent) the air temperature rises above 32°, the temperature of the body starts rising above 37°. This happens not merely because the body is unable to dissipate metabolic heat fast enough but also be-

cause the environmental stress ultimately causes a failure of the thermostat. When the thermostat fails, runaway feedback takes over: higher temperature causes metabolic reactions to go faster which produces more body heat which raises the temperature which causes metabolic reactions to go faster . . . and so on. This runaway feedback (if not stopped) leads to death. Below the lower temperature limit, a similar runaway feedback leads to death from stoppage of metabolism.

The sense of this situation is shown in Figure 8-11, which applies to any homeostatic system. The role of conscious effort in the maintenance of human homeostasis can be spelled out. Near the limits of physiological homeostasis it is advisable to augment the unconscious system with conscious, external controls—clothing, air-conditioning and room heating, for example. By these "artificial" means one seeks to keep the body on the **homeostatic plateau.** However, whenever the body is safely on this plateau, no conscious effort need be made to maintain constancy. The unconscious corrective feedbacks of physiology are adequate. Minutely detailed external control is not required. There is even some evidence that it may not be desirable—a reasonable amount of periodic stressing of the cybernetic system may be necessary to keep it in good functioning order.

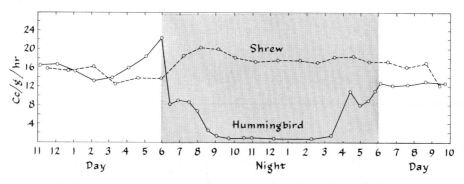

Fig. 8-10. *The savings in oxygen consumption effected by the daily hibernation of an Anna hummingbird, as compared with a shrew of the same size. (After O. P. Pearson, Condor (1950) 52:145-152.)*

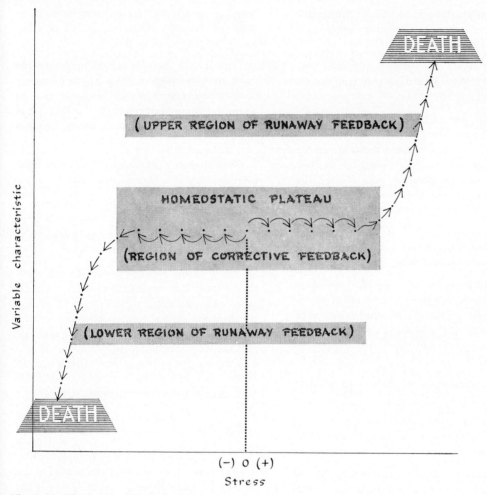

Fig. 8-11. *The limits of homeostasis.*

Questions and Problems

8-7. Make a list of the **boldface** terms in this chapter. Write out a definition or description of each. Compare your work with the text.

8-8. Write out a brief description of the contributions of each of the following men to the theory developed in this chapter: Maxwell, Wiener, Cannon.

‡8-9. Is mitosis a cybernetic scheme for assuring constancy in the numbers of chromosomes from one cell generation to another? Explain.

8-10. Account for the "howl" that may develop in public address systems.

‡8-11. P. Adams and J. Heath (1964) discovered the following facts about sphinx moths. At rest, the moth's temperature is that of the air. If the air temperature is between 16° and 27°C, before taking off the moth shivers until it raises its temperature to 38°. During flight, the body temperature fluctuates about 36°. Given a choice of temperatures, the insects

tend to collect where the ambient temperature is 37.7°. In terms of body temperature, how would you classify sphinx moths?

8-12. Sphinx moths are certainly not strict poikilotherms. What advantage can you suggest for their way of life?

8-13. A man who wishes to kill some bees spreads the hive apart when the external temperature is −12°C. The next morning, all the bees are still alive—as a clump of animals who are actively vibrating their wings. The temperature of the center of the clump is +14°C. Are bees poikilotherms?

‡8-14. A single bee, isolated at −12°C will die. In the most general terms, why does it die whereas a clump does not?

‡8-15. If a 70-kilogram man had to take in as many Calories per day in proportion to his body weight as does a hummingbird, what would be his daily Calorie requirement? How does this compare with his actual Calorie requirement?

8-16. Make a cybernetic diagram of endproduct inhibition (§41).

8-17. Discuss the etymological issues in the alternative terms *homotherm, homoiotherm,* and *homeotherm.*

8-18. In the early days of the automobile, the snake population of rural regions was rather severely reduced because snakes apparently liked to lie stretched out on the blacktop roads in the cool of a summer's evening. Why were the snakes there? Why were fewer run over in the middle of the day?

‡8-19. It can be calculated that it takes .085 Cal-

ories for a hummingbird to warm up its body from 10° to 40°. What fraction of its daily energy requirements is this?

‡8-20. The specific heat of human flesh may be assumed to be equal to that of hummingbird flesh. How many Calories would it take to warm a human body from 7° to 37°? What fraction is this of man's daily energy requirements?

‡8-21. Why doesn't man go into hibernation each evening the way a hummingbird does?

8-22. A fever of less than 40° in a human is usually treated by piling on extra blankets. Above 40°, one applies ice packs instead. Why the difference in treatments?

‡8-23. Look at the table in Appendix 10. Consider the column headed Critical Air Temperature—Lower Limit. At (and below) this temperature the animal fails to maintain its normal constant temperature. Excluding man, do you see any relationship between this statistic and the weight of the animal (which you already know with enough exactitude)? How do you account for the relationship, if any?

8-24. Why is man an exception to the rule deduced in the preceding answer?

‡8-25. If we had data for Peking man (500,000–1,000,000 B.C.), what would you predict would be (a) his normal temperature, and (b) the critical lower temperature of the air for him?

8-26. It has been stated as a matter of principle that every persistent, stable system must be regulated by feedback. Someone objects: a clock is a time-measuring system that does not have feedback. Discuss the issue.

Readings

Cannon's *The Wisdom of the Body* is pleasant reading. Schmidt-Nielsen's *Desert Animals* tells of some remarkable ways of achieving homeostasis under extreme conditions. Wiener has two books that discuss cybernetics: *Cybernetics* and *The Human Use of Human Beings.* The latter is the more

interesting because the author's political premises are more prominent. If your political beliefs are different from Wiener's, you may find it amusing to devise different cybernetic analyses of the everyday problems he discusses there.

9 Population Dynamics

67. Reproduction as Positive Feedback

In 1755, Benjamin Franklin (1706–1790), musing over the evident growth of human population in the Colonies remarked: "There are supposed to be now upwards of one million English souls in North America (though it is thought scarcely eighty thousand had been brought over sea), and yet perhaps there is not one the fewer in Britain, but rather more. . . ." The reason for this was, of course, obvious: reproduction in Britain had more than made up any losses by emigration. Franklin made the implication of such a fact explicit: "There is, in short, no bound to the prolific nature of plants or animals, but what is made by their crowding and interfering with each other's means of subsistence. Was the face of the earth vacant of other plants, it might be gradually sowed and overspread with one kind only as, for instance, with fennel. . . ."

Franklin's essay seems not to have been much noticed at the time. His point about the character of biological reproduction was made again in 1798 by an English clergyman, Thomas Malthus (1766–1834) in his *Essay on Population.* As Malthus put it: "Population, when unchecked, increases in a geometrical ratio. . . . Through the animal and vegetable kingdoms Nature has scattered the seeds of life abroad with the most profuse and liberal hand. She has been comparatively sparing in the room and the nourishment necessary to rear them. The germs of existence contained in this spot of earth, with ample food, and ample room to expand in, would fill millions of worlds in the course of a few thousand years."

Charles Darwin (1809–1882) returned to this point in his *Origin of Species,* published in 1859:

There is no exception to the rule that every organic being naturally increases at so high a rate, that, if not destroyed, the earth would soon be covered by the progeny of a single pair . . . Linnaeus has calculated that if an annual plant produced only two seeds—and there is no plant so unproductive as this—and their seedlings next year produced two, and so on, then in twenty years there would be a million plants. The elephant is reckoned the slowest breeder of all known animals, and I have taken some pains to estimate its probable minimum rate of natural increase; it will be safest to assume that it begins breeding when thirty years old, bringing forth six young in the interval, and surviving till one hundred years old; if this be so, after a period of from 740 to 750 years there would be nearly nineteen million elephants alive descended from the first pair.

The growth of a population, "when unchecked,"—to use Malthus' phrase—is very simply, though incompletely, represented by Figure 9-1. With the passage of time, an unchecked population increases faster and faster.

The units on the abscissa are not given in the figure. By a suitable choice of units, the curve can be made to fit equally well the potential population curves of all organisms. For viruses, the units should read in minutes, for fruitflies in days, and for elephants in decades. Popular articles sometimes point with fascinated horror to the reproductive potentialities of an oyster, which can lay half a billion eggs in a season. Darwin diverted the discussion to a more productive channel when he pointed out that even slow-breeding elephants are capable of prodigies of reproduction. In introducing his argument, however, Darwin used a phrase that might be misleading: ". . . every organic being naturally increases *at so high a rate* . . ." The word "so" unfortunately is ambiguous; the meaning of the sentence would be clearer if it read: "at a rate sufficiently high . . ." All organisms, no matter how slow breeding, increase at a rate sufficiently high to make the growth curve soar off "toward infinity."

Reproduction is positive feedback. Children have more children and these in turn produce still more children. The reproduction of an unchecked population is like money invested at compound interest. We can even use a modification of the compound interest formula (Appendix 6) to calculate the rate of increase of a population:

$$N = N_0(1 + i)^t \qquad (1)$$

where: N_0 = initial population
N = final population
i = interest rate per year, compounded annually
t = number of years

The assumption that the "interest" is compounded only once a year is unrealistic, but the resulting figure is sufficiently exact. On the basis of the growth of population in the American colonies Malthus assumed that the maximum possible growth rate for humans was a doubling in population every 25 years. To what annual interest rate (i) would this correspond? Using equation (1), we set $t = 25$, $N_0 = 1$, and $N = 2$, thus:

$$2 = (1 + i)^{25} \qquad (2)$$

To solve this we use logarithms:

$$\log 2 = 25 \log (1 + i) \qquad (3)$$

$$\log (1 + i) = \frac{\log 2}{25} = \frac{.30103}{25} \qquad (4)$$

$$\log (1 + i) = .01204 \qquad (5)$$

$$(1 + i) = 1.028 \qquad (6)$$

$$i = .028 = 2.8\% \qquad (7)$$

So a net increase of only 2.8 percent per year is sufficient to double a population in 25 years. This rate is decidedly less than the interest rate

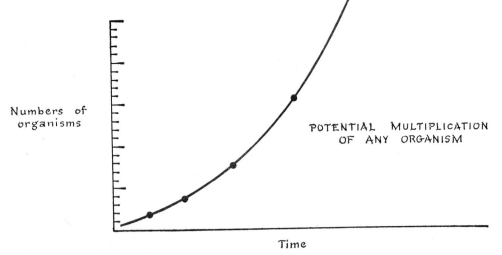

POTENTIAL MULTIPLICATION OF ANY ORGANISM

Numbers of organisms

Time

Fig. 9-1. *The positive feedback of reproduction produces a potential population growth that always accelerates, without intrinsic limit.*

earned on bank accounts during most of the existence of the United States of America. Even so, such a rate of increase (part multiplication, part immigration) was maintained only in the early years of the Republic.*

Those who have not experimented with the compound interest formula are often surprised at the way in which even a low rate of interest rather rapidly leads to a doubling of the numbers. Some representative values are given in Table 9-1. Notice that even so low a rate of

TABLE 9-1 *Doubling Times, in Years, for Various Rates of Annual Increase, Compounded Annually.*

PERCENTAGE RATE OF INCREASE	DOUBLING TIME
0.5	139
1.0	70
1.5	47
2.0	35
2.5	28
2.8	25
3.0	23
3.5	20
4.0	18

increase as half a percent per annum leads to a doubling of the population in 139 years— only a short segment of the time man has been in existence already (and, hopefully, only a small fraction of the future time that man will be on the earth).

As was pointed out previously, the assumption of discontinuous growth is not realistic. For a more exact treatment another equation is available, one which assumes continuous increase, continuously compounded. This equation is:

---

* 9-1. The first official census, in 1790, revealed 3,929,214 people. In 1960, the figure stood at 179,-323,175. What was the average annual rate of increase during this period?

9-2. If the population of the U. S. had doubled every 25 years from 1790 to 1960, what would the population have been in 1960? (Use log value given in equation 5.)

$$N = N_0 e^{bt} \qquad (8)$$

where: e = base of natural logarithms
     (2.718 . . .)

   b = a constant

The remaining symbols have the meaning given before. The constant b, which may be thought of as representing the "biotic potential" of the species, is always greater than zero; the faster the growth, the greater is b. For a population that doubles in 25 years, $b = .02772$. Calculations using equation (8) would be more difficult than ones using (1), were it not for the existence of printed tables of the "exponential function" as it is called. Unchecked growth follows the predictions of this function and is therefore said to be **exponential growth.** If one plots the logarithm of N against t (on ordinary, arithmetic scale) the result is a straight line during the period of exponential growth. Whenever, therefore, a plot of growth on semilog paper yields a straight line, growth is said to be **logarithmic growth.** Notice that the meaning of exponential growth and logarithmic growth is the same—it is just the image that is different. Any growth that increases at a regular rate (1, 2, 4, 8, 16, . . .) is of this sort (as you should verify on semilog paper).

68. The Malthusian Demostat

In a finite world (and we have direct experience of no other), there can be no stable, enduring system that includes an element of unopposed positive feedback. This principle was first pointed out in §62; it will now be given particular meaning in an economic example.

What the economist Kenneth Galbraith calls "the conventional wisdom" includes (during our time) the idea that in a proper economic system one should be able to set one's money out at compound interest for an indefinitely long time, ultimately reclaiming both principle and accrued interest without any diminution caused by depreciation of the currency (i.e., without inflation of prices). Is this a reasonable expectation? Is such a system possible? Let's see.

Suppose someone at the time of the birth of Christ (about 4 B.C.) had put one dollar in a bank that paid 4 percent interest, compounded annually. How much money would he have now, some 1970 years later? Using the compound interest formula, we find that the answer is 3.59×10^{33} dollars. Is this reasonable? Assuming money was pegged to the gold standard throughout that time, with gold at its present value of about $1.23 a gram, the initial deposit of slightly less than a gram-equivalent of gold would now have grown to about 2.92×10^{33} grams of gold. Could our hypothetical depositor demand to be paid in gold? Consulting Appendix 4 we find that the total mass of the earth is only 5.983×10^{27} gm. The answer is obvious.

The implications are almost as obvious, but not often faced. An economic system that includes the positive feedback of compound interest can endure only if it includes also one or more such counteracting forces as inflation, bank failures, confiscatory taxes, robbery, bankruptcy, revolutions, and repudiation of debts. Conventional wisdom regards these events as pathological. Undesirable they may be; but at least one such force must be included if the system is to endure. We might as well regard them as normal. This does not preclude us from regarding some of the counteracting forces as preferable to others.

Similar remarks can be made about all biological systems. In a finite world there can be no stability if the positive feedback of reproduction is unopposed. But it is always opposed, and by many different forces: starvation, crowd diseases, intraspecific conflict, and predation, to name the most obvious. These forces tend to depress the population whenever it reaches an unusually high level. On the other hand, if the population falls to an unusually low level, lightening of the restraints allows normal reproduction to increase the numbers. In a word, any natural population tends to equilibrate about a set point, even as the temperature of a thermostated room does. A basic idea of **demography** (Gr. *demos* = people)—the study of populations of any species—is the idea of the Malthusian **demostat,** the natural system that produces approximate stability in population numbers. Implicit in Malthus' writings is the demostatic control illustrated in Figure 9-2. In Malthus' quaint phraseology, overpopulation results in "misery and vice," by which he meant such things as starvation, disease, and warfare; these bring the population back down toward the set point. On the other hand, if a sudden decrease in population should take place, more wealth would be available per person, which would result in greater reproduction or greater survival rate and the population would rise to the set point again. Reproduction considered by itself is positive feedback; however, in its functional role illustrated in Figure 9-2 we may legitimately regard the *increased* reproduction which comes as a response to the *decreased* population as a negative feedback in the demostatic system.

Is the Malthusian model correct? Although Malthus was principally concerned with *Homo sapiens,* let us examine first the applicability of

Fig. 9-2. *Showing the operation of the demostat implied in the writings of Malthus.*

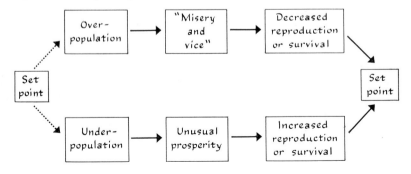

the model to nonhuman populations. For these, there is no question as to its correctness. Observations made in the field show that, over a long period of time, the population density of any species remains approximately the same; this density we speak of as the **carrying capacity** of the land. The carrying capacity can seldom be predicted *a priori* but must be determined by empirical measurement (just as the "normal" temperature of a homotherm can be determined only by observation). The variations in population from year to year may be scarcely noticeable, or they may be spectacular as they are in populations of Arctic lemmings; but in any case, there is a fluctuation about a set point. The most important negative feedbacks that control overpopulation vary from species to species and may vary within a species from one year to another, but there are always corrective feedbacks. For wild herbivores (e.g., antelope, elk) starvation is seldom as important a feedback as is predation; though the relative importance of these two controls is sometimes reversed when well-meaning but ignorant men kill off most of the wolves and coyotes in a region. It's difficult to remember that a stable system must include corrective feedbacks!

In recent years there has been an increasing realization of the importance that psychological factors play in the control of animal populations. Laboratory colonies of rats furnished a surplus of food stabilize at a level far below that made possible by food, because of the social disorganization produced by crowding. Fighting interferes with mating, distraught mothers fail to care for their young, and the adults of both sexes indulge in cannibalism.

In nature, the pathology of overpopulation is often prevented by the instinctive operation of "conventional conflict." The singing of a male bird may or may not please the female, but certain it is that it warns other male birds to keep their distance. In this way, as H. E. Howard showed in 1920, birds stake out territories for themselves that are large enough to support their families. Conventional, bloodless conflict enables them to avoid the damage produced by more sanginary encounters. The males

that lose in this ritualized conflict, having no private property, can attract no mates and so do not breed.

The foregoing examples show only a few of the many ways in which natural demostats work. The effective corrective feedbacks are often not obvious and must be discovered by patient observation and experiment.

69. Are Human Populations Demostatically Controlled?

Is man an animal? To a modern biologist this question seems hardly worth asking because the answer is so obvious. But, in one variation or another, this question has been at the bottom of some of the most acute intellectual and social conflicts of the last two hundred years. Nonbiologists are willing to admit the many similarities of man and (other) animals but they like to ask, "Is he *only* (or *merely*) an animal? Is he rigidly bound by the laws that determine the lives and reactions of the lower forms of life? After all, he has language and self-consciousness. He can learn, and pass on his learning to his descendants. He can make inventions and change his way of life. Do not these striking human characteristics exempt him from the general laws of biology?" Such questions cannot be lightly brushed aside.

From his demostatic model Malthus deduced that if the population of Great Britain were to rise, then the amount of misery would necessarily increase. Unfortunately for his theory, history dealt hardly with this particular prediction. In the 36 years that Malthus lived after the first edition of his essay both the population *and* the prosperity of Englishmen increased markedly, quite contrary to his prediction. In the century and a half since then the burgeoning of both population and well-being has been still more remarkable. What has been happening? Is modern man really exempt from the population principles that govern other forms of life?

The most meaningful way of grappling with this question is to take a long view of human existence. To begin with, we should note that the present phase of rapid population growth —about 2 percent per year—is most exceptional. *Homo sapiens* has been in existence at least since 50,000 B.C., at which time (it has been estimated) the human population exceeded one million. What average rate of increase would be required for that primeval population to grow to the 3.5 billion of today? Just 0.016 percent per annum—less than one one-hundredth the present rate of population growth. Was anyone aware that the population was growing at all during *most* of the last 50,000 years? It seems very unlikely. In any one community an epidemic might take off more than ten percent of the population in a single year; and, as the history of the Old Testament makes clear, there was always the threat of complete extermination by war. Fluctuations completely masked long term trends. The "population explosion" is a modern invention.

A growth rate of 0.016 percent per annum is only a statistical abstraction. Edward S. Deevey has pointed out a more meaningful way to view the demographic history of man as an assemblage of essentially static periods interrupted by times of relatively fast growth due to a "technological revolution." During a static period, as shown by Figure 9-3, the population would fluctuate about a constant mean, even as the temperature of a thermostated room fluc-

tuates about a set point. The number of people would tend always to be near the maximum determined by their technological ability to wrest a livelihood from the land. This equilibrium would remain essentially unchanged for hundreds, thousands, or even tens of thousands of years, until an important technological innovation occurred—say the invention of the bow and arrow, or the domestication of the hunting dog, or the cultivation of plants. With each improved means of gaining a livelihood the human population would move rapidly upward until it was near the new maximum made possible by the improved technology; there it would equilibrate about a new set point.

There have been many inventions and discoveries that have improved man's ability to earn a living. Without too great a violence to history we can subsume these under three headings: the tool-making revolution, the agricultural revolution, and the modern scientific-industrial revolution. We will never know their precise effects on population, but the simplified diagram of Figure 9-4 can be defended as a plausible picture. The scale is so coarse that the year to year fluctuations are completely ironed out. The tool-making revolution began even before the present species of man was evolved, with the development, hundreds of thousands of years ago, of flint knives (used for skinning animals) and spearheads. The resulting hunting economy was abruptly made obsolete with the domestication of plants, about 10,000 B.C. Some genetic selection of the plants and a few developments in the technology for growing them improved man's prospects somewhat in the next few thousand years, but the greatest revolution of all started about four hundred years ago—as near as one can date such a change—with the beginnings of modern science, modern methods of organizing work, and modern technology based on science. The rate of invention increased and even accelerated. Inventions in earlier ages had occurred at a pace implied by Aesop's saying, "Necessity is the mother of invention." Nowadays, however, there are thousands of people who make it their business to look for necessities that can serve as the excuse

Fig. 9-3. *How a technological revolution moves the demostatic set point to a higher level.*

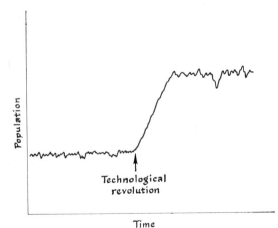

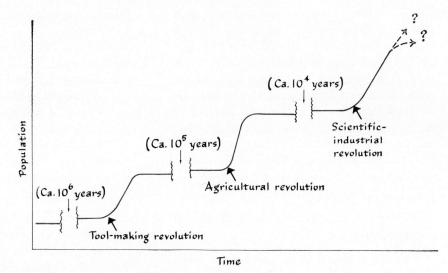

Fig. 9-4. *The three principal alterations of the set point of the demostat for* Homo sapiens. *The growth rate on each plateau is so slight as to yield a slope scarcely greater than zero; only by introducing a gap in a plateau can a change in set point between revolutions be made visible.*

for invention, or look for uses for things that have already been invented. What a fantastically different world ours is from that of five thousand or even five hundred years ago! As Alfred North Whitehead said, "The greatest invention of the nineteenth century was the invention of the method of invention."

Now we see how Malthus came a cropper. His demostatic model of population dynamics is adequate for describing the situation of man on earth for probably 99 percent of the time. But Malthus had the professional misfortune to live in the middle of the most rapid revolution of all times, and he didn't know it. Hence the temporary falseness of his particular predictions, which led to a general denial of his whole theory.

70. Is There a New Set Point in Man's Future?

Men quite naturally assume that what has been true for all of their lives will always be true. Only a knowledge and respect for history and theory can correct for the errors such natural assumptions produce. Because science and tech-

nology have continually moved the demostatic set point upward for the last four hundred years many men assume that this upward movement will continue forever. But there have been technological revolutions before, and they have come to an end. What reason do we have to think that this one is endless?

Space! some way—we shall go out into space and populate an infinite universe. Possibly; but we must distinguish between migration and colonization. It is remotely possible that we may colonize extra-terrestrial bodies, though the difficulties are greater than the tax-paying public is encouraged to appreciate. The planet Mars is about as hospitable to human life as an earthly mountain twice the height of Mt. Everest, which is hardly over-crowded yet. All other solar planets are even less favorable to life. As for the planets of other stars, they are at fantastic distances. The nearest star is Alpha Centauri—4.3 light-years away.* To accelerate the weight required to a speed that will get a human being that far in less than a lifetime requires many times the energy needed to keep the same man or woman alive on earth for an entire life-

---
* 9-3. How many kilometers is that? How many miles? (Use Appendixes 3 & 4.)

time. Therefore extra-terrestrial migration is no answer to the population explosion. Though some few humans may take off to found colonies on the planets of other stars, most of us must adjust our lives to the limitations of the earth. Sooner or later the earthly population must take up once more the responsibility of life under conditions of demostatic stability, and this time for good. If we act rationally—and it is by no means a foregone conclusion that we shall—two questions must be answered:

1. At what level shall we fix the set point?
2. What forms of corrective feedback should we encourage?

What forms of corrective feedback are available? We cannot list them all, but abstracting from human history and our observations of populations of other species we can say that the following are the most important choices available to us:

> Starvation
> Warfare
> Epidemic diseases
> Social disorganization
> Celibacy
> Continence in marriage
> Birth control
>> Rhythm methods
>> Appliance methods
>> Chemical methods
>> Abortion
>> Sterilization
> Infanticide
> Ritual homicide of adults

Surely no one would argue that all of these methods are equally desirable. We can reject most of them; but we cannot reject all of them. If, aghast at the thought of taking responsibility, we reject all the characteristically human methods of controlling population, then population will be controlled by natural, animal methods—starvation and the animal conflict found in the utter disorganization of human societies reduced to the starvation level. If we refuse to take human responsibility, Malthus' "misery and vice," in the simplest sense, will produce demographic stability at an inhuman level.

Questions and Problems

9-4. Make a list of the **boldface** terms in this chapter. Write out a definition or description of each. Compare your work with the text.

‡9-5. Until about four hundred years ago the lending of money at interest was called **usury** and was condemned by the Christian church. Now we use the condemnatory term "usury" only for "excessive" interest. The economist John Maynard Keynes (1883–1946) has suggested that we may some day return to the earlier view. Develop a line of argument supporting Keynes' position.

9-6. "The concept of 'carrying capacity' involves a tautology and therefore is scientifically indefensible." How would you answer that argument?

‡9-7. Solve equation (1) for t.

‡9-8. Give the general expression for finding the doubling time, t_2. (Set $N_0 = 1$, which means $\log N_0 = 0$; $N = 2$.)

‡9-9. Solve equation (1) for i.

9-10. Prepare a table of doubling times (like Table 9-1) to run from 0.1 percent to 1.0 percent, by tenths of a percent.

‡9-11. Assume that "standing room" for a human being is an area of 60 cm by 30 cm. What would be the standing-room population of the land area of the world? (See Appendix 4.)

‡9-12. Assume that the present world population is 3.5×10^9, and that the rate of increase is a uniform 2 percent per annum, without acceleration. How long will it be before there is "standing room only"?

9-13. If it were possible to convert the entire earth to human beings, what would the population be? (Assume average weight of people —adults and children—is 50 kg; use Appendix 4.)

9-14. If it were possible to convert the entire mass of the earth to human protoplasm, starting with a population of 3.5×10^9 people and multiplying uniformly at 2 percent per year, when would growth necessarily come to a stop?

9-15. Plot the population of the United States from 1800 to the present time, on semilog paper. (Data recorded in Table 9-2.) How

TABLE 9-2 *Population, in Millions, of the United States, Exclusive of Alaska and Hawaii.*

YEAR	POPULATION
1800	5.3
1810	7.2
1820	9.6
1830	12.9
1840	17.1
1850	23.2
1860	31.4
1870	38.6
1880	50.2
1890	62.9
1900	76.0
1910	92.0
1920	105.7
1930	122.7
1940	131.7
1950	150.7
1960	178.5

can you tell the growth rate has not remained constant? Can you correlate changes with known historical factors?

9-16. The U.S. Federal census officially announced that the American frontier came to an end in 1890. Is there any graphical correlate of this official fact?

9-17. Graph the data of Table 9-3 on the same piece of semilog paper used for Prob. 9-15. Has the growth rate of *any* of the regions graphed been constant?

TABLE 9-3 *Population, in Millions, of the World and Several Regions. Carr-Saunders' Estimates to 1900; United Nations Data Thereafter.*

DATE	EUROPE AND ASIATIC U.S.S.R.	ASIA, EXCLUDING U.S.S.R.	LATIN AMERICA	WORLD TOTAL
1650	103	327	12	545
1750	144	475	11	728
1800	192	597	19	906
1850	274	741	33	1,171
1900	423	915	63	1,608
1920	485	997	92	1,834
1930	530	1,069	110	2,008
1940	579	1,173	132	2,216
1950	594	1,272	162	2,406
1960	641	1,665	208	2,972

9-18. Which region had the greatest growth rate for the entire period recorded?

9-19. Which region had the greatest growth rate for the twentieth century?

9-20. For the decade 1950-1960 list the regions in the order of growth rate, with the fastest listed first.

9-21. As completely as you can, account for the surges in population growth rate of the various regions shown after 1950.

‡9-22. The crude birth rate is the number of births per year per thousand population. Assume that the fertility of a population remains unchanged, i.e., that the average number of children produced by each woman during her lifetime does not change. Suppose the crude death rate is markedly diminished: What will happen to the crude birth rate? Explain.

9-23. "Any factor which lowers the birth rate necessarily alleviates the population problem." True or false? Explain.

‡9-24. To escape the earth an object must have a velocity of 11.2 km per second, called the "escape velocity." (a) At this velocity, how long would it take to get to Alpha Centauri? (b) How fast is this in miles per hour?

‡9-25. You read in the newspaper that it is proposed to put up into the sky a communications

satellite which will circle the earth once every 40 minutes, remaining in a usable orbit for 3 years. Instantly, you know something is wrong with the report. What?

9-26. To reach Alpha Centauri in one generation (commonly taken as a third of a century) what would have to be the *average* speed of a spaceship? (a) Give the answer in km/sec. (b) What multiple of the escape velocity is this? (c) What is it in m.p.h.?

9-27. Consider the negative feedbacks listed toward the end of §70. Rewrite the list in the order of desirability as you see it, with the most desirable at the head of the list, the least desirable at the tail. Compare your list with that of, say, ten other people. What seem to be the most consistent and significant differences? How do you think these differences of opinion might be reconciled?

Readings

My *Population, Evolution and Birth Control* (San Francisco and London: W. H. Freeman and Company, 1964) has a collection of classical and modern contributions to population theory, as well as accounts of the development of the controversy over birth control.

Scientific American Offprints

144. LaMont C. Cole. *The Ecosphere*

601. Sherwood L. Washburn. *Tools and Human Evolution*

605. Robert J. Braidwood. *The Agricultural Revolution*

608. Edward S. Deevey, Jr. *The Human Population*

619. William L. Langer. *The Black Death*

10

Stabilizing Selection

71. Puzzle: The Stability of Species

The idea of evolution is very old. Since classical Greek times men have occasionally speculated that perhaps all living things are related to each other as cousins are related to one another, only more remotely. But though we can find many statements of the idea before Charles Darwin, we give little credit or attention to his predecessors, for two reasons. First, we note that the idea of evolution never really caught on until the publication of Darwin's *Origin of Species* in 1859; it was merely one possible view of the world. Secondly, Darwin was the first to propose in full detail a mechanism to account for evolution, supporting it with a body of evidence that for the first time "staggered" the intellectual world, to use one of Darwin's favorite words. A few men before him had glimpsed the same mechanism, but they had described it in such a tentative, cautious way that what they said had little enduring impact.

Darwin's greatest contribution was not the idea of evolution but a logical mechanism that could bring it about; and this mechanism does not necessarily cause change, but, in fact, most of the time it prevents change. This striking fact escaped most of Darwin's contemporaries. One of his many critics "refuted" him by asking him how could he account for the fact that the ostriches depicted in ancient Egyptian documents look exactly like those we see today,

some four thousand years later? If evolution is true, the critic asked, why haven't ostriches changed in this long time?

This question is of far more fundamental importance than the critic realized, and Darwinian theory is eminently competent to answer it. How in the world have ostriches managed to stay the same over so long a period of time? This is a deep question. We are protected from seeing the puzzle by the conventional wisdom of such sayings as "Like begets like." When we stop to think of it we know the cliché does not subsume the whole truth. Like begets like—but not always, and not exactly; and it is the error in the act of reproduction that creates the problem that Darwin solved.

We can put the problem in modern terms. The DNA content of ostrich cells has not yet been determined, but from the data in Table 6-3 we would estimate that there must be at least 10^9 nucleotides per ostrich genome. This means 10^9 units of information that must be exactly reproduced and passed on to the next generation if like is to beget like. In a million vulnerable loci there is ample opportunity for some change to take place, even if the probability of change at any one locus is very low. In a word, we would be astounded if each newly born ostrich did not contain at least one new mutation. Since mutants breed true most of the time, as the generations pass we would expect more and more unusual types of ostriches to appear, as mutations accumulate and are assorted into new combinations by the process of sexual reproduction. Lacking any counteracting force, we would expect that only a tiny minority of the ostriches of today would look anything like those known to Cheops or Queen Nefertiti. To explain the constancy of the species over many millennia we must find some process that acts counter to the dispersive force of mutation. This is the process that Darwin found: he called it **natural selection.**

72. Answer: The Phenostat

The mechanism that maintains the constancy of a species can be fitted into a cybernetic diagram of the type used previously in discussing thermostats and demostats. Let us first remind ourselves that any natural population is variable with respect to any measurable characteristic (height, weight, etc.) If we take a large sample of the population and measure it we find that the record of these measurements can be summarized in a **frequency curve** of the sort shown in Figure 10-1. The most frequent class produces the **mode** of the curve—the high point. The curve illustrated is a *unimodal* curve, but a curve may have more than one mode. For example, if the sexes are not separated, the frequency curve for height in humans is bimodal.

The unimodal curve shown in the figure is often said to be "bell-shaped." The theoretical

basis for this curve was first worked out by the great German mathematician K. F. Gauss (1777–1855); hence this distribution curve is often called a **Gaussian curve.** Gauss discovered that it fitted the distribution of errors made in taking astronomical observations. The Gaussian curve has also been found to apply to countless distributions of metric characteristics in nature. Because it is such a common distribution it is often called the **normal distribution;** but we should not suppose that it is the only natural one. In the typically Gaussian distribution the curve is symmetrical about the modal axis; in such cases the **arithmetic mean** ("average") corresponds to the modal value. In the discussion to follow this type of symmetric curve is, for convenience, implicitly assumed, though the conclusions reached do not depend on this assumption.

We start with the common sense notion that for any species, with respect to any measurable characteristic, there is probably a best value. Later, we will present objective confirmation of this notion, but for the moment we will just assume it. That is, with respect to the weight of ostriches we suspect that the average weight of the birds is probably about the best weight for birds in their environment, living the sort of life they do. This weight we will call the "fittest" weight—fittest to survive. We suspect that animals much larger are probably under some disadvantage, perhaps because they are not so fleet of foot. Contrariwise, unusually small animals may suffer from some other disadvantage, perhaps being less successful in intraspecies combat. Without committing ourselves to detail, we postulate that there is a set point for each measurable characteristic, as shown in Figure 10-2. Whenever the mean weight of a population rises much above this set point, **differential mortality** soon brings the mean back down to the set point. Similarly, the corrective feedback of differential mortality can correct also for divergence in the other direction. It is as though the variable characteristics of the species were kept within normal bounds by some sort of invisible **phenostat** (just as population size is controlled by a demostat).

Fig. 10-1. *A Gaussian ("normal") distribution. In a symmetrical distribution the arithmetic mean ("average") coincides with the modal value.*

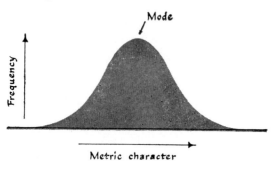

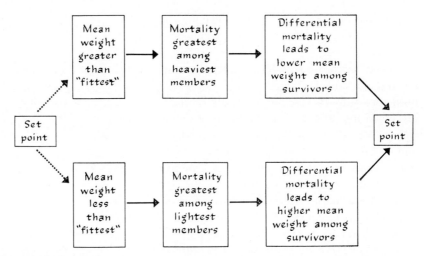

Fig. 10-2. *The phenostatic control of a species.*

The root *pheno-* is derived from a Greek word that means *to appear,* or *to show* (as in *phenomenon*). It is well known that the visible, measurable characteristics of an individual are determined by both hereditary and environmental characteristics. In a constant environment (if such exists!), differences among individuals will be solely of genetic origin. Developing in a variable environment even genetically identical individuals (assuming *they* exist) will come to differ one from another. In the real world, both heredity and environment vary simultaneously. Unless we have reason to think otherwise we assume that they vary independently of each other. This means that we cannot know *a priori* the relative importance of heredity and environment in determining the variation shown by any particular individual; heredity and environment are *confounded,* as a statistician would say. "Nature" is also unable to discriminate between the genetic and the environmental causes of the final result. A large ostrich is a large ostrich, whether by virtue of genes for large size or because it enjoyed an unusually good food supply as a youngster. "Nature" sees only appearances, the word appearances being understood in the broadest way to include not only that which may be seen by means of light rays but all objectively determinable aspects. Hereditary information is not directly readable, hence it would be inappropriate to speak of the "genostat" of the Darwinian model: "phenostat" is the proper term.

It should be noted that the differential *mortality* assumed in the model given in Figure 10-2 is not the most general kind of negative feedback, but is instead a special kind. To illustrate the more general case let us examine the working of selection in seals. In these polygynous animals there are bloody struggles between the males at the beginning of each breeding season to determine which males shall own the harems. The males that lose are seldom killed; they are banished to bachelors' quarters, and denied the right to breed. A male who lives a long life without ever winning the right to breed has no more effect on the genetic constitution of the next generation than he would have had had he been killed in his first battle. Such failure to breed is sometimes spoken of as "genetic death." This is clearly only a metaphor, however, and perhaps too vivid a one. We suspect that an individual male seal (given understanding and the choice) would see a considerable distinction between a genetic death and a literal one. The example of the seals should, however, make clear that **differential fertility** is the primary corrective feedback of the phenostatic system; differential mortality is merely one way of producing it.*

---

* 10-1. Include this improvement in a revised version of the phenostat.

The role of the environment in pruning the more aberrant members from the population reminded Darwin of the activities of animal and plant breeders. A hobbyist who maintains a particular breed of pigeons year after year must constantly *cull* the birds that do not measure up to the "standard of the breed" (the set point). He selects. With this human model in mind Darwin coined the term "natural selection" to indicate the effect of "Nature" in culling aberrant forms and so maintaining the constancy of the species. In response to critical objections, Darwin denied that he had personified nature; "natural selection," he said, is only one of those metaphorical expressions that "are almost necessary for brevity."

73. The Meaning of "Survival of the Fittest"

At about the same time that Darwin was publishing his observations on natural selection the popular philosopher Herbert Spencer (1820–1903) independently coined the phrase "survival of the fittest" to refer to the results of natural selection. It is a memorable phrase, and one which has led to considerable misunderstanding and needless controversy. Rather than unearth old arguments we will show the statistical reality to which the phrase refers.

Figure 10-3 should be read from the bottom upwards. The bottom curve represents the distribution curve of the young of the species. In the process of growing up many of the organisms perish, so that the second curve includes fewer individuals. (Actually, the difference between the first and second curve will usually be much greater; consider the oyster which produces half a billion offspring per pair, only two of which, on the average, reach breeding age.) In a population which has already stabilized about its set point the mean of the second

Fig. 10-3. *Stabilizing selection: the statistical reality underlying the phrase "survival of the fittest." (Read from bottom upward.)*

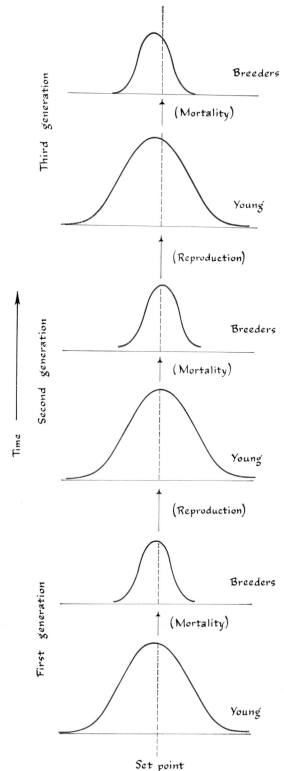

curve will be the same as that of the first. The distribution will be different, however: the post-mortality curve will have *proportionately* fewer of the extreme values in it. *Survival is biased in favor of values near the set point:* this is the real meaning of the phrase "survival of the fittest."

To continue with Figure 10-3, in the act of reproduction the amount of variability is increased. There are two reasons for this: mutation, and the recombination of genes that is brought about by sexual reproduction. As a result, the young of the next generation begin with a distribution curve much like the original one of the parental generation (3rd Gaussian curve). Again, pre-adult mortality diminishes the size of the population and diminishes the frequency of the extreme values disproportionately;—and so on.

It should be clear that the "fittest" is determined by the environment. The results of an interesting experiment carried out by F. B. Sumner illustrate this point well. Large numbers of mosquito fish of the genus *Gambusia* were exposed to predation by penguins. Two different color variants were used, light and dark; and tanks of two correspondingly different backgrounds (light and dark) served as the environments. The results are shown in Figure 10-4. Against a light background 61 percent of the light fish survived as compared with only 39 percent of the dark. When the background was dark, 74 percent of the dark fish survived, but only 26 percent of the light. The set point is determined by the environment. "Fittest" is defined by the environment; there is no such thing as an absolute "fittest."

Notice that being appropriately colored does not give absolute protection. Even against a dark background, 26 percent of the dark fish lost their lives. There is always an element of chance in mortality; that is, survival is in part **random,** and in part **biased** (in favor of the "fittest"). The preacher in Ecclesiastes (9:11) probably had something of this sort in mind when he said:

I returned, and saw under the sun, that the race is not to the swift, nor the battle to the strong, neither yet bread to the wise, nor yet riches to men of understanding, nor yet favor to men of skill; but time and chance happeneth to them all.

Fig. 10-4. *"Survival of the fittest" as a function of the environment. Percentages stand for percentage of fish surviving exposure to predation in the different environments.* (*Based on F. B. Summer,* Am. Naturalist (*1935*) **69:**245-266.)

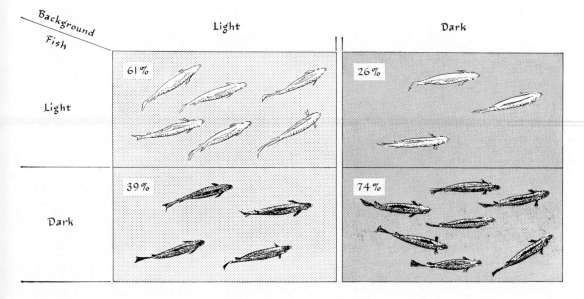

The sense of this passage surely implies that "not necessarily" should be inserted in each of the predications, e.g., "that the race is *not necessarily* to the swift . . ." etc. Or, more stiltedly, "it is *only statistically true* that the race is to the swift . . ." However worded, it is a matter of some importance in human affairs that this insight not be lost. The mere survival of a particular individual is not proof that he is one of the fittest.

Mortality is both random and biased. In the early days of evolution it was sometimes argued that if most mortality was a random matter natural selection could not exert its effect. "Since 499,999,998 of the offspring of a pair of oysters are going to die anyway, what difference does it make which 2 out of the half billion survive?" The implied argument is fallacious. It is possible to prove rigorously the truth of the following

Fundamental principle of natural selection:
When mortality has both random and biased components, the bias is always selectively effective, no matter how great the random component.

Genetic and environmental factors are always confounded in the Gaussian distribution. The confounding slows down the rate at which natural selection achieves its effects, but it does not nullify it as a force.

74. The Slow Growth of the Idea of Stabilizing Selection

Selection can cause either a change in the mean of a species, or it can keep the mean unchanged, depending on whether the environmentally de-fined set point is changing or not. Selection with change is the subject of the next chapter; selection with stability, which we have been discussing here, is called **stabilizing selection.** This idea has an interesting history which raises some puzzling questions about the rate of scientific progress.

Stabilizing selection may seem rather "obvious" now, but apparently the first person to clearly define its operation (though without modern terminology) was an obscure English naturalist named Edward Blyth (1810–1873). The extent to which Blyth's publications in 1835 and 1837 influenced the development of Darwin's thought is a difficult and disputed historical question. It is a remarkable fact that Blyth considered only the selection that produces stability, hesitating to consider the possibility that selection might also produce change.

The idea that species might change was heavily charged with emotion in Victorian days. For reasons that seem insufficient to us now it was felt that belief in the stability of species was a necessary part of religious belief. An area of resistance naturally provokes extended argument. It was natural therefore that Darwin, in his *Origin of Species,* should have emphasized change (which occurs only occasionally) and minimized stability, which is the rule. He did not even clearly distinguish the two sorts of selection. Stabilizing selection fell into the background of the early Darwinian discussions.

Of the two sorts of selection, stabilizing selection is the easier to demonstrate. The hypothesis of stabilizing selection has a simple, testable consequence which is illustrated in Figure 10-5. The population of individuals selectively removed from a population should form a **bimodal** distribution curve, that is, one with a

Fig. 10-5. *Distribution curves connected with the process of stabilizing selection.*

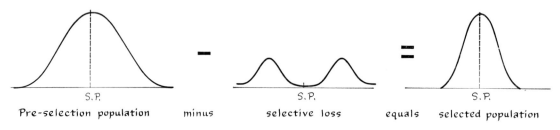

| Pre-selection population | minus | selective loss | equals | selected population |

hump on either side of the set point, as shown. Not until 1898 was this prediction tested. In that year H. C. Bumpus (1862–1943) reported some observations made at Brown University following an uncommonly severe storm of snow, rain, and sleet. 136 English sparrows were retrieved from the campus and brought into the laboratory where 72 birds revived. Bumpus did a comparative study of those that survived and those that did not, and found that the population of dead birds was characterized by the inclusion of birds with: (a) the greatest length and the least length; (b) greatest wingspread and least wingspread; (c) longest cranium and shortest cranium; and (d) heaviest weight, and one of the two lightest in weight. Some statistical variables (e.g., length of tibiotarsus) were distributed randomly among the two groups. It was clear, however, that mortality was at least in part biased against the extremes. As Bumpus put it: "Natural selection is most destructive of those birds which have departed most from the ideal type, and its activity raised the general standard of excellence by favoring those birds which approach the structural ideal."

Bumpus' study is now regarded as a classic in the establishment of Darwinian theory, but, curiously, at the time it was cited by many as a refutation of evolution. The critics reasoned thus: Darwin says that evolution is caused by natural selection; but in this study we see that natural selection produces stability; therefore the Darwinian theory is false.

The importance of stabilizing selection did not come to be sufficiently appreciated until the 1940's. Within a decade its importance was independently recognized by three different students, who signalized the event by christening the process with three different names: *stabilizing selection* (I. I. Schmalhausen), *centripetal selection* (G. G. Simpson), and *normalizing selection* (C. H. Waddington). A process that is named is always easier to recognize (even if it has too many names!). Following the christening of stabilizing selection its reality was attested to by a large number of studies. Stabilizing selection associated with growing from juvenile to adult has been demonstrated in sev-

eral different groups of snakes and lizards, for example. In these animals, the number of scales (in the head region, for instance) do not change as a given individual matures. Yet the adult population shows much less variability in scale number than does the juvenile population. Why an individual with a number of scales near the mean of the species should be competitively superior to ones with more or fewer is quite beyond our present powers of explanation. This example is quite typical of the multitude of puzzles nature throws in the way of biologists. We can easily ascertain the position of the set point, but seldom can we explain why it is where it is.

75. The Inescapability of Stabilizing Selection

More than a century elapsed from the time of Blyth's first description of the process of stabilizing selection to the final explicit incorporation of the idea into biological theory. Why so long? A historical question of the form, "Why didn't it happen sooner?" can probably never be given an entirely satisfactory answer, but it is worthwhile trying to answer this question as best we can, for this is undoubtedly not the last time a logically simple idea will have its progress into man's habitual thinking patterns impeded.

Impeded by what? In the case of the idea of stabilizing selection two plausible suggestions can be made. The first is the Idea of Progress —the idea that things are changing and getting better, constantly. This quite modern idea rapidly captured men's minds in the nineteenth century. Both in and out of science the seduction of the idea of change turned men's eyes away from stability, which just did not seem quite as interesting or as much worth investigating. Men did not deny stability; they simply ignored it all too often.

The second impediment that can be suggested is the fear men felt that the principles of biology might have direct applicability to *Homo sapiens*. That man is a rather special animal we need not deny; but an important part of the intellectual progress in the last two centuries has been concerned precisely with the elucidation of the ways in which man's problems have their roots in the nonhuman world. Every step of this progress has been taken reluctantly. Darwin hesitated twenty years before publishing his theory of natural selection, and when he did publish it he included only a single paragraph —the third-to-last in the book—which said anything at all about man. This is the entire paragraph:

In the distant future I see open fields for far more important researches. Psychology will be based on a new foundation, that of the necessary acquirement of each mental power and capacity by gradation. Light will be thrown on the origin of man and his history.

There was an immediate outcry that Darwin had said that man was descended from apes and hence was presumably not significantly distinguishable from them—which he had not said at all. But the volume of the outcry showed that Darwin's long hesitancy in publishing was justified.

Are there implications of the theory of natural selection that Darwin never discussed? One suspects so; and other biologists have probably been equally hesitant. Knowing what Freud has taught us about unconscious repression, it is not unreasonable for us to suspect that an investigator may have his vision clouded by a dimly felt anxiety that his line of research may threaten some of the conclusions of conventional wisdom. A fact that is felt to be threatening may have to be discovered several times before it becomes stabilized into the conceptual framework of science—recall the three christenings of the fact of stabilizing selection, a century after the first timid announcement of its discovery. Even as late as 1963 the zoologist Ernst Mayr spoke of "this somewhat elusive concept" in referring to the almost tautological fact of stabilizing selection.

Is mankind governed by the process of stabilizing selection?—this is probably the question we fear to ask. The answer can be bluntly put: *of course.* For a single line of evidence, examine the data shown in Table 10-1 (p. 181). The fate of more than nine thousand babies during the first ten days of their life was followed. Of those who weighed less than two kilograms at birth almost half died within ten days. This does not surprise us, for most babies this size have been born prematurely, that is to say, abnormally early. But, in running your eye down the column of figures printed in color, notice that the distribution of the remainder fits the bimodal curve given in Figure 10-5. That is, not only are very small babies less fit to survive, but so also are very large babies. There is, in other words, a set point for human weight-at-birth. Undoubtedly there is a multitude of other set points for human characteristics, most of which have not yet been ascertained.

The idea of a "golden mean" goes back to antiquity. The saying, "Nothing in excess," attributed to Solon in the sixth century B.C., evokes our praise—but is it more than lip service? Ours is the age of bigger and better; we find it hard to strive for anything less than the superlative. This may be one of the sources of the resistance to the idea of stabilizing selection.

Probably a more important aspect of our resistance springs from our dislike of the way stability is achieved—by losses, by elimination, by death. It is one of the glories of our age that we have eliminated literally millions of deaths from disease that would have occurred each year in a comparable population of four centuries ago. Losses that were regarded as "natural" losses before Pasteur and Koch are no longer tolerated. Intoxicated with success, we dream of eliminating all losses. Is this possible?

Let us look again at the way in which sense is maintained in the message of heredity. We can diagram the system as shown in Figure 10-6. The set point represents the "normal" genotype of the species. Most of the time, most of this hereditary message is successfully duplicated in the DNA replication process. But now and again one or more nucleotides are al-

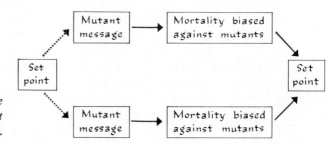

Fig. 10-6. *The cybernetic scheme whereby the hereditary message is kept constant from generation to generation.*

tered. The DNA replication process contains no provision for the elimination of errors in the message. At the nuclear level, errors are reproduced as faithfully as are the correct versions of the message. To use an analogy, it is as though we have a print shop that is well supplied with almost-perfect typesetters each of whom uses the type set by another man as "copy" (model) for his own typesetting;—*but the printshop has no proofreaders.* The end result of such an uncorrected serial process would be a steady degradation of the message.

There is, however, a negative feedback in the biological system (a proofreader external to the printshop, as it were). The external proofreader we call natural selection. This agent acts not at the nuclear level, but at the environmental level, measuring the individual against a thousand subtle criteria set by the environment. The judgment that is made is sometimes of the black or white sort—life or death—but more often is a merely quantitative judgment, a slightly depressed fertility imposed on the mutants, for example. However gentle or severe the judgment of nature may be, the end result is the same—a steady elimination of mutants, a steady purification of the hereditary message. In a constant environment, the opposing processes of mutation and natural selection reach a balance which produces a fairly constant amount of loss in each generation. In the human species, between two and four percent of all babies are born deformed to a significant extent, the percentage depending in part on one's definition of "significant." Of this loss, it is estimated that about half is attributable to environmental accidents, and half to defects in the hereditary message. That is, about one percent of all babies

born have a significantly defective message. The only corrective feedback available for the removal of the defects is differential fertility (which may or may not involve differential mortality). Losses are inevitable.

The losses due to mutation are actually much greater than these figures would indicate. In all organisms, the heaviest numerical losses take place at the earliest stages of development, whether the losses are caused by chance or by defective heredity. In a placental mammal like man it is not easy to detect losses in the earliest stages since these cause death and expulsion of the embryo before the woman is sure she is pregnant. A corroboration of this statement is found in the work of A. T. Hertig, John Rock, and E. Adams, 1956. For medical reasons connected with the health of the mother, the reproductive organs had to be removed from a number of married women. These were examined for embryos and a total of 34 in the first 17 days of development were collected. Of these, 13 were visibly abnormal—38 percent. There was no reason to suspect that the medical condition of the mother had influenced the development of the embryo. The study-sample was small, but since the true number of defectives would no doubt be augmented by more subtle biochemical aberrations without visible morphological correlates, 38 percent is probably an underestimate of the proportion of fertilized eggs that carry defective hereditary messages. The vast majority of these defective embryos are eliminated long before birth.

This finding of Hertig, Rock, and Adams has surprised many people, though few geneticists. The loss seems shockingly high—but should we really be disturbed by it? If loss is expressed only in terms of numbers, a loss of 38 percent sounds large. But what do we mean by the word *loss?* How do we measure it? In the human context these are deep questions with which mankind must grapple in the years to come.

Questions and Problems

10-2. Make a list of the **boldface** terms in this chapter. Write out a definition or description of each. Compare your work with the text.

10-3. Tell briefly the contribution of each of the following men, and the approximate date: Darwin, Blyth, Spencer, and Bumpus.

‡10-4. "The phrase 'survival of the fittest' is meaningless because it hides a tautology; the fittest are those that survive, which brings us right back around the circle to where we started." How can this objection be answered?

10-5. To the experiments with the mosquito fish and penguins (§73) someone objects that it does not demonstrate natural selection because it involves the unnatural bringing together of species that live thousands of miles apart in nature. Is this a valid objection? Explain.

‡10-6. Regarding the same experiments it is objected that the conclusions reached are not justified for, had the experiments been run long enough, the penguins would have caught *all* the fish, regardless of color; hence there is no selective advantage to color. How would you answer this?

10-7. An experimenter wishes to select for intelligence in rats. He subdivides, at random, a large population into two equal populations. Population A is maintained for many generations under very uniform conditions of food, temperature and housing. The environmental conditions are frequently changed for Population B. The training, testing, and selection methods are identical. In which population would you predict the greater progress toward genetic uniformity with respect to intelligence? Explain.

10-8. What, in your opinion, are the corrective feedbacks for the phenostatic control of height and weight in humans? Explain your hypotheses.

‡10-9. What, in your opinion, are the negative feedbacks for metabolic rate in humans? Explain your hypotheses.

10-10. Do you think that intelligence is phenostatically controlled in humans? What are the negative feedbacks? How would you gather evidence on these points?

10-11. Do you think it desirable that intelligence be phenostatically controlled in *Homo sapiens?* Your reasons?

10-12. Comment on the statistical reasoning embedded in the following quotation from Robert Maynard Hutchins (*Saturday Evening Post,* 15 Aug. 1942; p. 71): "Not intelligence but money decides whether the high-school graduate shall go to college. . . . A study in Kansas revealed that a majority of superior high-school graduates were not in college. Most of those who were presumably best fitted by mental ability to receive training in higher institutions were not candidates for such training, and 40 percent of those who did enter college had a mental rating below the average of their group."

10-13. In *Understanding Human Nature* (p. 118) Alfred Adler (1928) said: "It is well known that eight to ten-year-old children of well-to-do families are much more quick witted than poor children of the same age. This does not mean that the children of the wealthy are more talented but that the cause for this difference lies entirely in the circumstances of their previous life." Discuss.

‡10-14. If you will graph the data shown in Column (3) of Table 10-1 you will find they produce a uni-modal curve, rather than a bi-

TABLE 10-1 *Differential Mortality of Newborn Babies in the First Ten Days.* (*Source: Hosemann's Data in Mary N. Karn and L. S. Penrose, 1951.* Ann. Eug., **16**:147–164.)

(1) WEIGHT AT BIRTH, IN KILOGRAMS	(2) NUMBER BORN	(3) NUMBER OF DEATHS	(4) PERCENT OF GROUP DYING WITHIN 10 DAYS	(5) SURVIVAL PER 1000
Less than 2.0	53	24	45.3	547
2.0–2.49	275	24	8.7	913
2.5–2.99	1534	35	2.3	977
3.0–3.49	3779	62	1.64	984
3.5–3.99	2692	42	1.56	984
4.0–4.49	690	18	2.6	974
More than 4.5	123	8	6.5	935
Totals	9146	213	2.3	977

modal curve like the middle curve of Figure 10-5. Does this mean, then, that the reasoning in §75 is erroneous? Explain.

10-15. "Since the weight of the baby is affected by the mother's diet (an environmental effect) we are not justified in assuming that selective mortality of newborn children will have any genetic effect." Comment.

‡10-16. Examine Table 10-2. What is the set point for brood size in swifts? How is it maintained?

TABLE 10-2 *Survival of Young Swifts in Relation to Brood Size.* (*Source: C. Perrins, 1964.* Nature, **201**:1147–1148.)

BROOD SIZE	NO. OF BROODS	NO. OF YOUNG	NO. LOST	NO. FLEDGED PER BROOD
1	30	30	2	0.93
2	72	144	5	1.93
3	20	60	9	2.55
4	16	64	36	1.75

10-17. Is sterility ever favored by natural selection?

10-18. Women who have twins or triplets should outbreed the mothers of singlets. Yet only about 1 birth in 90 is multiple. How come?

10-19. What significance has the answer to 10-18 relative to the history of mankind?

‡10-20. It is commonly said in medical circles that 10 percent of all conceptions are terminated by spontaneous abortion. Is this a true measure of genetic error?

10-21. Consider two identical oyster beds, O and Y. A poacher steals 5×10^8 adult oysters from bed O. Another man removes 5×10^8 oyster eggs from bed Y. Which bed has its productivity more greatly affected? Explain.

10-22. From a strictly biological point of view, is the value of the life of an oyster independent of its age?

10-23. Is there any sense in which it can truly be said that the dying of 38 percent of the human population 17 days after conception is as serious a matter as the dying of 38 percent of the population of human 21-year-olds? Explain.

10-24. Note that the genetic message is protected against the disorganizing tendency of mutation by a corrective feedback *in the environment* (Fig. 10-6). Do you think it would be theoretically possible for the corrective feedback to be part of the genetic message?

10-25. If environmentally incurred losses are inevitable, is it preferable that they occur early or late? What is your personal opinion? Solicit the opinions of others. If there are differences, try to uncover the reasons for the differences.

Readings

Some insight into the origins of the idea of natural selection can be gained from Chapters 1-5 of my *Nature and Man's Fate.* Huxley and Kettlewell's *Charles Darwin and His World* is a splendidly illustrated brief introduction to the subject of this chapter and the next. The standard, and indeed only, account of Blyth's role is given by its discoverer, Loren Eiseley in the essay cited in the Bibliography.

11

Mechanisms of Evolution

76. Evolution Observed

The theory of evolution, though a scientific theory, leads to conclusions that lie in the realm of history—very distant history, in fact. The periods of time encompassed by historical evolution are immense—millions and even billions of years. One might therefore conclude that it would not be possible to observe evolution in the same sense that gravity may be observed, that is, in terms of processes taking place before our very eyes. Charles Darwin thought so when he praised a reviewer of his work for being "one of the very few who see that the change of species *cannot be directly proved"* (italics added). His conservatism was commendable; but we know now that Darwin was overcautious. We have, in the past hundred years, seen several species change "before our very eyes." The changes have not been great, it is true (no amoeba has changed to a dinosaur, for example). The changes have been only on a small scale, but they have been genuinely evolutionary changes none the less. One of the most interesting of these has been observed in certain species of European moths. Let's see what the story is.

The "peppered moth," *Biston betularia,* occurs in light and dark (*melanic*) forms, both of which are shown in Figure 11-1. The normal ("original") form is a light, peppered color. A specimen of the dark type was first captured in 1848, near Manchester, England, just 11 years

before the publication of the *Origin of Species.* In the years thereafter, in various parts of England, the relative frequency of the dark form was observed to increase until today, in some regions, only dark forms are found. Why the change?

The answer is almost self-evident from the photographs shown in Figure 11-1. In *A* we see a tree trunk of the sort found in rural England far from industrial centers: lichens covering the oak tree give it a variegated surface against which the lightly peppered moth is hard to see; the black form stands out prominently. By contrast, on trees growing in industrial areas, the lichens are killed and the trunk is blackened by soot; on such a tree (Fig. 11-1*B*) it is the black moth that is protectively colored, the light moth standing out "like a sore thumb." Birds that prey on the moths have been observed and photographed catching moths, and it has been proved that they bring about a differential mortality favoring the survival of the light forms in unpolluted woods and the dark forms in industrially blackened woods. The correlation of moth color with proximity to industries in Great Britain is striking, as Figure 11-2 shows.*

Evolutionary change in these moths has been a secondary consequence of human history. As the Industrial Revolution burgeoned, the smoke belched forth from factories blackened more

---

* 11-1. Striking, but not perfect. How would you explain the absence of dark forms around Plymouth?

Fig. 11-1. *Two color variants of the same species of moth* (Biston betularia) *in two different environments. Left: Tree trunk in an uncontaminated region; note how the light form of the moth harmonizes with the lichens.* Right: *A tree trunk from an industrial region; here the dark (melanic) form blends better with the background. (Courtesy H. B. D. Kettlewell.)*

and more of the countryside, killing the lichens on tree trunks and changing the selective conditions for the moths that rest on them. Gene mutation, an uncontrolled process, must always have been producing some melanic forms. Before the Industrial Revolution, such mutants must have been eliminated about as fast as they were produced. Once the English countryside became defaced by "progress," the melanic forms were adaptively superior to the peppered forms, and thus arose the phenomenon now called **industrial melanism,** which affects some seventy species of moths in England. The phenomenon is known also on the continent and in the United States, always in close proximity to industrial centers. Thus has man, even in the short period of modern history, affected, however unintentionally, the course of evolution.

77. Directional Selection

The process that accounts for the evolution of industrial melanism is diagrammatically explained in Figure 11-3. With the coming of industry the old set point for the color of the moths was replaced by a new one. The change in set point probably took place gradually, over many moth-generations, but for simplicity we diagram it as an instantaneous change. Selection biased in the direction of the new set point resulted in a progressive shift of the distribution curve of the population; during this period of change we speak of the selection as **directional selection.** Ultimately the mean of the population reached the new set point, following which the selection was merely stabilizing selection.

It is clear that the process of selection is no

Fig. 11-2. *Relative frequencies of dark and light forms of peppered moths in the British Isles. Note region of major industries. Solid sectors indicate dark forms, clear sectors the light. (After H. B. D. Kettlewell.)*

different in these two cases; the difference lies in the stability of the set point, or lack of it. Directional selection is sometimes called *progressive selection*. This term is somewhat objectionable because it raises the difficult question "What is progress?" Is it progress for moths to become darker? And, if coal is ultimately replaced by atomic fuels and the English moths become lighter, will that be a sort of retrograde evolution? Even the term directional evolution is not unobjectionable. It might be inferred that the direction is always the same, which is not necessarily so. In the evolution of horses, for example, prehistoric ancestors evolved at one

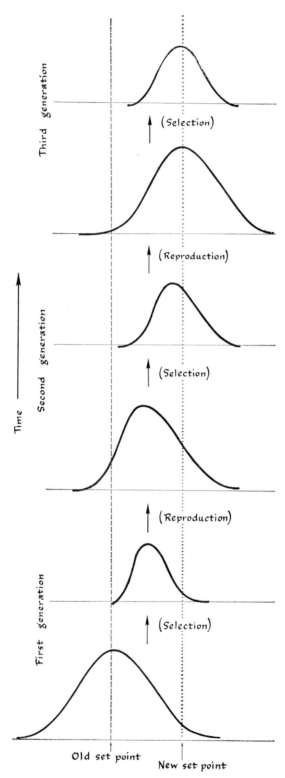

Fig. 11-3. *Directional selection.*

time toward larger size, at another time toward smaller, as the set point established by the environment changed from one geological age to another. There is no necessary direction to evolution. The relation, if any, of evolution to progress is subtle.

The change brought about by directional selection is called a **secular change** in the species. The word "secular" is derived from an old French word meaning a race, an age, or the world. It is generally contrasted with "sacred," the implication being that the latter is eternal, whereas the former changes or passes away. A change that takes place slowly and perhaps steadily in history, economics, or biology is called a secular change.

Secular changes in living things present, of course, problems in the field of **taxonomy,** the discipline that deals with the classification of organisms (Gr. *taxis* = arrangement + *nomos* = law). Carried sufficiently far, secular change produces great enough differences between the first and the last of a series of hereditarily related organisms so that taxonomists feel justified in applying different species-names to the extremes in the time series. How different the extremes must be to justify different specific names involves, of course, an arbitrary element in decision. In the example of the moths described above, the process has not yet gone so far.

78. Recent Secular Changes

Most secular changes in species take place very slowly, on the time scale of human history, for the simple reason that the secular changes in the environmentally defined set points take place with corresponding slowness. When, however, man deliberately modifies the environment, he often causes an environmental set point to change rapidly, thus sometimes causing a correspondingly rapid change in species. A few examples will be instructive.

Scale insects. Among the major pests of citrus trees in California are scale insects. Early in the twentieth century a means of killing them was developed: a tree would be completely enclosed by a tent within which hydrogen cyanide would be released. For a while this system worked admirably, but within a few years there appeared a mutant form of insect that could withstand the poison. By natural selection, this form was favored and it spread from one grove to another, thus putting an end to the use of cyanide fumigation. In fact, such mutants have appeared in three different species of scale insects, at different times and different places.

Houseflies. When the insecticide DDT was discovered, it was optimistically believed, for a while, that its use would shortly do away with the nuisance of houseflies. The illusion was speedily shattered. Around dairy barns, where the chemical had been used most generously (and where flies were most abundant), there soon were found DDT-resistant flies, which, by natural selection, rapidly replaced the standard type. The difference was due to mutation.

Bacteria. Penicillin is a marvelously effective killing agent for certain species of bacteria, but here, too, evolution has interfered with man's plans by producing mutant strains that are highly resistant to this antibiotic. The usefulness of other antibiotics is similarly limited.

We now see that evolution is not a mere hypothesis about the distant past, but rather that it is an ever-present fact which we must take into account in our daily living and planning. Confronted with a pest, we try to eliminate it by changing its environment. We are most likely to be successful if the change is great in extent, or rapid in rate. The extent of the change we can make is often limited by the tolerance of the organisms associated with the pest: too high a concentration of antibiotic, weed-killer, or insecticide may harm man, his crops, or his domestic animals. The success of a new "pesticide" * generally hinges on whether man can shift the environmentally defined set point farther or faster than the pest can achieve the necessary secular change. One way to thwart evolution is to cause more rapid alternations in

the set point than a species can possibly adjust to: thus do physicians use first one antibiotic then another in the treatment of a diseased patient. Another way is to create a complex new set point, for example, by using two different antibiotics simultaneously. Mutational adaptation is always an improbable event; the probability of two different mutations occurring at the same time in the same pest population is very much less than the probability of the occurrence of only one.

One other point needs to be made. When we find a DDT-resistant fly, we may be tempted to think of it as a sort of "Super-Fly." This is nonsense. It is the "fittest," but only in a DDT-treated environment. Take away the DDT, and the resistant fly turns out to be *less* vigorous, less "fit" than the "normal" fly. So also is it with cyanide-resistant scale insects and penicillin-resistant bacteria. Whatever the physiological mechanism involved in resistance, it is one that must, apparently, be paid for by a partial loss of some other element of physiological vigor.

79. The Multiplicity of Environments

In the laboratory study of biology there is a tendency to assume that species are uniform and constant. Physiologists commonly write about what *the* mouse or *the* rat will do under such and such circumstances. A laboratory worker often fails to become aware of the over-simplifications he is making because he works with strains of organisms that have a high degree of genetic uniformity.

In the field, things are otherwise. Both the organisms and the environments are diverse. A field biologist must be constantly aware of both diversities. One must never forget the interactions of organism and environment. The science that deals with these interactions is called **ecology** (Gr. *oikos,* house), a science that is concerned with all the interactions of an organism with its environment—which includes other species of living things.

The multiplicity of environments has been

---

* 11-2. What does this coined word mean? That is, what does the suffix *–cide* mean? Can you give other words with this suffix?

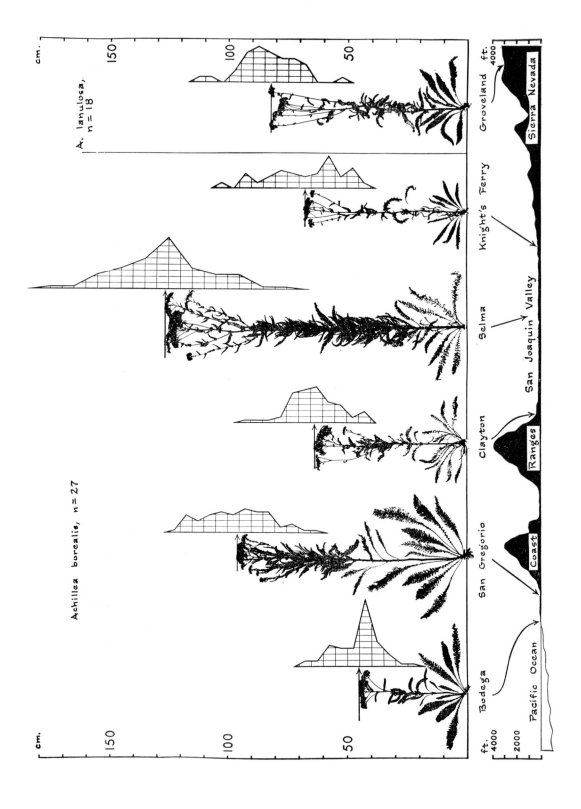

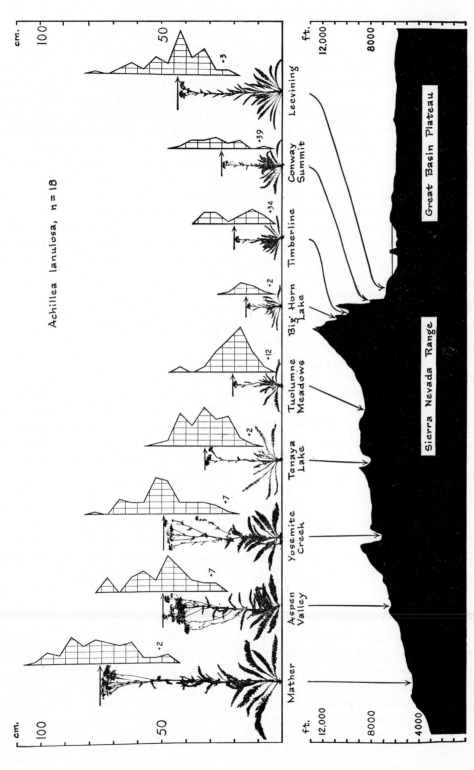

Fig. 11-4. *Variation with the genus Achillea, associated with a west-east transect. (After Clausen, Keck, and Hiesey, Pub. No. 581, Carnegie Institution of Washington.)*

well shown by some beautiful studies carried out with plants by J. Clausen, D. Keck, and W. M. Hiesey at the Carnegie Institution laboratories and field stations in California. Their results are worth examining in some detail at this point.

Yarrows of the genus *Achillea* are extremely widespread in the northern hemisphere; there are many species of these plants, and within a species there are often many distinguishable races. An east-to-west transect of California shows the variations indicated in Figure 11-4. In general, it will be noted, the greater the altitude, the shorter the plant. Are such differences due to heredity or environment? Fortunately, in plants, such a question can be settled very simply. It is possible to cut a plant into several different portions and plant these in different environments. Plants that are so derived from a single plant without the interposition of a sexual process are said to be members of the same **clone** (Gr. *klon* = twig, slip). Their heredity is identical; any differences that develop among them can be attributed to environment.

Figure 11-5 shows the result of planting clonal plants native to the coast at three different elevations: at Stanford, which is approximately at sea level; at Mather, about 4,600 feet; and at Timberline, at 10,000 feet. Figure 11-6 shows what happens when Mather clones are similarly distributed. Let us look at these two figures closely to see how many generalizations can be extracted from them. Several things should be noted: (1) Only one coastal plant transplanted to Timberline survived, and that but barely—showing that the Timberline races are genetically different. (2) Coastal plants transplanted to 4,600 feet are not only smaller, as we would expect from the environmental difference (shorter growing season at high altitude), but are smaller, on the average, than plants native to Mather growing at this elevation (Fig. 11-6)—again indicating genetic differences. (3) The comparative heights of different clones on the coast are only slightly related to their comparative heights in the new environment at 4,600 feet. A word like "height" may stand for but one "thing" in terms of measure-

ment, but it may stand for many "things" genetically; that is, height may be determined by many different genes, each with its own reaction pattern to new environments. (4) Mather races transplanted to the coast grow larger (environmental effect), but not so large, on the average, as coastal plants in that environment (genetic effect). (5) Mather plants are better able to survive transplantation to Timberline than are coastal plants, as we would expect, considering that the shift in the set point is less extreme. (6) The variability in Mather plants at Timberline is far greater than it is at their natural 4,600 feet. This is a general phenomenon: A harsh, extreme environment often uncovers genetic differences that are hidden in a population thriving in its optimal environment.*

80. Isolation and Speciation

Evolution includes not only adaptation and secular change but also, from time to time, the subdivision of a single species into two or more contemporaneous species—a process that is called **speciation.** How this may occur is hinted at in the story of the *Achillea* plants just told, but may perhaps be seen more clearly in another example, this one taken from the animal kingdom.

In the Grand Canyon region of the American Southwest there are two species of "tassel-eared" squirrels: one called the Abert squirrel (*Sciurus aberti*), and the other the Kaibab squirrel (*S. kaibabensis*).* The two species are in general very similar in appearance (Fig. 11-7); but whereas the Abert squirrel has a gray tail (usually) and white underparts, the Kaibab has a white tail and black underparts. Both species live in pine forests at high elevations. The Abert is widely distributed throughout the Southwest, but the other species, by contrast, is confined to the Kaibab plateau in

---

* 11-3. Does this statement have human implications?

* 11-4. Note that the *generic* name—the genus name—of *Sciurus* (L. squirrel) has here been abbreviated. Under what circumstances is such abbreviation advisable?

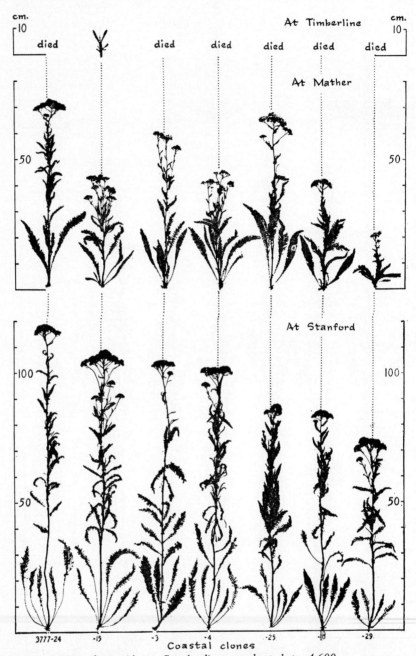

Fig. 11-5. *Growth of coastal* Achillea *plants (from Stanford) transplanted to 4,600 feet (from Mather) and 10,000 feet (Timberline). Dotted lines indicate members of each clone. (After Clausen, Keck, and Hiesey, Pub. No. 581, Carnegie Institution of Washington.)*

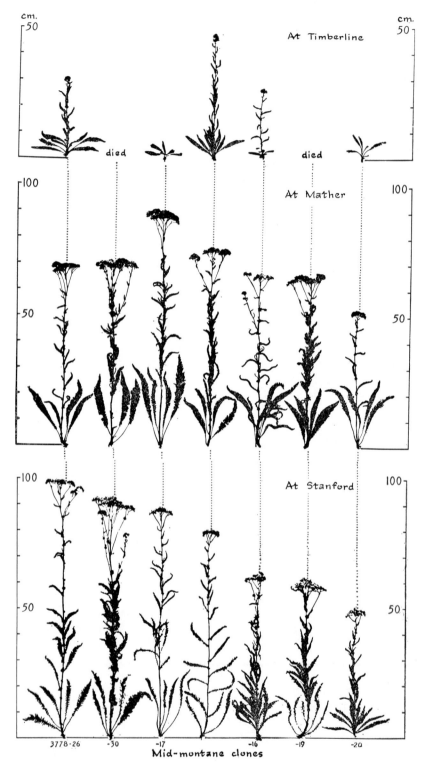

Fig. 11-6. *Growth of mid-montane* Achillea *plants (from Mather) transplanted to 10,000 feet (Timberline) and sea level (at Stanford). Dotted lines connect members of a clone. (After Clausen, Keck, and Hiesey, Pub. No. 581, Carnegie Institution of Washington.)*

northern Arizona. This plateau is about 40 miles long by 20 wide, bounded on the south by the mile-deep chasm of the Grand Canyon, and on the other sides by deserts.

The great similarity of these two species would indicate that their ancestors were members of but a single species in the not-too-distant past. But if this is so, why the differences now? The word "why" is ambiguous and has at least two different meanings that we must consider here.

By "why," we may mean: What is the adaptive significance of the differences? For this question, as for many finely detailed questions of evolution, we have no certain answer. We suspect that there are subtle differences in the environment that make the white-tailed, black-bellied form the "norm" in one region; the gray-tailed, white-bellied form the "norm" in others. But careful field studies (yet to be made) are needed to test this suspicion.

By "why," we may mean: How did the evolution of one species into two come about? This question is easier to deal with. Geological evidence indicates that the pine forests north and south of the Grand Canyon were once joined, that squirrels could once pass from one region to another without leaving the yellow pine trees which are the source of their food and to which their behavioral patterns confine them. Then, as the Grand Canyon formed and deepened and as the climate grew warmer, the pine forests were "squeezed upward" to higher elevations, until the woods north of the Canyon were separated from those south of it by many miles of pineless country. Thus were the Kaibab-squirrels-to-be isolated on a sort of island. The Kaibab region might always have been sufficiently different from the surrounding regions to demand a different norm than the rest of the Southwest; but so long as this region was part of a continuous forest, there would be interbreeding of all the squirrels, and genes would "flow," so to speak, from one region to another, thus preventing the development of sharply defined differences in possibly slightly different environments. Once two regions are isolated, however, gene flow is stopped, and then each

interbreeding population can adapt cybernetically to the set point of its environment. Thus can distinguishably different forms arise. In the early stages, when the differences between the types are slight and when interbreeding readily takes place (if and when there is opportunity), the two populations will be spoken of as **races** (or **varieties**) of the same species. As the differences become more extreme and as the possibility of interbreeding becomes more remote, we speak of the two populations as being different *species*. Speciation viewed as a process in time can be symbolized as shown in Figure 11-8. At what moment in time can we say that one species has become two? At T_2? At T_3? Clearly, an arbitrary element is involved in the decision.

81. The Competitive Exclusion Principle

In the same sense in which death is a normal part of life, so is extinction a normal part of evolution. What are the causes of extinction? They are varied, many of them as particular as the causes of individual death; but there are also some generalizations that may be made about extinction.

Let us look once more at the process of speciation, with an eye to its consequences. Suppose two populations isolated from each other have become somewhat different; and suppose, now, that the populations are brought together again in the same area. What will happen? If they have differentiated only as far as races, and if there are no psychological (or other) barriers to their interbreeding, they will rejoin into a single population, varying around a single norm which is a sort of compromise of the varying selective pressures. If the area occupied by the species is large relative to the mobility of the individuals, the stable condition may be one in which there are differences between individuals at the extremes of the range, but in which the differences smoothly intergrade from one end to the other. So a mammalian species may be larger at the northern part of its range, smaller at the south,* with a smoothly changing con-

---

* 11-5. Why? Give a simple theoretical explanation.

Fig. 11-7. *Abert and Kaibab squirrels, showing an early consequence of the speciation process. (From a painting by Louis Agassiz Fuertes, copyright National Geographic Society.)*

tinuum of forms between. Such a stable transition of geographical types within a species is called a **cline** (Gr. *klinein* = to slope).

But the rejoined populations may not interbreed, in which case we will generally refer to them as different species. What happens when two different species are brought together in the same territory? Clearly, there are only two possibilities: either they will coexist, or one will extinguish the other. A priori, these possibilities might seem equally likely, but in fact this is not so. In fact, in a very profound sense, *coexistence of completely competing species is impossible;* this principle we call the **Competitive Ex-**

Fig. 11-8. *At what precise point in time does one species become two? At T_2? At T_3? At T_4? The decision is necessarily arbitrary.*

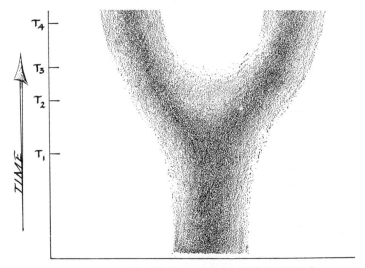

VARIABLE CHARACTERISTICS

clusion Principle. Its truth is not immediately apparent; in fact, a casual glance at nature seems to reveal many instances to the contrary. But the theory behind the principle is so simple and straightforward that it impels us to look very carefully at any supposed violation of it. Let us see what the theory is.

For our model we take a contrived one in the field of economics, one that is highly artificial and unreal in that field, but whose logic we can easily appreciate, and whose applicability to the biological situation is (as we shall see) very direct and meaningful. Let us imagine a savings bank with only two depositors, A and B. For some strange reason, the bank pays A compound interest at the rate of 3 percent per annum, whereas B receives 4 percent annual compound interest. Each is permitted to deposit money only once; each puts in $1,000. Even stranger, the bank has this rule: that whenever the combined totals of the two accounts (both capital and interest) shall reach $2,000,000, the management appropriates half the money to itself, taking from each depositor *in proportion to his holdings at the time*. Following this appropriation, their accounts grow again until the total is $2,000,000, when they are cut back again, in the same way.

If this goes on indefinitely, what will happen? Intuition tells us (and rigorous mathematics confirms) that every cycle of growth and cutback will see B with a larger and larger proportion of the funds. Ultimately (since a penny cannot be subdivided), B will have all the money; by virtue of his competitive advantage (4 percent versus 3 percent), he will have excluded the other depositor.

Obviously, this is strange economics, but it is normal biology. Mortality among competing organisms is both selective and nonselective. The selective component (due to different competitive efficiencies) is represented by the difference in interest rates in our model. The nonselective component (perhaps such factors as fire, tornadoes, and falling airplane parts) is represented by the periodic cutback (organisms cannot increase indefinitely in numbers). It is not difficult to see that no matter how small the competitive difference between species, one species will eventually replace the other. (If B receives 3.001 percent interest while A receives only 3.000, B will eventually have all the money.) Nor need the two species begin with equal numbers: a few invaders of a competitively superior species can replace a multitude of inferior natives. (So, in the United States, a few English sparrows introduced to the Eastern seaboard, multiplied to millions, excluding similar millions of native bluebirds from most, though not all, of their original haunts.)

Can competitors ever coexist? Only if they are competitively precisely equal. But here common sense insists on an **Axiom of Inequality:** no two things, no two processes are ever exactly equal. The axiom may be trivial when we are dealing with *things* because slightly unequal things may serve precisely equal functions. (Although no two postage stamps are precisely equal, they may serve equally well.) But with respect to competing *processes,* because of the compound interest effect, even the slightest competitive advantage is, in the long run, decisive. This makes the biologist's job especially difficult. Most of the competitive differences between species are so slight that he cannot directly verify them, cannot *predict,* which of two species will win out if they are put in competition; he can only set up the experiment, let it run to conclusion, and then say, "Aha! *this* species is competitively superior." The biologist is generally only a "Monday morning quarterback." In nature, said Charles Darwin, "battle within battle must be continually recurring with varying success"; but suppose that we should "try in imagination to give any one species an advantage over another. Probably in no single instance should we know what to do. This ought to convince us of our ignorance on the mutual relations of all organic beings; a conviction as necessary, as it is difficult to acquire."

82. Implications of the Exclusion Principle

The Competitive Exclusion Principle states that complete competitors cannot coexist—and yet, do we not often see them doing so? To this question biologists answer an unqualified *No.* Whenever a first glance reveals what appear to be two competing species coexisting in the same territory, our confidence in the theory underlying the Exclusion Principle leads us to predict that closer observation will show some critical sense in which the apparent competitors do not really live in the same place, or some important activities in which they do not compete. One species may draw on a source of food not available to the other. One may be active in midday, the other in twilight hours. The competitive efficiency of one species relative to the other may change with the changing seasons. Or the two species may not really live in the same environment, as when one bird lives in the treetops, another in the bushes beneath the trees.

In trying to decide whether competitors coexist, it is plainly not enough to look at maps of their geographical distribution. One must instead go into the field, and right into their homes, so to speak, to study the home-life of the species. Ecologists (following Charles Elton) make a distinction between the habitat of an organism and its ecological niche. The **habitat** means just what one would expect: the actual physical place where a species lives—its geographical distribution on a fine scale, as it

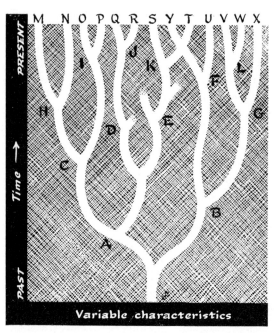

Fig. 11-10. *The consequences of secular change and speciation shown diagrammatically. Note adaptive radiation, as the species increase in numbers; note also convergent evolution (species Y and species T).*

were. The term **ecological niche** is, however, a metaphorical one; it is not the place where the organism lives, but what it does there. The habitat is the species' *address;* the niche is its *profession.* The term niche has reference to its whole way of life. An example may make the distinction clear.

Fresh-water ponds often harbor two different kinds of swimming insects that look much alike: "backswimmers" (*Notonecta*) and "water-boatmen" (*Corixa*). Both species are small—only a few millimeters long—and look much alike (Fig. 11-9), having legs modified into oarlike appendages for propulsion through the water. But though they look much alike, they are not at all closely related, in an evolutionary sense. Were we to trace their ancestries, we would find rather different-looking nonswimming ancestors for each, long before we came to the ancestors common to both. Their relationship is diagrammed in Figure 11-10, in which *Y* and *T* may be taken to be these two species.

Fig. 11-9. *A case of convergent evolution. Backswimmer* (Notonecta) *and water-boatman* (Corixa) *have evolved similar structures to adapt to similar modes of life.* (*From Usinger,* Aquatic Insects of California, *University of California Press. Berkeley, 1956.*)

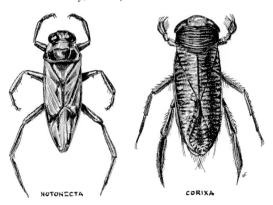

When two rather different stocks of organisms evolve species that resemble each other closely, we say that **convergent evolution** has taken place. The "oars" of backswimmers and water-boatmen are the result of convergent evolution. More familiar examples of the same process are the wings of birds and bats.*

Although backswimmers and water-boatmen are found in the same habitat, they do not share the same ecological niche. Backswimmers are predaceous animals, attacking various other insects, worms, and even tiny fish. Water-boatmen, by contrast, feed on decaying vegetation. The two kinds of organisms do not, therefore, compete. The backswimmers' "profession" is predation; that of the water-boatmen, scavenging. This is why the two species can coexist in the same habitat. Convergent evolution has occurred with respect to swimming, but not with respect to food habits.

The Competitive Exclusion Principle has this as a corollary: *No two species can share the same niche and the same habitat.* Ecological differentiation is the necessary condition for geographical coexistence. Species that are geographically isolated from each other may undergo convergent evolution so that they occupy closely identical niches. For example, among plants living in desert regions, the adaptations of the true cactuses (family Cactaceae) to survival in a dry climate are well known. The conservation of water is favored by the relatively impermeable epidermis, as well as by the relatively low surface:volume ratio of the above-ground portions of the plant. These organisms are found in the New World. In Africa, however, the same niche is filled by members of quite a different family, the Euphorbiaceae, a family that includes such uncactuslike plants as the castor bean, the rubber tree, and the spurges. In the African deserts, this family has evolved species that look remarkably like Cactaceae—a most notable case of convergent evolution.

Species that occupy the same niche but not the same geographical habitat are said to be **ecological equivalents.** The "jack rabbit niche" of North America is occupied, in South America, by a cavy (related to the guinea pig) which has big ears and long hind legs. The niche of the "large herbivore of the open grasslands," occupied by various species of antelopes, horses, and so on, throughout most of the world, is filled in Australia by the kangaroos. What has just been said is only a crude, first approximation to the facts. The determination of ecological equivalence is always only approximate. Nevertheless, it is clear that true ecological equivalents can continue to exist in the natural world only so long as they are kept geographically isolated from one another. We all know how the importation of other herbivores into Australia threatened the survival of the kangaroos—a threat that would have been made good except for man's subsequent interference with unhindered competition. The interchange of species between various parts of the world that man is now bringing about (whether intentionally or not) will, if carried to completion, produce a barrierless world in which the number of different species is no greater than the number of ecological niches. Man will thus reduce the variety of the living world—unless he takes thought and alters his behavior.

Such are the most important implications of the Competitive Exclusion Principle. By its very nature, the principle is one that cannot be proved in the most rigorous sense, since, at each stage in the gathering of evidence, one may dismiss instances of apparent coexistence of species in the same habitat and niche as spurious—a procedure that looks like circular reasoning. However, the principle has a wonderful *heuristic** value, since it leads the biologist who believes in it to look ever more closely at the homelife of species, thus sharpening his observational abilities.

83. Numbers and Naming of Species

In part, evolution is a process with positive feedback. The evolution of new species creates

---

* 11-6. The German name for bat is *Fledermaus*—which strongly implies the idea of convergence. Do you see why?

* 11-7. Meaning?

new environments into which other species can evolve. This is obvious in the phenomenon of parasitism: each new free-living species evolved is a potential new environment for one or more new species of parasites. But the environment-creating effect of speciation is not confined to parasitism; the evolution of trees, for example, has created the special environment of the forest floor, in which live many species of plants and animals that cannot live elsewhere.

Of course, this is not the only effect of evolution. Extinction of species is also part of the story. When a large or important species is extinguished, it may take with it many other species that depend on environments it formerly created. The disappearance of the various large tree ferns of the coal ages of geology was accompanied by the extinction of a host of smaller organisms that probably depended on the peculiar conditions created by these dominant plants. How many species of organisms have been evolved and extinguished in the course of geological time we will surely never know, but the paleontologist G. G. Simpson has gallantly "guestimated" between 50 million and 5,000 million species as the total number of different kinds of plants and animals that have been produced during the course of evolution. The imperfection of the geological record is such that we may never be able to agree on a more precise figure.

We don't even know how many species of plants and animals are now living. For this uncertainty there are various reasons. For one thing, when we take time into consideration, it is obvious from an inspection of Figure 11-8 that the concept of a species is not always sharp. One species or two? Sometimes we cannot say. Undecidable instances are a necessary consequence of the fact of evolution. In addition, so numerous are the papers describing species that no one even knows how many species have, up to the present time, been described and named. Besides, there are many species still to be discovered. Simpson estimates the total number of living species at 2,000,000. This figure will do as well as any to bring home to us the problem of keeping the multitude in order. The need

for universally accepted names is surely obvious.

In scientific publications we find references to *Homo sapiens, Musca domestica, Ulmus americana, Mimosa pudica,* and so on, when man, the domestic fly, the American elm, and the sensitive plant are being spoken of. Historically, the italicized names come to us from the days when Latin was an international language understood by all learned men. Our continued use of Latin and Greek names is *not* due to mere inertia or affectation. When exactness is desirable (as it is in science), there is grave danger in using common names, as will be shown.

There is a type of pine tree that bears the name *Pinus strobus.* Reference to a book on lumber trees reveals that this kind of tree may properly be referred to in English as a "white pine." Why not, then, in scientific publications, simply call this species a white pine? There are two reasons why we do not. In the first place, in common usage, "white pine" is applied to *P. flexilis* and *P. glabra* as well as to *P. strobus;* so if we referred to a "white pine" in a scientific paper, our readers might well wonder which of these trees was meant.

The common name is unsatisfactory for a second reason: It is only one of many common names. *P. strobus* is also, in various parts of the United States, referred to as the eastern white pine, the northern white pine, the northern pine, the soft pine, and the Weymouth pine. A biologist who knows the correct scientific name of a species is sometimes at a loss when he has to speak of it in common terms unless he knows the usage prevalent among the people to whom he is speaking. The example cited is by no means unusual; instances equally ambiguous could be cited by the thousands.

Often the ambiguity is of an even wider nature. In England, the word "corn" means any of a number of kinds of cereal, for example, wheat, rye, barley; in America, the same word means a unique species, *Zea mays,* which is not called "corn" in England, but "maize." A "gopher" in Florida is a tortoise; in California it is a rodent. Without multiplying instances, it is clear that if we wish to have our meanings understood exactly, we must use names that are completely unambiguous. Ambiguity is devastating to the progress of science. As Francis Bacon said: "Truth comes out of error more readily than out of confusion."

It will be noted that all of the scientific names used above consisted of two words. For this reason, we speak of the scientific method of naming things as the system of **binomial nomenclature,** first consistently applied to living things by the Swedish biologist Carolus Linnaeus, in 1735. There are several conventions connected with the use of this nomenclature that need to be known by every biologically literate person. The names are best written in *italics;* when a typewriter is used, the names are underlined. *The first name—the name of the* **genus**—*should begin with a capital letter.* On the other hand, the second name—the name of the **species**—usually does not begin with a capital letter. (In zoological usage a capital letter is never used for the name of the species—a rule not invariably observed by botanists.) The plural of the word "genus" is **genera;** the plural of "species" is **species.** The abbreviation of "genus" is *gen.;* of "species," *sp.* (sing.) and *spp.* (pl.). As an adjective, "genus" becomes **generic;** "species" becomes **specific.** Thus we speak of "generic names" and "specific names."

How are scientific names selected? There is no uniform system, but a few methods of selection may be mentioned. Sometimes the Latin or Greek word for the common name is used: Thus *Acer* is the Latin word for maple, and *Homo* is the Latin word for man. At other times, Latin or Greek roots are combined in such a way as to be descriptive of the appearance of the organism, or of someone's opinion of it; for example, *Chrysanthemum* means "superb flower" in Greek. Frequently, too, either the genus or the species is named after some man, either because of his association with the specific organism, or in simple honor, for example, *Gardenia, Dahlia, Bougainvillea.*

Why is the nomenclature *binomial?* Some examples may be instructive: *Acer saccharum* is the name for the sugar maple tree; *Acer rubrum* is the name for the soft maple tree (which has reddish twigs—hence the specific name); and *Acer nigrum* is the scientific name for the black maple tree. Notice that all of these maple trees are called by the generic name *Acer;* in other words, the binomial gives a partial indication of the classification of the organism. Species that are held to be very nearly related—nearly enough related so that they all bear similar common names ("maple" in this example)—may be given the same generic name (*Acer* in this example). Pine trees all belong to the genus *Pinus.* If there are no known closely related species, a given species may be the unique possessor of a generic name: *Homo sapiens* is the only species of man (genus *Homo*) present on the earth today, though some extinct species are put in the same genus, for example, *Homo neanderthalensis.*

In reading scientific literature, we frequently run across a reference to a genus only. For instance, it may be stated that a certain species of insect is found on *Pinus,* or that a certain mite is found only on *Crotalus* (rattlesnake). Such incomplete information may mean either that the author was unable to identify the species of the organism, or that the statements made are true of a number of species in the genus. The reader must tell from the context what is meant.

Another common usage needs to be mentioned. Frequently, the generic name will be abbreviated, as *A. saccharum, A. rubrum,* or *A. nigrum.* Again we must tell from the context what genus is meant; unless the context is clear, an abbreviation should not be employed. In no case is it justifiable to use the specific name alone, because, though generic names are, with few exceptions, unique, no attempt is made to keep specific names unique, except within the confines of a single genus. Such specific names as *domestica* and *americana* are used over and over again in different genera.

Although the Linnaean names are sometimes a little frightening to the student at first, the strangeness soon wears off. In fact, many of our common names for organisms are scientific names adopted into common parlance. When this stage of acceptance has been reached, it is quite proper to use the generic name without

an initial capital, and without italics; thus we may write asparagus, gardenia, verbena, and chamaeleon.

84. The Role of Museums and Herbariums

When a new species is discovered, how does a name come to be attached to it? It is a standing rule of biological nomenclature that a species cannot validly be named unless it has been adequately described in print. It is the privilege of the first person who describes it to give the species a name. Such a name must, of course, be *published,* as are all contributions to science, and the name must satisfy the conventions described in the preceding section.

What constitutes an "adequate description" of the species? There is no general answer to this; the requirements vary from one group of organisms to another. Frequently, the published description includes drawings of significant portions of the organism. But no description, whether verbal or pictorial, can be completely satisfactory. For this reason, it is advisable that the author deposit one specimen of his newly described species in a public museum or herbarium. (If a museum houses only plant specimens, it is called a **herbarium**.) A species, strictly speaking, consists of a population of similar organisms in nature; but since it is scarcely possible to preserve a whole population, the author of a new name is expected to select what he regards as a typical single specimen for deposit. This single specimen is called a **type-specimen,** or **type.** In the publication that gives the new name for the first time, the author states where this type-specimen has been deposited and gives its deposit number. Then whenever any other biologist is uncertain as to the exact meaning of a published description, he may examine the type at the museum where it is deposited.

Although in some groups of organisms an amateur biologist may, by consulting the literature, fairly easily determine the specific name of an individual at hand, in general the identification of species is a job for the specialist. It is therefore economical of time to consult taxonomists. As one would expect, most taxonomists are to be found where large collections are available: either in universities or, more particularly, in museums and herbariums.

Probably most nonscientists think of a museum as a place solely for the display of odd plants and animals. Historically, the great public museums of today are descendants of such private museums as the sixteenth-century museum shown at the top of Figure 11-11. But there is another side to a museum, one that is scarcely known to the public at large but which is equally, perhaps more, important. This aspect is suggested by the very word "museum," which means a temple of the Muses, that is, a place of study. In an active, modern museum the display specimens account for less than one per cent of its holdings. The rest of the specimens, including type-specimens, are part of the study collections maintained for specialists only, in rooms not open to the public (see Fig. 11-11, bottom).

In §3 we described the twofold nature of science: the conservative and the progressive. The role of museums in conserving knowledge is easily grasped; what is not so easily understood is the importance of the museum in contributing to the progress of knowledge. One might at first suppose that good taxonomic work could be done by men who were concerned only with knowledge already gained. Experience casts doubt on this supposition. There is, in fact, a strong correlation between the excellence of museums in their public-display function and their qualities as institutions in which knowledge is advanced. Moreover, those taxonomists who have the greatest store of conserved knowl-

Fig. 11-11. (Facing page.) *The sixteenth-century museum of Calzolari of Verona* (above) *contrasted with a small portion of the work area of a modern museum* (below). *Note the systematic storage of specimens.* (*Courtesy C. D. O'Malley and the Chicago Natural History Museum.*)

edge to draw upon are also usually the ones who are advancing knowledge most. Many scientists think it doubtful if knowledge in this (or any other) field can be conserved unless it is at the same time advanced.

Questions and Problems

11-8. Write a brief definition of each of the **boldface** terms in this chapter. Compare your work with the text.

‡11-9. "Fitness in the abstract does not exist." Explain and illustrate the meaning of this with an example.

11-10. Using the experimental results obtained with *Achillea* explain why we speak of the *phenostat* of natural selection rather than the *genostat*.

11-11. In 1947, according to Hubert W. Frings, a meeting of the National Pest Association (a group of professional exterminators) was seriously worried as to what would become of their profession when DDT had killed off all the insects. Explain how their fears were the product of ignorance.

11-12. What sort of place is an ecological niche?

‡11-13. In Figure 11-12 are shown the outlines of the heads of four species of rabbits and hares, from four different regions—namely (in alpha-

Fig. 11-12. *A problem in adaptation. Which animal comes from which region? (See Problem 11-13.) (After Hamilton; from Allee et al., Principles of Animal Ecology, W. B. Saunders Co., Philadelphia, 1949.)*

betical order), the Arctic, Arizona, Minnesota, and Oregon. Identify the correct region for each head, and give the general principle on which you base your identification. (Hint: One of the functions of the external ear is that of a cooling—radiating—organ.)

11-14. In Figure 11-13 are shown the results of transplanting clones of *Achillea* to the two lower elevations. What is the most surprising general result of this experiment?

‡11-15. Why are plant clones particularly useful in solving problems in heredity versus environment? Using vertebrates, what is the best attack one can make on such problems? Is it as good?

‡11-16. David Lack, in 1945, reported on two species of aquatic birds: the cormorant (*Phalacrocorax carbo*) and the shag (*P. aristotelis*). The diets of these two species are as follows, in percent:

| | Predator Species | |
Food Species	Cormorant	Shag
Sand eels	0%	33%
Clupeoid fish	1	49
Flatfish	26	1
Shrimps, prawns	33	2
Labrid fish	5	7
Gobies	17	4
Other fish	17	4

These two closely related species feed in the same waters and nest on the same cliffs. Are they an exception to the Competitive Exclusion Principle?

‡11-17. A taxonomist living in Kansas wishes to see a type-specimen deposited in the National Museum in Washington, D.C. Should he travel to see the specimen in the museum, or should the museum send it to him for examination in his own laboratory? Explain the practical issues involved.

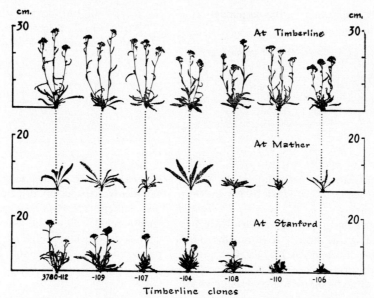

Fig. 11-13. *Comparative growth of* Achillea *plants native to Timberline* (10,000 *feet*) *when transplanted to 4,600 feet* (*at Mather*) *and sea level* (*at Stanford*). *Dotted lines connect members of a clone.* (*After Clausen, Keck, and Hiesey, Pub. No. 581, Carnegie Institution of Washington.*)

11-18. A paratype is a specimen collected (by the describer of the species) at nearly the same time and place as the type-specimen, and deposited in a museum—often in a museum other than the one housing the type-specimen. What advantages are there in this practice?

11-19. Interspecific hybrids among vertebrates are usually impossible to obtain, even by artificial insemination. Of the hybrids that are obtainable (e.g., the mule, from a horse and a donkey), most are sterile. Explain these facts in terms of information theory.

11-20. G. B. Shaw, in the Preface to his play *Back to Methuselah* has this to say of the concept of evolution: "It makes the killing of an animal murder in exactly the same sense as the killing of a man is murder." Shaw uses this statement as the basis for his vegetarianism.

Explain Shaw's reasoning. Explore the logic

TABLE 11-1 *Comparisons of the Yield of Wild and Domestic Animals on Different Types of Unimproved Land in Africa.* (*Source: E. B. Worthington, 1961.* The Wild Resources of East and Central Africa.)

TYPE OF LAND	YIELD EXPRESSED IN TERMS OF:	LAND GRAZED BY	
		DOMESTIC ANIMALS (CATTLE, GOATS, SHEEP)	WILD ANIMALS (BLESBOCK, ELAND, WILDEBEEST, SPRINGBOK)
Rangeland	Kg liveweight gain per animal per day	0.14	0.19–0.24
Acacia savannah	Kg liveweight maintained per hectare	20–28	157
Bushland	Kg liveweight maintained per hectare	3.7–13.5	52.5
Black cotton chernozem	No. animals per square kilometer	87	343
Depleted land	Kg liveweight per hectare	15.5, and land became more depleted	31, and land recovered

thoroughly and evaluate the argument as a guide to living.

11-21. Table 11-1 shows the results of grazing animals of European origin by themselves on African land, as compared with mixed herds of African animals. Explain the differences.

Readings

For general treatments of evolution see Grant's *The Origin of Adaptations,* Huxley's *Evolution in Action,* or Simpson's *The Meaning of Evolution.* Perhaps the best biography of Charles Darwin is the one by Gavin de Beer. An entrancing introduction to animal ecology is Elton's book of that title; no comparable book exists for plant ecology. A good general textbook is Odum's *Fundamentals of Ecology.* The mathematical derivation of the Competitive Exclusion Principle will be found in my paper, "The Cybernetics of Competition," which includes also a discussion of possible applications to a wider range of problems. Students plagued with unsubstantiated rumors of interspecific hybrids should consult Gray's careful checklist.

Scientific American Offprints

12. Verne Grant. *The Fertilization of Flowers*

22. David Lack. *Darwin's Finches*

108. Loren C. Eiseley. *Charles Darwin*

195. Stanley C. Wecker. *Habitat Selection*

Origin and Evolution of Life

12

85. Antiquity of the Rocks

That the earth is immensely old is common knowledge now, yet this knowledge is only about two centuries old. How did it happen that man, who was clever enough to build the pyramids and discover irrational numbers long before the birth of Christ, took so long to appreciate the antiquity of the earth? No simple, acceptable answer can be given to such a question, but we can point out one of the reasons: inadequate observation. One is not likely to puzzle about a thing unless one really looks at it, and we are least likely to look at ubiquitous things like the earth, which is always under our feet and fills half (or more) of our visual field. The scientific study of the earth was preceded by the artistic discovery of it. The idea of a landscape, which we take so for granted now, was (in the Western world) a discovery of Renaissance times. That mountains are not mere impediments to travel, but are also things of beauty was a discovery of the Italian poet Petrarch (1304–1374). As long as man merely hated mountains, he could hardly see them; one must, in a sense, love things to see them for what they are. Petrarch taught Western man to see and to love mountains.

The particular way of seeing mountains that we call scientific followed at a snail's pace behind the artistic way. Not until the new efflorescence of science in general did there develop a science of **geology** (Gr. *ge* = earth). The first noteworthy treatise on the age of the earth was published in 1785 by James Hutton (1726–1797). In his *Theory of the Earth,* this Scot laid down as a rule that the origins of rock formations should be explained in terms of this working hypothesis: *The past history of our globe must be explained by what can be seen to be happening now.* With respect to one class of rocks, this assumption led to no upsetting conclusions. In the outflow of present-day volcanoes, we can see rocks solidifying from molten material: such rocks we call **igneous rocks** (L. *ignis* = fire). Wherever on the face of the earth we find rocks that are physically and chemically similar to such known outflows, we call them by the same name and assume that they too have originated from the cooling of molten masses (not necessarily spewed out of a volcano).

But Hutton's interpretation of another class of rocks set off intellectual fireworks. Limestone, sandstone, and shale are not reasonably to be explained as having originated from molten material. Sandstone is clearly made up of layers, or **strata,** of fine particles, as though one layer had been laid upon another. If we look about us today, we see places where just this sort of process is taking place. At the mouth of a river, for instance, we find that, as the current of the river is slowed down on entering the ocean, the river's burden of tiny sand and clay particles drops to the bottom, there to be deposited layer upon layer. We know that such sediments have in historic times been laid down by the great rivers of the world, thus extending their delta lands into the oceans. Sedimentary deposits of recent origin are not as hard as rock, but we can easily understand how time and pressure could turn them into rock. It therefore seems most reasonable to suppose that rocks like limestone, sandstone, and shale have been formed by such processes acting in the past; we call rocks of this class **sedimentary rocks.** This hypothesis seems all the more reasonable when we find embedded in sedimentary rocks the shells of oysters and the skeletons of fish.

All this is accepted now, but when Hutton, at the end of the eighteenth century, proposed this interpretation of the rocks, his ideas met most determined opposition. To understand the vigor of this opposition, we must know the intellectual framework of Hutton's day. It was then almost universally believed (in the Western world) that the earth had had a definite and sudden beginning in the fairly recent past. One seventeenth-century Irish theologian, a Bishop Ussher, studying sacred Hebraic writings (and armed with a generous supply of assumptions), calculated that the world began in the year 4004 B.C. An even more ingenious contemporary of Ussher's figured out that man was created on precisely 23 October of that momentous year at precisely 9:00 A.M.

Now observe the revolutionary implications of Hutton's theory when we state it in roughly quantitative terms. Speaking very broadly, we may say that at the present time a "normal" rate of sedimentation is such that in 1,000 years about 30 centimeters of sedimentary materials are laid down. This is the order of magnitude of the process. Rocks laid down during only one of the great eras of the earth's history, the Mesozoic era (see Table 12-2), total about *32 kilometers* in thickness. The time required to produce so much sedimentation, however liberal our assumptions, is irreconcilable with Ussher's estimate of the age of the earth.

In such a situation what are we to do? Here is a question of choice, and one's choice is determined not alone by logic but also by tradition.

Hutton was a scientist, the inheritor of a scientific tradition. In the absence of evidence to the contrary, he assumed that the forces operating in the past must have been like those in operation in his day. The *rate* of a process taking place in the past may have been somewhat different from the rate today, but we should not gratuitously assume any difference in the *order of magnitude* of the rate. Because Hutton assumed a uniformity of processes throughout the earth's history, his doctrine was dignified by the title **uniformitarianism.** It should be realized, however, that this impressive word does not refer to a completely new method of thinking but rather to the extension of a venerable logical tradition into a new field. The doctrine of uniformitarianism is a lineal descendant of a doctrine promulgated by a medieval scholastic, William of Occam—namely, "Entities should not be multiplied beyond necessity." However obscure this classic statement may be, the mode of its application is clear. In practice, Occam's principle means that we should not suppose more forces or causes than are necessary to account for the phenomena observed. Because Occam's principle pares a theory down to its bare essentials, it is often referred to as **Occam's razor,** or the **Law of Parsimony.** Hutton's use of Occam's razor, or the principle of uniformitarianism (call it what you will), led to conclusions definitely, and painfully, in opposition to the popular beliefs of his day.

86. Determining the Age of Rocks

Although the argument just presented is sufficient to show, with a high degree of probability, that the earth is very old, it is hardly precise enough to show how old it is, or how old the various beds of sedimentary rock are. It is difficult to justify any particular quantitative assumption regarding the rate of deposition of sediments in the past. Fortunately, in the twentieth century, a method has been developed for determining the age of rocks with considerable precision—namely, the **radioactive clock method.** The logic of this method is easily understandable, and will be presented here by simplifying some of the technical details.

The element uranium 238 (U^{238}) is a radioactive one, that is, an element that spontaneously disintegrates to produce other elements. The disintegration of any radioactive element is independent of temperature, pressure, humidity, and other environmental conditions. The rate of disintegration is absolutely constant. The rate is conveniently indicated by stating the **half-life** of the element; the meaning of this term will become clear from what follows.

Suppose a chemist today, in the year 1966, purifies some U^{238} and puts some pure crystals of it into a bottle. Assume that the sample is a small one—say, only 1,000,000 atoms of U^{238} —and that there are no atoms of any other kind in the bottle. The uranium would continuously disintegrate, producing other substances. It would disintegrate at such a rate that in 4.5 billion years, half the original atoms of uranium would disappear, their place being taken by other atoms. And 4.5 billion years later, the number of uranium atoms would be halved again (see Table 12-1).

TABLE 12-1 *The Disintegration of Uranium Atoms In Time.*

DATE	NUMBER OF ATOMS OF U^{238} IN SAMPLE
The present, 1966 A.D.	1,000,000
4,500,001,966 A.D.	500,000
9,000,001,966 A.D.	250,000

We say that the element uranium has a half-life of 4.5 billion years, by which we mean that, however many atoms of it we may have at a given instant, only half of these atoms will still be intact 4.5 billion years later.

What happens to the uranium atoms that disintegrate? U^{238} breaks up to form thorium^{234}; this has a half-life of 24 days, disintegrating to yield proactinium^{234}, which has a half-life of only 1.18 minutes. From this comes . . . but better look at Figure 12-1, which shows the stepwise disintegration of the atoms in this "de-

cay series"—the final product, a stable one, being a form of lead, Pb^{206}. (This is an uncommon isotope of lead; the commonest is Pb^{208}.) Ultimately, every atom of U^{238} will have been transformed into Pb^{206}. Or, looked at from the other end, each atom of Pb^{206} on the earth today is a witness for the one-time existence of an atom of U^{238}.

We see then how we can use the radioactive decomposition of U^{238} as a clock for estimating the passage of time, or for estimating the age of a sample. When crystallization occurs in a mixture of substances, each crystal is composed of only one kind of substance. If we have a rock in which uranium-type crystals occur, we may assume that the crystals were of pure uranium at the time when they were formed. By determining the ratio of lead atoms to uranium atoms in such crystalline material, we can determine how long it has been since the crystals were originally formed; and if from other evidence it appears that the age of the rock layer is the same as that of the crystals in it, we know the age of the stratum itself. The radioactive clock method of determining the age of rocks is most readily applicable to igneous rock. Since sedimentary rocks are frequently associated in one way or another with igneous rocks, we can, by making various reasonable assumptions, arrive at a fairly accurate estimate of the age of sedimentary rocks also. It is the general belief of geologists today that it is possible to determine the absolute age of the various strata of rocks with an error not exceeding 10 percent. When we say that the earliest rocks of the Cretaceous period of the Mesozoic era were formed 120 million years ago, we imply that we would be surprised if they were older than 132 million years or younger than 108 million years. By such methods, the age of the oldest rocks has been determined to be about 2.8 billion years. This gives the date of the formation of a lasting crust of the earth.* From other evidence, the total age of the earth appears to be about 4.5 billion years.

---

* 12-1. If future studies show (as they probably will) that we must revise this estimate, will it be toward a greater age or a lesser one?

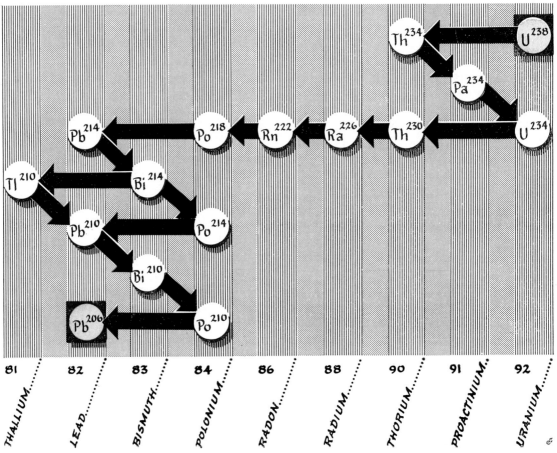

Fig. 12-1. *The degradative path leading from Uranium-238 to Lead-206. An alpha decay (marked α in figure) involves the loss of two neutrons and two protons, the equivalent of a helium nucleus. A beta decay (marked β) involves loss of one electron. The names of the atoms and their atomic numbers are given at the lower margin.*

87. The Fossil Record

Our knowledge of life in the past is based on fossils. A **fossil** (L. *fossilis* from *fodere* = to dig) is any material trace of a former organism. Sometimes it is no more than the imprint of a fern leaf in coal. Sometimes it is an actual part of an organism, for example, a tooth or an oyster shell. Exceptionally it is the whole organism —say, an insect preserved in amber (fossilized pitch of trees). Whatever its form, a fossil is always a rather improbable thing. Fungi and bacteria decay organic material whenever they can, and even such hard parts as bones have a great deal of decayable organic material in them. Adequate fossilization of an organism is

possible only under conditions in which the activities of decay organisms are inhibited, for example, low temperature, extreme dryness, or unfavorable chemical conditions such as are found in the oxygen-poor sludge at the bottom of an acid bog.

As geologists of the late eighteenth century and early nineteenth century pondered over fossils, they arrived at conclusions that were at variance with traditional beliefs. It had been known for centuries—at least since the time of the Florentine genius Leonardo da Vinci—that some of the fossils found in the rocks are clearly those of no species of animal or plant living today. This means that some of the species living in the past have perished completely. This conclusion was not by itself at variance with traditional beliefs, for Christian theology, like the theology of several earlier religions, includes an account of a Deluge. It was easy enough to explain away curious-looking fossils as remnants of species that had perished in the Deluge. But when the strata are studied thoroughly, it is found that different fossils disappear from the record in different strata. When the strata are deposited, they are laid down one on top of another; therefore, the upper strata are younger than the lower. The disappearance of different fossil species at different levels of the stratified record implies their extinction at different times. Must we, then, suppose many deluges? And how could a deluge cause the extinction of an aquatic species—say, a fish?

A more serious threat to traditional belief was presented when it was remarked that different fossil species made their first appearance in the geological record in different strata, that is, at different times. According to the theological tradition accepted in the nineteenth century, all forms of living matter (except man) had been created at the same time. The record of the rocks, read in the spirit of the Law of Parsimony, led to a different conclusion—in fact, to the creation of a new discipline of study called variously **paleontology** or **paleobotany** (Gr. *palaios* = old, ancient), the former usually meaning the study of the history of animals, the latter of plants.* On the basis of such studies, the prehuman history of the world has been divided into periods analogous to those used in human history. The names of these are given in Table 12-2, which also gives the approximate date of the beginning of each. Note that this table is oriented in the way undisturbed beds of sedimentary rock are oriented—with the oldest age at the bottom. You should read the table from the bottom upward.

It is difficult to imagine time measured in hundreds of millions of years. To help appreciate the *relative* lapses of time involved, we have included in the table a column printed in

color in which 4.5 billion years is compressed to 1 year.† If, then, we picture the earth as being "born" on 1 January, we discover that the year was more than half over before life probably appeared on it, about 20 July (a rather uncertain date). Not until 20 October did organisms appear that left good traces of their existence. All of these were water-dwelling species. More than a month passed before the first land plants showed up, perhaps as early as 27 November, certainly by 3 December. Within three "days" there were extensive forests. Animals, always dependent on plants, soon evolved onto land, too.

Dinosaurs, which figure so prominently in the popular picture of paleontology, had their heyday less than two weeks ago, around 19 December; by Christmastime they were extinct. Meanwhile the mammals, which first appeared as far back as 17 December, had multiplied in kinds and numbers to become the dominant forms they are today. The flowering plants, somewhat younger (née 19 December), also burgeoned rapidly, displacing many of the ferns and conifers that flourished earlier. By two days after Christmas, the world looked approximately as we know it today, with flowering plants, insects, birds, and mammals dominating the landscape. But man was absent. Not until the last day did *Homo sapiens* appear on the scene—with consequences to all the rest of the landscape that are spectacular, not always happy, and still to be worked out to completion.

88. Limitations of the Fossil Record

Paleontology is history, and like all history it is no better than its records. The rather special conditions required for fossilization have already been discussed. What fraction of the world's inhabitants at any one time become fossilized? We are unable to make a defensible estimate, but the fraction must surely be very, very small. Furthermore, there is little doubt that the probability of fossilization is not the

---

* 12-2. Such is the usage. What is unsatisfactory about these terms? How could the terminology be improved?

† 12-3. On this scale, 1 second equals how much geological time?

TABLE 12-2 *The Geologic Ages. (This table is constructed in accord with geologic convention: the oldest era is placed at the bottom, with succeedingly younger ages above. This is the order in which the sedimentary rocks are deposited. The table should be read from the bottom upward. Dates in color represent the time converted to the scale of a solar year.)*

NAME OF ERA	NAME OF PERIOD	APPROX. DATE OF BEGINNING (MILLIONS OF YEARS AGO)	RELATIVE TIME	BIOLOGICAL CHARACTERISTICS
(PRESENT)		0	31 Dec., Midnight	
CENOZOIC	Quaternary	1		Appearance and dominance (?) of man.
	Tertiary	58	27 December	Dominance of birds, mammals, flowering plants, insects.
	Cretaceous	125	21 December	Reptiles dominant; toothed birds, marsupial mammals appear. Insects and flowering plants increase in number and variety. Extinction of dinosaurs.
MESOZOIC	Jurassic	150	19 December	First flowering plants. Age of giant dinosaurs. Pterodactyls, bony fish, archaeopteryx. First hardwood forests.
	Triassic	180	17 December	Reptiles, conifers dominant. First mammals.
	Permian	215	14 December	First conifers. Diversification of reptiles, insects. Extinction of trilobites. Deserts common.
	Carboniferous	260		Extensive forests of giant ferns, club-mosses, horsetails (all spore-bearers). First appearance of reptiles, seed plants, insects. Trilobites almost extinct. Horseshoe crab (still living) appears. Swamps common.
PALEOZOIC	Devonian	310	6 December	First land forests—of ferns, club-mosses, horsetails. Corals, armored fish abundant. First amphibians.
	Silurian	350	3 December	Definite land plants. Eurypterids and primitive fishes dominant; corals, trilobites abundant. First cephalopods. Lungfishes. Scorpions.
	Ordovician	430	27 November	Land plants (?). Algae. Corals abundant. Bivalve and coiled shell molluscs. Eurypterids. First vertebrates (fishlike forms).
	Cambrian	510	20 November	Algae. Trilobites dominant. Many molluscs; *Lingula*. Sponges, jellyfish.
PROTEROZOIC		900	20 October	Evidences (some disputable) of sponges, radiolaria, bacteria, algae; all water-dwelling forms.
ARCHEOZOIC		2000	20 July	Presumptive origin of life.
AZOIC		4500	1 January	Origin of earth.

Fig. 12-2. Brachiosaurus, *a giant herbivorous dinosaur of the late Jurassic; found in Colorado and eastern Africa. (From Bernhard Kummel,* History of the Earth. *W. H. Freeman and Company, San Francisco and London, 1961. Drawing by Z. Burian under the supervision of Prof. J. Augusta.)*

same for all species but varies with the structure of the organism and its ecology. Numerous remains have been found of the largest dinosaur known, *Brachiosaurus,* shown in Figure 12-2. By contrast, aside from a few unimportant fragments, *Archaeopteryx,* the earliest recorded bird, is known only from two well-preserved specimens, one found in the Solenhafen lithographic limestone in 1860, and the other uncovered in 1877. This bird (shown in Fig. 12-3) was about the size of a crow. The teeth in its beak, and various other features, would probably have led to its identification as a flying reptile had it not been for the detailed impression its feathers left in the fine-grained limestone.*

When the first *Archaeopteryx* was found, in the year following the publication of the *Origin of Species* it made a tremendous impression on the public, being hailed as a "missing link" between reptiles and birds. The argument and logic of Darwin's theory were a bit too hard to carry conviction; spectacular finds like *Archaeopteryx* probably had more influence in swinging public opinion around. The finding of "*the* missing link" always gets a larger play in the newspapers than it deserves. The desire for a complete paleontological record has never been

---

* 12-4. Bird fossils in general are quite rare. Dinosaur fossils are numerous. Why the difference?

Fig. 12-3. Archaeopteryx, *the earliest known bird, looking down on a small Jurassic dinosaur. (From Bernhard Kummel,* History of the Earth. *W. H. Freeman and Company, San Francisco and London, 1961. Drawing by Z. Burian under the supervision of Prof. J. Augusta.)*

fulfilled and (we can predict with considerable confidence) never will be fulfilled. The low probability of fossilization must be multiplied by the low probability of uncovering the fossils under conditions suitable for scholarly study. Except for microfossils recovered in drilling (as for oil) only rocks exposed at the surface are ever examined for fossils. Many of the fossils uncovered are destroyed before an expert can see them. Most of the laying bare of new strata is done by practical men who are building roads or houses and who do not welcome the profit-destroying delays required for the careful uncovering of strata for the paleonotologist.

One of the striking facts about the paleon-tological record is the *suddenness* with which new major groups of plants and animals appear. When a major group—like flowering plants, or reptiles, or mammals—first appears it is almost immediately (in geological terms) represented by a great many species. The morphological gap between it and its supposed progenitors is great. The sudden appearance of a major group in full force, so to speak, has always been recognized as somewhat embarrassing to the theory of evolution from which one might (at first at least) predict a more gradual development of a new pattern of existence. Can we explain such "paleontological explosions" of new groups?

Perhaps not entirely; but certain relevant

facts and ideas can be pointed out. First of all we need to see that the operation of the Competitive Exclusion Principle militates against a complete fossil record. As Darwin said: "Competition will generally be most severe between those forms which are most nearly related to each other in habits, constitution and structure. Hence all the intermediate forms between the earlier and later states, that is between the less and more improved states of the same species, as well as the original parent species itself, will generally tend to become extinct."

Without being able to present a precise, clean-cut argument evolutionists suspect that a major group represents an adaptation which opens up a whole new ecological realm for exploitation (as when a land environment first became possible). The new realm includes a multiplicity of new ecological niches, with a multitude of new set points. Speciation takes place unusually rapidly, and as a result the probability of fossilization of intermediate forms is unusually low. Such at least is our current version of an answer to the puzzling fact of the large gaps in the paleontological record.

89. On the Strategy of Science

The biggest gap of all in the evolutionary picture of life is the gap at the very beginning, the gap between life and nonlife. What have evolutionists to say of this? In recent years, a great deal. But it is a noteworthy example of the strategy of scientific investigation that Darwin had almost nothing to say about the matter. Most of his followers were equally silent. The experimental work of Louis Pasteur had shown that life did not arise from nonlife under present-day laboratory conditions, and for many people this experimental fact closed the door to speculation about the spontaneous beginnings of life in the distant past. Most scientists refused to push the story of evolution back further. August Weismann was not content with this attitude. In 1881 he said: "I admit that spontaneous generation, in spite of all vain efforts to demonstrate it, remains for me a logical necessity." Karl von Naegeli agreed: "To deny spontaneous generation is to proclaim a miracle."

But one cannot find much more on the subject of the origin of life in the writings of scientists in the last half of the nineteenth century. Clearly, few problems could claim to be more basic to biology than this one. Why, then, did not biologists write more about it? The reason was essentially, and unconsciously, strategic. Looking backward, we can see that the necessary facts on which sound speculation could have been based were simply not available in that era. Good scientists of the time probably realized this "intuitively," and so turned their attention to matters of lesser importance that held greater promise of early solution. As Kenneth Boulding has said: "Science might almost be defined as the process of substituting unimportant questions which can be answered for important questions which cannot." This aspect of science has often led to external criticism on the grounds of triviality, but it has paid off handsomely in the long run. (Has philosophy progressed faster by attacking the "big" problems?)

In recent decades we have at last made some progress on the question of the origin of life. We are still far from a definitive answer, but we think we can see the *form* of the solution. The question of the origin is intimately related to the nature of life: progress in attacking the second question will undoubtedly facilitate work on the first. The rate of progress is at present so great that no textbook can hope to be up to date even at the time of publication, but it may help orient the student's thoughts so that he can evaluate the latest reports.

90. The Origin of Life

In the development of our ideas about the origin of life we can distinguish two major hypotheses:

The **Autotroph Hypothesis** states that the first living thing must have been an autotroph—

literally a "self-feeder"—something like the photosynthetic green plants of today. In favor of this hypothesis is the fact that such organisms are independent of other living organisms for their organic compounds, which they make themselves. Against the hypothesis is the awkward fact that a condition of autotrophism is attained only by an organism that includes the vast array of enzymes required for the synthesis of carbohydrates, proteins, and fats from such inorganic substances as CO_2, H_2O, and NH_3. The Autotroph Hypothesis implies that a most complicated organism was evolved first—an implication that is clearly not reconcilable with the tradition of parsimony in the making of hypotheses.

The **Heterotroph Hypothesis** states that the first "organism" must have been a heterotrophic one, something like the viruses. In favor of this hypothesis is the fact that the most extreme heterotrophs that we know of today are unquestionably the simplest of known forms of life. But—and here is the difficulty—the most extreme heterotrophs have to be surrounded by a medium (a living cell) made up of the most complex organic chemicals; and in the days before there were living organisms, where would such organic substances come from?

The difficulty, formidable as it appears at first sight, proves to be not insurmountable. It has its origin, it would seem, partly in the structure of common speech. In the world of today there is organic matter only because it is constantly resynthesized by living organisms. Organic matter is not stable in our world: "It decays," we say. Yet this is not true: we should say, *"It is decayed"*—by bacteria, molds, and other microbes. In other words, on the surface of the earth before there was any life, should any organic material have been synthesized, *it could have persisted*. The next problem is this: Can organic matter be synthesized by nonliving means?

Yes. In the laboratory it is possible, by irradiating a mixture of carbon dioxide, water, and ammonia with ultraviolet light, to obtain a multitude of organic compounds, which do not decay so long as they are protected from the attentions of microbes. The sun produces ultraviolet light in abundance. In the atmosphere today, CO_2 and H_2O are present. In the atmosphere of some of the outer planets, NH_3 has been detected spectroscopically; it is not unreasonable to suppose that it was present in the earth's atmosphere before living organisms were evolved. If so, then all the conditions needed for the creation of organic matter were present on the earth in early days.

But there is a great difference between organic molecules and organisms. Ordinary molecules do not reproduce themselves. It is a most extraordinary molecule indeed that can reproduce more of its own kind. Tobacco mosaic virus would appear to be such a molecule. If, among the variety of molecules produced in the abiotic period of the earth's history, even one such molecule were produced, it might then, by continued replication of itself (using the other organic molecules present), have started the chain of living things that reach down into our own time.

Was this the way life began? It is hard to see how we can ever know for sure. The hypothesis is, however, at least plausible. Under laboratory conditions, the number of different organic compounds that are formed when CO_2, H_2O, and NH_3 are irradiated is almost beyond estimation. The compounds first formed, as radiation continues, are converted to other organic compounds, and we know no limit to the numbers or complexities of the compounds that may so be synthesized. We have never yet observed the formation of a virus molecule or anything like it. Undoubtedly, the probability of forming so complicated a molecule by such a process is very low. But given time enough, even an extremely improbable event may happen. Since we do not know exactly when living things first appeared on earth, we do not know exactly how much time there was in which such an improbable event might occur; but it seems likely that 1 or 2 billion years may have passed before life began. And since the improbable event would have had to happen only once, the Heterotroph Hypothesis does not, in the present stage of our knowledge and ignorance, seem unreasonable.

91. The Evolution of Autotrophs from Heterotrophs

The Heterotroph Hypothesis just described was first clearly stated in 1928 in a popular essay written by the English biologist J. B. S. Haldane (1892–1964). The same thesis was more thoroughly developed in a book by the Russian biochemist A. I. Oparin, *The Origin of Life,* published in English in 1938. The idea was further developed by the American biochemist N. H. Horowitz, who, in 1945, showed how, utilizing genetic knowledge and Darwinian reasoning, we might account for the evolution of autotrophs from heterotrophs.

The synthesis of the first self-reproducing particle, which we may call a "proto-organism," must have taken place through a series of steps that we may symbolically represent thus:

$$A \longrightarrow B \longrightarrow C \longrightarrow D \longrightarrow \ldots \longrightarrow W$$
$$\longrightarrow X \longrightarrow Y \longrightarrow Z_y \text{ (proto-organism)}. \quad (1)$$

The capital letters represent chemical compounds of increasing complexity as we go from A to Z. (The 26-letter alphabet, we must suppose, is wholly inadequate to represent the full complexity of the situation.) In the first instance, all the stages of the process represented by arrows took place by nonliving means.

The proto-organism, Z, if it was capable of self-reproduction, must (if we make the simplest hypothesis) have been able to make its own kind of molecule using Y as a raw material; we indicate this fact by symbolizing the proto-organism by Z_y. Once the first Z_y molecule appeared (by whatever happy chance), it could make more and more Z_y molecules from the supply of Y molecules in its environment. But, in so doing, it would be in danger of "eating itself out of house and home," for what would happen to the population of Z_y molecules when the supply of Y was exhausted? Plainly—since *we* are here today—at least one molecule of Z_y must have undergone a change to enable it to bring about not only the reaction $Y \longrightarrow Z_y$, but also $X \longrightarrow Y$. Such a change must be called a mutation; the new "organism," capable of synthesizing its own substance from X, we may

symbolize by Z_{xy}. If we regard the first "organism" as consisting of a one-gene organism (say gene Y), then this "organism" is a two-gene organism (gene Y and gene X). (Whether the increase in genes was brought about only by a change in a single molecule, or by a union of two different molecules, is a detail.)

Notice the consequences of such a mutation. In a world in which both substances X and Y are abundant, it would be difficult to say, a priori, whether Z_y or Z_{xy} would be able to multiply faster. But as soon as the supply of Y became scarce, Z_{xy} would clearly have a competitive advantage. It would soon outnumber Z_y, which would probably become extinct as its food supply failed.

What next? Clearly, as the supply of X diminished, there would be an opportunity for a new mutant, a three-gene organism, Z_{wxy}, to become the predominant type. And after that, Z_{vwxy}, then Z_{uvwxy}, then Z_{tuvwxy}, and so on. Step-by-step-Darwinian-step the evolution of a multigene organism would take place. Ultimately, there would be produced an autotrophic organism—an organism capable of making all its organic compounds from inorganic materials. Once this occurred, the risk of living would be greatly reduced, and the way was opened for future evolution in many directions, in the direction of increase of synthetic abilities as well as in that of the loss of abilities that has characterized the evolution of parasites and, to a lesser extent, the evolution of animals.

92. Life on Other Worlds?

Space exploration has raised the possibility that we may someday land on other planets of our solar system, or even possibly on planets of other stars. If we do will we find life there? And if so, what kind? These questions titillate the imagination of all who explore the implications of space travel. They will be answered if and when we land on other celestial bodies. In the meantime, can we arrive at probable answers to such questions?

The first level at which we can tackle these questions is the most fundamental one: What do we mean by the word "life?" Our kind of life is based on carbon compounds in a watery medium. J. B. S. Haldane once suggested that life might alternatively be based on silicon compounds in a medium of liquid ammonia. Though the criteria of life (§4) are subtle and difficult to encompass verbally, if we were to find them satisfied by an utterly different chemical system we would have to apply the word "living" to it. Unfortunately, our knowledge of chemistry is really too rudimentary to make any estimate of the probability of the existence of such utterly different forms of life as a silicon-ammonia life. We can only admit the logical possibility and then pass on to a consideration of "life as we know it."

In all forms of "life as we know it" the basic polypeptides are composed of twenty different amino acids, all of the l-form; the energy currency is based on high energy phosphate bonds; and nucleic acids are the information carriers. Are these the only possibilities in a water-carbon compound world? We don't know. Certainly with respect to the amino acids we can see no a priori reason why the d-forms would not serve, or why many other kinds would not do just as well as the twenty now used. Perhaps, however, there are deep theoretical reasons for the apparent chemical restrictions of life.

Given a suitable supply of simple chemical precursors of amino acids, nucleic acids and ATP, together with a suitable form of energy (ultraviolet light, electricity, etc.) what is the probability that a living system will be evolved? If it is very small then the Oparin schema can be opposed by the fundamental objection that assuming the occurrence of an event of extremely high improbability is next door to assuming a miracle, and miracles (whether true or not) are not the domain of science. This objection could be countered with the statement that, after all, *we are here,* which shows that this event must have happened even if it was miraculous. This is certainly unanswerable, but if this is the best explanation we can reach it does not justify our assuming there is life elsewhere in the universe—for we can hardly justify making a habit of assuming miracles!

There are two lines of reasoning that indicate the origin of life may not have been an improbable event, and hence one that we are justified in assuming as having taken place at many places in the universe. The first point to make is this: even a very improbable event has a high probability of happening given enough opportunities. A bit of history should help illustrate this point. In 1931 one of the roulette wheels at Monte Carlo paid off on black 26 times in a row. Red and black are equally probable ($p = \frac{1}{2}$). The probability of 26 successive results of the same color is less than 1 in 32,000,000.* So was it a miracle when black turned up 26 times in a row? Not at all. It is only when we think of 26 blacks as an isolated run that it seems miraculous. But Monte Carlo was operating for many decades before this happened. Put another way, if one takes as a unit 26 spins of the wheel, there must have been millions, perhaps tens of millions of such units over the last century. When we say that the probability of an event is only 1 in 32,000,-000 we are not saying it won't happen; we are merely saying that we won't bet on it unless we are assured that there will be millions of opportunities for it to happen.

With respect to the problem of the origin of life, the probability of a particular key event might be very small, and the event might still occur. Suppose that this hypothetical key event had a probability of occurrence in any one second of only 1 in a million billion. That's a small probability. But there are 3×10^7 seconds in a year; and the earth may have been favorable for the origin of life for 2 billion years before life appeared. That means a total of $2 \times 10^9 \times 3 \times 10^7 = 6 \times 10^{16}$ seconds in which our improbable event could occur. Under the circumstances we would predict that the "improbable" event would be almost certain to occur.

There is a second line of evidence that suggests that the origin of life may not have been improbable. In discussing the structure of pro-

---

* 12-5. Show how this answer is derived.

teins (§55) it was pointed out that a polypeptide chain may spontaneously form linkages that produce secondary structure; that this secondary structure may spontaneously rearrange itself into a macromolecule of tertiary structure; and so on. The point is that the marvellous complexity of secondary and tertiary structures far from being improbable, must occur necessarily, given a certain primary structure. Some of the aggregations required for the evolution of life may also be necessary consequences of certain chemical relationships. If so, the origin of life becomes sufficiently probable so that we should assume that our world of life is but one among millions or billions. This is only a verbal argument which needs to be fleshed out with hard chemical facts, but it is the best we can do for the present.

It is possible that life is widespread throughout the universe. It is also *possible* that it is everywhere the same kind of life in the sense that it is built on the same system of water, *l*-amino acids, high-energy phosphate bonds plus nucleic acids. But it is practically impossible that *Homo sapiens* occurs anyplace but on this earth. Why do we say this? The argument is essentially historical. Consider the history of man on earth. Mankind has frequently been subdivided into different nations and cultures. Never has the history of one group repeated the history of another. Napoleon Bonaparte occurred only once. However similar two cultures may be, historical accidents of small dimensions ultimately cause great historical divergences. This idea was succinctly stated by the French philosopher and mathematician, Blaise Pascal (1623–1662): "If the nose of Cleopatra had been a little shorter the whole face of the world would have been changed." And what if Lincoln had had a bad cold that night and had not gone to Ford's Theatre? What if F. D. Roosevelt had been in good health at Yalta? The persistence of the consequences of small accidents in history is so great that we cannot conceive of two communities, however near identical at the outset, generating identical histories.

Evolution is history, history on a grand scale.

It follows no predetermined program. Adaptation and speciation are influenced by the accidents of population size, availability of mutants, geographical isolation, and alteration of set points by climatic and biotic factors. In human history, Napoleon occurred only once; in evolutionary history, *Homo sapiens* has occurred only once, for essentially the same reason. If we ever reach other planetary bodies that have suitable characteristics we may indeed find life, and perhaps intelligent beings. They may even be more intelligent than we. But they won't be *Homo sapiens*. Science fiction, to be believable, must never flaunt this inescapable conclusion.

93. How Common are Habitable Planets?

Will man ever colonize other planets? This question can be subdivided into two parts. Will we some day possess the technological ability to move small inocula of *Homo sapiens* to other astronomical bodies? Are there any other bodies that are suitable for human habitation? "In principle" the answer to the first question is *Yes,* though the technological cost will be fantastically great. Without asking whether we will be willing to pay it, let's see whether we can tell if any other heavenly body is worth going to.

In asking whether another planet is habitable we mean habitable in a practical sense. If there were some compelling reason for doing so, men could live on the moon, an airless, waterless body that is too hot on the side facing the sun, and too cold on the other side. Life would have to be carried on entirely in hermetically sealed rooms or suits. Under such conditions, is it the moon that is inhabited or the insulated room or suit? It will be the contention here that the moon is not habitable; if you wish, you may think of this statement as a definition of the word "habitable."

In this sense, no planet of our sun, other than the earth, is habitable. Table 12-3 summarizes the astronomical knowledge of the solar planets. Each check mark indicates the exclusion of the planet as a suitable abode for man; one exclu-

TABLE 12-3 *The Unsuitability of Solar Planets for Human Habitation. Exclusion as a Possible Home for Man Indicated by Check Marks; One Exclusion Is Sufficient.*

PLANET	NO BREATHABLE ATMOSPHERE	TOO HOT	TOO COLD	NOT ENOUGH WATER	GRAVITY TOO GREAT
Mercury	✓	✓		✓	
Venus	✓	✓		✓	
Mars	✓		✓	✓	
Jupiter	✓		✓		✓
Saturn	✓		✓		
Uranus	✓		✓		
Neptune	✓		✓		
Pluto	✓		✓		

sion is sufficient. Notice that every planet is unsuitable for at least two reasons.

To find a possibly suitable planet we must look beyond the solar system and that means a very long way indeed. The nearest star is Alpha Centauri, a triple star, and that is 4.3 light years away. At such a distance we cannot see planets, only stars. Nevertheless, there is a plausible (though not conclusive) line of argument that indicates that all stars have planetary systems. Let's assume the argument is sound. What are the conditions that must be fulfilled if a planet is to be habitable?

A thorough study of these conditions has been made by the RAND Corporation of Santa Monica for the U.S. Air Force, and reported by Stephen H. Dole (1964). In summary, the basic conditions for habitability are connected with the size of the star that serves as a sun for the planetary system, the size of the planet, and the rate of energy inflow to the planet from its sun (which is determined by the size of the star and the star-planet distance). If a planet is too small, it cannot hold oxygen in its atmosphere; this consideration sets the lower limit at about 40 percent the mass of the earth, which yields a gravitational force of 0.68 g. If it is too large, the gravitational force acting on man makes movements fatiguingly difficult; a force of about 1.5 g is the practical limit, which is

exerted by a planet 2.35 times the mass of the earth.

Oxygen is a necessity. Several lines of evidence indicate that O_2 was not a part of the earthly atmosphere until green plants were evolved; all free oxygen is a by-product of photosynthesis. If this is a necessary evolution, then only those planets that have evolved some plantlike forms of life will be suitable for man. The partial pressure of O_2 must lie between 53 millimeters of mercury (equivalent to a terrestrial altitude of 6,900 meters), and 400 mm Hg. Higher concentrations of O_2 are toxic.

The planetary atmosphere must have sufficient water to sustain life as we know it, and in addition it must have carbon, nitrogen, phosphorus, etc. in available forms. There must not be too much ammonia, chlorine, fluorine, formaldehyde, cyanides, methane, nitrogen oxides, ozone, or sulfur dioxide. In addition, the planetary surface should not be subjected to an excess of meteorite fall, earthquakes, electrical storms, atmospheric pressure, wind, dust, ultra-violet irradiation, or radioactivity. The more we look into the conditions required for comfortable human life, the more we suspect that the earth is rather a special place.

How special? This is obviously a very difficult question to answer; many assumptions must be made, and one is not sure how reasonable the assumptions are. Nevertheless the RAND group made an attempt to estimate the frequency of habitable planets in our galaxy and came up with the following picture.

Our galaxy, the Milky Way, has a total volume of 5.5×10^{13} cubic light years. It was estimated that it includes 6.5×10^8 habitable planets, or about one habitable planet in every 85,000 cubic light years. Put another way, the mean distance between habitable planets is estimated at 44 light years, which is about ten times the mean distance between stars. Of course the uncertainty of this estimate is great and unknown, but even if we assume that every star has at least one habitable planet this means that the habitable planet closest to the earth is more than 40,000,000,000,000 kilometers distant. This can scarcely be called an encouraging prospect to those who wish to escape earth's problems by fleeing to the stars.

Questions and Problems

12-6. Make a list of the **boldface** terms in this chapter. Write out a definition or description of each. Compare your work with the text.

12-7. Briefly tell what each of the following men contributed, with the approximate date: Petrarch, Hutton, Haldane, Oparin, Horowitz.

12-8. The following statement was made in a popular scientific journal in 1957: "Upon the authority of no less a personage than Professor Raymond A. Dart, there is no longer any room for doubt that the link between man and his ape-like progenitors is represented by the remains of Australopithecus africans, or South African ape, and so named by the Professor." Comment on the scientific validity of this statement.

‡12-9. "With the passage of time we may reasonably expect the missing links in the paleontological story to decrease in number." Agree? Explain.

12-10. One millennium of geological time equals how much time on the compressed scale printed in color in Table 12-2?

‡12-11. One day of the compressed scale printed in color in Table 12-2 represents how much geological time?

12-12. On the compressed (color) scale of Table 12-2, when did the Quaternary begin? Add this figure to the table.

‡12-13. Expressed in terms of days, a million years of geological time equals what on the compressed (color) scale of Table 12-2?

‡12-14. Complete Table 12-2 by filling in the colored date for the beginning of the Carboniferous period.

12-15. A painting is reliably identified as dating from 200 B.C. It is a landscape, with the plants accurately and sensitively drawn. Mr. Jones thinks the painting is Greek; Mr. Smith thinks it is Oriental. Which one is probably right?

‡12-16. The term "Azoic" included in Table 12-2 is not at all standard. What does it mean?

12-17. The French philosopher Auguste Comte (1798–1857) once said, "There are some things of which the human race must forever remain in ignorance; for example, the chemical composition of the heavenly bodies." By consulting a chemistry or astronomy text, or an encyclopedia, find out how helium was discovered. In the light of this bit of history, comment on Comte's statement.

12-18. A biologist-turned-philosopher, Hans Driesch (1867–1941) wrote in 1908: "The question of the so-called origin of life is as incapable of being discussed as is the problem of death, in spite of the great number of popular works written about it." Defend or attack Driesch's statement.

12-19. The rocketeer Eugen Sänger (1905–1964) in his book *Space Flight: Countdown for the Future* (1963) justified the attempt to get to other heavenly bodies thus: Man has an

insatiable thirst for knowledge . . . The tendency to expand the realm of human knowledge and power without question is deeply fundamental in human nature. Any infringement or abandonment of this primal urge would cut deep into the roots of man's very being. Therefore, since survival is the issue, man has no choice but to keep on expanding his fund of knowledge and command of his environment. . . . It can be said without fear of contradiction that in obedience to the very laws of his existence, man will reach out as a matter of course to know, and establish dominion over, the realm of space, as he has done over earth.

Give your personal reaction to these ideas, at some length.

12-20. Do you think man will ever travel to the other planets of our sun? Justify your answer.

12-21. Do you think that man will ever travel to the planets of other stars? Justify your answer.

12-22. Do you think that the following quotation has any proper relevance to the problem of interstellar travel? Fred J. Gruenberger (*Science*, **145**:1413–1415, 1964) coined the term *Fulton non sequitur*, explaining it thus: "The true crackpot can frequently be spotted on this test alone. He proceeds with an argument like this: 'They laughed at Fulton. He was right. They're laughing at me. *Therefore*, I must be an equal genius.' It is so obvious, but the Fulton non sequitur keeps recurring."

12-23. What would be the long-term evolutionary consequences of man's taking up residence on a planet with a surface gravitational force of 1.5 *g*?

Readings

Oparin's *Life: Its Nature, Origin and Development* gives a brief introduction to the problems of the origin of life. For published details of the technology of space flight see the *Space Handbook* by Robert W. Buchheim *et al.* A. G. W. Cameron has edited a fascinating collection of papers called *Interstellar Communication* which is concerned not only with the possibility of communicating with intelligent beings elsewhere in the galaxy, but also with the feasibility of interstellar travel. This last topic is also discussed in the essay "Interstellar migration and the population problem," republished in my book *Population, Evolution, & Birth Control*. The RAND study mentioned in the text is published as Stephen H. Dole's *Habitable Planets for Man*.

Scientific American Offprints

47. George Wald. *The Origin of Life*

144. LaMont C. Cole. *The Ecosphere*

210. William A. Fowler. *The Origin of the Elements*

811. Edward S. Deevey, Jr. *Radiocarbon Dating*

846. Loren C. Eiseley. *Charles Lyell*

III Our Plant-Dependent World

A discovery is great when one can communicate it in passing.
M. W. BEIJERINCK

13

The Role of Plants in the Biosphere

94. Atomic Energy and Its Utilization

There is only one important source of energy available to man and all other living things: atomic energy. For the release of this energy, a rather special setup is required, which may be at either of two distances from the terrestrial organisms utilizing the energy: *near,* that is, not more than 20,000 kilometers distant;* or *far,* that is, about 150,000,000 kilometers away.

Obtaining economically significant amounts of energy from a nearby installation has been recognized as a real possibility only since 2 December 1942, when, under the direction of Enrico Fermi, an atomic pile on the campus of the University of Chicago "went critical," that is, started producing externally usable energy. Since then, tremendous strides have been made in tapping the energy of the atom, but even today, in spite of the fact that several atomic-energy installations are feeding electricity into public power lines, it is by no means clear that terrestrial installations can ever be a safe way to satisfy a *large* part of man's energy demands. Every installation produces large amounts of radioactive waste products and contaminated apparatus, the radioactivity of which disappears only slowly during hundreds of years. No acceptable way has yet been found for disposing of the large quantity of wastes that would be produced by the many installations that would

be required to supply all of man's energy needs. We will, therefore, turn to the other type of atomic-energy installation on which all living things have depended for several billion years—namely, the sun, which operates at a distance of approximately 150 million kilometers from our planet.

The energy output of this atomic power plant is fantastically great. Even the small amount of its radiant energy that the earth intercepts is still enormous. The equivalent of about 10^8 Hiroshima-model atomic bombs reach the surface of the world every day. Much of this energy heats up the surface layer of the earth during the day—heat which is lost by radiation to the cold, starlit sky at night. Some of the heat vaporizes ocean water; this vapor is then moved by heat-generated winds to higher altitudes, where it precipitates, creating potential energy sources in the form of mountain streams. And a small fraction of the sun's radiant energy is captured by green plants, which use it in synthesizing energy-rich organic compounds. Of the quantity so produced, part is used by the plant later (later at night, later in the year, or years later) in supplying its own energy needs. Part is used by animals that eat the plants, or by animals that eat the animals that eat the plants. And part may be removed from the current scene of action by fossilization at the bottom of a swamp, to be dug up perhaps millions of years later in chemically altered form and burned as fuel.

---

* 13-1. Whence this value?

Thus man uncovers and uses coal, a high-energy residue of plants that captured energy from the rays of the sun shining on the earth in late Paleozoic times, some 300 million years ago. "Fossil fuels"—as coal, lignite, peat, petroleum oil, and gas are called—make up the most important part of man's energy budget at the present time, but this is only a passing phase of man's history. Practicable sources of these fuels will soon be exhausted—in a matter of 200 years at most.

What then? Prophecy is hazardous, but we can distinguish several plausible possibilities:

I. We may have no better nuclear technology than at present, a technology that produces large amounts of radioactive "garbage."

    1. With our present (or a larger) population, we may reconcile ourselves to large-scale radiation damage (e.g., a great increase in the numbers of deformed children) in order to enjoy the advantages of a high-energy income.

    2. We may somehow decrease the world's population to the point where the nuclear-energy production required is low enough to produce a more tolerable level of radiation damage.

    3. We may renounce nuclear energy and adjust our population to the much lower level that can be supported by incoming energy from the sun.

II. We may develop a completely safe nuclear technology, one with no radioactive garbage to dispose of.

The shape of the future will be markedly determined by the success of our present efforts to develop fusion power (which is "clean") to replace fission power, which is dirty. If we can follow the line indicated by II, one sort of world will develop, possibly an immensely crowded one, certainly a very wealthy one. If the promise of II is not realized, we must retreat to the possibilities of I. Whichever of these alternatives we elect, the capturing of solar energy will surely remain important. Possibly we may devise economical means of bypassing plants in the capture of this energy. Possibly we may not, in which case we will continue to be dependent on plant photosynthesis, as we have for the hundreds of thousands of years of man's existence on earth. It behooves us to learn something of the mechanism of photosynthesis.

95. Photosynthesis

We recall the over-all equations for photosynthesis and respiration, noting that, in their effects, they are opposing reactions:

Respiration:

$$\text{Organic compounds} + O_2$$
$$\longrightarrow CO_2 + H_2O + \varepsilon. \quad (1)$$

Photosynthesis:

$$CO_2 + H_2O + \varepsilon$$
$$\longrightarrow \text{organic compounds} + O_2. \quad (2)$$

In the above equations we use ε to represent energy, which takes the form of movement, metabolic work, and heat in Equation 1, and light in Equation 2.

Among the first to appreciate the opposition of the two processes was Joseph Priestley (1733–1804), an English minister and amateur chemist. In 1772, Priestley gave the following report of his experiments:

I have been so happy as by accident to hit upon a method of restoring air which has been injured by the burning of candles and to have discovered at least one of the restoratives which Nature employs for this purpose. It is vegetation. One might have imagined that since common air is necessary to vegetable as well as to animal life, both plants and animals had affected it in the same manner; and I own that I had that expectation when I first put a sprig of mint into a glass jar standing inverted in a vessel of water; but when it had continued growing there for some months, I found that the air would neither extinguish a candle, nor was it at all inconvenient to a mouse which I put into it.

Finding that candles would burn very well in air in which plants had grown a long time, . . . I thought it was possible that plants might also restore the air which had been injured by the burning of candles. Accordingly, on the 17th of August 1771 I put a sprig of mint into a quantity of air in which a wax candle had burned out and found that on the 27th of the same month another candle burnt perfectly well in it.

We see that in regard to the gases involved, Priestley had discovered the opposing nature of the processes of respiration and photosynthesis. Even though the synthesis of organic material had not yet been established, it was clear that plants were indispensable for the continued existence of animals—an implication that did not escape Priestley or his contemporaries. When the Royal Society awarded Priestley the Copley medal in 1773, the man who made the presentation speech remarked that Priestley's experiment showed that useless and even poisonous plants "do not grow in vain"; and went on to say: "Salutary gales convey to the woods that flourish in the most remote and unpeopled regions, our vitiated air, for our relief, and for their nourishment." Note the homocentric* attitude, typical of the times.

This presentation speech made an impression on a Dutchman, Jan Ingenhousz (1730–1799). Some six years later, Ingenhousz, a busy physician, took the opportunity of a short stay in England—less than three months—to carry out some classic experiments in the field of photosynthesis. The following is taken from Ingenhousz's summary of his work:

I observed that plants not only correct bad air in six or ten days, by growing in it, as the experiments of Dr. Priestley indicate, but that they perform this important office in a compleat manner in a few hours; that this wonderful operation is by no means owing to the vegetation of the plant, but to the influence of the light of the sun upon the plant. I found that plants have, moreover, the most surprising faculty of elaborating the air which they contain; . . . that they pour down continually a shower of this depurated air, which . . . contributes to render the atmosphere more fit for animal life; that this operation . . . begins only after the sun has for some time made his appearance above the horizon . . . ; that this operation

of the plants is more or less brisk in proportion to the clearness of the day and the exposition of the plants; that plants shaded by high buildings, or growing under a dark shade of other plants, do not perform this office, but, on the contrary, throw out an air hurtful to animals; . . . that this operation of plants diminishes towards the close of the day, and ceases entirely at sunset; that this office is not performed by the whole plant, but only by the leaves and the green stalks; that even the most poisonous plants perform this office in common with the mildest and most salutary; that the most part of the leaves pour out the greatest quantity of this dephlogisticated air from their under surface . . . ; that all plants contaminate the surrounding air by night; . . . that all flowers render the surrounding air highly noxious, equally by night and by day; that roots and fruits have the same deleterious quality at all times; . . . that the sun by itself has no power to mend the air without the concurrence of plants.

A few years later, a Swiss minister, Jean Senebier (1742–1809), showed that it was not air in general that was involved in the photosynthetic reaction but only that portion of the air that we now call carbon dioxide. He surmised that the capture of CO_2 by the plant resulted in an increase in plant substance, but a clear demonstration of this fact was first made by a fellow-countryman, N. T. de Saussure, in 1804. De Saussure weighed air before and after the removal of CO_2 by a plant; he also determined the dry weight of the plant before and after the experiment. He found that the increase in dry weight of the plant during the process of photosynthesis was *greater* than the weight of carbon dioxide removed from the air. It was only reasonable to conclude that water was the other raw material used in the manufacture of plant substance. From this he deduced a modern statement of the process of photosynthesis:

$$CO_2 + H_2O + \text{light energy} \longrightarrow O_2 + \text{plant material}. \quad (3)$$

This was a reasonable summary of the experimental implications—in fact, the only reasonable one—but the evidence for one phase of it was unsatisfactory for many years to come. It was difficult to give a quantitative proof of the

---

* 13-2. Meaning?

role of water in the process. The necessity of water is plain, but the weight of the water used by a plant exceeds by many times the weight of organic material synthesized by a plant. Most of the water taken up by the plant evaporates from the leaves, and it is not easy to show that this is not what happens to all of the water. It has only been in recent years that it has been possible to demonstrate unambiguously that water is used in the manufacture of the products of photosynthesis. This demonstration has been made by "tagged-atom" experiments.

The immediate motivation for carrying out these experiments was a desire to know where the oxygen in the photosynthetic equation comes from. Does it come from the CO_2? Or from the H_2O? A priori, one source might seem as reasonable as the other. For many years most investigators assumed—for reasons not worth detailing here—that the O_2 came from the CO_2. Then in the 1930's, comparative studies of the physiology of certain bacteria led the American microbiologist C. B. van Niel to postulate that the O_2 came from the H_2O. This view was generally opposed. The controversy was settled when the rare isotope of oxygen, O^{18}, became available in quantity. By making one of the reactants with this isotope, and the other with the ordinary isotope (O^{16}), it was possible to run a "tracer" experiment (§31) to see where the free oxygen (O_2) came from. Indicating O^{18} by a colored symbol, O, and O^{16} by O, the results were as follows:

$$CO_2 + H_2O + \varepsilon$$
$$\longrightarrow \text{organic compounds} + O_2. \quad (4)$$
$$CO_2 + H_2O + \varepsilon$$
$$\longrightarrow \text{organic compounds} + O_2. \quad (5)$$

So the O_2 comes from the water molecule, the hydrogen of which is incorporated into the organic compounds synthesized.*

Equations like *4* and *5* above are lacking in precision with respect to the term "organic compounds." Can this term be rendered more precise? It can. Careful quantitative study show that we can rewrite the photosynthetic equation thus:

—————————
* 13-3. How might this be demonstrated?

$$CO_2 + H_2O + \varepsilon \longrightarrow (CH_2O)_x + O_2, \quad (6)$$

in which the x stands for some integer. If the photosynthetic product is glucose ($C_6H_{12}O_6$), $x = 6$; if it is sucrose ($C_{12}H_{22}O_{11}$), $x = 12$. (The slight inaccuracy—sucrose lacks one H_2O unit of fitting the formula—is tolerated in such generalizing equations.) Substances of the approximate formula $(CH_2O)_x$ are called carbohydrates.

96. Where Does Photosynthesis Take Place?

Equation (6) with its over-all view of photosynthesis falls far short of giving us a satisfactory picture of the mechanism of the process. We will return to the chemical details in the next section. First we need to learn more of the morphology associated with the process.

Ingenhousz, in the passage quoted in the preceding section, stated that photosynthesis "is not performed by the whole plant, but only by the leaves and the green stalks." Later studies showed that sometimes even parts of leaves cannot photosynthesize. Among some ornamental plants, for example, ivy and geranium, there are strains that have *variegated* leaves, that is, green leaves mottled with white spots. When such leaves are tested for photosynthetic activity, it is found that only the green areas carry out the process. The constant correlation of greenness with photosynthetic ability naturally suggests a causal relation between the two.

Microscopic examination shows that the green areas contain green bodies called **chloroplasts.** Is it possible to show that photosynthesis takes place only in the immediate region of a chloroplast? Answering this question depended —as so often in biology—on the choice of favorable material (thus showing the importance for the experimenter of a wide knowledge of the variety of living things). Demonstrating a difference between chloroplast regions and nonchloroplast regions is hardly possible in cells that have a single large chloroplast extending throughout most of the cell, or in cells that have many small chloroplasts scattered throughout. But in filamentous algae of the genus *Spirogyra,*

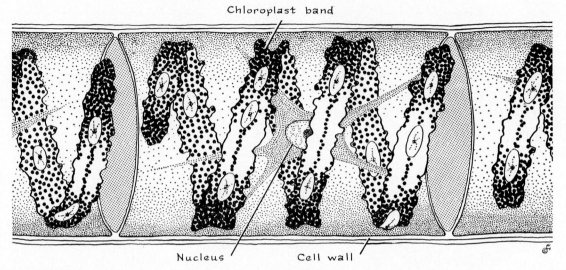

Chloroplast band

Nucleus   Cell wall

Fig. 13-1. *Spirogyra cell, showing chloroplast in the shape of a band. Many such cells make up a long green filament.*

there is a single ribbonlike chloroplast that occupies only part of the cell (Fig. 13-1). If the chloroplast is the site of photosynthesis, then it should be possible to show that oxygen is produced by an illuminated *Spirogyra* cell only in the immediate region of the chloroplast and not in other regions. But how can one demonstrate this in a cell whose diameter is perhaps only 20 microns? Clearly a microchemical test is needed.

To the German botanist T. W. Engelmann (1881) goes the credit for a beautiful solution of this problem. Engelmann had found that bacteria of the genus *Pseudomonas* move very actively in the presence of oxygen but are immobile when oxygen is absent. Only O_2 will

bring about their motility; no compound of oxygen, nor any other compound, activates them. The sensitivity of the "pseudomonas test" for oxygen is phenomenal; as few as 20 molecules of O_2 can be detected by this method.

Using *Spirogyra* and *Pseudomonas,* Engelmann demonstrated the site of O_2 production in photosynthesis as follows: He put the two organisms together on a microscope slide, in water (Fig. 13-2*A*), and then placed the mount—microscope and all—in complete darkness, during which time the respiring cells of bacteria and algae used up the O_2, thus causing (undoubtedly) the bacteria to become immotile (*B*). After allowing enough time for all the O_2 to be removed, Engelmann abruptly exposed

Fig. 13-2. *Engelmann's experiment, by which the photosynthetic activity of a Spirogyra cell was localized in the chloroplast. Pseudomonas cells were used as sensitive detectors of oxygen. See text.*

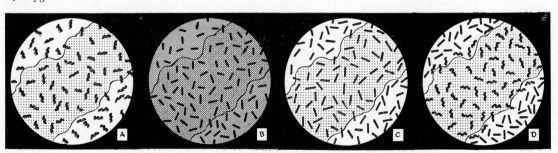

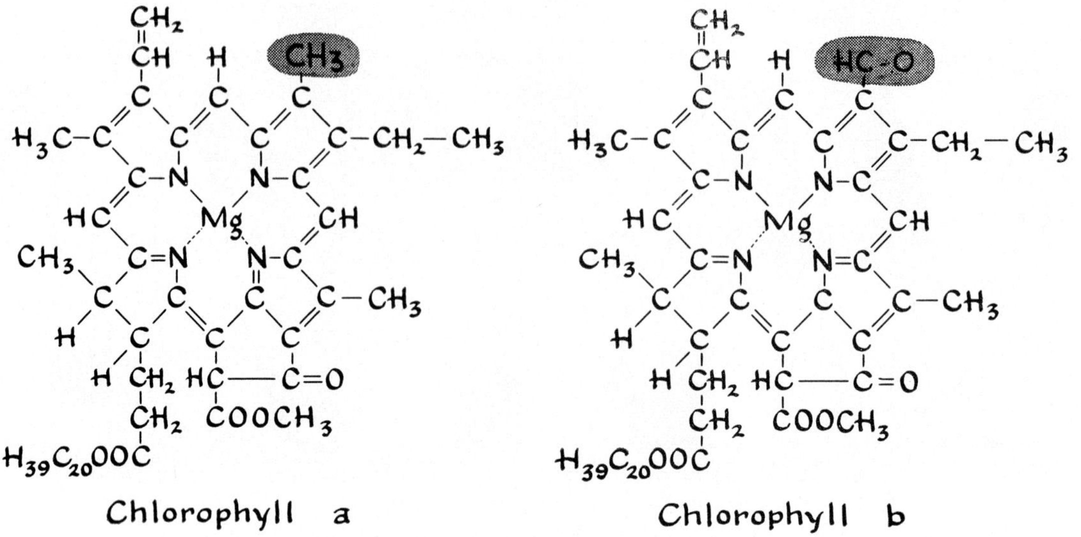

CH_2
CH H CH_3
C   C   C
H_3C-C   C   C   C-CH_2-CH_3
C-N   N-C
HC   Mg   CH
CH_3 C=N   N-C
C   C   C   C-CH_3
H   C   C   C
H CH_2 HC——C=O
CH_2 $COOCH_3$
$H_{39}C_{20}OOC$

Chlorophyll a

CH_2
CH H HC-O
C   C   C
H_3C-C   C   C   C-CH_2-CH_3
C-N   N-C
HC   Mg   CH
CH_3 C=N   N=C
C   C   C   C-CH_3
H   C   C   C
H CH_2 HC——C=O
CH_2 $COOCH_3$
$H_{39}C_{20}OOC$

Chlorophyll b

Fig. 13-3. *The chemical structure of chlorophylls* a *and* b, *as worked out largely by Willstätter, Fischer, and Conant. The significant difference is indicated in color.*

the setup to light, and immediately examined the mount. At first, all the bacteria were motionless (*C*), indicating the absence of O_2. In a very few seconds, however, the bacteria began to move, *at first only in the immediate vicinity of the chloroplasts* (*D*). Thus was it demonstrated that chloroplasts are the cell structures in which the process of photosynthesis takes place.

The chemical compound that is essential to the work of the chloroplasts is **chlorophyll;** or, more accurately, the chlorophyll*s*, for there are several slightly different molecules that serve the function of photosynthesis. In the higher plants, there are two chlorophylls, *a* and *b,* which have the structures shown in Figure 13-3. That it should have taken something like a half-century of work by some of the ablest chemists to establish the structure of such complex molecules is hardly surprising. In addition to the *a* and *b* forms, there are other chlorophylls (e.g., *c* and *d*) that occur in certain of the lower plants—diatoms and dinoflagellates—to the exclusion of *b*. Why there should be different forms is not known.*

_____
* There is a mildly amusing sidelight on chlorophyll. During the 1950's commercial interests decided to push the sale of "chlorophyll"—actually, breakdown

The general class of chemical compounds to which the chlorophylls belong is the class of **porphyrins.** In the center of the "porphyrin ring" is a magnesium atom (see Fig. 13-3 again); chlorophyll is therefore called a magnesium porphyrin. Chemically, the chlorophylls are not greatly different from a group of iron porphyrins that serve as respiratory enzymes in both plants and animals. Hemoglobin, present in the red blood cells of vertebrates is an iron porphyrin. The substitution of Mg for Fe in the porphyrin ring gives chlorophyll a light absorbing capacity several thousand times as great as that of the respiratory compounds.

In the chloroplasts, as in all parts of the cell, intricate structure is evident at the electron microscopic level. The chlorophyll is contained in flat membranous sacks called **lamellae;** a stack of lamellae is called a **granum** (L. grain; pl., *grana*). Figure 13-4 shows sections of grana

_____
products of chlorophyll—as a deodorant. The reasoning seemed to be this: green plants smell sweet and fresh; green plants have chlorophyll; *ergo* any organism that has chlorophyll inside it will smell sweet—therefore men should eat chlorophyll to smell sweet. The logic of this argument was neatly challenged by R. W. Marsh who commented:

The goat that reeks on yonder hill
Has browsed all day on chlorophyll.

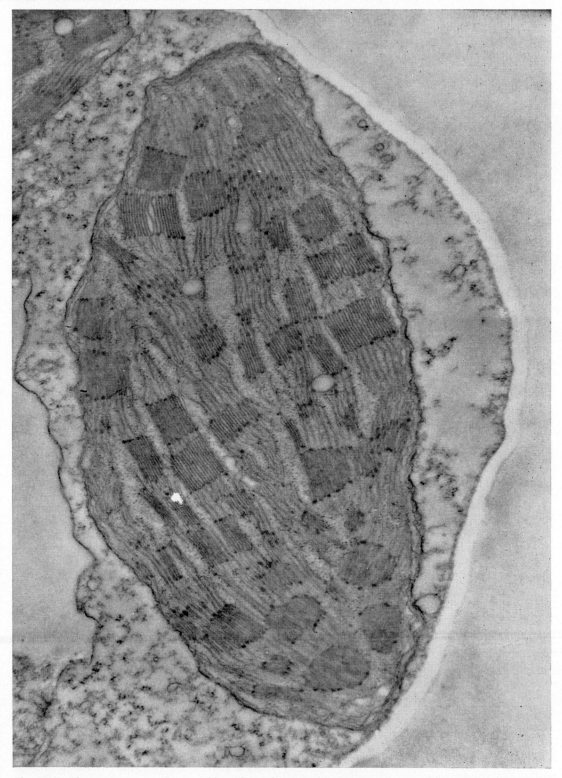

Fig. 13-4. *Electronmicrograph of a chloroplast, showing the grana in section. (Courtesy A. E. Vatter.)*

Fig. 13-5. *Electronmicrograph of the ruptured surface of a single granum, showing the quantasomes of which it is composed. (Courtesy R. B. Park.)*

inside a chloroplast; each granum has been likened to a stack of coins.

If a granum is examined at higher magnification it is found to consist of many hundreds of smaller units called **quantasomes** (Fig. 13-5). Each quantasome contains, among other things, about 230 chlorophyll molecules. There are even indications that the quantasomes are subdivided still further into **quantatropes,** which contain about 20–25 chlorophyll molecules each.

97. Molecular Basis of Photosynthesis

How does chlorophyll bring about photosynthesis? We still do not have the complete picture, but a great deal has been learned in the past half century. A small part of this knowledge—what seem to be the pivotal facts—will be described here in the hope that it can serve as a framework for organizing future discoveries.

The light that is absorbed by chlorophyll must do some kind of work if any utility is to result from the absorption. What kind of work? A hint is found in the behavior of chlorophyll in a test tube. If chlorophyll is exposed to light, it **fluoresces,** that is, it absorbs light at one wavelength and emits it at another. The physics of fluorescence is well understood (Fig. 13-6). When an atom absorbs energy from incoming radiant energy, an electron circulating around the nucleus is shifted to more distant orbit. It takes energy to make this shift. The electron in

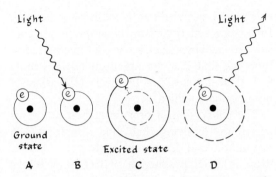

Fig. 13-6. *The mechanism of fluorescence. Absorbed light "excites" an electron, that is, puts it into an orbit more distant from the atomic nucleus. When the electron returns to its normal orbit, light is emitted.*

the more distant orbit has potential energy by virtue of its position; the molecule that has some of its electrons in this condition is said to be in an "excited" state. The excited state is unstable. In the test tube experiment the stable or "ground" state is restored when the electron returns to its original orbit. Energy is conserved by the simultaneous emission of radiant energy. Fluorescent light is almost always of longer wavelength than the original, exciting, light; some of it may, in fact, be in the range of heat waves, as it is in chlorophyll fluorescence.

This is all very interesting, but mere glowing won't make food. The fluorescence we have described is a test tube phenomenon. In the plant, the energy of the electrons in the excited state is captured for useful purposes. High-energy electrons are momentarily captured by a chain of substances called electron carriers (*A* through *E*, in Fig. 13-7); as the electron is passed from one to another some of its energy is removed and used to bring about the synthesis of ATP. After two molecules of ATP are formed, the less energetic electron is passed back to the chlorophyll molecule, which returns to the ground state, ready for another influx of light. The entire process is called **photophosphorylation.** Note that *in vitro* fluorescence is replaced by *in vivo* synthesis of ATP. This substance, it will be recalled, is like money to a cell (§38): it can be used to pay for a great variety of chemical syntheses.

This is only part of the complex of reactions that we collectively call photosynthesis. A second group of reactions is concerned with the splitting of the water molecule. About the mechanism of this there is not as much agreement, but it is clear that the source of energy here, as in photophosphorylation, is in the raising of chlorophyll molecules to the excited state and then tapping the energy of the high-energy electrons to split O_2 off of H_2O.

The usefulness of the process of photosynthesis is not realized until the amount of organic carbon in the cell is increased. This increase is achieved by coupling CO_2 (inorganic carbon) to a particular high-energy 5-carbon organic compound (ribulose-1,5-diphosphate) producing an unstable 6-carbon compound which immediately splits into two molecules of a 3-carbon compound (3-phosphoglycerate). The 3-phosphoglycerate is then reduced to 3-phosphoglyceraldehyde. The coupling of CO_2 to ribulose is a **dark reaction**—no light is required. The other reactions just mentioned also take place in the dark, but it must not be supposed that light has nothing to do with them. To pay for the reduction of glycerate to glyceraldehyde, ATP and NADPH must be used, and these high-energy substances are the "savings" accu-

Fig. 13-7. *Cyclic photophosphorylation. The energy of the excited electron is passed through a series of "carriers" (A through E), during which process two molecules of high-energy ATP are formed; at the conclusion, the electron returns to the ground state. (After "How Cells Transform Energy," by A. L. Lehninger. Copyright © 1961 by Scientific American, Inc. All rights reserved.)*

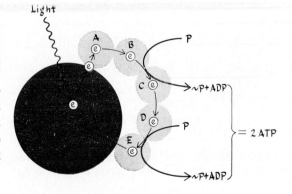

mulated from the process of photophosphorylation.

The 3-phosphoglyceraldehyde is a sort of crossroads in the metabolic network. From it, all the other compounds in the plant cell can be made; which ones *are* made depends on the synthetic abilities of the particular kind of cell, on the general environmental conditions (e.g., acidity or alkalinity), and on the availability of other raw materials (the synthesis of amino acids requires some kind of nitrogen, for example). Compounds like starch and sugar are eminently suited to the storage and transportation of energy in the organism; when finally used, they pay for the synthesis of ATP and NAD (§38, §39), which serve in the most immediate way to pay the costs of metabolism. If a financial analogy will help, ATP and NAD are like the coins required for the metabolic vending machines; sugar and starch are like bank checks which must be converted into coins before the metabolic machinery can be set in operation.

98. The Cycling of Carbon

I sometimes think that never blows so red
The Rose as where some buried Caesar bled;
That every Hyacinth the Garden wears
Dropt in its Lap from some once lovely Head.

Thus did Omar Khayyám (in the words of Edward FitzGerald) poetically state the idea of the cycling of the elements through living organisms. There are a number of ways of representing this process, one of which is by means of the abstraction we call the **carbon cycle.**

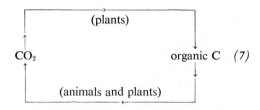

$$CO_2 \quad\quad\quad\quad \text{organic C} \quad (7)$$

Both decarboxylation and carboxylation (removal and addition of CO_2 to an organic molecule) can be carried out by all living organisms. In a nongreen organism, however, if we consider its activities over a considerable period of time, we find that the organism releases more CO_2 than it "fixes"; so the cycle (Equation 7) need not be qualified.

The conversion of organic carbon to CO_2 is carried out by living plants and animals in both respiration and fermentation. In green plants, there is a *net* production of CO_2 only in the dark.

The scheme we have just presented is oversimplified. To develop it closer to the complex reality, we may consider the ways in which carbon is passed from one individual to another. The passage of carbon from plants to animals is accomplished directly; animals eat plants. **Herbivores** (L. *herba* = herb + *vorare* = to devour), such as cattle and rabbits, feed on plants (herbs). **Carnivores** (L. *carnis* = flesh) are also fed by plants, though indirectly. The predaceous dog that eats a rabbit is eating grass "processed" by the rabbit. The chain of organisms *grass ⟶ rabbit ⟶ dog* is called a **predator chain.** There may be many links in such a chain. A bass may eat a minnow that has fed on water fleas that ate protozoa that were nourished by algae. Short or long, the predator chain is eventually anchored to green plants, which are therefore called the *primary producers,* or the *basic industry organisms.*

The passage of carbon *from animal to plant* is not so direct. Cartoons to the contrary, there are no man-eating plants, and the insectivorous ones are quantitatively unimportant. Carbon gets back to plants via the carbon dioxide released into the air by the respiration of both plants and animals. This part of the cycle (Equation 7) would be more accurate if amended to read: *animals ⟶ atmosphere ⟶ plants.*

The biological cycle is only one of the ways in which carbon is circulated. There are several carbon cycles, of which are depicted the most important in Figure 13-8. In each instance, transfer of carbon into the atmosphere (as CO_2) is shown by colored arrow; removal of carbon from atmosphere by black arrow. The

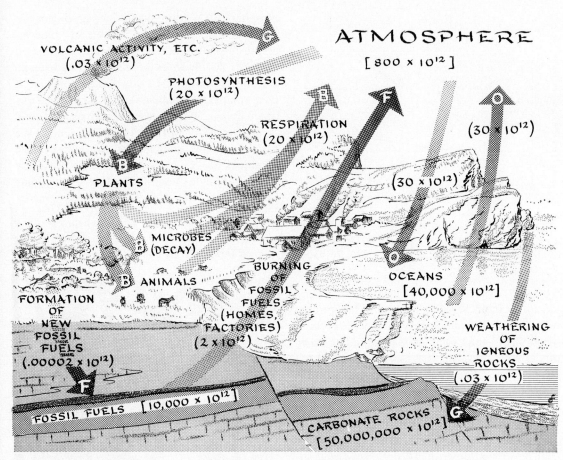

Fig. 13-8. *The major carbon cycles. Amounts of carbon expressed as kilograms of the element. Rates, per year, indicated in parentheses. Total amount in each reservoir shown in square brackets. Colored arrows show transformations to CO_2 of atmosphere; black arrows show removals from atmosphere. G = geological; B = biological; F = fuel; O = oceanic.*

quantities, expressed as kilograms of elemental carbon, are estimates; the errors of the estimates are not precisely known, but the order of magnitude is probably correct. The greatest carbon cycle is the one involving exchanges between the CO_2 of the atmosphere and the bicarbonate of the oceans; this is about 50 percent greater than the biological cycle. The cycle involving geological activities (volcanic eruption, weathering) is much less important* at the present time; during past geological eras it may have been otherwise.

Several cycles can be separated out of Fig. 13-8, as indicated by G for geological, B for

biological, etc. A little thought shows that the cycles so indicated are not mutually exclusive; for instance, the process of fuel formation could quite properly be labeled G for geological. It is labeled F for fuel to call attention to the lack of equality between the rate of formation of fossil fuels and the present rate at which man is using them (the other F arrow). We burn enough coal, petroleum and natural gas each year to put into the atmosphere 2×10^{12} kilograms of carbon, about one-tenth the amount produced by the respiration of all plants and animals. Yearly the amount we burn increases. What is the rate at which carbon is taken out of the atmosphere and returned to the reserves

---

* 13-4. How much less?

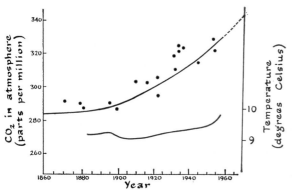

Fig. 13-9. *The rise in CO_2 content of the atmosphere, paralleled by a rise in the average yearly temperature of Vienna, Austria. (Data compiled by G. S. Callendar.)*

mospheric CO_2 (due, say, to increased decay in one year) would be corrected for by some increase in photosynthesis, and some increase in the CO_2 dissolved in the oceans, thus keeping the concentration of CO_2 in the air constant at its normal value of about 0.03 percent. Like any other system with negative feedback, it would be expected to work only within limits. We wonder, as we contemplate the considerable quantities of CO_2 being released into the air by man's burning of fossil fuels, whether the limits

Fig. 13-10. *The "greenhouse effect." Glass is transparent to light rays, but not to heat rays. Soil absorbs light, converting it to heat, which is thus trapped inside the greenhouse.*

of fossil fuel? We don't know. This process takes place in swampy regions where layers of dead plants (and some animals) are laid down under conditions unfavorable for complete microbial decay, there to become peat, the poor-quality fossil fuel that may (given suitable pressure, temperature, and time) become coal. The value given in the diagram for this process is based on the assumption that the present rate is somewhat less than it has been, on the average, for the 350 million years required to produce our present reserve of 10^{16} kilos of fossil carbon. The rate calculated, 2×10^7 kilos of C fossilized per year, is the least reliable of all the statistics given in the figure, but even so, the discrepancy between 2×10^7 (rate of fossilization) and 2×10^{12} (rate of burning) is impressive. We are using our fossil fuels about one hundred thousand times faster than they are being formed. Clearly, this is no balanced system.

99. The Cybernetics of Atmospheric Carbon Dioxide

The operation of three of the four carbon cycles illustrated leads to a cybernetic system that can be diagrammed according to the pattern illustrated previously (§62).† An increase in at-

---

† 13-5. Please do so.

of the adjustive system might not someday be exceeded; and if so, what the consequences would be.

Data gathered over the past century indicate that there has indeed been a rise in the amount of CO_2 in the atmosphere (upper curve, Fig. 13-9). Paralleling this, there has been a rise in the average temperature of the world, as indicated by records of many cities, of which we show only one (lower curve, Fig. 13-9). Is there a causal relationship here, or is this only coincidence? There is good reason to believe the former is the case: that, in fact, an increase in CO_2 in the air has caused a rise in the temperature of the earth. The argument for this belief was first developed by the English physicist John Tyndall, in 1861, before the data exhibited here had been gathered.

The basic concept is that of the **greenhouse effect** of CO_2. Let's see how a greenhouse works (Fig. 13-10). Light rays enter a greenhouse through the glass and strike the soil, which absorbs the radiant energy, thus becoming warmed. The warm soil emits heat rays to which, however, the glass is *not* transparent. The heat rays are thus trapped in the greenhouse. Consequently, the temperature of such a glass-covered house may rise many degrees above the outside temperature. Tyndall pointed out that carbon dioxide is like glass, being less transparent to heat rays than it is to light rays. Atmospheric CO_2 converts the whole earth into a sort of greenhouse, by diminishing the radiation of the earth's heat out into space. The more CO_2 in the air, the greater is this warming effect. Physical calculations indicate that burning all the fossil fuels would cause the average temperature of the earth to rise by at least as much as 6°C, which would give Iceland the climate of France.

This is not, however, the whole story. There is, as Tyndall was the first to postulate, a larger cybernetic scheme (Fig. 13-11) that lowers the CO_2 content of the air, and the temperature, once more. Increased CO_2 results in increased temperature, which melts the glaciers, thus increasing the amount of water in the oceans. Ocean water can absorb much more CO_2 than can the corresponding weight of glacial ice; consequently, CO_2 is now removed from the air faster, and the temperature falls. The rest of the cybernetic scheme can be read from the figure. This system is one with considerable lag in its reactions; consequently, it produces the fluctuations familiar to us in the waxing and waning of glacial ages. We were already well into an interglacial age when we started burning fossil fuels, thus accelerating the warming. In many respects, this might seem a desirable thing. However, we should not forget the vast quantities of water that are now trapped in the icecaps of the poles. Melting all of this ice would raise the level of the oceans by about 30 meters, an amount sufficient to ruin many of the great cities of the world: London, New York, Baltimore, New Orleans, Los Angeles, Bombay, Hamburg, and Amsterdam, to mention only a few. In addition, of course, many

Fig. 13-11. *Cybernetic relations between glaciers and CO_2 content of the atmosphere.*

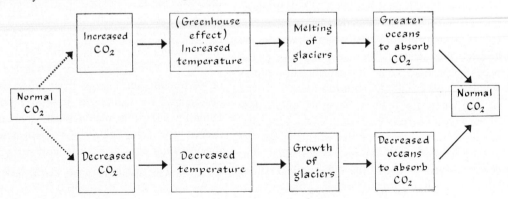

millions of square kilometers of agricultural land would be flooded.

Is this the necessary result of the burning of fossil fuels? So far as we can see at present, Yes. Nature is complicated, of course, and we may have overlooked something. But we must base our expectations (and our actions) on what we know now, not on what we might learn tomorrow. Even with our present knowledge, we can see ways in which the effects of fossil fuel burning can be counteracted. Since the effect of photosynthesis is to remove CO_2 from the air, by increasing the amount of photosynthesis we can remove more CO_2 from the air, thus decreasing the greenhouse effect. How can photosynthesis be increased? Here there is no general answer; rather, the many environments of the world must be examined individually to determine the **limiting factor** in each, that is, the nutrient or other environmental aspect that is keeping plants from growing to the extent that the other, more generously supplied factors would permit. In desert regions, water is obviously a limiting factor; this, man is supplying to an increasing extent by his engineering works. If and when we develop economically feasible means of distilling or de-salting ocean water, the possibility of watering coastal deserts will increase the amount of photosynthesis considerably.

Nitrogen is often a limiting factor, as is phosphorus; these (as well as other nutrients) can be supplied if we make the effort. There are many photosynthetic organisms in the sea, but vast regions of the open oceans are virtual deserts for want of phosphorus. The ocean bottom, by contrast, lacks light but is often rich in phosphorus, nitrogen, and other fertilizing elements. It has been proposed that atomic reactors be lowered into strategically selected places in the ocean to produce heat, thus causing upwellings which would bring rich bottom waters to the surface where the light is. Such are only a few of the as-yet scarcely exploited ways of increasing the photosynthesis of the world. It will be a matter of no small interest to see what man consciously does about the cybernetic systems of the world that he has so far meddled with only unconsciously.

100. The Role of the Biosphere

Among the useful abstractions contributed by Lamarck is that of the **biosphere.** The word is modeled after atmosphere (the sphere of air of the earth), hydrosphere, and lithosphere,* and is a collective term for all the living matter that forms, as it were, a thin scum on the surface of the earth. What is the role of this biosphere in the flux of energy from the sun out into the farthest reaches of interstellar space? We understand what it is when we compare the two pictures in Figure 13-12. The sun radiates energy to all of space. The earth intercepts a tiny fraction of this energy. Before the biosphere appeared (A), this amounted only to a redirection of the radiation (visible earthshine from the irradiated side) or a delay as the earth, warmed by absorption of the radiant energy on the side facing the sun, reradiated it as invisible heat waves later, when the warm side turned away from the sun. When the biosphere came into being, the situation changed somewhat (B). The capture of energy by photosynthesis delays its reradiation to outer space. Sometimes the delay is negligible, as when a molecule of sugar that is synthesized by a chloroplast is metabolized in the colorless cytoplasm a moment later. A bit longer delay occurs when a leaf-synthesized sugar molecule is transported down the phloem to the roots, there to be respired several hours after the capture of the sun's energy. If the molecule is deposited in a storage depot in the root—as it may be in a carrot or a sweet potato—its energy may not be released for many months. Or the plant may fall to the bottom of a swamp, there to be converted to coal or petroleum, the energy from which may not be released for a hundred million years or so. (Small wonder that such deposits are sometimes called "fossil sunlight.") Or, with much less time lag, the energy in a blade of grass may be

* 13-6. What mean these last two terms?

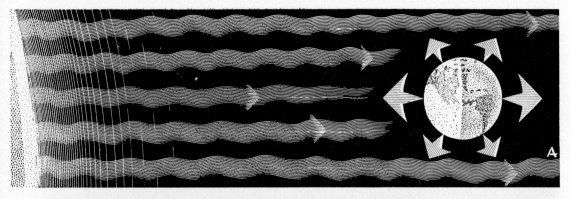

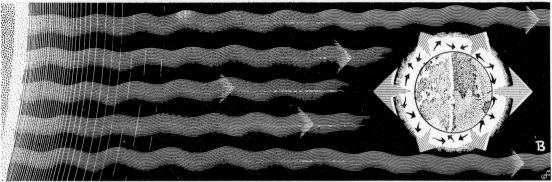

Fig. 13-12. *Effect of the Earth on the dissipation of the Sun's energy into space.* (A) *Before the biosphere developed;* (B) *after. Wavy arrows represent the Sun's radiation. Thick colored arrows represent the Earth's re-radiation of energy received from the Sun. The smallest colored arrows represent transformations of energy in the biosphere.*

transferred successively to a rabbit, to a fox, and then to a hunting dog. Once in the biosphere there is no predicting the exact history of any unit of energy except to say that, after an indefinite number of transfers from organism to organism, and after a greater or lesser delay, this energy, like all other solar energy, will be reradiated to outer space. The biosphere is just a sort of tortuous by-pass in the mainstream of energy passing from the sun to all of interstellar space.

The by-pass carries an astonishingly small fraction of the total flow of energy. A green plant, under optimal conditions, can operate with only about 3 percent efficiency. This is under very precise, expensive laboratory conditions. Under field conditions, a more typical efficiency is 0.3 percent. Even this is a misleading figure, for it fails to take account of the ra-

diant energy the plant cannot use (because of wave lengths of light that are not absorbed by the photosynthetic pigments). Of the total energy that falls on a well-cultivated field of grain, H. A. Spoehr (1922) found that only 0.04 percent was represented in the final product. But this cannot be taken as the efficiency of the whole biosphere, because the capture of solar energy is interfered with by lack of moisture (deserts), lack of needed nutrients (much of the open ocean), low temperature (winter), and the constructions of man. (J. J. Spengler, in 1957, estimated that the United States is covering up 0.5 percent of its cropland each year with highways, homes, and other buildings.) An accurate estimate is not available, but it is probably not too extreme to say that not more than 1 part per 10,000 of the solar energy that strikes the earth passes through the biosphere.

It is not surprising that the most intelligent member of the biosphere should wonder if the proportion cannot be increased.

The amount of energy the sun pours in on the earth is stupendous, but it comes to us so widespread in extent and in so gentle a way that we are seldom impressed by it. The energy of an atomic bomb exploding seems tremendous. Yet consider the area in which total destruction is achieved by this means; this same area receives just as much energy from the sun *in a single day*. But it is much less concentrated in time (fortunately!); and the problem of capturing it for "useful" (to us) purposes bears a resemblance, as the mathematician Warren Weaver has pointed out, to that of gathering a fortune from pennies widely scattered over a landscape: one must use up an appreciable fraction of one's income buying the food and shoe leather required to make the enterprise possible. Solar energy is enormous in amount but diffuse in distribution. Appreciating this geometric reality, we have more respect for the 0.3 percent efficiency of plants.

101. The Future of Life

In the light of the Second Law of Thermodynamics, what can we say about the future of life on earth? The sun is a gigantic atomic power plant in which 4.7×10^9 kilos of matter are converted to energy in every second (an amount roughly equal to the weight of 50 loaded ships of the *Queen Mary* class). So great is the solar mass that, in the approximately 4 billion years the earth has existed, the sun has lost only 0.03 percent of its substance by radiation. It should continue to furnish the earth with an adequate supply of energy for billions of years to come—how many, we are not sure. Sooner or later, it will "run down." So will all the other stars. As regards the cosmos as a whole, the Second Law of Thermodynamics tells us that the energy that is now very unequally distributed throughout the universe will ultimately be equally distributed everywhere, with only such variations as the

laws of probability "permit." Order will be replaced by disorder. In place of a mosaic of hot and cold spots, everywhere the temperature will be lukewarm. There will be no temperature differences to make some parts look light in contrast to other parts, to run any machines, or to maintain life. All will be dark and uniformly warm—but there will be no organisms to feel it. All will be changeless in time—perceptible time will no longer exist because the measurement of time depends on energy differences (a clock must be wound up periodically); and anyway, there will be no sentient beings to perceive time if it did exist. The end state of the universe as a world without light, without sensation, without change, without time—a world epitomized as a *Wärmetod* by German cosmologists —such is the logical conclusion of the Second Law of Thermodynamics.

Is this the whole story? We don't know. It is all we can see *certainly*. Are there other laws of nature that operate in a contrary way, but in so subtle a fashion that we have not yet discovered them? Possibly. Some cosmologists think so. Certain it is, that though the First and Second Laws of Thermodynamics adequately explain the running-down of the world as we observe it today, they do not at all explain how it got "wound up" in the first place, how energy came to be so unequally distributed to begin with. This aspect of cosmological evolution requires an explanation of another sort. When we understand this, we may have to revise our prediction of the ultimate future of life.

102. The Web of Life

Green plants are the primary producers in the economy of nature. Other organisms depend on energy garnered by the plants—energy that is passed on by way of the carbon compounds. When a sheep eats grass, it reprocesses the organic compounds, turning grass protoplasm into sheep protoplasm, converting the chemical energy of the grass into its own chemical energy. In this process, entropy increases. A measure of this is the extent to which the high-energy or-

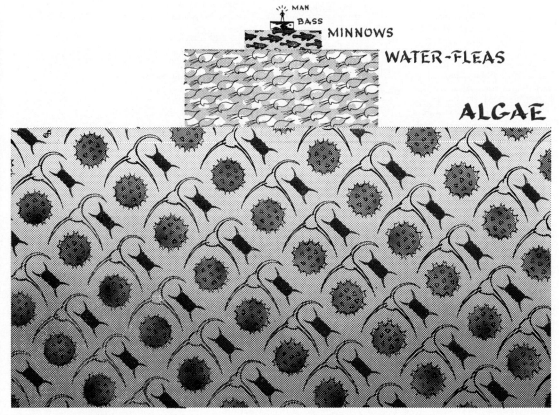

Fig. 13-13. *Biological consequences of the Second Law of Thermodynamics.*

ganic carbon compounds of the grass are degraded to zero-energy carbon dioxide. In round figures, it takes about 10 kilos of organic compounds in the grass to produce 1 kilo in the sheep; that is, about 90 percent of the energy is lost in the act of predation. The precise amount varies with every pair of organisms, but this figure is a typical one and well worth remembering.

Suppose a man living on a lake were to eat only bass. Where would his energy come from? Figure 13-13 is drawn to show the relative masses of protoplasm in each link of the **food chain** supporting man. To produce 1 kilo of man, it takes about 10 kilos of bass, 100 kilos of minnows, 1,000 kilos of water fleas, and 10,000 kilos of algae. The whole conceptual scheme illustrated in Figure 13-13 is called the **Pyramid of Protoplasm.**

Such a pyramid is an abstraction from reality,

for seldom is a predator confined to a single source of food. When we come to study the organisms in any region closely, we discover that a diagram of the food relations among its members produces a sort of **web of life** (a phrase suggested by Darwin). The results of one such study are shown in Figure 13-14. Note that the aspen park land studied can be broken down into smaller units called **communities.** A biological community is rather like a social class among humans, being composed of a number of species that have contact mostly within their own group, though some members also have contacts outside the community. Note, for example, that the insect-eating birds of the "mature poplar community" (a community is usually named after the most conspicuous plants in it) get their food from within the community, whereas the hawks cross over into other communities as well. The food interrelationships are

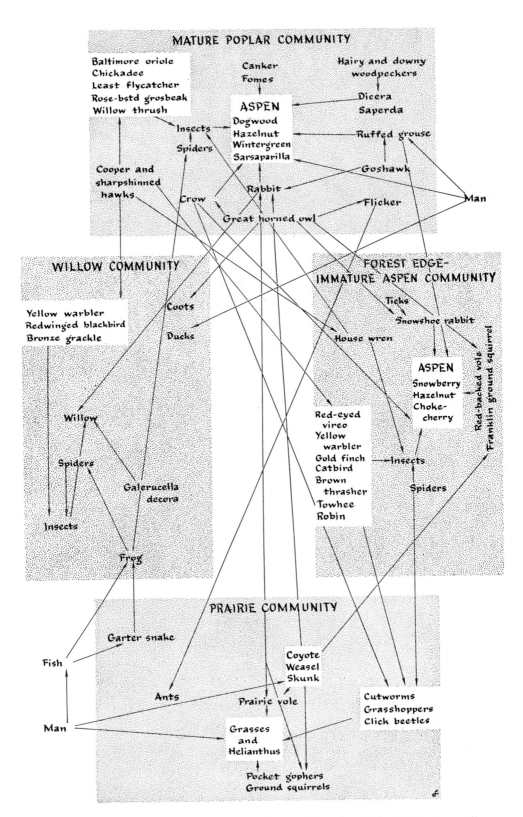

Fig. 13-14. *The web of life in an aspen parkland of Canada. (After Bird; from Allee, et al.,* Principles of Animal Ecology, *W. B. Saunders Co., Philadelphia, 1949.)*

patently complex; but however simple or involved they may be, they can all be ultimately traced back to green plants.

The study of the interactions of living organisms is part of the science of ecology, a science that may be said to be a sort of study of the economics and sociology of all organisms, rather than just the one organism that academic economics and sociology deal with. It is hardly possible to investigate the entire biosphere without having a considerable knowledge of many of its members; therefore, courses in ecology are usually placed late in a biologist's curriculum. Nevertheless, there are a few elementary generalizations from ecological studies that can be presented now.

The first of these concerns the fundamental nature of the struggle for existence, which appears to take many different forms in different species. Parasitic, cannibalistic, herbivorous, and carnivorous animals may appear to be leading very different lives; yet in terms of energy, they are "trying" (metaphorically) to do the same thing plants "try" to do as they grow upward and spread out their leaves. Each is "trying" to get the greatest share possible of the sun's energy. *The struggle for existence,* as Boltzmann said, *is the struggle for free energy.*

The struggle for existence is a struggle partly with other organisms, partly with the nonliving environment (we continue to speak metaphorically). Where the physical conditions of life are severe, as in the Arctic zone, most of the struggle is with the environment; in a tropical rain forest, by contrast, most of it is with other organisms. In the first case, there are few species and the web of life is relatively simple. In the second, there are so many organisms doing so many things that it is impossible to see any but the major interrelationships. The two situations contrast in another way: in their stability. A community with few species can be easily altered in its composition by "accidents." Everyone knows about the Arctic lemmings and their violent fluctuations in numbers. This is not the only example of this sort from the Far North, where the web of life is simple. A tropical forest, by contrast, shows no such epidemics. The

multiple interrelationships of species produces so many checks and balances, as it were, that any incipient epidemic is nipped in the bud. Complexity produces stability. In a tropical rain forest the members of any one species of tree, for example, are so widely scattered that an observer often cannot see from one to another. Only when man comes in and (for his own purposes) destroys the forest does a different development occur. In razed areas there may grow up immense stands of a relatively few species of plants, forming an impenetrable thicket (which the original and undisturbed "jungle" did not). This thicket is unstable; it changes decade by decade until ultimately something like the original stable forest is reestablished. Such a succession of communities in time is called an ecological succession.

103. What It Means to Be "Top Dog"

At about the time Charles Darwin was working on his *Origin of Species,* many thinkers, not all of them biologists, were becoming keenly aware of the all-pervasiveness of the struggle for existence. The poet Tennyson spoke of "Nature, red in tooth and claw." Yet many amateur naturalists thought this phrase a poetic exaggeration, since one almost never saw any bloodshed during one's Sunday walk in the park. It was one of Darwin's tasks to call attention to the illusion of noncompetition, and to correct it.

In a fundamental sense Boltzmann was right when he said that the struggle for existence is a struggle for available energy, and yet in a day-to-day sense—most of the time—in most places—it is not the available energy that determines the number of any species. It is, as Darwin said, "not the obtaining food, but the serving as prey to other animals, which determines the average number of a species." Starvation is a rare event in nature. It occurs occasionally (seasonally, for many over-wintering birds). It occurs in the simplest of food pyramids (e.g., in the Arctic). And significantly, it is most likely to occur at the top of the Pyramid of Protoplasm, to afflict the "top dog" of the pyramid.

Plants, at the bottom of the pyramid, compete directly for energy, and yet the greater part of their mortality is not directly, or solely, attributable to starvation. On one plot of ground, Darwin mapped 357 seedlings of the native weeds appearing in the spring; of these, no less than 295 were destroyed by their predators, mostly slugs and insects. And so it is for every one of the levels of the pyramid except one. Predation, not starvation, controls most populations.

Predation is often not a random matter. Careful observation of hawks, for example, has shown that the smaller birds that they catch are usually young, sick, or for some other reason in less than perfect vigor. Selective predation is one of the main reasons that we so seldom see sick or weak organisms in nature. If the thought of sanguinary nature disturbs our meditations, "we may console ourselves," as Darwin said, "with the full belief that the war of nature is not incessant, that no fear is felt, that death is generally prompt, and that the vigorous, the healthy and the happy survive and multiply."

Only at the top of the pyramid does starvation become a common phenomenon. One is far more likely to see a lean and hungry lion ("the king of the jungle") than one is to see anything but a plump and well-fed mouse. Starvation is one of the privileges of the "top dog." Man, who is assuredly at the top of a pyramid, has enjoyed this privilege during all of recorded history. Even today, the most competent students of population say that two-thirds of the world's population is either starving or living under the threat of starvation. Does that surprise you? Do you doubt it? Then remember the inevitable *bias* involved in the writing and reading of books. Only people who are well fed can indulge in the luxury of writing and reading books; it is small wonder that writers (well fed) so seldom write about what they have no direct, personal knowledge of, nor that readers (also well fed) show so little desire to read about so painful a subject.

All "top dogs" share the right of starvation. Man, the "toppest" dog of them all, has developed another right, one that is scarcely known elsewhere in the living world: the right to die a "natural" death. The quotation marks are amply justified. Only a minority of species with sharply defined life cycles (e.g., Mayflies, which die at the end of a day of adult life) enjoy a "natural" death. For the rest, predation selectively removes weakening individuals long before they can die of old age. It is no paradox to say that natural death is rather unnatural. As man diminishes the effectiveness of disease and starvation in controlling his numbers, he increases the likelihood of dying unnaturally—that is "naturally." Concomitant with this change there is an increase in the commonness of senility, a condition that is the greatest rarity in all organisms but man, a condition that creates problems for the solution of which man looks in vain throughout the rest of the living world.

It is no light matter to be at the very top of the Pyramid of Protoplasm.

Questions and Problems

13-7. Make a list of the **boldface** terms in this chapter and write a brief description of each. Compare your work with the text.

13-8. Give the contribution, and the approximate date, of each of the following men to the topics discussed in this chapter: Boltzmann, Darwin, de Saussure, Engelmann, Ingenhousz, Priestley, Tyndall.

13-9. List the foods you ate in your most recent dinner. Trace the energy available in each food back to its ultimate source by a plausible path.

13-10. Trace the energy available in the electric wires of your house back to its ultimate source.

‡13-11. Frederick Soddy, one of the co-discoverers of chemical isotopy, once remarked that we

should speak of "tomic energy" rather than "atomic energy." His argument was based on etymology. Reconstruct it.

13-12. At Abidjan, on the Ivory Coast of Africa, there is a temperature differential of 38°C in a depth of about 500 meters of ocean. It has been proposed that this differential be used to generate electricity. If the attempt is successful, will this be an escape from dependence on the sun for energy? Explain.

‡13-13. During the Second World War, the people of Holland, who were suffering from food shortages, cut their poultry flocks to one-quarter their usual size. In crowded countries like Holland, poultry are fed largely on grain. Was killing poultry a sound food conservation measure or not? Explain.

13-14. There was once a man who proposed to make money by setting up a rat and cat farm. He would grow rats to feed the cats. When the cats were big enough, he would kill them and sell the fur to furriers, who would make "mink" coats of them. The cat carcasses he would feed to the rats. With this closed carbon cycle, he figured he needed to buy a quantity of grain for the rats exactly equal to the weight of the cats' furs. Okay?

‡13-15. An automobile manufacturer makes two cars, one of which (model G) has twice as much glass area as the other (model A). Both cars are otherwise identically equipped, with heater, radio, air conditioner, cigar lighter, and spare tire. Which car gets the better gasoline mileage? Why?

13-16. You have probably noticed that the windows of greenhouses are whitewashed in summer. Why?

‡13-17. As regards only the greenhouse effect, the covering up of agricultural land by highways will tend to have what effect on the climate?

13-18. The maximum temperature inside the cylinders of a Diesel engine reaches about 480°C. Suppose we put an entire engine inside a chamber held at 480°C. Neglecting deleterious effects on oil, rubber, and so on, how would you expect the engine to run in that chamber?

‡13-19. Among "primitive" peoples, many vegetarian societies are known. There are also many societies that live almost entirely on the meat of such animals as deer and antelope. But no societies are known that subsist principally on the meat of such animals as wolves, wildcats, and lions. Why not?

13-20. A stable population of humans lives mostly on grain. Then a new religion arises that insists that salvation is open only to the eaters of meat. What would be the consequences to the tribe adopting the new religion?

‡13-21. Charles Elton (p. 148 of *The Ecology of Invasions by Animals and Plants*) tells how he once spent an hour lecturing on the subject of sudden insect outbreaks in forests, only to be met with polite uninterest on the part of his audience of three professional foresters. When he learned that these men worked in British Guiana, British Honduras, and tropical India, the reason for the uninterested attitude became plain. What was it?

13-22. What does the German word *Wärmetod* mean? What is its application to cosmology?

‡13-23. Careful measurements made early in the twentieth century showed that the mean CO_2 content of the air in early spring was 0.02971 percent; in the late summer it was 0.02905 percent. Account for the difference.

13-24. Suppose, by some strange quirk, all heterotrophs were destroyed instantly, leaving only autotrophic organisms; and suppose also that no further evolution occurs.

Describe the consequences as completely as you can.

13-25. A manufacturer of burial caskets boasts that his product will give "eternal protection to your loved ones." If his claim were true, and if all men used his product, what would be the eventual result?

Readings

Thirring's *Energy for Man* is an excellent introduction to problems of this sort. For two sound and interesting discussions of ecology, see Elton's *Animal Ecology* and Odum's *Fundamentals of Ecology*. If you find the cosmological implications of the Second Law of Thermodynamics depressing, you might read Bertrand Russell's essay, "A Free Man's Worship," published in his collection *Logic and Mysticism*.

Scientific American Offprints

91. Albert L. Lehninger. *How Cells Transform Energy*

122. J. A. Bassham. *The Path of Carbon in Photosynthesis*

14

Algae:
The Grass
of the Waters

104. The Classification of Organisms

Man, looking at the world and trying to make sense of it, classifies its diverse elements. There are at least a million different kinds of plants and animals. How one classifies these is determined by one's interests and the intellectual climate of the times. St. Augustine (354–430 A.D.), homocentric in his point of view (as was characteristic of his period), divided all animals into three groups: useful, hurtful, and superfluous. A thousand years later we find one L'Ecluse dividing flowers into two groups: those with sweet scent, and those with no scent. Another man, Carrichter, divided plants according to the twelve signs of the zodiac; and yet another, Frey, divided animals according "as they exhort us to virtue or deter us from vice." However interesting may be these systems of classification, they scarcely satisfy a modern biologist, who wants a "natural" system of classification of organisms, that is, one based on the probable evolutionary relationships. A century of investigation and thought has led to the general belief that the reproductive structures and systems are the most reliable indicators of fundamental (evolutionary) relationships, and it is for this reason that life cycles are emphasized in discussing plants.

Although we regard our system of classification as a more or less adequate reflection of the results of evolution, this system was in large part devised by men who did not believe in evolution. Linnaeus, who proposed one of the earliest schemes, believed in the fixity of species, as did almost all of his successors for the next century. In spite of this, the logical scheme devised by these taxonomists was substantially the sort that would have been developed by evolutionists, had they done the work from the beginning.

The basic framework of the modern system of classification is exhibited in Table 14-1, in the first column of which are listed the various categories, from the most inclusive, the kingdom, down to the least inclusive, the species; and in which, as particular examples, we give the classification of a dog in the animal kingdom, and a dandelion in the plant kingdom. For the beginner, learning the name of every classificatory category of an organism is too much of a chore; therefore, in this text an organism will

TABLE 14-1 *The Classification of Organisms, with Two Examples.*

CATEGORY	DOG	DANDELION
Kingdom	Animal	Plant
Phylum	Chordata	Pterophyta
Class	Mammalia	Angiospermae
Order	Carnivora	Asterales
Family	Canidae	Compositae
Genus	*Canis*	*Taraxacum*
Species	*familiaris*	*vulgare*

usually be referred to only by its generic name, and will be further classified only to its **phylum.** The *phyla* (plural) are the largest subdivisions of a kingdom.

Taxonomists differ in their opinions on the best way of subdividing the kingdoms. The issues involved are technical ones that we need not here concern ourselves with. It is, however, a convenience to use some system, and for that reason we present a classification of the plant kingdom in Table 14-2. The phyla there distin-

TABLE 14-2   *Plants: The Principal Phyla and a Few of the Classes.*

PHYLUM	APPROX. NUMBER OF SPECIES	SOME BETTER-KNOWN MEMBERS
Schizophyta		
Class: Schizomycetes	20,000	Bacteria
Class: Schizophyceae	1,500	Blue-green algae
Myxomycophyta	400	Slime molds (Myxomycetes)
Eumycophyta	74,000	True fungi; molds, mushrooms
Euglenophyta	300	Euglenoid algae, including *Euglena*
Chlorophyta	5,700	Green algae
Chrysophyta	5,700	Diatoms
Pyrrophyta	1,000	Dinoflagellates
Phaeophyta	900	Brown algae
Rhodophyta	2,500	Red algae
Bryophyta	24,000	Mosses, liverworts
Psilophyta	3	Genus *Psilotum*
Lycophyta	500	Clubmosses
Sphenophyta	100	Horsetails
Pterophyta		
Class: Filicinae	10,000	Ferns
Class: Gymnospermae	670	Conifers
Class: Angiospermae	200,000	Flowering plants

guished are widely (though not universally) accepted by contemporary plant taxonomists. The table is not complete: no phylum known only from fossil specimens is included, and a few of the "living phyla" of lesser importance have also been omitted.

105. General Characteristics of the Algae

Having presented a formal classification of the plant kingdom, we will now proceed to ignore it by talking about the **algae,** a group that has no official existence. The word is used as a collective term for at least seven different phyla. Algae is a Latin word that means seaweed (sing. *alga*). With few exceptions, "seaweeds" are algae, as are many thousands of microscopic species. All these plants are *nonvascular;* that is, they have no elements for the transport of fluids (i.e. no phloem or xylem). They can afford this simplicity, for they are, with only a few exceptions, water-dwelling forms. The exceptional species are generally small in size, for example, the "moss" (usually an alga species) that traditionally grows on the north side* of trees, as well as other algae that grow in the fur of sloths. Such land-dwelling species have not really solved the problems of land existence —of which we will have more to say later—and are metabolically active only in very moist places (e.g., on rocks near waterfalls) or in times of moisture (e.g., for a short while after a rain).

In spite of exceptions, algae are really water-dwelling forms. This is one of the many reasons for believing that included in the algae are the most "primitive" of plants, that is, plants that are most nearly like the first ones that appeared on earth. The "protoplasm" of all living things is mostly water (e.g., onion—87 percent; chicken—71 percent; human, newborn—76 percent; human, adult—60 percent). Obtaining and conserving water are great problems for land-dwelling plants and animals, for the solving of which many and complex adaptations have been evolved. It is unreasonable to suppose that the first living organisms could have come into being on land. The first plants must have been not too different from some of the present-day algae.

That does not mean that all algae are primi-

---

* 14-1. Why the north side? Since there's more light on the south, wouldn't the plant be able to photosynthesize more, hence thrive better, on the south?

tive—far from it. Many of the algae are quite complicated in structure, and some of their life cycles are as complicated as those of land plants. In other words, while evolution has been taking place on land, so also has it been taking place in the water. We will survey some of the results of this evolution. Much of the time we will be concerned merely with the characteristics of the organisms themselves. At other times, we will be interested in trying to figure out their evolutionary position. In the latter attempt, we will, for the most part, have to depend on plausible reasoning, because the geological evidence of ancient algae is meager indeed. Most algae have no hard parts at all, and few make good fossils. Nevertheless we now have convincing evidence of fossil algae at least two billion years old.

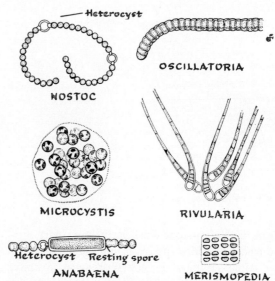

Fig. 14-1. *Some common blue-green algae. (Not drawn to the same scale.)*

106. The Blue-Greens

There are various reasons for believing that the blue-greens are among the most primitive of the algae. The oldest fossil algae yet found, in the pre-Cambrian rocks of Ontario, look like members of this phylum. No members of this group have ever been found to indulge in sexual reproduction: multiplication is by cell division only—hence the name of the class, **Schizophyceae,** or "splitting plants." (The phylum is **Shizophyta,** the other class of which includes the bacteria.) The nucleus, identified by its high concentration of DNA, does not seem to have the structure of the nuclei of higher organisms, and does not (so far as we can see) undergo mitosis. How, then, in the absence of equational division, do both daughter cells manage to get a complete set of genes, and a balanced one (i.e., not too many of one kind)? Or do they always manage to do so? These important genetic puzzles have not been solved. Obviously, in cells that have no sex, it is difficult to follow the distribution of genes.

Members of some common genera of blue-greens are shown in Figure 14-1. Some filamentous genera, such as *Oscillatoria,* are capable of slow, writhing movements, the mechanism for

which is still not understood. No other kind of motility occurs in this class. Many blue-greens live on moist earth and can withstand long dry spells; these are among the important colonizers of new, bare land, particularly in the tropics. Some species are capable of withstanding high temperatures, metabolizing at 70°C. Reports of algae living in waters much hotter than this are probably erroneous, either because the temperature of the precise spot (the **microenvironment**) where the alga occurs was not determined, or because it was not noticed that the alga was merely surviving for a while a temperature too high for it to carry on normal metabolism.

All blue-greens photosynthesize, but unlike other plants they have only one kind of chlorophyll, **chlorophyll** *a,* a pigment found in all photosynthetic plants with the exception of the photosynthetic bacteria. There are no chloroplasts in the blue-greens, the photosynthetic pigment being scattered throughout the cell in small granules. There is also always a blue pigment, called **phycocyanin,** which is probably involved in the capture of radiant energy. Many species contain additional pigments of uncertain function, the color of which may mask the basic blue-green color. The wide variety of colors seen in the outflow terraces of the gey-

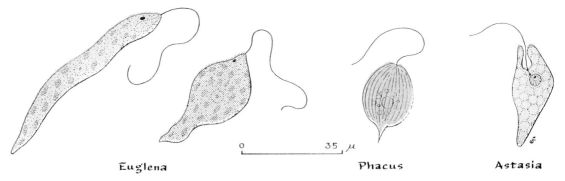

Euglena   Phacus   Astasia

Fig. 14-2. *Some euglenoids.*

sers of Yellowstone Park is in large part produced by various species of blue-greens.

Although they do not reproduce sexually,
many of the Schizophyceae produce a resistant
state called a **resting spore** (Fig. 14-1). Some
species produce thick-walled cells called **heter-
ocysts;** these are said to serve no function,
which is most remarkable.* Many species secrete a gelatinous material (stippled in Fig.
14-1); *Nostoc,* for example, is often seen on
bare rocks in the form of hard gelatinous hemispheres, perhaps a centimeter in diameter, and
frequently almost black in color.

107. The Euglenoids: Plants or Animals?

A characteristic feature of a euglenoid cell is
the **flagellum,** a whiplike structure at the anterior end. Some cells have an additional, much
smaller flagellum near the principal one, but
special microscopic techniques are required to
see it. Sexual reproduction is almost unknown
in this phylum. All members have a single, readily stainable nucleus. Most euglenoids are of a
clear bright-green color, containing the same
two kinds of chlorophyll found in the higher
plants—namely, chlorophyll *a* and **chlorophyll
*b***—in a definite chloroplast. The basic green
color is sometimes obscured by a red pigment,
particularly in cells that are in, or entering into,

a resting stage. A few genera are colorless, that
is, without chlorophyll, and hence incapable of
photosynthesis; such a one is *Astasia* (Fig.
14-2). Colorless forms live by absorbing dissolved organic foodstuffs from their environment, a kind of nutrition called **saprophytic** (Gr.
sapros = rotten). The nutrition even of the
photosynthetic green euglenoids is, apparently,
in part saprophytic, for they are most abundant
in waters that are rich in organic substances,
for example, in the well-manured puddles of
horse corrals. Experimentally, *Euglena* (which
is green) can be kept alive in the dark in organic solutions. Sometimes it loses its green
color when so maintained for a long period of
time, thus coming to resemble *Astasia.*

One of the classic questions of elementary
biology is: *Is Euglena a plant or an animal?* It
is important to see the sense in which it is an
unanswerable question. When we ask, "What
is a plant?" we really mean, "How do we *define*
a plant?" No single criterion for distinguishing
plants and animals has proved satisfactory, but
instead three are commonly cited. Plants have
(1) *chlorophyll,* (2) *cellulose,* and (3) *indeterminate growth,* that is, a pattern of growth in
which the precise limits and outlines of the
adult form are not determinable beforehand
(contrast ivy with an elephant). If an organism
shows all three of these characteristics, we un-
hesitatingly call it a plant. But if it has only one
or two, we are sometimes doubtful. *Euglena*
looks very animal-like in its movements—
though note, motility was not given as one of
the *differentia* of plants and animals in the

---

* 14-2. Why remarkable? What evolutionary pre-
supposition is responsible for making such a statement?

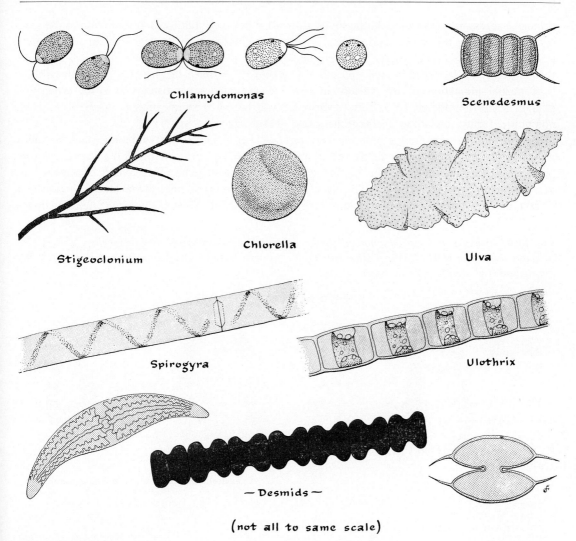

Chlamydomonas

Scenedesmus

Stigeoclonium

Chlorella

Ulva

Spirogyra

Ulothrix

— Desmids —

(not all to same scale)

Fig. 14-3. *Some green algae.*

above list. *Euglena* has chlorophyll; its growth is normally determinate (as is true of microscopic plants generally), but under certain conditions many euglenas will lose their flagella and clump together in a *palmella* phase. *Euglena* is discussed in both botany and zoology texts. What one *calls* it is a matter of definition, and, in a sense, unimportant. More important is it that the euglenoids look like connecting links between animals and plants, that is, intermediate forms through which plants may have evolved to become animals.*

_____
* 14-3. Or vice versa?

108. The Green Algae

The phylum **Chlorophyta** includes almost 400 genera, living in a wide variety of habitats, ranging from concentrated brine to fresh mountain water. "Red snow" is produced by species in which a red pigment masks the green, under certain environmental conditions. The phylum is a predominantly fresh-water phylum. It is generally believed that from this group evolved the higher plants. Among the characteristics in which the green algae resemble the higher plants are the following: The chlorophylls present are always chlorophyll *a* and chlorophyll *b*; the principal accessory pigments (xanthophylls and carotenoids) are the same as in the higher plants; the principal food reserve is starch; and the chlorophyll is localized in chloroplasts.

A partial indication of the variety in this phylum is shown in Figure 14-3. Besides various nonmotile forms, including filamentous ones, many species are rendered motile by two or more flagella. Most species exhibit sexual reproduction. In some species, the uniting cells are indistinguishable; in other species, they are clearly distinguishable as two different types.

It is believed that the differentiation of the sexes that characterizes the higher plants was evolved in this phylum. To indicate how such an evolution *might* have taken place, we shall consider a graduated series of species in the order Volvocales. (For the meaning of "order," see Table 14-1 again.)

The genus **Chlamydomonas** includes hundreds of species, all of which are single cells with two flagella. The basic structures and typical reproductive behavior are shown in Figure 14-4. Most of the time, reproduction is

Fig. 14-4. *Structure and reproduction of the green alga* Chlamydomonas. *Haploid cells in color; diploid in black.* (*From Fuller and Tippo,* College Botany, *copyright 1949, by permission Henry Holt and Co., Inc.*)

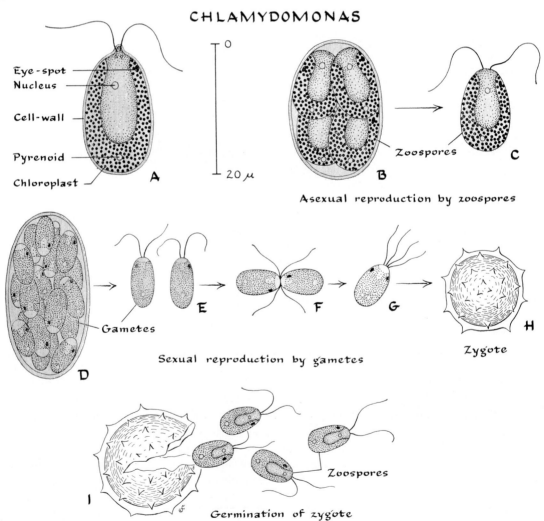

CHLAMYDOMONAS

Eye-spot
Nucleus
Cell-wall
Pyrenoid
Chloroplast
A
20 μ
B
C
Zoospores

Asexual reproduction by zoospores

D
Gametes
E
F
G
H
Zygote

Sexual reproduction by gametes

I
Zoospores

Germination of zygote

asexual. Within the rigid cell wall one or more fissions occur, producing two or more daughter cells, called zoospores, which break out of the parental cell wall and swim away as new cells (Fig. 14-4*B, C*). Occasionally, perhaps in response to an unfavorable environment, the cell divisions taking place within the parental cell wall are more numerous, resulting in the production of many smaller cells (Fig. 14-4*D*), which, because of their subsequent behavior, are called **gametes.** When the parental cell wall breaks, these gametes swim out and unite with one another.

In some species of *Chlamydomonas,* any two gametes can unite; in others, the gametes derived from different lines (or clones), although indistinguishable morphologically, prove to be functionally different. If one calls one type + and the other −, mating can occur only between a + gamete and a − gamete. A species in which uniting gametes must come from different clones is called a **heterothallic** species. (A species in which uniting gametes can come from a single clone is said to be **homothallic.**)

The union of two gametes produces a thick-walled zygote (Fig. 14-4*H*), which is usually a resting stage capable of withstanding unfavorable environmental factors. Before the zygote

germinates, it undergoes meiosis to produce four haploid zoospores (Fig. 14-4*I*). In homothallic species two of these are +, two −. After release from the zygote case, each zoospore, by mitosis, produces a clone of haploid cells like itself. The greater part of the life cycle of this alga is, therefore, haploid. For comparison with genera to be described below, we introduce another term: **isogamy.** *Chlamydomonas,* whose gametes (whether homothallic or heterothallic) look alike, is said to be **isogamous** ("equal gametes").

The genus *Pandorina* exhibits a further stage of complexity. Individuals of this genus are multicellular; typically there are 16 cells to an individual colony (Fig. 14-5). The individual cells look like compressed *Chlamydomonas* cells; indeed, when *Pandorina* is grown in laboratory culture under not quite optimum conditions, it "degenerates" into a culture of unicells indistinguishable from *Chlamydomonas* cells. Normal asexual reproduction is accomplished by the division of each cell of a colony into a complete new colony of cells, or zoospores (Fig. 14-5*B*). When the process of cell division is completed, the gelatinous covering of the parental colony ruptures, releasing the sixteen new colonies, which swim away independently. This

Fig. 14-5. *Structure and reproduction of the green alga* Pandorina. *Haploid cells in color; diploid in black.*

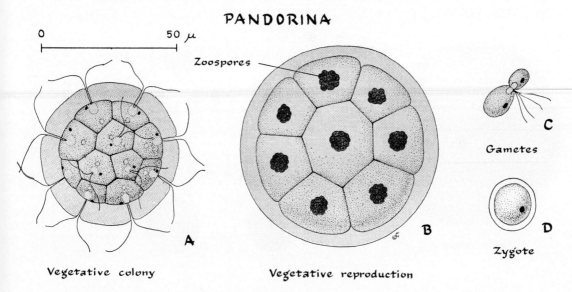

PANDORINA

0   50 μ

Zoospores

Gametes

C

A

B

D

Zygote

Vegetative colony   Vegetative reproduction

phenomenon reminded an early observer of the story of Pandora's box, hence the name of the genus.

When *Pandorina* reproduces sexually, it does so by the production of numerous small gametes, which, however, occur in two different sizes; hence the genus is said to be **heterogamous** ("different gametes"). The union of the unequal gametes produces a zygote. The subsequent events are much the same as in *Chlamydomonas.*

In the genus *Volvox,* differentiation of the two types of gametes is carried even further. A *Volvox* colony consists of a large number of *Chlamydomonas*-like cells (Fig. 14-6*A*), sometimes as many as 50 thousand. Asexual reproduction is accomplished by the formation of daughter colonies by repeated cell division within the parental colony; only some of the cells of the parental colony have the ability to form daughter colonies. From time to time, daughter colonies escape from the parental colony, increase in size, and repeat this part of the cycle. After about 10–20 asexual generations, sexual reproduction takes place. Most species of *Volvox* are heterothallic, as indicated in Figure 14-6*B,* in which is shown a small portion of each of two different colonies. One col-

ony, which we may properly call a male colony, produces only tiny biflagellate cells, called sperm. These cells are produced within a special structure of the parental colony, a structure called an **antheridium.** A female colony produces an analogous organ, called an **oögonium,** inside which a *single* female gamete, or egg, is formed. The egg is not only much larger than the sperm, but it is nonmotile. Organisms like *Volvox* are said to exhibit **oögamy.** The motile sperm swims to the egg; one sperm unites with each egg to form a diploid cell, the zygote. The zygote here, as in other Volvocales, is a thick-walled structure capable of withstanding unfavorable circumstances. During its germination, meiosis takes place.

In retrospect, several trends are apparent in the *Chlamydomonas-Pandorina-Volvox* series. First, there is a trend to multicellularity. The individual in *Chlamydomonas* is a single cell; in *Pandorina,* a colony of 16 cells; and in *Volvox,* a colony of thousands of cells. Second, specialization accompanies increase in cell number. In *Pandorina,* all of the cells seem to be alike; but in *Volvox,* the whole colony, as it rolls through the water, rolls in such a way that one portion is usually first, or anterior; furthermore, only some of the cells of *Volvox* are ca-

Fig. 14-6. Left: *A single* Volvox *individual.* Right: *Portions of male and female individuals shown in greater magnification. Note sexual reproduction and the production of a zygote, a diploid cell.*

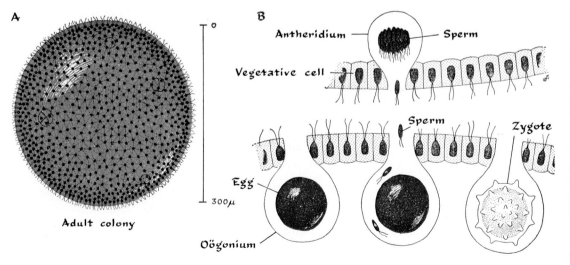

pable of vegetative (asexual) reproduction. Third, with respect to sex, the series shows a progressive change from isogamy to heterogamy to oögamy. All plants "above" the algae exhibit oögamy.

It must be emphasized that, in pointing out the "progressive" nature of this series, we do *not* assert that *Volvox* evolved from *Pandorina,* and *Pandorina* from *Chlamydomonas.* We do not have fossil records to justify such an assertion. This particular evolution *might* have occurred, but we do not know that it did. The series shows the *sort* of evolution that we suspect occurred, whatever were the genera involved. Seldom can we, with confidence, assert what species evolved from what. But as speculative beings (and all men are speculative), we like to figure out how things might have happened. Multicellular organisms most probably evolved from unicellular ones; organisms in which the sexes are sharply differentiated probably evolved, through several stages, from isogamous organisms. Consideration of a series of organisms such as this one in the Volvocales (and similar series exist in other orders of algae) shows us at least the sort of course evolution may have taken.

109. The Diatoms

The phylum **Chrysophyta** (the golden-brown algae) includes several subphyla, of which we shall consider only one: those organisms known as **diatoms.** The chlorophylls of these organisms are chlorophyll *a* and **chlorophyll *c*;** in addition, there is always present an accessory brownish pigment, **fucoxanthin.** The food reserves sometimes include an insoluble carbohydrate but never starch; a more characteristic food reserve in this group is oil. Many of the elongate, bilaterally symmetrical diatoms move by some poorly understood mechanism that perhaps involves the continuous movement of a thin sheet of "protoplasm" from one end of the cell to the other, much as the tread of a caterpillar tractor moves. Flagellated cells are rare. Sexual reproduction occurs in many species.

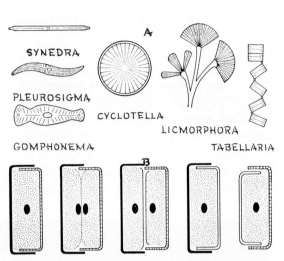

Fig. 14-7. (A) *Various diatoms.* (B) *The method of cell division. Recent evidence indicates that many (most?) diatoms are diploid, but more investigation of this point is needed. (From Wilson and Loomis, Botany, rev. ed., Dryden Press, New York, 1957, courtesy Holt, Rinehart, and Winston.)*

A most striking characteristic of diatoms is the possession of a cell wall made of two halves, or *valves,* one of which fits over the other after the manner of a typewriter-ribbon box (Fig. 14-7*B*). These valves, or "shells," are commonly said to be of *silica,* the substance of which common sand is composed, but this statement arises from a misinterpretation of experimental results. The valves of a diatom are strongly and characteristically marked; species are identified by their characteristic markings. To see the valve markings easily, diatoms are treated with strong, hot acid solution that destroys all of the organic material. Following this treatment, a chemical analysis of the remaining shell shows that it is composed of silica. But there is little question but that, before the destructive treatment, the element silicon is present in some other compound, probably as an organic silicon compound, that is, a compound that contains both carbon and silicon. The significance of the shells in the life of diatoms is not known. It is doubtful that a shell can furnish protection to such a small organism. Perhaps the large amount of surface presented by the sculpturing of the shell aids metabolic reactions; we don't know.

Figure 14-8 shows the markings on one of the larger diatoms. Whatever significance such sculpturing may have to the organism, it has excited the wonder of biologists ever since the resolving power of microscopes became great enough to reveal it. The nineteenth century was a time when, as never before or since, amateur scientists flourished and made important contributions to scientific knowledge. Diatoms were a great favorite with these amateurs. In our day of multimillion dollar research projects it is rather touching to read the confessions of scientific faith of this earlier, simpler day. Consider, for instance, the closing words of the

Fig. 14-8. *Structure of a large marine planktonic diatom,* Arachnoidiscus ehrenbergii; *diameter about 350 microns. (Photo copyright by General Biological Supply House, Inc. Chicago.)*

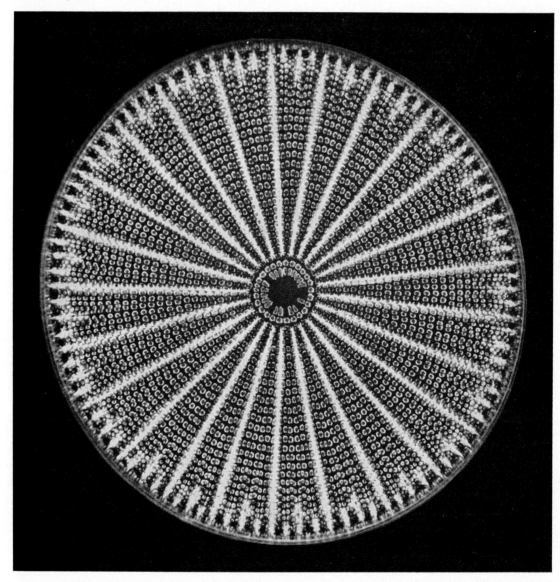

introduction to the Rev. William Smith's two-volume work (1853) on the British diatomaceae:

Weather permitting, the collector may always reckon upon well-filled bottles, provided his rambles are by the sea-coast, or through a district supplied with ponds or streams. I take my leave of him for the present, by recommending to his pursuit a study pregnant with interest and with beauty: which fills the mind with wonder in the contemplation of forms at once so minute and perfect, so humble in their individual capacity, and yet by their numbers and wide diffusion occupying an important position in the organic world, and fulfilling the purposes of Power, Wisdom and Benignity.

Though the diatoms may have been "humble", their observers were not always so. Imbued with the strong British spirit of sportsmanship, the wealthier amateurs competed with each other in resolving the minute markings of the most difficult diatoms. Microscopists subsidized the best microscope makers, whom they urged on to ever greater efforts with bonuses for higher resolving power. The activities of these "diatomaniacs" are generally credited with hastening the perfection of the optical microscope.

Diatoms are found almost everywhere there is water: in streams, in soil, and in the oceans. Marine diatoms, and to a lesser extent marine dinoflagellates (see the following section), carry out most of the photosynthesis that takes place in the ocean. Because, directly or indirectly, diatoms are the principal source of food of all marine animals, they are often called the "grass of the sea." It is probable that most petroleum is derived from ancient diatoms.

When diatoms die and their organic material has decayed, the residual silica shells sink to the bottom of the water, where they accumulate. The extent of past accumulations of this sort is almost unbelievable. Near Lompoc, California, there is a deposit of nearly pure diatom shells that is about 1 kilometer thick and covers an area of 30 square kilometers.

The material in such beds is called **diatoma-ceous earth.** The lightness of its intricately sculptured particles and their noninflammability makes this material well suited to the manufacture of insulating boards for buildings. Because of the great amount of surface presented by a mass of such shells, diatomaceous earth is a very effective filtering agent, and is used in the filtering of oil, beer, and other fluids. The minuteness and hardness of its particles make diatomaceous earth useful for scouring and polishing.

110. The Dinoflagellates

"In looking at Nature," said Darwin, "it is most necessary . . . never to forget that every single organic being may be said to be striving to the utmost to increase in numbers; that each lives by a struggle at some period of its life; that heavy destruction inevitably falls either on the young or old during each generation or at recurrent intervals. *Lighten any check, mitigate the destruction ever so little, and the number of the species will almost instantaneously increase to any amount.*"

The truth of the sentence we have italicized is periodically brought home to the people of Florida whenever "red water" appears off the coast. Acres of the ocean turn reddish-brown as the dinoflagellate organisms multiply by the billions. In red water areas, fish die by the millions (apparently because of a toxin produced by the microorganisms); the finny corpses, thrown up in fragrant windrows on the beach, remind the inhabitants of the profligacy of nature. This striking phenomenon serves also as a salutary reminder of our ignorance. Undoubtedly, such a great epidemic occurs because some normal "check" to increase is lightened, but what this check is we do not know. By the time we arrive on the spot to analyze the situation, whatever unusual condition it was that caused the exceptional multiplication has probably already been corrected by the multiplication itself. (For example, if an increase in vitamin B_{12} should cause an increase in population, as one theory holds, then the greater numbers of organisms would remove the excess concentration that brought them into being.)

Dinoflagellates are members of the phylum **Pyrrophyta.** These microscopic cells move by means of two flagella, one of which runs in a central transverse groove, while the other protrudes from the posterior end (Fig. 14-9). Some forms are enclosed in a sort of shell made up of many interlocking plates of some organic substance. The chlorophylls are chlorophyll *a* and chlorophyll *c,* and the accessory pigment is fucoxanthin.

There are many fresh-water dinoflagellates, but by far the greater number are marine. Some of them are **luminescent;** that is, they carry out a reaction that can be summarized thus:

$$\text{food} + O_2 \longrightarrow CO_2 + H_2O + \text{heat} + \text{light} . \tag{1}$$

In other words, respiration, instead of yielding heat as the only by-product, yields (also) light.

Fig. 14-9. *Dinoflagellates, the second most numerous group of plants in the sea.*

DINOFLAGELLATES

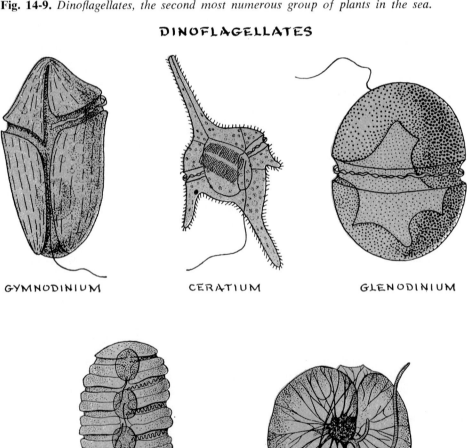

GYMNODINIUM   CERATIUM   GLENODINIUM

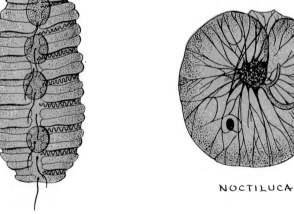

POLYKRIKOS   NOCTILUCA

At times the dinoflagellates are so great in number that every breaking wave of the sea flashes in the night as the agitation of the water stirs in oxygen from the air, thus increasing the metabolism of the microorganisms. On the Pacific Coast, one of the dinoflagellates responsible for this luminescence, *Goniaulax* by name, happens to produce a substance that is a deadly nerve poison for vertebrates. The sea water containing this dinoflagellate is harmless to man, even during times of their greatest increase, but the local mussels are not. These molluscs are filter feeders; they sieve out vast quantities of *Goniaulax,* and concentrate the toxin in their livers. They are themselves unharmed. The toxin is so poisonous that one milligram is sufficient to kill thirty-five mice. During a "bloom," the dinoflagellates may reach a concentration of 10^7 per liter. Such epidemics being unpredictable as to time and place (and modern men being so unobservant of nature), deaths from eating mussels are prevented (among the law-abiding) by making it illegal to collect and eat mussels during the months of May to October, which includes all the times of greatest abundance of *Goniaulax.*

It must not be supposed, of course, that all dinoflagellates are poisonous. The vast majority of them are harmless.

111. The Browns and the Reds

Brown algae are members of the phylum **Phaeophyta.** In these algae occur chlorophyll *a* and chlorophyll *c,* and the accessory pigment fucoxanthin. Red algae are members of the phylum **Rhodophyta;** in these the photosynthetic pigments are chlorophyll *a* and **chlorophyll *d,*** with the red pigment **phycoerythrin** as an accessory. In both phyla various other pigments may produce an over-all color of brown, green, purple, or red. Various sugars and other carbohydrates (never true starch) are stored in the cells.

The popular term "seaweed" includes botanically quite a diverse assemblage of plants, including some flowering plants (e.g., "eelgrass"), but the great majority of the seaweeds are brown algae or red algae. Most of the algae we have considered so far have been microscopic and **planktonic** (Gr. *planktos* = wandering) in habit; that is, they float at or near the surface of the water and are largely at the mercy of currents or tides. The adult stages of the red and brown seaweeds (Fig. 14-10) are, however, **benthic** (Gr. *benthos* = depth of the sea), that is, attached to the bottom. Being photosynthetic and needing light, they occur only in shallow water, at depths no greater than 80 meters. Some of the giant brown seaweeds, called *kelp,* may reach a length of 70 meters and a weight of several hundred kilograms. Because of the scale effect (§10), increase in size magnifies the problem of exchange with the external world. The kelp has "solved" this problem by evolving a body that is much flattened, thus presenting a large surface for diffusion of chemicals and for the interception of light. The attachment of the kelps to a fixed bottom in the region of active tidal and wave movements permits more rapid exchange of chemicals than is possible to a planktonic organism, which moves but little relative to its environing water.

The general structure of a large kelp plant (Fig. 14-11) reminds us of the leaves, stems, and roots of flowering plants. The internal structure is so different, however, that we use different names—namely, **blade, stipe,** and **holdfast** —for the corresponding structures. We are sure that there is no **homology** between these structures and leaf, stem, and root; that is, the latter have not been evolved from the former. The structures are not homologous; they are *analogous:* they are similar in superficial appearance and have some similarity in function, but there is no fundamental (evolutionary) similarity. A water-conducting tissue (xylem) is, for example, lacking, as it can well be in such water-dwelling forms (though note, eelgrass, a water-dwelling flowering plant, has such a tissue).

Sexual reproduction is universal in these two phyla; many of the life cycles are extremely complex. Note than in the kelp shown in Figure 14-11 there are two different phases to the life cycle. One is called the **gametophyte** generation because it produces gametes. When male and

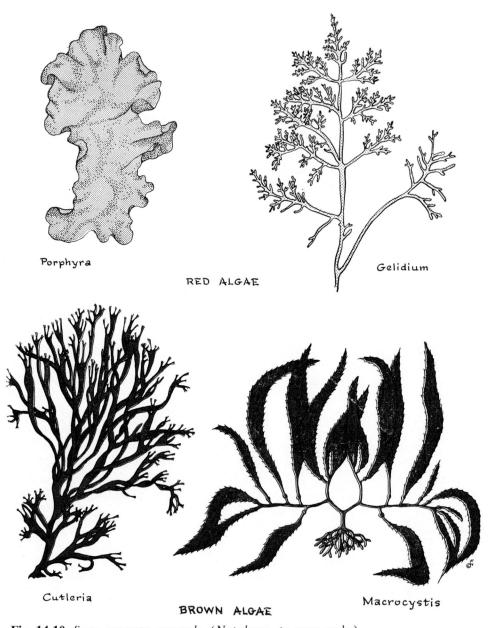

Fig. 14-10. *Some common seaweeds. (Not drawn to same scale.)*

female gametes unite, a zygote is produced; this then develops into a quite different plant called the **sporophyte** generation because it produces **spores.** These mature into gametophytes, and the cycle is complete.

Brown and red algae are important photosynthesizers of the seacoast. They furnish food and hiding places to myriads of other organisms. Some of them accumulate certain elements that are only dilutely present in the sea water around them, for example, iodine and potassium (potash). In addition, from some forms (e.g., *Gelidium*—see Fig. 14-10) may be derived **agar,** a carbohydrate that is extremely useful in the preparation of solid media for growing bacteria. Other seaweeds produce **alginates,** carbohydrates widely used in commercial ice cream, to which they impart a smooth consistency other-

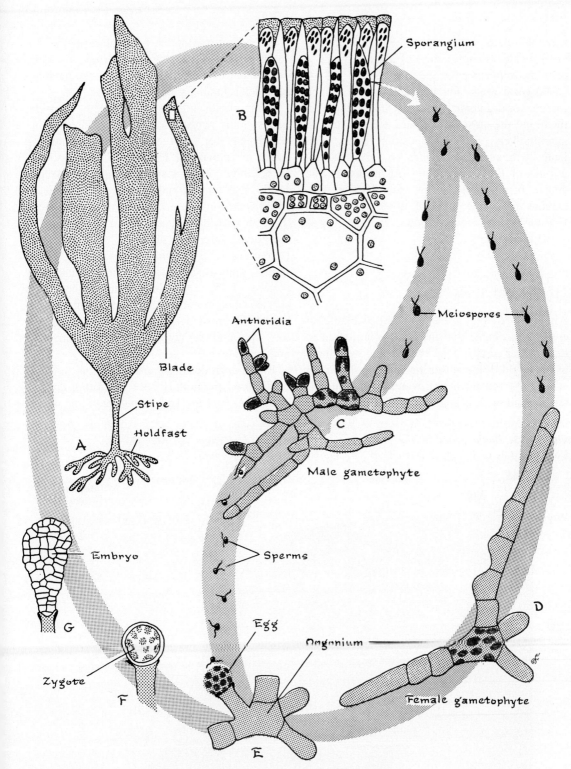

Fig. 14-11. *Life cycle of a kelp. Haploid cells in color; diploid in black. (After G. Papenfuss.)*

Sporangium

Meiospores

Antheridia

C

Male gametophyte

D

Female gametophyte

Oogonium

Egg

Sperms

E

Embryo

G

Zygote

F

Blade

Stipe

Holdfast

A

B

wise obtainable only with expensive butterfat. Geologically, some of the red algae have been of prime importance in the formation of the so-called **coral reefs.** These structures are named for the coral animals which are conspicuous in them; but the most careful studies indicate that, quantitatively, calcium-depositing algae, particularly the *coralline red algae,* are the most important of the reef-building organisms. In the course of time, staggering quantities of calcareous rock may be laid down. Drilling at Eniwetok Atoll revealed that the coral was 1,405 meters thick.

112. Ecology of the Sea

Although reliable figures are not available, it is highly probable that the plants considered in this chapter carry out most of the photosynthesis of the world, some authorities putting the figure at over 90 percent. Fresh waters being quantitatively minor, it is safe to say that most of the world's food production takes place in the sea. In discussing the ecology of the sea, it will be convenient to use some new terms, the meaning of which is indicated in Figure 14-12.

Some photosynthesis takes place in intertidal and subtidal zones, the reds and browns being responsible for most of this. This region we speak of as **neritic** ("near shore"), as opposed to **oceanic.** Neritic plants, though conspicuous to the eye, are of only minor importance as direct food for humans. The Orientals eat some three dozen different species of seaweeds, but use them more as condiments than as energy sources. The Irish make slight use of "Irish moss," and seashore farmers in a number of regions of the world have learned that some species of kelp can be fed with profit to livestock. But most neritic plants are too watery, too salty, and frankly unpalatable to both man and beast.

In the open ocean the plankton is at the base of the food pyramid. Plankton is often divided into *phytoplankton* and *zooplankton,* the mean-

Fig. 14-12. *Biotic zones of the sea and seashore. (After J. Hedgpeth, from Odum, Fundamentals of Ecology, 2nd ed., W. B. Saunders Co., Philadelphia, 1959.)*

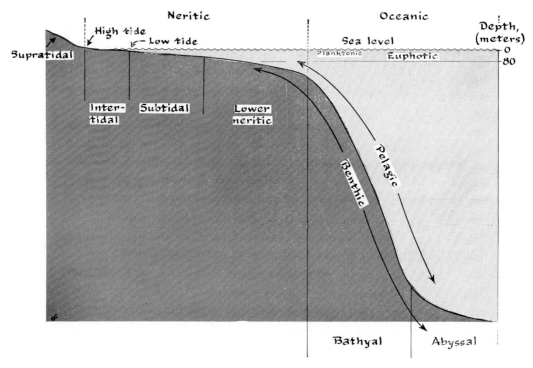

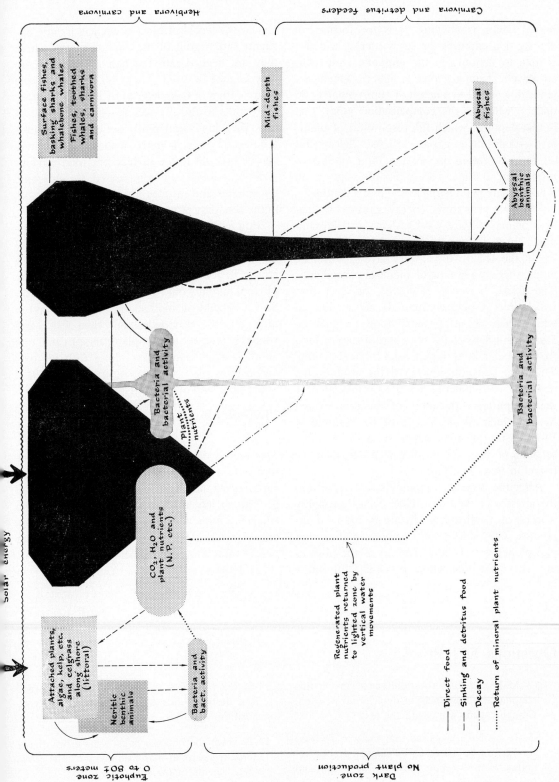

Fig. 14-13. *Elements of the food web of the sea. (After Sverdrup, Johnson, and Fleming; from Allee et al., Principles of Animal Ecology, W. B. Saunders Co., Philadelphia, 1949.)*

ing of which is obvious. It is the former, of course, that captures the sun's energy, which it is able to do only in the **euphotic zone** (Gr. *eu* = well, true + *photos* = light), which extends downward to a depth of approximately 80 meters, which is the **compensation point,** that is, the depth at which the respiration of plants just equals their photosynthesis. Below this depth, respiration is greater than photosynthesis, and so there is a net loss of energy at all times for any plant living at so great a depth.

What happens to the energy captured by marine plants? Figure 14-13 shows in diagrammatic form the principal threads of the web of life in the sea. In the surface layers, it will be noted, there is a cycling of chemical compounds. The abyss, however, is a *sink,* an area into which energy-rich compounds settle, but in which there is no primary food production. Deep-sea fishes depend on a sort of rain of food from above, a kind of perpetual Biblical manna. The total concentration of living stuff in the depths is, consequently, small, as is indicated by the comparative thickness of the two shaded figures which are derived from the Pyramid of Protoplasm, but are oriented so as to show the relation of mass of "protoplasm" to distance from the ocean's surface.

After the organic compounds that settle into the abysses of the ocean have been thoroughly worked over, all that is left are inorganic compounds, CO_2, H_2O, and (more significantly) phosphates and nitrates. Insofar as the abysses are true sinks, the whole process results in a loss to the world of life—needed inorganic nutrients settling out of the euphotic layer where they are needed into the lightless zone where they cannot be used. There is, however, some recirculation of this material by upwellings from the depths to the surface, though the extent of this upwelling is apparently not enough to make a balanced cycle. If more of the abyssal waters can be brought to the surface, the food production of the world can be increased, for inorganic phosphates and nitrates are the limiting factors in the economy of much of the ocean.

Man makes almost no *direct* use of the photosynthetic products of the open ocean. The total amount is enormous, but it is very dilute. To collect it, for example, by centrifuging out the phytoplankton would cost more than it is worth. So we depend on indirect means. Zooplankton filter out the phytoplankton, then fish (and whales) sieve out the zooplankton, or catch one another; then man comes along with his nets and fishing gear and harvests the crop. Man is at the small end of the food chain:

Phytoplankton $\longrightarrow$ Zooplankton $\longrightarrow$
Small Fish $\longrightarrow$ Large Fish $\longrightarrow$ Man

This means that, at the very most, he can capture only a thousandth of the energy originally captured by the plants of the sea. In practice, he gets much less than this. We suspect that the efficiency with which man exploits the seas is capable of being increased a great deal. Some people think this is desirable.

Questions and Problems

14-4 Make a list of the **boldface** terms in this chapter and write a brief description of each. Compare your work with the text.

‡14-5. It has been proposed that the world's food production be increased by placing atomic reactors in the deepest parts of the ocean and just leaving them there to produce heat. Explain the reasoning behind this suggestion.

14-6. Do you think the proposal just mentioned is a desirable one to carry out. Justify your position.

14-7. What the botanist calls "blue-green algae" actually occur in many different colors. How, then, can the name be justified?

‡14-8. Another name for the blue-green algae is

Cyanophyceae. What is the etymology of this term?

‡14-9. Consider the number of species shown for each of the several groups of Table 14-2. Which figure do you suppose is most exact, most reliable? Why?

14-10. Of the figures in Table 14-2, which do you think is second-most reliable? Why?

14-11. If *Astasia* were the only euglenoid known, would it be described in a botany text?

‡14-12. In the passage quoted in §110, Darwin said that "every single organic being may be said to be striving . . ." Why did he not simply say that "every single organic being *is* striving"?

14-13. You are out in a rowboat on the ocean, on a dark night without lights. Every time you dip your oars, the water seems to flash around the tips of the oars. Why?

14-14. Before white men came to the Pacific Coast of the United States, coastal Indians would, whenever the night waters were luminescent, post sentinels to warn any inland Indians who came along not to eat the mussels. Why?

14-15. Following the destruction of all life on the East Indian island of Krakatoa in 1883, blue-green algae were the first colonizers to appear on the volcanic ash. What characteristics of these algae make them particularly suited to this role of primary colonizers of bare places?

‡14-16. What is puzzling about the thickness of the coral on Eniwetok Atoll? Suggest an explanation.

14-17. In the diatomaceous earth of Lompoc there are about 2.5×10^6 diatoms per cubic centimeter. How many diatoms are there in the total bed?

‡14-18. To be quite unrealistic, suppose all the diatoms in the Lompoc beds were the descendants of a single diatom, by asexual fission. Suppose that none of the diatoms died or were destroyed until the final number was reached; then they all died at once and became the deposit we see today. If cell division took place once every twenty-four hours, how long would it have taken to produce this deposit?

Readings

For a popular account, see Tiffany's *Algae: The Grass of Many Waters*. For the economy of the oceans, read Carson's dramatic and beautiful *The Sea Around Us*. On the technical level, see *The Oceans*, by Sverdrup et al. For all ecological matters, consult Odum.

Scientific American Offprints

830. Herbert S. Bailey, Jr. *The Voyage of the "Challenger"*

853. Willis E. Pequegnat. *Whales, Plankton and Man*

864. Robert Cushman Murphy. *The Oceanic Life of the Antarctic*

15

Fungi: Trash Burners and Parasites

113. The Role of Microbes in the Carbon Cycle

Chlorophyll-containing plants play a larger role in the biological carbon cycle than do most other organisms: they not only produce CO_2 (by respiration), but they also use it (in photosynthesis). Only such autotrophs are capable of setting up, by themselves, a biological carbon cycle—a fact that is indicated by arrows *a* and *b* in Figure 15-1. Heterotrophic animals, feeding on plants, can increase the amount of CO_2 (arrow *c*), but they cannot decrease it. Most of the organic material synthesized by higher plants is soon turned into CO_2 by the respiration of either plants or animals, but not quite all. A dead tree, recumbent on the floor of the forest, has, locked up in it, a great deal of carbon, principally in the form of cellulose and lignin. (As a matter of fact, this carbon was taken out of the carbon cycle long before, when the cambium cells produced xylem cells, which presently died in the "living" tree.) Organic carbon is also removed from the carbon cycle when animals "naturally" die, though "natural death" is a comparatively rare phenomenon. Of more importance is the larger quantity of dead organic material produced all the time by living animals: excreted urea and uric acid, discarded hairs, feathers, and so on. All of this would accumulate in a sort of organic trash pile, thus

steadily diminishing the amount of carbon available for cycling, if it were not for other organisms that live on this trash, that is, respire it, degrading* the organic carbon to CO_2 once more, thus putting the carbon back into cycle again.

The organisms that are principally responsible for "burning" this trash are the fungi and the bacteria; collectively, they are often called *microbes,* a term of uncertain extension that also includes microscopic algae and the one-celled animals called protozoa.† Although many autotropic species are included among the microbes, in this and the next chapter we will be concerned only with heterotrophic species, and will use the word "microbe" without qualifying adjectives to indicate such forms. The importance of heterotrophic microbes in keeping carbon atoms in circulation is clear.

114. Microbes and the Nitrogen Cycle

Microbes are important also in the circulation of nitrogen throughout the biosphere. The nitrogenous compounds we call proteins are essential constituents of all plants and animals.

* 15-1. Why this word? It is standard usage in biochemistry; the metaphor indicated by position in Figure 15-1 suggests the answer.

† 15-2. Now complete Figure 15-1 by adding arrow *g* to show the role of the microbes.

Fig. 15-1. *Autotrophs, heterotrophs, and the degradation of organic carbon.*

Much of the organic nitrogen is constantly re-worked into one protein after another, into one amino acid after another; but sooner or later, nitrogen escapes from the plant or animal body either as an ammonium (NH_4) compound, or in some more complex form that is then converted to an ammonium compound in the soil. This process is indicated by arrows *1, 2,* and *3* in Figure 15-2. Some of the NH_4 salts may be taken up by the plant (arrow *4*), but if this does not happen soon, various species of microbes presently convert the NH_4 to NO_2 (nitrite) and then to NO_3 (nitrate) compounds. The last named is the most stable of the three in the soil

and is probably the principal source of plant nitrogen (arrow *10*). Unfortunately, however, many bacteria (arrow *11*) can convert NO_3 to N_2, "molecular nitrogen," which is a gas and escapes into the air. Now molecular nitrogen is useless as a source of nitrogen for all animals, and for almost all plants. It can be used as a source of nutritional nitrogen by some bacteria, some blue-green algae, and *possibly* by a few plants outside the phylum Schizophyta (see Table 15-1). Organisms that can so use it convert (arrow *12*) the N_2 back into organic nitrogen compounds which have more energy than N_2 and can be more readily transformed into

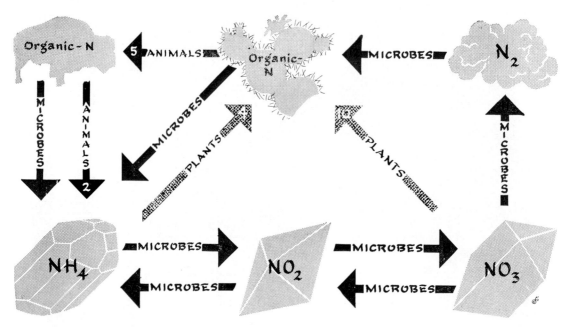

Fig. 15-2. *The basic transformations of nitrogen in the living world.*

other compounds. The constant degradation of organic nitrogen to N_2 presents various practical problems which will be taken up when we come to the bacteria in the next chapter.

In Figure 15-2, processes that are, for all practical purposes, carried out only by microbes are indicated by colored arrows. The very large role played by microbes in the nitrogen cycle is obvious. This cycle is, of course, an intellectual abstraction; in fact, in nature, the transformations of carbon and nitrogen take place together. In both cycles, microbes are important in degrading the element to its lowest energy state (CO_2 or N_2); but nitrogen compounds are, in general, more readily and more completely degraded than are carbon compounds. The great majority of organic nitrogen compounds are readily metabolized by one or another species of microbe. In contrast, cellulose, the most important carbon compound used in elaborating the structure of plants, is very insoluble in water and quite resistant to microbial action; hence its accumulation in swamps, in peat deposits, and—in altered forms—in coal. The microbial digestion of cellulose and other plant wastes is often limited by the supply of nitrogen (there is none in pure cellulose). For this reason, the

"composting" of garden wastes is accelerated by the addition of nitrogen-rich compounds, for example, animal manure. Manure and cellulose together make a balanced diet for many microbes of decay.

An interesting example of the results of unintentional composting is found in the "spontaneous combustion" of hay. This is a relatively rare accident. All respiration produces heat as a by-product, but this fact does not ordinarily cause any trouble. For a hay pile to be heated to the point where it catches fire, the relative humidity of the hay must be within the very narrow limits of 95 to 97 percent. Below 95 percent relative humidity, microbial respiration is slow enough so that the heat produced can be easily dissipated. Above 97 percent, although heat production is greater, so also is heat conduction along the moist fibers. Only in the narrow two percent range does heat production overshadow heat dissipation, setting up a positive feedback system which is operative up to a temperature of 70°C. At this point microbial respiration stops and nonmicrobial oxidation takes over, raising the temperature ultimately to the ignition point.

Because the common organic nitrogen compounds are soluble in water and metabolizable by microbes, there are few nitrogen deposits in the world analogous to the deposits of carbon we find in coal and petroleum. The most conspicuous exceptions are the deposits of **guano**—bird dung—on islands off the Peruvian coast. The coastal waters in these regions are rich in fish and crustacea, supporting a large population of sea birds. The bird droppings on the islands escape most microbial degradation because of the exceptionally dry climate: years pass without a single drop of rain.

115. The Classification of Fungi

The term "fungi," like the term "algae," is a rather inexact term. The classification to be used in this book is shown in Table 15-1. Fungi, "in

TABLE 15-1   *Classification of the Fungi.*

PHYLUM	MEMBERS
Eumycophyta	True fungi
Class: Phycomycetes	Black bread mold, water molds
Class: Ascomycetes	Yeasts, *Neurospora*
Class: Basidiomycetes	Mushrooms
Class: Fungi Imperfecti	Ringworm fungi
Myxomycophyta	Slime molds

the narrow sense," include only members of the **Eumycophyta** (Gr. *eu* = well, true + *myco,* a combining form, meaning fungi). Biology that is restricted to the study of this group is called **mycology.** Mycologists divide the objects of their interest into four classes as shown, only the first three of which we will consider at length in the sections that follow. The fourth class, the Fungi Imperfecti will be dismissed with a few words here.

The members of the first three classes all indulge in sexual processes and so are said to be "perfect"—a rather interesting implied definition of the adjective. There are other fungi in which sexual fusion has never been found, either because we have never found more than one sex, or because sexual practices have been abandoned by the species. Since the differentiation of the first three classes is partly based on the sexual phenomenon, the classification of forms in which sexual fusion has not been found is often quite uncertain. For this reason, the special class Fungi Imperfecti was created. There is no doubt that it is a grab-bag group that includes species properly belonging to the other classes. In fact, from time to time we discover sexual stages in a member of this class, following which we remove the species therefrom and assign it to one of the other classes. It is often said that the adjective "imperfect" applies not so much to the organism classified, as it does to the classifier, though in a different sense: it is a memorial to the imperfection of his knowledge.

Cells of the Eumycophyta are generally cylindrical in shape, as are those of many of the bacteria (discussed in the next chapter); but the true fungi are larger. As a very rough generalization, a true fungal cell is about 10μ in diameter; whereas a bacterial cell of similar shape will be, say, 1μ in diameter.* Because of the greater size, more morphological detail is discernible. Fungal nuclei are definite and easily stainable. What we regard as an individual generally consists of many cells rather than one; the cells are typically arranged end to end, in **filaments.** Spores are produced by most species. The resistance of fungal spores to heat is only moderate; boiling water always kills them. A single cell may produce many spores; hence, **sporulation** (spore formation) is a means of multiplication. Fungal spores are frequently quite resistant to drying; since they are small and often have a low specific gravity,† they are readily transported by the wind, thus disseminating the species. An incredible variety is found in the shapes of spores, only a small sampling of which is shown in Figure 15-3.

In their nutrition the Eumycophyta are without exception heterotrophic, some species being saprophytic (living on dead organic material, others parasitic (feeding on living or-

---

* 15-3. How do the volumes of two such cells compare? Assume the same relative proportions.
† 15-4. Explain why this is important.

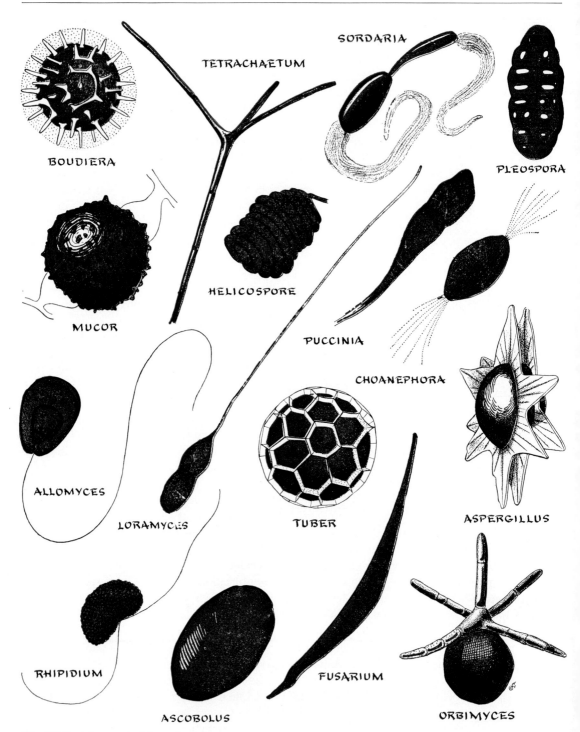

Fig. 15-3. *A bouquet of fungal spores.*

ganisms). The great majority of the fungi are **obligate aerobes;** that is, they are organisms which, like man, must have free O_2 to live. Some can live either with or without O_2, and so are called **facultative aerobes:** such are the yeasts that produce wine. Among the saprophytic fungi are to be found species that can grow under conditions one ordinarily regards as very unfavorable to life. Many of them can grow in surroundings with a very high osmotic potential—the surface of brine vats and opened jars of jelly of high sugar concentration, as well as nearly dry leather and cloth. (What is commonly called "mildew" is one or another species of fungi.) Some fungi can live in high concentrations of substances that are poisonous to most forms of life: phenol, picric acid, and arsenic, to mention a few examples. Almost any situation that is a bit moist will permit some species of fungus to grow. Whereas very few bacteria are active in the absence of free water, most fungi need only the water of very moist air to flourish: a relative humidity of 70–75 percent suffices. In the humid tropics, fungi cause rapid deterioration of many useful materials, particularly cloth. The advance of modern civilization into the tropics is to a considerable extent limited by man's ability to control fungi.

116. The Phycomycetes

In their active vegetative phase of growth, members of this class show either (a) no cross walls in their filaments, (b) few cross walls, or (c) many cross walls, but walls that are perforated. In any case, the result is a partial departure from the simple cell theory as presented in Chapter 2. Nuclei are not separated from one another by cell walls or cell membranes. Such multinucleate tissue is said to be **coenocytic** (Gr. *koinos* = common, shared + *kytos* = vessel—hence, a cell). As filaments age or run out of food, solid cross walls may be formed, thus presenting an appearance more consonant with the cell theory. Reproductive structures are separated from nonreproductive tissue by cross walls.

Botany texts often refer to the Phycomycetes as the "algal fungi" because the considerable resemblances between these molds and various algae suggests an evolutionary derivation of one group from the other. Many Phycomycetes, like the algae, are confined to a watery environment. Among the more interesting of the water-dwelling species are members of the genus *Allomyces.* These are tropical forms that can often be collected by placing boiled hemp seeds in water containing mud from the tropics. In a few days the seeds will be covered by a cottony growth which we call a **mycelium.** Under the low power of a microscope, a mycelium is seen to be made of many filaments, each of which is called a **hypha** (Gr. web; pl. *hyphae*). The distinctions between these terms may be made clear thus: The relations between *hypha, hyphae,* and *mycelium* are the same as those between *person, persons,* and *people.*

The life cycle of *Allomyces* is shown in Figure 15-4. The diploid phases are shown in black. The diploid hyphae (*A*) normally produce a type of spore case called a **mitosporangium** (*B*); the spores within are produced by mitosis, and are diploid. After release (*C*) each of these is capable of producing another diploid mycelium (*E*). This phase of the life cycle can repeat itself endlessly.

Sometimes, however, a different sort of sporangium is produced. This dark-colored thick-walled structure is called a **resistant sporangium** (*G*). It goes into a period of dormancy; it can survive periods of unfavorable environmental conditions, following which it can break open and release spores (*H*). These spores are produced by meiosis; such spores are haploid and are called **meiospores.** Each can give rise to a haploid mycelium (*J*). The hyphae of this plant are indistinguishable from diploid hyphae until they produce reproductive structures (*K*). These occur in pairs, at the tips of hyphae. The subterminal structure (*L*) looks like a mitosporangium and produces flagellated cells (*O*) that look like the spores already described. The terminal structure, however, is a bright orange in color, and it releases flagellated cells (*N*) that are quite small, and orange in color. Since these

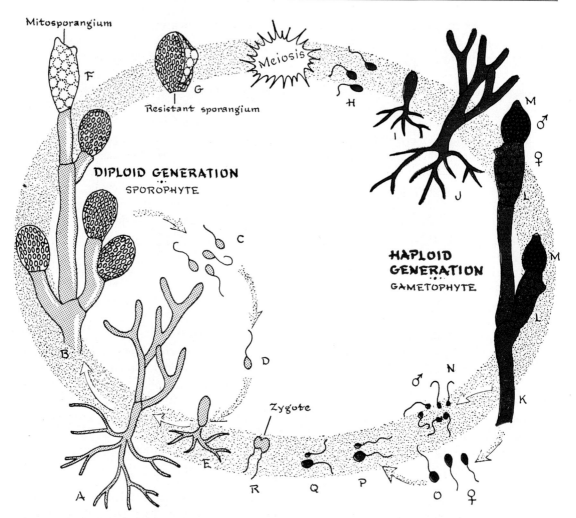

Fig. 15-4. *The life cycle of* Allomyces. *Haploid phase in color, diploid in black.* (*After Ralph Emerson.*)

two kinds of cells fuse (*P* and *Q*) to produce a zygote (*R*), the spores are evidently gametes. The larger gametes are called female gametes, the smaller male. The structures that produce them are called **gametangia** (sing. *gametangium*). An organism that can produce both kinds of gametes from the same individual is said to be **hermaphroditic** (after the myth of Hermaphroditus, a son of Hermes and Aphroditus, who, while bathing, became joined in a single body with a nymph). *Allomyces* is also homothallic.

Allomyces is especially interesting in that it shows how complicated the life cycle of a "sim-

ple mold" can be. There are many unknowns in such a cycle; for instance, how can diploid and haploid spores produce the same sort of young hyphae (*A* and *J*) which yet, as they mature, differentiate sharply in their reproductive structures? And what is the environmental difference that makes the terminal and sub-terminal gametangia produce different sexes of gametes?

Allomyces is saprophytic, as are most of the Phycomycetes. Other genera of water molds include parasitic members; one of these, *Saprolegnia*, deserves a few words here. This mold may easily be collected by leaving a dead fly in a glass of pond water for a few days; or a piece of dead fish will do. Under such circumstances, *Saprolegnia* is obviously a saprophyte. But the mold may also be found growing as a cottony mass on an injured area of a living fish. Is it, then, a saprophyte or a parasite? Studies indicate that the answer varies with the strain of mold: some strains live only on the fish cells killed by other means, while other strains can invade living tissues. This example points up the general principle that the evolution of parasitism from saprophytism must always be thought of as a possibility; what it requires are the proper mutations of genes for selection to act upon.

Among air-dwelling Phycomycetes, *Rhizopus nigricans,* the black bread mold, is well known. At one time *Rhizopus* was almost universally encountered on stale bread, but the fungi-inhibiting agents now added to commercial bread have changed the picture. *Rhizopus* grows readily on ripe bananas; it may often be collected by exposing overripe fruit to the air for several days, after which the fruit may be covered with a dingy white cottony mat. Under the microscope we see that the whiteness is due to the hyphae, the blackness being added by a peppering of black structures. On closer inspection (Fig. 15-5), each of these structures is seen to consist of a cluster of tiny black balls—spores

—each of which is able to germinate and produce a new mycelium. The delicate sack in which the spores are produced is a sporangium, and the erect hypha on which it is borne is a **sporangiophore** (Gr. *phoros* = bearing, wearing). Reproduction of *Rhizopus* is usually by the asexual means just described. The asexual spores are light and easily carried by air currents. Whenever a spore falls on a suitable substratum, it germinates to produce a new mycelium.

Rhizopus may also reproduce by sexual means, as shown in Figure 15-6. Projections of two different filaments grow toward each other. At the point of juncture, there is a union of nuclei from each filament to form a thick-walled zygote. Under proper environmental conditions the zygote germinates to produce new spores. Sexual reproduction is not often observed because it requires strains of two different types. These strains are morphologically identical and hence can hardly be referred to as male and female. To indicate their physiological difference, one strain is arbitrarily called + and the other −. Sexual reproduction takes place only between two strains of the opposite type in *Rhizopus,* and consequently *Rhizopus* is said to be heterothallic.

The only diploid nucleus to be found in *Rhi-*

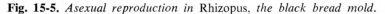

Fig. 15-5. *Asexual reproduction in* Rhizopus, *the black bread mold.*

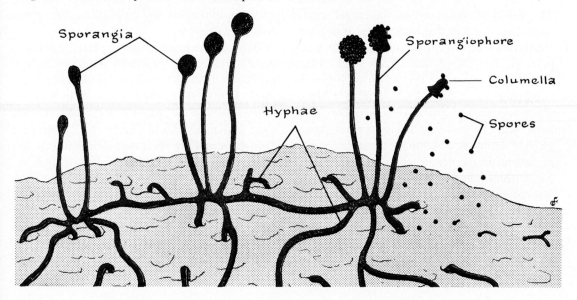

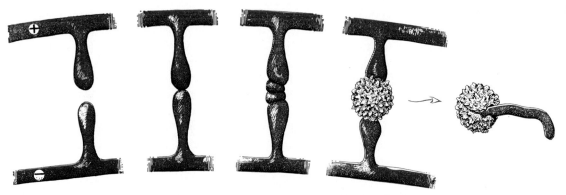

Fig. 15-6. *Sexual reproduction in* Rhizopus *by fusion of two haploid hyphae of oppo-site mating types, producing a zygote. Before germination, zygote undergoes reduction division.*

zopus occurs in the zygote. During the germination of the zygote, meiosis occurs, producing haploid nuclei. All of the vegetative tissue of the black bread mold is haploid.

Among the non-water-dwelling Phycomycetes there is another species that is far more important than the black bread mold; it is *Phytophthora infestans,* the parasitic species that causes the "late blight of potatoes." This organism has, in fact, been of considerable historical importance, particularly in the development of the United States. The mold infects first the leaves of the plant, becoming most apparent just at harvest time, and later the tubers, which it causes to rot in the ground and in storage. The historical importance of the fungal species stems from the fact that Ireland was at one time dangerously dependent on a single crop plant, potatoes. Introduced there from South America, the "Irish potato" thrived so well that the population of Ireland doubled from 1795 to 1845, reaching a figure of over 8 million in the latter year. In that year began a great famine brought on by destruction of potatoes by *Phytophthora.* In the next fifteen years, over a million Irishmen died of starvation and starvation-favored diseases; another million and a half emigrated to the United States and Canada, there to play an important role in the political, social, and religious development of the growing nations. Today the population of Ireland has stabilized at a little over 4.5 million, ap-

proximately the same as it was in the year 1800. Agriculture has diversified somewhat beyond the one-crop stage of the old days, and various means have been found for minimizing the inroads of the potato disease, but the Irish people, though well fed, are still not wealthy by American standards.

117. The Ascomycetes

The Ascomycetes, or sac fungi, produce at some stage an **ascus** (Gr. leather bottle or bag), a saclike structure within which are spores called **ascospores.** Some general features of this class may be illustrated by considering the genus *Neurospora.*

Neurospora is sometimes called "red bread mold" because it occasionally occurs on bakery products, particularly those made with corn meal. It is a fluffy, whitish growth in its early stages, turning orange as it gets older. Its life cycle is diagrammed in Figure 15-7. Vegetative growth occurs by the rapid elongation of hyphae, which, unlike those of the Phycomycetes, have, at all stages, numerous cross walls, or **septa** (sing. *septum;* L. partition). After a few hours' growth, there are formed at the ends of some of the aerial hyphae numerous small reddish spores called **conidia** (sing. *conidium*; Gr. *konidion* = dust). Each conidium is capable of germinating into a new hypha. Asexual reproduction is accomplished by this means, as well as by the growth of hyphal fragments that break off from the parent mycelium.

Sexual reproduction also occurs. One of the best-known species of *Neurospora* is heterothallic, and it is the life cycle of this species that we have diagrammed. When sexual reproduction has taken place, there are found on the mycelium dense black spheres easily visible to the naked eye; each such body is called a **perithecium** (Gr. *peri* = around + *thekion* = a case). Two ways in which sexual reproduction may take place are indicated in the figure. There may be a direct fusion of hyphae of the two different mating types (called *A* and *a*); or a structure called a **protoperithecium** may be formed and fertilization be brought about by the alighting of a conidium of the opposite type on this protoperithecium, as indicated in the figure.

Both routes of fertilization lead to the same result—namely, to the fusion of two haploid nuclei to produce a single diploid nucleus. This diploid nucleus, by a regular process of meiosis, divides to form four haploid nuclei inside the ascus. It happens that, in the species of *Neurospora* depicted, each of these haploid nuclei undergoes a further *mitotic* division to produce two haploid nuclei. Around each of these eight haploid nuclei is formed an ascospore. The mature perithecium contains many asci, inside each of which are found eight haploid ascospores. When activated by moderate heat, each of these ascospores is capable of germinating to produce a new mycelium. Note that almost the entire life cycle of *Neurospora* is haploid; for only a short while, in immature asci, are there diploid nuclei.

Among the more important members of the

Fig. 15-7. *Life cycle of the ascomycete,* Neurospora. *Haploid nuclei in color, diploid nuclei black.* (*After G. W. Beadle.*)

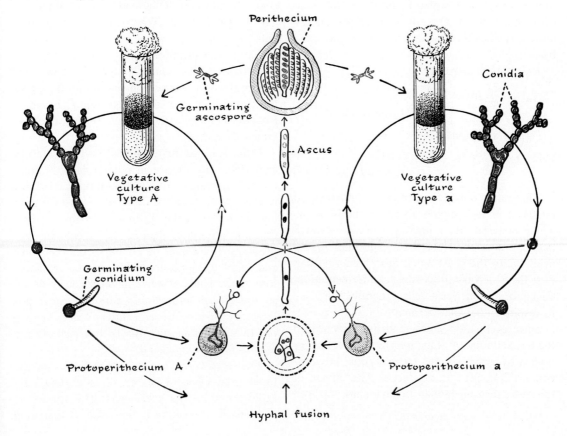

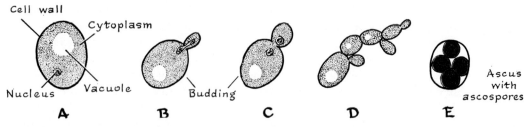

Fig. 15-8. *Common yeast. (B-D) Asexual reproduction by budding. The ascospores shown in E are haploid.*

Ascomycetes are the **yeasts.** Asexual reproduction among these organisms is accomplished by a modified type of cell division called **budding** (Fig. 15-8). The products of cell division usually soon separate, though in some species they may remain attached to each other for a time to produce a hyphalike chain of cells.

A most useful species of yeast is *Saccharomyces cerevisiae,* called baker's yeast, or wine yeast. This yeast is particularly useful because it has the ability to live anaerobically, that is, in the absence of oxygen. From the metabolism of glucose ($C_6H_{12}O_6$), it can derive energy either aerobically or anaerobically, as indicated below:

Respiration (aerobic):

$$C_6H_{12}O_6 \longrightarrow 6H_2O + 6CO_2$$
$$+ \; 674 \text{ Calories of } \varepsilon. \quad (1)$$

Fermentation (anaerobic):

$$C_6H_{12}O_6 \longrightarrow 2CO_2 + 2C_2H_5OH$$
$$+ \; 22 \text{ Calories of } \varepsilon. \quad (2)$$

The energy obtained is, of course, partly used by the cells in bringing about synthesis of organic material, thus making possible growth and cell division. Note that respiration makes available to the yeast much more* energy than does the anaerobic process we call **fermentation.** Given an option, yeast cells generally "choose" to respire rather than ferment.

Since prehistoric times man has encouraged the fermentation of grape juice and other sugary liquids by yeast. By this fermentation, ethyl alcohol (C_2H_5OH) is produced. The effects of this substance on human behavior are too well

* 15-5. How much more? Greater by which factor?

known to require description. Under anaerobic conditions, and in the presence of ample sugar, as much as 15 percent by volume of the liquid may become alcohol before the yeast cells are killed by this waste product of their fermentative activity. In the production of light *table wines,* fermentation is usually stopped when the alcoholic concentration reaches 10–12 percent. *Fortified wines* are produced by adding sufficient alcohol to the fermenting liquor to bring the concentration of alcohol up to about 20 percent, the addition being made before all the sugar is metabolized. When kept from contact with air, light table wines keep fairly well, particularly after filtration and pasteurization. Fortified wines keep much better. Beverages of higher alcoholic concentrations are produced by the distillation of a fermented liquor: brandies from fermented fruit, whiskies from fermented grains.

Although the first interest in fermentation came from an interest in potable liquor, today the greater part of the fermentation carried out in the United States is directed toward producing alcohol for other purposes. In the production of industrial alcohol, the incidental by-products ("bouquet"), so important in wines and distilled drinks, are of no importance; therefore, many kinds of waste materials can be used as sources of fermentable carbohydrates: potatoes, sugar-cane waste, cannery wastes, and so on. In some cases, not yeasts, but bacteria are used as fermenting agents.

The use of yeast in baking is based on the rapid production of carbon dioxide (CO_2) by rapidly multiplying yeast cells. The species of yeast used for baking is the same as that used for alcoholic fermentation, but the special baking strains produce CO_2 more rapidly than wine strains. The gas that is produced, both by respiration and fermentation, forms bubbles in the dough, thus raising, or leavening, it. Any alcohol produced is evaporated during the baking process.

In recent years, interest has developed in another product of yeast—namely, the yeast cells themselves. Yeast cells are rich in protein and can supply many of the dietary needs usually met by meat and dairy products. Growing aerobically on waste materials, yeast can produce proteins at a fraction of the cost of meat proteins. In a world becoming increasingly crowded with humanity, increasing attention is being given to the use of yeast in the everyday diet. A shift from meat to yeast involves problems of several sorts. There are hundreds of different species of yeast, and they do not all taste alike. The ones most suitable as food are not most suitable for bread making or the production of alcohol. The testing of yeast species for flavor has only begun. The development of recipes using yeast has scarcely been started by home economists. In addition, there are psychological and social problems in becoming used to a new type of food. The greatest educator here is hunger, but it should be possible to use practical psychology to obtain the same end with less discomfort. The substitution of yeast for meat should make possible larger populations of *Homo sapiens*—if such are desirable.

Among other genera assignable to the Ascomycetes, *Penicillium* and *Aspergillus* are notable. A large part of the spoilage of food products, leather, cloth, and so on, is caused by members of these genera, which include hundreds of species, most of which produce strongly colored conidia. Green is a common color among the penicillia, brown and black among the aspergilli. Only a few of the species have ever been observed to produce ascospores. For the rest, only asexual reproduction is known. How should such an asexual species be classified—among the Ascomycetes or the Fungi Imperfecti? Some mycologists follow one procedure, and some the other. Those who classify the nonsexually reproducing species among the Fungi Imperfecti apparently do so because they feel that any "imperfect" species must, by definition, be assigned to the Fungi Imperfecti; that is, they regard the name of the class as referring primarily to characteristics of the species. Mycologists of the other conviction think that the demonstration of sexually produced ascopores in a single species of the genus is sufficient reason for placing all members of the genus in the Ascomycetes, since it is hardly proper to put different members of the same genus in different classes.

Penicillium and *Aspergillus* may be differentiated under the microscope by their "heads" of conidia (see Fig. 15-9). Among the penicillia useful to man, *P. camemberti* and *P. roquefortii* contribute, respectively, to the flavor of Camem-

Fig. 15-9. *Microscopic appearance of the spore-bearing "heads" of two common genera of molds.*

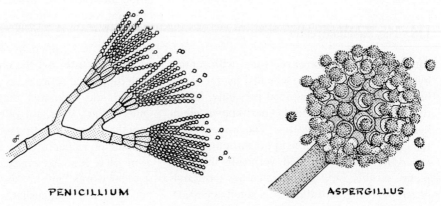

PENICILLIUM   ASPERGILLUS

bert and Roquefort cheeses. Other species have been shown, following the observations of Alexander Fleming in 1928, to produce a powerful antibiotic called *penicillin*. This organic chemical is bacteriostatic; that is, it stops the growth of susceptible species of bacteria. Some of the susceptible species produce important human diseases. Between the time of its discovery and the time of the successful production of penicillin, more than a decade elapsed. There were many reasons for this delay, principal among which were the extreme **lability** (destructibility, perishability) of the substance and the discouragingly small amounts of it produced by *Penicillium* cultures. The present large-scale production of this remarkable chemical has been made possible by the solution of problems of several different sorts. For one thing, it has been found that the amount of penicillin produced is greatly influenced by the kind of culture medium. Different strains of the same species of *Penicillium* vary widely in their penicillin productivity. Since the organisms are asexual, it has not been possible to combine the best qualities of different strains by interbreeding. Instead, strain improvement has depended on selection from among strains gathered from nature or produced artificially by mutagenic agents. So well have the various practical problems been solved that the cost of penicillin has been reduced from $100,000 per pound (in 1943) to $25 a pound (in 1960). Similar economies have been effected in the production of streptomycin, tyrothricin, aureomycin, and other antibiotics synthesized by microbes.

118. The Basidiomycetes

The Basidiomycetes are true fungi with septate hyphae; they reproduce sexually by means of basidiospores, to be described presently. Mushrooms (Fig. 15-10) are the best-known members of the Basidiomycetes. The underside of the cap of the common field mushroom, *Agaricus campestris,* is divided vertically into thin plates, or gills, on each of which are thousands of *basidia* (sing. **basidium;** L. a small pedestal),

each of which bears, when mature, four spores called **basidiospores.** Light basidiospores are forcibly thrown off the basidia in such a way as to fall vertically downward between the gills. Spores escaping from the gill cavities may be carried by winds to other localities, there to germinate into hyphae. A basidiospore is haploid, and the mycelium that arises from it is also haploid. Mushroom mycelia grow under the ground. When two hyphae of opposite mating types unite, a new mycelium is formed, each cell of which contains two haploid nuclei: one derived from one parent, and one from the other. Since the nuclei do not fuse, the cells containing them are not called diploid, but merely "binucleate." What we ordinarily call the "mushroom" is only the fruiting structure of the whole plant, most of which is underground and inconspicuous. Under suitable conditions, the underground mycelium sends up the mushroom, in which there is a fusion of the nuclei just prior to the formation of the basidia. The nuclear fusion is immediately followed by meiosis; the basidiospores are haploid. Note that here again the greater part of the life cycle is haploid, even though, during part of it, vegetative cells possess two nuclei. The formation of a diploid cell is but a prelude to reduction division.

The number of spores formed per individual mushroom runs into the millions or billions, but it has been calculated that not more than one spore out of 20 billion released by a common field mushroom succeeds in producing a new generation. Here we see an example of an important biological principle: the inverse correlation between the probability of survival of offspring and the rate of production of those offspring. When we find "offspring" produced in as prodigious numbers as are mushroom spores, we may be sure that the chance of survival for each individual spore is very slight indeed.

It should be noted that the popular word "mushroom" does not refer to any clear taxonomic entity, but to the fruiting body of a number of rather diverse Basidiomycetes, and even of a few Ascomycetes. In addition, the popular words "mushroom" and "toadstool" do not refer to distinguishable taxonomic entities.

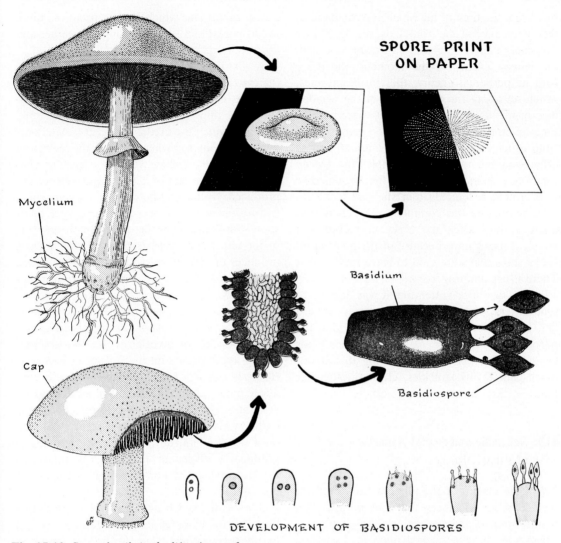

Fig. 15-10. *Some details in the life of a mushroom.*

The word "toadstool" comes from the German *Tod-Stuhl* (Death-stool). Popularly, any mushroom that causes sickness or death is likely to be called a toadstool, and such mushrooms are found in several genera—genera that include harmless species also. *There is no simple way to tell a harmful mushroom from a harmless one* (such as seeing if the mushroom will tarnish silver). Distinguishing species is a job for a competent taxonomist. Unless the student wishes to undergo the discipline of *learning* the mushrooms, he had best regard all mushrooms as being divided into two groups: mushrooms-found-in-the-stores and mushrooms-found-on-the-ground; and eat only the former.

Mushrooms are saprophytic. These and other saprophytic Basidiomycetes are responsible for a good deal of the decay that takes place in nature, including the decay of cellulose, the principal structural constituent of trees and other plants. Lumber that has not been sufficiently "cured"—that is, dried—is likely to be attacked by such fungi. Any wood continuously surrounded by damp air is liable to such "dry rot." The importance of fungi in the history of the British Empire is little realized, but is indubitable. From the time of the Spanish Armada until the appearance of the iron-clads, the Admiralty was continually engaged in two wars: one with the human enemy of the moment; the other with its perpetual enemy, the Basidiomycetes, which set about the destruction of the wooden men-of-war as soon as their keels were laid. In times of stress, when there was no getting away from using uncured lumber, the grateful fungi often won the race. For example, the *Queen Charlotte,* launched during the Napoleonic wars, rotted so quickly that she had to be rebuilt before she was commissioned. There was many a time when the Navy of record was largely a paper navy because of the great number of ships that were unfit to leave their docks. There is an amusing record of an old ship in 1780 which was so rotten that it was decided to scuttle her. A scuttling party was put aboard her, but one of the resident tars, learning the purpose of the visitors, saved them their labor by "clenching his fist and driving it, without much pain to his knuckles, clean through her hull."

119. Scientific and Social Aspects of Plant Diseases

All of the classes of the phylum Eumycophyta include some members that are parasitic on plants. Some of the consequences of such parasitism were briefly touched upon in discussing the "late blight of potatoes" (§116). Returning now to this general problem, we will consider one of the many Basidiomycetes that parasitize plants, and try to show how scientific and social factors interact in producing a problem and effecting its solution.

"Stem rust of wheat" is produced by *Puccinia graminis,* the life cycle of which is shown in Figure 15-11. The popular name is derived from the rusty appearance of certain spots that appear on wheat affected by this parasite. Microscopic examination of a rust spot reveals a cluster of a particular kind of spore, called a **uredospore** (L. a blight). Each uredospore, if it falls on a wheat plant, is capable of producing

a new mycelium, which in turn produces more uredospores; and so on, as long as weather and the supply of host plants permit.

As the host plant nears the end of its season, the *Puccinia* mycelium produces a different sort of spore, called a **teliospore** (Gr. end). A teliospore is thick-walled and resistant to cold weather, which the uredospore is not. After surviving the winter in wheat stubble, the teliospore germinates to produce very tiny hyphae (basidia), near the end of which basidiospores are produced. Notice that before this happens, there is a fusion of the two haploid nuclei of a teliospore, thus producing the only diploid nucleus of the entire life cycle. Meiosis of this nucleus produces the usual haploid basidiospores. These are of two mating types. To grow into a mycelium, a basidiospore must find a host plant, one that is not a wheat plant. *Only if a basidiospore lands on a barberry plant can it produce a mycelium.* Fusion of mycelia of the two different mating types occurs on the European barberry, *Berberis vulgaris,* following which there is produced a new kind of spore, called an **aeciospore** (Gr. injury). The aeciospores produced on the barberry *can infect only wheat plants.* Landing on a wheat plant, an aeciospore germinates to produce a mycelium that, in less than two weeks, produces a new cycle of rust spots of uredospores.

A parasite like wheat rust, which requires two hosts for the completion of its life cycle, is said to be **heteroecious** (Gr. *hetero* = different + *oikos* = house, home). Hundreds of heteroecious plant parasites are known. Perhaps as remarkable as the existence of such plants is the fact that man ever succeeded in working out the details of their life cycles. The principal details of the life cycle of *Puccinia graminis* were first determined by the German mycologist H. A. de Bary, between 1860 and 1865. Once the idea of heteroecism was planted in the minds of biologists by de Bary's achievement, it was a much easier matter to discover additional instances.

Without going further into the details of the biology of this plant pathogen, it is worth stopping to describe some of the methods of control available for this and other plant parasites. For

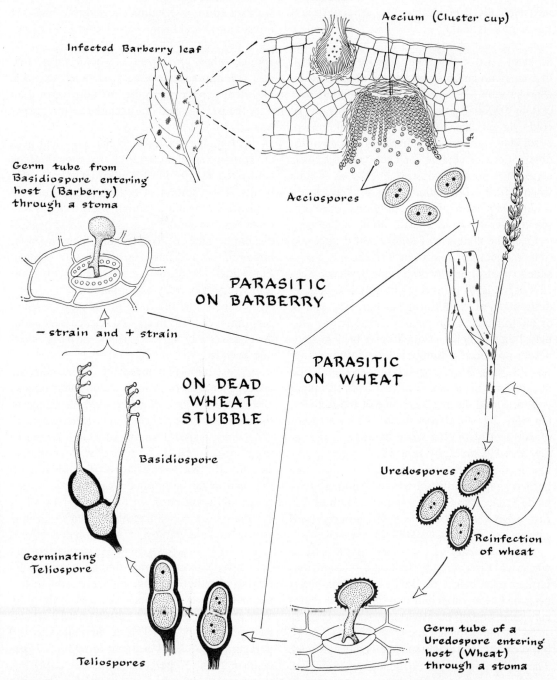

Fig. 15-11. *The life cycle of the wheat rust,* Puccinia graminis. *Haploid stages are in color, diploid in black.*

most plant parasites, climate is of considerable importance in determining the extent of the parasitism. The spread of uredospores on wheat is favored by warm, moist conditions. Given an initial infection of a wheat field, the seriousness of it in any particular year will be determined by the climatic conditions of that year. The transmission of the disease from one year to the next typically depends on the barberry; but if the winter is mild, uredospores may survive from one year to the next, thus by-passing the barberry part of the cycle. The farmer cannot, of course, do anything about the climate, but in a broad sense, humans can choose climate to a certain extent. By planting wheat in regions of cold winters, the rust problem is minimized. Also, in any given region there is a certain probable pattern of climate for each year, and it is sometimes possible to start a crop at a time when parasite infestation is least likely. Some traditional planting times—traditional since pre-scientific eras—have a justification of this sort.

From the life cycle of *Puccinia,* it is apparent that, in regions of cold winters, it should be possible to control rust by destroying barberry. Success depends on achieving close to 100 percent destruction of wild European barberry plants, as the following example illustrates. It was estimated that a single rusted barberry bush in Minnesota produced a number of aeciospores that was 38 times as great as the human population of the world. The spread of rust from this plant was measured during the course of the summer. On May 26, wheat was rusted within a radius of 100 feet of the barberry; by June 6, the radius was 1½ miles; by June 17, 4 miles; and by harvest time, wheat within 10 miles of the single barberry plant had been rusted. Another study made in Decatur County, Indiana, showed that rust originating from a single barberry bush caused a crop loss of $50,000 in one season.

That barberries are involved in the rust of wheat was discovered by several astute amateur farmers even before de Bary's studies on heteroecism. Laws compelling landholders to eradicate their barberries are known as far back as 1755 in the Crown Colony of Massachusetts, but such laws were only spasmodically enforced. They were viewed as infringing on individual liberties, an infringement that is tolerable only if it can be demonstrated that it is necessary for the public good. Until the life cycle of the wheat rust was demonstrated and verified, the assertion that barberries were "the cause" of wheat disease must surely have seemed like superstitious nonsense. More: in regions of variable

winters, close observation showed that bad rust infestations would sometimes occur in the complete absence of barberries (following a mild winter, when uredospores would survive to carry on into a second year). Detailed scientific knowledge makes possible, in more ways than one, the passage and enforcement of the proper laws.

Field studies have led to the empirical generalization that plant parasites can sometimes be controlled by altering the nutrition of the host plants. The addition of fertilizer sometimes diminishes a fungal infestation. Some cabbage diseases that are serious in acid soils are of negligible importance in alkaline soils; consequently, liming of the soil is used as a method of control. Fungicidal chemicals are frequently of great utility, provided they are applied at exactly the right stage in the life cycle of the parasite. Success in this field, as in applied science in general, depends on a broad background of basic scientific knowledge.

A most important means of diminishing the effects of parasites is by selecting plant stocks with a high degree of inheritable resistance to the parasites. The selection and development of genetically resistant strains of plants is one of the principal jobs of our agricultural experiment stations. It must be emphasized that this is a job that will never be finished. An example should make this point clear. In the late 1920's, plant geneticists developed and distributed to farmers a rust-resistant variety of wheat called "Ceres wheat." Within a few years after its distribution, field mycologists reported finding a new strain of *Puccinia* that could attack Ceres wheat; this strain was given the name "Race 56." In 1930, Race 56 constituted 0.2 percent of the wheat-rust population; in 1931, it amounted to 1.0 percent; in 1932, 2.1 percent; in 1933, 3.7 percent; in 1934, 33 percent. It was not surprising, therefore, that a severe wheat-rust epidemic occurred in the following year; and by 1938, Ceres wheat was regarded as such a rust-susceptible strain that farmers generally ceased to plant it.

What had happened? Had this once-resistant strain lost its resistance through some sort of degeneration? Not at all! In 1938 it was just as resistant *to the same parasites* as it had been in 1928, but *the parasites had changed*. For the parasites, the fields of Ceres wheat constituted a new selective environment in which new variants of *Puccinia* might thrive. Among the many natural variants of *Puccinia* that were produced, one (Race 56) was able to live on Ceres wheat; this variant outmultiplied the others and became the new type of *Puccinia* in the regions where Ceres wheat was grown. The appearance of Race 56 of *Puccinia graminis* was, then, a genuine case of evolution occurring before our eyes, brought about (unintentionally) by man's own activities.

What was done to combat Race 56? Before the severe rust epidemic of the middle 1930's, agricultural stations were already busy selecting and developing new strains of wheat that were resistant to Race 56. As speedily as possible, these new wheat strains were made available to farmers, and thus wheat rust was again brought under control—until new strains of *Puccinia graminis* evolved in response to the new challenge thrown out by man. By the time these new rust strains evolved, other strains of wheat had been developed in the agricultural experiment stations. As ammunition for this never-ending battle with wheat parasites, the experiment stations of many nations maintain a cooperative World Collection of Wheats of more than 13,000 strains on which to draw for genetic variability.

Because of the ever-present fact of evolution, there is no reason to hope that we will ever develop a breed of crop plant that is permanently resistant to all strains of parasites. The battle is endless. Man can combat the evolution that occurs in nature only by consciously bringing about a somewhat faster evolution in his experimental fields. In this realm of human endeavor (as, indeed, in all realms) there is no such thing as a static security; the only security lies in continued vigilance. As long as man is interested in wringing the maximum amount of returns from the soil, so long will he have to support numerous and expensive experiment stations, staffed by competent biologists. In these stations must be grown hundreds of varieties of crop plants that are "useless" at present but which may be needed in the future to breed new crop strains that are resistant to as-yet nonexistent races of parasites.

120. The Slime Molds

The Myxomycophyta are called "slime molds." They are of little practical importance, but this is no reason for ignoring them. Scientists agree with the mathematician Jacques Hadamard, who said: "Practical application is found by not looking for it, and one can say that the whole of civilization rests on that principle." What practically important discoveries may come out of study of the Myxomycophyta we cannot say in advance—*nor do we try;* it is enough that the slime molds are strange and wonderful organisms that raise a host of unanswered questions.

Poetically speaking, slime molds are "retiring" organisms. They are most likely to be found on the underside of damp fallen logs in the shaded depths of a forest. In its active stage a slime mold will be an extended mass of "protoplasm," perhaps a dirty white or bright orange in color, a millimeter thick at most and covering a few square centimeters of the log. If we look very carefully, we can see that it is slowly slithering along, changing shape as it goes. It reminds us of some giant amoeba; and it feeds like an amoeba, by engulfing food particles.

Microscopic examination shows that this mass of "protoplasm" has no cell walls or cell membranes, except the single membrane bounding the whole mass. The entire "organism" is coenocytic.

What we have described so far corresponds to stage 4 of Figure 15-12, and hardly seems like a description of a plant. But, under certain conditions, this very animal-like mass changes to a plant-like organism. The protoplasm may round up into a number of little "blebs" (stage 6), each of which then grows into a sporangium (stage 7), consisting of a stalk and a terminal spore case inside which spores are formed. These structures not only look like plants, but

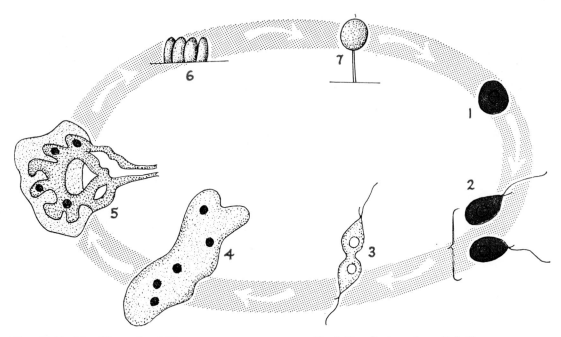

Fig. 15-12. *The life cycle of* Physarum, *a myxomycete. Haploid cells in color, diploid in black.*

Fig. 15-13. *Sporangia of various myxomycetes. (After William Crowder, courtesy National Geographical Society.)*

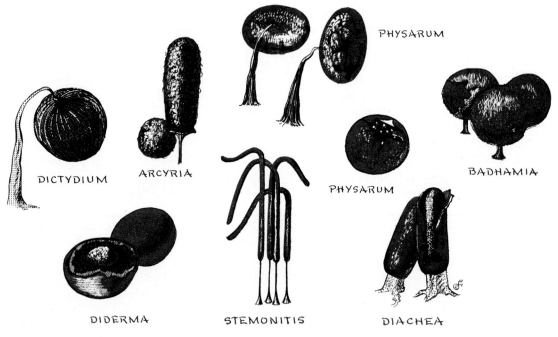

they are bounded by cellulose walls. In view of the difference between the active and the sporulating stages, it is not surprising to find that slime molds are claimed by both botanists and zoologists, the latter classifying them as Mycetozoa.*

In the formation of spores, meiosis is involved. The spores are therefore haploid. If a spore falls on a suitable moist substrate, it will germinate to produce a new morphological type, a flagellated cell (stage 2). Since these haploid

* 15-6. Etymological meaning?

cells unite by twos, they are gametes. The resulting diploid cell is a zygote. By repeated nuclear mitosis unaccompanied by cell cleavage, it produces the multicellular coenocytic mass (or, as the zoologists call it, a **syncytium**) that slides along in the hidden places of the woods. This active stage is amorphous; there is little to differentiate one species from another. Classification is based on the sporangial characteristics, which show great and wondrous variety—only a little of which is shown in the few examples illustrated in Figure 15-13.

Questions and Problems

15-7. Make a list of the **boldface** terms in this chapter and write a brief description of each. Compare your work with the text.

‡15-8. Some species of bats roost in caves, others in trees. Only the former are important sources of guano. Why?

‡15-9. When a good fisherman catches an undersized fish, he wets his hands before grasping the fish and uses the greatest care in taking it off the hook and replacing it in the water. Why?

15-10. Give an etymological analysis of the following terms which were used in this chapter without explanation: mitosporangium, meiospore, amorphous, syncytium.

‡15-11. How is it possible to protect foodstuffs from mold attack? Give examples in which the various methods are used.

15-12. What kind of mold do you see most commonly on bread? If it is not the black bread mold, why not?

15-13. Why are yeasts potentially important as human food? What problems will have to be solved before they are widely used as food?

‡15-14. To grow yeasts for food, would you grow them under aerobic or under anaerobic conditions? Why?

‡15-15. Equation 2 (§117) shows that 1 gram-

mole of glucose produces, on fermentation, 2 gram-moles of ethyl alcohol. If 1 gram-mole of ethyl alcohol is completely respired to CO_2, how much energy will be released? (Hint: An essential principle is found in §24.)

15-16. When fermentation is carried out in vats containing 100,000 gallons of medium, heat must be removed to keep the fermenting organisms from being killed. What is the source of this heat?

‡15-17. In contrast (see the preceding question), fermentation in a 1-gallon container can usually be carried out without risk of killing the organisms. Explain.

15-18. What is the best way to make wine: in well-filled barrels or shallow pans? Why?

‡15-19. Comment on the significance of the following title page of a book: *The Mycetozoa of North America, Based Upon the Specimens in the Herbarium of the New York Botanical Garden.* By Robert Hagelstein, Honorary Curator of Myxomycetes. New York, 1944.

15-20. Why are the slime molds often omitted from both botany and zoology textbooks?

‡15-21. If you were given a pure strain of a heterothallic fungus, how would you determine its mating type?

15-22. The American horticulturist Liberty Hyde Bailey (1858–1954) stated in 1892 that he thought it should be possible to breed a variety of apple that would be resistant to the fungus disease *apple scab*. "But," he remarked, "this is a common history of injurious insects and fungi; they take on new habits to accommodate themselves to new conditions. It is possible a good market apple may spring up that is scab-proof; but when we have learned to produce such kinds with tolerable certainty,

the fungi will have grown cunning too—I fear."

Recast Bailey's statement in terms of precise biological concepts and principles.

15-23. (Laboratory exercise.) Examine the basidia of some mushrooms bought in a store. What is odd about them?

Readings

Christensen's *Molds and Man* is full of delightful sidelights on the fungi. Large's *The Advance of the Fungi* has a particularly interesting account of the Irish potato famine in the first two chapters.

A fine history of the discovery and development of penicillin is given in Chapter 2 of Cohen. For a longer version of this humanly interesting story, see Maurois' *The Life of Sir Alexander Fleming*.

Scientific American Offprints

109. John S. Niederhauser & William C. Cobb. *The Late Blight of Potatoes*

115. Ralph Emerson. *Molds and Men*

16   Bacteria

121. General Characteristics and Discovery

The subtitle of the chapter on fungi, "Trash Burners and Parasites," would do almost as well for a chapter on bacteria, for these organisms also are saprophytes and parasites. However, they are not exclusively so, since there are a few autotrophic species; these we will discuss presently. For the most part, however, bacteria play essentially the same role in the "economy of nature" as that played by the fungi: they degrade organic compounds to inorganic ones.

There is much variation among the species of bacteria, but certain crude generalizations may be made about this group. To begin with, the filamentous type of morphology, common among fungi, is rare among bacteria. Soil bacteria of the genus *Actinomyces* are filamentous, but the diameter of their cells is only a twentieth to a fiftieth that of fungal cells. Sporulation, the rule among fungi, is exceptional among bacteria; and where it occurs, it is not a mode of multiplication, for only one spore is formed per cell. Sexual reproduction, in the few species in which it has been demonstrated, has no connection with spore formation.

When we look at bacteria with the optical microscope, we see little variation in form. The majority of the common species can be classified as one of the three types shown in Figure 16-1. Bacteria, unlike fungi, are active only when surrounded by water, though they may survive (inactively) in dry air. Because of their small size, bacteria (by virtue of the scale effect) typically exhibit extremely high metabolic rates. Accompanying these metabolic rates are correspondingly high rates of reproduction. For a population of cells to double in 20 minutes is not uncommon, and a doubling time of as little as 12.5 minutes has been recorded. Such a fan-

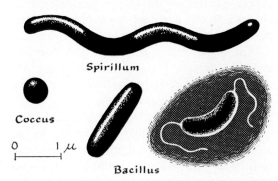

Fig. 16-1. *Some of the principal morphological types of bacteria, drawn to scale. The flagella shown at right are visible only on specially prepared bacteria.*

tastic rate of reproduction means that bacteria are likely to be very important members of any ecological system of which they are part.

Bacteria are everywhere, and they outnumber all other species of plants and animals. That they were not discovered until about three centuries ago is, however, hardly a cause for wonder, for seeing them is not easy. Small, generally colorless when seen individually, translucent, most often immotile, and with a morphology not very different from miscellaneous bits of trash, bacteria even today are a challenge to the student just learning to use a microscope. Considering how difficult it is to see them with a good compound microscope of 400–900 diameters magnification, we are most impressed with the fact that bacteria were first seen with only a "simple microscope" (a single magnifying lens) of about 200 power—and first seen by a man who didn't know what he was looking for, which makes seeing much more difficult. The discoverer of bacteria was Antony van Leeuwenhoek (1632–1723) of Delft, Netherlands.

By occupation, Leeuwenhoek was a draper and a surveyor. In addition, he held a political sinecure that made him responsible for the care of the town hall (but he was not a janitor, as has sometimes been asserted!). His moderate wealth permitted him to indulge his hobby of grinding lenses and focusing them on all sorts of things: rain water, sea water, vinegar, infusions made from ginger, cloves, nutmeg, and pepper—as well as such less proper materials as his own feces, scrapings from his teeth, and human semen. In these materials he saw and studied algae, fungi, protozoa, and bacteria, and thus became the first microbiologist. He was, in the strict sense, an *amateur,* that is, one who does what he does for the love of it (L. *amator* = a lover), not because he's paid to do so. That a science should be founded by an amateur rather than a professional should not surprise us when we stop to think of it, for no profession can exist until it is founded by one who, with respect to the profession that develops, is necessarily an amateur.

Leeuwenhoek's findings were revealed in a way quite different from present-day scientific publication. They appeared as parts of letters written to the Royal Society of London, and were read before meetings of the members. They were printed (in part) later. How different the world of the seventeenth century was from our own is emphasized by the fact that these communications of scientific discoveries passed freely between the Dutch microbiologist and his

English colleagues even during the years their countries were at war. Can we imagine such interchanges between belligerents today? It is not only the tools of war that evolve; so also do the customs and the meaning of war.

The discovery of bacteria was announced in the celebrated Eighteenth Letter of 1676. Since bacteria are so small and so poor in detail, and since Leeuwenhoek's lenses were so crude, how do we know that he was looking at bacteria and not at some other tiny objects—say, nematode worms? The evidence is of three sorts. *First,* he made sketches of the objects. (This is the weakest evidence.) *Second,* with that quantitative attitude that is so important an element of the scientific temperament (§10). Leeuwenhoek measured his "animalcules" by comparing them carefully with such identifiable objects as the eye of a louse and a human red blood cell; and from these quantitative comparisons, we can tell that his Eighteenth Letter is concerned with objects the size of bacteria. *Third,* his description of their motion unambiguously indicates that he saw certain kinds of bacteria. In his words:

They moved with bendings, as an eel swims in water; only with this difference, that whereas an eel always swims with his head in front and never tail first, yet these animalcules swam as well backward as forward, though their motion was very slow.

Of organisms within their size range, only bacteria move in this manner.

122. The Spontaneous Generation Controversy

One of the major problems of biology today is the problem of the origin of life. As explained in §90, we think we know (though only in the most general way) how life began on this earth several billion years ago. Consistency in evolutionary theory demands that life must once have been generated from nonlife. However, it is clear that the necessary conditions for this transformation would have been destroyed by living things themselves, so that once life began there would be no more originations of living things from nonliving matter. After the first birth, there was no other. The discrediting of the possibility of *spontaneous generation* under present-day conditions was one of the great negative triumphs of biology. The word "negative" is intended in no sense of disparagement; the achievement was negative only in the sense that it destroyed an almost universally held belief. Without this achievement, all of modern microbiology and a great part of modern medicine could never have come into being.

The first partial discrediting of the doctrine of spontaneous generation was brought about by experiments of the Italian biologist Francesco Redi (1626–1697), in 1668. It was then (and perhaps still is) believed by most people that maggots are spontaneously generated by decaying meat. By a controlled experiment, Redi showed that the evidence for the belief was quite insufficient. He enclosed pieces of meat in two types of vessels: one completely open to the air, the other covered by fine gauze. Only in the former did maggots appear. Redi observed further that the maggots, if allowed to develop, ultimately turned into flies, and also that flies were attracted to the meat in both the experimental and the control vessels, but were able to lay eggs only on the meat in the open vessels. In the controls, maggots sometimes appeared on the gauze, following the visitations of flies. Redi concluded that maggots are not produced spontaneously from decaying material, but that they are always the progeny of a previous generation of flies.

Redi's experiment discredited the doctrine of spontaneous generation, but only for a time. With the discovery of bacteria, the entire question was thrown open again, to be settled only two centuries later by experiments that were essentially similar to Redi's, though technically more difficult to perform. The meat in Redi's experimental vessels, though generating no maggots, had nevertheless become putrid. In putrid meat a microscopist can see bacteria. It was natural to conclude that the bacteria had arisen spontaneously. The most active period of conflict between the **biogenesists** (those who believed that life came only from life) and the **abiogenesists** (spontaneous generationists) began in 1749, with the publication of some experiments by the Englishman John Needham (1713–1781). He put some mutton gravy in a flask, which he closed with a cork and heated in a bed of hot ashes. The flask was kept closed for some time after the heat treatment; when it was opened, it had microbes swarming in it, and it smelled of putrefaction.

Needham's reports aroused the interest of the Italian Lazzaro Spallanzani (1729–1799), who repeated the experiments under more rigorous conditions. Instead of stoppering his vessels with corks, Spallanzani sealed them hermetically by melting the mouths closed after the introduction of the organic material. Then the organic soup was boiled for a long time. *Some* of such vessels, when examined later, proved to be free of both microbes and objectionable odors.* Spallanzani found that he could obtain such microbe-free organic soup only if he carried out the boiling process for several hours. He concluded that life could come only from previously existing life.

Needham interpreted Spallanzani's findings differently: the Englishman protested that the prolonged boiling of the soup had so enfeebled the *"vegetative force"* that the material was no longer capable of generating life. Spallanzani retorted that his long-boiled soups were perfectly capable of supporting life if it was introduced from the outside: When he broke open one of his flasks, the soup within soon swarmed with microbes. In reply, Needham said that opening the flasks permitted the "vegetative force" to re-enter the soup with the fresh air from the outside, thus supplying that which was lacking in the heated air inside the flask.

The controversy was given a dramatic new hearing in the nineteenth century by a new duo of antagonists, both of them Frenchmen: F. A. Pouchet (1800–1872) and Louis Pasteur (1822–1895). In 1858, a paper by Pouchet

---

* 16-1. Do you think it is significant evidence for the opposing view that *only* some of the vessels were free of life?

reviewed the evidence and told of experiments of his own that proved, he said, that life could be spontaneously generated. The following year, Pouchet brought out a book of some seven hundred pages. So ponderous a work might have swept the field before it, had it not aroused the fighting spirit of the chemist Pasteur. Pasteur repeated many of Pouchet's experiments, frequently obtaining quite opposite results. In addition, he designed a test of such simple elegance as to convince almost everyone.

The invisible and impalpable "vegetative force" of the abiogenesists was a formidable entity to rule out. The treatment of the liquid environment, or **medium** (pl. *media*), subsequent to the heating period was clearly crucial. Some scientists had admitted air to the experimental flask through glowing hot tubes; others had let air in only after it had bubbled through sulfuric acid; still others had filtered air through fibrous cotton. But to all such experiments the objection could be made, with more or less justification, that air admitted in the "unnatural" way had been deprived of its "vegetative force."

Pasteur answered all the objections by a classic experiment. He partially filled a flask with the organic soup that was to be heated. Then, before heating the medium, he pulled the neck of the flask out into a long tube with a curvature, as shown in Figure 16-2 (such a flask has

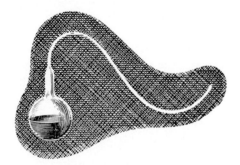

Fig. 16-2. *Pasteur's flask.*

been called a "swan-neck flask"). In this flask the medium was boiled for a long time. At the conclusion of the boiling period the flask was allowed to cool *very slowly.** After being

* 16-2. Why very slowly?

cooled, the flask was watched for signs of life developing within. When the experiment was performed with sufficient care, no living organisms ever appeared inside the flask, no matter how long it was kept. Note that normal air outside the flask, with whatever "vegetative force" it might contain, had complete access to the medium inside, for molecular movement and diffusion (Chap. 3) insured a continual, slow interchange of gases between the flask and the outside.

Pasteur's experiments indicated that the development of bacteria in ordinary flasks left open to the air is due to contamination of the contents of the flask by some sorts of particles or "germs" that fall into it, these particles being too massive to permit their being carried into Pasteur's swan-neck flask by the force of molecular bombardment. Such germs should then be found collected in the lowermost portion of the swan-neck. Pasteur showed that this was indeed true; for microbes soon appeared in the flask if he tipped it in such a way as to cause a few droplets of the soup to reach the lowermost portion of the swan-neck, and then subsequently tilted the flask so as to return these droplets to the flask.

By the elegance of his experiments and the vigor of his presentations, Pasteur won the argument. In 1863, another scientist stated the common opinion when he said: "M. Pasteur's experiments are decisive." For another decade no one seriously, publicly, questioned this judgment. And yet . . . we know now that both Pasteur and Pouchet were right (that is, partially right). During their years of controversy, they had repeated each other's experiments, *but never exactly.* Each had been careful in the repetition of physical details of the experiment, but for some curious, perhaps psychological, reason they had chosen different media. Most frequently, Pasteur had made his soup of yeast; and Pouchet his of meat. In this difference, slight though it no doubt appeared to be, lay the key both to their controversy and to some great general truths of bacteriology.

The question was reopened in England in 1872 by H. C. Bastian (1837–1915), who published a 1,100-page opus, *The Beginnings of Life*. Bastian's work is of little interest to modern readers, but in the mass of ill-digested and uncritical observations, there is this important fact recorded: The various media used by Pouchet and Pasteur differ significantly in their acidity or alkalinity. If an organic soup is made slightly acid before it is heated, it may remain free of living organisms indefinitely after it is cooled again. If it is made slightly alkaline before heating, it will, on the contrary, speedily develop living organisms after it is cooled. This difference Bastian saw through the eyes of an abiogenesist. But a compatriot of his, the physicist John Tyndall (1820–1893), showed that the new results did not contradict the biogenetic theory.

Tyndall showed that there are two forms of bacterial life: (1) an active form, which can readily be killed by the temperature of boiling water, or by even lower temperatures; and (2) an inactive form, which can survive the temperature of boiling water, *provided the liquid it is in is slightly alkaline*. If the inactive form survives the heat treatment, it may then, subsequent to cooling, turn into an active form and multiply rapidly. In retrospect, it appears that Pasteur achieved his experimental results because he chose (for whatever reason) slightly acid media; whereas Pouchet, choosing slightly alkaline materials, achieved contradictory results and arrived at opposite conclusions. Here we see clearly presented one of the reasons for the tradition of scientific publication (recall §3), for insisting on a full reporting of all known, relevant details, and for the most exact repetition possible of the experiments of the competitors with whom one disagrees.

The two forms of bacterial life with respect to heat resistance are distinguishable under the microscope. Some bacterial cells are capable of producing glistening, nearly spherical bodies called spores, first recognized by the German microbiologist Ferdinand Cohn (1828–1898) in 1875. A bacterial spore (Fig. 16-3) is highly resistant to heat and poisons. It exhibits no metabolism or any other characteristic of life; but it may, when placed in a suitable environ-

ment, germinate to produce new cells of the ordinary type, called **vegetative cells** (Fig. 16-3). Such vegetative cells then multiply in the ordinary way by cell division for a time until, perhaps in response to slightly unfavorable environmental conditions, some of the vegetative cells again produce spores.

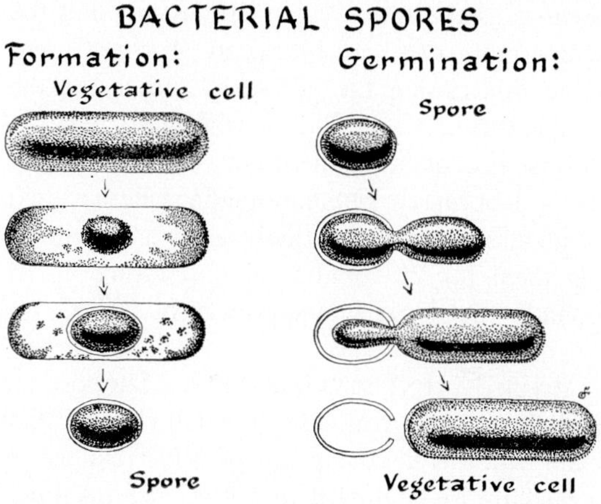

Fig. 16-3. *Formation and germination of bacterial spores.*

Not all species of bacteria are capable of producing spores; in fact, the majority cannot. The vegetative cells of all species, including those of spore-formers, have only moderate resistance to heat. Most kinds of vegetative cells are killed by exposure to a temperature of 60°C for 15 minutes; exceptionally heat-resistant species may be able to survive several minutes' exposure to 80°C. But all vegetative cells are almost immediately killed by exposure to the temperature of boiling water, 100°C. By contrast, many spores are capable of withstanding this temperature for several hours if the environment is slightly alkaline. It was by clearly demonstrating this fact that Tyndall was able to reconcile Pasteur's experiments with those of Pouchet and Bastian.

In addition to his contributions to the theory of microbiology, Tyndall made important practical advances by devising simple and reliable means of rendering media **sterile**, that is, free of all living creatures. He introduced the following two methods of sterilization by heat.

AUTOCLAVING. Spores are not readily killed at a temperature of 100°C, but they can be killed by exposure to a temperature of 121°C for a few minutes. A vessel of water in free communication with air at ordinary atmospheric pressure cannot be heated to so high a temperature; but if it is enclosed in a hermetically sealed container, the pressure around the vessel is increased as the water vapor comes off, and the temperature then can be raised. A closed container for raising the pressure, and hence the temperature, of the fluids within is called a "pressure cooker" in the home, or an **autoclave** in the laboratory. Organic media, whether acid or alkaline, may be routinely sterilized by holding them for 20 minutes at a pressure of 15 pounds, that is, at a temperature of 121°C.

INTERMITTENT STERILIZATION. Suppose an autoclave is not available? Tyndall showed that even with this handicap it is possible to sterilize a medium by heating it to 100°C several times at properly spaced intervals. The first heating kills all the vegetative cells. A few hours after the medium cools, the spores that are present germinate and produce new vegetative cells. If one now heats the medium again, these vegetative cells are killed. If the second heating is done too soon after the first, not all of the spores have germinated; if too late, some of the new batch of vegetative cells have formed new spores. For effective sterilization, the interval between the first and second heatings must be just right. For most media and with most species of bacteria, it has been found that an interval of one day is satisfactory. In practice, for greater surety, the heating is repeated again on the third day. Routinely, **intermittent sterilization** (or **tyndallization,** as it is also called) consists in heating media to the temperature of boiling water on three successive days, the media being held at room temperature in the intervals.

With these reliable methods of sterilization, Tyndall and other scientists repeated the essential experiments concerned with the problem of spontaneous generation and brought the con-

troversy to a close, for a time at least. It was repeatedly shown that media that were thoroughly sterilized remained free of life indefinitely, *provided proper precautions were taken to avoid contamination of the media subsequent to their sterilization.* The italicized phrase is important. How can one *prove* that life *cannot* be spontaneously generated? The experimenter prepares what he hopes are sterile media, establishes certain conditions, and then watches for the appearance of life. If living things do not appear, he cannot state that spontaneous generation is impossible; he can say only that under certain conditions he has not observed it. If he is a careless experimenter, that is, if he uses inadequate sterilization procedures or clumsily permits contamination of his media, he may report opposite results. As Pasteur said at a historic debate:

Every source of error plays into the hands of my opponents. For me, affirming as I do that there are no spontaneous fermentations, I am bound to eliminate every cause of error, every perturbing influence. Whereas I can maintain my results only by means of the most irreproachable technique, their claims profit by every inadequate experiment.

123. The Control of Bacterial Cultures

With the advent of microbiology, it has become apparent that our traditional language habits need modification. Colloquially, we say, "A piece of meat decays." Discoveries of the nineteenth century have shown the inaccuracy of this expression. Meat does not decay of itself —it is decayed by living organisms. The same may be said of all other organic substances that we ordinarily speak of as decaying—wood, leaves, flowers, and so on. Most organic substances are intrinsically stable, in terms of a human time scale; when they change rapidly, it is because they are decayed by living organisms. Our colloquial manner of speaking of decay is inaccurate, just as it is an error to say, "the sun rises." In both instances, the form of the statement reflects earlier, untrue conceptual schemes. Everyday speech will continue to be couched in traditional terms; so it is important to appreciate their scientific inexactness.

Any organic material dissolved in, or in contact with, water will be decayed; the watery medium will soon swarm with millions upon millions of bacteria. *What* bacteria? Are they all the same kind, or are they different? How do we know? In the nineteenth century, some biologists maintained that all bacteria were members of a single species. The discrediting of this belief was a fundamental step, involving the development of the basic techniques of bacteriology described below.

Under the optical microscope, bacteria show disconcertingly little differentiation. Even the electron microscope has been of little help in distinguishing species. Most bacterial cells can be readily classified as one of three basic morphological types: a rod, or **bacillus** (pl. *bacilli*); a sphere, or **coccus** (pl. *cocci*); or a corkscrew-shaped rod, or **spirillum** (pl. *spirilla*) (Fig. 16-1). Seldom can one see any detail inside the bacterial cell, and for a very good reason: the cells are too small. According to physical theory, it is possible to distinguish separate points, using light visible to the human eye, only if the points are at least 0.2μ apart. A typical bacterial cell is only about 0.5μ in thickness. This means that most of the structures inside the bacterial cells will be so close together that they cannot be seen as separate objects; hence, the interior of a bacterial cell will seem to be without structure.

It was easy to maintain, in the early days of bacteriology, that all the observable morphological differences among bacteria were due entirely to different environmental factors acting on a single species—an assertion that could be disproved only by effecting a separation of bacterial species. In principle the separation of species is simple, but in practice there are difficulties. If one opens a can of sterile bouillon and pours it into a glass container left open to the air, the soup is at first clear. Within two days, at room temperature, the soup is cloudy;

microscopic examination shows that the cause of the cloudiness is a swarm of bacteria, there being perhaps as many as a million bacterial cells in each cubic millimeter. Are all these cells of the same species or not? To settle the question, one must somehow obtain separate **cultures,** that is, separate populations, each of which has originated from a single cell. A single drop (approximately 50 cubic millimeters) of the bacterial soup will contain about half a billion bacterial cells. To separate individual cells out of such a concentrated swarm may at first appear to be impossible, but it is not. It may be accomplished by a dilution method first applied to this problem by the English surgeon Joseph Lister (1827–1912), and for that reason called **Lister's serial dilution method.**

The logic of this method may be understood by considering an artificially simple example. Suppose we begin with a tube that contains 2 cc of medium, in which there are just 10 living bacterial cells, as indicated in *A* of Figure 16-4. If (after thorough stirring) we remove 1 cc from such a tube and add it to a test tube that contains 1 cc of sterile medium (*B*), we will then have a tube with 2 cc of medium and, most probably, 5 bacterial cells (*C*). We have thus diluted the original culture (*A*) of bacteria, obtaining a culture with only half as many cells.

We can continue this procedure. By diluting *C*, we will produce a *D*, which probably will have 2 or 3 cells—say, 2, as indicated in the figure. The next dilution will produce a tube (*E*) with probably 1 cell in it. If we take 1 cc from *E*, we will pick up either 1 cell or none (*F*).

So much for logic. How do we know when we have any cells—whether *F*, for instance, has 1 cell or none? Here we depend on one of the primary characteristics of living organisms: the ability to reproduce. The various dilutions are made in an organic medium that will support life and cell multiplication. Therefore, every tube that has any living bacteria in it—even if only 1 cell—will, in a short time, be cloudy with millions of living cells (*A'*, *C'*, *D'*, *E'*, and *F'*). If *F* receives 1 cell, it will become

I. The basic operation:
   a single dilution

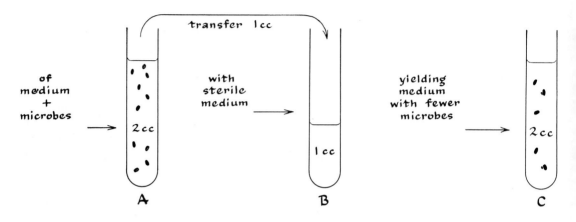

II. By repeating this basic operation, serially, we finally isolate single cells by
    SERIAL DILUTION:

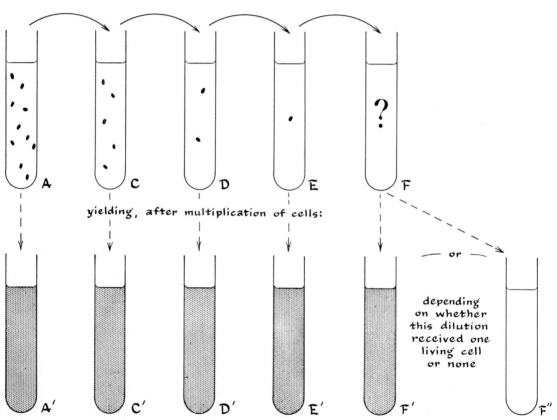

Fig. 16-4. *How a single microbial cell may be isolated, using Lister's dilution method, thus obtaining a "pure culture."*

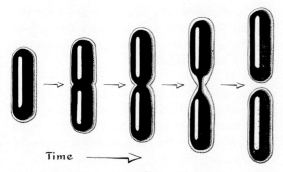

Fig. 16-5. *Division of a bacterial cell.*

cloudy (F'); if it receives none, it will remain clear indefinitely (F'').

The procedure used in Lister's serial dilution method has been somewhat simplified in this example—it is usually carried out in replicate, for instance—but the principles should be clear. To get a culture derived from a single cell, we carry out a serial dilution and save only turbid tubes of the highest dilution that yields some turbid and some clear tubes. Is such a culture *certainly* derived from a single cell? No—only probably. But the probability can be calculated, and if it is not as high as is desired, the serial dilution procedure can be carried out again, starting with a culture derived from the previous serial dilution procedure. And yet again, if desired.

The serial dilution method is a practically feasible one to secure a culture derived from a single cell, because bacteria multiply at a prodigious rate. Bacteria reproduce *asexually* by cell division. A bacillus, for instance, after growing in length for a while, divides across the middle to form two daughter cells (Fig. 16-5). A short time later, each of these divides to form two more, making a total of four. A new division every 20 minutes is common. At this rate, a culture started with but 1 cell would contain several million cells at the end of 8 hours.* Even though no turbidity is noticeable in a culture tube until there are about 10,000 cells per cubic millimeter, it does not take long to identify tubes that have received but a single living cell.

By the dilution method, Joseph Lister, in 1878, first obtained cultures that had a high probability of having been derived from a single bacterial cell. The importance of this technical advance in helping to determine the differences between bacterial species was immediately recognized. But Lister's method, with its multiplicity of tubes and its many operations, is laborious to carry out. Fortunately, simpler but equally reliable methods were soon developed. A German physician, Robert Koch (1843–1910), showed how the same end could be reached with much less labor by the use of a *solid* medium. One modification of Koch's method is shown in Figure 16-6. Assume that we have already brought a bacterial culture to a convenient dilution, say, such that the tube shown in *A* contains less than 100 bacterial cells. We now prepare a tube of nutrient medium to which has been added agar, an organic substance that is not nutritive for most species

* 16-3. How many million?

Fig. 16-6. *Obtaining pure cultures by spatially separating microbial cells in sterilized nutrient agar.*

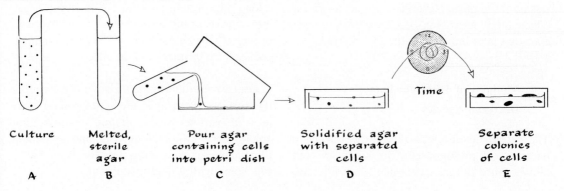

Culture	Melted, sterile agar	Pour agar containing cells into petri dish	Solidified agar with separated cells	Separate colonies of cells
A	B	C	D	E

of bacteria and that has the property of solidifying the medium to which it is added (the consistency is about that of Jell-o). An agar medium can be liquefied by heating it to 100°C, but it will not become solid until cooled to about 40°C. We heat a tube of sterile agar medium, thus liquefying it, then cool it to a lower temperature so there is no danger of killing the bacteria introduced into it. While it is still liquid, we **inoculate** it—that is, add the bacterial culture shown in *A*—rapidly mix the two together, and then pour the mixture into a flat **petri dish** in which the agar solidifies, thus fixing in place each bacterial cell. We store the petri dish at a suitable temperature for a day. At the end of that time, each spatially separated bacterial cell has multiplied to produce a **colony** of millions of cells, as represented in *E*. When a sample of each colony is examined microscopically, we see that it consists of one, and only one, kind of cell. If the initial dilution used was such that there were only 20 bacterial cells poured into a plate 100 mm in diameter, the probability that two bacterial cells would lie so close together as to form a single colony is small; hence it is reasonably certain that any particular colony represents the offspring of a single cell. **Koch's solid-medium method** accomplishes the same result as Lister's dilution method, with much less labor; for this reason the solid-medium method is generally preferred when we desire a **pure culture,** that is, a culture consisting of cells of only one species.

We have not given all the details of pure-culture procedures, but from the descriptions it is apparent that all the methods are based on probability procedures. No culture is absolutely certain to be pure. Nevertheless, on this probabilistic basis, microbiologists have erected a science that is of immense value to mankind.

124. Methods of Distinguishing Bacterial Species

The successful development of the science of bacteriology presupposed two kinds of techniques: pure-culture techniques, and differentiating techniques. The first have just been described. The second, the methods whereby pure cultures of bacteria are distinguished from one another, will be treated now.

MORPHOLOGICAL DIFFERENCES. The three principal types—bacilli, cocci, and spirilla—can be further subdivided. Cocci are differentiated with reference to the way in which successive cell divisions take place. If divisions occur in two or three planes, and the cells separate from one another or form irregular bunches, the species is assigned to the genus *Micrococcus*. If the plane of division in successive divisions is always the same, and if the cocci stick together, the result will be a long chain of cells, which, since it frequently appears as a twisted chain on the microscope slide, justifies the generic name *Streptococcus* (Gr. *streptos* = *twisted*). Among bacilli, species that can produce spores are assigned either to the genus *Bacillus* (L. a rod) or to the genus *Clostridium* (Gr. *klosteros* = a spindle). (The distinction between these two genera is a physiological one: The members of the genus *Clostridium* are unable to multiply in the presence of oxygen; whereas members of the genus *Bacillus* can, and usually do.)

Bacteria can also be distinguished on the basis of their motility. Motility is universal among the spirilla, rare among cocci, and common among the bacilli. Movement is brought about by cellular extensions (see Fig. 16-7) called *flagella* (sing. **flagellum;** L. a whip). Each flagellum is much too thin to be seen by ordinary microscopic examination: the dimensions of a flagellum are approximately those of a long thin protein molecule. A bacterial flagellum consists of but a single strand; the flagellum of any other cell consists of 2 central filaments enclosed by 9 others (11 in all).

COLONY DIFFERENCES. Bacteria growing on the surface of an agar medium produce colonies of various sizes, shapes, textures, and colors. Some colonies are flat and spreading, others are compact, some rounded, some flat on top, some with a depression, and so on.

STAINING DIFFERENCES. Though staining characteristics are detected visually, they are basically a reflection of differences in the chemical nature of bacterial cells. Many species are differentiated according to their reaction to the **gram stain.** This staining method, named after the Danish physician Christian Gram, who de-

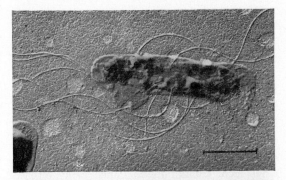

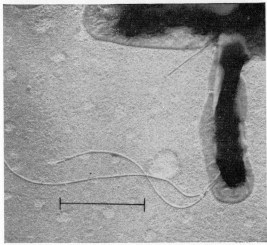

Fig. 16-7. *Electron micrographs of bacteria, showing flagella. Dimension lines are 1μ. (From W. W. Umbreit,* Modern Microbiology, *W. H. Freeman and Company, San Francisco and London, 1962.)*

veloped it in 1884, is really a double staining method. Bacteria are first heat-killed on a microscope slide; they are then immersed in a solution of crystal violet followed by iodine. Then the slide is subjected to a decolorizing agent, after which it is restained with a red dye, safranin. Bacteria that retain the first dye (violet) are called *gram positive;* those that are decolorized and hence take up the second dye (the red one) are called *gram negative.*

BIOCHEMICAL DIFFERENCES: PRODUCTS. On the basis of morphology, the great majority of bacteria can be differentiated no further than to genera. Identification of species is accomplished mostly on the basis of biochemical differences, not the least of which are differences of the products produced by different species metabolizing the same food. Fed the same sugar, one kind of bacteria will produce acetic acid, another propionic acid, another lactic acid, and another no acid at all.

BIOCHEMICAL DIFFERENCES: SUBSTRATES. Bacterial species differ enormously in the kinds of food, or *substrates,* they can utilize, and the conditions under which they can use them. Some bacteria are aerobic, others anaerobic; and they may be *obligate* or *facultative,** in either case. With respect to organic foods, "One man's meat is another man's poison." There are microbes that can feed not only on things that we recognize as food (e.g., sugars, amino acids) but also on what we habitually call waste products: urea, uric acid, hippuric acid (an increasingly scarce delicacy in these days of the decline of the horse), and the indole and skatole that abound in animal dung. Not only do microbes prosper on the waste products of higher plants and animals, but they also live on each others' waste products. Some of the putrefying bacteria of the marshes produce methane (CH_4), or marsh gas; other bacteria use this material as food. Many bacteria produce hydrogen (H_2) as a waste product; other species use it as food. Even carbon monoxide (CO), so deadly to man, is a nutritive substance for a few species of bacteria. In fact, no organic material has yet been found that cannot be used as an energy source by some species of bacteria. This applies even to those organic substances that we call **antiseptics,** substances that kill bacteria under suitable circumstances. Carbolic acid is an antiseptic, lethal to most kinds of bac-

---

* 16-4. Is there any difference between a facultative aerobe and a facultative anaerobe?

teria; but diluted to less than 1 percent strength, it serves admirably as food for a number of species.

Microbiologists believe that *every energy-rich substance is a potential food for some kind of microbe.* Since we have not tested every chemical compound, we cannot assert that this is true, but certainly it is a fruitful *working hypothesis.* The absence of enduring accumulations of any kind of organic compounds on the face of the earth is strong evidence of its truth. In evolutionary terms, the appearance of any new organic substance on the earth constitutes a new environmental niche that "invites" occupancy by whatever species can succeed in moving into it by mutation and selection.

Differences in nutritional demands are used routinely in distinguishing species of bacteria. Rapid, simple methods of determining these differences form the basis of the **differential media** used in routine bacteriology. As a single example, the colon bacillus *Escherichia coli* is unable to multiply when put in a medium in which citric acid is the only source of organic carbon; *Aerobacter aerogenes,* which is indistinguishable from the colon bacillus by microscopic examination, *can* utilize citric acid as a food. If one has a pure culture known to be either *E. coli* or *A. aerogenes,* the final differentiation may be made by inoculating a small amount of the culture into a tube of sterile citrate medium. If there is "growth of the culture," that is, multiplication of cells, one knows that the species is *A. aerogenes;* if not, it is *E. coli.*

125. Use of the Competitive Exclusion Principle

Suppose we suspect that a certain kind of microbe exists in the soil. How would we go about finding it? If it is in the minority (which will almost always be the case), it will be hard to obtain it directly, even with Koch's plating method. If by "kind" we have in mind some morphological distinction, success will be hard to achieve. But if we can specify the "kind" in terms of physiology, then it is often possible to find it quickly, even if it is very rare, by making use of the Competitive Exclusion Principle (§81). A few examples will show how this may be done.

Suppose we wanted to study the physiology of penicillin-resistant microbes. How would we secure such organisms? Simply by making up a nutrient medium with a high concentration of penicillin, inoculating it with, say, a bit of soil, and seeing what develops. This procedure we may speak of as *negative selection.*

Alternatively, we can use *positive selection* to bring about a relative increase of a wanted species. The colon bacillus is so called because it is a normal inhabitant of the human colon, or large intestine. *E. coli* does not live long in soil or water. Its presence in drinking water indicates fecal contamination. Since many disease organisms can be transmitted via feces, tests that reveal *E. coli* are of practical importance. Unfortunately, even in seriously contaminated water, *E. coli* cells may be only a small fraction of the total number of bacterial cells present, and consequently the chances of finding colonies of *E. coli* on a plate made directly are very slight. It has been found, however, that *E. coli* can multiply vigorously in a medium containing lactose (a sugar), at a temperature of 37°C, whereas most water- and soil-dwelling species of bacteria cannot. The colon bacillus can, therefore, be found more easily in a water sample if the sample is first "enriched" with lactose. If this enriched culture is kept at 37°C, there is a relative increase in the number of *E. coli* cells, thus facilitating the problem of finding colonies of this bacillus on a plate.

Any medium that permits one microbial species to outmultiply all others is called a **selective medium,** or *enrichment medium.* We owe the development of enrichment medium methods to the Dutch microbiologist Martinus Willem Beijerinck (1851–1931), who did his greatest work in the cradle of microbiology, Delft. Beijerinck's first love was botany, but under family pressure he trained as a chemist. In later switching to microbiology he combined the two professions, being one of the pioneers in working out the chemical role of bacteria in the biosphere. In developing selective culture media as a means of discovering and isolating new species of bacteria he was explicitly aware that he was applying Darwinian theory in the laboratory—in fact, he sometimes spoke of his method as a form of "darwinizing" cultures. Selective culture methods have been of great use in agricultural studies. Soil is an exceedingly complex material in which occur multitudinous, poorly understood biochemical reactions brought about by various species of microbes. Selective culture media are used in demonstrating that certain chemical reactions are brought about by microbes. For instance, in the soil, urea is destroyed. May this destruction be due to microbes? Urea in sterile soil is stable. If we make up a selective culture with urea as the only energy source and inoculate it with soil, we presently find a flourishing culture of microbes. When we isolate various species from the mixture, we find that most of them are capable of destroying urea. Thus we learn what microbes in the soil bring about what biochemical reactions.

The success of Beijerinck's selective culture method is limited, however, by another ecological principle, which we will introduce by an example. Mashed grapes in an open flask serve as a good selective medium for yeasts, which outgrow other organisms for a while. But if we wait too many days before investigating the culture, we may find that the predominant organisms are not yeasts but "acetic acid bacteria"—bacteria that turn the alcohol produced by the yeasts into acetic acid, the essential ingredient of vinegar. The change in the dominant organisms of the culture is brought about by the change in the environment. *In the act of exploiting the environment, a dominant organism often creates a new environment that favors other species.* Yeasts, exploiting the sugary medium that favors them, create an alcoholic medium that favors acetic acid bacteria. The succession of species brought about by species-induced environmental changes is spoken of as **ecological succession.**

The fact of ecological succession limits the

usefulness of enrichment procedures. The easiest way to avoid the limitation is by making rapid transfers of the mixed organisms to fresh enrichment media of the same sort. In fact, by many rapid **serial transfers** to the same medium, we can obtain cultures that are pure, or almost so. Many of the experiments Pasteur carried out before the development of Koch's pure-culture technique were performed with cultures obtained in this way. A better method was introduced in 1950 by A. Novick and L. Szilard, who perfected a **chemostat,** a culture system in which chemical equilibrium conditions are maintained by continuous additions of fresh medium and removal of old, thus preventing ecological succession.

126. Autotrophic Bacteria

Unlike the animals, many species of bacteria do not have to be furnished organic carbon, but can manufacture their own organic compounds from CO_2. But CO_2 is not a source of energy; and some of the bacterial autotrophs do not use sunlight. How, then, do they live on CO_2-carbon alone?

Let us first review some basic biochemistry. The over-all metabolic reaction of most organisms may be expressed thus:

$$\text{organic compounds} + O_2 \longrightarrow CO_2 + H_2O + \varepsilon. \quad (1)$$

While this equation may be said to be true, it conceals an important fact of life. It implies that the purpose* of metabolism is to release energy. Exceptionally this is true: the purpose of shivering is to heat up the body by releasing energy. But, in general, the *release* of energy is only an unavoidable concomitant of living. Since survival is the primary consideration, the primary needs of an organism are for growth and multiplication—both involving an increase

---

* In a discussion of this sort, the word "purpose" can hardly be avoided without awkward circumlocutions that add little to the exactness and clarity of the discussion. Those who object to the use of the word may rephrase the subsequent discussion in a more rigorous manner.

in living material. The primary purpose of metabolism is to increase the amount of "protoplasm" in living material. We can indicate this fact thus:

$$\left.\begin{matrix}\text{organic}\\\text{compounds}\end{matrix}\right\} + O_2 \longrightarrow CO_2 + H_2O + \mathcal{E} \overset{\text{waste energy}}{\uparrow}$$

$$\mathcal{E} + CO_2 + \left\{\begin{matrix}\text{organic}\\\text{compounds}\end{matrix}\right\} \longrightarrow \text{"protoplasm"}$$

(2)

(particular organic
compounds particularly
organized)

This formula emphasizes the fact that the first line of Equation 2 tells only half the truth, the lesser half. The energy that results from the oxidation of organic compounds is in part waste, but, more importantly, part of it is used by the living cell to build up "protoplasm." In organisms of the sort with which we have so far been concerned, living material is synthesized from a variety of organic compounds. For all such organisms, the synthesis of living substance, and hence the occurrence of growth and reproduction, is possible only so long as organic compounds are available as raw materials. It happens that almost all organic molecules on the surface of the earth today have been produced as a result of the synthetic activities of organisms. It follows, therefore, that any organism that exhibits the type of metabolism just described depends on other organisms for its continued existence and multiplication. Essentially, it feeds at the expense of other organisms; that is why we call it a *heterotroph*.

But there are bacteria that can flourish in the dark when furnished carbon only in the form of CO_2. To transform this into energy-rich organic carbon, such bacteria must be fed some other chemical compound that is energy-rich. Several such systems of nonphotosynthetic autotrophy are known. There is, for example, a genus of bacteria, called *Nitrosomonas,* which derives its energy from the oxidation of the inorganic molecule ammonia (NH_3). The over-all result of its activities is indicated in Equation 3.

$$NH_3 + O_2 \longrightarrow NO_2 + H_2O + \mathcal{E} \overset{\text{waste energy}}{\uparrow}$$

(3)

$$\mathcal{E} + CO_2 + H_2O \longrightarrow \text{organic compounds, used}$$
$$\text{in making "protoplasm"}$$

As usual, part of the energy is wasted, but the remainder is used to bring about the reaction indicated in the second line of the equation.

Other autotrophs among the bacteria include *Nitrobacter,* which oxidizes nitrites to nitrates (NO_3^-), and "sulfur bacteria," which oxidize hydrogen sulfide (H_2S) to sulfates, deriving useful energy. Then there are the iron bacteria, which use incompletely oxidized iron compounds as food, oxidizing them further to less-soluble compounds, thereby deriving energy which is used in the synthesis of organic substances. Such bacteria are believed to have caused the formation of iron deposits in pre-Cambrian times in what is now Minnesota; less welcomely, organisms like these cause the deposition of insoluble iron compounds in our water pipes today.

Organisms of the sort just described are also called **chemosynthetic** organisms, and the process of synthesizing organic materials at the expense of energy derived from an inorganic chemical reaction brought about by the organism is called **chemosynthesis.** The bacteria include also some photosynthetic members which capture radiant energy with *bacteriochlorophyll,* a compound slightly different from the chlorophylls of the green plants.

127. Thwarting the Saprophytes

Many men who concern themselves with the "purpose" of human existence feel that the best life is one that is lived "naturally." A plausible argument can be made for this point of view, but so also can an argument be made for the opposite—namely, that much of man's efforts are consciously devoted to creating an unnatural life for himself. Death by disease is natural —but do we really want to lead an entirely natural life? Likewise, it is natural for energy-rich organic substances to be rapidly degraded to inorganic CO_2, H_2O, and NO_3^-, through a chain of odorous intermediates. Microbes of decay are everywhere, and it is "natural" for them to "try" to increase and multiply on any suitable substrate. Men resent many of the consequences of the natural carbon and nitrogen cycles, and try to prevent them. We have learned a number of ways of thwarting the saprophytes, of which the following are the most important.

LOW TEMPERATURE. All metabolic activities, including those of saprophytes, proceed more slowly at lower temperatures. At sufficiently low temperatures, measurable metabolic activity ceases entirely. Refrigeration of foods is therefore an effective means of preserving them from attack by saprophytes.

FILTERING. With a sufficiently fine filter, it is possible to remove all microbial cells from liquid food. The finer the filter, however, the more energy must be expended in forcing liquid through it, and for this reason sterilization by filtration is confined, for the most part, to laboratory procedures.

HEAT STERILIZATION. A temperature of 121°C maintained for 20 minutes will sterilize any food (§122). This temperature is obtainable in an autoclave or pressure cooker. Alkaline materials, such as beans and meat, should be so sterilized. Sterilization is sometimes achieved at the lower temperature of boiling water (100°C), but not reliably, unless intermittent sterilization is used. The wisdom of eating home-canned meat or beans is questionable. With acid foods, such as most fruits and many vegetables (peaches, pears, and tomatoes), we need not be so cautious. These foodstuffs may be reliably sterilized at a temperature of 100°C. Sterilization is made more certain by the addition of quantities of sugar or salt, for reasons to be discussed subsequently.

STERILIZATION BY ATOMIC ENERGY. Since the development of practical sources of atomic energy there has been a great deal of research aimed at sterilizing foodstuffs by neutron beams and other forms of high-energy irradiation. There is no doubt that food can be so sterilized, but it is questionable if the technique should ever be adopted, for two reasons. The first, and less important reason, is that high-energy radiation causes a number of unusual chemical reactions to take place, producing "off-flavors." The second and more important objection comes from the implications of similar experiments carried out with bacteria and fruit-flies. If an organic medium is X-rayed and then fed to either of these organisms, the mutation rate is increased even though the organisms themselves were never irradiated. Since new mutations are almost invariably deleterious, the implications of these studies create a most serious objection to this method of sterilization, unless it can be shown that man is an exception to general biological principles (which would be most surprising).

INHIBITION BY HIGH OSMOTIC POTENTIAL. A microbial cell in contact with a medium of high osmotic potential (see §23) will lose water to the medium. If the osmotic potential is very high, the cell loses so much water that it either becomes incapable of carrying on metabolic activities or is killed. For this reason, foodstuffs can be preserved almost indefinitely by salting or drying—methods known to man since prehistoric times. Of the two methods of preservation, salting is the easier to carry out, but it yields a material whose dietary uses are limited by its extreme saltiness. Drying is readily carried out in very sunny climes (consider the sun-dried raisins, apricots, and other fruit of semiarid regions), but in colder or cloudier regions the process must be hastened by artificial heat, which is expensive.

Whatever method is used for increasing the osmotic potential of a food material, success depends on effecting a rapid change. Because of the scale effect (§10), the necessary osmotic potential will be reached in all parts of the foodstuff soon enough only if the pieces are not too large. For this reason, large fruits are cut into smaller pieces, and meat is sliced into thin strips before being dried.

USE OF ORGANIC INHIBITORS. Wine, perhaps the oldest preserved foodstuff, keeps well because, when properly prepared, the final concentration of ethyl alcohol is so great (12–15 percent) that all microbes, including even the yeasts that produced the alcohol, are killed. Various fermented milks (e.g., yoghurt), of poorer keeping qualities, have also been known since antiquity.

Lactic acid fermentations are also used to preserve foodstuffs. Shredded cabbage, to which some salt is added, when kept under nearly anaerobic conditions, undergoes a fermentation in which the sugar of the cabbage is turned into lactic acid by "lactic acid bacteria" of various species. The result is sauerkraut. Again, the organisms responsible for the fermentation are, in the end, killed by their own waste product.

Many foodstuffs are preserved by high osmotic potential combined with organic inhibitors. Cheeses fall in this category. Lactic acid and propionic acid are the microbial inhibitors frequently found in cheese. In cheese production, most of the water of the original milk is removed, thus raising the osmotic potential.

The resistance of microbes to high osmotic potentials and to organic inhibitors varies from species to species. For rule-of-thumb use, it is worthwhile remembering these generalizations:

1. The ability to resist high concentrations of inhibitors or high osmotic potentials is more common among fungi than among bacteria.

2. The fungi that are important as food spoilers are, with few exceptions, obligate aerobes. We see, then, why it is that pickles or fermented foodstuffs are best kept under anaerobic conditions. Wine keeps best in a fully filled, tightly stoppered bottle. Cheese is protected against the action of fungi by a coating of wax.

128. Human Exploitation of Saprophytes

The microbial destruction of organic compounds can even be desirable, if the substances attacked are ones man regards as junk. There are a number of ways in which man encourages and exploits saprophytes.

Linen is prepared from a fiber found in the stem of the flax plant. This useful fiber is separated from the rest of the plant by a controlled process of "retting," in which masses of flax are allowed to rot until all but the more resistant fibers have been rotted away. In the preparation of leather, a similar process, called "sweating," is used to rot the hairs off the hide. Undoubtedly the most important example of human encouragement and control of decay processes is to be found in sewage disposal. Uncontrolled sewage is, at best, a potent source of obnoxious odors; at worst, it is a disseminator of disease-producing bacteria. The conversion of dangerous sewage into harmless and even useful materials is brought about by the deliberate encouragement of microbial multiplication. The principal constituent of sewage is water—more than 99 percent of sewage, by weight, is just plain water. If a sewage-treatment plant is properly run, the effluent water is completely satisfactory for reuse. At present, most cities do not make use of sewage effluent; the few that do, use it only for industrial or agricultural purposes. Failure to use it for drinking purposes can be ascribed only to cultural inertia and prejudice. In the treatment of the solid portion of sewage, saprophytic activity is stopped short of completion, and the remaining "sludge," which is absolutely free of disease-producing bacteria, may be collected, dried, and sold as commercial fertilizer. In some plants, the inflammable gas methane (CH_4), produced by bacteria, is collected for fuel.

In addition to encouraging generalized saprophytic activity, man often utilizes particular metabolic activities of specific microbes to produce products desirable to him. Already mentioned have been the production of alcoholic beverages and cheeses. In addition, the controlled fermentation of various materials by pure cultures of bacteria and molds is used to produce a wide variety of substances of industrial importance: acetic acid, lactic acid, citric acid, butyric acid, butanol, and acetone, to mention but a few. The production of these substances is carried out on a huge scale. Pure-culture fermentations are typically carried out in 50,000-gallon tanks; maintaining pure cultures on such a scale is a triumph of biological engineering. The many products of the "fermentation industries," as they are known, are used in the manufacture of paints, explosives, detergents, and medicines.

129. Disinfection by Pasteurization

With few exceptions,* microbes that are parasitic in man do not multiply or live long in soil, air, or water. It follows, then, that the control of human disease depends principally on the control of the movements and activities of human (and to a lesser extent, other animal) carriers of disease. In the preparation of food products, wherever possible, machine methods are substituted for human handling. Where this substitution is not practicable, it is desirable to use germ-killing techniques after the final handling, before the foodstuff is made available to the public. One of the most important of these techniques is **pasteurization,** a technique of mild heating first developed by Pasteur for the treatment of wines and since adapted to many other products, the most important of which is milk.

With the single, and seldom important, exception of anthrax, parasitic microbes do not form heat-resistant spores. Therefore, it is not necessary to boil a foodstuff to kill the parasites in it; vegetative cells are killed at a much lower temperature. Fortunately, parasitic microbes are killed at a lower temperature than are most saprophytic vegetative cells. At the present time, for the pasteurization of milk, there are two alternative procedures: In the *flash method,* the milk is rapidly heated to a temperature of 75–80°C, held at that temperature for a few seconds, and then rapidly cooled; in the *holding*

method, the temperature is held at 60–65°C for 30 minutes. Neither method, be it noted, kills spores or even all vegetative cells; only the disease-producers are completely eliminated. Pasteurization **disinfects;** it does not sterilize.

Why not sterilize milk? For two reasons. The first is an economic reason: heat costs money. Milk, an alkaline material, could be sterilized only by autoclaving, an expensive procedure. Second, there is an aesthetic reason. Boiled milk, as all cooks know, is quite different from unboiled milk, both in taste and in consistency. It is also different nutritionally: much of its vitamin content is destroyed by the treatment.

Even pasteurized milk has a different taste from "raw" milk. In the early days of the pasteurization process, there was much opposition to the peculiar flavor of pasteurized milk. It took one or two generations for pasteurized milk to be completely accepted by the public. Now, many people who have never tasted any other kind of milk complain, when they taste raw milk, of its "unnatural" taste. Thus we see how taste can be modified by experience. Complete acceptance of pasteurized milk is a great gain in the field of public health, for raw milk is a notorious vehicle for diphtheria, typhoid fever, dysentery, streptococcus infections, and undulant fever.

130. Food Poisoning

Sometimes food is unsafe because it has become contaminated with parasitic microbes, the commonest of which are those that cause intestinal diseases, such as typhoid and dysentery. Discussion of such microbial action properly belongs in §131. For the present, we are concerned only with the spoilage of food by saprophytes. Ingestion of spoiled food is dangerous *not* because of the living bacterial cells taken in, but rather because of the microbial waste products present in the food.

There are many kinds of food poisoning; different saprophytes spoil food in chemically different ways. The consequence of ingesting microbially spoiled food may be nothing more

---

* The single exception among bacteria is *Bacillus anthracis,* the causative organism of the disease anthrax. Spores of this aerobic species may survive for years in soil. Among fungi, *Coccidioides,* the causative agent of "San Joaquin Valley fever," is similarly exceptional.

serious than a stomach-ache, or as serious as death itself. The most dangerous of all food spoilers is *Clostridium botulinum,* an anaerobic spore-former. This organism has been found in sausage (*L. botulus* = sausage) and other meats, as well as in other nonacid foods, including inadequately sterilized nonacid vegetables canned in the home.

The lethal effect of *Clostridium botulinum* is brought about by a powerful poison, or **toxin,** that it secretes into the medium. It takes only 1×10^{-10} of a gram of the pure toxin to kill a mouse. The lethal dose for man is much less certain, because it has been determined by follow-up studies of accidental poisonings, rather than by experiments; but the evidence is pretty good that it takes about 3,500 times as much to kill a man, that is, about 3.5×10^{-7} grams.* Of course, only a small percentage of any spoiled foodstuff consists of the toxin, but so powerful is this fraction that human beings have been killed by merely tasting suspected food without (consciously) swallowing any of it. The toxin is a protein of the class called "globular proteins." It attacks the efferent autonomic nervous system; this selectivity is one of the reasons why so little of it is required to kill. Thoroughly washed bacterial cells have been fed to guinea pigs with no harmful results. Presumably, the same procedure could be carried out with humans, but no one has volunteered for the experiment. However, it is undoubtedly true that we all, every day, ingest a few (say, a few hundred) cells of the ubiquitous *Clostridium botulinum* spores with our food with no untoward results.

Botulinum poisoning is completely avoidable. The principal safeguards are adequate techniques of sterilization and food preservation. However, even occasional technical failures need not be harmful if we are all alert to the danger. No preserved food should be eaten if it shows any signs of spoilage. In canned goods, the escape of gas when the can is opened indi-

cates microbial spoilage. Many species of bacteria, including *C. botulinum,* produce gases. Food spoilage may also be indicated by discoloration or slight softness of the food material; these signs should be looked for in inadequately salted hams. Any unpleasant odor of the preserved material should arouse one's suspicions. Suspect foodstuff should be thrown out. However, should economic considerations make this course of action impracticable, it is still possible to avoid the gravest dangers. Fortunately, the toxin produced by *C. botulinum* is destructible by heat, or as the bacteriologist says, it is *heat-labile.* Five minutes' boiling of the distrusted foodstuff will destroy all botulinum toxin, though it may leave unaltered other nonlethal, *heat-stable* microbial toxins.

131. The Biology of Parasitism

In the minds of most laymen, the word "bacteria" is almost synonymous with disease; yet, as one bacteriologist, Otto Rahn, has pointed out, at the very most not more than 1 bacterial cell out of 30,000 is harmful to man or any of his domesticated animals and plants. That does not seem like a bad record when we note that in a typical year about 1 man in every 17,000 in the United States commits murder. Nevertheless, the disease-causing, or **pathogenic,** activities of bacteria loom large in the minds of men.

With almost no exceptions, pathogenic bacteria are *obligate parasites* under natural conditions. When released into a world of competition with saprophytes, pathogens speedily succumb. Air and soil and water are potentially dangerous to humans only when they have been recently contaminated by humans or closely related animals. The only breeding grounds for the disease organisms of vertebrates are other organisms, usually vertebrates.

When we consider not pathogens in general, but particular species of pathogenic microbes, we discover even narrower restrictions to particular host organisms. Most of the microbes that cause diseases in man do not, in nature,

---

* 16-5. How much of the pure toxin would it take to kill 200 million people, approximately the population of the United States? Express the answer in grams, and in ounces (see Appendix 3).

infect any other host species; even under experimental conditions they are capable of infecting only a few other species of animals. This does not mean that wild animals do not have diseases; they have their own diseases. As a generalization, if a parasitic microbe is capable of infecting more than one host, the hosts are organisms which, from other evidence, are regarded as being closely related in an evolutionary sense. Many microbes that infect man can infect other primates—monkeys, apes, and so forth; a smaller number of human parasites can infect mammals other than primates; still fewer human parasites can infect birds; and no parasitic bacteria are known that can infect both man and fishes or any organism more distantly related to man than fish—with the important exception of the bacteria known as the **Rickettsias.**

The Rickettsias are a family of tiny microbes that are strict *intracellular* parasites. Infection by them seems to be universal among many species of arthropods—fleas, lice, cockroaches, and so forth. In their arthropod hosts they do little or no damage. They may, however, be transmitted to a mammalian host, in which the infection is more serious. Among diseases caused by Rickettsias are typhus, scrub typhus, Q fever, and Rocky Mountain spotted fever.

Why are parasitic microbes almost always obligate parasites? Laboratory experience in culturing microorganisms throws light on this problem. Most saprophytic bacteria are easily cultured in the laboratory in relatively simple media; many a saprophyte can flourish in a medium containing only a single organic compound. Moreover, most saprophytes can grow on a wide variety of foods.

Among parasitic bacteria the story is quite different. Most mammalian parasites require very particular conditions for multiplication. The temperature must be fairly close to 37°C, a typical mammalian temperature. (This is one reason disease bacteria perish outside the host body.) With respect to their nutrient media, mammalian parasites are extremely finicky. A single organic chemical is not enough. They must have a large variety, combined in rather particular proportions. Bacteriologists are unable to grow many mammalian pathogens on media made up entirely of substances whose chemical composition is known; frequently, such complex, chemically undefined substances as blood serum must be added to the medium.

When we take a broad view of all bacteria, both saprophytic and parasitic, we see a relationship that is of general biological application: the inverse relationship of *specialization* and *adaptability*. Most saprophytes can adapt themselves to a wide variety of environments. On the other hand, almost every parasitic species is specialized to attack a particular host in a particular way; and associated with this specialization, we find a very low order of adaptability: the parasite cannot adapt itself to living in a much different environment.

From these generalizations it follows that the infective powers of bacterial parasites furnish another evidence of the truth of evolution. Since parasites show a low order of adaptability, the fact that two host species have a number of parasites in common is evidence of deep-seated similarities between the host species—similarities that can be best explained on the basis of descent from a common ancestor.

Then what about the Rickettsias? We cannot deny that their "choice" of host species is exceptional. No evolutionist maintains that the arthropods and the vertebrates are closely related. While admitting that these facts are slightly embarrassing, we can still explain them. Only a few rickettsial species are capable of infecting man or other mammals. The great majority of Rickettsias—how many hundreds or thousands of species is not known—are natural and ubiquitous inhabitants of the cells of arthropods. How does it happen, then, that some of them infect mammals? In every such instance, the microbial species is one that is found in an *arthropod parasite* of the mammal—in a louse, a tick, or a mite. These arthropod parasites have been parasitic on mammals for hundreds of thousands, or millions, of years. The long association presented an opportunity for an evolutionary leap across the biochemical gap separating the arthropods and the mammals, and apparently (if these ideas are correct) some of the Rickettsias made the leap. No bacteria outside of this family have crossed such a wide gap. Other instances of the *transmission* of mammalian diseases by arthropods are known—for example, the transmission of human typhoid by houseflies—but the transmission is purely passive: the arthropod merely carries the disease organism, which does not parasitize the arthropod.

It must not be supposed that a parasite is necessarily pathogenic. The bacterium *Salmonella typhosa* is a parasite of men; it causes typhoid fever. It has been found that between 3 and 10 percent of the individuals who recover from typhoid pass feces or urine infected with living *Salmonella* cells for at least a year after their recovery from the symptoms of the disease. It has been found that a smaller fraction of the general population show living *Salmonella* cells in their excreta even in the absence of personal histories of typhoid fever. The conclusion is unavoidable: Some people become infected with the typhoid organism without being made ill. In other words, parasitism and pathogenicity are not perfectly associated. Similar findings have been reported for other intestinal diseases, as well as for scarlet fever. It now appears that for every man who shows the classical symptoms of scarlet fever during an epidemic of the disease, about twenty others become hosts to the *Streptococcus* without showing any symptoms worse than a sore throat.

It will be readily appreciated that the lack of parallelism of parasitism and pathogenicity presents serious public health problems. A person who is in good health though he harbors the parasite is called a **carrier.** Many epidemics of typhoid have been started by carriers working in restaurants. In most states, such carriers, when reliably identified by bacteriological tests, can be legally prevented from working in restaurants, dairies, and the like. The acceptance of such measures, which are infringements of individual liberty, is no doubt made easier by the fact that healthy carriers of typhoid are relatively rare. The reverse situation obtains with scarlet fever. At one time, scarlet fever was

almost everywhere a quarantinable disease; that is, individuals showing the disease were confined by law to their homes until some time after their recovery. Now that it is known that unidentifiable carriers of the disease organisms are many times more numerous than the sufferers, the quarantining of scarlet fever patients is being abandoned.

The natural history of diseases cannot be understood without the Darwinian principle of natural selection. How this principle influences us in our use of penicillin and other antibiotics has already been pointed out in §78. The principle also permits us to understand a phase of the history of every disease that otherwise would be puzzling—namely, the fact that a widespread parasite becomes less pathogenic as time passes. For example, descriptions of syphilis in Renaissance writings (see, for instance, Cellini's autobiography) present a picture of a malady that was far more severe in its primary symptoms than it is now. Syphilis was at that time a new disease, having, in all probability, been brought to Europe by Columbus's crew. Smallpox and influenza, diseases of long standing in Western Europe, when introduced among the people of the South Sea Islands, caused epidemics of a severity unknown in the Old World and contributed substantially to the eradication or enfeeblement of these populations.

There are several explanations of the phenomena just recounted; all of them indicate a gradual decrease in pathogenicity of a widespread parasite—and this, independently of medical advances. This generalization can be accounted for in two ways, both of them Darwinian in nature.

1. The parasitic species is undoubtedly subject to selection. It is important to realize that *it is not in the interest of a parasite to be pathogenic.* A parasite that confines its host to a bed, or worse still, kills him, is far less likely to be passed around to other host individuals than is a parasite that causes little or no illness. There is ample evidence that, within a single species of parasite, different degrees of inheritable pathogenicity occur. In the course of time, we should expect a parasitic species to

become less pathogenic. Also, *in general,* we may deduce that parasites of low pathogenicity have probably been steadily associated with their hosts longer than have those of high pathogenicity.

2. The parasite is a selective factor in the environment of the host. Even within a species, there are inheritable differences in susceptibility to diseases. Those host individuals that are less affected by a parasite will outmultiply those that are more severely affected, and will, in the course of time, become the predominant type.

In closing this chapter, it is appropriate to point out how an increase in knowledge may bring new problems to our attention—problems that are not always pleasant to face, but ones that cannot be caused to vanish by ignoring them. From the Darwinian analysis of parasitism and pathogenicity just presented, it follows that one possible way of taming a pathogen is to encourage its spread and accept the selective consequence. In the course of time, as a result of the action of natural selection upon both host and parasite, an equilibrium will (in general) be reached, in which condition the parasite may flourish with but little pathogenic effect on the host. This is one way to "conquer" disease. This is the way followed in nature. Occasionally, man even deliberately uses this approach with domesticated plants and animals.

For example, rust-resistant snapdragons were developed by exposing large fields of the plants to the parasite, and saving the few plants that survived. Man is reluctant to use the same method with his own species.

The other approach to disease is the medical approach: to try to prevent the spread of disease organisms, and to try to kill them in infected individuals. This is the traditional approach in our society. Is it the best one? There is little doubt that *in the short run* it is the more economical one, the one involving the least suffering. But what about *the long run?* Is it possible to completely eradicate all disease, or will some always remain with us, taking a small but cumulative toll in human suffering? When we kill the parasites in an individual, we thereby save that individual for reproduction; and if his susceptibility to attack by the parasite is in part inheritable, our medical action results in increasing the supply of susceptible individuals in future generations. Is the medical approach too risky in the long run, or not? Many of our important medical practices are possible only in a civilized community. What does the future hold in store for us? Is the future to be substantially like the present, or is there a serious danger that the relatively stable cultural conditions that we now enjoy will be significantly disrupted?

Questions and Problems

16-6. Make a list of the **boldface** terms in this chapter and write a brief description of each. Compare your work with the text.

16-7. Write out a brief description of the work of each of the following men, with the approximate date of each: Beijerinck, Cohn, Koch, Leeuwenhoek, Lister, Pasteur, Redi, Spallanzani.

‡16-8. You have a culture that is a mixture of only two species of bacteria: one a spore-former, the other not. How might you most easily obtain a pure culture of the spore-forming species?

16-9. A certain organic substance is unstable in acid solution. It can withstand 3 hours' exposure to 100°C but only 3 minutes' exposure to 120°C. How could you sterilize a solution of this substance?

‡16-10. Bacterial metabolism takes place much more slowly at 5°C than at ordinary room temperature, which is about 20°C. If you had to work in a laboratory at the lower tempera-

ture, how would the tyndallization method of sterilization be affected?

16-11. Non-spore-formers may be killed as thoroughly at 80°C as at 100°C. Why is the latter temperature usually specified?

‡16-12. Koch, in 1880, found that when he injected a mixture of streptococci and *Erysipelothrix muriseptica* into the ear of a "house mouse," he could later recover only the *E. muriseptica* from the blood stream. Explain the results. What general phenomena do they illustrate? Of what practical importance are the phenomena?

16-13. In the selective culture method for obtaining *E. coli* described in §125, why is a temperature of 37°C used? A priori, would you expect the same results if a temperature of 15°C were used?

‡16-14. An eminent microbiologist was once asked by a healthy young male student, "What is a good enrichment medium for beautiful women?" He answered with a single word. What was it?

16-15. Will pasteurized milk spoil if it is kept in a sterile container with a covering that is impervious to microbes? Explain.

16-16. To be "certified," milk must come only from cows that are periodically certified to be free of disease; cow barns and milking apparatus must be kept scrupulously cleaned; and the handling of the milk must be in accord with rigorously hygienic standards. "Certified milk" is *raw* milk; that is, it is not heated before use. Pasteurized milk, on the other hand, is collected under conditions not nearly so hygienic, but is heat-treated just prior to bottling. Which milk is safer for human consumption? Why?

‡16-17. An entire family dies of botulinum poisoning. When the health officer investigates their house, and questions neighbors and friends, he finds evidence that the family's last meal consisted of the following foodstuffs: home-canned beans that had been opened a week before and eaten intermittently during that time, being boiled each time before being

eaten; stewed tomatoes, probably prepared four days earlier; home-canned beef that had been made into a pie and warmed in the oven just prior to the last meal; home-canned peaches that had been opened several days earlier. Which of these foodstuffs is the most probable source of the botulinum toxin? Explain.

16-18. What fraction of an ounce of botulinum toxin is needed to kill a man? (See text and Appendix 3.)

‡16-19. A review paper on botulinum toxin has this statement: "The crystalline type A toxin is a white, odorless protein of high molecular weight and unknown taste." It is common for chemists to state the taste of chemicals. Why hasn't the taste of this substance been stated?

16-20. The amount of poison required to kill an animal is usually proportional to its body weight, but not so with botulinum toxin. Experiments have shown that the lethal dose for adult mice weighing 6–10 grams is the same as for adult mice weighing 18–22 grams. How come?

‡16-21. A bacteriologist, in discussing bacterial spores, asks: "Should we regard the process of sporulation as a bulwark hastily erected when the enemy is sighted, or as a fortress that happens to be there when the enemy arrives?" What's the answer?

16-22. How may the year of the discovery of bacteria be easily remembered?

‡16-23. The bottom mud in Lake Mead (behind Hoover Dam) has a temperature about 3°C above that of the overlying water. What is the probable explanation? If sediment were deposited more slowly, would you expect the temperature of the mud to be greater or less?

16-24. The flagellum of a bacterium consists of a single strand, and is thus unique in the living world. In what way is it unique?

16-25. According to the "Cosmozoic Theory" of the origin of life, life began when a bacterial spore arrived on earth and germinated. Is this a satisfactory theory of the origin of life? Explain.

Readings

The original descriptions of the discovery of bacteria and other microbes are fortunately available in Dobell's excellent *Antony van Leeuwenhoek and His "Little Animals,"* in which see particularly the Eighteenth Letter. For shorter excerpts from Leeuwenhoek, see Boynton or Moulton and Schifferes. For a general history of bacteriology, Bulloch's fine work should be consulted; unlike most histories of science, it is a history of ideas rather than a mere chronology of discoveries. A brief retelling of the spontaneous generation controversy may be found in Chapters 8 and 9 of Conant. Anyone interested in the human aspects of science can hardly afford to miss reading Dubos' *Louis Pasteur: Free Lance of Science,* which shows in an unusually perceptive way the roots of scientific activity and the interrelationships of knowledge and practice. R. N. Doetsch's *Microbiology* consists of a number of important classical papers in the field.

As may be gathered from the above paragraph, there are many excellent books available for cultural reading in the field of microbiology. From this embarrassment of riches, only a few more works will be cited here. Smith's *Plague on Us* and Roueché's *Eleven Blue Men* include many fascinating detective-story style accounts of problems in epidemiology. Haggard's *Devils, Drugs, and Doctors* depicts the escape of medicine from superstition to knowledge. A good general text emphasizing the human implications is Grant's *Microbiology and Human Progress.* For a more advanced treatment, see Stanier, Doudoroff, and Adelberg.

17

Conquest of the Land

132. Lichens

We do not know what were the first plants to live on land, so we can only speculate as to the kinds of things they might have been, using present-day organisms as models. Notice that we said "models," not "examples," because it is very unlikely that the organisms to be discussed here were the first land plants or gave rise to the land plants of today. But they will serve as models to illustrate some of the problems presented by a land existence.

Soil is to a large extent the creation of living things. Where there is no soil, the existence of land plants is precarious. Such a situation occurs today in mountainous and arctic regions. What are the first organisms to colonize such bare spots? Some algae are moderately successful, notably some of the unicellular green algae and some gelatin-encapsulated blue-greens. But the algal layer on an exposed rock is thin, and its photosynthetic activity is restricted to days of high relative humidity, or to brief periods after rains. This is a severe restriction because high humidity and sunshine—both needed—are generally mutually exclusive.

Far more successful than either green or blue-green algae is another kind of plant that is most remarkable in many ways: the **lichen.** Lichens occur as dark-colored patches of many hues on long exposed rocks, but most people are more aware of the forms known as "Old Man's Beard" or "Spanish moss," which hang from trees (Fig. 17-1). (However, what is called Spanish moss in Louisiana is a flowering plant, a relative of the pineapple.)

Lichens have been a bother to taxonomists from the earliest days. Linnaeus, who often seemed rather impatient with nonflowering plants, contemptuously referred to lichens as "rustici pauperrimi," that is to say, the "poor peasants" of the plant world. Linnaeus' successors, replacing invective with investigation, found these poor peasants puzzling. A lichen is not, in the strict sense, an individual at all. The word "individual" comes from a Latin root meaning indivisible. But in this sense, every lichen is composed of two individual species, one a fungus and the other an alga—a truth discovered by the Swiss botanist Simon Schwendener in 1867. For referring to cases in which two species live together, the German de Bary coined the term symbiosis (Gr. *syn* (*sym*) = together + *bios* = life, mode of life). In the lichen, we say that algae and fungi live together *symbiotically.* The term symbiosis, as used by de Bary, is a neutral term without commitment as to the beneficial or nonbeneficial relationships of the two *symbionts.*

There are about 15,000 different species of lichens. The algal component is always a green or a blue-green; the fungus is either a basidio-

Fig. 17-1. *The foliose lichen* Usnea barbata *("Old Man's Beard") hanging from a branch, on which a crustose lichen is also growing. (Courtesy Hugh Spencer.)*

mycete or (more often) an ascomycete.* Experimentally the two components can be separated and grown in isolated cultures. The algae often prove to be identical (so far as we can tell) with known free-living species. The fungi, however, are of species unknown except in the lichen combination. If one must classify the lichens in the conventional scheme, it seems best to add them as a fifth class of the Eumycophyta (Table 15-1, p. 267). They are, perhaps, no more anomalous than the Fungi Imperfecti, which also contain members of other classes. (Physicists no longer say that "nature abhors a vacuum," but biologists suspect that nature abhors pigeon-holes.)

What do the two partners get out of their as-

sociation in the lichen? For the alga, the mat of mycelium lessens the danger of drying. The saprophytic fungus gets food from the algae. In the *crustose lichens,* which occur as flat crusts on rocks, the fungus hyphae actually penetrate the algal cells; this relationship almost looks like parasitism. In the *foliose* and *fruticose lichens,* which grow as denser, more elevated masses (on rocks, ground, or trees), the algae are not penetrated; apparently, the fungi get only such organic materials as can diffuse out of the algal cells. Probably all lichen associations are to be considered as examples of **mutualism,** a symbiosis beneficial to both partners.

Economically, lichens are of little importance. Litmus and a number of other dyes can be extracted from some species, but the importance of these has been much diminished by the growth of synthetic organic chemistry. "Iceland moss" and "rock tripe," two very minor foodstuffs, are lichens. "Harris tweed" owes part of its characteristic odor to the lichens used in treating it. The Arctic is the region of the greatest importance of lichens. "Reindeer moss" is a lichen, *Cladonia rangiferina;* it is a major food of reindeer and caribou. Laplanders depend on it for at least part of the fodder for their reindeer. The growth is sparse, however, by temperate-zone standards; it takes 1–3 acres of *Cladonia* pasture per year per deer, and re-

Fig. 17-2. *Cross section of a lichen. Fungus cells are shown in color, algal cells in black. (After Fuller and Tippo,* College Botany, *copyright 1949, by permission of Henry Holt and Company, Inc.)*

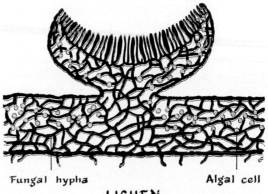

Fungal hypha Algal cell

LICHEN

* 17-1. What is the fungal component of the species shown in Figure 17-2?

growth after harvesting or grazing requires 30 years: so the stable allowance must be 30–90 acres per head.

Though lichens are of little importance in economics in a narrowly human sense, they are important in the over-all economy of the biosphere. As the first colonizers of rocky regions, they secrete acids which help break up rock into soil; thus they provide a foothold for other plants, which in turn ultimately nourish animals.

133. The Life Cycle of a Moss

By this time it should be clear that not everything a layman calls a moss is a moss to a botanist. Apparently, the lay definition of a moss is that it is anything green and fuzzy, indefinite of form, of low elevation, or hanging scraggily (Irish moss, Iceland moss, Spanish moss, and so on). To the botanist, a moss is necessarily a member of the phylum **Bryophyta,** a phylum that includes both liverworts and "true" mosses. We will not here define the phylum, but will exhibit some of its characteristics by considering the life cycle of a moss.

True mosses are rather inconspicuous pads of greenery, often growing at the base of trees, or on well-sprayed rocks near waterfalls. A true moss has a leafy appearance, but microscopic examination proves that moss "leaves" are not homologous with the leaves of a flowering plant. The principal vegetative structures of a moss plant are shown at the top of Figure 17-3. From a filamentous green body on the substrate spring "leafy" branches that, in exceptional species, rise a foot or so into the air, but which, more commonly, are less than an inch high. Downward into the soil the moss plant sends colorless, root-like anchoring processes, called **rhizoids** ("root-like"). From the substratum, water is taken into the plants, to be moved upward into the aerial portions of the moss where photosynthesis takes place. There are seldom true conducting tissues (vascular tissues) in mosses; never are they as well developed as they are in trees. In their anatomy we see the basic reasons for both the size and habitat of mosses. Having

little or no vascular tissues, the aerial portion of a moss plant is necessarily severely restricted in size; and the primitive devices for gathering water (rhizoids and "leaves") permit existence only in relatively wet environments. The mosses' conquest of the land is only partial.

Existence on land requires extensive modification of the reproduction of a plant. Recall that the act of fertilization in algae involves the union of two gametes, at least one of which is motile. How can such a union between delicate sex cells take place in the air? The tiny motile male cell, with its necessarily large surface:volume ratio, would soon die from loss of water. Mosses have, one might say, solved the problem by side-stepping it: fertilization still takes place in a watery medium.

When the moss plant has matured, the apex of its leafy part produces sex cells. In most species, a single plant produces either male gametes or female gametes, as shown in Figure 17-3. All of the haploid phase (shown in color) of a moss plant may be said to be one sex or the other. The female plant produces a multicellular sexual structure ("gametangium") called an *archegonium.* The corresponding male structure, the *antheridium,* consists of a large number of centrally located cells destined to become sperm cells, surrounded by a jacket of sterile cells. The mature, flagellated sperm cells are not released until the antheridium is surrounded by water. Then their problem is to get to the eggs produced by the archegonium. Now we see why it is that most mosses are of low elevation: only so is there a reasonable chance that rain (or waterfall spray) will produce a film of water that is continuous from antheridium to archegonium, or that the splash of a raindrop will, by chance, propel a droplet of sperm cells to an archegonium. (A hermaphroditic species can complete this phase of its life cycle somewhat more easily.) Whatever fair chance brings a sperm into the vicinity of an archegonium, once there, a directive, nonchance force enters in. The egg secretes a chemical substance that is attractive to sperm, which tend to move from lower concentrations of this substance to higher. Sperm are said to exhibit a positive **chemotaxis** to the

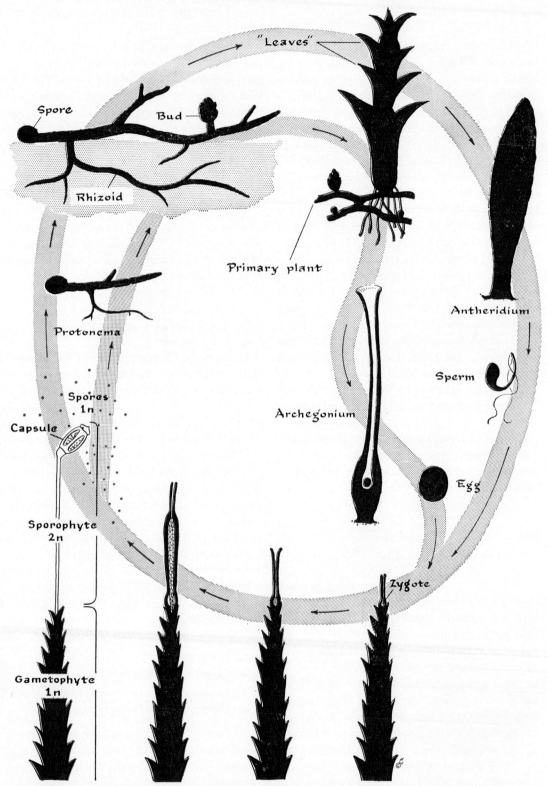

"Leaves"

Spore

Bud

Rhizoid

Primary plant

Protonema

Antheridium

Sperm

Spores
1n

Archegonium

Capsule

Egg

Sporophyte
2n

Zygote

Gametophyte
1n

Fig. 17-3. *Life cycle of a moss. Haploid tissues are shown in color.*

substance; their reaction to the egg is a *chemotactic* one. With the union of egg and sperm to form a diploid zygote, the **gametophyte generation**—the haploid phase of the life cycle—comes to an end.

The zygote, by mitotic division, produces a multicellular diploid plant, shown in black in Figure 17-3. Notice that the diploid embryo begins its development at the site of its formation, surrounded by parental (haploid) tissue. Such protection of delicate embryos by parental tissue characterizes all of the plants that have in any real sense conquered the land. In a moss, the diploid plant remains attached to the parental plant, on which it depends for water and minerals. The diploid portion of the life cycle is completed when the moss produces a **spore capsule,** within which spores are formed. These spores result from meiotic divisions and hence are haploid. The plant that produced them is the **sporophyte generation.**

Spores are light and easily borne by breezes. The spore that lands on a favorable substratum germinates to produce a new primary gametophyte, called a **protonema,** shown in the figure. The protonema looks so much like some of the filamentous green algae that some early botanists mistook it for an alga.

134. The Role of Bryophytes in the Living World

In this phylum, as in all phyla, there is much more variety than the consideration of a single textbook example would imply. The phylum Bryophyta includes over 20,000 species, divided into two main groups: the *Hepaticae* (liverworts) and the *Musci* (mosses), of which we have considered only the latter. The example given is typical, however, in that it shows how imperfectly this phylum has solved the problems of a terrestrial existence. All bryophytes are small and confined to localities that are at least periodically quite wet. They are among the first colonizers of such localities, thus contributing to the formation of soil on which other organisms may grow.

Among the aquatic mosses, *Sphagnum* is noteworthy. Species of this grow in fresh-water ponds, particularly in colder regions. The water of a "sphagnum bog" is acid and is said also to contain antiseptic organic chemicals; at any rate it inhibits microbial decay. In the bottoms of old bogs have been found portions of Viking ships hundreds of years old, still in a state of good repair; even fairly well preserved human bodies of considerable age are occasionally reported from such waters. Organic materials, including the substance of the sphagnam moss itself, may be preserved for a long time. The *peat* of Ireland (and elsewhere) is the compressed residue of old sphagnum bogs.

135. The Phyla of Vascular Plants

The conquest of land could not be complete until good vascular tissues were evolved. Plants possessing a well-developed system of this sort are called *vascular plants*. According to a recent classification, there are four phyla of vascular plants: **Psilophyta, Lycophyta, Sphenophyta,** and **Pterophyta.** The first three phyla are noteworthy chiefly for their extinct species, which dominated the flora of the land at times in the past, contributing greatly to the formation of coal. Figure 17-4 shows a meticulous reconstruction of the earthly scene as it must have been during the Carboniferous period. Except for some ferns (members of the phylum Pterophyta), most of the plant species in this restoration are members of the other three phyla of vascular plants.

The phylum Pterophyta is divided into three classes:

> **Filicinae:** *ferns* and related plants
> **Gymnospermae:** *conifers* and related plants
> **Angiospermae:** *flowering* plants

In the phylum Pterophyta, we find the highest development of the vascular tissues, one of the features that has made possible the large size of many of the species of this phylum. The arrangement of the vascular tissues in the stem differs somewhat in the three classes.

Fig. 17-4. *A reconstruction of a swamp as it must have appeared in a coal-forming period of the late Paleozoic Era. (Courtesy the Chicago Natural History Museum.)*

136. The Life Cycle of a Fern

During the late Renaissance, as men began to really look at the world around them, among the more puzzling features of the plant world were the ferns. Plainly they reproduced themselves; but how did they do so without flowers? And where were the seeds? Some thought reproduction took place mysteriously under the cover of darkness, others that ferns produced seeds but that the seeds were invisible. From this hypothesis, by a plausible pseudologic, there arose the belief that the possession of fern seed was a sure way for a man to make himself invisible. It is this superstition that is referred to in Shakespeare's *Henry IV*, when one of the characters says: "We have the receipt [recipe] of fern seed, we walk invisible."

Fern seeds are indeed invisible: *they don't exist*. If one focuses on the function of dispersal,

Fig. 17-5. *Life cycle of a fern. Haploid cells in color, diploid in black.*

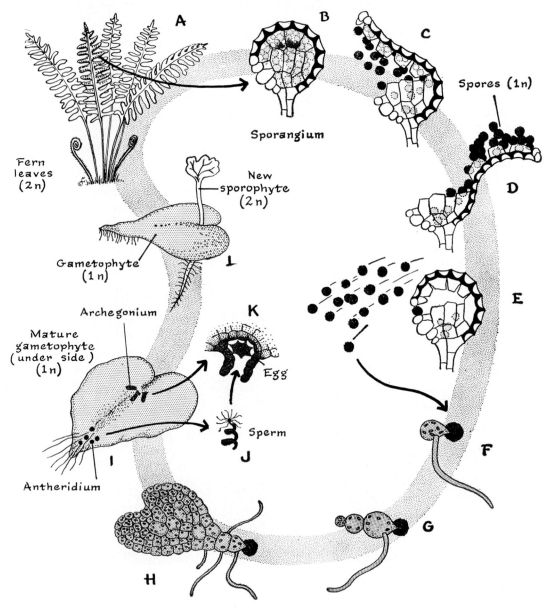

Fern leaves (2n)

Sporangium

Spores (1n)

New sporophyte (2n)

Gametophyte (1n)

Archegonium

Mature gametophyte (under side) (1n)

Egg

Sperm

Antheridium

the object in the fern life cycle that plays the role of the seed in this respect, is the **spore** (Gr. *spora* = a sowing, seed). This object is produced by the leaves. If one looks on the underside of a fern leaf at the proper season, he will see protuberant brown spots, arranged in a pattern characteristic of the species. These are not (as laymen often mistakenly suppose) either disease spots or insect parasites, but are normal reproductive structures called *sori*. Each **sorus** (Gr. a heap) is composed of many microscopic structures called *sporangia* (Fig. 17-5*B*). Inside each **sporangium** (Gr. *angeion* = receptacle) the process of meiosis (§58) takes place, producing the tiny haploid bodies we call spores. Under the proper atmospheric conditions, a mature sporangium is capable of opening and ejecting its spores forcibly in the manner shown in *C–E* of Figure 17-5. As occurs with random dispersal generally, most of the spores fail to find a place suitable for further development, but the few that do, develop as shown in *F–I* of Figure 17-5.

A spore that lands on a suitable spot of damp, shaded ground will, by mitosis (§14), produce a flat, multicellular body about half a centimeter in length, and called a **prothallus** Gr. young shoot), or *gametophyte* (Fig. 17-5*I*). Note that the spore produces a plant quite unlike the plant it came from. The prothallus is, in most of its parts, only one cell in thickness; it is green, and it photosynthesizes. It has no roots, stems, or leaves; though it does have, on its ventral surface or underside, some root-hair-like structures called **rhizoids** (Gr. *rhiza* = root + *-oid* = like). Also on the ventral side (L. *ventralis* = belly) are the sex organs. A female sex organ is called an **archegonium** (Gr. *archegonos* = the first of a race); it produces an egg. The corresponding male organ is called an **antheridium** (diminutive of Gr. *anthos* = flower) and produces motile sperm cells. At maturation, provided there is a film of water under the prothallus, sperm cells swim toward the egg cells, attracted by a diffusible chemical substance. Although several sperm cells may enter an archegonium (not necessarily of the same prothallus), only one can fuse with the egg. The fusion

produces a diploid zygote. As a rule, only one zygote per prothallus will develop further. Since *one* prothallus normally produces only *one* zygote, the sexual part of the fern life cycle does not involve multiplication. Multiplication occurs earlier in the life cycle, in the nonsexual part, the process of spore formation.

The zygote undergoes further development *in situ* in the archegonium. By mitosis it produces a multicellular plant that matures into the familiar fern plant that we all know. Before it has gotten very far in this development, the prothallus from which it sprang deteriorates and dies. The mature fern plant has true roots, stems, and leaves, only the last of which, in the most familiar ferns of the temperate regions, are visible above ground. In the tropics, however, there are "tree ferns" (Fig. 17-6), in which the stem is above ground. Some of these are as much as 75 feet in height, the leaves at the crown ranging up to 12 feet in length, the trunk being substantial enough to furnish wood for man's dwellings.

Such is the life cycle of a fern, which was first explained in 1841 by Wilhelm Hofmeister (1824–1877), a German music publisher whose avocation was botany. In the process of elucidating the life of a fern Hofmeister had to create a new conceptual scheme, the idea of an **alternation of generations,** a sporophyte generation and a gametophyte generation. Plants of the two different generations resemble each other so little that no one ignorant of their genetic identity would be likely to guess that they were of the same species. One might even assign them to different classes or phyla, on the basis of morphology alone. How can organisms that possess the same genes (though in different dosages) develop so differently? We don't know.

137. Gymnosperms and Angiosperms

We have studied the first of the three classes of the phylum Pterophyta, namely the Filicinae, or ferns. We will next look at the second and third classes, the Gymnospermae and the Angio-

Fig. 17-6. *Tree ferns. (Courtesy Chicago Natural History Museum.)*

spermae. In considering these two classes bear in mind that the ferns have a life cycle that is clearly divided into two phases; that gametophyte and sporophyte generations are both green and independent; that a watery environment is required for the male gamete to meet the female; and that there are no seeds.

The gymnosperms and angiosperms, by contrast, have sporophyte generations that much overshadow the gametophyte in size and duration; they have developed a method of fertilization that does not require free water; and they have developed seeds, special structures that are admirably suited to dispersal and survival under adverse conditions. In large part because of these adaptations, the seed-bearing plants have spread over most of the earth's land areas. In

our time, gymnosperms and angiosperms dominate the visual landscape.

The gymnosperms (Gr. *gymnos* = naked + *sperma* = seed) include such well-known types as pines, firs, junipers, hemlocks, spruces, yews, and redwoods. As a crude generalization we may say that most gymnosperms are "evergreens," that is, plants that do not shed their leaves in a mass at one time but rather lose them and replace them at a slow rate all the time. By contrast, the evergreen habit is the exception rather than the rule among the angiosperms or "flowering plants," a class that includes not only such obvious flowers as roses, lilies, and dandelions, but also forms in which the flower is less obvious, such as many of the trees that we call **deciduous** (L. *decidere* = to fall off), that is, trees that lose their leaves in a mass at the beginning of winter. Maples, sycamores, willows, and walnuts are all angiosperms and are deciduous; live oaks and eucalyptus are of this class, but are not deciduous. The "hardwoods" of commerce are angiosperms; "softwoods" are generally, though not always, gymnosperms.

138. The Life Cycle of a Pine

The life cycle of a pine involves an alternation of generations, but this is by no means obvious. The gametophyte generation is almost entirely enclosed and protected by sporophyte tissue. The details of reproduction are shown in Figure 17-7.

A large pine cone, called an **ovulate cone** (Fig. 17-7*A*), produces a considerable number of structures called **ovules,** which, since they swill produce large spores, are called **megasporangia** (Gr. *mega* = great), shown in *B*. Each scale of a pine cone produces two such ovules. Study of the maturation of an ovule has shown that at a very early stage there is present within it a diploid cell called a **megaspore mother cell.** This cell, by a process of meiosis, produces four haploid cells called **megaspores.** A pine tree is, therefore, the sporophyte generation. It differs from the sporophytes that we have previously considered in that *it produces two kinds of spores,* only one of which is found in the familiar large pine cones. (The other type of spore is found in a small pine cone, to be described presently.) Of the four megaspores visible in Figure 17-7*E,* only one is functional. By cell division, this spore, still completely enclosed in the ovule of the parental plant, produces a gametophyte called a **megagametophyte** (*G*). At one end of this megagametophyte are produced two archegonia, in each of which is produced one egg (*H* and *I*). Thus is the female gamete protected by the sporophyte generation.

A pine tree also produces many small cones, which the nonbotanist usually does not notice. These cones are called **staminate cones.** Within them, **microsporangia,** by meiosis, produce

many spores called **microspores;** each microspore germinates to produce a **microgametophyte,** or immature pollen grain. The mature **pollen grain** is a four-nucleate structure (*K*). One of these nuclei is destined to function in fertilization and is hence called a **sperm nucleus;** the other nuclei, which do not fertilize eggs, are called **vegetative nuclei.** Pollen grains, when mature, are released from a pine tree by the millions, to float passively in the air. A very small percentage of these pollen grains succeed in reaching ovulate cones, where they may lodge in the **pollen chambers** of the ovules (*L*). The **pollen tube** of a germinating microgametophyte grows into the tissues of the ovule until it reaches the megagametophyte; then one sperm nucleus unites with one egg nucleus to produce a new diploid zygote, which grows into a new diploid sporophyte. Notice that **pollination** (*C* and *L*) takes place long before the megagametophyte is mature: Pollination occurs 12 or 13 months before the act of fertilization takes place. After fertilization, the zygote undergoes many cell divisions and considerable differentiation to produce an embryo sporophyte, which is surrounded by tissues of the female gametophyte as well as by tissues of the parental sporophyte. Development of the new sporophyte proceeds for a while, then stops. The new sporophyte, together with the tissues surrounding it, constitutes a resistant structure known as a **seed.** In some gymnosperms, the seeds are shed soon after they are completely formed. But in many pine trees, the seeds remain enclosed by the scales of the pine cones for years. In some species, the scales of the pine cone do not spread apart and release the seeds until the cone has been subjected to the action of a forest fire. The significance of this adaptation is clear. It is one of the many reasons why gymnosperms can flourish in regions that are too dry for most angiosperms.

Notice that a pine tree produces two kinds of spores: a microspore and a megaspore. The pine tree is **heterosporous.** Heterospory is universal in the classes Gymnospermae and Angiospermae. It is rare among the Filicinae, most of which are **homosporous,** as are all the Bryo-

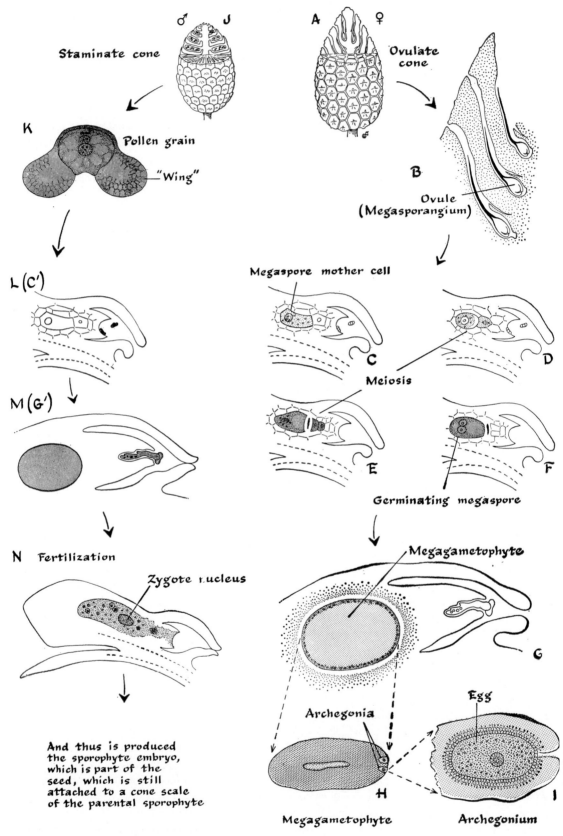

Fig. 17-7. *Details of the life cycle of a pine, to be studied in close conjunction with the text. Haploid tissues in color, diploid in black.*

phyta. Note that the pine tree, thoroughly adapted to a land existence, has no motile sperm (which would require water to reach the egg). The male gamete nucleus is in a structure that *grows* in to reach the female. Among the Gymnospermae, motile sperm are found only among the cycads and the ginkgo tree.

As compared with the Angiospermae, the Gymnospermae do not include many species—only about 700. Among these species are, however, some of great commercial importance. The size of some of these giants is ample evidence that an adequate vascular system has been evolved in this group: Douglas firs sometimes attain a diameter of 10 feet and a height of 200 feet; the "giant sequoia" of the Sierra Nevada reaches a maximum diameter of more than 30 feet and a height of more than 300 feet.

Questions and Problems

17-2. Make a list of the **boldface** terms in this chapter and write a brief description of each. Compare your work with the text.

17-3. What were the important conceptual contributions (and the dates thereof) of these men: de Bary; Hofmeister; Schwendener?

17-4. According to astronomical theory, before the Middle Paleozoic era the moon was only half its present distance from the earth. As a consequence, ocean tides may have been several hundred feet high. What significance would such a situation have had on the development of the biosphere?

17-5. Lichens are very hardy in many respects, but they are quite sensitive to smog and other man-polluted atmospheres. What evolutionary consequences have followed from this? (This is a test of your memory!)

‡17-6. The following argument is one often advanced by the newcomer to evolutionary ideas, and it is wrong. It is important that you be able to explain the basic error. Try to do so.

"Mosses can live perfectly well in water, as is shown by the sphagnum moss. Since living on land is so difficult, it obviously is not to the interest of a moss (or any other kind of plant) to try to live on land when it can have an easier life in water. It's stupid to move from an easy environment to a hard one. Therefore, if evolution did take place as the textbooks tell us, there must have been some inner driving force to make organisms evolve in a way that was not to the interest of the individuals that did the pioneering. Darwinian competition does not favor pioneering."

17-7. How does the answer to the preceding question help explain our failure to find fossils of the first pioneers in any new ecological niche?

‡17-8. With respect to their adaptation to life on land, the ferns remind you of what group of vertebrate animals? Explain.

17-9. When planted by man, ferns can survive and flourish in many places where they are incapable of reproducing more of their own kind. How come?

17-10. In the writings of Ben Jonson there occurs the following passage: "I have no medicine, sir, to walk invisible, no fern seed in my pockets." Explain.

17-11. The spores of fern were first seen in 1669. Could Shakespeare have been referring to fern spore when he spoke of "fern seeds" in the passage quoted in §136?

17-12. In Figure 17-5, the following structures are not labeled: sorus, rhizoid, prothallus. Please label them.

‡17-13. In Figure 17-5, the ring of dark-walled cells around the sporangium is called an **annulus** (L. ring). Please label it. What ancient engine of war does it remind you of?

17-14. The underground stem of a fern is often called a **rhizome.** Explain the significance of the name.

‡17-15. The antheridia of a fern usually mature long before the archegonia of the same prothallus. What will be the genetic consequences of this fact?

17-16. (Laboratory exercise.) Estimate the number of spores per mature fern plant. If there were no mortality, how many descendants would this one plant have three life cycles later?

17-17. Occasionally, a portion of a fern sporophyte will produce a gametophyte directly, without the intervention of spores; this phenomenon is called **apospory** (Gr. *apo* signifies away from, detached—a general negative idea). Also, vegetative cells of a gametophyte now and then grow into a sporophyte; this is called **apogamy.** Do these phenomena help dispel the mystery spoken of at the end of §136? Explain.

Readings

Andrews' *Ancient Plants and the World They Lived In* traces the evolution of land plants and gives some idea of the problems confronting the early invaders of the land habitat.

Scientific American Offprints

111. I. Mackenzie Lamb. *Lichens*

865. George A. Llano. *The Terrestrial Life of the Antarctic*

18 The Flowering Plants

139. The Life Cycle

The Cenozoic era, as regards animals, is often said to be the age of insects, mammals, and birds; as regards plants, it is clearly the age of the flowering plants, members of the class Angiospermae, of the phylum Pterophyta. The angiosperms first definitely appeared in the Cretaceous period (a few disputable fossils from the Jurassic are known) and evolved rapidly to produce many genera and species. Today, about one hundred million years after the origin of the class, the angiosperms include approximately two hundred thousand species, ranging all the way from almost microscopic plants to large hardwood trees.

The characteristic feature of this class is the **flower.** Flowers vary greatly in appearance, but we may learn the basic structures of them from a study of idealized diagram of Figure 18-1. Within a ring of **sepals and petals** are a number of **stamens,** the male parts of the flower. Placed centrally is a **pistil,** the female part of the flower. If a flower includes both sexual parts, it is called a **perfect flower;** otherwise it is said to be **imperfect.**

In the life cycle of a flowering plant, antheridia and archegonia are no longer identifiable, but there are still megaspores, microspores, and megagametophytes, and microgametophytes. The swelling of the pistil is the **ovary,** within which are several **ovules,** or **megasporangia.**

Each megasporangium, by meiosis, produces haploid megaspores. A megaspore may divide mitotically to produce the eight-nucleate structure, the megagametophyte, seen in the figure. Of the eight nuclei, five disintegrate during the development of the seed. Of the remainder, one is the **egg nucleus,** or female gamete; the role of the other two, the **polar nuclei,** will presently be seen. Note that, as in the gymnosperms, the megagametophyte is entirely enclosed within, and protected by, tissues of the sporophyte.

The male gametophyte, or **microgametophyte,** is tiny. Within the **anther,** which tops the filament of the stamen, there are produced microspores. Each microspore is haploid and produces the haploid gametophyte that we call a **pollen grain.** Such a mature microgametophyte is shown in Figure 18-1C. The pollen grain is usually carried from the stamen to the **stigma** of the pistil by wind or insects. After adhering to the sticky stigma, the pollen grain germinates to produce the three-nucleate structure shown in C; the lowermost of the nuclei is called a **tube nucleus,** and appears to be concerned with the downward growth of the **pollen tube.** The two nuclei behind it are called **sperm nuclei,** and function in fertilization. As the tube of the microgametophyte grows down the **style** of the pistil, the three nuclei remain near the growing tip. After the tip of the pollen tube penetrates the **micropyle,** the two sperm nuclei function in fertilization in a manner that is unique to this group of plants, exhibiting the phenomenon of **double fertilization,** as follows. One of the nuclei unites in the ordinary way with egg nucleus, thus forming a diploid zygote nucleus. The other sperm nucleus, however, unites with both polar nuclei to form a *triploid* **endosperm nucleus.** By repeated mitotic cell division, the zygote nucleus produces the embryo proper, while the endosperm nucleus produces a mass of tissues called **endosperm,** which nourishes the embryo for a time.

As the embryo grows within the protecting tissues of the parental sporophyte, some of the surrounding sporophyte tissue changes in character so that it becomes impermeable to water and often very hard or tough. As the water

supply is cut off, the development of the embryo stops, and its metabolism sinks to a low level. The arrested embryo, together with the hardened wall of parental sporophyte tissue around it, constitutes the seed of a flowering plant. This seed always includes some food supply. The endosperm is a visibly significant food reserve of the mature corn seed. In peas, by contrast, the food reserves of the endosperm are transferred to the cotyledons (see §140) during early embryogeny; the principal food reserves of mature pea seeds (or bean seeds or peanuts) are clearly the two plump cotyledons.

The life cycle of a flowering plant may perhaps be seen more clearly if presented as a cycle, which it is in Figure 18-2. As usual, hap-

Fig. 18-1. *A flower, schematically represented. Haploid tissues are shown in color, diploid in black.*

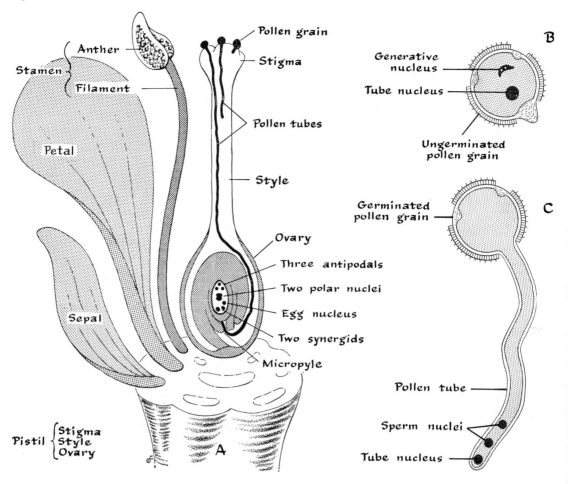

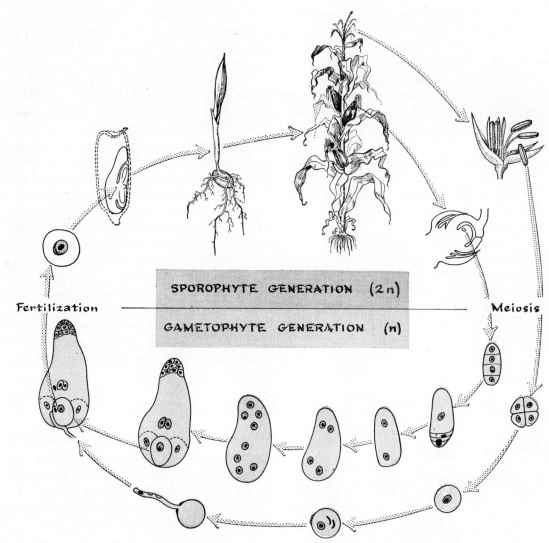

Fig. 18-2. *Life cycle of corn (maize). Haploid tissues are in color. (From Wilson and Loomis,* Botany, *rev. ed., Dryden Press, New York, 1957, by permission of Holt, Rinehart, and Winston.)*

loid stages are shown in color. For our particular example we have chosen a corn plant, which differs in some respects from the idealized flower discussed previously.*

There is almost endless variation among flowers in the number, shape, and arrangement of their sepals, petals, stamens, and pistils. Within a single species, the morphology of the flower is very constant, much more so than are many other characteristics of plants (e.g., the size and proportions of the whole plant and of the leaves). Experience has shown that floral morphology is a most useful way of distinguishing the genera of flowers; discrimination to the specific level generally requires a consideration of other, more variable characteristics.

It is hardly possible to overemphasize the evolutionary importance of the seed. It is unquestionable that this structure has contributed

* 18-1. Is a corn flower perfect?
  18-2. Is corn monoecious or dioecious? (Consult the Glossary.)

greatly to the dominance of the gymnosperms and angiosperms in the modern flora. Consider some of the most obvious advantages of seeds and the process of seed formation:

1. The process of seed formation involves a thorough protection of the earliest—the most delicate—stages of development of the individual by the mature sporophyte of the preceding generation.

2. The storage of food within the seed means that the later germination of the seed can occur rapidly, with the resultant growth of a fairly large, fairly rugged new sporophyte within a short period of time.

Fig. 18-3. *Germination of the seed of a monocot. Compare with Figure 18-4. (Reprinted with permission from W. W. Robbins, T. E. Weir, and C. R. Stocking,* Botany, *John Wiley and Sons, Inc., New York, 1957.)*

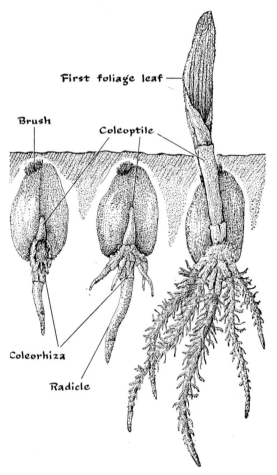

First foliage leaf

Brush

Coleoptile

Coleorhiza

Radicle

3. The great environmental resistance of seeds to such adverse environmental factors as cold and dryness permits seeds to survive long exposure to unfavorable conditions.

4. Seeds are modified to function as agents in the distribution of the species. Recall the light fluffy seeds of a dandelion.

It is worthwhile to contrast seeds with the spores of the lower plants, with regard to the characteristics just listed. As regards the fourth point, the problem of distribution, we may say that spores function just as well as seeds. Certainly, the spores of fungi are much lighter and more easily transported by the wind than is any seed. As regards the third point, the resistance to unfavorable environmental influences, fungal spores come off second-best to angiosperms, though they do fairly well. (Bacterial spores are, however, much more resistant than seeds.) But with respect to the first two characteristics, the storage of food and the protection of the delicate stages of early growth, the spores of lower plants are very poor indeed.

140. Monocots and Dicots

The class Angiospermae is further subdivided into two subclasses, the monocotyledons and the dicotyledons, a distinction first recognized by the Greek philosopher Theophrastus (371–287 B.C.). The classification of the flowering plants may be exhibited thus:

Class: **Angiospermae**
   Subclass: **Monocotyledonae**
      Families: Gramineae, Liliaceae, Iridaceae, Orchidaceae.
   Subclass: **Dicotyledoneae**
      Families: Salicaceae, Ranunculaceae, Magnoliaceae, Cruciferae, Rosaceae, Leguminosae, Malvaceae, Umbelliferae, Labiatae, Solanaceae, Cucurbitaceae, Compositae.

The primary distinction between *monocots* and *dicots* (as they are familiarly called) may best be seen by comparing Figure 18-3 and Figure 18-4. During embryogeny, the dicot seed

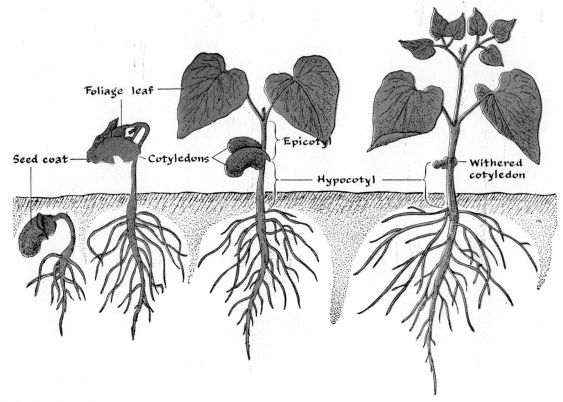

Fig. 18-4. *Germination of the seed of a dicot. Compare with Figure 18-3. (Reprinted with permission from W. W. Robbins, T. E. Weir, and C. R. Stocking,* Botany, *John Wiley and Sons, Inc., New York, 1957.)*

produces *two* special organs called **cotyledons** (Gr. *kotyle* = cup). The monocot seed, by contrast, produces only one cotyledon. In addition to this basic difference, the two subclasses are further distinguished as follows: The venation of the leaves is generally parallel in the monocots, as you can easily see by examining any grass, lily, or iris; whereas there is most often a netted venation in the dicots (e.g., roses, legumes, tomatoes, and cucumbers). Moreover, the flower parts in monocots are typically in groups of three or multiples thereof; whereas dicot flower parts are more often in fours or fives.

141. The Evolutionary Trend from Haploidy to Diploidy

We are now ready to bring together information on plant reproduction scattered through Chapters 14–18, to show a significant point. Sexual reproduction, we have said, involves two complementary processes occurring alternately, in cyclical fashion: fertilization and reduction division. Between fertilization and reduction lies a diploid phase; between reduction and fertilization is the haploid phase. The relative duration of the two phases is determined by the temporal placing of one process with respect to the other. Although there are many irregularities and exceptions, the following generalization is permissible: passing from the algae and fungi through the mosses, liverworts, and ferns to the gymnosperms and angiosperms, the haploid (gametophyte) phase becomes progressively less prominent and the diploid (sporophyte) phase more prominent. The sense of this generalization is shown in Figure 18-5.

Why is this so? If haploidy has been replaced by diploidy in the higher plants (and most ani-

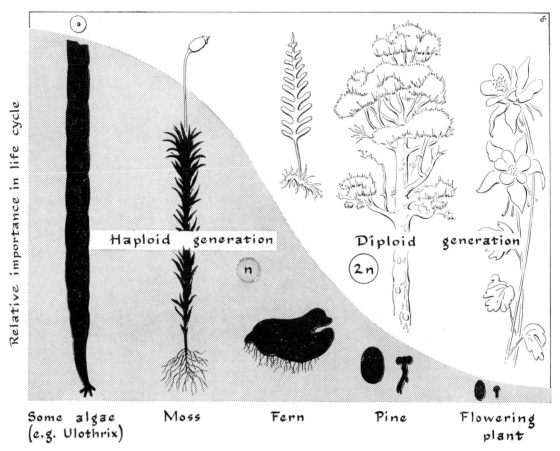

Fig. 18-5. *The broad evolutionary trend from haploidy to diploidy, i.e., from dominance of the gametophyte generation to dominance of the sporophyte.*

mals are diploid), it must be because there is some sense in which diploidy is an advantage. The answer lies in genetics, and can best be appreciated by reviewing Chapter 7 first. . . . *Assuming that has been done—*

Recall that, almost without exception, each new mutation is a detriment to the organism that receives it. Recall also that most new mutations are recessive; that is, a new mutant (a) produces little or no effect when combined with its "normal" allele (A) in the heterozygote (Aa). But the concept of genetic recessiveness has no meaning in haploid individuals. Which type of organism (haploid or diploid) is more susceptible to the deleterious effects of mutation? Plainly, the haploid individual is, because the bad effect of a new mutation is not modified by any corresponding normal allele. Having

two of each gene locus is a kind of insurance, just as is having two lungs or two kidneys. Diploidy is a sort of "safety factor," to use an engineering term. The process of mutation cannot be stopped. *Other things being equal,* a diploid organism is less susceptible to mutation damage than is a haploid.

However, this is not the whole story. Because deleterious genes are not immediately eliminated from diploids, they can accumulate. The best genotype of a diploid species in a particular environment may be, say:

$$AABBCCDDEEFFGG\ldots$$

But as a result of the mutation process acting on successive generations, a population of diploid organisms may include, say, these genotypes:

AaBBCCDDEEFFGg . . .

AABbCcDdEEFFGG . . .

AaBBCcDDEEFfGg . . .

The new mutant genes we have printed in color, to catch the eye. Since mutant genes have the best chance of survival when they are recessive, we can assume that all the mutants shown above are recessive, which we indicate by using small letters to represent them. They are recessive *in the normal environment*—the "old" one. But in a new environment, a mutant allele may not be recessive at all. This is the phenomenon that probably explains the facts illustrated in Figure 11-6. (It is essential that you turn back to page 193 to view this.) Plants that are apparently identical in one environment reveal their genetic heterogeneity when transplanted to a new environment in which "recessive" alleles are no longer recessive. Evolution continually involves the creation and occupation (or "attempted" occupation) of new environments. Diploidy is a way of preserving genetic diversity so that a new environment can be rapidly exploited, if exploitation is at all possible, without waiting for the needed new mutations to appear.* If one thinks of this situation in terms of "stimulus" (or "challenge") and "response," it is as though the response appeared in advance of the challenge. When the response is one that is advantageous in a new environment, the phenomenon is called one of "preadaptation." Most new mutations are, of course, neither adapted (to the present environment) or preadapted to any particular new environment that may be realized. But a few are, and it is this fact that gives diploid organisms flexibility in meeting the challenges of changing environments.

Whether the force of natural selection is capable of selecting for adaptability per se is still a matter of controversy. It is not necessary to settle this matter to know that diploidy is an advantage, for the lesser vulnerability to mutation damage is alone of sufficient selective value.

---

* 18-3. Lamentable teleology is hidden in this sentence. For the salvation of your biological soul, correct it.

The added flexibility of the species can be regarded as an unplanned-for extra dividend which has helped in making diploid organisms the diverse and dominant forms they are today.

Before leaving the haploidy versus diploidy problem, one more point must be made: *We must beware of the danger of proving too much.* After showing the advantages of diploidy, we must then account for the fact that there are, after all, tens of thousands of predominantly haploid species living successfully in this world. There must be circumstances that make haploidy an advantage. What are they?

It is doubtful if we know the complete answer to this question yet. However, it is probably not without significance that the most predominantly haploid species—many species of algae, almost all fungi, and especially the bacteria—are ones that reproduce with great rapidity. Since, over a long period of time, the population of every species is maintained in cybernetic equilibrium, a high reproductive rate is necessarily coupled with an equally high death rate. A species in which the death rate is necessarily high even in the absence of mutations will be least damaged by the mutation process. It can most easily afford to be haploid. Diploidy can be achieved and maintained only by a reproductive process that involves fusion, for example, sexual reproduction. In the nature of things, sexual reproduction is more complicated and less suited to speedy multiplication than is asexual. Therefore, an ecological situation that favors the most rapid reproduction will favor the elimination or minimization of sexual reproduction and a corresponding emphasis on haploidy.

142. Vegetative Reproduction

The Pterophyta are, as a group, "committed" to sexual reproduction, foregoing the advantages of asexual processes. But even in the highest phylum of plants, some species have evolved means of asexual reproduction called **vegetative reproduction.** A pretty example is shown in Figure 18-6; whenever a specialized leaf of a "walking fern" touches a suitable substrate, roots and stems develop from the point of contact, creating a new plant which can exist as a separate individual if the leafy bridge between it and the parent plant is severed. By successive repetitions of this process, the fern can "walk" from one spot to another.

Other examples of vegetative reproduction are shown in Figure 18-7. A detached leaf of *Bryophyllum* (also called *Kalanchoë*) is capable of growing new little plants at its margins. The common potato, which is really an underground stem (not a root), can grow new plants from each one of its "eyes" (buds). Bamboo normally spreads by underground stems called **rhizomes.** A strawberry plant accomplishes the

same process by aerial stems called **stolons.** Canada thistle spreads by horizontal roots.

Why do higher plants resort to vegetative reproduction? What are the advantages? There are several. For one thing, sexual reproduction is often a relatively slow process, particularly if it is tied to the seasons so that it can occur only once a year. By bypassing this process, a plant may spread much more rapidly. Notable is a wild blackberry plant (genus *Rubus*) that was imported to the west coast of the South Island of New Zealand; a single plant there is now believed to be more than 100 miles long. (That this belief has not been carefully checked is understandable: picture to yourself the painful consequences of trying to do so!)

In bypassing sexual reproduction, a plant also

Fig. 18-6. *Vegetative reproduction by a "walking fern." (Courtesy H. Lou Gibson.)*

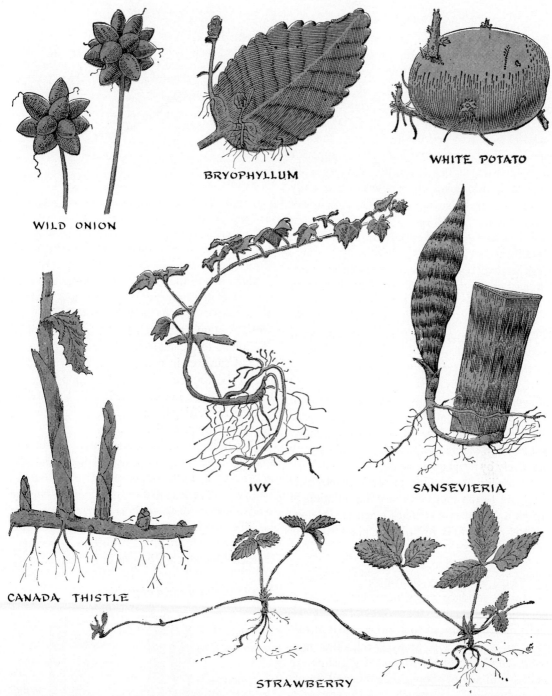

WILD ONION

BRYOPHYLLUM

WHITE POTATO

IVY

SANSEVIERIA

CANADA THISTLE

STRAWBERRY

Fig. 18-7. *Some examples of vegetative reproduction in plants.*

bypasses the recombination of genes that meiosis and fusion bring about. This may be an advantage or a disadvantage, depending on the circumstances. A plant that owes its success to its "hybrid vigor" can reproduce its own kind far more efficiently by vegetative reproduction than by sexual reproduction. Suppose, for example, its genotype is symbolized thus:

AaBbCcDdEeFfGg . . .

If it reproduces sexually, only a small fraction of its offspring will have the same genotype, or any specified genotype. (How small a fraction we will learn later when we take up the subject of genetics.) But vegetative reproduction, involving only equational divisions of the genetic material produces genetically identical individuals.* If the heterozygote is markedly superior to any existing homozygote, this stability is an advantage. Moreover, if a species habitually resorts to vegetative reproduction only, it will soon become heterozygous at many different gene loci as a result of successive, unavoidable mutations.

Vegetative reproduction confers another advantage: escape from the sterility that often afflicts a hybrid. As most people know, a mule is a hybrid between a horse (mare) and a donkey; it is a wonderfully vigorous animal, but it is sterile. If mules could only be propagated vegetatively, the necessity of re-creating them each generation by fresh species-crosses could be avoided. Such vegetative reproduction is not possible in higher animals, but it is in higher plants. Many wild flowering plants (e.g., many grasses) are sterile "mules" that multiply very effectively by vegetative means.

The ability of plants to multiply vegetatively is related to the fact that the differentiation of organs and tissues that takes place in development is more easily reversed in plants than in animals. Man exploits the advantages of this mode of reproduction. For example, by "layering" (Fig. 18-8), it is often possible to induce a plant to produce many daughter plants, all members of the same clone. **Slips** of stems can sometimes be induced to form roots if thrust into well-watered soil. Many species that normally "slip" poorly, do so well if the slips are treated with any of about thirty different "rooting compounds," of which indoleacetic acid, indolebutyric acid, and naphthaleneacetic acid are best known. The discovery of the rooting compounds (beginning in 1935) has made the

Fig. 18-8. *"Layering" as a means of inducing vegetative reproduction of a plant.*

work of the professional horticulturist much more effective.

Some of the most important modes of artificial vegetative reproduction are the **grafting procedures.** One of these is shown in Figure 18-9. A stem or branch is cut from one plant and joined to the cut stem of another by placing the cut surfaces in contact. The plant that furnishes the root in this artificial union is called the **stock;** the other element is called the **scion.** Success in grafting usually requires close contact of the cambiums of the two.

Vegetative reproduction of plants is useful to man in many ways. Garlic, a plant that has never set seed in the thousands of years man has known it, is propagated only by subdividing the bulbs. Seedless fruit, such as navel oranges, can be (indeed, must be) reproduced by grafting. With many horticultural varieties, we have learned that we can, by grafting together stock

Fig. 18-9. *One method of grafting.*

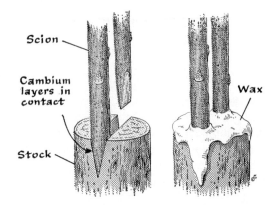

Scion

Cambium layers in contact

Wax

Stock

---

* 18-4. And these are all said to be members of the same *what*?

and scion from different varieties, or even from different species, combine the good qualities of both. For example, European wine grapes are very susceptible to root damage by aphids (*phylloxera disease*), whereas some American grapes, of inferior wine-producing qualities, are resistant to these plant lice. The wine industry of Europe, which was threatened with destruction by phylloxera toward the end of the nineteenth century, was saved by grafting scions of the choice wine-grape varieties on stocks imported from America.

Most economically important fruit trees— apples, pears, and others—are heterozygous for dozens or perhaps hundreds of genes. Seeds from fruit trees produce a highly heterogeneous collection of offspring; of these, a negligibly small fraction are like the parent or are of any use to man. Therefore, propagation of fruit trees is almost exclusively vegetative.

Grafting also furnishes a valuable means of settling some of the questions of plant physiology. For instance, by making grafts between tobacco plants and other species, it has been shown that the grafted pair develops nicotine in the leaves only if tobacco is used as the stock, thus indicating that, even though nicotine is found concentrated in the leaves, it depends on the roots for its synthesis.

There is a widespread misconception that by grafting, one can produce new types of plants. This is not so. Grafting is merely a means of maintaining and propagating genes that have already been produced by mutation. The tissues of both partners of a graft reproduce by mitotic division; there is no interchange of genetic material between these two types of cells, though, at the juncture, they lie side by side. There may be translocation of dissolved materials—such as nicotine mentioned in the preceding paragraph —between stock and scion, but there is no change in the genetic constitution of either tissue. There are numerous examples of apple-tree stocks on which have been grafted more than 100 varieties of apple scion; each of these scions produces its own variety of apples true to type, uninfluenced by the genetic constitution of the stock. A single scion strain grafted in series from

one tree to another reproduces true to type *indefinitely*. Thus has the Washington navel orange been maintained since its origination as a single mutant in South America early in the nineteenth century. But though true reproduction continues indefinitely, it does not continue forever. Mutations occur not only in germ cells but also in vegetative cells; such **somatic mutations** not only can originate a desirable variety, but can also put an end to it. Horticultural propagation of fruit trees requires careful selection of scions.

143. Pollination of Plants

Sexual reproduction in conifers and flowering plants depends on the transport of a male gametophyte—a pollen grain—to the immediate neighborhood of the female gametophyte. In some species, transport is nondirectional, being brought about by wind (usually) or water (rarely). In other species, transport is, we might say, directional: the pollen grains are moved by living agents (birds, bees, and other animals) from flower to flower.

Wind pollination is characteristic of the gymnosperms, and is found also in many angiosperms (e.g., cottonwood, walnut, oats, and wheat). Wind-pollinated plants typically produce large quantities of pollen, as they must if the probability of pollination by such a nondirectional means is to be made sufficiently great. Naturally, most of the pollen grains fall uselessly to the ground or into water. The shores of lakes in regions of conifers will at times have a visible windrow of wasted pollen grains. In some waters, particularly in acid waters, pollen grains frequently survive for long periods of time, and accumulate. Since it is usually possible to recognize the genus (and sometimes the species) of the plant that produced the pollen (see Fig. 18-10), examination of pollen deposits in an old lake bottom tells us what plants flourished in the past. From such **pollen analysis,** we can deduce the climate of an ancient period.

Plant species that are pollinated by animals

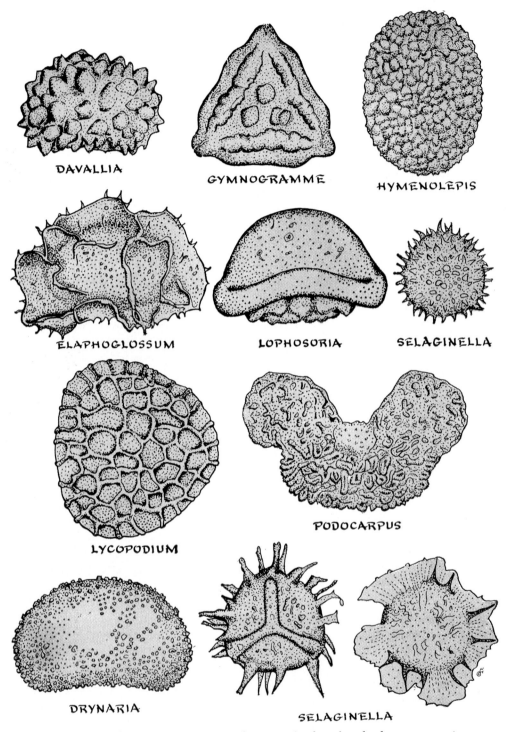

DAVALLIA

GYMNOGRAMME

HYMENOLEPIS

ELAPHOGLOSSUM

LOPHOSORIA

SELAGINELLA

LYCOPODIUM

PODOCARPUS

DRYNARIA

SELAGINELLA

Fig. 18-10. *Pollen shows a great variety when examined under the low power microscope.*

produce less pollen than do wind-pollinated species. Since animals move preferentially from flower to flower, the reason for the difference is clear. Showy, conspicuous flowers are a form of advertisement: they tell the animal where he can "come and get it." Of course, there has to be "something in it" for the animal, for *no feature of one species can be selected solely for its benefit to another*. This is the **Paley-Darwin Principle,** a truth that was often overlooked by theologians (particularly in the eighteenth century) who were wont to explain the adaptations of species on an altruistic basis, particularly with reference to man, for whose benefit they supposed other organisms to have been created. The English theologian William Paley (1743–1805) said, however, that it is best to regard the adaptations of each species as being "designed" for its own benefit. Rattlesnakes have rattles not to warn away men so as to protect the men, but to protect the rattlesnakes themselves. This idea fitted very neatly into the Darwinian scheme, it being necessary merely to substitute the word "evolved" (by natural selection) for the word "designed."

The Paley-Darwin Principle resembles a basic principle in law that holds that no contract is valid unless both parties receive something for executing it; there must be a *quid pro quo* (L. something for something). The flower that takes advantage of an insect's instinct to fly toward brightly colored objects, by which stratagem the flower tricks the insect into pollinating it, gives the insect a *quid pro quo* in the form of a bit of **nectar,** a sugary liquid located so deep in the flower that the insect cannot get the nectar without rubbing against anther or stigma. Pollen itself is often the *quid pro quo*—bees use it as food—but obviously a successful one only if (as is true) the insect does not harvest all the pollen for his own use. The instincts of the insect must make it "wasteful" or "careless," from the insect's standpoint, if the plant species is to endure.

Odor is often an attractant, too. We suspect* that a flower odor that pleases us pleases insects also. The converse is not necessarily true: flow-

ers pollinated by carrion flies produce substances that smell like decaying meat. The odoriferous substances produced by a flower may not be produced continuously. Some plants that are pollinated by animals active in the daytime produce their odors only during the daylight hours, and some night-pollinated flowers produce their odors only at night.

The colors of flowers show analogous adaptations. Experimental studies made by means of the technique of conditioned learning (see §270) show that bees are unable to distinguish scarlet-red from black—that is, they are blind to the red end of the spectrum of colors. Birds, however, can perceive red. With almost no exceptions, scarlet-red flowers are pollinated by birds and not by bees. One exception, a scarlet-red poppy (*Papaver*) that is pollinated by bees, has been shown (by appropriate instruments), to reflect ultraviolet light, to which the human eye is blind. In other words, such poppy flowers, which appear red to humans, must appear—well, perhaps blue-blue?—to the bees. This example shows us how our human sensory limitations may lead us astray in the interpretation of experimental facts.

144. The Leaf: A Photosynthetic Organ

Although the stem of a land-dwelling plant is often green, leaves are responsible for carrying out most of its photosynthesis. Plants compete with each other for a place in the sun. *Other things being equal*—and we admit that's a dangerous phrase—the plant that succeeds in intercepting the most of the sun's rays will have a competitive advantage in survival. A flat leaf is admirably suited to such interception: it presents a maximum of light-gathering surface with a minimum of material (living cells). But this large surface: volume ratio raises the threat of a rapid loss of water. The plant "solves" this problem (if we may personify the plant) by having the outer layer of its leaf cells (Fig. 18-11), its **epidermis** (Gr. *epi* = over + *derma* = skin), thicker-walled and less pervious to moisture than most other cells. In addition, the

---

* 18-5. Why the cautious verb?

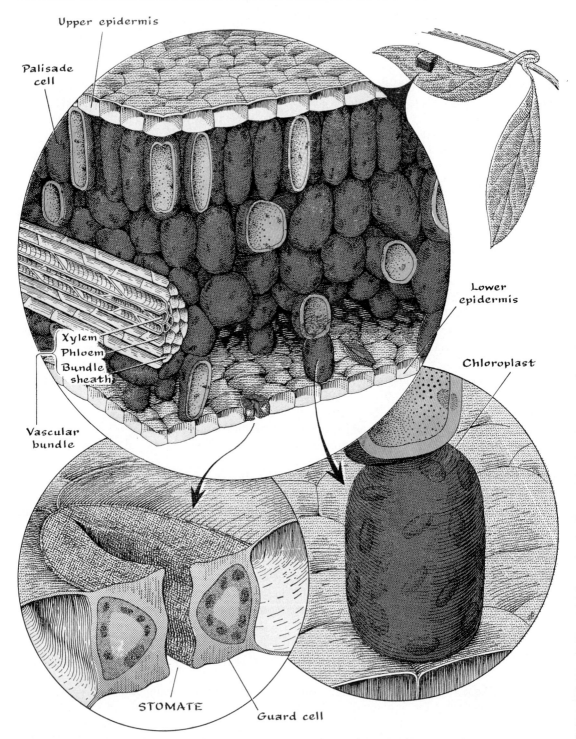

Fig. 18-11. *Detailed structure of a leaf. (From Bonner and Galston,* Principles of Plant Physiology, *W. H. Freeman and Company, San Francisco and London, 1952.)*

epidermis is often covered with a **cuticle** (L. *cuticula,* diminutive of *cutis* = skin), a thin, noncellular layer of wax, sometimes called *cutin*. This layer is not shown in the figure.

Thus the loss of water is minimized, but by raising another problem: How are exchanges of CO_2 and O_2 to be managed through such an epidermis? The plant's answer is a kind of specialized cell called a **guard cell** (Fig. 18-11), a pair of which surround an opening called a **stomate** (Gr. *stoma* = mouth). When the stomates are open, CO_2 and O_2 (and also water vapor) can be exchanged between the leaf and the surrounding air. The dimensions of open stomates vary considerably in different species: typical dimensions are 20μ by 10μ. The number of stomates per square millimeter is usually of the order of 100–200 (with a high of 1,300), there being usually more stomates in the lower epidermis than in the upper*—which may even have none, as is true of nasturtiums and apple, oak, olive, and birch trees. An entire corn plant will have approximately 2×10^8 stomates, which, when fully open, account for about 1.5 percent of the leaf surface.

How is the opening and closing of a stomate regulated? The guard cells are so constructed that when they are limp, or *flaccid,* they collapse together, closing the stomate between them. When they are swollen with fluid, or *turgid,* they spread apart, opening the stomate. What induces a state of **turgor** in guard cells? The exact mechanism is still under research, but the basic reaction underlying it seems to be this:

$$\text{1 molecule of starch} \underset{\longleftarrow}{\overset{\text{(enzyme)}}{\longrightarrow}}$$

many molecules of sugar. *(1)*

When the reaction goes to the right, the osmotic potential (§§22, 23) of the guard cells rise, bringing in water from surrounding tissues, increasing the turgor of the guard cells, and opening the stomate. Such a chain of events follows illumination of the leaf, *perhaps* because photosynthesis lowers the concentration of CO_2 in the leaf spaces, thus lowering the acidity in the

guard cells, thus favoring enzymatic action toward the right. If the leaf is suffering a water deficit, the guard cells will collapse, thus closing the stomates. The behavior of the guard cells is in general adapted to keeping the stomates closed as much as is consonant with the necessary photosynthesis.

Transport of material to and from the leaf takes place in **vascular bundles.** As the bundle leaves the stem and enters the leaf, it becomes known as a **vein,** because of the resemblance of the ramifications of the veins of a leaf (Fig. 18-12*B* and *C*) to the ramifications of the veins and arteries of an animal. Each vein includes (*A* of Fig. 18-12): **xylem tissue,** in which water is brought to the leaf; **phloem tissue,** which transports the **photosynthate** (i.e., the chemical products of photosynthesis) to other parts of the plant; and certain structural tissues. These latter serve to stiffen the leaf, which would otherwise be rather limp and unable to intercept much light. The extensive ramification of the leaf vein system (*C* of Fig. 18-12) not only gives rigidity to the leaf but also serves to put every cell of the leaf within a few cell-distances of the transport system. The pattern of venation varies considerably among the various kinds of plants.

Leaves of many plants serve other functions in addition to photosynthesis. In *Portulaca* and century plants, thick leaves act as water-storage organs. In insectivorous or carnivorous plants, for example, Venus's-flytrap, bladderwort, and pitcher plant, leaves are modified for the capture of small animals. The usefulness of leaves to man hardly needs mentioning. Indirectly, most of our food comes from these photosynthetic organs. Directly, many leaves serve as food for man, for example, the leaves of cabbage and lettuce. Most leaves are rich in ascorbic acid (vitamin C), an important element of the diet. Among the less common, but useful, substances obtainable from leaves: the flavoring materials of peppermint, sage, and wintergreen; many drugs, among them cocaine and digitalis; and those commercially important items, tobacco and tea.

---

* 18-6. Why?

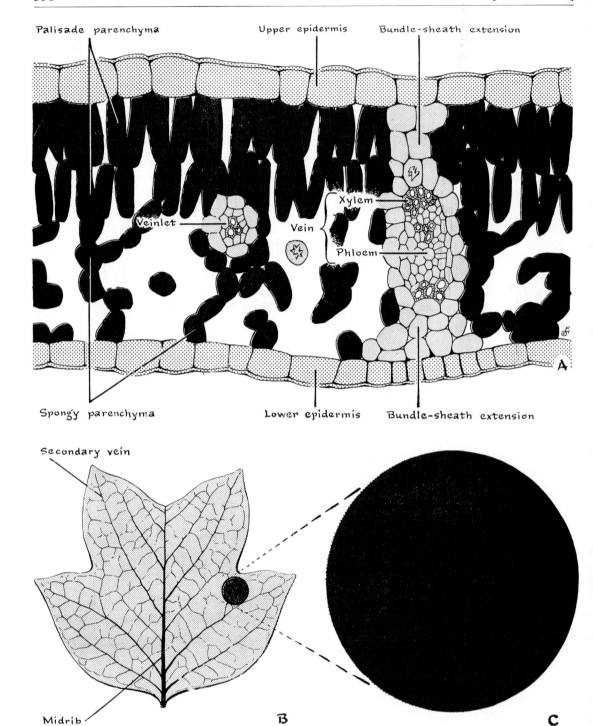

Fig. 18-12. *Structure of a leaf. (After Foster and Gifford,* Comparative Morphology *of Vascular Plants, W. H. Freeman and Company, San Francisco and London, 1959.)*

145. Roots

The CO_2 needed for photosynthesis comes in through the leaves; the other raw material, H_2O, comes in through the roots. Obtaining water entails another set of problems, for which the solutions are of more than a little interest. Again the basic problem is connected with the surface:volume relationship; the geometry of roots is such as to maximize the surface. Everyone knows that roots are sometimes quite long. In well-drained, porous soil, alfalfa roots may extend downward some 30 feet. (In packed or poorly drained soil, they will be confined to a narrow layer near the surface because the root cells cannot otherwise get enough of the oxygen they need for respiration.*) But the great extent of a root system cannot be appreciated unless we go to the trouble of working plant roots free of the soil around them by a careful washing process, when something of the sort illustrated in Figure 18-13*A* is seen. Even this, however, is by no means the whole story. By still more careful work, we find that there is a region just behind the growing tip of each small rootlet that is covered by hundreds of tiny **root hairs** (Fig. 18-13*B*), each of which is just an extension of a single epidermal cell. It is these root hairs, which are in intimate contact with the soil particles, that are responsible for most of the absorption of water from the soil.

How extensive the root system is has been most impressively shown by the studies of H. J. Dittmer (1937). This plant physiologist grew a rye plant in the soil of a container 12 inches square by 22 inches deep. When the plant was 4 weeks old and 20 inches tall, he carefully washed the root system free of dirt. Then, by measurement and estimation, he found that there were, in this small volume, 390 *miles* of roots† with a surface area of 2,500 square feet. The 14.5 billion root hairs had an estimated total length of 6,600 miles and an area of 4,300

square feet. From Dittmer's data it may be calculated that the surface:volume ratio is 734:1, a ratio approximately equal to that of a human hair. That is, the entire root system of the rye plant had as much surface in relation to its volume as it would if all 390 miles of roots were human hairs.

Roots absorb water. How? As is true of so many basic problems in biology, we can give only a partial answer. Undoubtedly, one of the phenomena involved in bringing about the intake of water by the roots is the osmotic potential of the root cells. In general, the osmotic potential of the cytoplasm within root epidermal hairs is higher than the osmotic potential of the soil water around them. As a result, the net movement of water molecules is from soil to root. Were no factors other than the osmotic movement of molecules involved, an equilibrium would eventually be reached, and no more water would enter the roots. However, water is continuously being used by the plant in photosynthesis, and lost from the above-ground portions by evaporation. As it is so used and lost, more water is moved up the stem and away from the roots, and more water enters the roots.

Besides water, the plant absorbs from the soil many other kinds of molecules, principally ones of inorganic compounds. Among the major elements needed by plants are calcium, potassium, phosphorus, nitrogen, sulfur, and magnesium, which are present in the soil as salts. Also needed, but in much smaller quantities, are boron, cobalt, molybdenum, copper, manganese, chlorine, and zinc. Plants can *accumulate* salts of these elements until the concentration of them within the plant is greater than it is in the soil outside; which, according to the principles developed in §23, can happen only if the plant performs *work*.

That a plant needs only water and inorganic salts from the soil is a discovery of only the past hundred years. Earlier, almost mystical properties were attributed to the soil. (This attitude is still not completely dead.) Proving exactly what elements are needed by plants required the development of the most meticulous techniques of chemical purification. From the resultant de-

---

* 18-7. Why does grass die down in a footpath? (The above discussion may suggest an additional factor you never thought of before.)

† 18-8. It took 4 weeks for this growth to take place. *On the average,* what length of roots was grown each day?

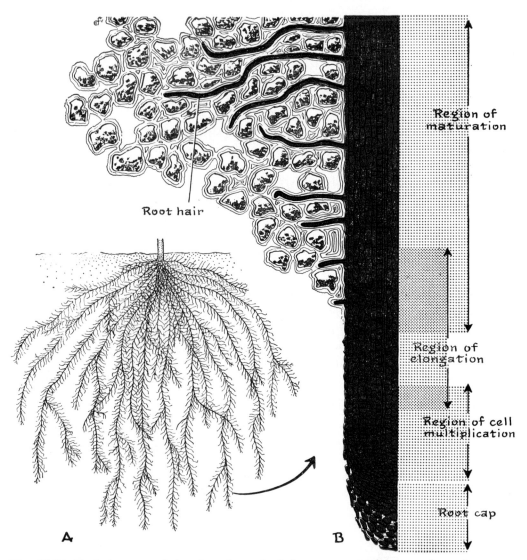

Root hair

Region of maturation

Region of elongation

Region of cell multiplication

Root cap

A   B

Fig. 18-13. *Each tiny root of the plant shown in* A *has many root hairs, as shown in* B. *Each root hair is an extension of a single epidermal cell, and is not visible in* A. B *also shows the processes that take place in the various regions of a growing root.*

velopments in pure science came many practical benefits. Soils that fail to support good plant growth can now be analyzed and "corrected" by chemical additions.

Soil being so complex and unrefinable a material, the critical proof of the necessity of any element requires the use of **soilless culture,** or **hydroponics.** Now that the techniques have been worked out for experimental work, hydroponics have been used for other purposes:

(1) for growing fresh vegetables in isolated military camps on barren islands; (2) for growing the early stages of delicate, expensive plants like orchids; and (3) for growing "sprouts" (e.g., bean sprouts, alfalfa sprouts) for food either for animals (dairy cows in winter) or humans (for use in salads or chop suey), where the absence of soil particles produces a product that can be eaten in its entirety without washing.

A few enthusiasts have proposed that soilless

culture be substituted for all traditional agriculture, but economic analysis indicates that this will not be feasible in the foreseeable future. **Nutrient solution** (water plus salts) is cheap, but vats to hold it are expensive, and must be shielded from the light to prevent the development of algae, which would deprive the larger plants of nutrients. Support for the plants must also be provided, since they are deprived of their usual method of bracing themselves in the soil by their roots. All in all, it appears that man will require soil for a long time to come, and had better learn as much as he can about its characteristics and conservation.

146. The Movement of Fluids in Plants

The photosynthetic reaction requires that both H_2O and CO_2 be brought together in the same cell. But CO_2 enters by way of the leaves, whereas H_2O enters through the roots, some

Fig. 18-14. *Important cells and tissues in the bark and adjoining regions of a dicotyledonous plant, as seen in cross section. (From Wilson and Loomis,* Botany, *rev. ed., Dryden Press, New York, 1957, courtesy Holt, Rinehart, and Winston.)*

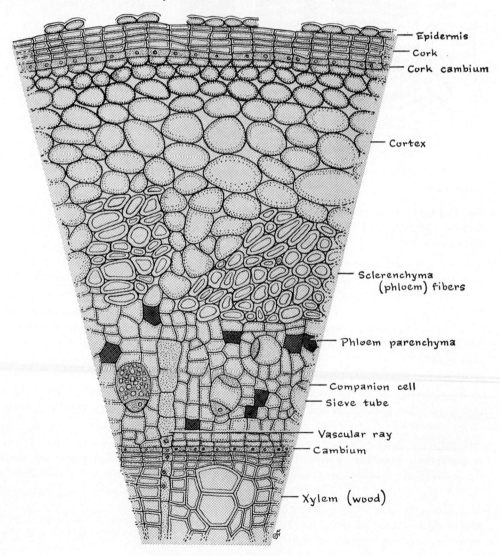

Epidermis
Cork
Cork cambium

Cortex

Sclerenchyma
(phloem) fibers

Phloem parenchyma

Companion cell
Sieve tube

Vascular ray
Cambium

Xylem (wood)

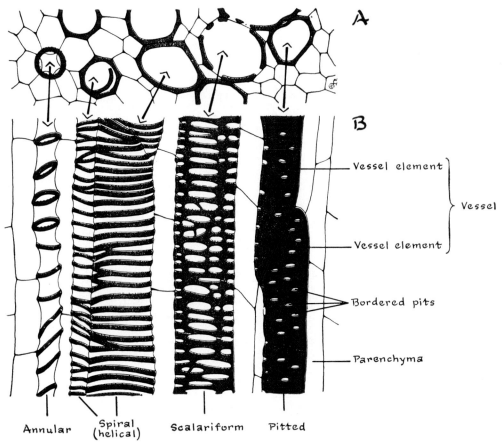

Fig. 18-15. *Different types of xylem cells. (After Esau; from Foster and Gifford,* Comparative Morphology of Vascular Plants, *W. H. Freeman and Company, San Francisco and London, 1959.)*

distance away. How is water brought from the roots to the leaves? And, after the photosynthate is formed, how is it conveyed to the living cells of the roots, which, being in the dark and without chlorophyll, are unable to make their own food?

Water transport in the plant presents us with an impressive problem. The water used is far in excess of what appears in the photosynthate. Great quantities of water are evaporated and diffused from the leaves—a phenomenon called **transpiration.** Typically, about 95 percent of the water taken up by the roots is so transpired, only 5 percent being used in photosynthesis. Measurements have shown that a single corn plant will transpire as many as 200 liters of water in a growing season (as many as 2 liters a

day when mature), that an acre of corn plants may use 1,300 tons of water during the season —the equivalent of 28 centimeters of rain. Equally impressive is the height through which water may be lifted by a plant: one great redwood tree in Humboldt County, California, is 110 meters high.

The mechanism whereby water is raised in the plant cannot be that of a simple "suction pump," for "suction" * would not raise the water more than about 9 meters, and the plant has no pump. The plant has, however, what might be called pipes. These are seen as more or less circular in cross section, when a stem or

---

* 18-9. Why does a knowledge of physics make us want to put quotation marks around this word? And whence the figure 9 meters?

trunk is cut across (Fig. 18-14). They are of two sorts, called **tracheids and vessels.** These, together with various fibers, make up the layer of tissue called **xylem** (Gr. *xylon* = wood). Both tracheids and vessels are produced by living cells, and are living cells to begin with; but in the maturation process, the cells die, leaving the dead cell walls. In forming the vessels, the end walls also disintegrate, producing continuous tubes. By far the greater part of an older tree is dead xylem; paradoxically, most of a living tree is dead, perhaps as much as 99 percent by weight.

A plant is a sort of wick soaked with water. As water is lost from the leaves by transpiration, and as photosynthesis produces osmotically active molecules, the osmotic potential of the cells in the leaves becomes greater. This tends to bring more water to them from the nearby xylem. There is thus exerted a "pull" on the tiny thread of water inside each xylem vessel, and water moves upward. Is there not danger that a "break" will occur in the long column of water in the plant stem, resulting in the fall of water to about 9 meters? No; in very thin columns of water, a break is improbable because of the *cohesive* force of water. Water molecules have a strong attraction for each other, and when supported in thin columns (a few microns wide in a xylem vessel), each column of water acts like a thread of great tensile strength. Thus is water pulled upward in the plant.

Such is the **Transpiration-Cohesion-Tension Theory** of water movement in plants, a theory originated principally by H. H. Dixon and J. Joly in 1895. There are several lines of evidence that favor this theory. *One:* an opening can be made into a stem and a pressure gauge sealed in; during rapid transpiration the gauge registers *less* than atmospheric pressure. *Another:* the walls of many vessels are strengthened by rings (Fig. 18-15), as are the flexible hose of a vacuum cleaner, the windpipe of man, and other vessels that must withstand greater pressure outside than in.

The movement of the photosynthate from the leaves elsewhere is accomplished by the phloem.

In Figure 18-14, note that the phloem is near the periphery of the stem or trunk. Because of this, it is possible (as practical men have known for centuries) to kill a tree by **girdling** it, that is, by excising a complete ring of the phloem, thus depriving the roots of a supply of food. One of the early students of the movements of fluids in both plants and animals, the Reverend Stephen Hales (1677–1761) in England, observed that a bulge develops in the tree trunk above the girdle (Fig. 18-16). This is the result of increased growth accompanying the accumulation of sugars in this region. The fluid in the phloem is very concentrated as compared with that in the xylem, the sugar concentration being often as high as 10 percent.

Phloem transport differs from xylem transport in another respect: live cells are needed. If a stem is subjected to live steam all around, the result is as though it were girdled. Why is this? We can get a partial answer by looking more closely at the microscopic structure of the phloem (Fig. 18-14 and Fig. 18-17). The **sieve tubes,** it has been found, are responsible for the flow of fluid: the dye eosin selectively blocks these tubes, bringing phloem transport to a halt. The cells of the sieve tubes are remarkable in that their end walls are perforated by

Fig. 18-16. Left: *A woody stem is girdled by removing a ring of bark, leaving the xylem intact.* Right: *Its appearance a few weeks later. (After Stephen Hales; from Bonner and Galston,* Principles of Plant Physiology, *W. H. Freeman and Company, San Francisco and London, 1952.)*

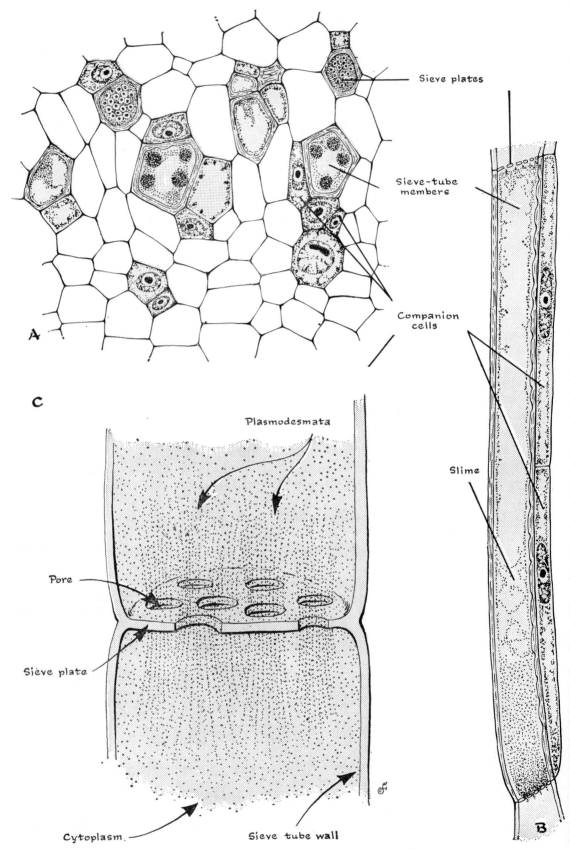

Fig. 18-17. *The structure of sieve tubes.*

many holes, from 0.5μ to 5μ in diameter; hence the name. These cells, when originally formed, have solid end walls; but, as they mature, the end walls become perforated, and the nuclei disintegrate. What is left? Cells? Are they alive? Because they lack intact end walls (as well as cell membranes), it is hard to say where one cell stops and another begins. When the nucleus dies, what is left? Should we call it "cytoplasm" or "protoplasm" (as some botany texts do); or, more noncommittally, "slime" (as other texts do)? Strands of this material connecting successive chambers of a sieve tube are often called **plasmodesmata** (Gr. *desmos* = chain). The facts are hard to fit into a rigid cell theory. Whether a sieve tube cell is or is not alive, certainly the cell that is juxtaposed to each of them, the **companion cell** (see Fig. 18-17) is. For one thing, it has a nucleus. The cell division that produces a sieve tube produces a companion cell; only the latter remains alive in the ordinary sense. Companion cells are presumed to be required in some unspecified way to make it possible for the sieve tubes to carry out their functions.

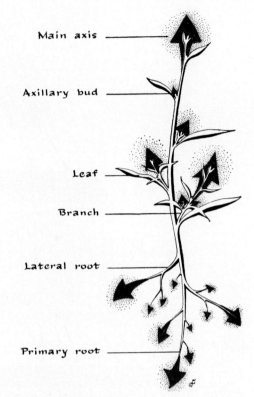

Fig. 18-18. *Growing regions of a plant. (From Foster and Gifford,* Comparative Morphology of Vascular Plants, *W. H. Freeman and Company, San Francisco and London, 1959.)*

147. The Growth of a Plant

The larger plants differ from animals in having **indeterminate growth.** There is no fixed, final adult form: growth in size continues so long as the plant is alive. Increase in the linear dimensions of a plant is brought about by an indeterminately large number of growing points or *apical regions,* indicated in Figure 18-18.

Figure 18-19 is a diagram of the terminal region of the stem of a plant. Increase in the number of cells occurs principally in the **meristematic zone** (Gr. *merizein* = to divide). A short distance back of this lies the **zone of elongation,** in which the cells increase in size, principally in length, becoming in some cases ten or more times as long as the cells in the meristem. The activity of cells in this region continuously elevates the meristematic zone, which always remains at the tip of the stem. In a typical tree all the linear growth is confined to the terminal 15 centimeters of the trunk. Below this is a **zone of differentiation and maturation,** in which the differentiation of the various types of cells, already begun in the zone of elongation, continues as the cells take on their "adult" form. In the case of many of these cells, as we have seen with the sieve tube cells, this means ultimately losing their nuclei and dying, leaving behind only the cell walls. Undoubtedly, all the cells derived from the meristematic cells by cell division (mitotic) have the same chromosomes, the same genetic make-up. The differences that develop among them must be brought about by environment, that is, by the different physical and chemical forces brought to bear on each cell by virtue of its position in the stem. We are far from understanding the processes of maturation.

The process just described leads to what is

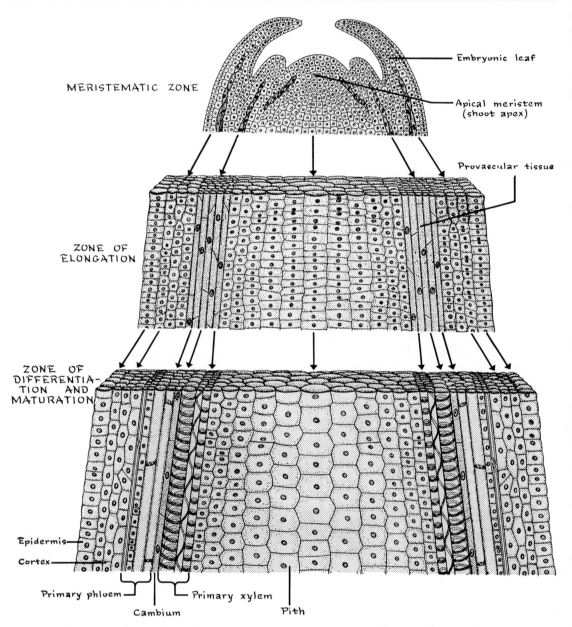

Fig. 18-19. *Zones of growth in the terminal portion of a stem. (From Wilson and Loomis,* Botany, *rev. ed., Dryden Press, New York, 1957, courtesy Holt, Rinehart, and Winston.)*

called the **primary growth** of a stem, growth that is mostly lengthening, and only slightly includes growth in thickness. At the end of this process of primary growth, there is left a meristematic tissue called **cambium,** which continues to produce new cells and in such a way as to

cause an increase in the thickness of the stem, resulting in **secondary growth.** The way this is brought about may be best appreciated by reference to Figure 18-20, which shows a cross section of a tree. The cambium layer, which lies between phloem and xylem, slowly and continuously produces more cells by cell division, the more peripheral cells becoming phloem, the more central ones becoming xylem, always leaving an intermediate layer of cells as cambium. The cross-sectional area of the xylem cells produced is greatest when the water supply is greatest. Because of this, there is a seasonal difference in the average diameter of the xylem cells, a difference easily seen in a cut tree trunk as alternate light and dark rings. The comparative favorableness of different years can be inferred from the relative thickness of the growth rings: a wet year will produce a thick ring; a year of drought, a thin one. Because of the variability of climate, the *pattern* of rings is always changing; so it is possible, by comparing different trees, definitely to identify the year when a particular ring was formed. Timbers used in the construction of dwellings at successive epochs can, by cross-comparison with others in the same region and with living trees, be accurately dated. Thus can the dates of prehistoric dwellings be de-

Fig. 18-20. *The structure of a woody stem, showing how the pattern of tree rings can be used for dating an ancient piece of wood.*

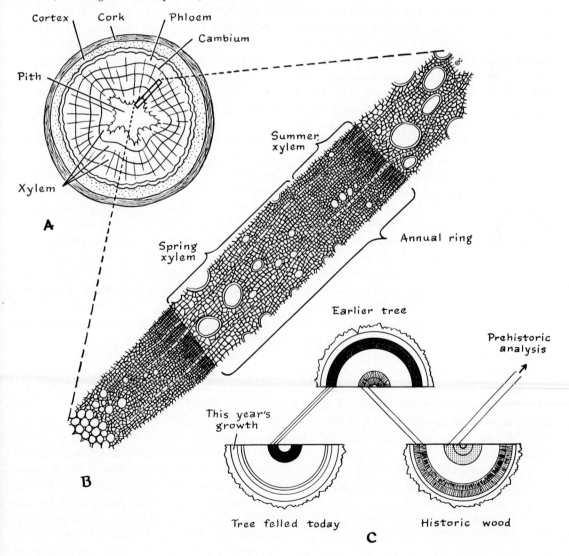

termined.* The possibility of using this botanical approach to historical and archeological problems was recognized in the early nineteenth century by three men independently: Twinning, Kuechler, and Charles Babbage (an ingenious inventor of calculating machines). But the method was not really perfected until this century, when the American astronomer A. E. Douglass became interested in it and showed how the pre-Columbian ruins of the southwestern United States could be accurately dated. Although the method has been very powerful in this region, it has its limitations. To obtain a unique pattern of rings, we need a pretty long "run" in one piece of wood—about 50 years, generally. More serious is the fact that the rings do not necessarily correspond to years, but to growth periods. We may consequently be misled when comparing trees that have been subjected to marked local variations in rainfall, groundwater supply, damage by insects, and so on. In some regions, the results of tree ring analysis are too ambiguous to be of much use.

Before leaving trees, a few words are in order about the chemical constitution of wood. Wood is about 60–75 percent **cellulose,** an insoluble carbohydrate, and 15–25 percent **lignin,** an even more insoluble organic compound(s) of unknown structure. Both substances are extremely resistant to decay—especially the latter, which tends to accumulate in the soil as part of the "humus," an ill-defined mixture of organic chemicals that are left after the more easily decayed compounds of plants and animals have been broken down. In the making of paper from the cellulose of "pulpwood" derived from poor lumber trees, the lignin is removed by dissolving it in a sodium bisulfite solution. The resulting waste is difficult to get rid of without adversely affecting the life of any streams it is dumped into. We need to find new uses for lignin.

As a tree ages, colored substances and insoluble materials are deposited in the older vessels

---

* 18-10. Suppose a certain dwelling has in it wood beams cut from three trees that lived from 1756 to 1820, from 1720 to 1820, and from 1743 to 1821, respectively. How old is the dwelling?

of the xylem, thus putting an end to their usefulness in the conduction of water. Their supportive ability is, however, thereby enhanced; and this portion of a tree, the dark central core known as **heartwood,** is stronger and less subject to decay than is the lighter, more porous **sapwood** surrounding it.

148. Tropisms and Plant Hormones

Every organism faces the problem of adjusting itself to the environment, or rather, to that mosaic of environments that makes up the world. The world is spotty. Not all places are equally suited, or even suited at all, to the existence of an organism of a given species. An animal adjusts to this situation by moving from place to place; many of the adaptations of an animal are concerned with the detection of places (sometimes at a considerable distance in space, or even in time) and with moving toward or away from them. But most plants do not have such abilities, and so must, in larger measure, be dependent on chance. Of hundreds of seeds that fall to the ground, only a few fall in a place suitable to germination and subsequent growth. During its entire life, as a plant increases in size, it is constantly growing into, or is in danger of growing into, regions of lesser suitability for its kind of life. How does a plant adjust its growth so as to make the best use of its spotty surroundings? This is the subject of the following brief introduction to an important phase of plant physiology.

When a seed falls passively to the ground, it may land in any orientation. But a seedling is a thing of predetermined structure: it has a definite root and shoot. As it develops, the seedling, by growth, corrects its initial orientation until it is growing properly, with the shoot growing up and root growing down, as shown in Figure 18-21A, B, C. Such a reaction is called a **geotropism** (Gr. *ge* = earth), the word **tropism** (Gr. *tropos* = a turning) being used for any differential growth. The root is positively geotropic; the shoot is negatively geotropic. Other tropisms exhibited by plants are **phototropism,**

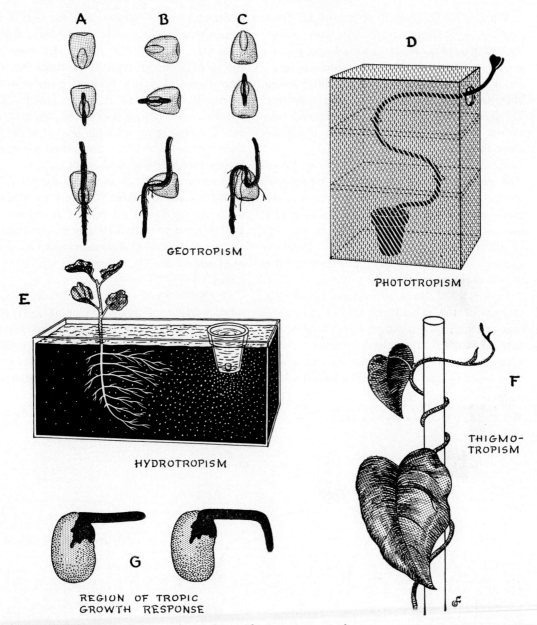

A   B   C

GEOTROPISM

D

PHOTOTROPISM

E

HYDROTROPISM

F

THIGMO-
TROPISM

G

REGION OF TROPIC
GROWTH RESPONSE

Fig. 18-21. *The principal tropisms (directed growth responses) of plants.*

the reaction to light; various **chemotropisms;** and **thigmotropism,** the reaction to contact exhibited by the climbing organs of some plants. The existence of such tropisms was known more or less unconsciously for probably hundreds of years, but scientific observation and investigation of them was initiated by Charles Darwin in the closing years of his life, aided by his son Francis. It is a strange fact in the history of science that the investigations initiated by this great and respected scientist were not followed up for almost 30 years, at which time the Dane Boysen Jensen (beginning in 1910) and the Hollander Frits Went (beginning in 1928), with the aid of many other physiologists, unraveled the mechanism of tropistic response and showed how it explains many of the phenomena of plant growth.

What is the mechanism of a tropism? If the root of a seedling is marked with equally spaced lines (Fig. 18-21*G*), it is found that the region in which the adaptive curvature occurs is the most actively growing region. Other studies show that such adaptive curvature results from the *differential growth* of cells on opposite sides of the plant, the cells on one side elongating more than the cells on the other side.

What makes the cells grow longer or faster? This problem can best be attacked by studying the more general problem of the causes of any plant growth. The greatest light has been shed on this problem by studies of the growing tips of oat seedlings, the *coleoptiles* (Gr. *koleos* = sheath), so named because the primary leaf is at first enclosed in a sheath.

Figure 18-22 shows, in a simplified way, the essence of the experiment that demonstrates that one part of a plant produces a substance that can stimulate the growth of another. If the tip of an oat coleoptile is removed and placed on a block of agar (a gelatinlike material from

seaweeds), there diffuses into the agar a substance that can stimulate growth in a decapitated oat coleoptile. A decapitated coleoptile will not grow otherwise. A control block of agar, which has not been in contact with a coleoptile tip, will not stimulate growth. Since the effective chemical substances diffuse to, and affect, tissues other than the ones that produce them, these substances are called **plant hormones** (Gr. *hormao* = to excite).

Hormones that can stimulate the *growth* of plants are called **auxins** (Gr. *auxe* = a growth or increase). Having established the existence of auxins, we next ask: How can these substances explain the differential growth observed in tropistic responses? The following experiment gives a clue.

If, on the tip of a decapitated coleoptile, we place a piece of auxin-containing agar (Fig. 18-23*A*), *being careful to place it asymmetrically,* the subsequent growth of the coleoptile is also asymmetric, being the greatest on the side overlain by the agar. Evidently, the auxins pass,

Fig. 18-22. *Demonstration of a diffusible growth-promoting substance in the tips of oat coleoptiles.*

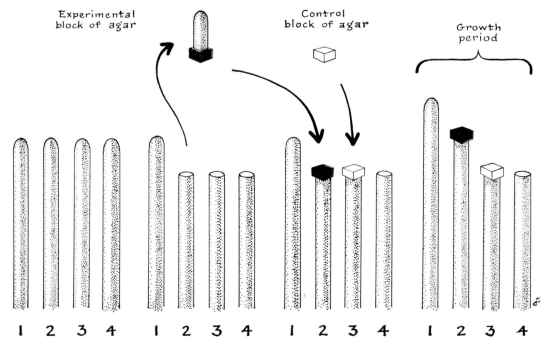

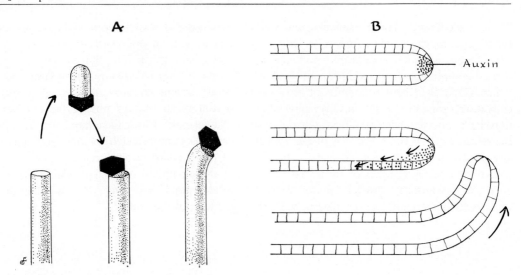

Fig. 18-23. *Differential growth of a decapitated coleoptile* (A) *brought about by asymmetrical application of auxin.*

for the most part, straight downward, giving the greatest stimulation to the cells that are directly beneath the source of the auxin.

Can we now explain tropistic growth? Figure 18-23B shows an attempt to do so. A coleoptile normally grows vertically. If one is placed in a horizontal position, it presently shows the usual differential growth and heads upward again. It is believed that this effect results from the differential translocation of auxin from the producing tip to the cells on the lower side of the prostrate shoot. Various other tropisms can be explained in similar fashion, though it is not always clear that the necessary differential translocation of auxins does, in fact, occur.

Before leaving the subject of auxins, it would be well to point out some of the practical benefits that have resulted from research of the sort just described. In the search for substances that affect growth, a number of chemicals have been found that either inhibit or stimulate plant tissues. Some of these substances are natural plant products; others are products of the chemist's art. One of the best known of the latter is one that bears the grandiloquent name of *2,4-dichlorophenoxyacetic acid,* mercifully shortened to **2,4-D.** In tiny quantities, this substance stimulates respiration and growth. In larger quan-

tities, it stimulates respiration to such an extent that the plant burns itself out, so to speak, and dies. Broad-leaved plants are more sensitive to this effect than are narrow-leaved plants, such as the grasses. It is, therefore, possible to spray a lawn with the proper concentration of 2,4-D and kill dandelions, plantain, and many other broad-leaved weeds without injuring the grass.

Numerous other uses have been found for this and other natural or synthetic auxins. With them, plant cuttings can often be induced to form roots. Such treatment has proven particularly valuable in the propagation of apple and pine trees, species that can be rooted only with difficulty under natural conditions. The ripening of many fruits, for example, bananas, pears, apples, and pineapples, can be hastened by auxins. For the last named, the successive use of an auxin on different parts of a field has made it possible to extend the harvesting period of pineapples over a longer time, thus easing the pressure on harvesting facilities.

In recent years a new class of plant growth stimulaters—the **gibberellins**—has been turned up by Japanese researchers. For many generations, rice growers had observed that their seedlings would sometimes show the most fantastic elongated growth forms; these were called "foolish seedlings." The causative agent was a fungus, given the name *Gibberella fujikuroi*. This fungus secretes a mixture of chemically related compounds, now called the gibberellins, which cause spectacular activity of the plant cells in the zone of elongation. How physiology may be connected with genetics appears from the recent work of B. O. Phinney of the University of California at Los Angeles, who has shown that some genetically dwarf strains of corn can be caused to grow normally by treatment with gibberellins. This suggests that gib-

berellins (or something like them) are normal constituents of nondwarf strains—a suggestion that is strengthened by the observation that extracts of normal plants can cause the same dwarf strains to grow to normal height. But that a given unitary phenotypic characteristic ("dwarfness") may have more than one genetic cause is demonstrated by the fact that only 5 of the 9 dwarf strains tested reacted favorably to the gibberellin treatment. This general theoretical point was made before, in a different context, at the end of §79.

Questions and Problems

18-11. Make a list of the **boldface** terms in this chapter and write a brief description of each. Compare your work with the text.

18-12. Give the approximate date and the contributions of each of the following men: Dixon and Joly, Douglass, Jensen, Paley, Theophrastus, and Darwin.

‡18-13. In very general terms, which are better suited for experiments designed to analyze the interactions of heredity and environment—mammals or flowering plants? Explain the genetic principles involved.

18-14. Strains of mammals that are most valuable in animal husbandry possess little genetic heterozygosity. By contrast, most of the horticulturally valuable strains of fruit trees are highly heterozygous. Why the difference?

‡18-15. What will be the genetic and evolutionary consequences if a flowering plant relies exclusively on vegetative means for its reproduction?

‡18-16. You are holding a garlic plant in your hand. How old is it? (What is the methodological problem in determining its age?)

18-17. "This oak tree had the beginning of its life 125 years ago." In what sense might one find fault with this statement?

‡18-18. What do you think of the legend of Johnny Appleseed?

18-19. Two identical "flats" of tomato plants in

rather dry soil are taken the same distance over a very rough road and then transplanted. Flat *A* is carried in a car with excellent springs; flat *B* travels in a truck with hard tires and broken springs. The day after transplanting, it is noticed that the plants from flat *B* are much more wilted than those from *A*. Why? How might this have been prevented?

‡18-20. It was stated in the text that life is necessary for the functioning of the sieve tubes, the evidence being the effect of a steam collar on a plant. Suggest another possible explanation based merely on the general effect of heat on dead proteinaceous material, such as eggwhite.

18-21. Leonardo da Vinci observed that he could tell the north-south orientation of a tree trunk from the rings. How did he do it?

‡18-22. Study of the cliff dwellings of Mesa Verde, Colorado, has led to the discovery that this region suffered a severe drought from 1276 to 1299 A.D. What sort of evidence established this?

18-23. Some water-dwelling flowering plants have stomates on the upper surface of their leaves, but not on the lower. Why?

‡18-24. Following transplantation, it is desirable to remove an appreciable fraction of the leaves of a plant. Why?

18-25. Why is it possible to sow seeds with no regard to "right-side-upness"?

Scientific American Offprints

107. W. L. Butler and Robert J. Downs. *Light and Plant Development*

110. Frank B. Salisbury. *Plant Growth Substances*

112. Frank B. Salisbury. *The Flowering Process*

113. Aubrey W. Naylor. *The Control of Flowering*

117. Dov Koller. *Germination*

118. J. B. Biale. *The Ripening of Fruit*

154. Martin H. Zimmermann. *How Sap Moves in Trees*

167. F. C. Steward. *The Control of Growth in Plant Cells*

19

Plants in the Biosphere

149. Coevolution of Insects and Angiosperms

Wind pollination is the rule in gymnosperms. Among the Angiospermae, however, there is a great variety of methods of getting the pollen from the male inflorescences to the female. Some flowering plants are wind pollinated; and some are pollinated by birds, bats, or snails; but the great majority are pollinated by insects. Speaking broadly, the Angiospermae, as a group, depend on the Insecta. Geologically, these two classes had their beginning at approximately the same time, the first big spurt of evolution taking place in the Mesozoic era. They have evolved together, many of the adaptations of the members of one class having a clear relevance to adaptations of members of the other. We have seen how plant flowers are modified to obtain the services of pollinating animals. Animals, in turn, frequently show complicated and beautiful adaptations that benefit the plant. The hairiness of the body of a bee, for instance, increases greatly its efficiency in picking up pollen from the plants that it visits, and thus makes more probable the transfer of pollen from flower to flower. In the behavioral realm also, bees show many nice adjustments to the needs of flowers. For instance, at the beginning of each day, the bees of one hive select a single species of flower to visit. Should the supply of nectar-producing flowers of that species

be exhausted before the end of the day, the bees will stop work rather than start visiting another species of flower the same day. The next day they will select another species of flower. It is not easy to perceive the utility of such a habit to the bees, but the advantage to flowers is clear; it makes more probable the transfer of pollen from flower to flower within the species, rather than the useless transfer of pollen between species.

The dependence of many flowers on insect pollination has sometimes complicated man's affairs. When settlers first took red clover into Australia, it failed to set seed, and, consequently, the immigrants were for a while dependent on other countries for their red-clover seed. Presently, the Australians imported bumblebees to pollinate their own clover. Similarly, the Smyrna fig depends on certain wasps for its fertilization. When Smyrna fig trees were first brought to the United States, the wasp was brought also, to insure fertilization and the setting of fruit.

In talking of evolution, we frequently use such phrases as "the evolution of man" and "the evolution of the horse," from which one might infer that each organism evolves in a vacuum, or in a world in which it is the only living thing. The preceding examples show the falseness of such an inference. The following example illustrates the point even more clearly.

There is, in the southwestern part of the

United States, a flowering plant named *Yucca filamentosa,* which can be fertilized by but a single species of moth, *Pronuba yuccasella.* The moth gathers pollen from a flower by means of highly specialized mouth parts, shapes the pollen into a ball, and then flies to another flower. There she thrusts her sawlike ovipositor into the ovary of the flower, lays an egg or two therein, and then pushes the pollen pellet down the style of the flower. The larvae that develop eat some, but not all, of the seeds produced by the plant. The adult moth, by pollinating the flower, makes seeds possible. The larval moth, by not eating all of the seeds, makes the continuation of the yucca species possible. The *yucca* is completely dependent on the *Pronuba* for its continued existence, and the moth is completely dependent on the *Yucca* for its continued existence. Were one to die, the other, perforce, would perish. This extreme instance of the interdependence of two species emphasizes the truth of a saying of Pope Sixtus V: "He that has partners has masters."

150. Mycorrhizas and Truffles

Man loves to organize and classify, but nature continually makes a shambles of his systems. It is convenient, in organizing a biology text, to put the algae in one chapter, the fungi in another, and the flowering plants in still another. But the facts do not compartmentalize themselves so neatly. We have seen before how certain species of algae and fungi associate themselves into a new "organism," a lichen, which is as logically (or illogically) considered with the algae as with the fungi. We will now look at another association, that of fungi with flowering plants.

If a survey were made of the mushrooms, it would surely be found that more mushrooms grow under trees than out in the open. Why? Partly no doubt because many mushrooms are easily damaged by drying, and the shade of a tree gives protection. But this is not the whole story. If the ramifications of the underground mycelium are followed (no easy task!), it will

often be found that they lead to a network of hyphae surrounding the roots of a tree. Hyphae may even penetrate the roots. What is the relationship of the two? One first suspects that the fungus is a parasite, or at any rate a saprophyte of the tree. This may be partly true, but it is not always the whole truth. Studies have shown that many species of trees do but poorly without their symbiotic fungi, particularly in poor, sandy soil. A conifer tree will often have 90 percent of its roots covered with hyphae, and at the same time be lacking root hairs. This suggests that the hyphae have taken over the absorptive functions of the root hairs. The association of fungal mycelium and plant root is called a **mycorrhiza,** that is, "fungus root." That mycorrhizas are of benefit to countless numbers of plants, particularly conifers and orchids, there is now no doubt.

Among the most interesting of the mycorrhizal species are the ones that produce the underground mushrooms called **truffles.** It might be thought that an underground fruiting body is poorly adapted to disseminating the species, but truffles are clever: they smell. Their odor and taste are attractive to many animals (including man). Some animals can locate underground truffles by smell, dig them up, and then eat them. Many of the spores pass through the intestine unharmed and are geographically dispersed when the animal defecates. Much as man loves truffles, he is poorly equipped for finding them and must enlist the aid of other species. Let the mycologist Clyde M. Christensen tell us how he does this:

Truffles have been hunted with dogs and even, so it is claimed, with goats, but the French professionals prefer pigs. In the first place, any pig has a strong inherent craving for the flavor of a good truffle and hankers after them as much as we do. Second, a pig has a keen sense of smell and can readily locate any truffle within range, needing no training to distinguish a truffle from a rabbit. In addition, a pig does not merely point at the truffle, but sets to and roots it up. The last but not least reason why the frugal Frenchman favors a pig for this delicate work is that when the animal's hunting days are over she can be served up on the table garnished with the very truffles she helped find.

The procedure of hunting truffles is about as follows: On a quiet evening of the truffle season, when the scent is likely to be most heavy and not blown about, the pig is taken under the arm or carried in a wheelbarrow to the wood where experience has shown the hunting to be good. The pig is carried or wheeled so that she may not get too tired—a good truffle-hunting pig is a wage earner and an artist, and is treated as such. Once in the woods, a rope is put around her neck, and she is given her head. When she smells a truffle she starts to root it out. She is pulled up, tied, and the hunter digs out the truffle, rewarding the pig with an acorn or some special titbit. This continues until both partners are tired or the evening's quota has been gathered.

The whole business sounds a bit fantastic, but almost the only fantastic thing connected with it is the price of the truffles. They are one of the most highly priced vegetables on the market, and have been for centuries. Many a landowner in southern France has used truffles as a good cash crop year in and year out. They have been cultivated in southern France for decades, but it is not an ordinary sort of cultivation. Oak or beech trees first are planted and, after they are established, pieces of truffle are scattered on the soil and covered. The first harvest comes after from six to ten years, and an annual crop can be gathered thereafter for two decades or more.*

151. Plant Dispersal

The methods whereby most plant seeds become geographically dispersed are a bit less exotic than that used by truffles in disseminating their spores. The ways in which dispersal is accomplished are at least as various as the solutions to the pollination problem, and involve the same principal agents—wind and animals. The seeds of many plants are enclosed by tissues with hairy extensions that provide buoyancy in the air, enabling the seeds to be carried long distances by comparatively feeble winds. Such adaptations are exhibited by dandelions, salsify,

and clematis. Another spectacular form of wind dispersal is shown by the tumbleweed, which inhabits open plains regions where there are strong winds. When the seeds mature, the whole plant breaks off at the base of the stem, and then, wind-driven, blows end-over-end across the plains, scattering seeds as it goes. Other plants have adaptations for throwing seeds to some distance. The seed pods of legumes, when dry, curl and expel the seeds forcibly. The seeds of many plants are enclosed by tissues that are esteemed as food by various animals. Such, for instance, are the plant structures popularly known as "berries." When a berry is eaten by a bird, seeds may pass through the intestinal tract unharmed and be deposited in the bird dung many miles from the parent plant, there to germinate. Plants exploit, so to speak, animals as carriers of seed also by producing seed cases with hooks that can attach to animal fur, for example, cockleburs, Spanish needles, beggar-ticks, and unicorn plant. Some of these adaptations are shown in Figure 19-1.

The problem of modifying the natural mechanisms for dispersal of seed has often been one of the major problems in the domestication of plants. It is usually to the interest of a plant (under natural conditions) to shed its seed. The "heads" of grasses, for instance, naturally shatter; but such shattering is contrary to the interest of man when he wants to harvest the seed for his own use. Probably much of the early progress in the domestication of wheat, rye, barley, and so on, was concerned with the selection of non-shattering grains.† In the environment of these early plants, man constituted a new environmental factor selecting for a factor (nonshattering) that had earlier been selected against. Progress was probably slow because so important a characteristic as shattering had probably come to be caused and ensured by many genes (as a sort of safety factor). As evidence of this, we have our recent experience in developing a new domestic crop, the sweet lupine. As in other lupines (see beans in Fig. 19-1), the seeds are naturally thrown out by a

* *The Molds and Man*. Minneapolis: University of Minnesota Press (1951), pp. 57–58. By permission of the publisher.

† 19-1. Did this selection have to be conscious selection?

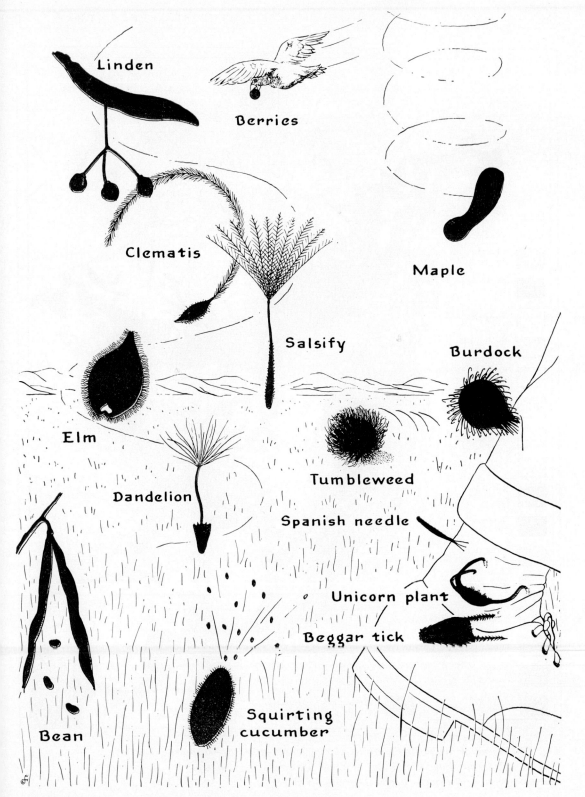

Fig. 19-1. *A few of the many methods of seed dispersal.*

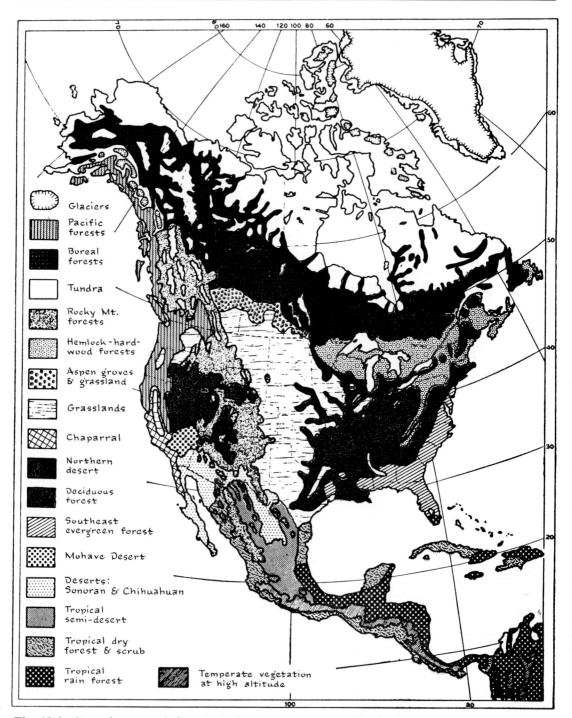

Fig. 19-2. *General ranges of the principal vegetation types of North America.* (*After Transeau; from Oosting,* The Study of Plant Communities, *2nd. ed., W. H. Freeman and Company, San Francisco and London, 1956.*)

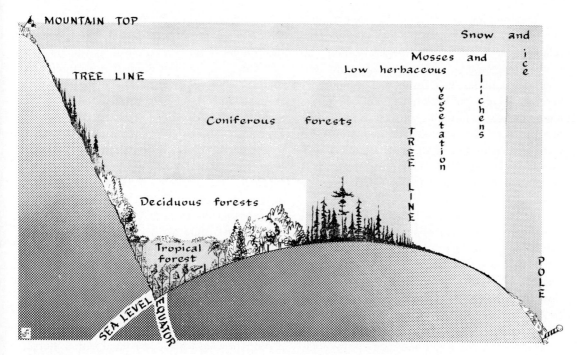

Fig. 19-3. *Parallelism in sequence of life zones produced by altitude and latitude. (After Wolcott; from Allee et al.,* Principles of Animal Ecology, *W. B. Saunders Co., Philadelphia, 1949.)*

curling and splitting of the dry pod. Finding a single plant that did not have this (humanly) objectionable characteristic required an examination of some 10 million different individuals.

The dispersal of species in time as well as space is made possible by the survival of seeds for long periods of time. The food supply of a seed is limited, but its metabolism proceeds at a very low level and so makes only slight demands on the supply. Some very small seeds can survive for less than a year (onion seed, for example); larger seeds can, in general, survive longer. Stories of the sprouting of wheat seeds taken from the tombs of ancient Egypt are false; careful observation shows that these seeds are contemporary ones slipped in by the profit-seeking guides. Cereal seeds in general have a life expectation of less than ten years. The large seeds of the water lily or sacred lotus (*Nelumbo nucifera*) are, however, spectacularly long-lived. Robert Brown, in 1850, succeeded in germinating some from a reliably dated collection 150 years old. Recently seeds

of the same species from an old Manchurian lake bed were successfully germinated. The geological evidence indicated an age of 50,000 years. However, carbon-14 determinations indicated an age of only 1040 ± 200 years, which must be taken as the more reliable figure. A thousand years of quiescent life is still pretty impressive—in a quiet sort of way.

152. Climate and Communities

That the natural landscape of a region is to a considerable extent determined by climate is well known. The dominant plants vary from region to region in objectively specifiable ways. Plant ecologists, speaking of "vegetation types," have mapped their distribution in North America, as shown in Figure 19-2.

Much of the relationship of vegetation type to region is determined by the temperature of the region. Part of this correlation is for direct reasons, and part for indirect reasons: humidity and precipitation are affected by temperature, and insolation* is also, for obvious reasons, correlated with it. As a *broad* generalization (no more), temperature varies inversely with altitude and latitude. As a result, the sequence of vegetation types encountered as one ascends a mountain at one latitude is also to be found as one keeps at the same altitude and moves toward a pole of the earth. This parallelism is shown in Figure 19-3. The area in which a given vegetation type is found is called a **life zone.**

Different life zones are, in part, characterized by different species of plants. There are some species (and even more genera) of plants that extend over many life zones. Even when a single species can occupy more than one life zone, close analysis reveals genetic differences between members of the same species in different zones, as was pointed out in §79. The differences involve many genes and many physiological characteristics. One of the most thoroughly studied of these is the relationship of flowering time to length of day, the study of which was initiated by W. W. Garner and H. A. Allard in 1920.

It is possible to alter the time of flowering by altering the ratio of hours of light to hours of darkness. Some plants are **short-day plants** and are brought to flowering by *decreasing* the amount of light received daily: such are poinsettias, asters, and dahlias. Under normal conditions, short-day plants flower in late summer or in the autumn. If, however, when they are mature, their days are "stretched" by using artificial illumination at the close of the normal day, the plants are prevented from flowering for some time, in some cases indefinitely. Other species of angiosperms are **long-day plants:** such are lettuce, corn, wheat, and gladioli. These plants usually flower in the spring or early summer; but if, by artificial shading, the daylight period is kept from increasing, the flowering of a mature plant may be prevented. Still other plants are **indeterminate,** for example, sunflower, tomato, dandelion, and cotton.

---

* 19-2. If you don't read this word carefully, you'll get off on the wrong track. What does it mean?

The mechanism whereby the amount of illumination causes or prevents flower formation has not yet been worked out in satisfactory detail, but there are indications that hormones are involved. **Photoperiodism** may affect plant phenomena other than flowering: tuber formation in Irish potatoes and Jerusalem artichokes is favored by short days. Since such tubers grow by the deposition of carbohydrates in them, and since carbohydrates are the product of photosynthesis, the swelling of tubers during short days may seem at first a little surprising. It appears that the carbohydrates deposited in the tubers at the time of their most rapid swelling are derived from carbohydrates that had, until then, been stored in the above-ground portions of the plant.

The photoperiodic characteristics of a strain of plants are due to inheritable genes. Garner and Allard first discovered the phenomenon of photoperiodism when confronted with a mutant strain of tobacco that failed to flower at the time normal for this species. Within a species there are frequently many strains with respect to photoperiodic response. Particularly is this true of species that occur over a wide geographical range. It is probably not possible for a wild species to live in different habitats unless it undergoes genetic differentiation into different *varieties* (§80). Since the varieties necessarily have different ecologies, they are often called **ecotypes.**

The principle of ecotype formation has its equivalent in the development of agricultural plants. A breed of corn selected because it does well in Minnesota can hardly be expected to flourish in Tennessee. When, by selective breeding, a strain is developed that does unusually well in one environment, its success is due to its particular reaction to the temperature, light, and other environmental factors of that environmental habitat. Such fine adaptation is almost always accompanied by limited adaptability to other environments. This is one of the reasons why every state or province needs to have its own agricultural experiment station to develop breeds suited to its own environmental conditions. Indeed, unless a state is quite small and uniform in its climate, the central scientific administration must maintain experimental plots at more than one locality.

Light is one great environmental factor for plants; water is another. Problems of collection, transport, and conservation of water are markedly different in the various life zones. With respect to the wateriness of the habitats in which they flourish, plants may be divided into three ecological classes: hydrophytes, mesophytes, and xerophytes. **Hydrophytes** live in a watery environment: water lilies and water hyacinth are examples. For such plants the collection, transport, and conservation of water are not problems at all. **Mesophytes** are land-dwelling forms that live in a moderately moist environment: this class includes most of the angiosperms. **Xerophytes** (Gr. *xeros* = dry) live in a dry environment: cactuses and yuccas are examples. Xerophytes show many structural adaptations to their environment: heavy cutinization of the leaves and stem; reduction in the number of stomates per unit surface; stomates sunk in pits in the leaves; thick stems or leaves that serve to store water; and reduction in the total amount of leaf surface. Some xerophytes drop their leaves after the rainy season is over, and during the hot dry summer go into a period of inactivity comparable to the winter inactivity of temperate-zone mesophytes. In addition to the structural adaptations mentioned above, the xerophytes undoubtedly have many physiological adaptations, the nature of which is more obscure. The physiological adaptations required of a plant that gets along with little water are shown also by an ecological class of plants called **halophytes,** plants that are capable of living in very salty soils (Gr. *halos* = sea). Such soils, even when they contain much water (e.g., salt-water marshes), are *physiologically dry,* because of the high osmotic potential of the soil water.

153. Organisms Make Environments

The statements of every science involve certain terms that we call "elementary." In biology,

two of these are certainly "organism" and "environment." We elect to use these words because the meaning of them seems self-evident— as it is, at first. But we will find, as we go more and more deeply into the study of biology, that the exact delimitations of the terms become less and less clear. Thus it is with the "elementary" terms of every science.

We first think of the environment as something *given,* as something external to the organism to which the organism must adapt itself, as something which *molds* the organism, as it were. But organisms also mold the environment. We have already seen (§125) how a microorganism can poison itself out of house and home, creating a new environment in which some other microbe can live better. The result of this sort of process is what we call an ecological succession of niches and organisms.

Landscapes have an embryology, based on many such ecological successions. Every freshwater pond or lake is, geologically speaking, only a temporary entity. The inflow of sediments tends to fill it up; the breaking down of its margins tends to convert it into a stream. But in addition to these geological processes, there are biological ones (study Fig. 19-4). As the hydrophytic plants (rushes, sedges, sphagnum moss) extend inward from the margin of a northern pond, they create, by degrees, solid ground, which is increasingly less suitable to their own kind and more suitable to mesophytes. Thus ecological succession takes place. The details of the process of pond destruction vary with the amount of drainage and sedimentation, as well as with the climate, but some sort of ecological succession occurs everywhere.

Rushes and sedges give way to sphagnum, and the latter yields to hydrophytic trees, which in turn are replaced by mesophytic trees. Is there no end to this process? As a matter of fact, there is. In each habitat there is a particular association of plants that finally develops and that seems to be stable—at least over long periods of time, as human history is reckoned. For example, in much of the east central part of the United States, there is a specifiable community of plants called an oak-hickory **climax,**

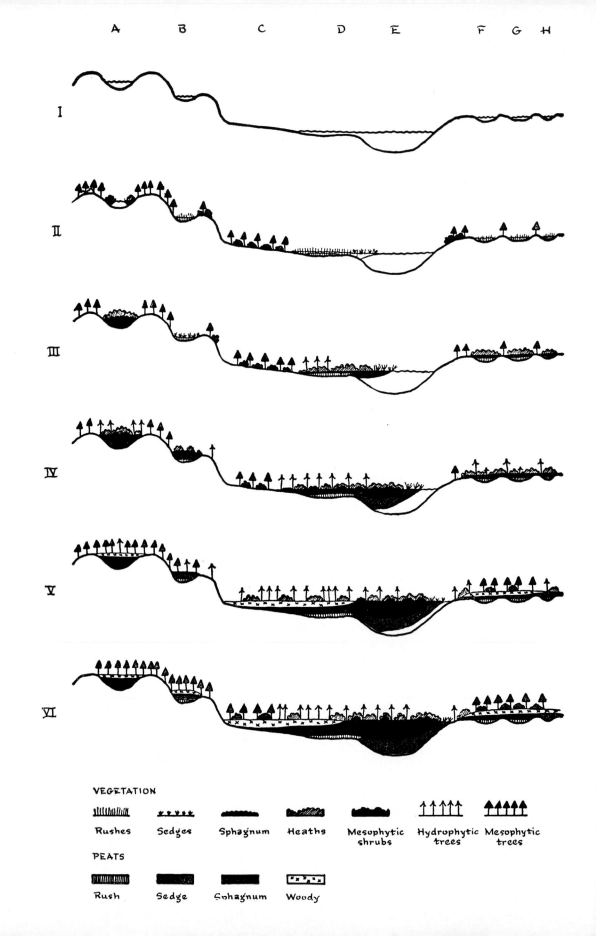

A   B   C   D   E   F G H

I

II

III

IV

V

VI

VEGETATION

Rushes   Sedges   Sphagnum   Heaths   Mesophytic   Hydrophytic   Mesophytic
                                           shrubs   trees   trees

PEATS

Rush   Sedge   Sphagnum   Woody

which terminates an ecological succession. A climax is named after its most obvious plant members, but of course with these are associated many other plants, as well as animals.

Organisms not only create a *series* of environments in the manner just described, they also cause a multiplication of environments. A canopy of trees creates a multitude of environments beneath it—environments that differ with respect to light, humidity, air movement, and presence of decaying organic matter. (Figure 19-5 will remind you of the variety, if you have ever experienced it; if you have not, it may well be meaningless to you.) W. C. Allee has shown that a tropical rain forest includes at least seven different major environments, from the treetops down to the forest floor. Each level, or "story," has its characteristic set of plants and animals, and some of the organisms at one level have as little direct contact with organisms at another as if they lived on different continents.

There is no general theory to give a quantitative relationship between organisms and the number of environments created, but there are a few general statements that can be made. For one thing, the number of ecological niches seems to increase with successive stages of an ecological succession; correspondingly, the number of different kinds of organisms tends to increase. The climax stage usually shows the greatest variety—a point not without aesthetic significance. Also, the amount of variety increases as the physical conditions become more favorable to life. Arctic tundra is a simple, relatively impoverished vegetational type, as compared with a tropical rain forest, which is as complex as an elaborate symphony. Coupled with this natural complexity there is, as we pointed out in §102, greater stability. Epidemic fluctuations in numbers—whether of hosts, predators, or parasites—characterize simple environments.

The climax formation is not always the most interesting or significant ecological community; sometimes it is a **sub-climax** that is most desired by man. An example in point is the sequoia forests (*Sequoiadendron giganteum*) of the Sierra Nevada of California. The magnificent open vista of these great trees that met the eyes of the first white settlers was a sub-climax stage of development. The first grove was put under national protection in 1864. The trees have since then been protected not only from lumbermen but also from fire. In the century that has elapsed various smaller species like white fir and incense cedar have grown up and spoiled the view of the big trees, as is shown by photographs taken at identical sites over a period of years. The smaller trees certainly must compete with the sequoias for water; the ultimate effect of this competition is not known.

Studies of tree rings show that, before white men came, there was a fire in these forests on the average of once every eight years, dating back at least to 450 B.C. Many of the more recent fires are known to have been started by Indians; others were undoubtedly set by lightening. These fires were mostly ground fires, each of which destroyed the fir, cedar, and other low-growing plants that had sprouted since the last fire, leaving the lofty sequoias largely undamaged. Thus it was that the first white settlers had a clear view of these great trees.

The present growth of fir and cedar not only obscures the view but it also emperils the sequoias. The plant community is now much more vulnerable to fire. One uncontrolled blaze, fed by a century's accumulation of tinder, may produce a "crown fire" that will destroy countless giants that would have survived a normal ground fire.

Systems of this sort create a peculiar kind of problem in the application of scientific knowledge to human affairs. For decades, publicists

Fig. 19-4. *Probable evolution of bogs in northeastern North America. (A, B, F, G, H) Evolution under condition of closed drainage. The conditions shown in C, D, and E are more applicable when there is more seepage, water movement, or wind action. (After Dansereau and Segadas-Vianna; from Oosting,* The Study of Plant Communities, *2nd. ed., W. H. Freeman and Company, San Francisco and London, 1956.)*

Fig. 19-5. *Organisms create environments. Trees, by their growth, create a complex of environments beneath them. (Courtesy U.S. Forest Service.)*

have labored to create in the general public an appreciation of the importance of protecting our forests from fire. The most effective propaganda has no doubt been that with a simple emotional appeal, not too cluttered up with rational arguments—consider, for example, the appeal of the lovable "Smokey the Bear." Now we know that in *some* situations (the sequoia forests are not unique) it would be better to have frequent, controlled forest fires. But how would the public react to the sight of its forest rangers setting fires? How are we to get across the message that sometimes deliberately incurred waste and destruction are good? It is comparatively easy to get across the message *"Thou shalt not set fires;"* it is much more difficult to create an enthusiasm for a directive that says "Thou shalt not set fires *except under certain circumstances which experts only are capable of determining."* This sort of problem has yet to be solved.

154. The Soil and Its Vicissitudes

Soil is an undefinable material, though "we all know what we mean" by the term. It is composed of a variable mixture of minerals, rock particles, clay, and animal and plant tissues in various stages of decomposition. One of its most important characteristics is its texture. Good soil is loose and spongy, not compacted like clay, which is not soil. What is properly called soil is only a thin layer in most parts of the world, underlain by *subsoil* (usually clay) and rocks. In the United States, the average thickness of the soil layer is about 18 centimeters.

Soil is formed by a complex of processes, both physical and biological. The first stages in its formation are predominantly physical: rocks are oxidized and cracked apart by freezing water, and otherwise *weathered*. Soon, however, living organisms enter into the process. Lichens (§132) play an important role in decomposing rocks, as do the roots of plants as they follow cracks, "seeking" water and breaking apart the rocks by their expansive growth. In later stages, both plant roots and burrowing animals (e.g., earth-worms) are important in producing the granular, friable texture so characteristic of good soil.

Plant roots are the most important agent in preserving the soil that they themselves need. The microscopically fine network of roots holds the soil together in the face of the erosive forces of wind and water. The above-ground portion of the plant also helps in this process by tempering the force of both wind and water. Careful measurements of actual erosion of soil protected by various plants has yielded the results shown in Table 19-1. Note that whereas the

TABLE 19-1 *The Calculated Time Required to Remove 18 Centimeters of Topsoil from an Erodible Soil in the Southern Appalachian Region. Slope: 10 Percent. (From Bennett, 1947.)*

TYPE OF GROUND COVER	YEARS TO COMPLETE EROSION OF SOIL
Virgin forest	575,000
Grass	82,150
Rotation cropping	110
Cotton	46
Bare ground	18

complete removal of 18 cm of soil in a virgin forest would take about one half million years, the same amount of unprotected soil would be removed in a mere 18 years, under the conditions studied. Soil formation (the rate of which is not easy to measure) would surely proceed fast enough to replace the losses in a virgin forest, but not (as we well know) fast enough to keep soil on bare ground. The results of just 26 years of erosion are dramatically shown in Figure 19-6.

There is another way to look at the soil problem; namely, in terms of what happens to the inorganic elements that are essential for plant and animal life—phosphorus, magnesium, iron, and so on. The chemist Justus von Liebig

(1803–1873) was the first to turn our thoughts to this problem, in the 1840's. Under "primitive" conditions, when agriculture was practiced little or not at all, the nutrient elements underwent a *cycling* process of the sort shown in Figure 19-7A. Plants took up magnesium, iron, phosphorus, and so on, all of which were eventually returned to the soil when decay processes worked on: (a) the plants, (b) the non-human animals that ate the plants, or (c) the humans who ate either of the preceding. Every act of defecation by man or other animals returned elements to the soil. Streams, protected from soil erosion by plants growing to their very margin, were clear and supported an abundance of fish feeding on their plant life. The wind blew then as now, but it could pick up little dust from the vegetated ground.

Such "primitive" conditions still exist many places, but "progress" is rapidly eliminating them, producing the situation illustrated in Figure 19-7B, in which the elements are not so much cycled as *stripped* from the soil. Civilized man no longer deposits his feces on the ground, but dumps them in rivers, which carry their precious elements out to sea to accumulate there, far from the land plants. Excessive and unwise farming bares the land to erosion, thus furthering the stripping process. Winds periodically pick up millions of tons of dirt and carry them out to sea. "Clean farming," carried to the very brink of the streams, results in a muddying of the streams and a decline in plant and animal life living therein. Floods are consequently more frequent and more damaging to man's property (Fig. 19-8). The **siltation** of the lakes behind dams destroys the value of these structures as a means of both holding water and generating hydroelectric power. Figure 19-9 shows two views of a dammed pond, the lower photograph having been taken only a few years after the upper. The total useful life of this body of water was only 14 years. This is an exceptionally short life, but the useful life of most dams is probably much shorter than most taxpayers realize.

The principal effect of civilized practices to date has been to substitute stripping for cycling

Fig. 19-6. *Twenty-six years before this photograph was taken, this gulch did not exist. Improper farming or over-pasturing, by reducing the network of roots holding the soil, can start a runaway process of erosion. (Courtesy U.S. Soil Conservation Service.)*

of the elements, to the cumulative impoverishment of the soil. The remedies are various, but they all amount to the same thing: a reinstitution of cycling, while retaining as many of the advantages of civilized living as possible. Because of the seriousness of feces-borne disease, we do not contemplate returning our raw sewage to the land in the old way, but sewage-treatment plants produce solids that are safe and valuable as fertilizer, as well as effluent waters that are safe both for drinking and agriculture and need not be wasted by being dumped into the rivers. Erosion can be mini-

mized by many procedures, among which **contour farming** (Fig. 19-10) is prominent. In one experiment, planting cotton in contoured rows interspersed with vetch (a good soil holder) decreased soil losses by 96 percent over an uncontoured, pure cotton stand. Among the difficulties in the way of more contour farming is a sociological one. The contours of the land do not respect property lines; hence, good contour farming can often be achieved only through coercing or (more desirably) persuading individual landholders. Traditional beliefs about the sanctity of private property need to be sig-

Fig. 19-7. *The change from A to B is one of the unsolved problems created by "progress."*

Fig. 19-8. *One flood was enough to half bury this farmhouse under silt washed down from improperly farmed lands upstream. (Courtesy U.S. Conservation Service.)*

nificantly modified to take greater account of community interests, in which each individual shares.

Cycling is also reinstituted by fertilizing the soil. For example, crushed phosphate rock (from deposits laid down by the oceans millions of years ago) can be added to soils deficient in phosphorus. In a similar way, farmers in Ireland add potash (potassium) to their soil by spreading freshly gathered seaweeds on them. In some cases, fertilizing may not be a way of completing a cycle, but rather a matter of making up for a deficiency of the region. Some Florida soils are low in copper, and some Australian ones deficient in cobalt, though the error in the latter instance does more harm to the sheep that feed on the plants than it does to the plants themselves.

At the base of the problem of the conservation of soil lie two psychological difficulties. The first is connected with men's occupations. In the eighteenth century 4 families out of 5 lived on the farm; today the proportion is less than 1 out of 6 in Europe and the United States. With this change there has come a diminution in the proportion of the population that is genuinely aware of the real source of our national income: the soil and its products. To the city-dweller, the farm and the forest may seem to be remote places inhabited by strange people who are insensible to the superiorities of urban life. Most city-dwellers act as if what occurs on a farm or in a forest a thousand miles away were no concern of theirs. Unfortunately, the means of communication and education—radio, television, magazines, and books—are for the most part (and naturally) controlled by city-bred people. The whole tone and emphasis of our social intercourse have thus become biologically unsound and dangerous to our continued existence and prosperity.

The second difficulty is connected with time. The ruin that follows improper management of the soil may take several generations to occur —and how are men to recognize the causes of such slow events? The impoverished and semi-desert areas to the south and east of the Mediterranean Sea were once green and prosperous regions. The land of Iraq once harbored 40 million people; now it has 5 million. There is good

Fig. 19-9. *In ten years' time, as silt was deposited from a stream that drained improperly farmed and overlumbered lands upstream, the attractive man-made lake shown at the top was changed to the man-made marsh shown below. (Courtesy U.S. Soil Conservation Service.)*

Fig. 19-10. *Contour farming. By such means the soil is conserved and, eventually, farm income increased. Frequently, successful contour farming can be carried on only by combined operation of more than one farm. (Courtesy U.S. Soil Conservation Service.)*

evidence that the decay of such once-flourishing regions was in large part brought about by neglect of the soil and its needs. Responsible rulers knew not what they did; it all happened so slowly. When changes take place slowly, we can be aware of them and of their causes only by giving our attention to records and to history, which, in the words of John Selden, a seventeenth-century scholar, can "so accumulate years to us as if we had lived even from the beginning of time." The impressions of mere day-to-day living are not a sufficient guide to wise action: we must also give our attention to the revelations of history. As George Santayana said: "Those who cannot learn from the past are doomed to repeat it." The downfall of past empires has been brought about to no small extent by men who had no understanding of the functions of plants and of the magnitude of the effects of small forces, long compounded.

Questions and Problems

19-3. Make a list of the **boldface** terms in this chapter and write a brief description of each. Compare your work with the text.

19-4. Make a list of the plant foods you ate yesterday. If you had been deprived of plants that came from the New World, how much difference would this have made in your diet? After you guess, consult Appendix 8.

‡19-5. Flowering plants are fairly sharply divisible into those with sticky pollen and those with nonsticky pollen. The members of one group are almost all insect pollinated, while most of the members of the other are wind pollinated. Which is which? Explain.

19-6. Would you expect species with sticky pollen or species with nonsticky pollen to be more often used in the pollen analysis of the geological deposits? Explain.

‡19-7. The wild ancestor of domestic corn (maize) is not known. In looking for it, would you look for a plant that had ears of corn tightly enclosed within the shucks at the mature stage, like maize?

‡19-8. Imagine two tribes of prehistoric men, both of which take to planting seed from a primitive grain. Tribe *A* stays in one place, year after year. Tribe *B* is nomadic, moving after each harvest. After a few decades, which tribe will have the better strain of grain? Explain.

‡19-9. Under completely natural conditions, a wild progenitor of a domestic plant always outcompetes the domesticated form. With respect to the grains, give one reason for this natural superiority.

‡19-10. In what basic ecological sense may it be said that man creates the epidemic problems of domesticated plants with which he struggles?

19-11. *Leavenworthia* is a crucifer, of which there are a number of species in the eastern United States. The flowers are perfect. Some species are self-compatible, that is a given individual plant can successfully pollinate itself. Other species are self-incompatible, and must be cross-pollinated. Species of the first group have nonodoriferous flowers; those of the second, odoriferous. How do you explain the association?

Readings

Baker's *Plants and Civilization* is recommended as a good over-all view. For a technical discussion of problems connected with the evolution of wheat, potatoes, etc., see Hutchinson's *Essays on Crop Plant Evolution*. How man has in the past fouled his nest is made evident in Osborn's *Our Plundered Planet,* Sears' *Deserts on the March* and Vogt's *Road to Survival.* Dasmann takes up the same theme in his nostalgic and sensitive book, *The Last Horizon.*

Scientific American Offprints

840. Edward S. Deevey, Jr. *Bogs*

852. Frits W. Went. *Climate and Agriculture*

856. David B. Ericson & Goesta Wollin. *Micropaleontology*

IV The Animal Way of Life

All we know is still infinitely less than all that still remains unknown.
WILLIAM HARVEY

20 The "Lower" Invertebrates

155. What Do We Mean by "Lower"?

The phyla of this chapter are a heterogeneous group of invertebrate animals, that is, animals without backbones. Some of the forms that are more complicated or more "advanced" (in an evolutionary sense)—for example, the insects —are postponed to later chapters. The invertebrate phyla considered here are often spoken of as being "lower," an adjective of somewhat uncertain extension, but meaning approximately that each such phylum as a whole was probably evolved earlier than one of the so-called higher phyla. (This remark does not necessarily apply to individual species, some of which may have been evolved quite recently.) Some zoologists think of these animals as being "simpler," rather than "lower," forms. This may be true, though it should be clear, before we have gone any further, that many of the species are far from simple. Some of the complications in structure and life cycle have no equal among the "higher" forms. *Simplicity* is not an easy concept to deal with.

156. Protozoa: Flagellates and Rhizopods

The first animals, like the first plants, must have been water-dwelling, single-celled forms, for the problem of living in water is not nearly as severe as that of living on dry land. The present-day descendants of these primitive animals we place in the phylum **Protozoa** (Gr. *protos* = first + *zoon* = animal). In a minority of species, several daughter cells adhere to each other, forming a colony; but in most of the protozoa, the individual consists of but a single cell. In size, protozoan cells range from 2 or 3 microns in length to more than 1,000 in a few free-living forms that are easily visible to the naked eye. The majority of the species are less than 100 microns in length. Their dependence on a watery medium is even greater than that of the algae; this is in part attributable to the lack of a cellulose cell wall, for, like all truly animal cells, active protozoan cells have only a cell membrane. Some species can produce a thick-walled resting phase, called a **cyst,** which is fairly resistant to drying but without notable resistance to elevated temperatures.

Since the individuals of this phylum are, in the main, small, it follows that the surface:volume ratio is large. Because of the scale effect (§10), it likewise follows that there is little need of special organs to facilitate exchanges between organism and environment. We are not surprised, therefore, to find no protozoan structures comparable to the lungs and gills of vertebrates. The interior of many protozoa looks rather simple on first examination (Fig. 20-1*A*), though recent studies with the electron microscope are showing that the simplest of the protozoa are not as simple as was once sup-

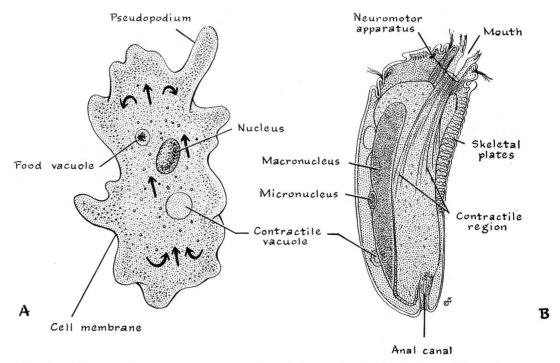

Fig. 20-1. Left: *Amoeba. Arrows show direction of movement of cell substance as the whole animal moves.* Right: *Ciliate from intestine of cow. Note the complexity within the confines of a single cell.*

posed. Even with the optical microscope, it is apparent that many protozoa are quite complex (Fig. 20-1*B*). In higher organisms, there is a segregation of functions among different kinds of cells, organized into tissues and organs. In the protozoa, all such segregation of functions must take place within the confines of a single cell. A portion of a cell specialized as to function is called an **organelle.** In speaking of the protozoa as "single-celled" forms, we have followed the custom of the majority of the zoologists, but it is worth pointing out that one able protozoologist, Clifford Dobell, has insisted that the protozoa should be regarded as *acellular* organisms, that is, organisms to which the cell concept does not apply. In effect, Dobell said that *if* protozoa were the only kinds of organisms known, no biologist would ever have conceived the cell theory.*

The organelles of protozoa are so different in

appearance from the organs of familiar multicellular animals that it is seldom safe to guess their function merely by looking at them. As an example of the use of experimental method to ascertain the function of an organelle, it is worthwhile considering the **contractile vacuole** (Fig. 20-1). In an amoeba, this clear, fluid-filled vesicle may be seen to undergo a regular cycle of changes. It is first noticeable as a very tiny droplet that steadily increases in size. As it reaches its maximum size, it approaches the cell membrane. When it reaches the membrane, it abruptly discharges its contents to the exterior, and disappears as a discernible organelle. A moment later a new contractile vacuole forms in the interior of the animal and starts on a new "pulsation cycle"—a cycle that takes about a minute to complete.

What is the function of the contractile vacuole? Comparative studies suggested an answer. It was observed that protozoan species living in fresh water almost invariably have contractile

* 20-1. What do *you* think—are protozoa unicellular or acellular?

vacuoles, whereas many closely related species living in brackish or marine waters lack them. The osmotic potential (§22) of sea water is higher than that of fresh water. The observations suggest that the osmotic potential of the protozoa is higher than that of fresh water, but about equal to (or less than) that of sea water; and that the contractile vacuole is an organelle for removing the excess water that passes through the cell membrane by osmosis. Experiments yield supporting data. Some fresh-water species are capable of withstanding a wide range of osmotic potentials. When individuals of such a species are placed in various media, the rate of pulsation of the vacuole is inversely proportional to the osmotic potential of the surrounding fluid. In the media of high osmotic potential, the contractile vacuole may even disappear entirely. The hypothesis that this vacuole is a water-removing organ fits the experimental data.

Several types of nutrition occur in this phylum. Some of the autotrophic unicells, for example, the photosynthetic *Euglena,* are often considered to be algae (plants) rather than protozoa (animals), though this is a matter of definition. If such organisms are to be considered animals, we say that they exhibit **holophytic** (autotrophic) nutrition. The indubitable protozoa are *heterotrophic*. These are subdivided into the **holozoic** forms, which take in solid *particles* of food (e.g., bacteria), often through a restricted part of the cell surface, which may be called a mouth; and the *saprophytic* (or **saprozoic**—the synonym preferred by many zoologists) forms, which take in *dissolved* molecules of organic foodstuffs, probably through all parts of the cell membrane. In addition, the heterotrophic protozoa include many parasites, which may take in either solid particles (parts of the host) or dissolved molecules.

Both sexual and asexual reproduction are known. Asexual reproduction is commonly brought about by ordinary cell division, though other methods are also found (as we shall see presently). Sexual reproduction occurs in many

species: Two individuals adhere together in **conjugation** and exchange nuclear material. Thus from one sexual act there arise two fertilized cells.

Of the five classes of protozoa, four will be considered in this book.

CLASS FLAGELLATA. These organisms (Fig. 20-2) move themselves by one or more long, thin, flexible whips, called *flagella* (sing. flagellum). The Flagellata are believed to be the most primitive animals, both because of their relative simplicity and because many of them e.g., *Euglena* and the dinoflagellates) contain chlorophyll and hence are capable of living autotrophically. Such organisms are studied by both botanists and zoologists, and would seem to form an evolutionary bridge between plants and animals.

Most of the flagellates are colorless but free-living, that is, nonparasitic, and are abundant in soil and water. Among the more important parasites are the many species of the genus **Trypanosoma,** which may be found in the blood of various vertebrates. Some of the trypanosomes that live in antelope in Africa are capable of producing the serious disease **nagana** in European cattle introduced into the region, although the native animals are apparently not harmed by these parasites.* The trypanosomes are transferred from one animal to another by the bite of bloodsucking flies of the genus *Glossina.* An organism that disseminates a disease (as does this fly) is called a **vector** (L. carrier) of the disease.

A trypanosome is also responsible for the disease **African sleeping sickness** in man. **Tsetse flies** (*Glossina*) are the vectors. These flies, which breed in bushy areas and along the margins of streams, are extremely difficult to eradicate. Some success is now being encountered in treating sleeping sickness with drugs. There are vast areas ("fly belts") of tropical Africa that will be suitable for human habitation only

---

* 20-2. Why the difference between native and introduced species of host organisms? Give an evolutionary explanation.

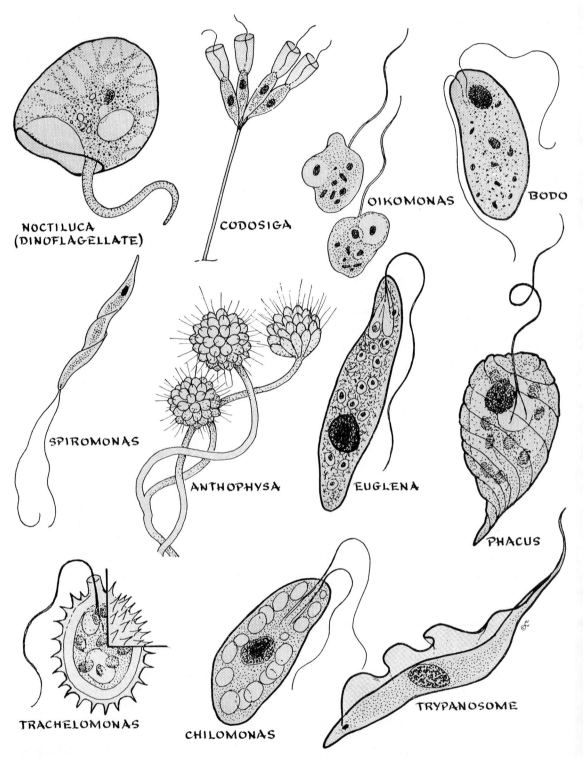

Fig. 20-2. *A flurry of flagellates (no uniform scale). (From Kent, A* Manual of the Infusoria, *David Bogue, London, 1880; and from life, by E. P. Catts.)*

when man has learned either to cure the disease or to eliminate the vector. It is natural to try to get rid of the tsetse flies by mass spraying of insecticides, but this may not be successful, for two reasons: the probable evolutionary adaptation of the flies to the poison (§78); and the unknown, and possibly harmful, disturbance of the local "web of life" (§102) by poisons that affect many species, both beneficial and harmful. The solution of the sleeping-sickness problem will not be easily achieved; it will undoubtedly require most careful studies of the whole ecological situation.

CLASS RHIZOPODA. The name of this class, signifying rootlike feet, is justified by the extensions of the body by which a rhizopod moves. *Amoeba* (Fig. 20-3) is a well-known example. In moving, it varies in shape as first one part of its body and then another extends, as the animal slithers along the substrate. Each temporary extension is called a **pseudopod** (Gr. *pseudes* = false + *podos* = foot). The largest of the soil-dwelling amoebae is put in the genus *Chaos,* which was originally a grab-bag category created by Linnaeus to hold all the odd species he didn't know what to do with, when he was trying to complete his classification of the world of living things.

There are some organisms that possess both pseudopods and flagella. Should they be considered members of the class Rhizopoda or the class Flagellata? Obviously, the decision must be an arbitrary one. The important point is that such species are probably evolutionary links between the two classes. We have shown one such form, *Naegleria,* on the plate of rhizopods (Fig. 20-3), but we could just as well have included it with the flagellates.

Most amoebae are free-living, but a number of species live in the gut of various animals, usually without harm to the host. One species living in the human intestine is *Entamoeba histolytica,* which is associated with the disease **amoebic dysentery.** Under unsanitary conditions this organism may be passed from one human to another, with the production of some illness and mortality. Modern diagnostic methods show that approximately 20 percent of the population of the United States is infested with this species of rhizopod, though the frequency of diagnosed amoebic dysentery is much less. Parasitism and pathogenicity are not necessarily associated.

Included in this class are the **Foraminifera** (Fig. 20-3), which produce microscopic shells that are characteristically different for each species. When marine Foraminifera die, their shells settle to the bottom, where they form an ooze that in the course of geological time may be turned to chalk. The white cliffs of Dover are former marine deposits of Foraminifera, now elevated; and now in the process of being eroded and returned to the sea once more. As fossils, "forams" are useful in identifying specific strata of rocks. They have been particularly important in the development of petroleum geology.

157. Protozoa: The Ciliates

Of all the protozoa, the members of the class **Ciliata** are unquestionably the most beautiful and spectacular. The variety is enormous—a hint of which is given by the diverse forms shown in Figure 20-4. A few species are parasitic, but the vast majority are not. Numerous species are easily found in any body of fresh water, particularly if it abounds in bacteria. Marine species also exist. In the Pyramid of Protoplasm (§102), the ciliates occupy a block just above bacteria and algae; above them come such multicellular forms as water fleas.* In many locations they are by no means indispensable for this ecological action, which is brought about also by various worms; but in the clarification of sewage waters, certain species of ciliates appear to be of prime importance.

The best known of all ciliates is, of course, *Paramecium.* There are a number of species, ranging in length from about 50μ to nearly 200μ; when illuminated from the side against a black background, the largest of them can easily be seen with the naked eye. One species,

* 20-3. Convert this sentence into a sketch on a margin of the page.

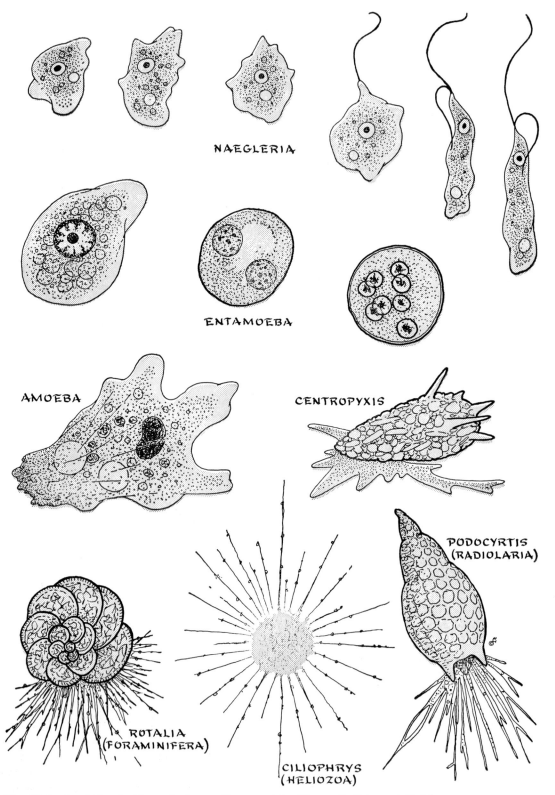

Fig. 20-3. *A rabble of rhizopods (no uniform scale). (From Doflein and Reichenow,* Lehrbuch der Protozoenkunde, *Fischer, Jena, 1927.)*

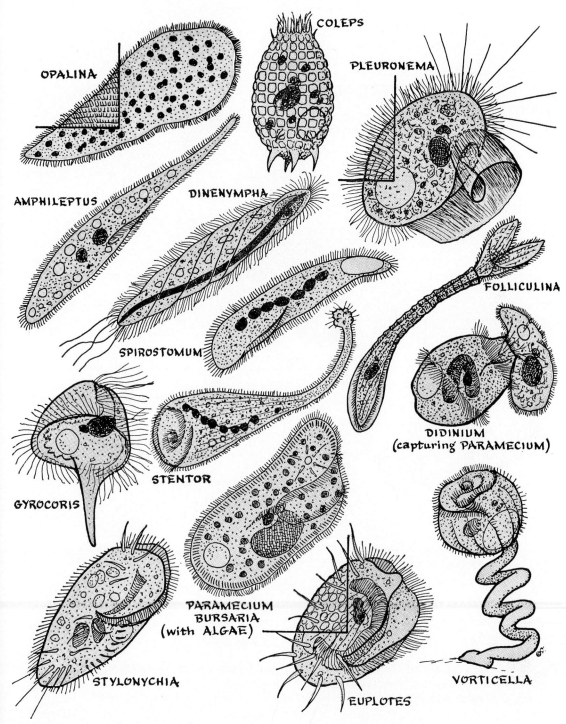

Fig. 20-4. *A slurry of ciliates* (*no uniform scale*). (*From Kent,* A Manual of the Infusoria, *David Bogue, London, 1880; and from life, by E. P. Catts.*)

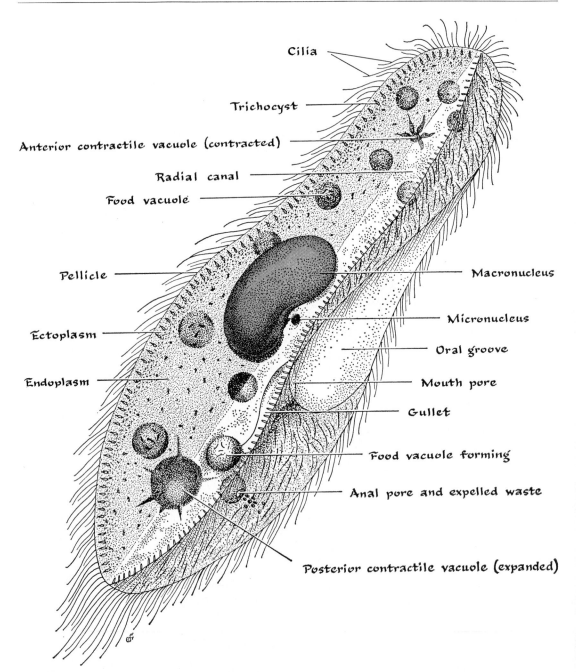

Cilia

Trichocyst

Anterior contractile vacuole (contracted)

Radial canal

Food vacuole

Pellicle

Ectoplasm

Endoplasm

Macronucleus

Micronucleus

Oral groove

Mouth pore

Gullet

Food vacuole forming

Anal pore and expelled waste

Posterior contractile vacuole (expanded)

Fig. 20-5. *Some (not all) of the structures of a paramecium; note how complicated a single cell may be. Nuclear material is in color. (From Johnson, Laubengayer, and DeLanney, General Biology, 1956, by permission of Holt, Rinehart and Winston, New York.)*

P. bursaria (Fig. 20-4), has within it symbiotic† green algae; all the other species of *Para-* *mecium* do not. The complexity of the body of a paramecium—which is by no means the most complicated of the ciliates—is evident from the *simplified* diagram of Figure 20-5. The animal

† 20-4. Meaning? In what context was this term used earlier in this book?

propels itself through the water by the beating of its **cilia** (sing. *cilium;* L. eyelid—later applied to eyelash); because of the asymmetry of its body,* the animal revolves on its long axis as it moves forward. Studies made with a strobo-scope show that the cilia beat in a regular, organized way. The integration of the action of the several thousand cilia is brought about by the fibers—analogous to the nerve fibers of multicellular animals—that interconnect the cilia. (For simplicity, this part of the *neuro-motor system* has been omitted from the figure.)

Food is swept into the body of the parame-cium by the cilia of the **oral groove.** Entering through the **mouth pore** and going down the **gullet,** the food becomes surrounded by a body of fluid, the whole forming a **food vacuole.** This food vacuole then slowly circulates around the body of the animal while digestion of the food particles (principally bacteria) takes place. When digestion is complete, the food vacuole may disappear; or it may discharge the undi-gested residue through the **anal pore,** a fixed spot in the **pellicle** (L. *pellicula,* diminutive of *pellis* = skin).

Water balance within the body is maintained by the periodic pulsation of **contractile vacu-oles,** as in *Amoeba.* In *Paramecium,* however, these structures are fixed in position and are considerably more elaborate in structure.

A most notable feature of the ciliates is a di-vision of the nucleus into two kinds of bodies: a **macronucleus** (large nucleus) and a **micro-nucleus.** (Some species have several micronu-clei.) The nuclear functions are likewise di-vided. The macronucleus takes care of *somatic* functions only, apparently elaborating enzymes that function in cellular metabolism. The micro-nucleus is concerned only with heredity, with passing genetic information on to the next gen-eration. This unusually clear-cut separation of functions has made the ciliates very favorable organisms for experiments in physiological ge-netics.

In cell division (often, for no adequate rea-

son, given the special name *fission,* in ciliates), both macronucleus and micronucleus divide. In the sexual fusion ("conjugation") of ciliate cells, the behavior of the nuclei is unusual, as will become apparent from a close study of Figure 20-6. After two paramecia press to-gether at their oral grooves (*A*), their macro-nuclei degenerate (*B* and *C*). Meanwhile, the diploid nucleus initially present in each (*A*) has undergone meiosis (*B* and *C*), producing the usual four haploid nuclei (*C*). Three of these haploid nuclei disintegrate (*D*); the re-maining nucleus then divides once more, by mitosis. Of these two nuclei, one stays where it is, while the other one migrates to the other cell; there is a mutual interchange of this sort (*F*). Following this interchange, the two haploid nu-clei fuse (*G*) to produce a diploid nucleus (*H*) in each cell. By this time the process of conjuga-tion is at an end, and the exconjugants separate. The nuclear consequences of conjugation are still not complete at this time.

Since the history of both exconjugants is the same, we will follow only one. Without cell di-vision, the nucleus divides mitotically twice (*I* and *J*) to produce four diploid micronuclei. Let us stop here. *The process indicated in the stages A through J is one that occurs pretty generally throughout the ciliates.* It is not yet complete, but the way it is completed varies considerably among the ciliates. We will consider only one of the possible variants, the one occurring in the species *Paramecium caudatum.* In this species, yet another mitotic division of the micronuclei occurs, producing a cell (*K*) with eight diploid micronuclei. Four of these then differentiate into four macronuclei; and three disintegrate; thus leaving only one micronucleus (*L*). This animal then goes through two cell divisions (*M* and *N*), in each of which the micronucleus is di-vided in the fashion usual to cell division, but in which the excess macronuclei are merely segregated without further division. Thus, finally, at stage *N,* we have typical paramecia once more. From this point on, for many cell generations, cell divisions (*O–Q*) are typical somatic mitotic divisions.

Not simple, is it? It is hardly possible, in the

---

* 20-5. What is the most notable external feature (see Fig. 20-5) that destroys the symmetry parame-cium might otherwise have?

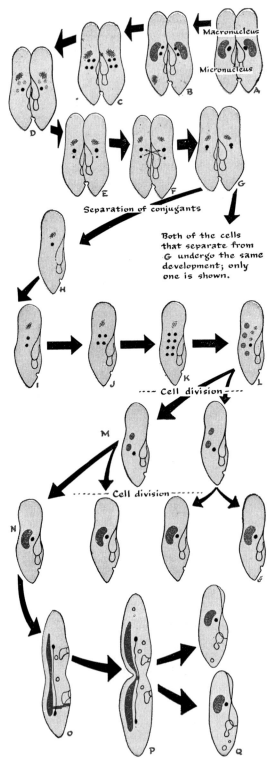

Separation of conjugants

Both of the cells
that separate from
G undergo the same
development; only
one is shown.

---- Cell division ----

······· Cell division·······

Fig. 20-6. *Sexual reproduction in Paramecium.*

light of such facts as these, to think of the Protozoa as "simple, one-celled organisms." The ciliates are particularly complicated. Yet, in spite of many peculiarities, they show fundamental similarities to "higher" organisms. Fertilization is preceded by meiosis; and most of the cells in the life cycle are diploid. A most striking peculiarity of the ciliates is the possession of a macronucleus. It was stated before that this structure takes care of somatic functions, while the micronucleus takes care of hereditary matters. We have just seen the evidence for the second part of this assertion: only the micronucleus functions in cell division. A single bit of evidence for the first will be given. Among the many strains of paramecia cultured in biology laboratories, there is one that has been carried on for more than 30 years without sexual conjugation. Cytological examination has demonstrated that this strain has no micronucleus at all. Its inability to reproduce sexually is thus explained. The macronucleus alone is enough to permit these organisms to carry on all the somatic functions and to multiply indefinitely by nonsexual cell division.

158. Protozoa: The Sporozoa

All members of this class are parasitic, and in their adult stages have no means of locomotion. Almost all are intracellular parasites at some stage of their existence: many of them live in the intestinal cells of a wide range of invertebrates; many others live in the blood cells of vertebrates. The silkworm disease *pébrine* is caused by one species; "redwater fever" of cattle, by another. All sporozoa have complicated life cycles, during one stage of which they reproduce by "spores." These "spores" do not serve the same functions as do bacterial spores or the spores of higher plants. They are more closely comparable to algal or fungal zoospores or conidia: they are a means of asexual reproduction by multiple cell divisions.

Sporozoa of the genus *Plasmodium* cause malaria in man and other animals, different species of parasites occurring in different hosts. Historically, malaria has limited man's success in colonizing many areas of the world. The name of the disease is Italian for "bad air"; for centuries, men recognized the *association* of the disease with swampy areas, supposing that the "bad air" coming from swamps was itself the cause of the disease. A good case can be made for the Pontine Marshes of Italy being an important factor—though only one factor among many—in the fall of Rome. Until very recently much of the mortality of wars was actually caused by malaria. During the American Civil War there were more than a million cases of malaria among the white troops on the Union side; reliable statistics are not available for the Confederate Army. In the Mexican War, 25 percent of the hospitalizations of United States troops at Vera Cruz were caused by the disease. In 1923, as an aftermath of World War I and the Russian Revolution, there were more than 5 million cases in Russia, with at least 60,000 deaths. In the early years of the Second World War, the incidence of malaria among American troops in the South Pacific theatre was 750 per 1,000 men per year. In peacetime, malaria has for centuries been a *contributing cause* of more than half the annual deaths of the world, the sporozoan disease weakening the people so that they easily fall prey to other diseases. Not until the middle of the twentieth century was a significant decrease in worldwide malarial infection brought about.

We now have the knowledge needed for a complete conquest of the disease—or rather of the diseases, for there are several, of which the three most important are the following: "tertiary ague," caused by *Plasmodium vivax,* in which the fever and chills recur every third day, that is, after an interval of 48 hours; "quartan ague," caused by *P. malariae,* which recurs at intervals of 72 hours; and "quotidian ague," caused by *P. falciparum,* which has an irregular cycle. Between bouts of fever, the patient is moderately comfortable. (Especially unlucky is he who gets more than one type simultaneously!) The organisms that cause malaria are, everyone now knows, transmitted by mosquitoes, but this is no mere passive transmission (as is the transmission of typhoid by houseflies). The disease organism causes a disease in the mosquito as well. The living of one "pest" upon another brings to mind an old English verse:

> *Big fleas have little fleas*
> *Upon their backs to bite 'em;*
> *And little fleas have lesser fleas,*
> *And so ad infinitum.*

Which is more or less true. (Should we feel sorry for the mosquito?)

The life cycle of a malaria parasite is shown in Figure 20-7. The sexual part of the life cycle takes place in mosquitoes of the genus *Anopheles;* the asexual phase occurs in man. In life cycles involving two (or more) hosts, the host in which the sexual phase occurs is called the **definitive host;** a host in which only asexual phases occur is called an **intermediate host.** Asexual reproduction of *Plasmodium* in man is brought about by multiple fission, or **sporulation,** which takes place inside the parasitized red blood cells. All of the parasitized red blood cells burst at once, releasing spores into the blood stream. The fever of malaria appears to be due to decomposition products released by the bursting of the red blood cells.

Attacks of malaria can be controlled by the administration of specific drugs. The classical drug quinine, derived from the bark of the cinchona tree, is now being superseded by a galaxy of other substances synthesized by chemists. But prevention of the disease is more important than its cure. *Plasmodium* cannot continue to exist if it does not have both hosts to live in. By eliminating mosquitoes, we can eliminate the disease. In this line of attack, insecticides such as DDT are useful, though usually not sufficient. Waters in which mosquito larvae live are best covered with insecticidal oils, or drained. Wherever a vigorous mosquito-eradication campaign is launched, the results are spectacular. On the island of Cyprus, 40 percent of all school children suffered from malaria in 1945; by 1948, the incidence had dropped to only 1.3 percent, as the result of an intensive

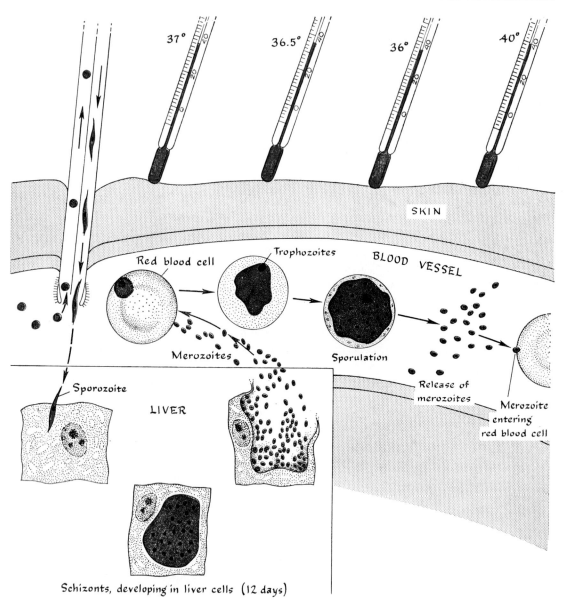

Fig. 20-7. *The life cycle of the malaria parasite in its two hosts, mosquito and man.*

anti-*Anopheles* campaign that cost $1,000,000. The elimination of mosquitoes costs money. This is one of the reasons that malaria is such an important problem in the poverty-stricken regions of the world. Unfortunately, there is a vicious circle involved here: Malarious people are sickly and indolent and, hence, unproductive. A highly malarious population is unable to accumulate the capital needed for more than subsistence living, and may lack the will to try.

Breaking the circle usually requires help from the outside, that is, from nonmalarious, energetic people.*

159. The Porifera

The animal kingdom is sometimes divided into three *subkingdoms:* the Protozoa (which we

---

* 20-6. Quickly controlling malaria in a formerly heavily malarious region often quickly raises a serious problem of another sort. What is it?

have just studied); the multicellular *Mesozoa* (a very odd group that we shall ignore completely); and the **Metazoa,** which includes all other phyla of multicellular animals.

Although some of the protozoa are visible to the naked eye, the vast majority of animals large enough to see are metazoans, and hence multicellular. There are many "reasons" for this, some of which are connected with the scale effect (§10). The larger an organism is, the more difficult it is for it to carry out exchanges with the environment at a fast enough rate. A common way for an organism to "solve" this problem is to alter its shape so as to increase the amount of its surface. The increase is often achieved by complicated inpocketings of part of its surface. A cellular construction is admirably suited to the achievement of a complicated architecture.

Of course, no organism solved the problem of growing large by sitting down and thinking out a logical solution and then evolving in the proper way. More likely, the multicellular condition was first found as a loose aggregation of daughter cells that failed to separate following cell division; some present-day dinoflagellates show this condition. From such a beginning as a mere colony of cells, we can imagine how, step by step, more and more organization and structural elaboration might have been evolved.

Direct knowledge of the path of evolution we do not have, and probably never will, since the early multicellular forms were most likely soft-bodied and unsuited to fossilization. We suspect, however, that the sponges show the type of loose organization that some of the early multicellular organisms may have possessed.

Sponges, the simplest of the Metazoa, belong to the phylum **Porifera,** or "pore animals." The sponges with which we are most familiar these days are products of the chemist's art; but natural sponges, which are knobbier in appearance, are still used to considerable extent. Natural sponges are skeletons of rather simple water-dwelling animals. Most sponges (the animals, that is) are marine organisms that grow in shallow water. They are collected by sponge-fishers, who use long, hooked poles or who dive for

them. After being collected, sponges are allowed to decay until only their skeletons remain.

If an organism is to be both large and metabolically vigorous, it must either move through the environment or move the environment through or past itself (which amounts to the same thing—facilitating exchanges between organism and environment). A sponge moves the environing water through itself. The organism is essentially a hollow sack of living material (Fig. 20-8). The principal opening of the body conducts water out of the body. (In no other phylum is the principal opening an exit opening.) Water is taken into the body through many small **incurrent pores;** tiny bits of food are filtered out of the water by cells that line the cavities of the body, and the waste water is extruded from the large **excurrent opening.** The current required for this "filter feeding" is created by the beating of thousands of small flagellated cells called **collar cells** (Fig. 20-8). One investigator found that a single sponge about the size of a small fountain pen moved 5 gallons of water through its food-gathering passages in a single day.

Most sponges have skeletons, which consist of interlocking elements called **spicules.** The basic substance of a spicule is a proteinaceous material called **spongin.** This substance includes as one of its constituents 3,5 di-iodo tyrosine, which is a specific remedy for one type of human goiter (enlargement of the thyroid gland in the neck)—a fact that was known to the ancient Greeks, who recommended the eating of ground sponges for the relief of goiter. Later, and until comparatively recently, this remedy was viewed as superstition. Now we know it is not, and we know why the remedy works; but we now have other sources of the effective substance.

In addition to spongin, the skeletons of some groups of sponges contain silica (of which sand is composed) or calcium carbonate (limestone). We can hardly recommend such sponges for the bath.

The collar cells of a sponge are almost indistinguishable from certain free-living flagellates —a fact that points to the evolution of the Porif-

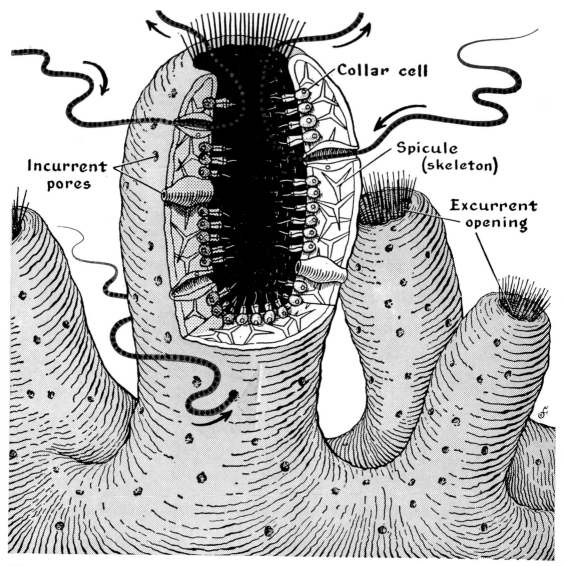

Fig. 20-8. *Sponges, the only phylum in which the largest opening is an exit rather than an entrance.*

era from the Protozoa. All available evidence indicates that evolution proceeded no further along this line, that the Porifera are a dead end in evolution. Their multicellularity has been reached in almost the simplest possible way: by a certain amount of differentiation and organization among the cells, with only traces of a higher level of organization—that of the tissue of similar cells. For this reason the Porifera have been said to be Metazoa of the "cellular grade of construction."

One of the most remarkable things about sponges is their power of **regeneration,** that is, their ability to re-produce parts that are damaged or lost. The zoologist H. V. Wilson in 1907 performed the ultimate experiment in regeneration, when he forced a small sponge through a fine sieve, thus separating the cells and destroying the intercellular organization. After separation, the isolated cells wandered around until they came together again in an unorganized aggregation, which within a few weeks, re-formed itself into a sponge of the original kind.

160. Hydra and Other Coelenterates

With the coelenterates, we come to Metazoa of the "tissue grade of construction." In these animals, cells are organized into two tissues: the **ectoderm** and the **endoderm** (Fig. 20-9). Between these two layers of cells, there is a sheet of nonliving jelly, which is more or less thick depending on the particular species. Present in the ectoderm are special **stinging capsules** (Fig. 20-9*C*), about which more will be said presently.

There are two different forms of coelenterates. One is attached to the substrate, with its mouth uppermost: this sessile form is called a **polyp.** The other is a free-floating form, with its mouth opening downward: this is called a **medusa.** The homology of the parts of the two is made clear in Figure 20-9*A, B.* In both, there is only a single opening into the **gastrovascular cavity;** this opening serves both for ingestion and for expelling undigested fragments of food materials.

Most species of the phylum Coelenterata are either polyps or medusae. There are, however, some species in which both forms occur, in which the medusae first appear as buds attached to a polyp. These buds later break off and develop into adult medusae that reproduce sexually. The zygote so produced develops into a new polyp, which produces new medusae, which . . . ; and so on. This alternation of forms

Fig. 20-9. *Coelenterata. The fundamental similarity of the polyp* (A) *and the medusa* (B) *is evident.* (C) *Cross section of the wall of a coelenterate, showing the stinging capsules that are produced only in this phylum.*

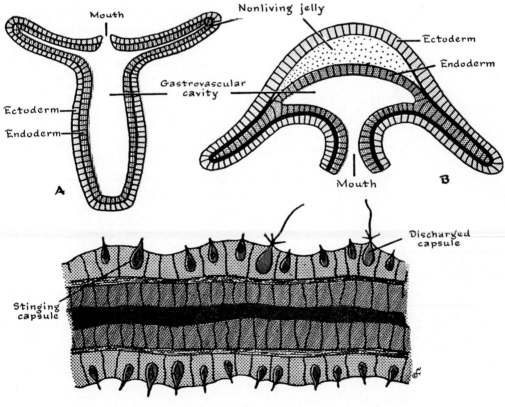

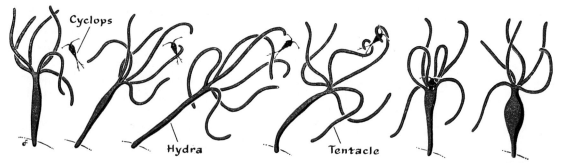

Fig. 20-10. *A hydra catching and eating a microscopic "water-flea." (Adapted from Buchsbaum,* Animals Without Backbones, *1948, by permission of University of Chicago Press, Chicago.)*

should not be confused with the alternation of generations in plants (Chap. 18), for in these animals both forms are diploid.

For the most part, this phylum is confined to

Fig. 20-11. *The nerve net of a hydra (in color). Note the concentration of nerve cells around the mouth; this region is the nearest thing to a brain the hydra has. (Adapted from Buchsbaum,* Animals Without Backbones, *1948, by permission of University of Chicago Press, Chicago.)*

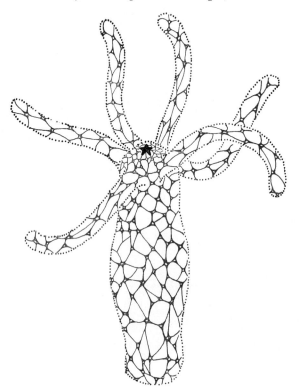

the ocean, where it is a conspicuous part of the fauna. Along the shores are found various kinds of polyps known as sea anemones and corals— animals that are often mistaken for plants by the neophyte. In the open ocean waters occur numerous medusae, commonly called jellyfish. Fresh-water members of the phylum are fewer in number, smaller in size, and quantitatively less important. Fresh-water jellyfish are small and very rarely encountered; fresh-water polyps are common but so tiny (only a few millimeters in length) as to escape the notice of all but biologists. The commonest of these, called **hydras,** * have been favorite objects for laboratory study since their discovery in 1740 by Abraham Trembley (1710–1784). Trembley found these strange little creatures in a ditch on a Dutch estate where he was employed as a tutor. His reports created a considerable controversy because they threatened long-standing notions of what constitutes an animal and what a plant. Trembley wrote, in a letter to his biologist friend Charles Bonnet: "I have studied it ever since last June, and have found in it striking characteristics of both plant and animal. It is a little aquatic being. At first sight everyone imagines it to be a plant; but if it be a plant, it is sensitive and ambulent; if it be an animal, it may be propagated by slips or cuttings, like many plants."

Hair-thin, a delicate, transparent hydra can capture a vigorous cyclops, daphnia, or other

* 20-7. What is the mythological origin of the name "hydra"?

water flea that is larger than itself. This it does by means of its stinging cells, or **nematocysts** (Fig. 20-9C), of which it has a great abundance in the ectoderm of its **tentacles.** The prey is immobilized by a poison contained in the stinging cells and thus made ready for capture by the tentacles, which convey it to the mouth (Fig. 20-10). The poison of the nematocyst is an unusual type of collagen, a class of proteins found in tendons. The nematocyst poison inhibits electron transfer in the reduction of the cellular respiratory enzyme, cytochrome *c*. The nematocysts of small coelenterates are quite harmless to man, but not so those of some of the larger pelagic species. The "Portuguese man-of-war," which has transparent tentacles as much as 15 meters in length, is a definite hazard to unwary swimmers, though there seem to be no authentic records of deaths caused by this jelly-fish. There are, however, other species of jelly-fish in the tropical waters of northern Australia and the western Pacific whose sting is known to be fatal within a few minutes.

The coelenterates' ability to catch prey implies some mechanism for coordinating the movements of its various parts. There is present, in fact, a very primitive nervous system. In a hydra, coordination is brought about by a sort of **nerve net**—a system in which nerve cells are joined one with another, but in which there is no concentration that could be referred to as a brain (Fig. 20-11). The reactions possible in such a system are quite restricted, but the nerve net is at least a step in the evolution toward mentality.

The most important coelenterates are the marine **corals,** inhabitants of clear tropical waters. These polyps secrete a surrounding skeleton of calcium carbonate, as do the coralline red algae. Coral reefs and coral islands are formed by the slow deposit of skeleton upon skeleton of these diverse organisms. Between them, algae and corals are responsible for the greatest structure ever created by living organisms—the Great Barrier Reef, which stretches for some 800 kilometers along the east coast of Australia.

The coral of commerce, which varies greatly in color and beauty, is only the skeletal remains of such organisms. The most beautiful coral, used in jewelry, is harvested from the ocean bottom off the coast of Algiers. The harvesting grounds are divided into 10 districts; 1 district is harvested each year, with a 9-year interval for regrowth.

Questions and Problems

20-8. Make a list of the **boldface** terms in this chapter and write a brief description of each. Compare your work with the text.

20-9. What is the function of the contractile vacuole in protozoa? Give the evidence for your statement.

‡20-10. Although about 20 percent of the American population is infected with *Entamoeba histolytica,* the incidence of reported cases of amoebic dysentery is much less. How do you account for the difference?

20-11. Richard Burton (translator of *Arabian Nights*) in his *First Footsteps in East Africa,* published in 1856, wrote: "The mosquito bites bring on, according to [the people of Somali] deadly fevers: the superstition probably arises from the fact that mosquitoes and fevers become formidable about the same time." Was Burton right in dismissing the belief as a superstition?

‡20-12. The number of deaths in the United States caused by malaria declined, in 30 years, from more than 5,000 per year to less than 10 per year. The decline was fairly steady except during the years 1932–1936, when the malarial death rate rose. The cause of the rise was not

a medical factor—not in the narrow sense. What was it?

20-13. In India, in 1948, about 100 million people suffered from malaria, of which 2 million died. In the same country, in 1963, only 50,-000 had attacks of malaria and (it is thought) none died of it. Why the great difference?

20-14. Can it be said that modern medical science has decreased the misery in India? Justify your answer.

‡20-15. In 1951 the first DDT-resistant mosquitoes were found in Greece, after several years' heavy use of DDT in eradicating anopheline mosquitoes. Since then, dieldrin has been widely substituted for DDT. Now dieldrin-resistant mosquitoes are appearing. What is the explanation for the appearance of these resistant forms? What is the solution of the problem they pose?

20-16. African sleeping sickness is endemic among the natives of West Africa, among whom it takes a slow and steady toll. At the beginning of the twentieth century, as a result of improved transportation, it invaded East Africa. Within 5 years, it killed a quarter of a million East Africans. There is no record of such an explosive epidemic in West Africa. What general biological principle may account for the difference?

‡20-17. In general, marine organisms are more sensitive to slight changes in environmental conditions than are fresh-water organisms. Can you give a general explanation of this fact?

20-18. What protozoan closely resembles the collar cells of sponges? What significance do you attribute to this fact?

‡20-19. Linnaeus, after neatly cataloging most of the animals he knew, threw the remainder into the grab-bag genus of *Chaos*. Is this a scientifically defensible procedure?

20-20. You want to observe the movement of the cilia of *Paramecium* under the microscope. You have available three sources of illumination: an incandescent bulb, a fluorescent light, and a bare neon tube. Which one will probably work best? Explain.

‡20-21. Are the bacteria inside the food vacuole of a paramecium also inside the paramecium?

Readings

Chapter 14 of Cohen tells of the use of foraminifera in identifying geological strata, and the importance of this use in prospecting for oil. Carson's *The Sea Around Us* tells something of the life of invertebrates in the ocean. For more systematic accounts of the invertebrates, see the MacGinities' *Natural History of Marine Animals*, Borradaile's *The Animal and Its Environment,* or Buchsbaum's superbly illustrated *Animals Without Backbones*. For a fascinating study of detective work in running down the causes of an amoebic dysentery outbreak, read "The Case of the Plumber's Patchwork" in Smith's *Plague on Us*.

21

Worms and Molluscs

161. Existence on Land: Challenge and Response

Because the first living organisms were probably soft-bodied and hence unsuited for fossilization, we may never know when life first appeared on earth, but the available evidence indicates that it was at least a billion years ago. Life must have been evolved first in a watery environment; all our oldest fossils are of aquatic forms. Not until less than half a billion years ago did land-dwelling forms appear. Why such a long time between the origin of life and its migration to land? What challenge does a land existence present, and what are the responses to the challenge?

The most obvious problem that faces a land-dwelling organism is that of survival in a dry environment. Water, the major constituent of every living cell, is essential for living activities; land organisms are in constant danger of losing water faster than it can be replaced. A second major problem of land existence is that of support; again this is connected with the lack of water. A living organism, being mostly water, is buoyed up and supported by its environment when it lives in water; in tenuous air it lacks this support, which it must obtain in other ways. The problem is particularly acute for large organisms. A third important problem of land-dwellers, which is a sort of composite of the first two, is that of reproduction. The gametes of a water-dweller are suspended and disseminated by the medium around them, which does not (obviously) threaten to dry them. The gametes of land forms—or other reproductive or disseminative structures, such as the spores of plants—because of their small size, are especially susceptible to drying.

And yet a fourth problem of land existence is that of withstanding a great range of variation in the environment. Many of the differences in variability are connected fairly directly with physical differences in the two materials. A given volume of air, for instance, requires only $\frac{1}{3000}$ as much heat to raise its temperature a given amount as does the same volume of water. Heat from the sun consequently causes much greater fluctuations in air temperature than in water temperature. From this effect spring many secondary effects, for example, the high winds that intermittently sweep over the land. By and large, a watery environment is much more constant than a land-and-air environment.

With all these seeming disadvantages of the land, why are there any land forms at all? In answering this, we must first point out, as has been emphasized before, that evolution is opportunistic. Where opportunities for a livelihood exist, there we may expect that, sooner or later, suitably adapted organisms will appear, as a result of evolution. The land is a great assemblage of environmental niches available for habitation by living things. As compared with the water, land may indeed have some disadvantages as a place for living—but do environments compete for inhabitants? Is it not, on the contrary, that organisms compete for environments? If so, the comparative merits of different environments are irrelevant, so long as the environments will support life at all.

It perhaps should be pointed out that land has some advantages, too. The relative thinness of the air as a surrounding medium makes it possible for poorly streamlined organisms to move at considerable speeds. The fastest organisms are land-dwellers: Some running forms (various antelopes) can travel in excess of 80 kilometers per hour, and some fliers (pigeons) can fly at nearly 160 km p h. The fastest water animals swim at about a third this speed. (For speeds of various animals, see Appendix 12.)

Air has another property that makes it more advantageous than water for living. Air is a mixture of gases of which nearly 21 percent by volume is oxygen; the amount of oxygen dissolved in water, on the other hand, is only about 1 percent by volume. An organism can, then, obtain from a given, easily movable volume of air more oxygen than is present in the same volume of heavier water. This circumstance has undoubtedly favored the development on land of organisms with a higher metabolic rate.

In evolving, how have organisms responded to the challenge of a land existence? It is part of the purpose of the succeeding pages to answer this question; but it is desirable here to sketch general answers, using as examples the plants already studied and those animals everyone knows about. First, in meeting the threat of drying, plants and animals have used similar devices. Land plants have developed a waxy cellular secretion, cutin, which greatly diminishes the loss of water. In addition, the outer layers of a plant often consist only of dead cells, for example, the bark and cork of trees. Mammalian skin also includes outer layers of dead cells, covered with water-impermeable substances (oils, more commonly than waxes).

The problem of support has been met by the evolution of special structural tissues, for example, xylem in plants, chitin and bones in animals. Almost all of the structural material in plants is dead, as is much of that in animals. Engineering theory tells us that a large organism must have proportionately more of its tissues serving as support. This fact serves to limit the size of land organisms. The largest water animals (whales) are far larger than the largest land animals (elephants). Strangely, however, the largest land plants (trees) are far larger than the largest water plants (algae called kelps). Among the factors that contribute to this difference in the two kingdoms is the lack of mobility among large plants. The structural problems of supporting a large stationary structure are not nearly as great as those of supporting a large structure in motion.

The problem of reproduction on land has been met by various, sometimes roundabout, means. Among land plants, mosses and ferns have not, in respect to reproduction, become completely terrestrial: an external film of water is still required for the male gamete to travel to the female. Flowering plants are, however, completely adapted to land: the male gametophyte can be transported through dry air to the stigma of the female, where it grows (rather than swims) down the style, needing no more moisture than that normally present in living tissues. No animal has achieved so great an independence of water. Motile male gametes are the rule, and they require moisture to swim in to reach the egg. In land-dwelling animals, fertilization in a liquid medium is made possible by a coming together of the two sexes in the act of copulation.

Regarding the adaptation of organisms to the variability of the terrestrial environment, only a few generalizations can be made. Many of the adaptations are physiological, but we know little of the details of the adaptations beyond the fact that, in general, land- and air-dwelling organisms are less affected than aquatic organisms by changes in the chemical and physical factors of their environment. Marine organisms are the most sensitive to environmental changes. In adapting to variable temperatures, some land animals have evolved a homeostatic system for maintaining a nearly constant temperature. This has been discussed in Chapter 8, and will be taken up once more when we come to study the vertebrates. The temperature control system is only one among many systems designed to maintain* a relatively constant internal environment in the presence of a fluctuating external one.

Movement itself is one means of minimizing the fluctuations of the external environment. It is not merely that an animal moves from where food is scarce to where it is more plentiful, but, in general, it "tries" to move so as to keep environmental factors near the optimum. To live well, most animals must move. Mobility brings with it changes in the symmetry of an organism. A slowly moving organism with few sense organs may have no symmetry whatever. *Amoeba* is such an organism: it is **asymmetrical.** Slightly more rapidly moving organisms, with better-developed sense organs, may show the **radial symmetry** of a jellyfish, in which the sense organs are distributed about the periphery of the mass and one point of the bell-edge is as likely to be going in a given direction as another. In a radially symmetrical animal, any of a number of vertical planes passed through the center will divide the body into like halves.

When we come to the most rapidly moving organisms, we find another type of symmetry, **bilateral symmetry.** A tiger has this type of symmetry; so does an airplane. For both of these, there is only one plane that can divide the body into equivalent right and left halves. (In passing, it should be noted that we do not demand perfect symmetry in applying the appropriate term; some of the internal organs of the tiger—as well as of the airplane—are asymmetrically disposed, but we nevertheless call both beasts bilaterally symmetrical.)†

Why do rapidly moving organisms have bilateral symmetry? (We mean, teleologically speaking, *why?*) Various relevant considerations can be pointed out. In gaining its livelihood, an animal needs to constantly "sample" its environment. This it may do most efficiently, that is, with the least duplication of effort, if it moves directionally, rather than at random. Directional movement is facilitated by having one part of the body predominantly in the lead. If morphological differentiation distinguishes this part of the body, bilateral symmetry results: The animal has a head end and a tail (anterior and posterior), a dorsal side and a ventral side (next to the substratum), and a left side and a right.

162. The Platyhelminthes

Occasionally, a greenhouse-keeper will be surprised to come across a ribbon-thin worm perhaps 15 centimeters long, slowly gliding along moist soil. Such a worm is a member of the phylum **Platyhelminthes** (Gr. *platys* = flat + *helminthos* = worm), a few members of which —like this natural denizen of tropical rain forests—have managed to come out onto land, but just barely. Most free-living flatworms are water-dwellers. In temperate regions, the easiest to come across are the **planarias** (Fig. 21-1), dun-colored organisms only a few millimeters in length which live under rocks and vegetation in fresh-water ponds and streams. They may often be collected with a submerged trap consisting of a bottle with a bit of liver inside. A planaria moves slowly over the substrate, laying down a film of mucus as a sort of carpet to move upon. On its ventral surface it has cilia, which may contribute to its motility, but careful studies show that nearly invisible muscular movements are largely responsible. A planaria is bilaterally symmetrical and shows considerable concentration of sense organs (the two eyes, and organs of touch and taste) at the anterior end, where the amount of nervous tissue present is sufficient to justify our speaking of a "brain." Experiments have shown that planarias are even capable of an extremely simple kind of learning.

---

* 21-1. What's objectionable about this sentence?

† 21-2. The symmetry of a *Volvox* (§108) was not described or named. Describe it, and propose a name for it.

21-3. Diagram and label all the types of symmetry considered to date.

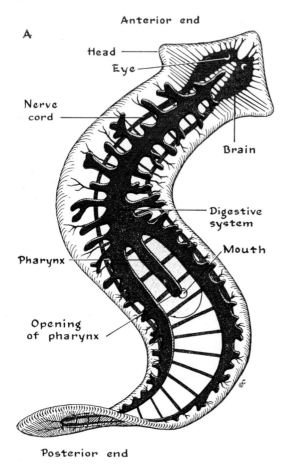

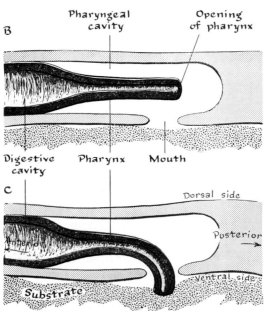

Fig. 21-1. *The structure of planaria.*

Like the coelenterates, the platyhelminthes have only a single opening into the gastrovascular cavity. This opening is at the end of a flexible, protrusile proboscis called a **pharynx;** the opening is called the **orifice of the pharynx.** How the animal takes in food may be best appreciated by studying *B* and *C* of Figure 21-1. When the animal finds a bit of fresh meat, it glides up on it, with its ventral side in contact with the food. The pharynx is then extruded out of the **mouth** and food is taken into the gastrovascular cavity through the pharyngeal orifice. In the cavity the food is fragmented somewhat, probably by muscular action, but all digestion appears to be *intra*cellular, occurring after fragments of food have been taken into the cells lining the digestive cavity.

In the Platyhelminthes we find an advance in the number of cell layers from which the tissues are derived. To the ectoderm and endoderm present in the coelenterates, the platyhelminthes have added an intermediate third layer, the **mesoderm.** All the animal phyla above the platyhelminthes also have this layer.

In the economy of nature, planarias are of only minor importance, but they are among the more interesting inhabitants of the experimental laboratory. These little creatures possess, to an unusual degree, an ability to regenerate lost parts. A single worm may be cut into several pieces (Fig. 21-2), each of which will, in a few weeks, heal and regenerate its lost parts. Because processes of regeneration are both interesting and practically important (e.g., in human medicine), regeneration has been much studied in these animals, and answers to some questions found. What, for example, determines which end of a piece cut out of the middle of a worm shall become the head end of the new worm? The answer is connected with the relative rates of metabolism of the two ends: the end with the higher metabolic rate becomes the head. Since there is a **metabolic gradient,** running from a high rate at the front to a low at the back of an intact worm, any section cut out has the same differential at its two ends and regenerates a head at the end that was more anterior before the operation.

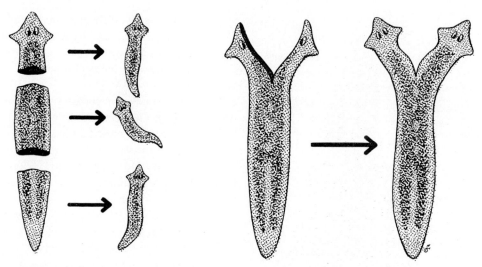

Fig. 21-2. *Regeneration of planaria.*

Although free-living platyhelminthes are of little practical importance, it is otherwise with the parasitic species. Millions of Chinese suffer seriously from the effects of the **Chinese liver fluke,** *Clonorchis sinensis,* a parasitic flatworm (Fig. 21-3). This fluke has three hosts in which it lives in succession: man, water snail, and fish. In the fish, the flukes occur in resting stages and are embedded in the muscles. When a man eats uncooked fish, the flukes come out of their resting stages and turn into active forms. To prevent the spread of this fluke, only one thing is necessary: to cook the fish. This sounds simple enough, but the millions of Chinese who live in affected localities have neither fuel nor money to buy the fuel needed for cooking the fish. This is but one of the many modern medical problems that are not medical problems at all, in the strict sense, but problems involving economics and the relation of population size to productivity of the land.

Another parasitic flatworm is the beef tapeworm, *Taenia saginata.* The life cycle is shown in Figure 21-4. The definitive host is man, who harbors the species as a multisectional worm living in his intestine. What is ordinarily regarded as a single adult tapeworm is perhaps better considered to be a colony of individuals connected in tandem. Each section consists of an almost complete set of organs, with emphasis on the reproductive. Each worm is hermaphroditic; the advantages of hermaphroditism to a parasite are obvious. As mature eggs and embryos develop within, sections break away from the whole and pass out in the feces. If a cow happens to eat grass contaminated with human dung that contains tapeworm embryos, these embryos then pass through other stages of their life cycle, leading to the ultimate formation of resting stages within "bladders" in the muscles of the cow. When these bladders are ingested by man, they "hatch," producing a new tapeworm.

Any parasite with a life cycle that necessarily involves more than one host is in a conspicuous way dependent on probabilities for its continued existence. With the beef tapeworm as an example, if *Taenia saginata* is to complete a life cycle, a man must defecate where a cow is feeding, and some time later the infested beef meat must be eaten, insufficiently cooked, by (another) man. The chance that a particular embryo excreted by man will be ingested by a cow before the parasite has perished from exposure must be very small. It is not surprising, therefore, to note that the embryos defecated by an infected man number in the hundreds of thousands. Throughout the living world there is a general inverse relationship between the *crude reproductive rate* (e.g., number of fertilized eggs

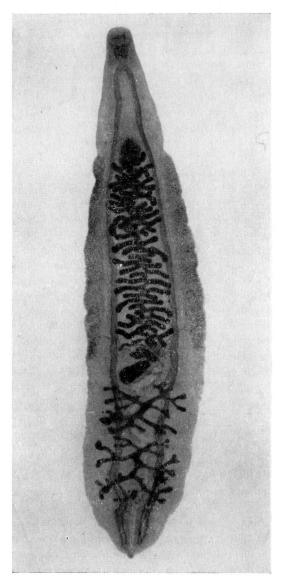

Fig. 21-3. *Stained specimen of the Chinese liver fluke,* Clonorchis sinensis. *Length about 1 centimeter. (Copyright General Biological Supply House, Inc., Chicago.)*

produced) and the chance of survival of an individual egg or embryo. A species in which the chance of survival is extremely low can survive only if immense numbers of individuals are produced. Parasites, particularly those with multiple hosts, have very high crude reproductive rates. The *net reproductive rates* depend on the success of each stage in the cycle, which will

differ under different conditions, and can be consciously altered by man, once he has discovered the life cycle.

Control of the beef tapeworm can be effected in three ways:

1. By always cooking beef thoroughly.

2. By inspecting beef at the slaughterer's and condemning meat that has bladders in it. (These are easily visible in certain muscles.)

3. By always disposing of human dung in a sanitary manner.

The first form of control can be effected by the individual. Anyone who wishes may prevent tapeworm in himself by refusing to eat rare meat. The other forms of control must be carried out by society, and can, in fact, make the first unnecessary. To put it another way, safe indulgence in the delight of eating rare beef depends on the adequate performance of the community functions of meat inspection and sewage disposal.

We have cited only two instances of parasitic flatworms. There are many other parasitic species of worms, and there is much variety in their life cycles. As a generalization, we may say that the two most common ways in which a parasitic species is passed from one host to another are via feces and by the eating of one host by another. In a society that enjoys a "high standard of living," as Occidentals understand the term, parasitic worms are of negligible importance. By contrast, consider the situation in Egypt where flukes of the genus *Schistosoma* (synonym: *Bilharzia*) are a major public health problem. During the 1950's it was estimated that the productivity of the population was depressed by 33 percent by **schistosomiasis** (infection with schistosomes; also called *bilharziasis*). On the average, 22 percent of the army recruits from Lower Egypt were rejected for physical defects, as compared with 3 percent from Upper Egypt. The difference was correlated with the difference in frequency of schistosomiasis. To eliminate the conditions leading to infection, the population would have to be prosperous, but it is not prosperous because it is diseased—an unlovely example of positive feedback. Such vicious circles are a

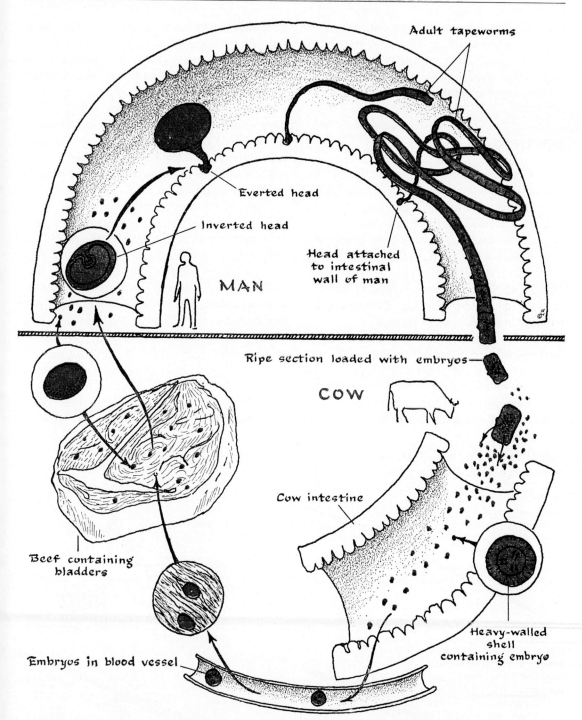

Adult tapeworms

Everted head

Inverted head

Head attached
to intestinal
wall of man

MAN

Ripe section loaded with embryos—

COW

Cow intestine

Beef containing
bladders

Heavy-walled
shell
containing embryo

Embryos in blood vessel

Fig. 21-4. *Life cycle of the beef tapeworm,* Taenia saginata. (*From Buchsbaum.* Animals Without Backbones, *1948, by permission of University of Chicago Press, Chicago.*)

constant threat to all populations. Whenever the standard of living goes down, or the organization of society is disrupted by war or other catastrophe, parasitic worms become an important threat to community health.

163. The Nemathelminthes

The Greek word *nema* means thread; the **Nemathelminthes** (or nematodes) are "thread worms" or "roundworms." This fact alone distinguishes them from the Platyhelminthes; but in addition the roundworms have a digestive tract that has *two* openings: a mouth and an anus. As a result, the animal has a "tube-within-a-tube" construction, as is apparent from an examination of *Ascaris* (Fig. 21-5), a genus parasitic in man and other animals.

There is a branch of mathematics called **topology** (Gr. *topo* = place), which deals with those aspects of the shapes of things that are unaltered by distortion, so long as no surfaces are torn; topology is often called "rubber-sheet geometry." To the topologist the shape of a nematode is the same as that of a doughnut; the general name **torus** is given this shape. A doughnut is a torus, and so is a nematode; *so also is a man.* Neglecting minor modifications, all animals from nematodes on up are tori. One of the topological consequences of this is that what is inside the intestine is not really inside the body. To get inside the body, an object must pass through an intestinal wall. Biological consequences of this topological fact will be pointed out, from time to time.

Nematode worms are about as close to being ubiquitous as are any organisms larger than protozoa and bacteria. Free-living species are present in large numbers in all soils, where they feed on bacteria. In the days when vinegar was made the "natural" way, it was always possible to find roundworms in the "mother of vinegar" that settled to the bottom of the container. This cottony material included cells of the "acetic acid bacteria" that were responsible for making the vinegar, and a host of nematodes that could thrive in this most unusual environment. Now that vinegar is made from pasteurized apple juice, by the use of pure cultures of bacteria,

Fig. 21-5. *The structure of* Ascaris, *a roundworm.* (*In part, from Brown,* Biology, *by permission of D. C. Heath and Company, Boston.*)

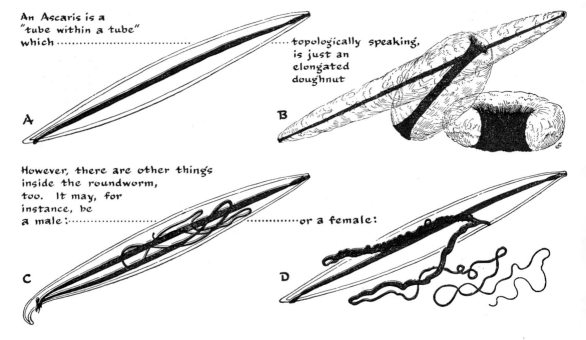

An Ascaris is a "tube within a tube" which .... topologically speaking, is just an elongated doughnut

A

B

However, there are other things inside the roundworm, too. It may, for instance, be a male: .... or a female:

C

D

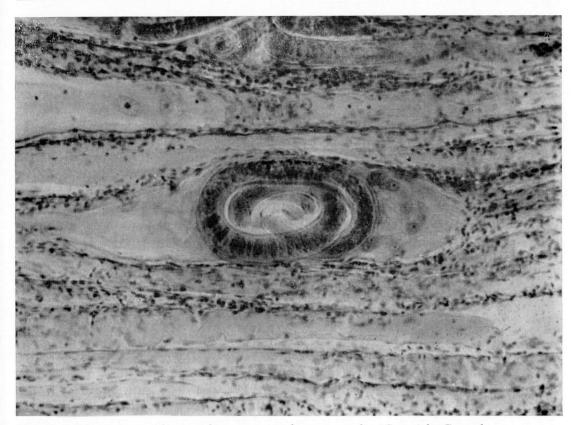

Fig. 21-6. *Photomicrograph of trichina worm in human muscle. (Copyright General Biological Supply House, Inc., Chicago.)*

one no longer sees the little worms once found in the vinegar cruet on every family dinner table.

There are many parasitic species of nematodes. Some of the plant parasites are of considerable agricultural importance. Human parasites include such relatively unimportant species as the "pinworms" that infect a considerable fraction of small children at one time or another, as well as more serious parasites such as the three described below.

The **hookworm parasite** is a minute worm called *Necator americanus* (the "American killer"). Thousands of these nematodes may sometimes be found attached to the intestinal wall of a single man. The fertilized eggs pass out with the feces. The eggs hatch in the soil, producing immature worms that live in the dirt for some time, ultimately re-entering man by burrowing through his skin, for example,

through the sole of a bare foot. The immature worms can live only in warm, moist soil, and hence the cycle cannot be maintained in cool regions. The control measures needed in warm countries are obvious: the sanitary disposal of human feces and/or the wearing of shoes. In many impoverished regions of the southern United States, neither measure can be invoked without outside aid or influence. Since hookworm infestation causes a very debilitating disease, its victims are often despised for their "shiftlessness."

The **trichina parasite,** *Trichinella spiralis,* can infest the flesh (Fig. 21-6) of a number of animals (pigs, rats, bears, man), passing from one to another when one animal devours another. It is *not* transmitted through feces. The most important source of infection for man is pork. As with tapeworm, this avenue of infection can be closed by thoroughly cooking the meat. Condemnation of infected meat is also theoretically possible, but not very practicable. Trichina worms are exceedingly minute and must be searched for with a microscope. In some European countries such an examination is routinely made. In the United States it is not favored, on the grounds that it is dangerous to have an officially sanctioned examination that is not thoroughly reliable.

Trichina worms burrow through the intestinal wall of man and ultimately migrate to the muscles. Symptoms of the early stage of infection resemble "intestinal flu"; later there are rheumatic muscular pains which, in heavy infections, may be severe. Each worm that reaches a muscle becomes encapsulated there, where it remains for the rest of the life of the host. It can reach a new host only if the flesh it is in is eaten by another animal. In our civilization, successful infection of a human by a trichina worm puts a terminus to the life cycle of the individual parasite.

Post-mortem examination of human muscles in Germany nearly a century ago revealed that about 90 percent of the human population was infected with trichina. Today, in the United States, the figure is about 16 percent. It should be possible to reduce the figure still further now that the practice of "deep freezing" of meats has become common. The time and temperature required to kill trichina are shown in the following table:

Temperature	Time
−15°C	20 days
−23°C	10 days
−29°C	6 days

These figures apply to pieces of meat that do not exceed 15 centimeters in thickness.* Dried sausage may require up to 40 days of freezing to kill the trichina, depending on the temperature, dimensions, and spices† added.

The **filaria worm,** *Wucheria bancrofti,* is another kind of roundworm of considerable

medical importance. The immature worms are so small that they are transmitted from person to person by mosquitoes of certain species. In humans, filarias cause trouble by blocking lymph passages, causing permanent swelling of the part of the body that is normally drained by the particular lymph passages. As a result, the affected part swells to a tremendous size; hence, the name of the disease, **elephantiasis.**

164. The Mollusca

This phylum includes clams, oysters, scallops, limpets, whelks, snails, slugs, and abalone—not to mention squids, the chambered nautilus, and octopi. The Latin word *molluscus* means soft, which aptly describes the impression one gets of the flesh of most of these forms, a large majority of which are, however, protected by a hard shell, of which calcium carbonate is usually the basic component. Although many snails are terrestrial, the phylum as a whole is predominantly aquatic. Clams, oysters, mussels, and other relatively sedentary forms usually get their sustenance from microscopic particles suspended in the water—bacteria, algae, and protozoa. The structure of a clam (Fig. 21-7) is admirably adapted to the function of sieving minute particles out of the water. A clam of ordinary eating size may filter as many as 3 liters of water an hour. (No one has measured the quantity of water passing through *Tridacna,* the giant clam of the Great Barrier Reef of Australia. This clam, whose shell is much favored for birdbaths and other garden bric-a-brac, weighs hundreds of pounds.) Since their food is the suspended material of the water around them, the flavor and quality of clams and oysters are markedly determined by the environment. Oysters living too near sewer outfalls may accumulate living typhoid or dysentery bacteria, and so be dangerous to eat in the raw condition. The accumulation of poisonous dinoflagellates by mussels has been referred to (§110).

One of the more curious aspects of the economic importance of shellfish is that connected with pearl production. A clam or oyster secretes

---

* 21-4. Why does the thickness matter?
† 21-5. Why should the spices matter? Any hypothesis?

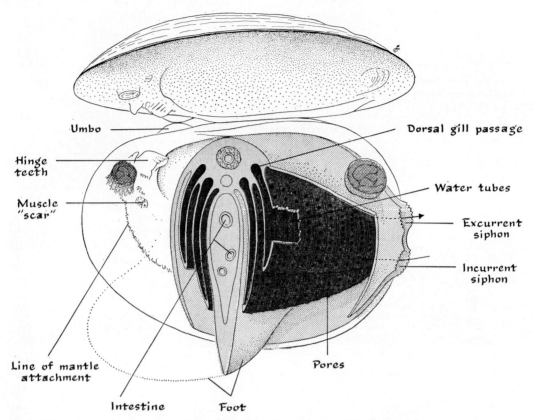

Umbo

Hinge teeth

Muscle "scar"

Dorsal gill passage

Water tubes

Excurrent siphon

Incurrent siphon

Line of mantle attachment

Pores

Intestine   Foot

Fig. 21-7. *The anatomy of a clam.* (*From Buchsbaum,* Animals Without Backbones, *1948, by permission of University of Chicago Press, Chicago.*)

new shell material continuously through the activity of the **mantle,** the layer of living tissue next to the shell. The innermost layer of the shell is, in many species, beautifully iridescent, and is called the *pearly layer*. If a foreign object comes in contact with the proper region of the mantle, it will be covered with pearly material. If it retains its discreteness as an object (rather than becoming plastered to the shell), it may be turned into a pearl, the shape of which is partly determined by the shape of the primary irritant. For the animal, the process has its utility in the protection it affords against various parasites; for man, its utility is found in its production of jewelry. The yield of pearls by pearl oysters under natural conditions is low. In the past half-century, Japanese technicians have developed means of deliberately inserting symmetrical irritating particles in young oysters, thus greatly increasing the supply of good pearls. "Cultured

pearls" are, as a matter of fact, superior in quality to the natural ones. But so perverse is human nature that they are less esteemed than "natural" pearls, precisely because they are less rare.*

It is a most remarkable thing that the phylum that includes such sluggishly moving organisms of minimal intelligence as snails, slugs, oysters, and clams should also include such alert, speedy carnivores as the squid (Fig. 21-8). Molluscs of this sort are put in the class **cephalopoda,** literally "the head-footed," so named because what is called the foot in other forms has evolved a brain and the highly specialized sense organs (e.g., eyes) that we associate with the word "head." The foot has also become sub-divided into a number of actively moving, sucker-armored arms, the number being eight

---

* 21-6. Are they less "natural"?

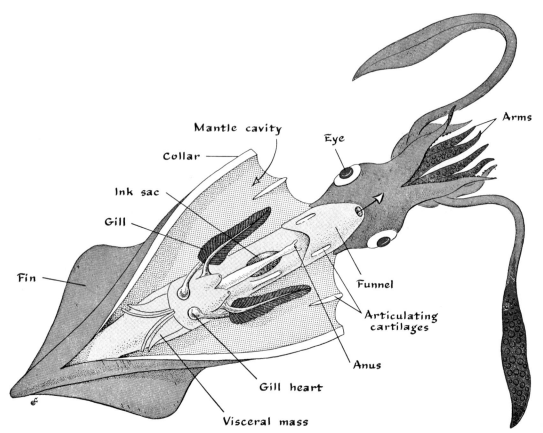

Fig. 21-8. *Internal anatomy of a squid. (From Buchsbaum,* Animals Without Back-bones, *1948, by permission of University of Chicago Press, Chicago.)*

in the octopi and ten in the decapods (of which squids are members).*

In adaptive capabilities, no other phylum of invertebrates can match the cephalopod molluscs; no other phylum comes as close to the vertebrates in their potentialities. Yet (or therefore?) they excite loathing rather than admiration in most humans. The octopus is the very stereotype of the animal villain in fiction, from Victor Hugo's *Toilers of the Sea* to the banal horror movies of our day. Yet octopi, far from being aggressive enemies of mankind are shy and retiring connoisseurs of shellfish. Squids, also, avoid men as much as possible. To the close student of biology, squids are particularly admirable. They have two large and excellent image-perceiving eyes (as contrasted with the

many *eyespots* of a limpet, which merely perceive light and dark); they have a well-developed brain and nervous system, and such experiments as have been carried out indicate considerable of what we would call intelligence. The motions of a squid are graceful. Normally it moves head forward by the undulations of its body (note the **fins**); but when in need of speed, it moves itself rapidly in the opposite direction by squirting water at high speed out of the **funnel.** Thus squids are among the oldest living exploiters of jet propulsion. The escape of a squid from enemies is aided by two other tricks. First, it has specialized color cells in its skin, cells called **chromatophores,** which (under nervous control) it can rapidly expand and contract, thus changing its color in a most confusing manner. Second, it can squirt ink out of its **ink sac,** thus creating a dark cloud in the

---

* 21-7. What is the singular of "octopi"? What does it mean? What is the etymology of "decapod"?

water that acts as an alternate target which the predator may attack in place of the formerly dark, but now light, squid. (Just as a bird may attack the tail freshly broken off a lizard while the main body of the prey escapes.) Such a diversionary tactic, even though successful only for a few seconds, may make the difference between life and death some of the time, which is enough for it to be selected for in evolution. (Perfection is not demanded.)

Most of the squids normally seen by man are small, from a few inches to a few feet, but we know that much larger forms are found in the depths of the ocean, below 450 meters. The largest of all invertebrates is *Architeuthis,* with arms as long as 15 meters, the rest of the body 9 meters and a weight of at least 2000 kilograms. We know this form almost entirely from portions of it found in the stomachs of sperm whales, which feed on it. The heads and bodies of these toothed whales often show great scars made by the beak and suckers of the squid, witnesses to epic battles that took place in the absolute darkness of the ocean depths.

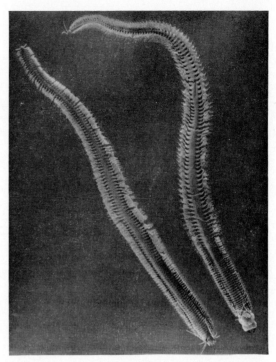

Fig. 21-9. *Some sandworms of the genus* Nereis. (*Copyright General Biological Supply House, Inc., Chicago.*)

165. The Annelida

The largest class of this phylum, the **Polychaeta** (Gr. *poly* = many + *chaite* = hair), includes such forms as the marine "sandworms" or "clamworms." The reason for the class name is readily apparent from an inspection of Figure 21-9. The **chaetae,** or bristles, are projections of locomotory organs, the **parapodia** (literally, the "side-feet"). Notice the **segmentation,** which is a characteristic of this phylum. Most of the body consists of repeated, almost identical segments; only a few of the terminal segments are *differentiated* from each other.

The polychaetes, unknown to inland dwellers, are quite conspicuous members of the marine fauna of many shores. In the South Pacific a species called the "palolo worm" puts on a spectacular show every November, just at dawn one week after the full moon. The posterior parts of many millions of worms break off and swim to the surface, where they release eggs and

sperm into the water in which fertilization takes place. Natives, aware of the precise timing of this process, scoop the worm fragments up by the basketfull and have themselves a feast. Meanwhile, the anterior portions of the worms, hiding in the corals below, set about regenerating the lost parts. After fertilization, each worm egg differentiates into an immature swimming form called a **trochophore larva** (Gr. *trochos* = wheel + *phore* from *phorein* = to bear; so called from the ciliated ring which gives the appearance of a moving wheel). A typical polychaete trochophore is shown in Figure 21-10. Such larvae eventually give rise to adult worms.

More familiar than the polychaetes are annelids of the class **Oligochaeta** (Gr. *oligos* = few), of which earthworms are the best-known examples. In the process of evolving into a subterranean habitat, earthworms have lost their parapodia, and their locomotory bristles have been reduced to near invisibility. Most earthworms are only a few centimeters long, but

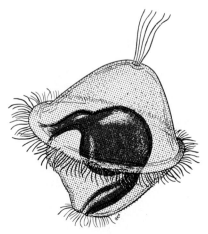

Fig. 21-10. *A trochophore larva.*

Australia boasts a now nearly extinct monster that reaches a length of more than 3 meters; it is about 2 centimeters in diameter and may weigh as much as 680 grams. The Laughing Jackass or Kookabura bird catches it much as robins catch our smaller earthworms.*

The segmentation of an earthworm is more than skin deep; some of the internal structures are segmentally disposed. For example, an earthworm has five pairs of hearts (Fig. 21-11*A*). The nerve cord also shows a swelling (a "ganglion") and branches in each segment (Fig. 21-11*B*). Notice that the annelid nerve cord is on the belly, or **ventral** side, of the animal, as it is in invertebrates generally, in contrast to the vertebrates, in which the nerve cord is **dorsal** in position (L. *dorsum* = back).

The intestinal tract of an earthworm is not, however, segmental in arrangement. It is a continuous tube from the mouth at the anterior end to the anus at the posterior. Like the roundworms, the annelids are built upon a tube-within-a-tube plan. The space between the two tubes (Fig. 21-12) is called a **coelom** (Gr.

koiloma = hollow); we will encounter this cavity frequently as we study other animals, including man.

An earthworm's diet consists of dirt and whatever nutritious remains of plants and animals are in it. Food enters the mouth at the extreme anterior end and passes the length of the intestinal tract, undergoing digestion along the way. Eating, for the earthworm, is both a means of securing nutrition and an aid in burrowing through the soil. A great deal of material of no nutritional value to the earthworm is thus moved around.

The soil, however, is probably benefited by the stirring up that it gets. In the course of their activities, earthworms carry much soil to the surface of the earth and deposit it as little coiled lumps of material called worm castings. Measurements in one worm-rich soil indicated that on each hectare in the course of 1 year there were deposited 7 metric tons of worm castings. At this rate, there would be deposited on the surface of the ground about 5 centimeters of reworked soil every 10 years. How much net increase in soil this represents is not known. The translocation of soil from below to above has the effect of gradually burying both rocks and small man-made objects, if the latter go unattended.

The reproductive system of the earthworm is segmentally arranged, but is confined to the ninth to fifteenth segments inclusive. The earthworm is hermaphroditic; it does not fertilize itself, however. Two worms come together and fertilize each other. Hermaphroditism is found here and there throughout the animal kingdom. It is not confined to any one phylum, but rather is characteristic of animals leading a certain kind of life. Though there are exceptions, it is generally found among animals of sedentary habits. It seems reasonable to suppose that an animal that does not get around much would be more likely to reproduce itself if it were certain that the first individual of the same species that it encountered would be of the right sex(es) for mating. At any rate, hermaphroditism is frequently found among the relatively slow-moving forms, such as the earthworm, and among parasitic species, such as tapeworms.

---

* 21-8. The Kookabura grabs hold of a protruding end of the worm, braces himself and waits. Pretty soon the worm "gives" a little and the bird secures a new purchase, braces himself and waits for the next relaxation. What role do the bristles play in the protection of the worm? Secure a giant earthworm and, by palpation, see if you can figure out the answer. If you are one of the deprived classes without ready access to giant earthworms, make do with what you have.

The final class of annelids to be considered is the class **Hirudinea,** or leeches. That these are segmented worms is obvious, but curiously the visible appearance is deceptive—there are three times as many external rings as there are internal segments. Leeches are without bristles; they move in water by undulations of the whole body; on land, they move slowly after the fashion of a "measuring worm," using their suckers for attachment. The suckers are also useful for attaching to vertebrate hosts. Once attached, a leech erodes a hole in the skin of the host by using tiny teeth hidden in the anterior sucker; the operation is skillfully and painlessly done, aided by a chemical substance called **hirudin,** which prevents the host's blood from clotting. In a few hours a leech will engorge enough blood to swell to several times its unfed size, then will drop off the host and live for many months on one blood meal. For centuries in Europe, leeches of the species *Hirudo medicinalis* were used as a means of bleeding a patient,

Fig. 21-11. *Anterior end of an earthworm. Color used to delineate: in A, circulatory system; in B, nervous system; in C, reproductive system.*

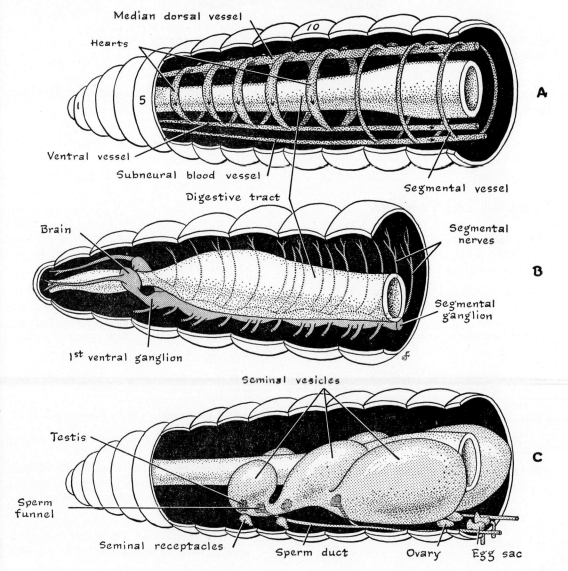

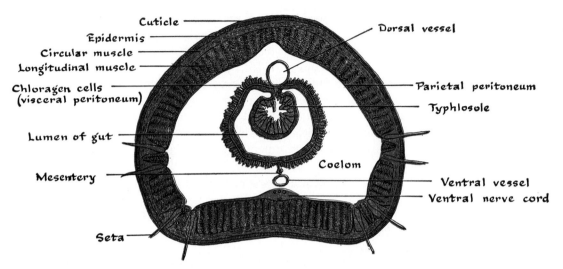

Fig. 21-12. *Structure of an earthworm. (From Johnson, Laubengayer, and DeLanney,* General Biology, *1956, by permission of Holt, Rinehart, and Winston, New York.)*

when bleeding was believed to be of therapeutic value. Even today, some drugstores in the foreign sections of large American cities keep live leeches in stock.

Questions and Problems

21-8. Make a list of the **boldface** terms in this chapter. Write a brief definition or description of each. Compare your work with the text.

‡21-9. In general, marine organisms are more sensitive to slight changes in environmental conditions than are fresh-water organisms. Can you give a general evolutionary explanation of this fact?

21-10. Among marine organisms, *littoral* species (i.e., species living between high and low tide marks) are less sensitive to slight environmental changes than are species of the open ocean. Give a general evolutionary explanation.

‡21-11. The largest plants are land-dwelling forms (redwoods), whereas the largest animals (whales) live in water. How do you account for this difference?

21-12. Consider plant spores, which serve to disseminate the species. From a quantitative point of view, compare large and small spores with respect to (a) optimum supportability by air, and (b) optimum water-retaining ability.

‡21-13. What kind of symmetry is exhibited by (a) a sugar bowl; (b) a coffeepot; (c) an automobile? In which one(s) is the symmetry perfect?

21-14. The three-toed sloth moves with a slowness that is almost painful to watch, yet it has bilateral symmetry. How come?

‡21-15. A planarian can move upside down at the surface of a bowl of water. What is the substrate in this case?

21-16. Some people think that the Jewish proscription of eating pork has a naturalistic explanation. *If* this is so, can you suggest what it is?

‡21-17. The polychaete "fireworms" of Bermudian waters find one another in the dark

night sea by the exchange of luminescent signals. As the male and female come together, they both burst, shedding gametes into the sea. The adults perish in the act of reproduction. (Rather a poetic death, is it not?) But is this not going contrary to the idea of natural selection?

21-18. As recounted in §162, schistosomiasis has reduced the productivity of the people of Egypt by 33 percent, whereas only 22 percent of the draftees are rejected by the army. Should not these percentages be identical? Or if not identical, should not the latter figure be greater because army standards are more rigorous than civilian standards?

‡21-19. "But is it safe?" asks Mrs. Mulligatawny. "Certainly," replies her butcher, slapping the pork roast; "I've had it in me own freezer at minus ten degrees for two weeks." Is it safe?

21-20. Add another column to the table in §163 giving the Fahrenheit degrees for killing trichina.

‡21-21. Give a cybernetic analysis of parasitic disease viewed as social problems.

21-22. In the works of Shakespeare and Molière a doctor is often called a "leech." Why?

‡21-23. The wound left by *Hirudo medicinalis* may bleed for a long time. Why?

21-24. Why are slow-moving planaria bilaterally symmetrical, whereas jellyfish, which may move much more rapidly on occasion, are radially symmetrical?

‡21-25. Some fresh-water clams produce a larval stage called a *glochidium,* which attaches itself to the gills or fins of fishes. In the life history of such clams, what role do the glochidia play?

21-26. Julian Huxley, biologist brother of Aldous, and grandson of T. H., in 1942 made the following statement:

To assert that man is the highest product of evolution to date is a statement of simple biological fact. There are, however, some other points concerning man's position relative to evolutionary progress that are less obvious. First is the curious fact that the human species is now the sole repository of any possible future progress for life. When multicellular animals first appeared, they all had reached a new level of progress: later, some cut themselves off from further advance by entering on blind alleys, such as the fixed vegetative existence of the polyps and corals or the headlessness and radial symmetry of the starfish and other echinoderms. The process of restriction has now gone so far that all future progress hangs on human germ plasm. It is a biological impossibility for any other line of life to progress into a new dominant type—not the ant, the rat, nor the ape.

In reviewing the animals of this chapter, try to develop a rebuttal to Huxley's argument.

Readings

There is a wealth of good books about the sea and its denizens, including the invertebrates. Carson's *The Sea Around Us,* the MacGinities' *Natural History of Marine Animals,* Buchsbaum's *Animals Without Backbones,* and Hardy's *The Open Sea* are only a few of the books available.

For a thorough treatment of the problems of animal parasites see *Parasitology* by Noble and Noble. Darwin's *Formation of Vegetable Mould through the Action of Worms* is a charming account of a classic discovery of the long-term importance of humble actions.

22

The Arthropoda

166. General Characteristics

The name "Arthropoda" literally means "jointed-footed"; its appropriateness can be verified with the first beetle that passes by. Crabs, spiders, lice, and butterflies are all arthropods. On the surface of the earth today, arthropods and vertebrates are clearly the two dominants groups of animals. Which one might be said to be *the* dominant group is a question to which neither man nor bug may give an unbiased answer. We think *we* are—particularly if we live in cities. But just let the city dweller try to walk across a northern tundra throbbing with mosquitoes in the summertime, and he may change his tune. Certainly if numbers of individuals are the deciding criterion, the arthropods win the crown easily. There are more ants, bees, and flies in a few square miles than there are humans in the entire world. As for the numbers of species in each group, there are only about 60,000 species of vertebrates, whereas the number of kinds of arthropods can be dramatized by the following calculation. According to a traditional account, Noah was required to gather together "of every living thing of all flesh, two of every sort . . . male and female." If this included the arthropods, and if we assume that Noah checked them on board at the rate of one species per second, working only a forty-hour week, it would have taken him at

least one month, and maybe two, to have put all the Arthropoda on board.*

Among the many conspicuous differences between arthropods and vertebrates is the skeleton. The internal position of the vertebrate skeleton is well known; the arthropod skeleton is external and is both a protection for the soft parts of the body and a locus of attachment of the muscles. It is called an **exoskeleton.** It is made of a nitrogen-containing organic compound called **chitin.** In its pure state, chitin is a soft and flexible material reminiscent of many manmade plastics. The smaller arthropods are, in general, covered with comparatively pure chitin. Larger arthropods, however, need a stronger exoskeleton, which may be achieved by (for example) impregnation with calcium compounds (as in lobsters and crabs). If the exoskeleton were everywhere so hard and inflexible, movement would be impossible. Mobility is made possible by a retention of thin, unimpregnated chitin at the joints. The mode of construction is much like that of a knight's articulated suit of armor, which must satisfy the same conflicting criteria of mobility and protection.

With the skeleton on the outside, the mode of

---

* 22-1. So, using the higher figure, how many different kinds of arthropods are there? How does this compare, by percentage, with the number of kinds of vertebrates?

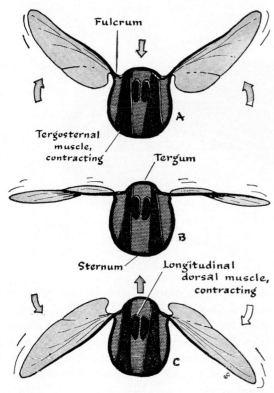

Fig. 22-1. *Mode of action of insect muscles. See text for explanation. (By permission, from Snodgrass,* Principles of Insect Morphology, *copyright 1935 by McGraw-Hill Co., Inc., New York.)*

attachment of the muscles must be different in the arthropods than it is in the vertebrates. The vertebrate plan is well known to most; for review, you might look ahead to Chapter 24. A typical mode of action among the arthropods is shown in Figure 22-1, which shows, diagrammatically, a **transverse** section through the thorax of a fly. The muscles, shown in color, consist of two sets. The vertical muscles run from the *tergum* (dorsal part of the exoskeleton) to the *sternum* (ventral part of the exoskeleton). When these muscles, the *tergosternal muscles,* contract (going from *B* to *A*), they pull down on the tergum. The exoskeleton from the tergum out to the leading edge of the wing acts as a lever operating about the fulcrum as indicated. So when the tergum is flattened, the wing is raised. The lowering of the wing is brought about by the *longitudinal dorsal muscles,* which run lengthwise and are attached at

the ends of each segment. When they contract, they diminish the length of the thorax, thus bulging up the tergum and causing the wings to drop (going from *B* to *C*).* Muscles that work against each other in this way are called **antagonistic muscles.**

The rapidity with which antagonistic muscles can cause wings to vibrate has long been a source of wonder. Robert Hooke, the ingenious demonstrator of the early days of the Royal Society, figured out a way to determine the frequency of the wing beats, but the diarist Samuel Pepys (1633–1703) was sceptical: "Mr. Hooke . . . told me that . . . he is able to tell how many strokes a fly makes with her wings . . . by the note that it answers to in musique during their flying. That, I suppose, is a little too much refined; but his discourse in general of sound was mighty fine." Using Hooke's method it can be shown that one species of midge has a beat frequency of 1,000 cps (cycles per second).† For comparison, consider these cps values among the birds: swan, 2; gull, 5; pigeon, 10; and hummingbird, 50.

The chitinous exoskeleton of arthropods is an admirable system for achieving protection without sacrificing mobility. It produces a splendid suit of armor that has probably contributed to the success of the phylum. But it has one conspicuous disadvantage: it does not readily permit growth. To increase in volume, an arthropod must first split open his old hard armor, pull himself out of it (still covered by a thin underlayer of flexible new chitin), and then swell rapidly before his new skin hardens into an armor once more. This process of molting (called **ecdysis**) is a complicated one, and the period immediately following a molt is a vulnerable one for the individual.

There seems to be little question that the arthropods evolved from the annelids. Like the annelids, they show segmentation, but it is considerably reduced in extent. External segmentation is still present, though it is less obvious, and

* 22-2. Make diagrams of longitudinal sections of a fly's thorax to show how the longitudinal dorsal muscles do their work.

† 22-3. What musical note (fundamental) do such wings produce?

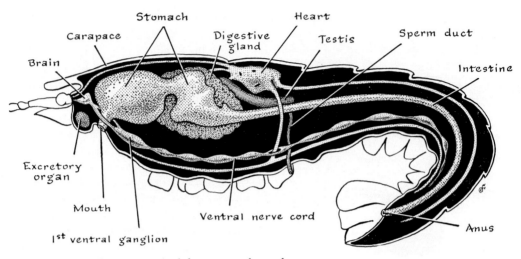

Fig. 22-2. *Internal structure of a lobster, an arthropod.*

the ventral nerve cord is definitely segmented (Fig. 22-2); but most of the other organs are unsegmented.

The phylum Arthropoda is divided into several classes, of which the three most important will be discussed here.

167. The Class Crustacea

The **Crustacea** are mostly water-dwelling forms. The best known of them are the various large edible species of lobsters and crabs, but actually the smaller species, ranging from shrimp on down to various microscopic water fleas (*Daphnia* and *Cyclops,* for example), are of greater economic importance since they are very near the base of the Pyramid of Protoplasm (§102). Such small forms feed on algae, protozoa, and bacteria, in various mixtures. They in turn are typically the food of small fishes, which in turn are eaten by larger. The concentration of small crustacea is so great in some parts of the ocean that it has made possible the evolution of large vertebrates feeding directly on them, for example, the basking shark and the largest of all vertebrates, the whalebone whales, which support their great bulk entirely on shrimplike crustacea sieved out of the water by their whalebone apparatus.

Among the more curious of the crustacea are the barnacles, which do not (at first glance) look at all like arthropods (Fig. 22-3). Inside the calcareous shell (which reminds us of a mollusc, if of anything) is an active arthropod with typically jointed appendages which it protrudes from time to time, waving them through the water to collect its microscopic food. All barnacles are marine. The adults are sessile, but they produce a motile juvenile form. The settling of barnacles on ships ("fouling") is expensive to man. The increased flow resistance caused by a 7-centimeter growth of barnacles on a ship may cut its speed by 50 percent and greatly increase fuel consumption. Dry-docking one of the largest liners and removing several hundred tons of barnacles may cost around 10^5 per year. Obviously, there is a need for an efficient antifouling procedure or device. So far only limited success has been achieved. Basic studies have shown that many substances that are directly damaging to barnacles are of little use as antifouling agents. Other organisms, for example, algae and bacteria, may settle on an anti-barnacle agent and furnish an acceptable support for the barnacles. Among the most effective antifouling agents found to date have been various copper preparations noteworthy for discouraging algae.

Most of the crustacea are marine, a few live in fresh water, and a very few live on land. The land-dwellers, such as the "pill bugs," have

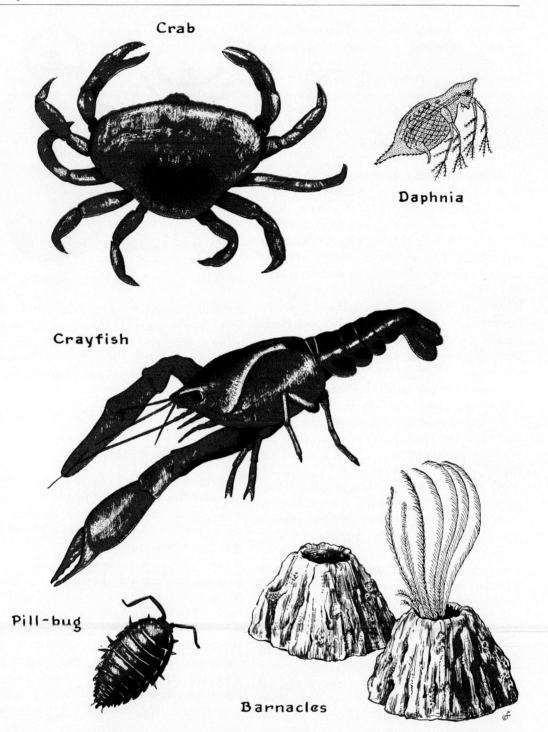

Fig. 22-3. *A miscellany of crustacea. (Not drawn to same scale.)*

made only a limited conquest of the land. Their breathing apparatus is essentially that of a water-dweller and functions only in moist environments, such as that found under rocks.

168. The Class Arachnoidea

To the class **Arachnoidea** belong the spiders and their relatives: scorpions, "daddy longlegs," the ticks, and the mites. All of these forms have eight legs, which distinguishes them from the insects, which have only six. Most of the members of this class are "lone wolves," each individual keeping to himself; an occasional brief flurry of sexual activity is the only form of social intercourse. Many of them—all the spiders, for instance—are wholly carnivorous, being tempted only by living flesh. Because spiders live mainly on insects, they are important agents in controlling the numbers of insects. The toxic bite (not sting) of spiders is well known, but seldom experienced by man. In the temperate zone, few spiders are large enough to bite or hurt man. The black widow is a notorious exception in the United States; but it is a very shy species, and forcing it to bite a man is difficult. There are no authentic cases of adults being killed by black widow bites, though possibly some children have been. More noted (though less dangerous) are the very large hairy spiders known as tarantulas. In the Latin countries the wild dance form known as the *tarantella* has a legendary origin as (1) a dance produced by a tarantula bite, or (2) a dance that can magically prevent the dire results of such a bite. Actually, tarantula bites are not very serious. Far more serious are the bites of certain large tropical scorpions, which may be lethal.

Ticks are bloodsucking arachnids. A tiny, flat individual can, in less than an hour, swell up to the size of a pea (Fig. 22-4) as it gorges itself on the blood of its host. As is frequently true of habitual parasites, ticks act as vectors of various diseases, among which are one kind of cattle fever, typhus, relapsing fever, and Rocky Mountain spotted fever. Many tick-borne dis-

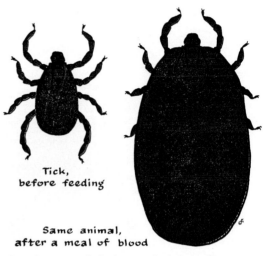

Tick, before feeding

Same animal, after a meal of blood

Fig. 22-4. *A tick, before and after feeding.*

eases are caused by Rickettsias, intracellular bacterialike organisms. These may be harmless or even beneficial to the ticks. The generally great pathogenicity of Rickettsias for man suggests that man is only a more or less accidental host for the microbes.*

169. The Class Insecta

It is characteristic of common classes of organisms that they become confused in the lay mind with quite different forms of life that (in some sense) are functionally equivalent. The point is well illustrated in a story told by the poet Robert Graves. It seems that an old lady was traveling by train from London to Edinburgh, taking a pet tortoise in a basket. She wanted to know whether she should buy a dog-ticket for it, as one is required to do in England for cats, because cats are officially counted as dogs. "No," said the ticket-taker, "No, mum. Cats is dogs, and rabbits is dogs, and dogs is dogs; and squirrels in cages is parrots, but this here turkle is a hinsect. We won't charge you nothing, mum!"

We cannot be quite so lenient as the ticket-taker in our definition: *insects are arthropods with three pairs of legs.* The class **Insecta** is a

---

* 22-4. By what line of reasoning?

conspicuously successful group. In number of species they outrank all other kinds of living things except, possibly, the microbes. Their variety and beauty are such that they have long been favorite objects for collectors. The hundreds of thousands of species of insects alive today fall into some 20 well-defined orders (§104). About half of these orders are described below, representatives being shown in Figure 22-5.

ISOPTERA. The termites, often mistakenly called "white ants," are important in the economy of nature in that they hasten the rate of decomposition of cellulose, the structural material of plants, including trees. Man, who appropriates this material to make his houses and his books, complains when termites continue to eat the kind of food they have eaten for some 200 million years.

ORTHOPTERA. Grasshoppers, katydids, roaches, crickets, and the praying (preying) mantis belong to this group. Most of the noise-makers of the insect world are orthopterans.

ANOPLURA. Lice, though descended from winged forms, are wingless. Being completely parasitic on vertebrates, including man, they no longer need wings, for the sociality of the host species easily enables a louse to transfer from one perambulating meal ticket to another. There is a 1915 record of a lousy Russian prisoner of war who had 3,800 lice living on him. The Rickettsial disease typhus is carried by lice.

SIPHONAPTERA. The fleas also are wingless, but they are more active about transferring from one host to another, having developed remarkable jumping abilities. Moussorgsky honored these animals with one of his finest songs. Properly unhonored are the fleas that carry plague and typhus.

DIPTERA. The word "fly," as an entomologist uses it, refers only to the two-winged flies, or Diptera. Houseflies, horseflies, cow flies, deer flies, mosquitoes, gnats, and midges belong to this order. These insects have evolved from four-winged ancestors. The second pair of wings, in the course of evolution, has "degenerated" into a pair of tiny knobs, which are not, however, without function. When these knobs (called **halteres,** or *balancers*) are removed, the fly is no longer able to fly correctly. It appears that, by vibrating while the insect is in flight, the halteres act as gyroscopes and help keep the animal on an even keel. Many diseases are caused by flies; in some of them (the ox warble), the insect is the direct cause, while in others (malaria, yellow fever), the fly (mosquito) is a vector of the disease organism.

HEMIPTERA. A precise entomologist restricts the use of the word "bug" to members of this group. Bugs have two pairs of wings, but one pair, half leathery in texture, folds over the other in rest. Bugs have mouth parts designed like a hypodermic needle, to pierce and suck. The attention of the great majority is confined to plants, entailing considerable destruction of man's crops. Chinch bugs, squash bugs, stinkbugs, backswimmers, and water striders are members of this order.

LEPIDOPTERA. These are the scale-winged insects—moths and butterflies—so beloved of collectors. About 80,000 species have been described and named. Probably only a few of the larger and more conspicuous species remain to be discovered. Some of the moths, for example, clothes moths and codling moths, cause considerable damage to man's possessions and crops. On the other hand, the larva of the silkworm moth furnishes us with genuine silk, which is a good substitute for rayon and nylon.

HYMENOPTERA. These have two pairs of thin, membranous wings; but frequently (e.g., in the honeybee), the hind wing hooks onto the fore wing, so that one has to look carefully to see the true structure. Bees, wasps, and ants are the conspicuous members of this order. Though there are many solitary forms, the order is notable for the development of elaborate social organizations in many different species.

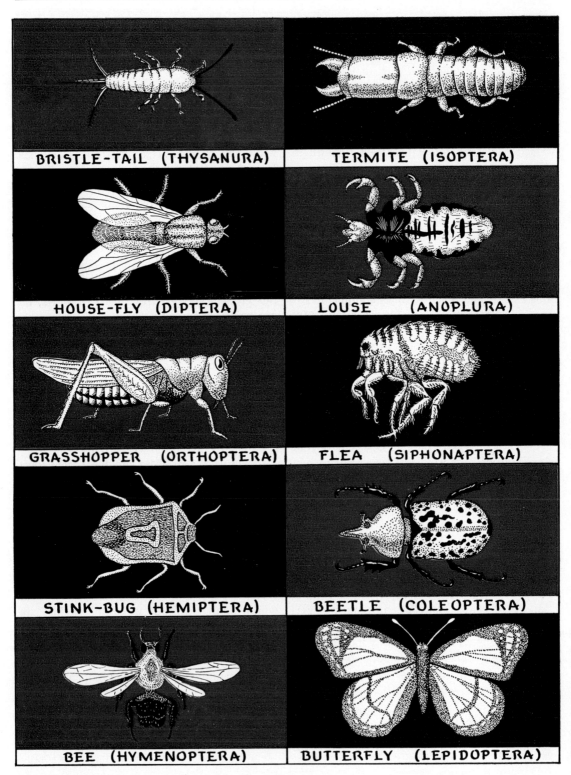

Fig. 22-5. *Representatives of some of the orders of insects.*

COLEOPTERA. In popularity with collectors, the beetles have been a close second to the Lepidoptera. About 180,000 species have been described and, unquestionably, many more remain to be discovered. In the bettles, the fore wings do not function in flying, but have been modified into tough covers that fold over the hind wings when the flight is ended. The markings of the body are frequently vivid and interesting. Noteworthy in this group are the potato bugs, June bugs, ladybirds, scarabs, and many destructive weevils, such as the boll weevil. The firefly is also a beetle, though its wing covers are much more delicate than those of most coleoptera.

170. The Metamorphosis of Insects

Some insects mature much as do the crustacea: by alternating periods of growth and molting, each new stage being much like the old. The grasshopper exhibits such a maturation process (Fig. 22-6*A*). The body proportions change at each molt, and usable wings gradually appear, but there is no striking change in appearance. The young stages are recognizably similar to the adult ones.

It is quite otherwise with the development of many other insects. A moth or a butterfly, for example, leads a double life (Fig. 22-6*B*). The egg first develops into a wormlike being called a **larva.** After a period of growing (without substantial change of form), the larva forms around itself a chitinous case. The whole individual, case and all, is then called a **pupa.** Pupation superficially appears to be a resting stage, but inside the pupa case there is feverish activity. Almost all the structures of the larva are completely broken down, and from the raw materials the adult structures are developed.

Fig. 22-6. *Metamorphosis in two different kinds of insects.*

GRADUAL METAMORPHOSIS OF GRASSHOPPER

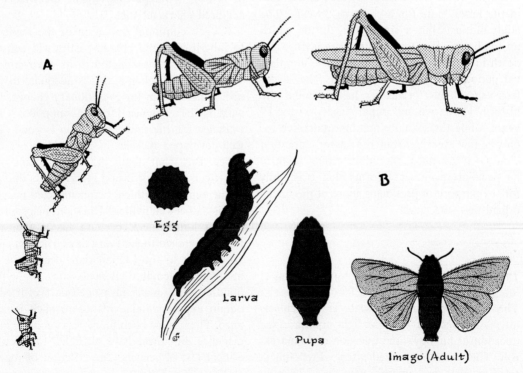

A

B

Egg

Larva

Pupa

Imago (Adult)

COMPLETE METAMORPHOSIS OF MOTH

When this transformation, or **metamorphosis** (literally, "change of form"), is complete, the new adult, called an **imago,** ruptures the pupa case and steps forth fully formed.

The double life led by such insects extends to the minutest details. The morphology of the insect larva is very different from that of the adult: the larva resembles an annelid worm and has many pairs of footlike appendages. Its daily life is different: a moth larva chews up leaves; the adult sips on flower nectar. A midge-fly larva lives continuously underwater; the adult drowns if submerged for a short time. The instincts of the two forms are different; they are attracted and repelled by different things.

When we think of a species, we habitually have the adult form in mind as being *the* species; immature forms we unconsciously ignore. In keeping with this tendency, the descriptions of the orders above were descriptions only of the adults. But, in insects that show metamorphosis, the emphasis should perhaps be placed on the larval forms. Some species of May flies, belonging to an order not described above, live in the larval state for as long as 3 years. The adult life lasts but a single day, during which no food at all is eaten. Mating, egg-laying, and death in a few hours; then begins the long larval period for the new generation. The seventeen-year "locust" (cicada) has a similar life history. The larval and pupal stages last for 17 years, while the sexually mature adults live for only a few weeks. From the insect's point of view (if it has one), the adults would seem to be peculiar, evanescent forms that exist only for the purpose of producing more of the "real" organisms—the larvae.

171. The Lamarckian Theory of Evolution

The metamorphosis of insects is particularly interesting because it throws light upon a vexed question of biology—the question of **Lamarckism.** This theory is named after a Frenchman, the Chevalier de Lamarck, who, in 1809, published a book in which he asserted that evolu-

tion was a fact and gave an explanation for it. In a famous quotation, he said:

The giraffe lives in places where the ground is almost invariably parched and without grass. Obliged to browse upon trees it is continually forced to stretch upwards. This habit maintained over long periods of time by every individual of the race has resulted in the forelimbs becoming longer than the hind ones, and the neck so elongated that a giraffe can raise his head to a height of eighteen feet without taking his forelimbs off the ground.

From this and other writings of Lamarck, it appears that he accounted for evolutionary change of species by the following conceptual scheme:

1. Use causes an increase in the development of an organ or ability; disuse has a contrary effect.

2. Offspring tend to inherit organs or abilities from their parents in the state of development to which they have been brought by use or disuse in the parents. ("The inheritance of acquired characteristics.")

3. The continual operation of the tendency to inherit acquired characteristics will cause a species to become adapted to its environment.

As a logical scheme, this is adequate to furnish a mechanism for evolutionary change. But what is the evidence for its assumptions? The evidence for the first assumption is good. The well-developed muscles of any athlete are evidence. But what about the second point—are the effects of use or disuse inherited? Is the arm of the son of an athlete better muscled because of his father's activities? Does the baby giraffe have a longer neck because his mother and father stretched theirs every day? The facts give no support to the Lamarckian idea of the inheritance of acquired characteristics. In the past hundred years many investigators have tried to obtain experimental evidence of such inheritance. There have been many reports of positive evidence, but these have all failed to meet the critical test of science: the criterion of repeatability (§3). To date, in spite of the expenditure of much time and energy, no supportable evidence has been found for Lamarck's hypothesis. Even in Lamarck's day, his idea did not enjoy much support by the scientific community. It might have eventually been forgotten entirely if Darwin had not published his theory in 1859. A half-century was not quite long enough to forget the Lamarckian idea, which was presently revived and offered as an alternative to Darwin's concept of evolution by natural selection. Many felt that so simple an idea as natural selection could not possibly account for such marvelous structures as the vertebrate eye and the wings of a bird—that these must somehow have been developed by use, which produced a modification in the adult, which was then somehow passed on to the offspring.

It is in connection with this last argument that insects with complete metamorphosis present us with significant evidence on Lamarckism. Consider, for example, one of the structures of the adult honeybee: the "antenna cleaner." It is important to an insect to keep its antennae free of debris, since important sense organs (smelling, hearing) are located on them. For this purpose the honeybee has a very neat device, shown in Figure 22-7 in two positions: open and closed. To clean an antenna, the bee places the two parts of its antenna cleaner around the base of the antennal filament, closes them, and then pulls the leg out to the tip of the filament, thus scraping and brushing off any debris that may be on the antennae.

The antenna cleaner is a highly adapted structure. Could it have been developed by a Lamarckian "inheritance of acquired characteristics"? That is, could the brush in the notch of an antenna cleaner improve with use, and the improvement be passed on to the offspring? Certainly not, for all the structures of the imago are present in their final form at the conclusion of ecdysis. Their size and shape is rigidly determined before they can ever be used. After that, the only changes that can take place are deteriorative ones, caused by the normal wear and tear of daily life. The evolution of the structures of the imago of an insect with complete metamorphosis must be by non-Lamarckian means.

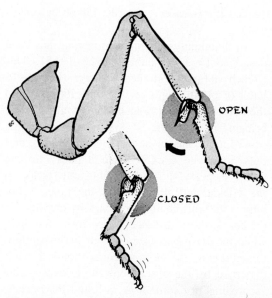

Fig. 22-7. *Antenna cleaner of a honeybee, one of the many specialized structures on the legs. (From Snodgrass,* Anatomy of the Honey Bee, *1956, courtesy Comstock Publishing Associates, Ithaca.)*

Which, in a way, is rather a pity. The Lamarckian explanation seems in some ways simpler and more direct than the Darwinian. But we must accept what T. H. Huxley ironically referred to as "the great tragedy of Science— the slaying of a beautiful hypothesis by an ugly fact."

172. Behavior: Instinct versus Intelligence

We all have heard of the marvelous things that insects such as ants, bees, and wasps can do; of their complex social organization; and of the complicated structures they can build. The remarkable thing about their actions is that they are not the product of learning. A spider knows how to make the kind of web that is proper for its species without ever having seen one. A female *Pronuba yuccasella* moth (§149) knows how it "should" lay its eggs in yucca flowers without being told. We attribute such actions to **instinct.** An instinct may be thought of as a complex chain or network of innate reflexes. When one of the reflexes is set off by a stimulus (called the **releaser**), the rest follow automatically.

An illuminating example of instinct has been described by J. H. Fabre (1823–1915). This French naturalist studied a wasp that has a habit of paralyzing a cricket with its sting and then storing it in a hole in the ground. When bringing in a cricket, it follows an invariable procedure. It flies close to the hole, alights, and puts down the cricket. Then it goes into the hole; "inspects" it; and, coming out, picks up the cricket and stuffs it into the hole. Fabre interrupted this chain of reflexes by moving the cricket a short distance away from the hole while the wasp was carrying out its inspection. On emerging, the wasp acted as though it were disturbed by the absence of the cricket. After "searching" for some time, it found the cricket, brought it back to the neighborhood of the hole, deposited it, and *again went down into the hole* on an "inspection tour." While it was in the hole, Fabre again moved the cricket; and again the sequence of events recounted above was repeated. Although Fabre repeated this experiment some forty times before he (the man, that is) tired of the game, the deposition of the prey at the mouth of the hole was always succeeded by an inspection of the many-times-inspected hole. The chain of automatic responses that constitutes an instinct clearly cannot be easily disrupted.

Instinct is a splendidly efficient way of reacting to an environment—on the predication that the environmental problem is a constant one. As is shown by the example just cited, the efficiency is purchased at the expense of flexibility, the ability to adapt actions to new circumstances. Although not all insect behavior is as completely governed by instinct as the above example would imply, it is nevertheless true that, by and large, instinct plays a predominant role in the lives of insects; intelligence (i.e., the ability to adapt behavior to new situations) plays a very minor role indeed. In this, the arthropods contrast markedly with the vertebrates, particularly with the mammals. Why is this so?

Basically, the development of instinct rather than intelligence among the insects is necessitated by their small size. Their size, in turn, seems to be a consequence of their basic body plan. The necessity of molting during growth imposes serious limitations on an organism. During the short period of ecdysis, the organism is relatively unprotected from enemies; the larger the members of a species that grows in this fashion, the more vulnerable to extinction it *is*. Furthermore, since the exoskeleton *is* the skeleton, during the period of molting, the tissues of the organism are deprived of support; again, the larger the organism, the more serious is this factor. In insects, exchanges of gas take place in many long tubules (**tracheae**) that ramify throughout the body, ending blindly; this system is much too elaborate (as compared with lungs) to get oxygen efficiently to all the cells of a large organism. Again, arthropods have an "open" circulatory system, that is, one in which the blood is not at all times made to flow smoothly in one direction in well-defined channels, as it is in the "closed" circulatory system that characterizes mammals; the relative inefficiency of an open system increases with increase in size.

For all these reasons, insects are severely restricted in size; the largest of living insects, a tropical beetle, is about as heavy as a fat mouse. What does size have to do with intelligence? Both observations and general theory show that there is a strong correlation between intelligence and the number of cells (neurons) in the brain of the central nervous system. An organism with many neurons is not *necessarily* intelligent, but one with few neurons *cannot be*. The neurons of insects are about the same size as the neurons of a vertebrate. Apparently, there is a lower limit to the size of a neuron. That being so, it follows that a small organism cannot have as complex a brain; hence the possibility of intelligent reactions is severely limited. For a small organism, the utilization of those "built-in" reaction systems we call instincts offers the only possibility of dealing with many or complex situations.

Insects are, nevertheless (within their size limits), extraordinarily successful inhabitants of the world. They achieve part of this success through sheer numbers. Like most small organisms, they have a high potential rate of multiplication; and the death of an individual counts for little. Looking at the class Insecta as a whole, we may say that there is great specialization among its member species: Each has its own environmental niche in which it is highly successful and to which it is largely restricted. No single species shows the range of adaptability exhibited by a mammalian species. Again, in specialization, we see a consequence of small size and a low order of complexity of internal organization.

The importance of insects in the pollination of flowering plants has been discussed in §§143 and 149, which should be reviewed at this point. In the course of evolution, many species of insects have evolved instinctive reactions that tend to lead them to the nectar and pollen of flowers. At the same time, the Angiospermae have (in a manner of speaking) evolved to take advantage of the instincts of the Insecta to gain their own ends; principally that of pollination, which leads to fertilization. The colors and odors of flowers are designed primarily to secure the attentions of insects, which result in pollination. Sometimes a moiety of the pollen serves as the *quid pro quo* for the service the insect renders the flower, but more often it is a sweet, nutritious nectar. Darwin, who made a classic study (1862) of the pollinating mechanisms of orchids, was much puzzled by a nectarless orchid genus, *Ophrys,* which seemed to give the insect nothing in return for pollination. Not until the twentieth century was the surprising explanation discovered. Some of the floral parts bear a striking resemblance to the abdomen of the female of certain insects—so striking that the vision serves as a releaser to the male who alights and attempts to copulate with the flower. In the course of such repeated **pseudocopulations,** pollination is effected. This is certainly a rather whimsical *quid pro quo.*

173. The Social Insects

In some insects there is an instinctive social organization. The best known of these are bees,

ants, and termites. The American zoologist William Morton Wheeler (1865–1937), one of the leading students of social insects, has stated that some sort of social organization has been independently evolved no less than 24 times in the Insecta. So many instances of convergent evolution clearly indicate some advantages in sociality. What are they? How have social organizations been evolved? We can hardly expect the fossil record to aid much in answering these questions. We must rely on reasoning and the comparative study of related species of social and near-social animals. The conclusions from such studies are necessarily tentative.

Among insects, as among men, it is probable that social habits arose from family relationships. In the solitary wasps there occur two modes of life that suggest what the beginning of the evolution of social organization may have been. Some wasps make provision for the next generation in the following manner: The female lays an egg at the bottom of a burrow, stuffs food materials on top of the egg, closes the burrow, and goes away. She normally never sees her own offspring beyond the egg stage. In other species of nearly similar habits, the mother provisions the burrow continually through the larval period of her offspring. In such species there is at least an acquaintanceship between the two generations.

In more social species of wasps, the relationship of parent and child is strengthened by an instinct of the larva to give a sweet-tasting salivary exudate to the parent, in exchange for food. This mutual feeding is called **trophallaxis.** The instinctive reactions involved may well have been important in strengthening and broadening simple family relationships into complicated social organizations. Trophallaxis among all the members of the colony plays an important role in the life of many social insects, including ants.*

In the most highly developed social insects there is a division of labor within the colony,

---

* 22-5. Admittedly, no trophallaxis in a *substantial* sense occurs in humans. But do you perceive any sort of psychological trophallaxis? Do you think it has been of any evolutionary significance?

with each morphologically distinguishable **caste** specialized for only certain functions. In honey-bees a colony consists of only one reproductive female, a *queen,* together with thousands of *workers* and a much smaller number of males called *drones.* The queen copulates only once; the spermatozoa she receives last her entire life-time of 10 to 15 years. The male or males with which she copulates die (had they not been so "lucky" they would have lived 4 to 5 months). The fertile queen can lay either fertilized or unfertilized eggs. The unfertilized eggs, which are haploid, develop into males. Diploid fer-tilized eggs develop into females. If the diploid larvae are fed a rich diet, they develop into fertile queens; on a more restricted fare they turn into workers, which are small, sterile fe-males. Only the queen of the hive lays eggs—at the rate of 1,000–1,500 a day for 2–6 years.

The behavior of worker bees has interested man for centuries. Their sensibly adaptive ac-tivities suggest intelligence, but close study has shown that their life, like that of other insects, is largely ruled by instinct. Workers can be "conditioned," however, to react to various colors—a process that undoubtedly occurs as they learn to distinguish nectar-containing flowers from others. In the daily communal life of these animals, it is not necessary for each individual to learn by direct experience where the best flowers are; they learn from each other. Such learning is possible only because bees have methods of communicating with one another, as has been clearly shown by the Austrian biol-ogist Karl von Frisch.

In the early part of each day, scouts locate flowers that will repay exploitation by the hive. Knowledge of the kind of flower is communi-cated when a returning scout-worker shares its load of identifiable nectar with other bees in the hive. More surprising, the scout can also tell the others how far away the flowers are and in which direction, which it does by means of various "dances." Von Frisch has described the dances so carefully that a human observer can correctly deduce the location of the flowers from the dances of the bees in the hive. However, under natural conditions these dances take

place in the dark, which casts doubt on the idea that other bees get the message by seeing the dance. Possibly communication takes place by the jostling of bees against each other; but more plausible is the suggestion of Adrian Wenner that sound is the significant feature. Wenner has recorded a considerable repertoire of bee sounds and has demonstrated predictable reactions of the bees to some of them.

The resemblance of insect societies to human societies in certain of their aspects has long fascinated speculative thinkers. He who would derive lessons from the one to apply to the other must not, however, overlook fundamental dif-ferences between them. The rigid social organ-ization and the segregation of functions to dif-ferent castes are consequences of the whole insect plan of life. Because insects have a chi-tinous exo-skeleton, they are severely limited in size. Because they are small, the complexity of their brains is necessarily much less than ours. Because of this, inflexible instinct rather than adaptable intelligence is almost the only pos-sible mode of reaction to a complex situation. Insect societies are themselves, consequently, inflexible in organization. The range of adapt-ability of the society as a whole is, however, increased by the segregation of functions to different castes, of which some termite species have a half-dozen or so, each with its own duties and instinctive reactions.

In all insect societies there is a more or less complete separation of reproductive and nonre-productive (should we say somatic?) functions. Because of the separation, natural selection acts, not primarily on the individual, but on the colony as a whole. Sterility, normally a characteristic quickly eliminated by natural se-lection, has been produced in worker bees by a process of natural selection acting upon the whole colony. Sterility is undoubtedly of value to the colony as a whole because the accom-panying division of labor increases the effi-ciency of the colony. Sterile castes have struc-tures and instincts that either are not present in the reproductive castes or are not so well developed among them, for example, the pollen-collecting structures present in worker bees, but absent or poorly developed in the reproductive forms.

In social insects, with their various castes, the totality of specific attributes is to be found in no one individual, but in the group. For this reason, many biologists apply the term **super-organism** to the social group that is the unit of natural selection and evolution. A hive of bees or a hill of ants is called a superorganism.

174. Biocides and the Control of Pests

Since the Biblical times of locust plagues man has looked on insects as competitors. For centuries the evil of insect competition was regarded as unavoidable; then the development of modern chemistry gave rise to a serious expectation that we might some day eliminate our enemies. This expectation was particularly strengthened by the discovery of the insecticidal properties of DDT. This substance was first synthesized in 1874 in Germany, but its insecticidal effect was not discovered until 1942. By 1944, the annual production of DDT in the United States was several thousand pounds; by 1958 it had risen to over 145 million pounds. Visions of a world free of unwanted insects embellished the advertizements of chemical companies and were largely accepted as gospel by the general public.

Suddenly in 1962 this euphoric bubble was pricked. Rachel Carson (1908–1964), who had achieved great popularity with her beautifully written *The Sea Around Us,* published a new book, *Silent Spring,* in which she attacked with great vigor the use of pesticides. Documenting her case with reports published in scientific journals she pointed out the tremendous loss of life among bird, fish, and small animal populations following the broadcasting of pesticides, not to mention the occasional loss of human life as a result of careless handling and distribution of the poisons. Near Sheldon, Illinois, for example ground-feeding birds, muskrats, rabbits, and ground squirrels were virtually eliminated by mass application of insecticides. In the lower Mississippi River fish by the thousands died; chemical analysis revealed their heavy load of pesticides. These were but a few of the many instances recorded in the literature.

Miss Carson's attack was promptly met by a spirited counter-attack. The pesticide industry had grown from a business with 40 million dollars in annual sales in 1939 to 300 million in 1959. Countless entomologists and field workers owed their livelihood to pesticides. Numerous reviews complained that *Silent Spring* was not sufficiently judicial in tone—which is perhaps true. It was also argued out that if we abruptly stopped the use of all pesticides, agricultural productivity would drop disastrously —which may also be true. The end result of a year of bickering in the press left the general public confused, but more cautious.

The problem of pest control is one in which we need a great deal more facts—hard facts that can survive suspicious analysis by financially interested parties. We are in the process of getting these. What the final picture will add up to we don't know, but in the meantime there are some important biological principles that can be underlined.

The first point to make is an important semantic one emphasized by Carson. "Insecticide" means insect-killer; "pesticide" means pest-killer. By using these words we risk deceiving ourselves into thinking these killers kill *only* the things named. This is far from the truth. Some of the organic phosphates used are identical with or similar to nerve poisons that have been proposed for chemical warfare between men. One of the most magnificent accomplishments of biology has been the demonstration of the biochemical unity of life from microbe to man. The enzymes that can be poisoned among the lowest forms of life occur also among the highest. There are chemical differences of course; but these are *relatively* few. If we can find these specific differences and use them for specific attacks on unwanted species, well and good. But until we do we should assume that any poison that we use is a general one, and should be called a **biocide.** When we use the word "pesticide" we unconsciously employ primitive word-magic; we try to control facts with words. There are no true pesticides or insecticides—only biocides. The question is, can we control the application of the biocides so as to produce more good than harm, from the point of view of *Homo sapiens?*

The problem of an economic accounting of biocide use has many facets. First, consider this problem. When we spray a forest with biocides from an airplane to kill insects, we kill also thousands of birds. The birds, had they lived, would themselves have killed many insects. Have we gained or lost? This is a rational question that can be answered only by a quantitative study. Such studies have seldom been made.

A more difficult problem is the one in which the gains accrue to one segment of society, the losses to another. A farmer in Iowa may increase his income this year by spraying biocides on his crops; but the income of a commercial fisherman a thousand miles away may be decreased next year when some of the same biocide molecules, dissolved in water or carried in plankton reach the lower Mississippi. How is the fisherman's loss to be paid for out of the farmer's gain? This is a problem for social engineering.

More difficult in the problem of cost accounting is the problem of reconciling incommensurables. Dutch elm disease is caused by a fungus carried by bark beetles. The beetles can be fairly well eliminated by massive sprayings with DDT—which kills song birds in droves. If we don't spray we lose the lovely shade of eastern elm-canopied streets; if we do spray we save the shade, and lose the song of birds. How do we weigh one value against the other?

The use of such words as "insecticide" traps us into making predictions from a too simple view of life. Implicitly, we may work with an equation of this sort:

Live insects + insecticide $\longrightarrow$
$$\text{dead insects,} \quad (1)$$

which of course is just what we want. But a truer equation would be:

The Web of Life + biocide $\longrightarrow$ What? *(2)*

This, of course, is a problem, not an answer. Assuming the truth of the first equation, national and local governments combined forces in 1957 to try to eradicate the fire ant from southeastern United States. Eight years and $15,000,000 later the fire ant was still there—but fish, wildlife, livestock, and poultry suffered great losses from the chemicals used. Under local pressure the campaign was almost entirely abandoned.

The biosphere is immensely complex, and we meddle with it at our hazard. The ecologist Charles Elton has told an illuminating story of the consequences of blind alterations of the web of life, in this instance not by chemicals but by living agents—but the moral is the same.

Some keen gardener, intent upon making Hawaii even more beautiful than before, introduced a plant called *Lantana camara,* which in its native home of Mexico causes no trouble to anybody. Meanwhile, some one else had also improved the amenities of the place by introducing turtle-doves from China, which, unlike any of the native birds, fed eagerly upon the berries of *Lantana.* The combined effects of the vegetative powers of the plant and the spreading of seeds by the turtle-doves were to make the *Lantana* multiply exceedingly and become a serious pest on the grazing country. Indian mynah birds were also introduced, and they too fed upon *Lantana* berries. After a few years the birds of both species had increased enormously in numbers. But there is another side to the story. Formerly the grasslands and young sugar-cane plantations had been ravaged yearly by vast numbers of army-worm caterpillars, but the mynahs also fed upon these caterpillars and succeeded to a large extent in keeping them in check, so that the outbreaks became less severe. About this time certain insects were introduced in order to try and check the spread of *Lantana* and several of them (in particular a species of Agromyzid fly) did actually destroy so much seed that the *Lantana* began to decrease. As a result of this, the mynahs also began to decrease in numbers to such an extent that there began to occur again severe outbreaks of army-worm caterpillars. It was then found that when the *Lantana* had been removed in many places, other introduced shrubs came in, some of which are even more difficult to eradicate than the original *Lantana.*

M. W. Beijerinck has said that "A discovery is great when one can communicate it in passing." In this spirit we can summarize the meaning of ecology to the agricultural engineer in this phrase: *We can never do merely one thing.*

This working hypothesis is no mere counsel of despair. If we are observant and intelligent, we can sometimes achieve considerable gains with minimal losses. In most general terms, if we must use biocides let us try to bias their action so as to affect the unwanted species more than others. As a matter of principle we should neither use biocides blindly like some great panacea, nor from irrational fear outlaw them entirely. What agriculturalists are working toward is an **integrated control concept** in which all kinds of control—chemical, behavioral, ecological, parasitological, and climatic—are drawn upon to achieve the ends desired. Problems of pest control are problems in the field of ecological engineering. A few examples of successful solutions along ecological lines will show the sort of thinking that is needed.

1. A serious parasite of cattle is known as the "screw-worm fly." In this species the female mates only once, whether or not she becomes pregnant as a result of the mating. Normally, of course, she does. Males are polygamous. Making use of these behavioral characteristics, it has been possible to eliminate the parasite from some areas. Flies are artificially reared in great quantities and sterilized by X-radiation. When released, sterile but sexually potent males compete with normal males. Every monogamous female they mate with is functionally cancelled out as a mother.

2. The danger of a biocide can be restricted if it can be combined with a species-specific attractant. The male of the gypsy moth, a serious pest of lumber trees, responds to a specific chemical produced by the female. Such externally secreted substances are called **pheromones** (analogous to hormones within the body). This sex attractant has now been isolated (from some half-million female moth abdomens!), identified, and synthesized, and shows promise as an attractant for poison baits. Males respond to a quantity of less than 10^{-13} gram.

3. Hornworms, a pest of tobacco, have sometimes been controlled by handpicking the larvae off tobacco leaves. A cheaper form of labor is found in a paper wasp which preys on the hornworms. By constructing artificial shelters of a type favored by the wasp at the margins of a field, large numbers of them can be brought to where they are most useful to man. The shelters can be moved from field to field as needed. Comparable methods for encouraging bird populations have been used in Europe. The combination of wasps plus minimal dosages of biocides has proved most effective. In ecological engineering, as in so much of practical life, the *either-or* approach is not the most productive of good.

Questions and Problems

22-6. Prepare a list of the **boldface** terms in this chapter. Write out a brief description or definition of each. Compare your work with the text.

22-7. Give a brief description of the work of the following people, with approximate dates: Carson, Darwin, Fabre, Hooke, Lamarck, Wheeler.

22-8. Find the etymological derivation of each of the following terms, and point out its aptness: (a) Diptera, (b) Lepidoptera, (c) Hymenoptera.

‡22-9. The May flies, whose life history is recounted at the end of §170, are put in the order Ephemeroptera. Explain the aptness of this name.

22-10. In §166 the terms transverse section and longitudinal section were used, without explicit definition. To show that you understand them, make simple sketches of (a) a median transverse section and (b) a median longitudinal section, of an automobile.

22-11. In tabular form, compare and contrast exoskeleton with endoskeleton with respect to the following characteristics: (a) phyla in which it is found, (b) protection furnished muscles, (c) chemical composition, (d) flexibility, (e) ease of growth of organism.

22-12. Why is it an error to refer to a spider as an insect?

‡22-13. A child notices two houseflies (*Musca domestica*) on the table. One is twice as large as the other. The child asks: "If we feed it plenty of sugar, how long will it take the little fly to grow as big as the big one?" What's the answer?

22-14. What animal has a grandfather but no father?

‡22-15. This may sound like a Zen *koan,* but it is not: Why don't we call seagulls hummingbirds?

22-16. Describe a convenient method of determining the wingbeat frequency of at least some insects. Who first used this method?

22-17. The temperature in the middle of a brood nest of honey bees seldom is outside the range of 30° to 35°C, even though the external temperature may go as low as −40°C or as high as +50°C. Suggest mechanisms to account for this relative stability. How would you classify bees in respect to temperature control?

‡22-18. Experimentally, a cluster of a fixed number of bees has a diameter that varies directly with the temperature. For instance, in one experiment, a cluster which had a diameter of 25 cm at 10° shrank to 21.5 cm at 0°C. Don't these observations violate the principle of the Scale Effect? Explain.

22-19. The behavior of bees includes "communication fanning" in which wing vibration is combined with a release of material from abdominal scent glands. Other bees react to the scent. What general term is applied to such substances?

‡22-20. Two new insecticides are discovered. One of them has the odor of one of the food substances favored by the insect. The other smells like the female of the species (the male is attracted to the female by her odor). On a priori grounds, which insecticide should be the most effective in the long run? Why?

22-21. Quite commonly, after several years' use of the same insecticide in a region, the dosage has to be stepped up to get the same effect. Explain why. What is the practical significance of this fact?

‡22-22. What simple evolutionary development might make the screw-worm fly immune to the biological method of control described in the text?

22-23. Is length of life subject to selection? Explain, with an illustrative example.

‡22-24. If all flowers were wind pollinated, what difference would it make in the earth's landscapes?

22-25. In the formation of sperm cells in the bee, there is no reduction division as there is in spermatogenesis in most animals. Teleologically speaking, why not?

‡22-26. Can sterility be inherited?

22-27. Compare and contrast insect societies and human societies.

‡22-28. It has been predicted that the pesticide industry will have an annual sales of a billion dollars a year by 1975. Confirm or deny this prediction, and explain the basis on which you do so.

22-29. At the risk of an illegitimate second-guessing of history, can you suggest a reason why pseudocopulation was not discovered during the nineteenth century?

‡22-30. Suppose a species of plant that is now successfully pollinated by pseudocopulation should produce a mutant that synthesized nectar. Would this mutant have a selective advantage?

22-31. Is pseudocopulation an example of mutualism?

‡22-32. The United States government, through various agencies associated with space and health research, financially supports research into communication among bees, dolphins, and other animals. Aside from the value for "pure" research, can you see an applied angle?

Readings

For pleasure, two splendidly illustrated texts can be recommended: *The Lower Animals* by Buchsbaum and Milne, and *Living Insects of the World* by Klots and Klots. The social insects have stimulated a lot of sleazy literature, for instance, Maeterlinck's work; for a *good* essay see Wheeler's "The ant colony as an organism," in his *Essays in Philosophical Biology;* also recommended are Wheeler's *Social Life Among the Insects.* Von Frisch's *Bees* is a delightful account of the scientific method in operation. Public health problems are treated in Herms' *Medical Entomology*.

To learn about the problems of biocides one should begin with Rachel Carson's *Silent Spring* and Lewis Herber's *Our Synthetic Environment,* published in the same year and also excellent, though it received much less notice. Robert Rudd's *Pesticides and the Living Landscape* is a careful, judical assessment of the dangers and potentialities of biocides.

Scientific American Offprints

135. Conrad Limbaugh. *Cleaning Symbiosis*

157. Edward O. Wilson. *Pheromones*

173. C. G. Johnson. *The Aerial Migration of Insects*

181. Adrian M. Wenner. *Sound Communication in Honeybees*

413. T. C. Schneirla & Gerard Piel. *The Army Ant*

23

Up to the Vertebrates

175. The Echinodermata

Beginning with Chapter 24 we will be concerned at length with the detailed functioning of the vertebrates, particularly with man. In the present chapter we want to display some of the forms of animal life believed to be on the main road of evolution to the vertebrates, and run briefly through the main subdivisions of this group.

We begin with the phylum **Echinodermata**, one of the very few phyla confined entirely to marine habitats; it includes starfish, sea urchins, sea cucumbers, brittle stars, sand dollars, and sea lilies. Adult members of this phylum are sedentary or relatively slow-moving. The characteristic rough, spiny skin is in part composed of calcium carbonate, the calcium being derived from the sea water. Starfish, then, like coralline red algae, corals, and molluscs, tend to decrease the calcium content of the oceans. However, at death, most of the calcium of these organisms is usually returned to the sea as a result of microbial action and chemical solution. Where conditions favor accumulation of such animal remains, deposits are laid down that may, in the course of geologic time, become limestone or marble.

Perhaps the best known of the echinoderms are the starfish (Fig. 23-1). Inside the spiny exoskeleton of a starfish may be found a remarkable **water vascular system** that is unique

to this phylum. The **tube feet** are moved by a combination of direct muscular action and hydrostatic pressure exerted by the **ampullae** connected with them. By the action of its hundreds of tube feet, a starfish crawls slowly along. It also uses these feet in opening the shells of a clam or other bivalve mollusc, pulling steadily until the mollusc opens. Each tube foot has a nervous reflex system that is, to a large extent, independent of the others; because they often work at cross purposes, many tube feet pull themselves loose from a starfish in the normal course of a day's activities. An echinoderm is sometimes referred to as a "reflex republic."

After a starfish has opened a bivalve mollusc, it proceeds to digest it in a most remarkable way. The stomach of the starfish is extruded (the way a glove might be turned inside out) around the food. Digestion takes place outside the body of the starfish; only the digested products are taken back into the predator.

It may seem strange that a discussion of the echinoderms should be included in a chapter on the vertebrates. That the Echinodermata should be considered to be more than very remotely related to vertebrates—to such organisms as dogs, cattle, and men—is superficially unreasonable. Neither externally nor internally does an adult starfish resemble a man. The spine-encrusted exoskeleton reminds us of the Arthropoda. The radial symmetry recalls the

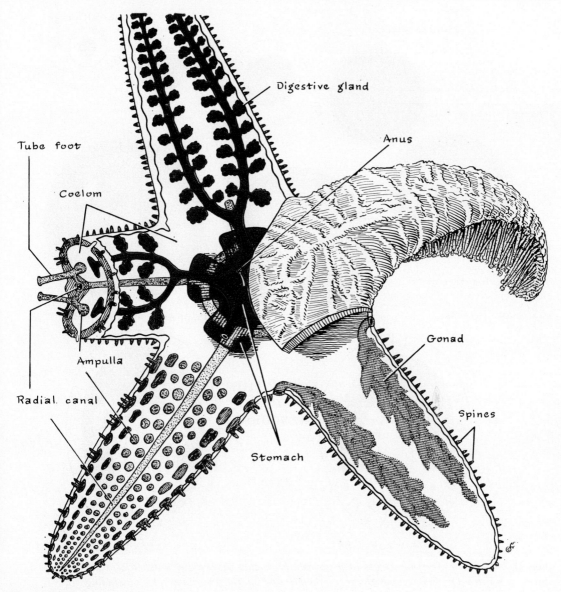

Fig. 23-1. *The structure of a starfish.*

Coelenterata. The slowly waving, hydraulically actuated tube feet are *sui generis.** Why, then, do biologists think starfish are related to guinea pigs?

The principal evidence of relationship is the similarity in early development of echinoderms and vertebrates. It has been found that forms which, on other grounds, are held to be closely related in an evolutionary sense show strong similarities in their embryological development: *close evolutionary relationship—similar embryology.* Because this generalization is backed by literally thousands of instances, it is legitimate to make the reverse implication: similar embryology—close evolutionary relationship; or, more exactly, *the degree of similarity in embryological development indicates the closeness of the evolutionary relationship.* Application of this principle indicates that the echinoderms are

* 23-1. Meaning?

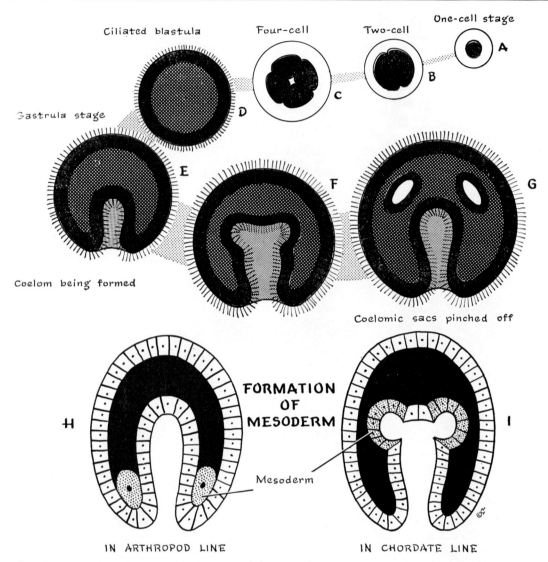

One-cell stage
Ciliated blastula   Four-cell   Two-cell

A

B

C

D

Gastrula stage

E   F   G

Coelom being formed

Coelomic sacs pinched off

FORMATION
OF
MESODERM

H   I

Mesoderm

IN ARTHROPOD LINE   IN CHORDATE LINE

Fig. 23-2. (A-G) *Embryonic stages of a starfish. Note that the way in which the meso-derm is formed (F, G) resembles the method found in the chordates (I) (including vertebrates), rather than that found in the arthropods (H).*

derived from the evolutionary stem that gave rise to the vertebrates, rather than that which produced the arthropods and their allies.

In the formation of the germ layer called the *mesoderm* among the higher animals, two alternative modes are employed, as shown in Figure 23-2H, I. The mode of origin of the mesoderm in the chordate line, that is, the line that includes the vertebrates, is found also in the echinoderms (Fig. 23-2F, G). Because of the fundamental nature of this aspect of develop-

ment, the echinoderms would appear, therefore, to belong to the chordate branch of the family tree of the animals.

Figure 23-2A–G shows selected stages of the early embryology of the starfish. The formation of the mesoderm at the close of the gastrula stage results in the development of coelomic sacs. The *coelom* is the body cavity; in man, this is the cavity that surrounds the viscera. The star-fish embryo with a coelom is a ciliated form, or ciliated larva, which moves actively

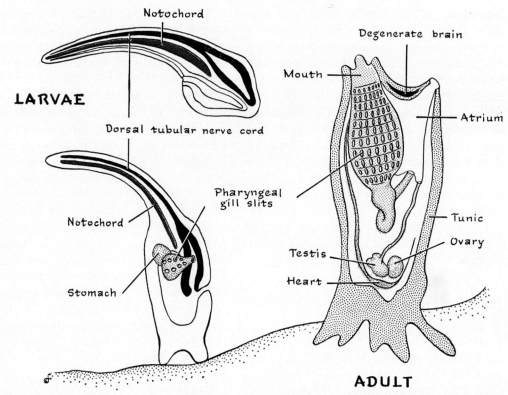

Fig. 23-6. *Structure and development of a tunicate. Notice the notochord in larval stages.*

sufficient to justify assigning an organism to one kingdom or the other. Certainly no biologist thinks for a moment that tunicates should be called plants. The presence of cellulose in them is an unresolved mystery.

Another biochemical characteristic of the tunicates is more enlightening, since it strengthens our belief in their relationship to the vertebrates. Hormones from the pituitary gland, which hangs beneath the brain in vertebrates, produce reactions generally throughout the vertebrates, but not among such invertebrates as the arthropods. However, it has been found that three of the pituitary hormones may be extracted from the nerve tissue of a tunicate, in which they presumably play a physiological role.

The subphylum **Cephalochordata** includes

Fig. 23-7. *Structure of* Amphioxus.

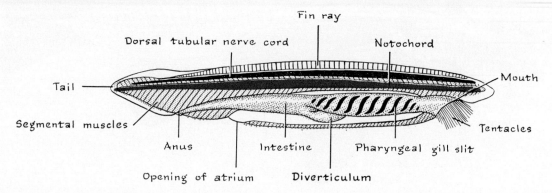

Amphioxus, a little fishlike worm, long a familiar creature in the biological laboratory. It exhibits, in almost diagrammatic fashion (Fig. 23-7), the three characteristics of the phylum Chordata. The notochord extends the whole length of the body and persists throughout life. Along some marine coasts, these animals are quite numerous. Although they are good swimmers, they spend much of their lives buried in clean sand up to their necks, straining microscopic food out of the water pumped past their gill bars. Some species are several inches long, but most are smaller. Along part of the China coast, these primitive chordates are found in great enough abundance to be collected as food for man.

177. Fishes

There are four classes of vertebrates that we call fishes: the **Agnatha** or jawless fishes (lampreys and hagfish); the **Placodermi,** an extinct group; the **Chondrichthyes,** or cartilaginous fish (sharks, rays, skates); and the **Osteichthyes,** or bony fishes (perch, bass, cod, trout, and so on).

The greater part of the body of a bony fish is made of muscles by which the animal swims. In most species the fins (with the exception of the caudal fin—see Fig. 23-8) serve only for steering. In many species the specific gravity is adjusted to facilitate maintenance at a given depth by secretion of gas into a **swim bladder.** Exchange of respiratory gases is effected by the **gills,** which are so constructed as to present a great amount of surface to the water that moves across them. By these structures, the otherwise unfavorable surface:volume ratio of a large organism is obviated. The gills are furnished with a fine network of blood vessels. The blood is pumped around the body by a simple two-chambered heart (one auricle, one ventricle). The gastrointestinal tract is relatively simple, and terminates in a chamber called a *cloaca* (L. sewer), into which the products of both the reproductive system and the kidneys are poured. In reproduction, fertilization typically takes place externally when the gametes of the two sexes meet in the water; then the fertilized egg is "on its own." However, there are many deviations from this typical situation. In some fishes (e.g., the common "guppy" of the home aquarium) the male has a fin that is modified

Fig. 23-8. *The structure of a bony fish.*

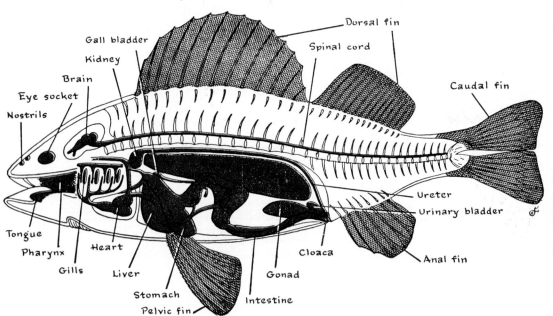

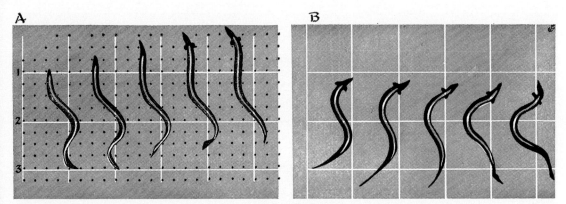

Fig. 23-9. *An eel, out of water, showing how its forward progression requires that it have something to press against laterally. (From Gray,* How Animals Move, *1953, courtesy Cambridge University Press, Cambridge.)*

into an intromittent organ, for conveying sperm into the female, and the eggs are retained inside the body until they are hatched; the young are then "born alive," * as the expression goes. Guppies are "live bearers."

Land vertebrates undoubtedly arose from fishes. An indication as to how this evolution might have taken place is given by the contemporary "lungfish" (Polypterus) of South Africa. In this fish, in addition to the gills, there are lungs, which permit it to survive the periodic droughts that characterize the region in which it lives. Although, for various anatomical reasons this species is believed not to be near the direct line of the ancestors of the land vertebrates, this double system for exchange of respiratory gases probably characterized the true "connecting links." There are other fishes in which the swim bladder arises as a paired structure from the ventral side of the esophagus (in contrast to the dorsal swim bladder shown in Fig. 23-8); such swim bladders probably gave rise to lungs, which have a similar embryological origin.

Successful adaptation to land also made necessary the evolution of an effective mode of locomotion. We can see how this could have come about if we first study the fish's mode of locomotion. The left half of Figure 23-9 shows how an eel (a fish) can progress on dry land, over a board studded with pegs. By pushing

outward and backward with its body against the pegs, it can push itself forward. The curves it throws its body into pass in waves backward as it moves forward. This is the same way it moves through the water, pressing against the water, the inertia of which gives it (so to speak) something of the solidity of the pegs shown here.

An eel on a dry board without pegs, though throwing itself into the same curves, cannot progress. The animal that moves on land needs something to push against, and something to push with. The "something to push with" of land vertebrates is found in the limbs, which were undoubtedly evolved from ventrally placed fins. We see something of this sort in the contemporary fish called "mud-springers" (Fig. 23-10), which can move around on mudflats with considerable ability. Not these particular animals, but some similar fish must have been at the base of the evolutionary tree of land animals. It is a striking fact that early in this evolution the limbs of vertebrates standardized on five toes (the **pentadactyl limb**). The only departures from this plan evolved since then have been in the direction of reduction in digital number, in the extreme cases (horses) to a single digit.

178. The Amphibia

"Most amphibia are abhorrent," said Linnaeus, "because of their cold body, pale color, carti-

---

* 23-3. Why the quotation marks?

Fig. 23-10. *The mud-springer,* Periophthalmus. *Note the fins modified into footlike organs which permit movement on land, an early stage of possible evolution to land. (Courtesy Shedd Aquarium.)*

laginous skeleton, filthy skin, fierce aspect, calculating eye, offensive smell, harsh voice, squalid habitation, and terrible venom; and so their Creator has not exerted his powers to make many of them." Be that as it may, we note that this class, which includes frogs, toads, mudpuppies, and salamanders, is only partially adapted to land. Note for instance, the way a salamander moves over dry land. The legs are thrust out at the sides (rather than being fully beneath it, as a dog's are), and its body is thrown into curves much like those of a fish, particularly when it moves as fast as it can. Furthermore, although many adult amphibians live in comparatively dry environments, they must return to fresh water to breed, for their eggs are not equipped to withstand dryness. The force of this generalization is not essentially diminished by the remarkable ways in which some species have divorced themselves from literal dependence on bodies of water at breeding time, for example, the way of the Chilean frog, *Rhinoderma,* the male of which carries the eggs in his mouth cavity until they have developed into tiny, fully formed frogs ready to hop out.

The name of the class is derived from the Greek *amphi,* meaning double, and *bios,* meaning life. Amphibia live two lives: one in the water, one on land. The zygote laid in the water develops into a sexually immature, or *larval,* form, with gills for exchange of respiratory gases. After a few weeks or months the larva undergoes *metamorphosis* to produce a sexually mature land-dwelling form with lungs. In salamanders (Fig. 23-11) the two life stages are

Fig. 23-11. *Two phases in the life of a salamander.* Top: *Larval, water-dwelling, stage; note gills.* Bottom: *Adult stage; animal has lungs and lives on land. (Courtesy Hugh Spencer.)*

usually noticeably different, though not as different as in the tailless amphibians (e.g., frogs), which have a tailed, fishlike larval stage: the tadpole. Metamorphosis is brought about by thyroid hormone. Extirpation of the thyroid gland causes a tadpole to remain permanently in the larval stage, though it may grow abnormally large. Alternatively, the addition of enough thyroid extract to the water surrounding a tiny tadpole will induce metamorphosis early, producing a tiny frog.

Larval and adult stages of amphibia differ in other important respects. A tadpole is a herbivore, feeding on microscopic algae; a frog is a strict carnivore, living on flies and other objects that attract its attention by moving. Correlated with this dietary difference are differences in the structure of the gut and in intestinal microbes.

Although adult amphibia crawl or jump on land, their adaptation to terrestrial locomotion is only a partial one. Since the legs are at the side of the body, the amphibian belly is in contact with the substratum—a position that does not make for speedy locomotion. No doubt this failure to evolve a better type of limb arrangement is one of the reasons for the lack of large species in the class. Also of probable importance is the fairly simple type of lung: while it is not as simple a sac as a swim bladder, it is much less complicated in structure than the mammalian lung, having relatively less surface available for gaseous exchange. Its deficiency is partly offset by the moist, highly vascularized skin of frogs and salamanders, through which O_2 and CO_2 can be exchanged. In one family of small * salamanders (the *Plethodontidae*) there are no lungs, the skin and the mouth serving as the sole organs of gaseous exchange.

Amphibia, like fishes, have a cloaca, a common chamber for excretory, fecal, and reproductive products. The heart is more complicated than in fishes, being three-chambered (two auricles, one ventricle), which apparently makes for greater efficiency in a lung-possessing organism.

---

* 23-4. Why are they small?

179. Reptiles

With the class **Reptilia,** a truly land-dwelling type of vertebrate may be said to have been evolved. No longer is the skin an organ for gaseous exchange: it is covered with scales (Fig. 23-12), and it prevents the loss of water. Breathing is carried out entirely by lungs, which are better developed than those of amphibians. The reptilian system of blood circulation closely approaches the mammalian system of a complete separation of pulmonary and systemic circulations (Chap. 27): there are two auricles and two ventricles, with an almost complete separation of the latter two chambers from each other.

In their reproduction, reptiles have achieved independence of water by developing a leathery egg covering that prevents loss of the water inside. The embryo thus develops in a watery medium furnished by its mother. Spermatozoa

Fig. 23-12. *A harmless water snake. (Courtesy Hugh Spencer.)*

cannot penetrate the leathery covering of a reptilian egg. The eggs must, therefore, be fertilized before this coating is put on, which means before the egg is laid. Fertilization is, therefore, internal, and depends on **copulation** (L. *copula* = a bond), that is, the temporary "union" of two sexes as the male thrusts an intromittent, gamete-delivering organ into the cloaca of the female. Reptiles have no true penis, but they have an intromittent organ that serves the same purpose. The cloaca is still present in both sexes.

As a group the reptiles have been quite successful land-dwellers. In the Mesozoic era, by **adaptive radiation,** reptiles invaded land, water, and even the air. Today the flying reptiles are gone, and the number of species in the other two environments is much reduced, with no giant forms like the dinosaurs. What caused this decline from predominance in the Mesozoic has long been a matter of speculation. The two most probable factors are climate and the appearance of mammals. From the difference in dominant plants between Mesozoic and modern times, it seems likely that the average air temperature is now several degrees cooler than then. This difference may be enough to make the reptilian lack of a constant temperature a serious disadvantage. (Reptiles are today much more abundant in the tropics than in temperate zones.) However, it may not have been a lowering of the temperature in the late Mesozoic, but a raising of it that put the skids under the Reptilia. R. B. Cowles (1946) has pointed out that, in a climate that is hot too much of the time, an animal as large as a dinosaur and possessing no heat-dissipating device (such as sweating) would be in serious straits. The only reptiles living in deserts today are small lizards and snakes, and these can retire to the shade of a plant or, better, descend into a cool subterranean burrow in the middle of the day.

Whether the late Mesozoic became too hot or too cold, we do not yet know, but in either case, we suspect it was the lack of a temperature-controlling mechanism that put the giant reptiles at a disadvantage vis-à-vis the tiny mammals that had by this time made their appearance. Undoubtedly, the evolution of a superior intelligence among the mammals soon hastened the extinction of the giant reptiles.

Today the class Reptilia is represented by turtles, crocodiles, lizards, and snakes. In the last-named group, the evolution of an elongated form fitted for entering burrows and other small openings has resulted in the reduction or loss of one lung, the elongation of internal organs, the loss of the forelimbs, and the reduction or complete loss of the hind limbs. As a result, to move on the open ground, a snake must perform essentially the same "swimming" motions shown by the eel in Figure 23-9. Minute irregularities of the surface play the role of the pegs there shown. The scales of the snake are designed to obtain a purchase on a rough substratum.* If the substratum is quite smooth (e.g., a piece of glass), the snake is as helpless as the eel shown in the right half of Figure 23-9.

That the limbless condition is a secondary evolution (rather than a primitive condition) is shown by the skeleton of a python, which includes **vestigial** remnants of the bones of the hind limbs, deeply hidden in the flesh, where they do little or no good.

180. Birds

The class **Aves** is one of the two classes of constant-temperatured, or *homothermal,* animals. The normal temperature varies from one species to another (see Appendix 10), but is typically several degrees higher than mammalian temperatures. Most birds fly, some of them magnificently well, as Figure 23-13 bears witness. This activity limits their size because of the proportionately greater amount of muscle and supporting bone required with increase in the size of a flying form. The conservation of heat in a cold environment presents a problem to a small animal, because of the scale effect (§10). This problem has been well solved in the Aves by the evolution of feathers, which are modified reptilian scales. (Scales are still re-

---

* 23-5. Handle and examine a snake carefully. How are its scales adapted to locomotion?

tained to some extent, for example, on the feet of birds.) Some of the feathers are modified to serve as flight surfaces of the wings, but most of them are adapted to produce a great amount of insulation. Some species of birds, for example, penguins, are thereby enabled to live in the coldest regions of the world.

Comparative anatomists can point to dozens of evidences of the relationship of birds and reptiles, and there is now no question but that birds were evolved from reptiles. Like reptiles, birds lay eggs, but ones that are better protected by a calcareous shell. The heart is completely divided into four chambers, a cloaca is present, and fertilization is internal. Like reptiles, birds have but small brains and limited intelligence. The elaboration of instinctual activities in courting and nest-building of birds has long excited the pleased wonder of man. One of the most remarkable characteristics of many birds is their ability to migrate accurately thousands of miles from a winter home to a summer home.

Birds are exceptionally favorable objects for observing the results of adaptive radiation, the end result of the process of speciation, producing many modifications of basic structures that allow the resultant forms to live in a wide variety of environments. The architectural dictum that *form follows function* was first stated by Lamarck, the biologist, with reference to the adaptive structures of living things. Figure 23-14 admirably illustrates Lamarck's thesis.

181. Mammals

Classification is frequently thought to be a rather automatic, noncreative procedure. This may be true of the classifying of objects into already accepted categories. But the discovery of the categories themselves frequently—perhaps always—involves an intellectual act that is genuinely creative. This is clearly seen in the discovery of that category of animals that we call the **mammals.** Until Linnaeus coined the term "mammal" (or rather, its Latin equivalent *mammalis*), there was no word in any of the

Fig. 23-13. *Successive stroboscopic pictures (left to right) of a hummingbird flying backward. (By Walker Van Riper, courtesy University of Colorado Museum of Natural History.)*

European languages to denote those organisms that have hair and suckle their young. (In English, "beast" is the nearest equivalent, but it may also be applied to large reptiles.) It took keen insight to see that the mammals constituted a natural, well-delimited group.

Mammals, like birds, are homotherms, though their temperature is somewhat lower: the temperature of man (98.6°F or 37°C) is typical. The heat-conserving device in mammals is hair. Like birds, mammals are clearly derived from reptiles. An interesting intermediate form between the two classes is the Australian mammal the platypus, or *Ornithorhynchus* (Fig. 23-15), a "warm-blooded" animal that lays eggs but nourishes its young by mammary glands. The platypus has a cloaca, in contrast to other mammals, in which there is a separation of reproductive and excretory orifices.

Some of the more primitive mammals are those called **marsupials.** In this group there is a pouch (L. *marsupium* = pouch) on the belly into which the very small, newly born young climb or are lifted by the mother. Inside the pouch are teats, to which the young attach and remain attached for several weeks while they continue their development. The marsupial mammals include the kangaroos, wallabies, wombats, bandicoots, and others. Most marsupials are restricted to the Australian region, a region that has been isolated from the rest of the world for about 30 million years. Since the date at which migration of land animals between Australia and the rest of the world stopped, another type of mammal—the **placental mammals**—has been evolved elsewhere. Placental mammals are competitively superior to the marsupials; they have almost entirely displaced the marsupials in all regions in which both types have lived together. The opossum of the Americas is one of the few marsupials naturally living outside of the Australian region.

The placental mammals are those mammals that nourish their young internally by means of a placenta (§279). These organisms are divided into a number of orders. Below are listed the principal orders, with specific examples and a brief mention of one or more salient characteristics of each order.

Order **Insectivora.** Hedgehogs, moles, shrews. Insect-eaters with pointed cusps on molar teeth.

Order **Chiroptera.** Bats. Structural modifications for flying.

Order **Primates.** Apes, lemurs, monkeys, man. Nails instead of claws; large brains; eyes directed forward.

Order **Edentata.** Armadillos, anteaters, sloths. Incisor teeth lacking.

Fig. 23-14. *The phenomenon of adaptive radiation, as illustrated by the bills of birds.*

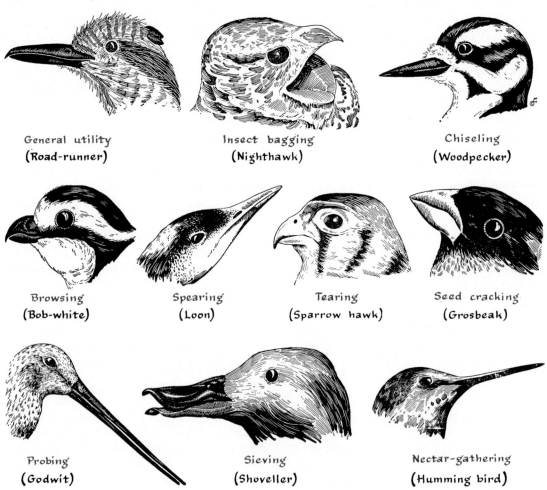

General utility
(Road-runner)

Insect bagging
(Nighthawk)

Chiseling
(Woodpecker)

Browsing
(Bob-white)

Spearing
(Loon)

Tearing
(Sparrow hawk)

Seed cracking
(Grosbeak)

Probing
(Godwit)

Sieving
(Shoveller)

Nectar-gathering
(Humming bird)

Fig. 23-15. *The duckbill platypus, an egg-laying mammal. (Courtesy New York Zoological Society.)*

Order **Rodentia.** Beavers, guinea pigs, mice, rats, squirrels. Chisel-shaped incisor teeth.

Order **Lagomorpha.** Rabbits. Formerly included in the Rodentia, but show differences in dentition.

Order **Carnivora.** Cats, dogs, bears, badgers, minks, seals, walruses. Flesh-eaters with strong, tearing teeth.

Order **Cetacea.** Whales, dolphins, porpoises. Modified for fishlike existence.

Order **Proboscidea.** Elephants. Incisors modified into tusks; prehensile proboscis.

Order **Perissodactyla.** Horses, rhinoceroses. "Ungulates" with digits reduced to uneven number.

Order **Artiodactyla.** Camels, deer, cows, pigs, hippopotamuses. "Ungulates" with digits reduced to even number.

Of all the orders of mammals, undoubtedly the most interesting to us are the primates, to which man belongs. The resemblances between men and apes and monkeys are too numerous to dismiss as coincidental. Unless parsimonious thinking is abandoned by making the origin of man a unique exception to that of all other living things, no one who studies the data of anatomy and paleontology can avoid concluding that man, monkeys, and apes have sprung from a common ancestral type. What that ancestral type is, is very much a matter of debate.

The fossil record, though improving from decade to decade, has far too many gaps in it to allow us to sketch surely the course of the evolution of man.

However, from such evidence as there is, and from general principles, it is possible to point out certain interesting features involved in the evolution of *Homo sapiens*. Undoubtedly, man's remote ancestors lived, at one time, in the trees. This habitat puts a premium on manual dexterity, which is aided by the development of opposable thumbs, which later made possible the extensive use of *tools*. Progression through the trees is unquestionably also aided greatly by the development of the stereoscopic ("two-eyed," depth-perceiving) vision that characterizes primates.

There must have been a time when man's ancestors came down out of the trees and walked upright on their hind feet—an ability almost completely lacking in other contemporary primate species. Also, and of the greatest importance in affecting the future course of evolution, was the development of speech. True speech is more than the mere use of sounds to communicate emotion (a use common in the animal kingdom); it includes also the ability to indicate objects by sounds. In its higher reaches, actions and even abstract ideas may be so communicated. Many animals are perhaps prevented from speaking by inadequate vocal apparatus (vocal cords, tongue, and so forth), but this is not the whole story. To the anatomist, chimpanzees would appear to be entirely capable of speech. Psychological studies show that they have a considerable amount of abstracting ability. Yet they do not speak, though numerous attempts have been made to teach them. Clearly something (in the way of motivation?) is lacking from their hereditary make-up, preventing them from developing this characteristic human ability, with all its immense power for good and evil.

Questions and Problems

23-6. Make a list of the **boldface** terms in this chapter and write a brief definition of each. Compare your work with the text.

‡23-7. A deep-sea fish that has a swim bladder must keep within a certain depth range. If it rises too high (as it might in the excitement of the chase), it then "falls upward" to the surface of the ocean and dies. Why? Give a cybernetic analysis.

23-8. Starfish are motile. Could you, from the type of symmetry they exhibit, predict how rapidly they move? Explain.

23-9. The following aphorism, coined by Ernst Haeckel, is sometimes called the **Biogenetic Law:** "Ontogeny recapitulates phylogeny." With the aid of a dictionary, figure out the meaning of this sentence, and cite three examples.

23-10. Systematically, and at some length, compare and contrast the mosses, the flatworms, and the amphibia, with respect to the extent to which each group has conquered the land.

23-11. What features enable the reptiles to prosper better on land than do fishes or amphibia?

23-12. An intromittent organ for copulation (e.g., a penis) is more common among land forms than among water-dwelling animals. Why?

‡23-13. Though they live in the water, whales and porpoises have penises. Why?

23-14. A male guppy has an intromittent organ. Why? Is the answer to this question essentially the same as the answer to question 23-13? Explain.

‡23-15. The following statement (from an otherwise excellent book on evolution) fails in what way to conform to taxonomic conventions? "Whales are divided systematically into a number of phyla, of which three principal ones are the Archaeoceti, the Mystaceti, and the Odontoceti."

23-16. Endothermal animals that live in cold climates are usually larger than their close relatives living in warmer climates. This generalization is called **Bergmann's Rule.** What is the adaptive significance of the correlation of size and climate?

‡23-17. Among ectotherms, the reverse of Bergmann's Rule is generally true; for example, the largest snakes are all of tropical habitat. Why the difference?

23-18. Linnaeus, discussing the birds, spoke of them as "cavalry, light, nimble, resplendently clad." Contrast this with his attitude toward the amphibia. If his attitudes were taken up by his followers (as they seem to have been) what effect would you predict they had on the development of taxonomy in the several classes?

‡23-19. Bushtits, quite small birds, must capture about 24 average-size insects per bird every minute of the day. Give a theoretical explanation for this fact.

23-20. Consider two communities: one is a primitive one with no weapons more powerful than bow and arrow, and depends on the hunting of deer for its food; the other is a modern community, hunting only for sport, with high-powered rifles, and putting a great premium on beautiful trophy animals. Raymond B. Cowles has pointed out that, as selective agents, these two communities will have quite different effects on the deer. What will be the long-term effects? Does either community work against its long-term interests? Explain.

‡23-21. In the domestication of animals, how has man avoided acting as an adverse selective agent? (That is, avoided selecting adversely to his own interest?)

23-22. Among the anthropoids it is generally true that carnivores are more likely to share their food than are herbivores. Give an evolutionary explanation.

‡23-23. S. L. Washburn and Virginia Avis have pointed out that when the ancestors of man became principally carnivorous, a change in their reaction to the idea of territory became necessary. What change? Explain.

23-24. List and discuss all the biological reasons you can discover for the remarkable success of *Homo sapiens*.

Readings

Vertebrates have so long been favorite objects of study that there is an embarrassment of riches in the way of a bibliography. Particularly beautiful are the books of the *"Living"* series: *Living Mammals of the World,* by Sanderson; *Living Reptiles of the World,* by Schmidt and Inger; *Living Birds of the World,* by Gilliard; *Living Fishes of the World,* by Herald; and *Living Amphibians of the World,* by Cochran. To these should be added the Goins' *Introduction to Herpetology,* Welty's *The Life of Birds,* and Walker's three-volume *Mammals of the World.*

Behavior and Evolution, edited by Roe and Simpson, is a stimulating collection of essays. For a general discussion of the origins and meaning of social habits see Allee's *Cooperation Among Animals.* Scott's *Animal Behavior* deals largely with vertebrate behavior, with one eye cocked on human problems.

For the historical controversy connected with the idea that man evolved from monkeys, see Part II of Hardin, *Population, Evolution & Birth Control.*

Scientific American Offprints

124. Evelyn Shaw. *The Schooling of Fishes*

133. E. G. F. Sauer. *Celestial Navigation by Birds*

145. W. H. Thorpe. *The Language of Birds*

412. Konrad Z. Lorenz. *The Evolution of Behavior*

414. N. Tinbergen. *The Curious Behavior of the Stickleback*

470. Irenaus Eibl-Eibesfeldt. *The Fighting Behavior of Animals*

601. Sherwood L. Washburn. *Tools and Human Evolution*

603. Charles F. Hockett. *The Origin of Speech*

614. S. L. Washburn and Irven DeVore. *The Social Life of Baboons*

24

How a Vertebrate Moves

182. Why Study Man?

Of the animal kingdom we have just made a survey, once over, lightly. The amount of detail included was certainly not enough for professional biologists, and scarcely enough for laymen. But there is no help for it. There are at least a million species of animals, of great diversity, and with a great wealth of individual detail. We could hardly discuss them all thoroughly in one book.* Selectivity must be the order of the day.

We cannot discuss all the kinds of animals thoroughly. To get a fairly good appreciation of the problems of animal life, it will be best to give close attention to one only. But which one? We might choose a "typical animal"—if only that phrase had any meaning! There is no adequate objective basis for the choice, so we will choose otherwise. We will settle on man. Why?

Here are a couple of answers: "The proper study of mankind is man," said the poet Alexander Pope, more than two centuries ago. "The proper study of mankind is man, says man," retorted James Thurber, humorist and seer of

our day. There are two points of view. Prefer which you will, we're going ahead on that basis.

In the chapters to follow we will consider in some detail the structure and functioning of man. But our approach will not be narrowly confined to this species. Many—perhaps all—of the structures and functions of this one animal cannot be understood without some knowledge of other animals. After all, man has descended from unmanlike forms. More: many of his biochemical functions are so general that they are shared by all plants and animals; to discuss these, it may sometimes be most convenient to talk about rats, worms, cuttle fish, or plants.

183. Vesalius

In a sense, man is most interested in himself; but as we survey the history of human progress, we see that there have been powerful resistances to the acceptance of *Homo sapiens* as a legitimate object of study. Opposition has taken various forms at different times; progress at each stage has depended on breaking down the relevant resistances. Some of them are still with us today; we may discuss these later. But first we want to learn about some earlier victories in the fight for intellectual freedom.

Medicine clearly depends on a minute knowledge of the human body, but for hundreds of

---

* 24-1. Suppose we did nothing more than list the species by their official names, and suppose the average name was the length of *Musca domestica*. How many pages like this one would it take for such a mere listing of a million species? How many volumes of the present size? And wouldn't that make an interesting book!

years many impediments were thrown in the way of obtaining this knowledge. The progress of anatomy was much delayed by the ecclesiastical Edict of Tours of 1163 A.D., which forbade the shedding of blood. This obviously made both surgery and anatomical dissection difficult (to say the least). The edict was later liberalized by "interpretations" to make surgery possible; but anatomical studies, not being so directly connected with therapy, were longer in gaining sufferance. With the coming of the Renaissance, interest in the human body was rekindled, both in its exterior form as it was treated by painters and sculptors, and in its internal structure. A great turning point in the study of anatomy came in 1543 with the publication of *De Humani Corporis Fabrica* by a Belgian working in Italy, one Andreas Vesalius. He was 29 years old at the time.

The opposition of the Christian Church to the study of the human body is a matter of official record, but it must not be supposed that this was the only opposition. It may not have even been the most important impediment to learning. The medical men themselves conducted their work in such a way as to make the acquiring of accurate knowledge difficult. It was the practice of anatomists to sit on a high seat in the teaching amphitheater, far away from the cadaver, pointing to the structures as they were uncovered by the ignorant and often unskillful barbers (the only surgeons of the time) who did the dissection. Under these circumstances it is hardly surprising that many erroneous beliefs about the body were successfully transmitted from one generation to another.

Most of the students were no more anxious than the teacher to get near the body. Vesalius was an exception. While a student in Paris, he became enraged at the slovenliness of the presentation, grabbed the scalpel from the clumsy dissector, and himself revealed the true structure of the human body. The day Vesalius stepped down to the dissecting table marked the beginning of a new era in biology.

More important than the mere anatomical knowledge that was gained was the introduction of a spirit of inquiry without which science

is sterile—the determination of scientists to see and do things for themselves. The highest kind of creative and investigative activity cannot be delegated. Only men who understand this truth can work at the frontiers of knowledge. It is an attitude that has never been lost completely, but it has had its ebb periods. Vesalius came at one of these and played a key role in developing the temper that characterizes modern science.

Vesalius' greatest days were spent in Padua. There he lectured and demonstrated in an amphitheater with 500 seats, filled with an overflow crowd of not only medical students but townspeople of all professions who had caught the excitement of the new learning. The course they undertook was most strenuous: it occupied the entire day for three weeks,* usually in the winter. New dissecting instruments were developed, and diagrams and charts were displayed and even made on the spot. Fortunately, Vesalius had the services of an excellent draftsman, a man named Jan Stephan van Calcar, another Belgian, trained under Titian. The figures he made for the *Fabrica* are still delights to behold.

184. The Systems of the Body

Before we can begin to understand anything as complex as a human or other animal body, we need to analyze it into some sort of components. Traditionally, the human body is first analyzed into systems—a **system** being roughly defined as a group of organs or structures that serve one function or a group of related functions, for example, support, digestion, reproduction. Figure 24-1 shows a medieval version of some of these systems. While grossly inaccurate in many of its details, this Persian representation is animated by the same analytical spirit that has led to the more modern interpretation shown in Figure 24-2.

There's nothing sacred about the set of sys-

---

* 24-2. Why didn't Vesalius spread it out over a longer time—say, with 3-hour sessions each day for eight weeks?

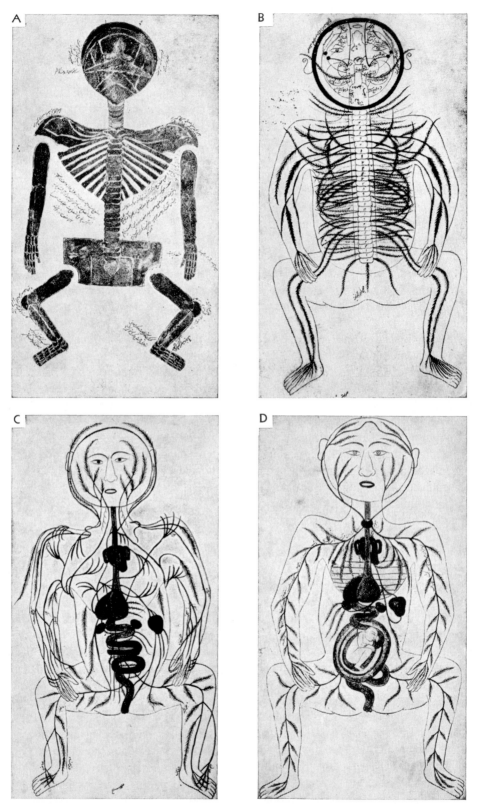

Fig. 24-1. *Medieval Persian analysis of the human body into systems. (A) Skeletal system. (B) Nervous system. (C) Venous system. (D) Arterial system of a pregnant woman. Compare this analysis with the modern version shown in Figure 24-2. (From the text* Tashrikh-i-Mansur, *courtesy Welch Medical Library, Johns Hopkins University.)*

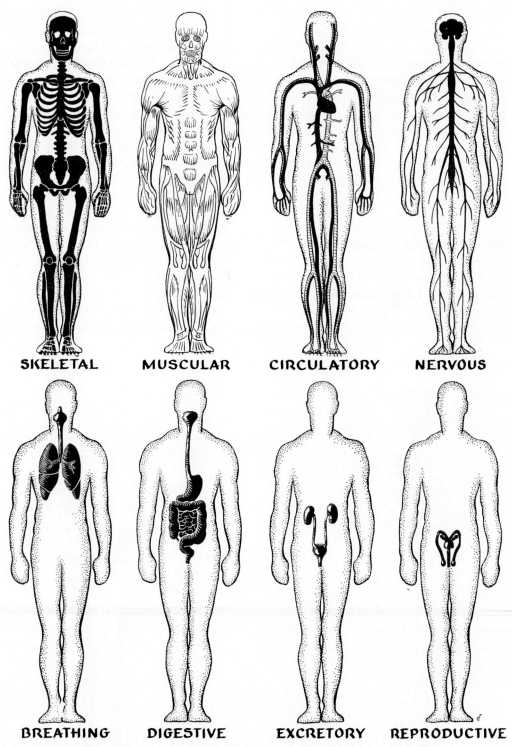

SKELETAL   MUSCULAR   CIRCULATORY   NERVOUS

BREATHING   DIGESTIVE   EXCRETORY   REPRODUCTIVE

Fig. 24-2. *The human body functions as a well-integrated unit, but it is advantageously studied in terms of separate "systems," such as those shown in color above.*

tems presented. Another expositor, with different ends in view, might divide the body into somewhat different systems. We must not forget that in carrying out even the simplest function, the body uses more than one system. The muscular system, for instance, moves the body, but it can do so only because the muscles are firmly attached to the skeleton; the muscles are stimulated to move by nerves; and repeated movements are possible only as long as the breathing, circulatory, and digestive systems are functioning.

185. The Skeletal System: Its Protective Function

The skeleton fulfills three major functions: *protection, support,* and, in conjunction with the muscles, *movement.* The skeleton may be said to consist of two divisions: the **axial skeleton,** a central axis on which is hung, so to speak, the **appendicular skeleton** (Fig. 24-3). The axial skeleton consists of the **vertebrae** (backbone), the **skull,** and the **ribs** and **sternum.** The appendicular skeleton consists of the **appendages** (legs and arms), together with the **pelvic girdle** to which the legs are attached, and the **pectoral girdle** to which the arms are fastened. Altogether, the body contains more than 200 bones.

Among the most delicate portions of the human body are the brain and the spinal cord. These structures control in large measure the activities of the entire body. The material of which they are composed has little intrinsic strength. It is not surprising, therefore, to find that no other part of the body is so thoroughly protected. The brain, located in what would otherwise be a dangerously exposed position at

Fig. 24-3. *The human skeleton analyzed into axial and appendicular components.*

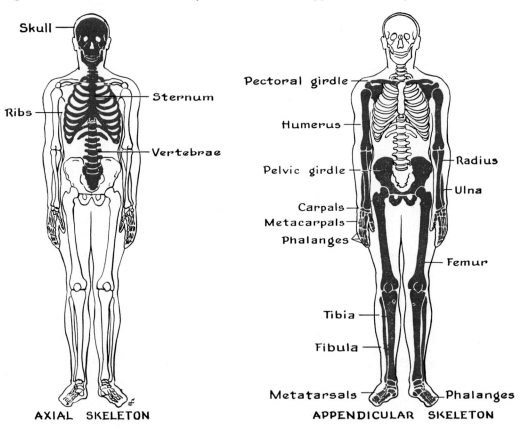

AXIAL SKELETON   APPENDICULAR SKELETON

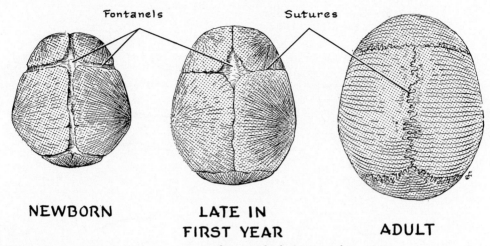

Fontanels   Sutures

NEWBORN   LATE IN FIRST YEAR   ADULT

Fig. 24-4. *The brain case develops from separate bones which fuse as they grow.*

the very top of the axial skeleton, is almost completely enclosed in a bony box—the skull. The skull is not a single bone, but rather a number of variously shaped, platelike bones that grow together and fuse at their edges as the individual grows older. During development, which starts before birth, the skull bones begin as widely separated, growing plates. By the time an infant is born, these plates have grown until they are touching each other in most regions, but not in all; where they do not touch are soft areas called **fontanels** (Fig. 24-4), the most prominent of which in a newborn is one near the top of the head. Moreover, even where the skull bones have already met by the time of birth, the **sutures** (L. *sutura* = a seam) between the bones are not very firm, permitting considerable distortion of the shape of the skull. The pliability of the infant skull is of importance at this time, for it permits a more easy passage of the rather oversize head down the birth canal.

Such a pliable skull would not, however, be good protection after birth for a brain exposed to the myriad dangers of this world; on the other hand, once the crisis of birth is passed, there is no advantage in retaining the pliability. Within a year or so after birth, the fontanels close as the skull bones grow together, and the sutures of the skull bones become more firmly knit. The outline of the sutures increases in complexity, year by year (Fig. 24-4). The skull bones do not, however, become completely welded together until after the twentieth year. Since the time of closure of the various sutures is fairly constant, their development enables the archaeologist to determine the age at death of an individual whose skull he finds.

The brain is protected by the skull. the other great part of the central nervous system, the spinal cord, is equally well protected by vertebrae (sing. vertebra; L. a joint, from *verto* = turn). Note, in Figure 24-5*A*, how small is the hole occupied by the spinal cord itself, as compared with the amount of protective bone in the surrounding vertebrae. The construction of the vertebrae represents an admirable compromise between the ideals of complete protection and complete mobility. The delicate nerve cord extends from the mid-region of the body to the head. It is most important that the nerve cord not be injured in the slightest way. From this point of view, the ideal protection would be a solid bony tunnel running the length of the back. Such a solid structure would be very inflexible and, hence, would not allow much movement of the body. The way in which the protective bony covering of the nerve cord is actually constructed affords nearly as much protection as would a solid bony tube, while conferring an amazing amount of flexibility to the body (Fig. 24-5).

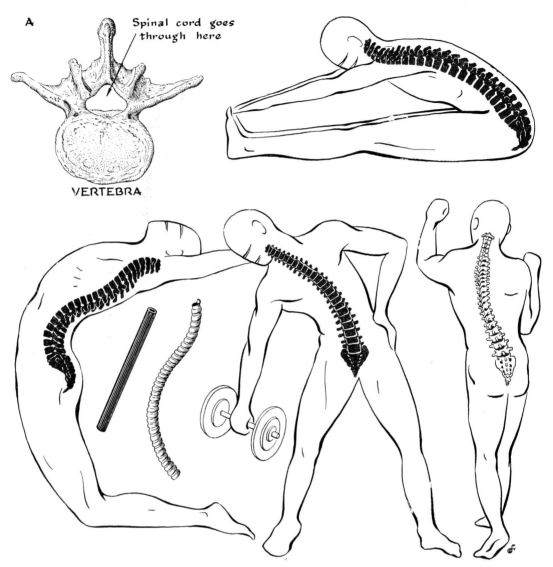

Fig. 24-5. *The pliability contributed to the backbone by its construction, which is analogous to that of flexible armored cable rather than rigid pipe. The individual vertebrae* (A) *furnish massive protection to the delicate spinal cord, while their articulation with one another permits movement.*

In humans, the skull and the vertebrae constitute the major portion of the skeleton that is protective in function. Most of the body is not protected from external blows by anything more solid than skin. This is in marked contrast to the arthropods (Chap. 22), in which the exoskeleton protects everything. A few vertebrates, for example, turtles and armadillos, have added an extensive external skeleton (the internal skeleton is still there) but, in so doing, they have sacrificed considerable mobility to gain protection.

186. The Skeleton as Support

Most of the bones of the human body are concerned with support. The heaviest load falls on the leg bones, which, be it noted (Fig. 24-3), are more stoutly built than the otherwise similar arm bones. *The heavier the load it must bear, the greater must be the diameter of a bone.* This is a commonplace: The legs of an elephant are thicker than those of a mouse. What is not so easily remarked is that they are disproportionately thicker. In Figure 24-6, the front legs of mouse and elephant are drawn *to the same size;* notice how much more slightly built the mouse's leg is. We have taken two particular animals for comparison, but the same relationship would hold for any two animals of similar mode of life but of great difference in size.

A large animal has proportionately larger bones. As a consequence, large size is correlated with lack of agility. A mouse is much quicker in its movements than an elephant. Also, since the larger animal has bones that are disproportionately large, the nonbony part of its body must be disproportionately small. The larger the animal, the smaller the proportion of muscles and internal organs. If an ani-

Fig. 24-6. *The larger a land animal is, the larger, proportionately, must its bones be to support its weight.*

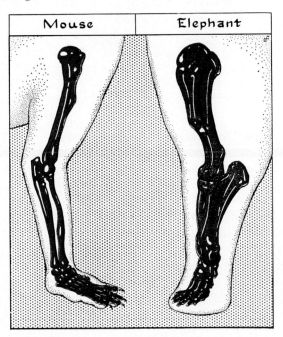

Mouse	Elephant

mal were to grow indefinitely, there would come a time when it would have to consist of nothing but supporting structure, so heavy that it would be unable to support anything else. Actually, of course, growth would have to stop considerably short of this. It is not possible to state precisely the upper limit in size for land-dwelling animals, but it should be apparent that the problem of adequate support is one of the factors that determine the limit.

187. How Does a Bone Grow?

The way in which bones grow can be determined by fastening small metal markers to the bones of a young animal, letting the animal grow for a while, and then determining the new positions of the markers. The outcome of such experiments is shown diagrammatically in Figure 24-7*A, B*. Notice that, as growth proceeds, the spacing between markers 2, 3, and 4 remains the same, whereas the space between 1 and 2 increases, indicating that the region of growth is somewhere between markers 1 and 2. The growth region is, in fact, quite near the end of the bone.

Bones, however, grow not only in length but also in thickness. How is this accomplished? Again, an experiment with a metal marker answers our question. This time, a metal ring is fastened around a long bone of a very young animal. The subsequent positions are diagrammed in Figure 24-7*C–E*. Notice that the ring is first covered over with bone, indicating that bone is added from the outside. Later, the ring appears free in the marrow cavity as the bone in which it was embedded is destroyed, thus making room for the enlarging marrow cavity.

Growth in thickness of the bone is brought about by a layer of tissue called the **periosteum** (Gr. *peri* = around + *osteon* = bone), a thin nonbony sheath that encircles the bone and lays down new bone on the outside. It can readily be understood how activity of the cells of the periosteum results in covering the ring with bone.

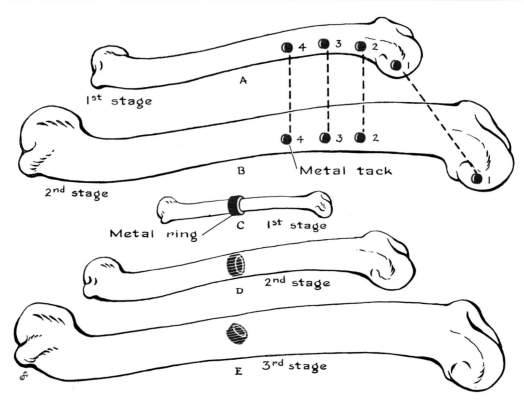

Fig. 24-7. *The experimental observations that reveal the location of the growing regions of a long bone. See text for discussion.*

The freeing of the ring, as it appears in Figure 24-7*E*, is also the result of cellular activity. As the wall of a long bone increases in diameter, certain cells digest the bone on the inner surface of the cylinder, thus making room for the marrow, which also consists of cells and their products. Because the marrow is soft, the metal ring is no longer rigidly held in position once the bone has grown to a diameter greater than that of the ring.

By experiments, we have shown that growth of the long bones of the body occurs by two different processes: growth in length, and growth in thickness. Normally, both kinds of growth continue until about the twentieth year. There is a hereditary condition (due to a dominant gene) in which growth in length ceases prematurely, producing a short-limbed, or **chondrodystrophic,** dwarf (Fig. 24-8, fourth and fifth from the left). Such short-limbed dwarfs were favored as court jesters in the

Middle Ages and beyond. Velasquez includes such dwarfs in many of his paintings of the Spanish court of the seventeenth century. The same growth abnormality is known in other kinds of animals and has been deliberately bred for in certain fancy breeds—notably, the dachshund and the basset hound.

188. How Muscles Move the Bones

It is important to realize this fact: A *muscle is capable of only one positive action*—namely, **contraction.** Its only other action is a passive one, **relaxation.** Muscles move the parts of the body in various directions. To take a simple example, the forearm can be either **flexed** (Fig. 24-9*A*) or **extended** (Fig. 24-9*C*). Both flexion and extension are results of muscular action. Since all muscles have the same primary action (contraction), different movements must be possible only because muscle contractions are utilized in different ways. The relationships of the muscles to the associated bones show how this is possible (Fig. 24-9*B, D*).

In the example illustrated, the two bones act as two parts of a lever: the upper arm bone, the **humerus,** acts as the fulcrum; while the forearm bone, the **radius,** acts as the lever arm. (There are actually two bones in the forearm, the radius and the **ulna**—see Fig. 24-3—but for simplicity, we speak here of only one.) There are several muscles involved in moving the forearm, but no harm will be done if we focus our attention on only two of them: the **biceps** muscle on the "front" part of the upper arm, and the **triceps** on the back part.*

Both muscles are attached, in part, to the shoulder bones above the humerus. Knowing the point of attachment to the radius (Fig. 24-9*C*), we can readily predict that contraction of the biceps will lead to a flexing of the arm. Similarly, since the triceps is attached to the other side of the forearm, contraction of this muscle will result in extension of the arm. By the proper cooperative use of the two muscles, the arm can be flexed or extended to any degree. Muscles that act contrary to one another in this way are called antagonists, or are said to be antagonistic to each other.

These terms are partly apt, partly inept; for in muscles we note the paradoxical situation that *antagonistic muscles always cooperate* in carrying out the movements of the body. Theoretically, an arm could be flexed by the use of the biceps alone. Actually, the triceps, too, is always called into play during flexion. To verify this, the reader can slowly flex his right arm while feeling, with his left hand, the lower side of the right arm. During flexion, a noticeable tenseness develops in the triceps muscle, showing that it contracts to a certain extent. The triceps does not contract as forcibly as the biceps, for if it did, the two equal and counteracting forces would prevent any movement at

all. Similarly, in extension, the biceps contracts, though less strongly than the triceps. The cooperative action of antagonistic muscles is important in bestowing smoothness to the movements of the body.

Sometimes a muscle appears to be attached directly to a bone; more frequently the muscle terminates in a **tendon,** which in turn is attached to the bone (Fig. 24-10). Tendons belong to a class of tissues called **connective tissue**—of which cartilage is another example—tissue that serves principally to connect and tie together other tissues of the body. A tendon is made up largely of cell secretions, rather than of cells, and is very tough and flexible, but not elastic. The tendon acts as a cable to transmit the pull from a contracting muscle to a bone.

There is an important benefit conferred by the tendons: a tendon permits a muscle to act at a considerable distance from the bone that it

Fig. 24-8. *All the individuals in this photo are more than twenty years of age. From left to right: a cretin imbecile, the result of insufficient secretion of thyroid hormone; two midgets of the symmetrical (Lorain) type; two short-limbed dwarfs of the chondrodystrophic type; a normal man. (From Major,* Physical Diagnosis, *W. B. Saunders Co., Philadelphia.)*

---

* 24-3. Using a pencil of one color, add humerus, radius, and ulna to Figure 24-9*A*; with another color, add biceps and triceps muscles. Label the additions.

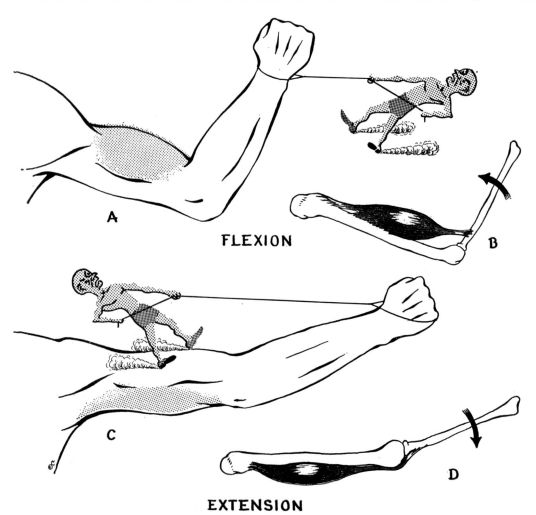

FLEXION

EXTENSION

Fig. 24-9. *The points of attachment of a muscle determine whether the muscle's only action—contraction—brings about flexion* (A, B) *or extension* (C, D).

moves. Notice, in Figure 24-11, that the muscles that move the fingers in the left hand are actually at a considerable distance from them, being well up in the forearm. The reader can verify this by moving his fingers vigorously while noticing the ripple of muscles under the skin of the forearm. The position of these muscles explains the feeling of fatigue experienced in the forearm following long-continued and intensive use of the fingers, as in typing or playing a musical instrument.

Thinking of activities of this sort, we can easily appreciate the advantage of the tendon system of transmitting power: If muscles had to be always fastened directly to the bones that they move, our fingers, if they were as powerful as they are now, would be great, clumsy, muscle-padded digits, quite incapable of the delicate movements they now perform. Many of man's arts and skills would no longer be possible, except at a very crude level. Without the action at a distance permitted by slender tendons, we would be truly "muscle-bound." (Notice the right hand in Fig. 24-11.)

Another sort of connective tissue that plays an important part in movement is the cartilage at the ends of the bones. Where two movable bones meet, this cartilage surrounds a pocket

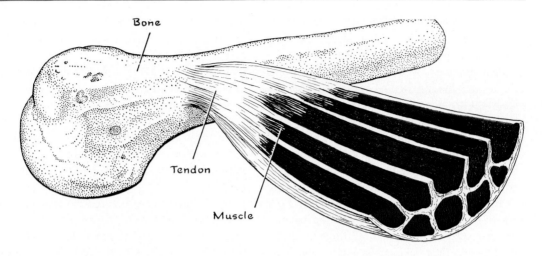

Fig. 24-10. *The attachment of a muscle to a bone by means of a tendon.*

of fluid, called the **synovial fluid.** This fluid is a watery, protein-rich solution resembling the white of an egg, hence the name (Gr. *syn* = with + L. *ovum* = egg). The synovial joint is what an engineer would call a "weeping bearing"—fluid is constantly oozing into it. The coefficient of friction of the synovial joint is unusually low, as is apparent from the following list:

Bearing Substances	Coefficient of Friction
brick against wood	0.5
copper against copper	0.8
teflon against teflon	0.05
ice against ice	0.02
synovial joint	0.01 to 0.02

The coefficient of friction of a weeping bearing rises during the time it is static. Movement

Fig. 24-11. *How tendons enable muscles to act at a distance is shown by the natural hand at the left. At the right is the artist's conception of what the human hand would be like if muscles had to be attached directly to the bones they move.*

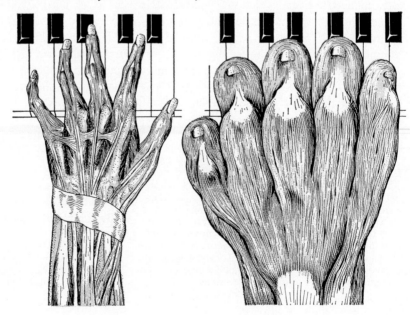

brings the coefficient down again. It is noteworthy that horses, which sleep standing, change their posture about every half hour.

There are over 600 recognized skeletal muscles in the human body. The number varies somewhat from person to person; smaller and relatively unimportant muscles are frequently missing. The more important muscles are almost always present, but they show considerable variation in their points of origin and insertion. In one study of over 500 human cadavers, it was found that, in more than 20 percent of them, one or both of the biceps muscles had *three* heads—that is, three points of attachment—thus belying the name, which implies two heads. Many other variations in muscle attachment are known. Probably some of the individuality shown in gait is attributable to such variations.

189. The Structure of Skeletal Muscle

No microscope is needed to tell that a muscle is not a homogeneous structure. A beefsteak is a cross section of cow's muscle. Either inspection or eating makes it apparent that there are three sorts of tissue present in such meat: muscle tissue, which makes up the bulk of the steak; fatty connective tissue, which in a good steak is flecked throughout the muscle; and tough connective tissue,* or gristle, which, from a gastronomic point of view, is better absent.

To the animal, the presence of fat in a muscle is perhaps of no particular benefit; this is just one of the many places where fat can be stored. The presence of tough connective tissue,

---

* Histologists, that is, scientists who study tissues (Gr. *histos* = web, tissue), recognize about a dozen different kinds of connective tissue, among which are loose connective tissue, fatty tissue, tendons, cartilage, and bone. Corroborative evidence that bone is but one variety of connective tissue is furnished by a rare disease (bearing the impressive name of *myositis ossificans progressiva*) in which the connective tissue of muscles gradually turns into bone. The eventual result is complete immobility of the muscles affected, and the sufferer could be said to "turn to stone."

however, is of first importance. The strands and sheaths of connective tissue that surround the muscle fibers (Fig. 24-12) join with each other and with the tendon; through them, a muscle is connected with a bone in such a way that contraction of the muscle moves the bone. The proportion of connective tissue to muscle tissue increases with age. As evidence, compare the dated sections shown in Figure 24-12, or the masticability of genuine lamb and admitted mutton.

In its fine structure a muscle is made up of fibers running parallel to its long axis. When these muscle fibers contract, the muscle contracts. Not all fibers contract at the same time. The greater the number of fibers contracting at any instant, the stronger the contraction of the whole muscle.

The microscopical anatomy of skeletal muscle fibers presents us with a problem in scientific methodology. Within each muscle fiber are several hundred nuclei, *which are not separated from each other by cell membranes.* What is the cell in this instance? Are we to say that each nucleus, together with an unspecified amount of cytoplasm, constitutes a cell? If so, the cell is a rather hazy concept. Or should we say that the whole fiber is a single cell? If we adopt this course, we must admit that muscles are composed of most atypical cells. A single muscle fiber may be 100μ in thickness—remember, that is the thickness of a human hair—and several centimeters in length. The membrane surrounding the fiber is much thicker and tougher than any ordinary cell membrane; in fact, it is usually given a distinct name—**sarcolemma** (Gr. *sarkos* = flesh + *lemma* = rind). And finally, the fiber is a *multinucleate* structure; such a structure is sometimes called a syncytium (Gr. *syn-* = together + *kytos* = cell; the name thus implies that each nucleus is part of an individual cell).*

In the maintenance of muscle health, the fol-

---

* 24-4. Multinucleate cells (if that's the right term) are also found among what fungi? And what synonym do botanists use for "syncytium"?

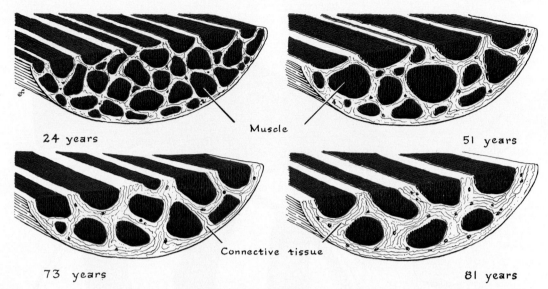

24 years

Muscle

51 years

73 years

Connective tissue

81 years

Fig. 24-12. *Cross-sections of muscles taken from men of various ages. With age, connective tissue (white) increases at the expense of muscle tissue (colored). This is one reason why young men are stronger than old men.*

lowing fact is of prime importance: A muscle that is not continuously used *atrophies*—it shrinks in size and hence becomes weaker. The **atrophy** takes place in every fiber. Apparently, a fiber can maintain its normal size only if it is worked frequently. In "polio" (poliomyelitis, or infantile paralysis) some of the nerve fibers attached to a muscle may be destroyed; as a result, the muscle is not stimulated to activity; as a secondary result, atrophy sets in. These facts have led to the use of massage (a substitute for nervous stimulation) in the treatment of polio. Again, following any major operation there is a period of enforced inactivity, during which the patient's skeletal muscles grow daily weaker. In modern hospital practice, this effect is minimized by massage and by having the patient get on his feet as soon as it is safe for him to do so.

One of the most remarkable features of skeletal muscle fibers is the crossbanding, or **striation,** visible under the microscope (Fig. 24-13). Every skeletal muscle has alternating light and dark bands oriented at right angle to the long axis. When a muscle fiber contracts, the light bands become dark and the dark bands light.

190. The Kinds of Muscle

Not all muscles show striations. Muscles that move the skeleton do; hence, skeletal muscle is frequently called **striated muscle.** But there are other muscles that are not striated, for example, muscles in the wall of the stomach. Such muscle, called **smooth muscle,** is made up of well-defined, uninucleate cells. In general, the organs in the central body cavity possess smooth muscle, striated muscle being comparatively rare. Smooth muscle differs from striated muscle in a number of ways, the most conspicuous of which is in the speed of action. Smooth muscle contracts and relaxes very slowly, striated muscle much more rapidly. Completion of contraction may take several seconds with smooth muscle, but less than one second with striated. On the other hand, smooth muscle does not fatigue as easily as striated; it may remain continuously contracted for hours at a time.

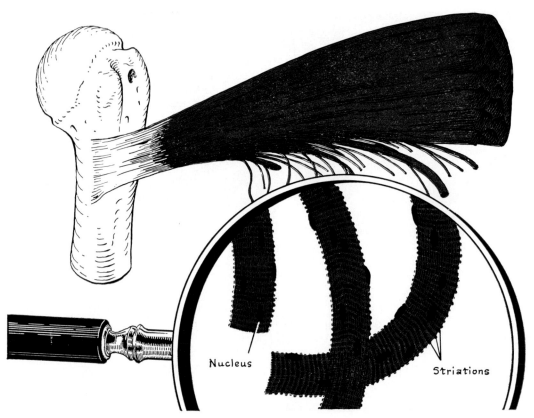

Fig. 24-13. *The striations to be seen in skeletal (voluntary) muscle when it is examined with a high-power optical microscope.*

There is yet a third kind of muscle, called **cardiac muscle** (Gr. *kardia* = heart), present in the heart. This muscle is structurally intermediate between smooth and striated muscle: Like smooth muscle, it has uninucleate cells—but these are striated. The functional demands on heart muscle are also intermediate between those of the other two types of cells: A heart must work, with only momentary rests, from the time of its first beat, eight months before birth, until death, scores of years later; so it needs, like smooth muscle, to be relatively indefatigable. But, like striated muscle, it must contract rapidly.

191. Where Does the Energy Come From?

"Muscular contraction," A. Szent-Györgyi, a Hungarian biochemist, has said, "is one of the most wonderful phenomena of the biological kingdom. That a soft jelly should suddenly become hard, change its shape and lift a thousand times its own weight, and that it should be able to do so several hundred times a minute, is little short of miraculous." How do muscles perform such prodigies? Where does the energy come from, and how can a muscle obtain the energy?

The details of the process of muscular contraction are still being worked out by molecular biologists. Only a few words will be said about it here. Muscle action is the result of chemical processes, of course, and most of these processes are anaerobic, i.e., they do not require oxygen. For the complete cycle of muscle processes to take place oxygen must be furnished, but contraction does not have to wait on the delivery of O_2. In vigorous muscular activity a man may incur a considerable **oxygen**

debt, which must be paid for during the rest period that follows. A man running a hundred-meter dash may end with an oxygen debt of more than 6 liters of O_2.

There are two kinds of protein in muscle, called **myosin** (Gr. *mys* = muscle) and **actin.** Put together in solution these two proteins form a higher-order complex called **actomyosin,** which can be separated out of solution in the form of fibers. Szent-Györgyi discovered that if ATP (§38) was added to actomyosin in a test tube the protein fibers contracted strongly. In the process, ATP was converted to ADP. So muscle contraction, like so many other metabolic activities, is paid for by the energy-coin of ATP.

This observation has led to intensive investigation of the way myosin and actin are distributed in the muscle fibrils and how their distribution is changed by ATP. Such work requires the combined efforts of biochemists and electron microscopists. Whether viewed as a problem in pure science or one in applied science, the investigation of muscle contraction is well worth considerable effort. As a machine, muscle is quite efficient. We reckon efficiency as the fraction of input energy that appears as useful work (the rest appearing as heat). A reciprocating steam engine has an efficiency of about 15 percent; of an ordinary auto engine, about 30 percent; of the best diesel engine, 45 percent. The efficiency of muscle in converting chemical energy to work is about 30 percent. Not bad.

Questions and Problems

24-5. Make a list of the **boldface** terms in this chapter and write a brief description of each. Compare your work with the text.

24-6. Although the text is not explicit, would you hazard a guess as to whether the periostea (sing. periosteum) of dwarf humans exhibit normal activity?

‡24-7. A whale has proportionately less of its body weight in skeleton than a land animal of corresponding size would have. Explain.

24-8. The largest of the dinosaurs, approximately 100 feet in length and weighing an estimated 40 tons when alive, are believed to have been swampdwellers. Without knowing the detailed evidence, can you guess why swamps seem a more reasonable habitat for such large creatures than solid land?

‡24-9. Once metal markers are placed on a bone in a living animal, as in Figure 24-7, how could the changing positions of the markers be followed without further surgical operations?

24-10. Although the total *amount* of phosphorus in the skeleton is approximately constant, it has been shown that 30 percent of the atoms of this element deposited in the skeleton of an adult rat at any time is removed therefrom within 20 days. What must be the evidence for this statement?

‡24-11. A muscle has only one positive action: contraction. How does it happen that opposite movements of an appendage are possible?

24-12. Under what circumstances might the definition of muscle efficiency given in §191 be regarded as completely wrong?

‡24-13. In the mouse, there is an autosomal-recessive gene for "fetal muscular degeneration" which produces embryos without any muscles. Shortly after birth, these mice die. Why do they die at this particular time?

24-14. A muscle from a young frog is compared with a muscle from an old frog. Both muscles are of exactly the same size and weight, and both are treated the same; yet the old muscle cannot lift as heavy a weight as the young one. Suggest at least one factor that may account for the difference.

24-15. The *palmaris longus* is one of the muscles

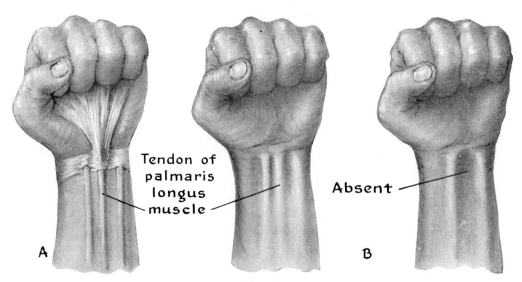

Fig. 24-14. *Demonstration of the tendon of the palmaris longus muscle. This muscle and tendon are absent in many humans.*

involved in flexing the fingers. Its presence or absence can be easily determined on a cadaver (Fig. 24-14*A*), and with some accuracy on a living person, by placing the forearm, palm up, on a table, flexing the middle finger, and looking for a dimpling of the surface of the lower forearm, as shown in Figure 24-14*B*. Do you have this muscle? In both arms? Is it present in your parents and siblings?

24-16. Consider Table 24-1. Could one use the presence or absence of the *palmaris longus* in an individual human as a means of determining his "race"?

24-17. The Christian religion emphasizes the primacy of the soul over the body. Why, then, have Christian sects been so often opposed to the use of dead bodies for dissection?

‡24-18. Is *D* of Fig. 24-1 male or female?

TABLE 24-1   *Frequency of Presence of Palmaris Longus Muscle in Different Ethnic Groups and Nonhuman Species.*

Ethnic Group	PERCENTAGE OF INDIVIDUALS POSSESSING THE MUSCLE
Chinese	98
Japanese	97
Negroes, U.S.A.	95
Russians	87
Whites, U.S.A.	86
Poles	81
French	75
Nonhuman Species	
Gibbons	100
Chimpanzees	95
Gorillas	15

Readings

For further reading in the subject of human physiology, there are many excellent texts. Among the shorter ones may be mentioned Best and Tay-

lor, and Carlson and Johnson. Some of the original papers dealing with bone and muscle physiology are to be found in Chapter 4 of Fulton's *Read-*

ings. The special topic of bone structure viewed as an engineering problem is treated in detail in D'Arcy Thompson's fascinating *On Growth and Form.*

Scientific American Offprints

19. H. E. Huxley. *The Contraction of Muscle*

62. Carl J. Wiggers. *The Heart*

140. John Napier. *The Evolution of the Hand*

25

Breathing and Its Problems

192. Definitions

For a long time the word "respiration" (L. *re* = back, again + *spiro* = breathe) was merely a fancy synonym for "breathing"; but with the development of the science of physiology, it came to be recognized that there were two separable events which required two nonsynonymous terms. Although medical and common speech still often treat the two words as synonyms, biologists differentiate them as follows:

Respiration

Definition: organic material + $O_2 \longrightarrow$
$$CO_2 + H_2O + \mathcal{E}. \text{ (in living cells)}.$$

Breathing

Definition: The process by which O_2 is taken into the animal body and CO_2 is expelled therefrom, the organs of breathing—in land-dwelling vertebrates—being the lungs and associated structures.

It took a while to develop this distinction. The great French chemist Lavoisier supposed that the chemical process of using the oxygen and producing carbon dioxide took place in the lungs. It was left for his compatriot, the mathematician J. L. Lagrange (1736–1813), to propose first that respiration took place in all parts of the body. We now recognize that respiration takes place in all aerobic organisms (whether they breathe or not); and by enlarging the

meaning of the term, we may even speak of "anaerobic respiration" in anaerobic organisms or tissues. It should be clear by now that respiration is not a single process, but a complex of biochemical processes.

193. Processing Our Air

Our interest in this chapter is with the phenomena associated with breathing in such a vertebrate as man. But first we want to see how the air is "processed" before it gets to the lungs. Normally, we take in air through the nostrils. The nasal passages constitute a nicely designed air-conditioning system. Most of the time, the air outside is colder and dryer than air should be to come into contact with the lungs. The walls of the nasal passages bring about rapid modification of the temperature and humidity of the air. The over-all distance between nose and **pharynx** (Gr. throat) is only a few centimeters, but the route through the nose is greatly complicated by the presence of bony structures (Fig. 25-1*B*) called **turbinates** (L. *turbinis* = anything that whirls around, such as a whirlwind or a top). The turbinates create eddies in the incoming air and thus increase the contact of the air with the extensive surface of the nasal passages. The bones of the turbinates are covered with a warm, moist tissue called **mucous epithelium,** which secretes **mucus.** Contact with

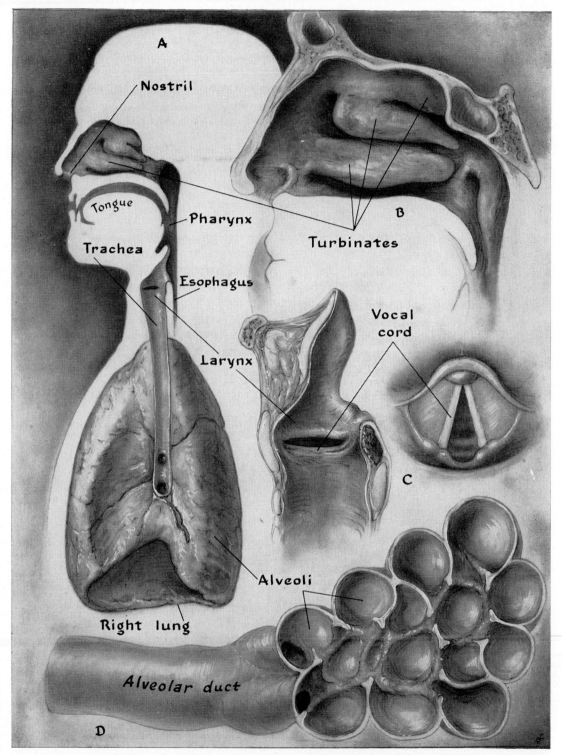

Fig. 25-1. *The structure of the breathing system. The long and somewhat tortuous path taken by the air in getting to the alveoli permits "air conditioning"—humidifying, warming, and cleansing of the incoming air.*

the warm, watery mucus both warms and humidifies the incoming air.

The air is air-conditioned in another way by the nose. Large particles of dirt are filtered out by the hairs lining the more forward parts of the nasal cavities. Dirt particles stick to the mucus and are eventually discharged with it. The filtering function of the mucus is brought home to us when we note the color of the nasal secretion following a sailboat trip (through a nearly dirt-free atmosphere) as compared with the color following a trip over a dusty road.

In filtering out small air-borne particles, the mucus performs a hygienic function. A man breathes in more than 15,000 liters of air a day, which in a clean atmosphere will contain about 150,000 bacteria. A few of these may be pathogenic. Most of the bacteria become trapped in the mucus, which has marked bactericidal properties. Moreover, the mucus is moved in such a way as to facilitate its disposal. The epithelial cells are ciliated. The cilia of the upper nasal tract move the mucus downward; those of the trachea move it upward. Arrived at the pharynx, the mucus is normally (and usually unconsciously) swallowed. The acid environment of the stomach is even less favorable to most pathogenic bacteria.

In many diseases, for example, "colds," the rate of mucus secretion is greatly increased. The increase in rate of secretion of this bactericidal material undoubtedly serves a useful function. However, the secretion of mucus and the attendant swelling of the mucous epithelium often proceed to such an extent that breathing through the nose becomes impossible, and air must then be brought in through the mouth, thus by-passing the excellent air-conditioning apparatus of the nose. We see here an example of a type of reaction that is fairly common in

Fig. 25-2. *Smog over Los Angeles. (Courtesy Air Pollution Control District, County of Los Angeles.)*

the human body—an adaptive response that overshoots the mark, so to speak. The human body is wonderful; but it is not perfect.

The imperfection of the human body is especially noticeable when it is confronted with new challenges for which it has not had a chance to evolve responses. Among these is **smog** (a neologism constructed by hybridizing "smoke" and "fog"). The term was first used in discussing the atmosphere of Los Angeles, but the phenomenon periodically blankets many of the large cities of the world (Fig. 25-2). Modern smog consists in part of smoke, some of which is an **aerosol** of carbon, that is, suspended carbon particles of about the dimensions of bacteria and hence removable with fair efficiency by the nasal epithelium. Smog contains also much smaller particles, down to molecular dimensions, of various other substances thrown into the air by industries and automobiles. This aerial garbage includes nitrogen oxides, ozone, peroxides, and other noxious substances formed by ultraviolet light shining on the primary refuse. At 25 ppm (parts per million), the mixture acts much like a war gas, causing **pulmonary edema** (edema of the lungs), that is, oozing of body fluid into the lungs. At lesser concentrations, its principal proved effects are eye irritation and unpleasant odor. The bad effects of heavy and prolonged smoggy spells are statistically demonstrable. One such period in London, 1952, brought on some 4,000 excess deaths, that is, deaths in excess of the normal number for the length of time.* In the most general way we may say that smog is one of the consequences of overcrowding, a new version of the "misery and vice" that Malthus postulated as population controls. It is, however, amenable to human control and regulation, though (as with sewage and ordinary garbage) controlling it costs money and may infringe on what some people regard as their "natural rights."

194. Getting Air to the Lungs

Once air is in the pharynx (Fig. 25-1), two courses are open to it: the **esophagus** and the **trachea** (Gr. *trachys* = rough—because of the bumpiness of this tube). The esophagus, which leads to the stomach, is normally collapsed, and little air passes down it. Instead, air passes into the trachea ("windpipe"), which is kept permanently open by rigid rings of cartilage in its walls. Near the upper end of the trachea is the **larynx** ("voice box"). This specialized part of the trachea supports the paired "vocal cords" (Fig. 25-1C), which are responsible for the primary production of the voice. These cords are stretched across the air passage. When the tension on them is increased and air is forced past them, a tone is produced, just as it is when we blow against a stretched rubber band. The vocal cords yield a higher-pitched note when they are stretched tighter. The length of the cords also determines the pitch of the voice. Longer cords are pitched lower than short ones. Since the length of the cords is determined by the diameter of the larynx, men, whose larynges are usually larger than those of women (and hence more often externally noticeable as the "Adam's apple"), generally have deeper voices than women. The pitch of the voice is therefore said to be a "secondary sexual characteristic," that is, a characteristic of only secondary importance, in which the sexes differ.

The vocal cords are the primary producers of the voice,* but they are only part of the mechanism. The cavities of the pharynx, the mouth, and the nose also act as resonating chambers and vary the relative strength of the different overtones of the sounds produced by the vocal cords. These overtones can be greatly altered by modifying the resonating passages through movement of the tongue, the uvula, and other movable parts. The effect of the resonating chambers on the tone of the voice is

---

* 25-1. However, following such a period, there is a period with a deficiency of deaths. What is the explanation of this; and the significance?

* 25-2. By the way, is the voice normally produced on *inspiration* or *expiration?* Can it be produced both ways? Try it.

obvious when the nasal chambers are blocked off, for instance, by congestion with mucus or by squeezing the nostrils shut. The tone produced is known as a "nasal" tone. We speak of "speaking through the nose"—which is rather curious, because that is precisely what we do *not* do in such a case.

An important characteristic of the voice, particularly the singing voice, is *vibrato:* a regular, but limited fluctuation in the pitch of the voice. This phenomenon is part of a cybernectic system whereby constancy of tone is maintained. Any slight deviation in pitch perceived by the ear results in negative (corrective) feedback brought about by nervous instructions sent to the brain and thence to the larynx. With a continuous vibrato, greater accuracy and control of pitch is possible than with a monotone. A skilled singer can hit the desired pitch to within 1 percent, and can begin to correct an error of pitch within 0.1 second.

Some distance below the larynx, well within the chest region, the trachea divides into two tubes called *bronchi* (sing. **bronchus;** Gr. windpipe); these bronchi in turn subdivide repeatedly, the ultimate subdivisions being blind-end sacs called *alveoli* (sing. **alveolus;** L. a small hollow). It is in the alveoli (Fig. 25-1*D*) that the real function of the lung is fulfilled—namely, getting oxygen into the body and carbon dioxide out of it. But more of this later.

195. The Process of Breathing

In the preceding section, the movement of air into and out of the air passages was often referred to but not accounted for. A little thought shows that there is a real problem here: How does air get from the outside all the way to the alveoli—a distance of perhaps 50 centimeters? An oxygen molecule might, of course, traverse the entire distance by virtue of its own molecular movement. But the diffusion of an appreciable number of molecules is a slow process because of the jostling of molecules against one another.

As everyone knows, the movements of the chest have something to do with breathing. Simple observations show that when the chest increases in diameter, air moves into the body; when the chest decreases in diameter, air is expelled from the body. We might guess that the expansion of the lungs causes the chest to expand. The cause-and-effect relationship, however, is precisely the opposite—a fact which has some practical consequences.

It is important to realize that a lung is incapable of expanding actively; in other words, there are no muscles in the lung that can cause it to expand. Functionally, the lung is but an elastic bag, living and complicated, but not too different from a rubber balloon. Once expanded, it can contract again by virtue of its elasticity,

Fig. 25-3. *How air is taken into the lungs. Muscular contraction causes the chest wall and diaphragm to move as shown in center figure. The elastic lungs, which are open to the outside through the trachea, are passively expanded by the external air pressure, and thus they fill the chest cavity at all times.*

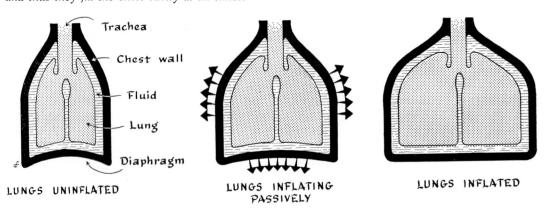

LUNGS UNINFLATED   LUNGS INFLATING PASSIVELY   LUNGS INFLATED

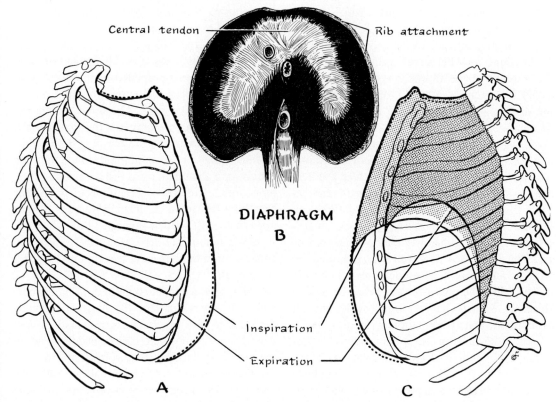

Central tendon — Rib attachment

DIAPHRAGM
B

Inspiration

Expiration

A   C

Fig. 25-4. *The movements of the ribs (A) and of the diaphragm (C) increase the volume of the chest cavity, thus causing an intake of air. (B) The diaphragm, as seen from below. Note that the muscle fibers are attached to the ribs and to one another by means of the central tendon.*

but it cannot expand itself any more than a rubber balloon can expand itself.

Stripped of all particularities of structure, the situation of the lungs is as represented in Figure 25-3: that of an elastic bag completely surrounded by the chest walls and the diaphragm, except for the single opening, the trachea, leading to the outside. Since the lungs are open to the outside, the pressure of gases in the lung cavity will at all times be the same as the air pressure outside. Should anything tend to increase the pressure in the lung cavity, gas will go out through the trachea until equality of the pressures is achieved. Anything tending to decrease the gas pressure within the lung cavity will bring about an intake of gas.

We take air into the lungs as follows: The diaphragm moves downward, and the chest walls move outward. The elastic lungs follow suit, thus increasing the volume of the lung cavity. This increase in volume *tends* to decrease the pressure, but the opening of the trachea permits more air to enter instead. Thus the process of **inspiration** takes place. The expelling of air, **expiration,** is brought about by a reversal of the sequence of events.

Particularities of the machinery involved in bringing about these changes in volume of the chest cavity are shown in Figure 25-4. The ribs, hinged to the backbone, are moved forward and upward by muscular action. The **diaphragm** is itself a muscle attached to a central tendon; when the strands of diaphragmatic muscle contract, the whole diaphragm becomes taut and necessarily moves downward, thus pushing the contents of the abdominal (belly) cavity downward and outward. As a result, there is an increase in the volume of the chest cavity and a concomitant protrusion of the belly.

Breathing may be carried out principally by the muscles of the thorax, in which case it is called "thoracic breathing"; or principally by the diaphragm, in which case it is called "abdominal breathing"; usually both types of breathing are employed. There are considerable individual differences in the types of breathing. At one time, it was thought there was a difference in the two sexes in this regard—and, in truth, there was. Studies made around 1900 A.D. showed that most women were thoracic breathers, whereas many men were abdominal breathers. The difference observed was regarded by some as an inherent "secondary sexual characteristic," like the presence of a beard or a deep voice. It was, perhaps, a reasonable enough assumption; but when similar studies made around 1925 failed to reveal any difference between the breathing of men and women, it was realized that the earlier observed predominance of thoracic breathing among women was occasioned by the formidable corsets that once were fashionable. . . . An error of interpretation of this sort makes the experimental scientist cautious about ascribing biological significance to any sex difference when the observation is made in only one society at one period. Folkways and customs can also corset or harness the minds of men and women and thus cause striking differences between the adult sexes. These remarks are not made to deny the existence of biological differences but only to enjoin caution in interpreting observations.

196. Some Practical Matters

That our lungs are expanded passively and indirectly by the enlargement of the enclosing chest cavity might seem to be a technicality of small practical importance, since the result is the same as if the lungs actively expanded themselves. In a sense, this is true; but situations sometimes arise in which the particular way our breathing mechanism works is of great importance. We will consider two: pneumothorax and resuscitation.

Pneumothorax, literally air in the thorax (thoracic cavity). As a result of war or accident, a hole may be opened in the chest wall. When this happens, air enters the chest cavity and surrounds the lung. The air is, of course, under the same pressure as the outside air; that is, the pressure inside the lung is the same as that of the air surrounding it. Since the lung is elastic, it then collapses, just as a rubber balloon would. Collapsed, the lung is of no use for breathing. Fortunately, in man, there is a wall, not too flexible, which separates the two lungs, so that a hole in the left side of the thorax will collapse only the left lung, leaving one lung still functional.

Collapsing a lung is sometimes done deliberately. In tuberculosis of the lungs, it may be desirable to give one lung a rest. This is simply done by inserting a fine hollow needle between the ribs and letting clean, germ-free air enter the thoracic cavity. After enough air has been admitted, the needle is removed and the hole closed. The lung promptly collapses and remains thus for a good many days. It eventually becomes active again because air introduced into the thoracic cavity is gradually dissolved in the fluid of the moist chest wall and is removed by the circulatory system. If it is desired to keep a lung collapsed for a long period of time, air must be repeatedly introduced into the thoracic cavity.

Resuscitation. If breathing is stopped by drowning or electric shock, there is a short period of time during which the person's life may still be saved if breathing can be started again. If it is a case of drowning, one should first try to empty the water out of the lungs. Then how does one get air into the lungs? How re-establish the breathing rhythm? For centuries a great variety of techniques has been used. Many of them work, but most of them have the disadvantage of requiring either a considerable period of training on the part of the rescuer or elaborate equipment or both. Since the person who drowns seldom plans his experience so as to have a trained technician standing by, many lives have been needlessly lost. In the middle of the twentieth century two United States Army physicians, R. J. Johns and D. Y. Cooper, III, perfected **mouth-to-mouth resuscitation,** which can be successfully used by any normally intelligent person.

The method is almost adequately described by the name. The rescuer puts his open mouth to the open mouth of the victim and blows the lungs full of air, gently but firmly, and in normal rhythm, keeping this up until the victim does his own breathing, or hope is abandoned. The details of the technique are few and easily remembered if one focuses on the simple principles underlying them. (1) It will do no good to blow into the mouth if all the air comes out the nose. With an adult victim, the nose must be held closed (a clothespin is useful). With a small child, the rescuer can put his mouth over both nose and mouth of the victim. (2) The tongue must be kept from falling back and covering up the opening of the trachea (see Fig. 25-1 again); otherwise the stomach will be blown up—to no purpose. Exerting pressure on the upper abdomen may help keep the stomach from inflating. The best way to control the tongue is this: With his hand, the rescuer moves the victim's jaw into a "jutting-out" position, so that the head is tilted back. When all this is done, if there is still an obstruction in the air passage, this fact will be readily noted by the rescuer.

Experience has shown that the mouth-to-mouth method produces a higher percentage of rescues than does any other method. Why did it take so long to discover it? The following account gives a clue. Shortly after this method was perfected, a class of 164 medical students was asked to use the method on some volunteers who had been anaesthetized with curare, a South American herb preparation that stops breathing. There was considerable resistance from the medical students (ordinarily a rather "liberal-minded" group), three of them flatly refusing to use the method except in a genuine emergency. Why the resistance? Clearly, it was connected with "aesthetic" considerations, that is, with attitudes that were strongly developed

as a result of the nineteenth-century triumphs in bacteriology and hygiene. The idea that mouth-to-mouth contacts are unhygienic and likely to spread disease was thoroughly inculcated in the general population of the Victorian days. There is, of course, a grain of truth in the belief. But this danger should certainly be regarded as of secondary importance under the circumstances.

It is interesting in retrospect to note that Johns and Cooper did not so much discover as *re*discover the method. In the Bible, in II Kings 4:32–35, there occurs this passage:

And when Elisha was come into the house, behold the child was dead and laid on the bed. He went in therefore, and shut the door upon them twain, and prayed unto the Lord. And he went up, and lay upon the child and put his mouth upon his mouth, and his eyes upon his eyes, and his hands upon his hands: and he stretched himself upon the child; and the flesh of the child waxed warm. Then he returned, and walked in the house to and fro; and he went up, and stretched himself upon him: and the child sneezed seven times, and the child opened his eyes.

This sounds suspiciously like mouth-to-mouth resuscitation. Whether it is or not, there have been many instances of distraught but intelligent mothers who revived their own children by breathing into their mouths, in defiance of hygienic taboos.

197. The Capacity of the Lungs

In giving measurements of the capacity of the lungs, we will use a metric unit, the liter, which is a volume almost exactly equal to 1,000 cubic centimeters, a bit more than 1 quart. (See Appendix 3 for equivalents.)

A man at rest inspires and expires only a small amount of air each time he breathes, approximately 0.5 liter, or about 1 pint. This "air," which goes in and out as quietly and regularly as the tides, is called **tidal air.** Notice the special definition, implied in this term, of "air" as *a volume of air;* this special (not general) definition will be observed throughout this section.

If, at the end of a normal, resting inspiration, a man makes an extra effort and breathes in as much air as possible, he can take in an additional 3 liters of air. This extra air which can be taken in is called **complemental air.**

On the other hand, if, at the end of a normal expiration of tidal air, a man makes an extra effort and expels all the air he possibly can, the extra air expelled amounts to about 1 liter. This is called **reserve air.**

Reserve air + tidal air + complemental air = **vital capacity,** the total amount of air a man can breathe in and out by the most strenuous efforts. Notice that it is about nine times the volume of the tidal air alone. The magnitude of the vital capacity varies from one individual to another; it is generally greater in men than in women (heredity? training?), greater in athletes than in sedentaries, greater in healthy persons than in invalids.

The vital capacity is about nine times the tidal air; or, with different emphasis, the ability of the body to take in air upon extreme demand is nine times as great as the need in quiet living. The lungs show, we might say, a considerable **physiological reserve** available for meeting unusual demands. The principle of physiological reserve is illustrated also in the fact that we have two lungs, but we can (if injured) get along on only one. Many other organs show a "safety factor" of this sort.

Considering the position of the lungs (Fig. 25-3) and the fact that the chest cavity cannot be completely collapsed, we can easily see that there must be air in the lungs after even the most forcible expiration. This volume of air is called **residual air** and amounts to about 1.5 liters. Part of this air can be released by letting air into the thoracic cavity from the outside, as previously described. But even removing the lungs from the body does not result in their complete collapse. The remaining volume of air, called **minimal air,** is never released once it is taken in. A newborn child has no air in his lungs until he takes his first breath. Thereafter, his lungs always have at least the minimal air in

them. By placing a portion of the lung in water, we can tell if a dead infant was stillborn, or if it died after taking a breath—a difference that is often of legal importance. The lungs of the stillborn child sink, whereas those of the child born alive float.

198. Getting O_2 into the Body and CO_2 Out

So much discussion of the mechanism of breathing, and still we have made no mention of getting air or any of its components into the body. In an important sense, *air that is in the lungs is still outside the body.*

Figure 25-5 illustrates the point. In all four instances (*A–D*), the molecule indicated as a black ball is outside the body. In *D*, the molecule is almost entirely surrounded by the body, but logically we have to say that if the molecule in *A* is outside the body, so is the molecule in *D*. What we have illustrated is a basic principle of topology (§163), and the body, as we shall see later, acts as if it understood this branch of mathematics. To get truly inside the body, a molecule must cross some sort of limiting membrane such as that indicated by the continuous limiting line of each "body" in Figure 25-5.

Fig. 25-5. *The black ball is not inside the colored body no matter how convoluted the clear passageway is. So it is with an oxygen molecule "inside" an alveolus. The molecule is not truly inside the body until it has passed through the epithelium of the alveolus.*

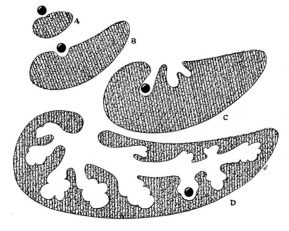

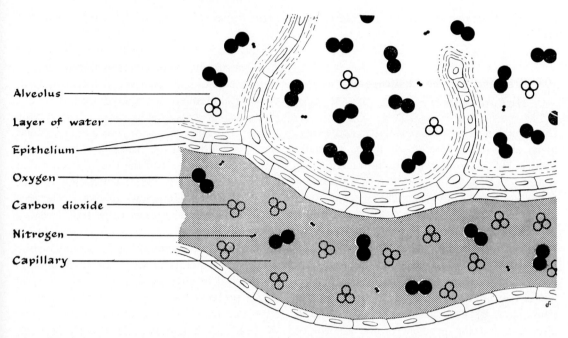

Fig. 25-6. *Alveolus and capillary, where oxygen* (*colored*) *truly enters the body and carbon dioxide* (*black*) *leaves it.* (*Because there is no net change in nitrogen, the N₂ molecules are shown too small and too few.*)

Air in the dead-end alveoli of the lungs is still outside the body. How does it get into the body? To understand this problem, let us examine a diagram (Fig. 25-6) in which the alveoli are magnified to show the relations of the air, the cells, and the blood in a blood vessel that winds around the alveoli.

As usual, the diagram is not a representation of reality, but is intended only as an aid in visualizing reality. The reader must imagine a picture, of the sort described in Chapter 3, of millions upon millions of molecules bouncing against each other in a random fashion and "obeying" the "laws" of probability. No attempt is made in this diagram to represent the relative numbers of the different kinds of molecules, but the relative abundance of a single kind on the two sides of the alveolar walls is correct. Water molecules are not shown, but the presence of water in the blood vessel is indicated by the shading. Molecules of the three kinds depicted can pass freely through the epithelial cells that bound the alveoli.

Notice, in the diagram, that molecules of O₂ are relatively more abundant in the alveolar space than in the fluid in the blood vessel. As a result of random molecular motion, O₂ molecules will move in both directions through the alveolar membrane, but, by the principles of probability, the *net* movement will be from the alveolar space to the blood in the blood vessel. Thus will oxygen enter the body. Carbon dioxide, on the other hand, is more concentrated in the blood than in the air, since it is being continuously produced by the respiration of all the body cells. Hence the net movement of CO_2 molecules will be from blood to alveolar space; and thus CO_2 will leave the body. Nitrogen molecules, on the other hand, are not used by the body, and their concentration in the blood is in equilibrium with their concentration in the alveolar air; hence there is no net movement of N_2 molecules.

In recounting the story above, we have assumed that the blood is a homogeneous liquid in which the various kinds of molecules are simply dissolved. The true situation is slightly different, as will be shown in Chapter 27, where the oxygen-carrying role of the red blood cells is described.

199. Breathing and the Challenge of High Altitudes

Every analytical procedure leads, in some way, to an abnormal separation of things normally together. In analyzing the body into anatomical systems, we necessarily run into occasional difficulties when studying functions, for a single function usually—perhaps always—involves the coaction of several systems. So it is with the function of breathing. If we ask: How is breathing controlled? we find that we must discuss the actions not only of the breathing system but also of the circulatory and nervous systems. These last two systems have not yet been discussed, but the problem of the control of breathing can nevertheless be taken up here, for it involves functions of these two systems that are now common knowledge: (1) the circulatory system circulates the blood throughout all parts of the body; and (2) the nervous system transmits "messages" (stimuli) from the brain to the various parts of the body via nerves.

A man can deliberately stop breathing for only a short period of time. After a minute or so, no matter how "strong" his "will power," he starts to breathe again. Why? What is the mechanism that makes him breathe? A little thought about what must go on during suspended breathing will suggest possible answers. *Respiration* (recall the definition, §192) goes on all the time. If *breathing* is stopped, that is, if exchange of gases between the body and the outside world is stopped, it is apparent that inside the body the *concentration of carbon dioxide will increase and that of oxygen will decrease*. Will either of these changes be effective in causing breathing?

Simple experiments with a human (or other mammal) who is breathing freely reveal that *either* low oxygen or high carbon dioxide content in the inspired air can cause an increase in the rate of breathing, but that *high carbon dioxide content is by far the more effective factor.**

How does carbon dioxide exert its effect? Anatomical observation reveals nerves that go from a part of the brain called the **medulla** to the breathing muscles (diaphragm, rib muscles). Physiological experiments show that varying the concentration of carbon dioxide in the blood circulating through the medulla will affect the rate of breathing: when the CO_2 concentration is high, breathing is rapid; when CO_2 is low, the rate of breathing slows or stops. The medulla is, therefore, spoken of as the *breathing center* of the body.

This method of control is rather interesting from several points of view. To begin with, if we guessed in advance of the experiments, we would probably guess that oxygen is the more important factor, for it is oxygen, after all, that we need. Carbon dioxide is a waste product; yet the mechanism is tied to carbon dioxide. In the second place, this observation broadens our viewpoint regarding the significance of "waste products." A substance may be waste material, produced in excess and requiring to be disposed of; yet it still may perform important functions: witness carbon dioxide.

The mechanisms of the body have been evolved to meet the "natural" situations, the ones that man and his ancestors met and solved (by natural selection) over millions of years. As we saw before, when considering smog (§192), a new challenge may be one for which man has no ready answer. We will now see that flight at "unnaturally" high altitudes is a similar challenge.

Gases are compressible. Consequently, a given volume at the bottom of a tall column of gas subjected to the influence of gravity will contain more gas molecules than will the same volume near the top of the column. The atmosphere surrounding the earth, under the influence of gravity, packs itself so that the concentration of molecules is greater near the surface of the earth than at a distance from it (Fig. 25-7).

---

* 25-3. Describe, in detail, experiments that would adequately test these bald textbook statements.

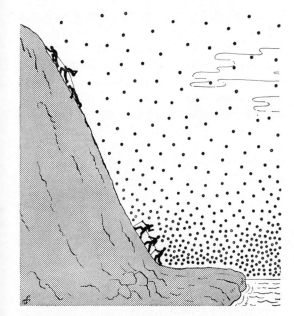

Fig. 25-7. *Air is compressible. At sea level the concentration of molecules is great, and men work easily. On mountain tops men faint readily because the concentration of oxygen molecules (as well as the concentration of other kinds of molecules) is low.*

The problem presented by an ascent in altitude may be made clear by study of Table 25-1, based on data obtained from humans in altitude chambers. At sea level (0 meters altitude) the total number of molecules per cubic micron of gas is about 27×10^6. In the alveoli, there are about 3.6×10^6 molecules of O_2 in this volume of gas, and about 1.4×10^6 molecules of CO_2. When a man ascends to 6,000 meters, the concentration of both kinds of molecules decreases: the former to 1.2×10^6 per cubic micron, the latter to 1×10^6. At this altitude, the concentration of O_2 molecules is not great enough to support continuous activity in a man accustomed to sea-level conditions. He *should* breathe more rapidly to permit more rapid intake of O_2. But the breathing mechanism responds most readily to CO_2 concentration, and unfortunately this has *decreased;* as a result, the man may breathe less rapidly, and may even faint. There are considerable differences in the extent to which individuals react to the lower

O_2 content of the air at high altitudes. Those who are almost insensitive to O_2 concentration —who react only to CO_2 concentration, as described above—are poorly suited to aviation or mountain climbing.

In aviation, two methods are used to get around the difficulty of great altitude. Up to about 11,500 meters it is possible to increase the efficiency of the flyer by fitting him with a mask that furnishes him with nearly pure oxygen instead of ordinary air, about 80 percent of which is useless N_2. In this way it is possible to increase the concentration of O_2 molecules until, even at 6,000 meters, it may approach a concentration of 12×10^6 per cubic micron of alveolar air. In practice, it is not feasible to furnish pure O_2 to an aviator, for two reasons: (1) at very high concentrations—approximating 100 percent—oxygen is poisonous, for reasons that are not well understood; and (2) to stimulate the medulla, a slight admixture of CO_2 is desirable.

As the air becomes rarefied at high altitudes, the total number of molecules per cubic micron becomes too small to sustain human life, even if 100 percent of these molecules are O_2 molecules. In practice, about 11,500 meters is the highest altitude to which aviators can ascend with an oxygen mask. Ascent above this level is possible only if the concentration of oxygen

TABLE 25-1 *Concentration of Molecules in Alveolar Air as Affected by Altitude. (Expressed as Approximate Number of Molecules per Cubic Micron of Gas.)*

ALTITUDE (METERS)	MILLIONS OF MOLECULES (ALL KINDS) PER CUBIC MICRON ALVEOLAR AIR	MILLIONS OF O_2 MOLECULES PER CUBIC MICRON ALVEOLAR AIR	MILLIONS OF CO_2 MOLECULES PER CUBIC MICRON ALVEOLAR AIR
0	27.0	3.6	1.4
1,200	23.3	3.0	1.3
2,400	19.9	2.3	1.2
3,600	17.0	1.9	1.2
4,800	14.6	1.5	1.1
6,000	12.5	1.2	1.0

molecules per volume of space is kept sufficiently great by pressurizing the cabin of the plane. With a cabin that can be hermetically sealed, there is no limit to the height that can be achieved, as far as the passengers inside are concerned, so long as no leaks occur. However, under battle conditions, flying in such a plane at great altitudes is clearly risky when there is serious danger of puncture. Not only would a hole in the plane's fuselage immediately subject the inhabitants to too low an oxygen pressure, but, at elevations exceeding 19,000 meters, the total air pressure is so low that the water of the body literally boils away.

200. Problems Posed by Sudden Changes in Pressure

If the human body is subjected to *sudden* changes in air pressure, special physiological problems arise. Almost everyone has experienced the peculiar stuffy feeling accompanied by slight, momentary deafness, following a sudden change in altitude. The cause of this can be understood by reference to Figure 25-8. Note that the cavity of the middle ear is shut off at one end by the eardrum, or **tympanic membrane,** but is open at another place via a canal called the **Eustachian tube,** which opens into the pharynx. This canal is a tiny one, and its walls are normally pressed together, closing the

Fig. 25-8. *Communiation of the middle ear cavity with the exterior via the Eustachian tube.*

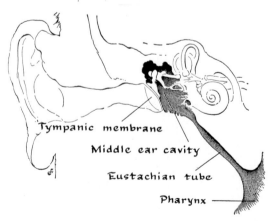

canal. What happens, now, when we change altitude? As we go up, we go into a region of lower atmospheric pressure; as a consequence, the pressure in the cavity of the middle ear is, for a while, higher than that outside. As a result, the eardrum may bulge outward slightly, hearing may be impaired, and a stuffy sensation be felt. Sooner or later, the excess pressure in the middle ear is relieved by the escape of air down the Eustachian tube and into the pharynx; this passage is sometimes accompanied by a "popping" sound. Chewing and swallowing often hastens this adjustment.

Other, more serious consequences of sudden change in pressure are related to the fact that *nearly 80 percent of the atmosphere consists of molecular nitrogen (N_2), which is biochemically useless to man.* The concentration of nitrogen in the blood is normally in equilibrium with the nitrogen in the atmosphere. But if the pressure around our bodies changes, an adjustment must be made, and sometimes this adjustment is painful.

The greater the pressure, the more gas can be dissolved in a liquid. Everyone has seen evidence of this fact. An unopened bottle of a carbonated beverage—one that contains a large amount of CO_2 in solution (e.g., ginger ale)—is clear; no gas bubbles are present, showing that all the gas is in solution. When we remove the cap of the bottle, there is an outrush of gas, indicating that the contents were bottles under greater than atmospheric pressure: The pressure on the contents has been reduced, and bubbles of gas have started immediately to form in the liquid and to escape to the surface, because under the lower pressure conditions the liquid is more than saturated with the gas.

Much the same sort of thing can happen to man (Fig. 25-9). When a man is put in surroundings where all the gas around him is under pressure, more gas is dissolved in the fluids of his body. This, by itself, is not harmful; but if the pressure of the gas around him is suddenly decreased, there is more gas in the man's fluids than can be held in solution; consequently, bubbles of gas are formed, just as they are in an opened bottle of ginger ale. In man, such bub-

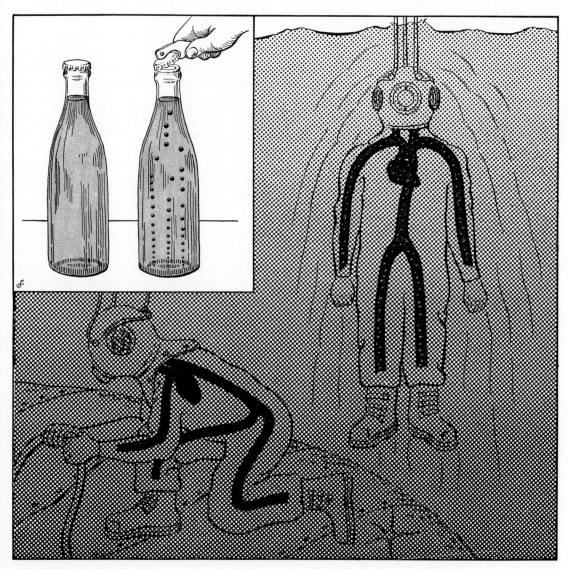

Fig. 25-9. *The greater the pressure, the more gas can be held in solution in a liquid. When a diver ascends to a region of lower pressure, gas bubbles may form in his blood and occlude blood vessels.*

bles may plug up blood vessels, thus stopping circulation in the parts affected, often with serious consequences. The symptoms are extremely variable, depending on where the bubbles happen to lodge, which seems to be largely a matter of chance. Bubbles may stop circulation in the spinal cord, thus causing partial paralysis; frequently, they affect organs of the mid-region of the body, causing the individual to bend over in extreme pain—hence the common name "the bends." A more general name is **decompression sickness;** this name indicates the invariable cause, rather than a variable symptom. The principal gas responsible for the effect is nitrogen, because it is present in the largest concentration and because, being biochemically inert, it is not used up by the body, as oxygen is.

The probability of bubble formation depends on a number of factors (not all well understood), including the amount of gas dissolved in the body and the rate of release of the gas under decompression. How much extra nitrogen will dissolve in the body of a diver depends on how deep he goes (i.e., how much pressure he is subjected to) and how long he stays down. Whether the gas will produce bubbles when he is decompressed depends on how rapidly the process takes place. If the diver is brought up slowly, he can get rid of the excess gas by breathing; when he is brought up rapidly, he may suffer decompression sickness. If this happens, the diver should be put in a pressure chamber, and the pressure within raised until his bubbles redissolve; then, by releasing the pressure slowly, a slow ascent may be simulated, allowing ample time for release of the excess gas from the body. When an airplane ascends, it moves into regions of lower pressure. In air there is much less change in pressure per unit height than there is in water. Decompression sickness is very unlikely to occur until the aviator has ascended to at least 6,000 meters, where the air pressure is about 40 percent of normal. In water, a similar pressure change takes place in rising only about 25 meters. The speed of ascent is important: in the days of the first sluggish airplanes, it was not possible to rise fast enough to experience decompression sickness. The development of more powerful motive forces brought this problem of the deep-sea diver to the attention of aviation physiologists.

There are individual differences in susceptibility to decompression sickness. These differences for the most part are not understood, but one thing is clear: fat men are more susceptible than thin men. The difference is apparently due to the fact that N_2 is about *five times as soluble in fat as it is in water*. A fat man, therefore, can accumulate a greater reserve of dissolved nitrogen that will have to be expelled when he is decompressed. It has long been known that fat men do not make good deep-sea divers.

The realization that the speed of elimination of dissolved gases is an important factor in decompression has led to a search for gases that can be eliminated more rapidly. Of gases that can be safely introduced into the body, *helium* is the most useful. It is chemically inert and quite harmless to animals. A surplus of it is eliminated about twice as rapidly as nitrogen. By breathing a mixture of helium and oxygen (instead of nitrogen and oxygen) before ascending, an aviator or diver becomes less susceptible to decompression sickness.

For descent to extreme depths, divers must use massive steel diving bells that protect them from the pressure. In such a contraption Jacques Piccard descended to 10,900 meters in 1959, the greatest recorded depth of the ocean. But such a bell permits no easy "communication" with the surrounding ocean. If work must be done, a diving suit is called for, and this places a practical limit at about 100 meters, if ordinary air is breathed. The greatest recorded dive is to 165 meters (1948). Even this is not very great as compared with the depth at which a sperm whale was once found entangled in a submarine cable—some 1,000 meters.

How can a whale dive so deep without getting the "bends"? Several partial answers are known. (1) Whales have blood system mechanisms for shunting the blood from the muscles, which work anaerobically during the dive, to the brain, which needs the O_2 more. (2) Since a submerged whale is not breathing continuously, as is a man in a diving suit, the whale is not soaking up as much nitrogen as is the man. The longest submergence time recorded is 2 hours, by a bottle-nosed whale. Pretty good breath-holding.

Questions and Problems

25-4. Make a list of the **boldface** terms in this chapter and write a brief description of each. Compare your work with the text.

‡25-5. Dogs have no partition dividing the thoracic cavity into two chambers. Could the operation of pneumothorax be used successfully in treating canine disease? Explain.

25-6. Suppose an explosive shell blew up and injured a man near you by opening two small holes in his chest wall: one on the left side, one on the right side. Can you suggest an immediate first-aid measure that might save the man's life? Explain the rationale of the measure.

‡25-7. An unwed mother is accused of having killed her newborn child. The medical officer attached to the coroner's office performs a very simple test that exonerates her. What is the test and the reasoning behind its interpretation?

25-8. Trace the course of a molecule of oxygen from the time it enters the nose until it is in the blood stream. At what point would you consider it inside the body?

‡25-9. Each human alveolar duct opens into about 20 alveoli. Figure 25-1 shows only about 13–15 alveoli coming from the alveolar duct. Explain the discrepancy.

25-10. The total lung structure of man is essentially one of a system of successive dichotomous branchings, from trachea to alveolar ducts. There are about 14 million alveolar ducts. How many "generations" of dichotomous branching does it take to produce that number?

‡25-11. The total alveolar surface of a man has been estimated to be about 40 to 80 square meters. Suppose a man is 2 meters tall and (for simplicity) regard him as a cylinder with a radius of 20 cm. If he rolls on his long axis across the floor, how many revolutions will he have to make to roll over an area equal to his alveolar area?

25-12. How many alveoli are there in one man?

‡25-13. Why, when you take your temperature, should you place the thermometer *under* your tongue? (See Fig. 25-1.)

25-14. If an animal had the ability to close completely all of its sweat glands and to stop all urination, could it, in a dry atmosphere, avoid losing water? Explain.

‡25-15. If we lived, and could live, in an atmosphere made up of 98 percent O_2 and 2 percent CO_2, would the problems of the deep-sea diver and the aviator be more, or less, serious than they are now? Explain.

25-16. "Decompression sickness" is a synonym for "the bends." Is there any reason to prefer the former term, aside from the fact that it is longer and hence more likely to impress our friends?

‡25-17. On a per capita basis, what is each person's "share" of the atmosphere, expressed in metric tons? (A metric ton is 1,000 kg; other data in Appendix 4.)

25-18. In 1849, a European physiologist noted that men were usually abdominal breathers, women usually thoracic breathers, and considered this difference a secondary sexual characteristic. Later, it was noted that Indian and Chinese women were abdominal breathers. Is it probable that this difference between Oriental and Occidental women is an inherent racial difference?

‡25-19. Do you think a man can commit suicide by wilfully holding his breath? Explain.

25-20. In reviving a person who has fainted at high altitude, why is a gas mixture of 95% $O_2 + 5\%$ CO_2 better than either 95% $O_2 +$ 5% N_2, or 100% O_2?

‡25-21. The "Delaney clause" of the 1958 amendment to the Food, Drug and Cosmetics Act (U.S.) forbade the addition to food of any amount whatever of any substance that had been found to cause cancer in man or other animals. Is such a "zero-tolerance" standard defensible on general scientific grounds? Point up your discussion with a relevant example.

25-22. The general rule is: Every muscle has an antagonist. Cite an exception.

25-23. Make a cybernetic diagram (Chap. 8) of the system that controls the pitch of the singing voice.

25-24. With an electronic system it is possible to delay the sound of a person's voice reaching his own ears. When the delay is about one-third of a second, the vibrato of his singing voice becomes "wider" and slower. Explain.

‡25-25. The concentration of noxious substances in tobacco smoke is about 300–1,500 ppm. Why doesn't the smoker suffer from edema of the lungs?

25-26. A group of rats were fitted with mechanical respirators, which were adjusted according to two different patterns: (a) slow inspiration with rapid expiration, and (b) rapid inspiration with slow expiration. Both groups were exposed to air containing *Pneumococcus* bacteria. The incidences of infection were (a) 0 percent and (b) 48 percent. Explain.

‡25-27. Public swimming pools often have available a short length of plastic tube to be used in mouth-to-mouth resuscitation. Why the tube?

25-28. Does it ever happen that a discovery in science that may be an advance in one respect may make advance in another way more difficult? Give an example.

‡25-29. For most people, the equilibrium of middle-ear air pressure is more difficult to make when going down than when going up. Why?

25-30. "Every time we breathe, we take in a molecule of air that was expelled in Napoleon's dying breath." True or false? (Assume a static atmosphere with no interchange with the rocks, oceans, and so on.)

Readings

Chapter 4 of Fulton's *Readings* includes a number of classical papers on the physiology of breathing. A brief discussion of the concept of physiological reserve may be found in Chapter 15 of Cannon's *The Wisdom of the Body*. The question of "inside-outside" taken up in the present chapter is part of the subject matter of topology, to which field the student may obtain an easy introduction by reading Chapter 8 of Kasner and Newman's witty and stimulating book, *Mathematics and the Imagination*.

Scientific American Offprints

612. Walsh McDermott. *Air Pollution and Public Health*

26

Digestion and Nutrition

201. Through the Alimentary Canal

About a century ago a member of the British House of Commons took the London School Board to task for introducing the subject of physiology into the curriculum, protesting: "Physiology, besides being costly and useless, is an immodest subject. When the Author of the Universe hid the liver of man out of sight He did not want frail human creatures to see how He had done." If you agree with this orator, read no further. The present writer's attitude is that of Robert Boyle, who, some three centuries ago, held that it is "highly dishonorable for a Reasonable Soul to live in so Divinely built a Mansion as the Body . . . altogether unacquainted with the exquisite structure of it."

One of the basic aspects of the structure of the body is that it is a *torus* (§163), that is, essentially an elongated doughnut, with a rather convoluted central **lumen** (hole), as Figure 26-1 should make clear. The path that food follows in this lumen—or alimentary canal or **gastrointestinal tract** (*G-I tract*) or *gut*—is quickly told. From the mouth, food passes through the pharynx into the **esophagus,** thence to the **stomach.** After considerable churning around, it moves on into the **small intestine,** where much of the foodstuff passes from the intestinal cavity across the wall of the intestine and into the body itself. What remains in the cavity at the conclusion of this process goes into the large intestine, or **colon;** and, at intervals, leaves the body by way of the **anus.**

Topologically it is clear, of course, that anything that is in the lumen of the alimentary canal is truly outside the body. This is a point of more than theoretical importance. The food that we take "into" the body via the mouth is not, at first, fit to enter the body. If, for instance, we should take this food, grind it fine, and inject it into the body proper (e.g., into the blood vessels), the consequence would be a very sick man; death might even result. The most delicious menu is composed largely of substances that would be violently poisonous if taken directly into the body. Before they can safely be taken in, they must be modified. The task of modifying them suitably falls to the G-I tract. The process takes place in stages, different parts of the tract specializing in different phases.

Digestion involves only one kind of enzymatic action: hydrolysis (§35). In this type of reaction the energy change is inconsequential; what is important is that large molecules, which cannot pass through cell membranes, are broken down to small ones that can. In preparation for digestion food is first cut into small pieces by the teeth. (In birds, which have no teeth, the same service is performed by the gizzard, a highly muscular portion of the G-I tract.) As the food is chewed it is mixed with **saliva,** a viscous liquid produced by the **salivary glands** (Fig. 26-2). Saliva contains an enzyme named

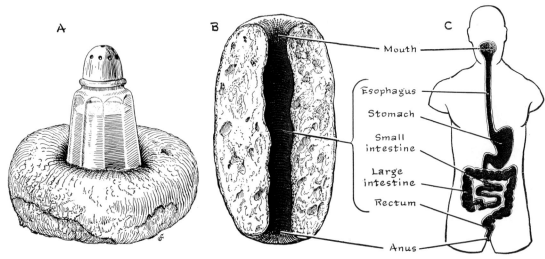

Fig. 26-1. *A standard doughnut* (A), *an elongated doughnut* (B), *and a man* (C) *are topologically equivalent. Objects inside the hole of the doughnut are outside the doughnut; objects in the lumen of the digestive tract are outside the man.*

ptyalin (Gr. spittle), which can catalyze the splitting of starch (a large carbohydrate molecule) into the smaller molecules of maltose (a sugar). After the food is mixed with saliva it is moved on to the next part of the alimentary tract.

202. Peristalsis

Besides water and ptyalin, saliva contains also **mucin,** a slick material which covers the food particles, making them easier to swallow. After the food has been chewed suitably, a small lump

Fig. 26-2. *The salivary glands occur in pairs. The location of the right member of each pair is shown. The largest gland, the parotid, is the gland whose infection by a virus causes the swelling known as "mumps."*

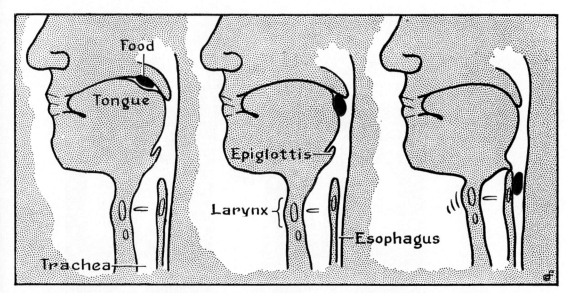

Fig. 26-3. *How a bolus of food (colored) is swallowed. The air passage is closed by the epiglottis, and the food drops into the esophagus. In this process, the larynx ("Adam's apple") moves upward.*

of it is moved to the back of the tongue and then swallowed. In Figure 26-3, it will be noted that the lump coming off the back of the tongue has two paths open to it: the esophagus and the trachea. To insure its getting into the right opening, the entrance of the trachea needs to be closed. This closure is effected by a complex series of movements, the most prominent of which, the upward movement of the larynx, can be observed readily from the outside. By its upward movement, the larynx crowds the opening of the trachea against the **epiglottis** and thus prevents food from entering the windpipe—usually.

Once in the esophagus, food moves rapidly to the lower end. Fluids move passively under the influence of gravity, but solids are helped along by a process called **peristalsis** (Gr. *peri* = around + *stalsis* = constriction), a process occurring throughout the entire length of the digestive tract. Peristalsis can best be understood by studying Figure 26-4. Put into words, the process may be described as the movement of a wave of muscular relaxation along a tube (the G-I tract), followed by a wave of contraction. Since the lump of food is just in front of the contracted area, it is moved through the tube.

The total time taken for a lump to go from the upper to the lower end of the esophagus is, at most, a few seconds.

203. Digestion in the Stomach

From the esophagus, food passes into the stomach. Here, slow churning movements mix the food with **gastric juice** (Gr. *gaster* = stomach) produced by cells lining the walls of the stomach. Gastric juice is a watery mixture of several substances among which the following should be noted:

Hydrochloric acid
Pepsin, an enzyme that partially digests a miscellany of proteins
Rennin, an enzyme that partially digests milk proteins

An important characteristic of enzymes is their sensitivity to changes in acidity. Each enzyme works best at a particular acidity or alkalinity; if the environment changes markedly in this particular, the enzyme will no longer be active. Ptyalin, the salivary enzyme, works only in neutral or alkaline solutions. At the acidity

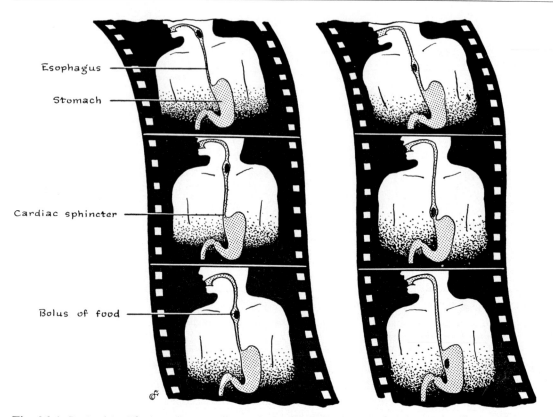

Fig. 26-4. *Peristalsis. The circular muscles in the wall of the digestive tract (esophagus in this example) relax in front of the bolus, while the muscles behind the bolus contract.*

of the stomach juice, ptyalin can no longer digest starch. Since food is so quickly swallowed, we might wonder if ptyalin has a chance to act. However, though food is soon in the stomach, it is not at once thoroughly subjected to the action of the stomach juice. Some time is required for the acid, and other substances, to penetrate to the center of the mass of food, during which time alkaline ptyalin acts on starch.

Another important characteristic of enzymes is their specificity. The digestive enzymes are relatively less specific that the intracellular enzymes; each digestive enzyme works on a large class of substrates, rather than being restricted to one or a few compounds. The substrate of pepsin is proteins, which it hydrolyzes to smaller polypeptides. Protein digestion is not completed until the food gets into the small intestine.

204. Social Implications of Ulcers

Meat is largely protein. The stomach produces protein-digesting enzymes. The stomach, being meat, is itself protein. *Why does it not digest itself?* If, in asking "why," we are referring to purpose, the answer is obvious: it would be disadvantageous for the stomach to destroy itself. But if by "why" we mean, "What is the mechanism that prevents the stomach from digesting itself?" we must reply that we do not know. We do know, however, that this protective mechanism, whatever it is, does not always work—that sometimes the stomach juices do digest away part of the stomach wall, or of the first part of the small intestine, the **duodenum.** The erosion produced is called a **peptic ulcer:** if in the stomach, it is a *gastric ulcer;* if in the duodenum, a *duodenal ulcer.*

Ulcers are particularly likely to develop in a man whose position in society produces continuous anxiety or nervous tension. As long ago as 1857, one physician (a Dr. Brinton) wrote: "Mental anxiety so frequently coincides with ulcers that we are fully entitled to regard it as a more or less immediate cause." But this insight was largely lost sight of during the latter half of the nineteenth century, when the success of Pasteur and others in tracking down the bacterial causes of many diseases led medical men to neglect the emotional and psychological elements in ill health. As late as 1929, a 544-page monograph on ulcers devoted only three sentences to emotional factors. This attitude changed rapidly in the decade that followed, years that saw the rising influence of psychology.

A leading ulcer specialist has estimated that at least 10 percent of the adult male population suffers, at one time or another, from ulcers. Why? Part of the answer is to be found in that vague factor we call "personality." Generally speaking, the "peptic-ulcer type" is a hard-driving individual who craves superiority. He is given more to action than to introspection; he is seldom "neurotic." But personality is only part of the answer; a remaining and important part is to be found in the nature of our society itself. Ulcers show an especially high frequency among bus drivers, taxi drivers, and railroad engineers. Executive positions in highly competitive fields are great breeding grounds for ulcers. Faced, or threatened, with this ailment, the individual can usually (if he will) control or get rid of his abnormal condition by changing his occupation and, more important, changing his way of life and thinking in a fundamental way. From the standpoint of society as a whole, ulcers should be regarded as an unavoidable by-product of our particular brand of civilization; eliminating them would require social reorganization of the most profound sort. Here is an ailment a principal cause of which—and perhaps its cure—lies in the field of social affairs, rather than in the field of biology in the narrow sense.*

205. The Role of Secretin

How long food stays in the stomach is determined by several factors: the kind of food, the quantity of food, and, perhaps, individual differences. Only a few substances, notably alcohol, are absorbed through the stomach wall into the body. The bulk of the food, after being reduced to a uniform consistency by peristaltic and other movements of the stomach, passes on to the small intestine.

The lower end of the stomach can be closed by a ring of muscle called the **pyloric sphincter** (Gr. *pyloros* = a gate keeper; *sphincter* = that which binds tightly). During much of the time that food is in the stomach, the pyloric sphincter is closed tightly but, after an hour or so, it opens periodically and lets a squirt of fluid food enter the small intestine. This process continues until the stomach is emptied.

The first part of the small intestine is dignified by a special name: **duodenum** (L. *duo* = two + *decem* = ten; so called because in man the duodenum is about twelve finger-widths long). It is in this region that **pancreatic juice** —perhaps the most important of the digestive juices—is added to the food. The course of events leading to the addition of this juice is worth recounting.

It was early observed in experimental animals that soon after food moves from the stomach into the duodenum, the **pancreas,** a small organ situated just below the stomach, starts to secrete pancreatic juice, which enters the duodenum by way of the pancreatic duct (Fig. 26-5*A*). It is natural to assume that a message is sent by way

---

* 26-1. Try to explain these facts: A statistical-historical study indicated that between 1850 and 1900, two-thirds of patients with peptic ulcers were women; since 1920, only one-tenth have been women.

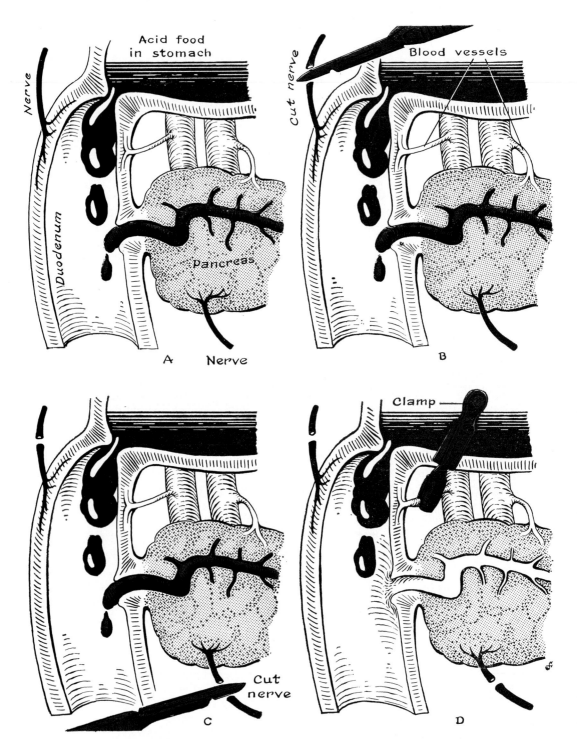

Fig. 26-5. *The experimental evidence for the hormonal elicitation of pancreatic secretion. When acid food from the stomach enters the duodenum* (A), *the pancreas secretes pancreatic juice. Cutting nerves attached to the duodenum* (B), *or to the pancreas* (C) *does not change the response. But stopping the exit of blood from the duodenal wall prevents the passage of the "message," i.e., of the hormone* secretin, *from the duodenum to the pancreas.*

of the nerves from the duodenum to the pancreas, "telling" the pancreas to begin secreting its juice. However, a very simple experiment shows that this is not so. When all the nerves leading to the pancreas are cut, the secretion of pancreatic juice is still elicited by the passage of food from stomach to duodenum (Fig. 26-5*B*, *C*). Clearly, messages are still getting through from the duodenum to the pancreas—but how? Under the conditions of the experiment, the only obvious connection of the pancreas with the rest of the body is by way of the blood vessels. The most reasonable assumption is that some sort of message is carried by the blood stream from duodenum to pancreas. That this is so can be shown by preventing the passage of blood from duodenum to pancreas, which can be done by either stopping the flow of blood *away* from the duodenum (Fig. 26-5*D*) or stopping the flow of blood *to* the pancreas.* Either experiment leads to the failure of the pancreas to respond to the presence of food in the duodenum. Evidently, the blood stream can carry a "message" from one organ to the other. Such a message, really a substance dissolved in the blood stream, is called a *hormone.*

The full story is this: The food mass that comes from the stomach is strongly acid. The duodenum and small intestine are alkaline. Certain cells that line the walls of the duodenum are stimulated by the acid, producing a hormone called **secretin.** (It is most unfortunate that this word looks so much like secre*tion.* Read carefully.) Secretin enters the blood stream and is carried to all parts of the body. In most places the hormone has no effect, so far as we know. But the pancreas responds to secretin by secreting pancreatic juice at an increased rate.

206. The Enzymes in Pancreatic Juice

Our food is made up of substances belonging to three different chemical classes: proteins, carbohydrates, and fats. Pancreatic juice contains enzymes that attack all three. It contains several proteolytic enzymes, one of which is called **trypsin;** a carbohydrate-splitting enzyme often called **amylase;** and a fat-splitting enzyme, **lipase.**

Pancreatic enzymes continue the work begun by the enzymes of the stomach and mouth. Trypsin splits proteins into polypeptides, which are later split by intestinal enzymes into amino acids, which can be absorbed into the body. The action of amylase appears to be a duplication of the action of salivary ptyalin: it changes starch to disaccharides (C_{12} compounds like maltose, $C_{12}H_{22}O_{11}$).

Lipase, the fat-digesting enzyme, is aided by other juices. One of the many functions of the liver is the production of **bile,** which enters the small intestine by way of the bile duct. Bile helps in the digestion of fats, but *bile is not an enzyme.* It has a soaplike action; it causes the large fat globules, consisting of many molecules, to break down into small globules in which, however, the chemical constitution of the molecules is unchanged. These small particles can remain suspended in water. Bile is said to **emulsify** fats. When fats are thus finely dispersed, they present a greater surface for the enzyme lipase to act on. The end products of lipolytic action, glycerine and fatty acids, are absorbed into the body through the intestinal wall.

207. Other Digestive Enzymes

The digestion of carbohydrates, carried as far as to disaccharides by pancreatic amylase, is brought to a conclusion by the enzyme **maltase,** which is produced by cells in the wall of the small intestine. This enzyme converts disaccharides (C_{12} sugar molecules) to monosaccharides like glucose (C_6 sugar molecules), which can be absorbed through the intestinal wall.

It should be noted that in digestion the principle of physiological reserve (§197) is once again exhibited. The action of salivary ptyalin is duplicated by pancreatic amylase. There is evidence that lipolytic enzymes are produced not only by the pancreas but also by the stom-

---

* 26-2. The former experiment is the better one. Why?

ach. Proteins are attacked by enzymes produced by the stomach, the pancreas, and also by the walls of the small intestine. The actions of these various enzymes represent, in part, duplication. Such duplication constitutes a safety factor. Considerable portions of the G-I tract may be put out of commission by disease or removed by surgery without seriously affecting the digestive abilities.

Because of the large numbers of bacteria present, it is difficult to determine exactly what digestive enzymes are produced by the intestines of man. Bacteria produce their own hydrolytic enzymes. To a certain extent, bacteria act as competitors for a common food supply. It is also possible that significant amounts of the products of bacterial digestion are absorbed by man. Man, so far as we know, is not dependent on these intestinal guests. In some other ani-

mals, however, intestinal bacteria seem to be essential. Cellulose, the woody material of plants, is a carbohydrate that is almost completely indigestible by man. Cows, horses, and termites, however, get much of their nutriment from cellulose. It has been shown that the intestines of these animals swarm with bacteria and other microorganisms that produce cellulose-hydrolyzing enzymes. The host animals (as well as the microscopic guests) benefit from the action of these enzymes.

208. Absorption of Food

The wall of the small intestine (Fig. 26-6A), when examined under a microscope (Fig. 26-6B), is seen to be composed of millions of tiny fingerlike projections pointing into the cavity.

Fig. 26-6. *The wall of the small intestine (A) is lined with thousands of tiny villi (B), each of which has the structure diagrammatically shown in C.*

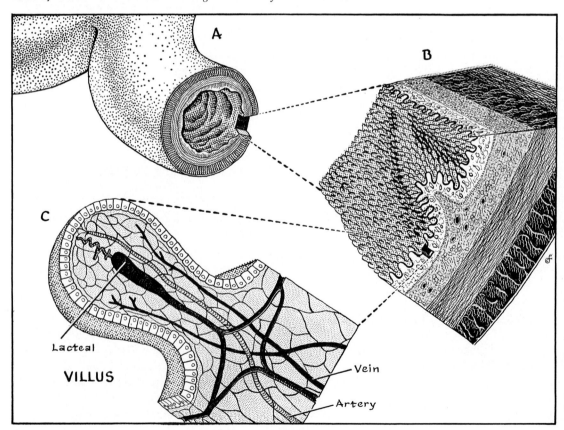

Lacteal

VILLUS

Vein

Artery

These are the **villi** (sing. *villus;* L. shaggy hair). Villi, when cut lengthwise, exhibit the structure diagrammatically shown in Figure 26-6C. Note that each villus contains vessels of two different kinds: blood vessels and lacteals. The function of the blood vessels will be considered first.

The end products of protein digestion are amino acids. The end products of carbohydrate digestion are monosaccharides (simple sugars). Amino acids and simple sugars are both soluble and readily pass through the walls of the villi to the blood vessels. In the blood vessels, blood is in continuous motion, owing to the pumping of the heart. Dissolved in the blood stream, amino acids and sugars are carried to all parts of the body.

The absorption of the products of fat digestion is a different story. If a fasting animal, or one fed a low-fat meal, is killed and opened, the lacteal vessels are inconspicuous. If, however, an animal recently fed a meal rich in fats is opened, the lacteals are readily visible as swollen, milky channels. The name **lacteal,** derived from the Latin *lactis,* meaning milk, was suggested by the appearance of these vessels when full. Microscopic examination of the contents reveals small droplets which can be chemically identified as fats.

How do fatty materials get into the lacteals? There appears to be no fat in the epithelium of the intestinal villi. After a fat-containing meal, fatty acids and glycerine, produced by the hydrolysis of fats by lipase, can be demonstrated in the intestine. Concomitantly, fat droplets appear in the lacteals of the neighboring villi. It is possible that fatlike materials pass through the villous epithelium as fatty acids and glycerine to be resynthesized into fats inside the villi.

The lacteals are part of a second circulatory system: the so-called **lymphatic system** (L. *lympha* = clear water). This system has no well-developed pump (such as the heart); it depends on the squeezing movements of the surrounding tissues. Microscopic examination of living intestine shows the villi to be in constant motion, weaving back and forth and pumping up and down. The movement of the villi probably aids in stirring the intestinal contents, thus aiding absorption; it undoubtedly helps to alternately squeeze and relax the lacteals, thus forcing the contents on. Ultimately, the lymphatic system joins with the blood system, the lymph entering the blood stream by a vein near the heart.

209. The Function of the Large Intestine

The food mass enters the large intestine in a fluid state; when it leaves, by way of the rectum and anus, it is solid. This change is brought about by absorption of water into the body. Since much of this water originally came from the body, we speak of the *re*absorption of water. Reabsorption is the principal function of the large intestine. There is no evidence that enzymes are produced by this part of the G-I tract.

At the end of its journey through the large intestine, the mass is fairly solid and is known as dung, or **feces** (L. dregs). This material is passed at intervals into the last part of the G-I tract, the **rectum.** The presence of feces in the rectum leads to characteristic sensations and the desire to defecate.

It is usually said that the "normal" frequency of defecation is once a day, but there is great individual variability. For some individuals, evacuation at intervals of two or three days may be normal. Whenever defecation is difficult or delayed beyond the normal interval, we speak of a state of **constipation.** A constipated individual may exhibit foul breath, headache, depression, or irritability. The causes of constipation are many: poor health, poor diet, and "nervous tension" are chief among them. It has been estimated that at least 1 adult in 5 in the United States is constipated most of the time, and about half of these take laxatives regularly. Most laxatives, however, when repeatedly taken, tend to lose their efficacy and hence are a questionable solution to the problem of constipation, which is better attacked by partaking of a sensible diet or by learning to cope with nervous tension.

210. The Role of Smooth Muscle

Peristaltic movements, as well as other movements of a more random sort, occur throughout the digestive tract and serve to churn the food and mix it with the digestive juices. Movements of the intestine are made possible by the action of two different muscle layers, shown in Figure 26-7. The muscle fibers in both layers are oriented in a helical fashion; but the muscle cells of the outer layer are oriented almost parallel to the length of the intestine, and this muscle layer is, therefore, called the **longitudinal muscle layer.** Bearing in mind that when muscle fibers act, they shorten their length, we can easily understand that the contraction of longitudinal muscles will shorten the length of the intestine. The inner layer is composed of cells oriented almost at right angles to the axis of the intestine; this layer is called the **circular muscle layer.** Contraction of this layer will constrict the diameter of the gut and, hence, in-

crease the length. By the varied cooperation and antagonism of these two layers, a variety of movements can be imparted to the intestine.

The muscles of the intestinal wall are *smooth muscles,* which differ from skeletal muscles in several ways (§190). They have no striations; each cell is definitely limited by a cell membrane, and has but one nucleus. Most of the muscles of the **viscera** (L. entrails) are of this kind. Physiologically, there are also significant differences between smooth muscle and striated muscle. The latter is capable of rapid contraction, but fatigues easily; the former is slow to contract and slow to relax, and it can remain contracted for long periods of time without fatigue. Striated muscle does its owner's bidding —it is "voluntary muscle"; smooth muscle almost seems to have a mind of its own—it is called "involuntary muscle."

With these differences in mind, we can predict with almost complete accuracy where each kind of muscle will be found, on the reasonable assumption that need determines presence. All the muscles that move the bones of the body are striated, for movements of the skeleton must be quick and subject to voluntary control. On the other hand, we need not concern ourselves with the movements of the viscera. Quite often, such movements must be long continued. The intestinal muscles, for instance, are almost constantly at work. Correlated with these needs, we find that visceral muscles, with few exceptions, are smooth muscles.

Fig. 26-7. *The muscles of the gut are smooth muscles. Contraction of the longitudinal muscle layer shortens the gut; contraction of the circular muscle layer constricts and lengthens it.*

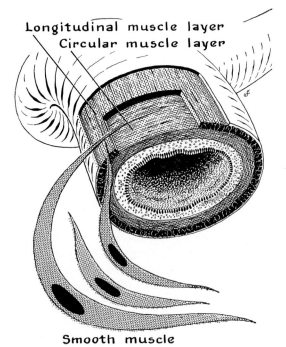

Longitudinal muscle layer
Circular muscle layer

Smooth muscle

211. Nutrition: The Cost in Energy

With the clarification of the concept of energy during the nineteenth century and the explicit statement of the conservation of energy, numerous workers began to study man as an "energetic" machine with a view to verifying (or disproving) the application of the First Law of Thermodynamics to man and other animals. The energy that an animal ingests in the form of potential chemical energy of organic molecules is released in various ways. With some of this energy, an animal can perform work: Considered as a working engine, man and other animals exhibit an efficiency of about 30 percent, which compares favorably with the working efficiency of the best gasoline engines. What happens to the other 70 percent of the energy taken in? The greater part of it appears as heat. In man, some of this heat is used in the evaporation of water (sweat).

Determining the total energy released by a metabolizing organism is a detailed and technical job, first carried out with sufficient accuracy by the German biologist Max Rubner in 1894. In his most careful determination of the expenditure of energy by dogs, Rubner accounted for the energy taken in with an error not exceeding 0.47 percent. Within the decade, the American physiologist F. G. Benedict showed a similar equivalence of intake and outgo with an error not exceeding 0.2 percent. Considering the difficulty of determining such energy budgets, we need not doubt the applicability of the First Law of Thermodynamics to living phenomena.

How much energy does a man require for a day's living? The answer to this depends on many factors: his size, the temperature, and the work he does, to mention only the most obvious. To generalize, in round figures we may say that a man of 70 kilograms weight—an average-size man—requires about 2,500 Calories per day, if he is a man of sedentary occupation. If he is moderately active, 3,000 Calories per day are required; a very active man—such as a lumberjack—will require 4,500 Calories or more. The requirements of "average" women in the same *verbal* categories are only about 80 percent as great. Women who are pregnant or are nursing children have somewhat greater needs. Children require less food than adults, but *not* in proportion to their body weight. During the first year of life, a baby requires around 100 Calories per kilogram body weight. This rate falls off steadily during maturation. An adult requires only about 36 Calories per kilogram, if sedentary, or about 65 Calories per kilogram, if very active. So we may say that even the most active adult is not as active as a baby.

What is the minimum number of Calories an adult can get along with? Many studies, both experimental and observational, indicate that the minimum number of Calories on which adult life may be maintained without impairment is about 1,600 Calories per day. If the number of Calories falls below this level of **maintenance Calories,** the individual must make up the deficit by respiring his own body tissues —a procedure that cannot (obviously) be followed indefinitely. An individual living on maintenance Calories alone is quite useless to himself or anyone else, for these Calories will sustain only life itself in a man who is lying down 24 hours of the day. Calories required over and above the maintenance Calories are called **work Calories.** From the figures given earlier, we see that a sedentary man requires nearly 1,000 work Calories per day; a moderately active man, about 1,500 work Calories; and a very active man, 3,000 or more work Calories. A housewife (in an American city) requires about 800 work Calories per day.

The minimum food requirements of the inhabitants of a spaceship present one of the serious limiting conditions of an extended voyage into space. For an astronaut to remain healthy he probably must be active to the extent of requiring 2,000 to 3,000 Calories a day. The dry weight of edible organic matter that will yield this much energy is at least 500 g, and more likely 800 g. This bulk cannot possibly be reduced to the dimensions of the "food pill" so essential to the craft of the science-fiction writer. The most economical trajectory for a round trip to Mars requires about 515 days under ideal conditions, allowing no time for exploration. The food for this period for one man would weigh 412 kilograms, or about 6 times the man's weight. Of course, the duration of the trip could be cut down by higher velocity, but the weight saved in food would be more than balanced by the increased weight of fuel required.

212. Inorganic Nutrients

But not all foodstuffs are needed to furnish energy. The quantitatively most important exception is water, which must be ingested in comparatively large quantities to replace the unavoidable losses due to sweating and other biological processes. There is no energy available in water. This substance is the solvent in which all biochemical processes take place.

In addition to water, other inorganic substances are required for continued life. Nearly everyone knows of the "craving" of cows and other plant-eaters for sodium chloride, a substance usually not sufficiently abundant in plants. Discovering the necessity of other inorganic substances has usually entailed more difficulty; typically, such discoveries have been initiated when it was found that people or other animals in a certain region of the world were suffering from a poorly understood malady. In this way the necessity of the element iodine was discovered. In extensive areas of the central part of the United States and in Switzerland, there was once an unusually high incidence of **goiter,** a swelling of the thyroid gland in the neck. A particular kind of goiter, called "simple goiter," was found to be most prevalent where the diet was deficient in iodine. This discovery led to the routine addition of very small quantities of iodine to the table salt (sodium chloride) sold in stores—a measure that diminished greatly, and at small expense, the incidence of goiter.

More or less as the result of similar "happy accidents"—happy, that is, in leading to scientific discoveries—the dietary necessity of iron and copper was also discovered. Both of these elements are required for the manufacture of the red blood cells. The element calcium is required in large quantities for the synthesis and maintenance of the bones. The daily calcium needs are equivalent to the quantity present in two large glasses of milk. It is of interest to note that in China, where, for the vast majority of the adult population, milk is an unknown luxury, animal bones form an important part of the diet; some recipes call for dissolving bones in vinegar preliminary to making a soup of them.

A recent discovery in the field of inorganic or *mineral nutrition* is that of the role of the element fluorine in the development of sound teeth. It has been observed that in some parts of Montana the teeth of the inhabitants are frequently mottled with brown. Surprisingly, it was found that such teeth, though unsightly, were sound—seldom being affected by decay or *dental caries.* Further study revealed that the single cause of both the soundness and the mottling was fluorine, ingested daily as fluorides present in the drinking water. On still further investigation, it was found that it was possible to control the intake of fluoride and so to improve demonstrably the health of teeth without causing noticeable discoloration of the enamel. More than 2 ppm of fluoride in the drinking water causes discoloration; around 1 ppm decreases caries without causing discoloration. This concentration has no known harmful effects. As of 1959, 20 percent of the people in the United States were living in communities that added fluoride to their water; another 4 percent were using local water that already had enough fluoride in it.* Controlled experiments (using closely similar cities, with and without fluoridation) show that when fluoride is added for five years or more, the incidence of dental decay among children is cut in half. There seems, however, to be no improvement in the teeth of those who are already adults at the time they start taking such water.

Many other inorganic elements are known to be required for healthy existence: zinc, magnesium, manganese, cobalt, potassium, sulfur, and phosphorus, to mention only some. Most of these are required in very small quantities, and the discovery of their indispensability is usually made only under unusual circumstances. As a practical dietary matter, the inhabitants of most parts of the world need not worry about getting sufficient quantities of the various inorganic nutrients, since almost any natural varied diet will inevitably furnish them in sufficient quantities.

---

* 26-3. Why, in reporting this, did not the author contrast the communities with natural fluoride and those with artificially fluoridated water supplies?

213. Vitamin Needs

The history of the discovery of vitamins is an involved and tortuous one. It begins either about a half-century ago or many centuries ago, depending on our interpretation of the meaning of the word "discovery." In this history are recorded many independent discoveries of needs for what we now call vitamins, and almost as many instances of the forgetting of the discoveries by society as a whole. In recent times the Dutchman Eijkman (1897) is frequently given credit for the first clear-cut demonstration of the existence of a vitamin; yet the way in which he missed arriving at a clear conception of a vitamin throws light on the methods and development of sciences.

Eijkman's studies were initiated by official action when the Dutch government became concerned with the high rate of the disease **beriberi** —a nervous disorder—among servicemen and prisoners in the Dutch East Indies. This was a time when the "germ theory of disease," promulgated principally by the Frenchman Pasteur and the German Koch, was winning over the minds of scientists everywhere. The idea that disease could be caused by microscopic living organisms constituted a new "conceptual scheme" that was proving fruitful in the explanation of many otherwise puzzling matters. In such an atmosphere, it was natural that Eijkman should first try to apply this conceptual scheme to the problem facing him; but without success. No disease organism could be demonstrated as the cause of the malady.

In delving further into the problem, Eijkman had recourse to animal experimentation. Observing that the venality of the suppliers of food to the Dutch barracks and prisons led them to purchase the cheapest sorts of foodstuff, Eijkman set about feeding some chickens the diet furnished these humans. The principal item in this diet was low-grade, but polished rice. When Eijkman fed his chickens solely on this material, they too developed a kind of beriberi, or **neuritis** (G. *neuron* = nerve + suffix *-itis* denotes inflammation). At this point Eijkman fell back to another conceptual scheme and decided that the polished rice fed to these chickens, being of low quality, must have some poisonous substance in it. When he varied the diet, he discovered that even a very small amount of *un*polished rice added to the diet would wholly prevent the development of neuritis. He explained this as being due to the neutralization of the poison in the polished rice by some unknown material present in the hulls of unpolished rice.

The first correct interpretation of such facts was put forward by the English biochemist F. Gowland Hopkins in 1906. As much as a generation earlier, some other workers had observed that it is not possible to maintain experimental animals on a diet made up solely of pure amino acids and carbohydrates to which have been added all the inorganic substances known to be required for life. Animals fed on such diets languish and die. If, however, to such a diet was added a *very small* quantity of some such complex organic material as an extract of yeast, the animals could be kept alive and in good health. Analysis revealed that the value of the enrichment materials was not due to any inorganic substance. Since the enrichment material was required in extremely small quantities, it was obvious that it was not satisfying any significant portion of the energy needs. Apparently, there was in such material some organic compound(s) essential to life. To such, Hopkins gave the name "accessory factors." A few years later another chemist, Casimir Funk, gave them their modern name: **vitamins.**

What is a vitamin? *A vitamin is an organic substance that is indispensable for life but is not required as a source of energy.* Eijkman's chickens, fed on polished rice, were suffering and dying from neuritis caused by the lack of the vitamin **thiamine.** This vitamin is abundant in the hulls of natural rice, but virtually absent from the white central part. In removing the hulls from the rice, we remove this vitamin; the addition of even a tiny amount of rice hulls to a diet of polished rice supplies enough thiamine to prevent neuritis in chickens or men.

TABLE 26-1   *Vitamins of the Greatest Practical Importance in Human Nutrition; Dietary Sources; and Consequences of Severe Vitamin Deficiencies.*

GROUP AND NAME	GOOD SOURCES	EFFECTS OF SEVERE DEFICIENCY IN MAN
Ascorbic Acid (Vitamin C; water-soluble)	Fresh fruits and vegetables, particularly citrus fruits	Scurvy: sore mouth, teeth fall out
B-Complex Vitamins (water-soluble):		
Thiamine (Vitamin B_1)	Yeast, whole grains, meats	Beriberi, a nervous disease
Riboflavin (Vitamin B_2)	Approximately as above	Various skin ailments and photophobia
Pyridoxin (Vitamin B_6)	Approximately as above	Not certain in man; anemia in dogs and pigs
Niacin (Nicotinic acid)	Approximately as above	Pellagra
Fat-soluble Vitamins:		
Vitamin A	Fish liver oils, butter, eggs, yellow vegetables	Night blindness, skin diseases
Vitamin D	Fish liver oils, eggs, irradiated milk	Rickets, abnormal calcium and phosphorus metabolism
Vitamin K	Widely distributed in plants	Prolonged clotting time of blood

Why are vitamins needed? What is their role in the life of an organism, in the life of cells? Less than 1 part in 10,000, by weight, of the diet needs to be composed of vitamins. Yet this small part is indispensable. This fact itself furnished a clue to the role of vitamins. As the physiology of cells came to be better understood, it was pointed out that there are, inside cells, enzymes that are an essential part of the living material, and that these enzymes, quantitatively speaking, make up only a very small part of a living cell. The quantitative parallel of vitamins and enzymes made it natural to suspect that the two were intimately related. Research has shown this to be true. We now know enough of the biochemistry of vitamins and enzymes to be able to state that *probably every vitamin is a part of some enzyme molecule*—a part which the animal itself cannot synthesize and so must derive from its diet.

The concept of the vitamin, once made clear by Hopkins, proved a fruitful one in biology. Less than half a century's work has revealed more than a dozen vitamins. Every one of these is of importance in the metabolism of cells, but many of them are so universally present in the diet of mankind that they are of little practical importance. Those of proved practical importance—those for which there is some probability of a deficiency in a diet—may be divided

into three groups: (1) ascorbic acid; (2) water-soluble vitamins of the B-complex; and (3) the fat-soluble vitamins. The most common of these vitamins and their food sources are given in Table 26-1, which also lists the effects of severe vitamin deficiencies in man. Results of mild deficiencies cannot be so sharply characterized or so easily recognized.

214. Starvation

For most of the peoples of the world during all of man's history up to and including the present time, one nutritional problem has overshadowed all others: *getting enough food.* It is the considered opinion of population experts that more than half of mankind, at the present time, suffers from starvation or its imminent threat. That a statement of this sort should be so shocking and questionable is evidence of the wide social gap between those for whom food is the principal daily concern and those who are so little concerned with the problem that they can afford to spend part of their time reading books like this. Hundreds of millions of people in China and India and the East Indies (to mention only distant places) must devote the greater part of their working days—and thus of their thinking as well—to the garnering of food. With few and conspicuous exceptions, only in the Western world is any appreciable proportion of the population sufficiently above the grubbing necessity of finding food to be able to afford, for instance, the luxury of formal education. Most of the people of the world seriously need one thing above all others: more Calories.

Even in our part of the world, men are occasionally brought face to face with the stark reality of starvation. In the industrial district of the Ruhr, Germany, during the Second World War, there developed (as elsewhere) shortages of food. For the good of the people as a whole, the government was forced to ration food. With the same end in mind, it tried to get as much work for as little food as possible. Over a period of several years a careful record was kept of the variations in food allotment, expressed in Calories, and in work performed by the industrial workers. It was found that there was an exact parallelism between the amount of food given to each worker and the amount of work performed. Each worker required, of course, his maintenance Calories, but above this level there was a simple conversion of work Calories into work. Whenever the food allotment was cut, the amount of work decreased; when the amount of food was increased, more work was performed.

The only exception to these statements does not contradict this principle and throws further light on physiological problems. It was found that the simple proportionality between work Calories and work disappeared when men were given cigarettes as a bonus for exceptional work. From this fact we might suspect a violation of the First Law of Thermodynamics, or an exceptional efficiency on the part of the workers. Investigation gave no support to either suspicion. On the contrary, the explanation was simple. The extra work performed under these conditions was "bought" at the expense of the flesh of the workers themselves: these workers lost weight. Obviously, such an incentive could not for long achieve the end desired by the management—namely, more work for less food.

During the same war, civilians in Holland were restricted to a legal diet of less than 1,500 Calories per person per day. They lost weight rapidly. In the early stages of starvation, individuals became irritable and belligerent. This attitude was soon succeeded by one of unresponsiveness, suspiciousness, and impassive lack of cooperation even with those who were attempting to improve their nutrition. There was also, as any reasonable man would expect, a general deterioration of morality as concerned food and its procurement. As one observer stated, it was clear that many individuals "were getting not a little extra food by hook or by crook, mainly by crook."

In discussions of world politics it is often said that we must see to it that no people starve, because starvation breeds revolution. There is a grain of truth in this; but a misconception needs to be guarded against. *Starving men do not revolt.* Careful observations made in prison camps and oppressed countries during World War II showed that men who are genuinely starving, no matter how idealistic their previous characters, become the simplest and most egotistic of anarchists, "every man against every man," in Hobbes' phrase. Each starving man has only one goal—food for himself, *now*. He does not combine forces with others to work for the good of the group; he is incapable of making long range plans even for his own good —a plan for tomorrow would be impossibly long range for him. Revolutions are not made by starving men; they may be made by men who have known starvation and now fear its recurrence; but it takes a full belly to revolt. This is a physiological fact.

215. Kwashiorkor

Man must have a mixture of amino acids to live. In the natural diet, we get our amino acids in the form of proteins, so we usually speak of amino acid needs in terms of protein needs. As a rule of thumb, we may say that a human being requires about one gram of protein per kilogram of body weight per day. This figure is perhaps too high for adults, and it is certainly too low for children, but it will do as an over-all approximation. The ordinary diet yields about 5 Calories per gram dry weight. For a daily intake of 2,500 Calories the dry weight of the food must be about 500 grams. To supply the protein needs of a 70-kg man, 14 percent of this food must be protein. On a carnivorous diet there is no problem, but if the food is all vegetable matter, protein supply becomes a problem. Even the most protein-rich of plant materials—seeds of cereals, and some tubers—have a protein concentration of only about 10 percent. This means that either the vegetable diet must be augmented with meat, or that an excess of vegetable Calories must be taken in in order to get enough protein. For most of the peoples of the world, living near the edge of starvation on a largely vegetable diet, protein deficiency is an ever-present reality.

On a global basis protein shortage shows itself most importantly in the disease of **kwashiorkor.** The word is African and means "the re-

jected one"; the word originally referred to the child that was displaced from the mother's breast by the arrival of a new baby. In a poorly nourished population living largely on a vegetable diet, the high protein requirements of a rapidly growing child can be most easily met by its mother's milk. Shocking though it may seem to us, the "normal" pattern of family formation over most of the world involves the bearing of eight or ten babies, all but two or three of which die before reaching the age of three years. About half of these infantile deaths are caused by kwashiorkor—protein deficiency as a result of too many children for the protein supply.

The approximate geographical distribution of kwashiorkor is shown in Figure 26-8. The same map would do, of course, to show the distribution of people living under serious threat of starvation because of over-population. Kwashiorkor is merely one particular, easily

Fig. 26-8. *The geographical distribution of kwashiorkor, as of 1960. (N. S. Scrimshaw and M. Béhar,* Science *(1961)* **133:***2040.)*

identifiable manifestation of human failure in population control.

216. Vitamin Deficiencies

Starving people often show no symptoms of vitamin deficiencies, for several reasons. First of all, above a very low minimum level, the need for vitamins is roughly proportional to the total amount of food taken in. Vitamins form parts of enzyme molecules that are important in the respiration of food; if little food is taken in, the individual can get along with fewer enzyme molecules, hence with less intake of vitamins. Ascorbic acid, for instance, is an important component of the enzyme system involved in the respiration of carbohydrates; the need for ascorbic acid is proportional to the carbohydrate intake. The need for the B-complex vitamins has been shown to be markedly increased by an increase in bodily activity; a starved man, being relatively inactive, has a minimum need of the B-complex vitamins. Some of the vitamins, notably vitamin D, are closely tied up with processes of growing. A well-fed baby (well-fed in terms of Calories) needs much more vitamin D if it is not to develop rickets than does a poorly fed one. Under starvation conditions, of course, there are few well-fed babies, growth is retarded, and the need for vitamin D is diminished.

But there is undoubtedly another reason why semistarved populations seldom develop vitamin deficiencies: consciously or not, they eat more wisely than most "well-fed," civilized men. The tendency of a hungry man to eat everything that comes his way is, in the main, good. Well-fed people refuse to eat many wholesome foodstuffs because of cultural or psychological prejudices, and for the same reasons eat many foods of low nutritional value. Under the spur of hunger, psychological and cultural prejudices are speedily sloughed off.

It is clear that many of the vitamin deficiencies suffered by civilized men are due in considerable part to diets that are unnecessarily refined and restricted. In earlier days, bread was made from the whole grain. Now we make it from only the white part of the grain. The resultant product is a lovely bread with a fine crust and excellent keeping qualities. But, as compared with whole-wheat bread, it is lacking three-fourths of the iron, one-half of the calcium, three-eighths of the copper, thiamine, and riboflavin, and almost all of the magnesium and manganese. Few people, however, who have tasted both kinds of bread will consent to eat "dark bread," even when informed of its dietary superiority. Nevertheless, the consequences are no longer serious, for since 1941 it has been mandatory in the United States to enrich white bread with thiamine, the most important of the vitamins present in whole wheat. As a result, at a cost of about 25¢ per person per year, commercial white bread is now equal or superior in thiamine content to the best whole-grain bread.

The nutritional principles just illustrated find other applications in dietary problems. Ascorbic acid is easily obtainable from fresh fruits and vegetables, as well as from some acid-preserved plant material, for example, sauerkraut. But there are many people who can be induced to eat such materials only with difficulty. The B-complex vitamins are present in large quantities in meat, particularly in the viscera of animals—the livers, kidneys, spleen, pancreas, and others. Many persons have a strong prejudice against vitamin-rich viscera.

An unsatisfactory feature of our knowledge of vitamins is our inability to state with precision what the quantitative needs for these important substances are. In the United States, the National Research Council has published a list of the minimum daily requirements of various vitamins. That this list allows for adequate intake of vitamins is clear, but to what extent it overestimates vitamin needs is a matter for debate. There are clinical and anthropological data that indicate that other peoples, living on markedly different foods, do quite well on diets which, by our standards, include inadequate amounts of various vitamins. No simple reason can be given for such discrepancies, but one factor probably involved may be pointed out—namely, the role of the intestinal bacteria in consuming and producing vitamins. Among other animals, it is known that guinea pigs (to take a single example) must be fed ascorbic acid, whereas rabbits need not be. It can be shown that the flesh of both animals contains ascorbic acid, which functions in their enzymes in a similar way. The difference in dietary needs of these animals is associated with the differences in their intestinal bacterial populations. In the gut of the rabbit there are bacteria that manufacture an excess of ascorbic acid, some of which passes through the intestinal wall and into the rabbit; whereas the guinea pig gut has different bacteria that do not supply this need.

To return to man, it is known that not all humans have the same bacterial flora in their intestines. To what extent the differences in intestinal inhabitants are responsible for individual differences in nutritional need is not a matter of direct demonstration, but it has been shown that there are differences among various species of bacteria in their ability to synthesize vitamins, or in their need for an external source of vitamins in *their* diet. Undoubtedly, some of our intestinal bacteria augment our supply of vitamins, and others diminish it by their competitive action. Since we cannot, at present, make more explicit statements than these, it is clear that any precise statement of the quantitative needs of man must be taken with at least a grain of salt.

Few primitive societies living in their traditional manner show significant signs of vitamin deficiencies. Why is this? In general, we may say that any society eating a diet that has long been traditional has survived because this diet *is* adequate to healthy existence. Difficulties arise when, due to the inroads of civilization or other upsetting factors, a traditional diet is altered. The substitution of refined white flour for some coarsely ground native meal may devastate a population.

Similarly, among men of the Western world, vitamin deficiencies most frequently develop when conventional modes of living have to be abandoned. A common situation of this sort is that of sailors. Until recent times, embarking on an ocean voyage of more than three months'

duration was extremely likely to lead to the development of the disease **scurvy**—a disease in which the gums bleed, the teeth fall out, the skin and flesh decay, and, finally, death results. The explorer Vasco da Gama lost 100 out of 160 men to this disease on his voyage rounding the Cape of Good Hope in 1498. There are historical records of the finding of derelict vessels with all hands on board dead of scurvy. We know now that such happenings could have been entirely prevented by fresh fruits and vegetables, or acid ones. In the days of sail, the preservation of fresh vegetables on a long ocean trip was not possible, but the prevention of scurvy by citrus fruits or sauerkraut was practicable, as was discovered by James Lind, a seventeenth-century physician in the British East Indies service. The importance of this discovery failed to penetrate the bureaucratic minds of the British admiralty, and the same discovery had to be made again in the eighteenth century by the explorer Captain Cook. Cook's account of the facts, fortunately, impressed the proper authorities; after his time, lemons (called limes) became a standard part of the ships' stores. The compulsory eating of these by British sailors led to their being called "limeys." As evidence of the effect of the new regulation, we have the records of one British naval hospital which show treatment of 1,754 cases of survy in the year 1760, and only 1 case in 1806, eleven years after the adoption of the new regulation.

It would not do to leave the impression that bureaucratic stupidity alone held up the recognition of the vitamins. There was another cause, which is a by-product of the scientific attitude. It was pointed out earlier (§119) that measures for controlling plant diseases were not really accepted until the theory underlying them was developed. It is part of the modern temper not to accept measures that work if they cannot be related to a rational theory. (How else could we distinguish them from superstition?) This attitude undoubtedly held up the acceptance of valid rules of nutrition. For a long time, all that practical men could say was "What you don't eat will make you sick," which didn't make good sense. The stability of valid rules of nutrition was not assured until Hopkins clearly delineated the concept of a vitamin in 1906 and Funk named it in 1912.

What advice can be given the man on the street about vitamins? If they are available, and if he has the money, vitamin concentrates and pills are a feasible means of insuring sufficient intake of vitamins. However, pills are expensive, and it may be, as one physiologist has maintained, that "those who need vitamin pills can't afford them, and those who can afford them don't need them." The question is principally one of economics. If the price of meat and fresh vegetables relative to the price of such starchy, low-vitamin foodstuffs as flour and potatoes continues to rise, while the cost of vitamin pills remains the same, the preceding quotation may cease to be applicable. In the meantime, it is possible, without carrying out chemical analyses and physiological tests, to have a diet that includes adequate amounts of the various vitamins. An inspection of Table 26-1 shows that an adequate natural diet includes liberal amounts of fresh fruits and vegetables (for vitamin C); of meats—particularly viscera—or whole grains and nuts (for the B-complex vitamins); and some fatty animal materials such as eggs and butter, or yellow or orange vegetables such as tomatoes (for vitamin A). Vitamin D is available in irradiated animal fats, or it may be synthesized directly by the human himself upon exposure to the ultraviolet light in the sun's rays. Vitamin K is so widely distributed that one can scarcely avoid getting sufficient quantities of it if he eats a natural diet that supplies the other vitamins.

In general, a sound diet avoids excessive restriction and excessive refinement. The greater the variety of natural foods eaten, and the less "purified" they are, the less likelihood there is that a vitamin deficiency will develop. In passing, it may be noted that a good diet, which includes considerable amounts of vegetable material, will also serve another dietary need— that of supplying sufficient **roughage,** that is, indigestible materials, to stimulate the walls of the large intestine, causing a healthy motility of the colon and preventing constipation.

Questions and Problems

26-4. Make a list of the **boldface** terms in this chapter and write a brief definition of each. Compare your work with the text.

26-5. Trace the path of food from mouth to anus, naming the parts of the G-I tract in order, indicating what enzyme acts in each region, where the enzyme is produced, what sorts of food it acts on, and what the digestive products and their routes of absorption into the body are. It may be convenient to organize this information into a table.

‡26-6. When a man eats, his "Adam's apple" bobs up and down at intervals. Explain the significance of the laryngeal agitation.

26-7. From the knowledge of etymology already gained, deduce the meaning of the following words: gastritis, laryngitis, colitis, tonsillitis.

‡26-8. In December 1944, the Committee of Terminology of the American Society of Parasitologists delivered itself of the opinion that the terms *infect* and *infection* are "properly applicable wherever the parasite invades and establishes itself within the body of the host, including, in this sense, the gastrointestinal tract." Why did the committee feel it necessary to insert the qualifying phrase "in this sense"?

26-9. How is it possible for a horse, drinking with his head down, to move water upward to the stomach?

‡26-10. **Achlorhydria** is an abnormal condition in which the stomach fails to secrete any hydrochloric acid. As a consequence, the food mass in the stomach is usually alkaline. As further consequences, what enzyme would fail to

work, and what other enzyme should be active for a longer time than usual?

26-11. In **obstructive jaundice,** the bile duct is plugged with gallstones; consequently, bile cannot reach the small intestine. As a result, the digestion of one of the three great classes of foodstuff is interfered with. Which one? Why?

‡26-12. What is the etymology of "pancreas"? In what way is it apt?

26-13. Consider these two statements:

a. The blood stream carries secretin from the duodenum to the pancreas, where it stimulates the production of pancreatic juice.

b. The blood stream carries secretin to all parts of the body, including the pancreas, which it stimulates to produce pancreatic juice.

Which is the better statement? Why?

‡26-14. In St. Jerome's *Life of St. Hilarion* there occurs the following passage: "From his thirty-first to his thirty-fifth year he had for food six ounces of barley bread, and vegetables slightly cooked without oil. But finding that his eyes were growing dim, and that his whole body was shrivelled with an eruption and a sort of stony roughness he added oil to his former food, and up to the sixty-third year of his life followed this temperate course . . ." with the result that he did not again suffer from the affliction described. Though diagnosis at a distance of one and a half millennia is risky, what would you say was the probable affliction of St. Hilarion, and why did his later regimen cure it?

26-15. When Vizcaino sailed up the coast of California in 1603, his men suffered grievously. Only six of his sailors could walk, and but two could climb to the maintopsail. Finally they pulled ashore and found what was probably the fruit of *Opuntia imbricata.* According to a contemporary account: "God like a father of mercy caused to be provided in these islands a small fruitlike agaves, called *jocoistles.* These because of their strength, when eaten by the men who had sore mouths, caused the ulcers to slough off and bleed profusely; but such was the efficacy of the fruit that within six days there was not a single per-

son whose mouth was not healed." Give a probable explanation of this historical event.

‡26-16. In his *Geography of Hunger* (1952), Josué de Castro has this to say of vitamin D: "The sun pours forth this vitamin like a divine manna from the cornucopia of the heavens." Comment on the accuracy of this statement.

26-17. Heard in a radio ad: "Use Doe-Smith's Spaghetti. It supplies that much needed energy in generous amounts without those unwanted calories." What does this statement mean?

‡26-18. A certain religious sect in the land of Erewhon is opposed, on theological grounds, to the use of medical measures. The sect is not opposed, however, to eating or to legal measures designed to insure good nutritional quality in foods offered for sale to the public. The sect opposes compulsory vaccination. It does not oppose the compulsory disinfection of municipal drinking water with chlorine, but opposes the addition of fluoride to the drinking water. Are the actions of this Erewhonian sect consistent with its principles? Explain.

26-19. Where is Erewhon?

‡26-20. The records of one New York hospital show the following sex ratio, ♂♂:♀♀ (males:females), for cases of perforated ulcer:

Years	Sex Ratio
1901–1906	2:5
1907–1914	6:0
1915–1930	16:1
1932–1939	12:1

Can you explain the changes?

26-21. In the first half of the twentieth century it was noted that stomach ulcers were almost unknown among the Negroes of the southern part of the United States; whereas in the North, they were nearly as common among Negroes as among whites. Suggest a reasonable explanation of these facts.

‡26-22. What would you predict will be the effect of continued desegregation on the digestive systems of Negroes?

26-23. Prior to about 1925, Dr. A. C. Ivy, in the course of his experimental work, autopsied some 2,000 adult dogs in the Chicago region and noted that about 98 percent of them suffered from goiter. Then, following experimental nutritional studies with dogs and other animals, it was found that a form of human goiter common in this region of the country could be prevented by the addition of the proper amount of iodine to the diet. After 1925, most of the table salt sold in grocery stores was "iodized," that is, had iodine added to it. Also after 1925, Dr. Ivy noted that goiter all but disappeared among his experimental dogs. What bearing does a case history of this sort (and there are others like it) have on the arguments for and against vivisection?

‡26-24. The lethal dose of botulinum toxin taken by mouth is 10^5 times as great as the lethal dose taken intravenously. Why?

26-25. Rats are much more resistant to food poisoning than is man. It is not known why. But what hypothesis is suggested by the answer to the preceding question? How could you test it?

‡26-26. A man of average size works at such a rate that he needs 2,000 work Calories per day. If he works 3 days, what will be his total dietary need, expressed in Calories?

26-27. Two men, both of average size, work at the same job. Mr. *A* works at such a rate that he must take in 2,600 Calories of food per day to maintain a constant weight. Mr. *B* works at such a rate that he needs 3,600 Calories per day to keep his weight constant. How much more work per day, expressed as a percentage, does Mr. *B* do?

‡26-28. Two teams of men are competing with each other at work. Each team is *allowed* a maximum of 600,000 Calories of food a day. Team *C* has 4 men; team *D*, 3 men. The members of each team work at the maximum rate possible while maintaining a constant body weight. Which team will accomplish the greater quantity of work? How much greater, in percentage?

‡26-29. Suppose, in the situation described in the preceding question, each team has a daily food allowance of only 8,000 Calories. Which team accomplishes the greater quantity of work, and how much greater?

26-30. The Calories available in foodstuffs, if not needed as food, can be used to help manufacture other things—plastics, machinery, "luxuries." If a self-sufficient society is willing to determine the size of its population of humans, what size population should it aim for: the maximum population sustainable on its food resources, or something less? Explain.

26-31. Consider the military situation alone. *Other things being equal* (which they never are), does the larger of two warring populations necessarily have the greater military potential?

‡26-32. The principles governing human nutrition govern the nutrition of other animals. On a farm where plowing and other work is done by horses, by what rules should an efficient farmer determine the number of horses he should support to run his farm? Explain.

26-33. Farming is highly seasonal in its demands for work. How has this fact, in the light of the general principles of animal nutrition, contributed to the displacement of the horse by the tractor?

TABLE 26-2 *Time and Food Needed per Man to Complete Round Trip to Planets along Hohmann Ellipses.*

PLANET	YEARS	FOOD, DRY WEIGHT	
		IN KG	AS MULTIPLE OF BODY WT.
Mercury	0.565		
Venus	0.79		
Mars	1.41		
Jupiter	5.5		
Saturn	12.2		
Uranus	32.2		
Neptune	61		
Pluto	91		

26-34. In 1945 James A. Reyniers achieved the first germfree culture of rats through an entire life cycle. Organisms grown in species-pure culture are called **axenic** ("no foreigners"). When grown in known mixture (as with only one species of intestinal bacteria), culture is called **gnotobiotic** ("known life"). What kinds of questions can axenic or gnotobiotic cultures be used to settle?

26-35. Anorexia is one of the symptoms of kwashiorkor. Comment on this from a cybernetic point of view.

‡26-36. Assuming the lower of the two figures given in §211, what dry weight of food must a man eat per year? What fraction or multiple of his body weight is this?

26-37. What multiple of his weight will a man eat in his lifetime? Assume he lives 70 years and eats 500 g per day; what are the errors involved in these assumptions, and how serious are they?

26-38. Using the same assumptions as in preceding problems, complete Table 26-2.

26-39. "The present difficulties of space travel will evaporate when we perfect—as we soon will—(1) a gravity shield, (2) a food pill, (3) dehydrated water, and (4) suspended animation for human beings." Which of these predicted advances are beyond foreseeable achievement?

Readings

Some of the classic reports in the fields of digestion and nutrition are to be found in Chapter 5 of Fulton; particularly worth reading are reports of Spallanzani, Beaumont, and Bayliss and Starling. Spallanzani's report is to be found in Boynton, and Beaumont's in Moulton and Schifferes. Captain Cook's report on scurvy in the British navy is in both Fulton and Boynton. For an up-to-date discussion of human nutrition, see Mottram.

Human starvation in all its aspects is treated encyclopedically by Keys *et al.;* in spite of its size, *The Biology of Human Starvation* is fascinating to browse in. An extremely brief and simple retelling of some of these data is to be found in Guetzkow and Bowman. An interesting case history illuminating the relationship between nutrition and industrial productivity is presented by Kraut and Muller.

Scientific American Offprints

425. Joseph V. Brady. *Ulcers in "Executive" Monkeys*

27

The Circulatory System

217. The Nature of a Circulatory System

Recall once more the equation of respiration:

$$\text{food} + O_2 \longrightarrow CO_2 + H_2O + \varepsilon. \quad (1)$$

Respiration takes place in all the cells of the body, but the raw materials it requires enter only at certain portals. To get these materials from the lungs and the gut to all parts of the body, a method of transport is required. This function is carried out by the **circulatory system,** which consists of heart, blood vessels, and blood. The lymph and lymph channels may also be considered part of the system.

In many of the invertebrates, there are considerable areas in which the blood is not confined to well-defined channels, but moves in a poorly directed way in large reservoirlike regions; such a system is spoken of as an "open circulatory system." Man and other vertebrates have a **closed circulatory system,** however: with few exceptions, the blood is confined to definite channels and moves in only one direction. There are three types of vessels: arteries, capillaries, and veins. These vessels differ significantly in both structure and function. By definition, *an* **artery** *is a vessel that carries blood away from the heart; a* **vein** *is a vessel that carries blood toward the heart.*

And what of the capillaries? To understand their relation to the other vessels, let us follow the blood as it circulates through the system, as diagrammed in Figure 27-1. Blood leaving the human heart is at first enclosed entirely in one large artery, the **aorta,** but this soon divides into smaller arteries; these subdivide repeatedly, and finally the blood is flowing in vessels so fine that they can be seen only with a microscope, though a moderate magnification suffices. Each of these tiny vessels is called a **capillary** (L. *capillaris* = hairlike).* The multitude of them is scarcely imaginable. A single cubic millimeter of skeletal muscle is interlaced with 1,400–4,000 individual capillaries. Because of the many cross-connections among these vessels, and because of the great number of capillaries, no single capillary is indispensable. In this provision for getting nutrients to the cells, we see once more an example of the principle of physiological reserve: When any particular capillary is accidentally put out of service, its work is taken over by numerous neighboring capillaries.

The length of an individual capillary is not very great: perhaps half a millimeter is typical. The capillaries, which may be regarded as the final divisions of the arteries, themselves unite to form the first small veins (Fig. 27-1). These veins in turn unite repeatedly to form larger veins until, in man, the blood returning to the heart runs in two great veins: the **anterior vena**

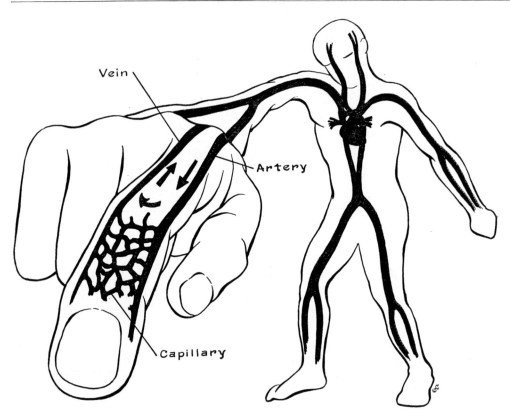

Fig. 27-1. *The relation of arteries to capillaries to veins. Oxygen-rich blood is indicated by color.*

cava (L. *vena* = vein; *cava* = cave, hollow place), bringing blood from the upper regions of the body; and the **posterior vena cava,** coming from the lower.

The threefold system, arteries-capillaries-veins, may be called a "circuit." There are several blood circuits in the body. The one that takes care of most of the body is called the **systemic circuit.** Implicitly, it is the one described in the preceding section. But there are other circuits as well—less extensive, but also important. One of these is the **pulmonary circuit** (L. *pulmo* = lung), which serves the lungs. The first man to appreciate the existence and significance of the pulmonary circuit was a Spaniard, Michael Servetus (1511–1553), but he announced his discovery in a theological work (a heretical tract for which he paid with his life), and so his findings had to be rediscovered by others later.

218. The Heart: Evolution and Function

Among the mammals, the heart is, in a sense, a double organ. The two parts of it work together, but pump blood to different regions, as Figure 27-2A indicates. The right side of the heart is a pump for the pulmonary circuit; the left side, for the systemic circuit. There is no direct channel connecting the two sides. Contraction of a common set of muscles works both pumps at the same time.*

The double pump of a mammal has had a long course of evolution. The simplest hearts we know of, in various invertebrates, are simply regions of the blood vessels that possess the ability to contract peristaltically and thus squeeze the blood onward. In fish (Fig. 27-3A) the contractile regions are differentiated into

---

* 27-2. Suppose the pumps worked independently. What then?

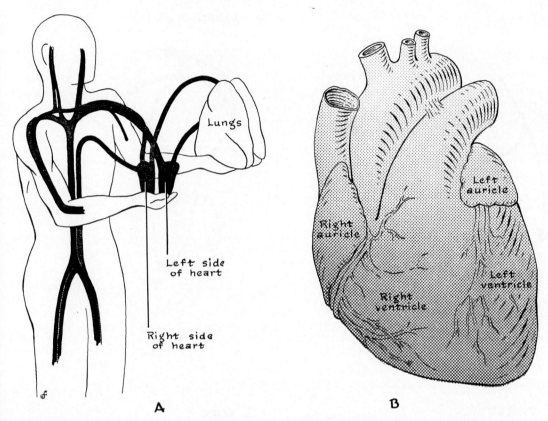

Fig. 27-2. *The heart is really two pumps* (A). *The right one supplies the lungs with blood, and the left one supplies the rest of the body. Oxygen-rich blood is shown in color.* (B) *A realistic view of the heart.*

two portions: a single auricle, and a single ventricle. The blood that comes out of the ventricle goes to the gills, where it is spread out in a capillary bed and oxygenated. The oxygen-rich blood is then gathered into vessels which go to other parts of the body where a second capillary bed occurs, this time for the purpose of getting oxygen (and food) to all the tissues. After this, the blood is gathered into veins and taken back to the heart. In the diagram, oxygen-rich blood is indicated in color, oxygen-poor blood in black.

In the amphibians (Fig. 27-3*B*) the heart is a bit more complicated, having two auricles, but only one ventricle. Since the separation of oxygen-rich and oxygen-poor blood is far from perfect, there is a certain inefficiency in the system. Reptiles (Fig. 27-3*C*) carry the evolution of separate pulmonary and systemic systems

further; but not until we reach the mammals (Fig. 27-3*D*) is it complete.

Let us follow the blood through a mammalian heart. If we start with blood returning from the systemic capillaries by way of the large veins (the venae cavae), we find that the blood first goes to the **right auricle.** This chamber is so named (L. *auricle* – little ear) because externally it is an earlike flap appended to the rest of the heart (Fig. 27-2*B*). From the chamber of the auricle, the blood goes to the **right ventricle** and, from there, out the **pulmonary artery** to the lungs, where it flows through capillaries surrounding the alveoli. These capillaries unite to form veins, which unite repeatedly to form, finally, the **pulmonary vein,** which brings the blood back to the heart, this time to the left side, to the **left auricle.** From the left auricle it goes to the **left ventricle** and then out

A. FISH

B. AMPHIBIAN

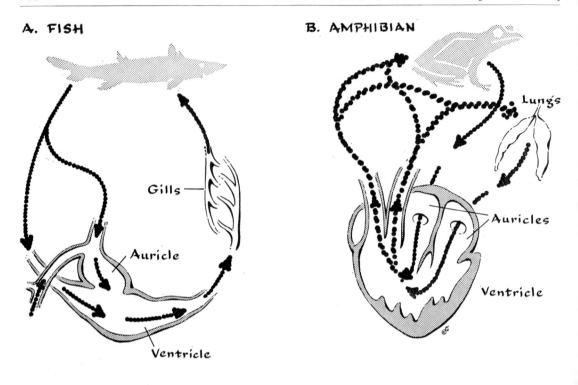

C. REPTILE

D. MAN

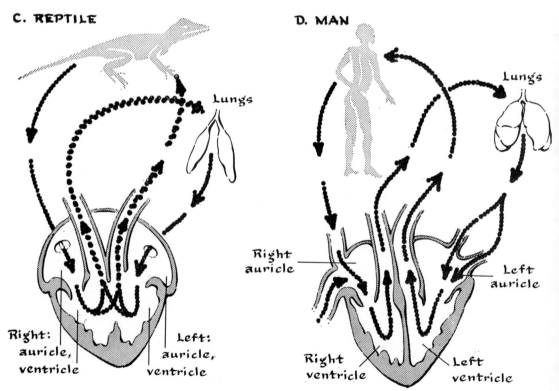

Fig. 27-3. *Detailed comparison of the hearts of four vertebrates.*

by way of the **aorta,** which supplies all the arteries of the body except those in the pulmonary circuit.

In the above account, the movement of blood was spoken of as though it occurred spontaneously. This is, of course, not the case. Blood is a passive fluid that must be moved. The principal moving force is the heart. The way in which the heart moves the blood can be understood by careful study of the series of diagrams in Figure 27-4. Contraction of the muscles of the heart reduces the volume of the chambers. Blood, like all fluids, is almost incompressible; hence, when the heart contracts, the blood must go somewhere. Where it goes is determined by the valves. It will be noted in the figure that each **valve** (L. leaf of a door) is so constructed that it permits passage of blood in only one direction. When the ventricles contract, for instance, the increased pressure of the blood closes the valves between the auricles and ventricles, thus preventing backflow of blood into the auricles. The valves leading to the pulmonary artery and the aorta are so arranged, however, that the same pressure opens them, thus permitting blood to flow out to the lungs and to the rest of the body. This phase of the heart's action, in which blood is forced out of the ventricles, is called **systole** (Gr. contraction). The opposite phase of the heart's action, in which relaxation of the heart muscle results in expansion of the chambers, is called **diastole** (Gr. expansion).

Most of the muscles and glands of the body are inactive unless stimulated by nerves or hormones. The heart, however, is a remarkable exception to this rule. When a living heart, removed from the body, is kept at normal temperature and is supplied with suitable food, it will continue to beat for a considerable time; clearly, it is not subjected to nervous or hormonal stimulation under these circumstances. The heart of a turtle, a "cold-blooded" animal, is especially hardy and can easily be kept beating for many hours after its removal from the body. Not only does the excised heart continue to contract, but—even more remarkable—its beat is regular. Close observation shows that the pattern of contraction is the same as that of an unexcised heart. Both the *automaticity* and the *rhythmicity* of the heart are *intrinsic.* This does *not* mean that the heart is indifferent to outside influences. In humans, sudden fear is accompanied by a marked slowing of the heartbeat, an effect caused by stimulation of the heart by certain nerves.

Observation shows that the heart does not contract all over at the same time; rather, a wave of contraction starting from one small area spreads throughout all the heart muscle. The area that contracts first is located near the junction of the systemic veins and the right auricle (Fig. 27-5). Depressant drugs or cold objects applied locally to other parts of the heart do not affect the rate of heartbeat; applied to the above-mentioned region, they cause the heart to beat more slowly. Because it determines the activity of the whole heart, this region is called the **pacemaker** of the heart.

We cannot but be impressed with the untiring character of the heart's activity. The heart be-

Fig. 27-4. *How contraction of the heart forces blood in one direction through it. Systole (contraction) begins in the auricles and spreads to the ventricles.*

 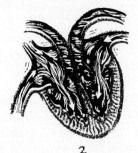

1 DIASTOLE   2   3 SYSTOLE

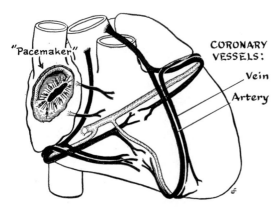

Fig. 27-5. *The heart has its own circulatory system. From the "pacemaker" region a wave of cardiac contraction spreads outward as the heart goes into systole.*

gins to beat, at first slowly and irregularly, eight months before birth, and continues beating until stopped in death, normally seventy or more years later. In the course of a long life the heart will beat 4,000 million times, more or less, depending on the activity of the individual. What remarkable muscle to be so untiring! Heart muscle is indeed a special kind of muscle, called *cardiac muscle.* In both structure and function it is intermediate between striated muscle and smooth muscle. Like the former, it must be able to contract and relax rapidly; also like skeletal muscle, it shows cross-striations. But the necessity of continuous functioning of the heart demands muscle that resembles smooth muscle in its ability to carry out long-sustained activities; microscopically, there is evidence that cardiac muscle is made up of single-nucleated cells, as is true of smooth muscle. The demand for *continual* activity is greater in the case of the heart than it is for any other organ; but its activity is not *continuous.* Although it beats without ceasing for a half-century or more, there is a very short pause between each two beats. During this fraction of a second the heart gets a momentary rest—and this is enough.

Cardiac muscle, like all the other tissues of the body, must be supplied with food and oxygen, and must be freed of wastes. These services must, of course, be performed by the blood

stream, and, as always, exchanges between circulatory system and body cells take place only in the neighborhood of capillaries. From this it follows that although many gallons of blood flow through the auricles and ventricles in a day, the blood in these great chambers furnishes the heart with no food at all. There are no small vessels to transport blood from the heart chambers to the heart muscle. Instead, there is a separate circulatory system (Fig. 27-5) for the heart muscle; this system is called the **coronary circuit** (L. *corona* = crown; perhaps applied in this case because the principal vessels encircle the heart like a crown). The principal arteries of this system, the right and left coronary arteries, branch off the aorta near its base and supply all the heart with blood. Like other circuits, this one consists of arteries-capillaries-veins. In keeping with its importance and great activity, *heart muscle is more richly supplied with capillaries than is any other tissue;* indeed, it is said that there is one capillary for every cardiac muscle fiber.

219. William Harvey and the Discovery of the Circulation

The story of the discovery of the circulation of the blood by William Harvey is worth recounting for the light it sheds on the problem of method in science. Harvey's great work, *On the Movement of the Heart and Blood in Animals,* was published, in Latin, in 1628. The chapters of this work are of uneven quality, but at their best they show a critical spirit that is completely modern.

In the birth of science, one of the major pains was that occasioned by the necessity of breaking free from the medieval tradition of reliance on authority. In the introduction to his work, Harvey remarks that no true lovers of learning are

so narrow-minded as to imagine any of the arts or sciences transmitted to us by the ancients, in such a state of forwardness or completeness, that nothing is left for the ingenuity and industry of others;

very many on the contrary maintain that all we know is still infinitely less than all that still remains unknown; nor do philosophers pin their faith to others' precepts in such wise that they lose their liberty, and cease to give credence to the conclusions of their proper senses. Neither do they swear such fealty to their mistress Antiquity, that they openly, and in sight of all, deny and desert their friend Truth. But even as they see that the credulous and vain are disposed at the first blush to accept and to believe everything that is proposed to them, so do they observe that the dull and unintellectual are indisposed to see what lies before their eyes, and even to deny the light of the noonday sun.

In studying the motion of the heart and blood, Harvey was hemmed in on all sides by authoritarian statements, particularly those of the Greek physician Galen (131–201 A.D.). Harvey's reaction to one of the beliefs perpetuated by Galen and his followers is clearly evident in the following passage:

The blood is supposed to ooze through tiny pores in the septum of the heart from the right to the left ventricle, while the air is drawn from the lungs by the large pulmonary vein. According to this many little openings exist in the septum of the heart suited to the passage of blood. But, damn it, no such pores exist, nor can they be demonstrated!

One looks in vain for such colorful language in modern works of science. Its presence in Harvey's work is understandable from a psychological point of view: Science, just breaking away from the principle of authority accepted in the Middle Ages, was in what we might call an adolescent stage of development. It exhibited some of the well-known symptoms of adolescence, such as that apparent in the passage just quoted.

In his investigation of the circulation of the blood, Harvey employed many lines of attack, which may be classified under four heads: simple observational studies, comparative studies, pathological studies, and quantitative (analytical) studies.

By direct and careful observation of the anatomy of the circulatory system, Harvey established, with a considerable degree of probability, the direction in which blood must flow. The arrangement of the valves in the heart indicates, to anyone analyzing the heart as a mechanism, the direction of flow within the heart. Similarly, as emphasized by Harvey in the preceding quotation, the evident solidity of the wall between the left and right sides of the heart argues against the possibility of a movement of blood directly from one side to the other. Moreover, in some of the veins of the body there are valves that indicate the direction of movement of blood.

But direct observation is sometimes insufficient to settle a disputed point. The exact mode of contraction of the heart—that is, the sequence of muscular contractions in the various parts—is difficult to determine in a rapidly beating heart. It can, however, be determined by carefully following the procedure used by Harvey:

When the chest of a living animal is opened . . . one may see that the heart alternates in movement and rest. There is a time when it moves, and a time when it is quiet.

This is more easily seen in the hearts of cold-blooded animals, as toads, snakes, frogs, snails, shellfish, crustaceans, and fish. It is also more apparent in other animals as the dog and pig, if one carefully observes the heart as it moves more slowly when about to die. The movement then becomes slower and weaker and the pauses longer, so that it is easy to see what the motion really is and how made. During a pause, the heart is soft, flaccid, exhausted, as in death.

Note that Harvey solved this difficult observational problem by using two sorts of material: various animals that lent themselves well to observation—the comparative approach; and the hearts of mammals nearing death—this one might call a pathological approach. In both cases the movement was slowed sufficiently to permit the observer to follow accurately the various movements. Of course, such studies would not, by themselves, establish the *normal* movements, but having worked out the sequence of events in unusual or abnormal hearts, Harvey was then able to verify the same sequence in normal mammalian hearts. Today we might achieve the same end by studying a "slow-motion movie."

The fourth type of investigation employed by Harvey, the quantitative, or perhaps we might better say the *analytical* method, is worth considering at some length. It was known in Harvey's day that the heart pumped blood, but it was not accepted that the blood flowed continuously in one direction, nor that it made a circuit of the body, the same blood circulating through the heart time after time. Rather, one of the most widely accepted theories was that blood was continuously formed anew from food supplied by the intestine, pumped through the heart and out to the extremities, there, presumably, to be soaked up by the tissues. That this could not be the true story was shown by Harvey by a few simple observations and a most ingenious argument. "Let us consider," said Harvey,

that the left ventricle of the heart when filled in diastole, contains two or three ounces, or only an ounce and a half. In a cadaver I have found it holding more than three ounces. Likewise let us consider how much less the ventricle contains when the heart contracts or how much blood it forces into the aorta with each contraction, for during systole, everyone will admit something is always forced out . . . and apparent from the structure of the valves. As a reasonable conjecture suppose a fourth, fifth, sixth, or even an eighth part is passed into the arteries. Then we may suppose in man that a single heart beat would force out either a half ounce, three drams, or even one dram of blood, which because of the valvular block could not flow back that way into the heart. . . .

So it may be inferred that if the heart in a single beat in man, sheep, or ox, pumps one dram, and there are 1,000 beats in half an hour, the total amount pumped in that time would be ten pounds five ounces; if two drams at a single stroke, then twenty pounds ten ounces; if half an ounce then forty-one pounds eight ounces; and if one ounce, then a total of eighty-three pounds four ounces, all

of which would be transferred from the veins to the arteries in half an hour. . . .

Suppose even the smallest amount of blood be transmitted through the lungs and heart at a single beat, a greater quantity would eventually be pumped into the arteries and the body than could be furnished by the food consumed, unless *by constantly making a circuit and returning*. [Italics added.]

Several aspects of this passage are worth emphasizing. Everyone nowadays knows that measurement is an important part of scientific activity, yet many nonscientists do not appreciate the value of making measurements. In the last analysis, measurements are not made for their own sake: their purpose is to determine facts—facts that can often be stated in nonquantitative terms. Notice that in the present instance the question was this: Is the blood continuously formed anew, or is the same blood pumped around and around the body? Notice that, as this question is worded, it contains no explicit references to quantities or to measurements. Yet Harvey showed how, by making a quantitative study, one could settle this qualitative point. Studies of this sort are now common in science, but Harvey's work is perhaps the first example of such an approach in the biological sciences.

Second, notice the method by which Harvey determined the quantities employed in his argument. He did not determine the quantity of blood pumped in a single beat of the heart with the greatest possible accuracy; rather, he used merely *reasonable estimates* and deduced the unavoidable conclusions. Since he did not want his argument invalidated by quibbling over the exact magnitude of the quantities, he minimized the error by making almost ridiculously conservative estimates, as is apparent in the passage: ". . . we may suppose in man that a single heart beat would force out either a half ounce, three drams, or even one dram of blood . . ."

The reader must not suppose that all scientific arguments can be settled by using estimates as crude as Harvey's. As science has matured and the simpler questions have been settled, greater and greater accuracy has been needed to settle more difficult questions.

Harvey did not completely prove the circulation of the blood. To him is due the honor for developing this conceptual scheme, and he showed how it was the only scheme that fit the known facts reasonably well. He did not, however, observationally prove the complete circuit of the blood. Although the compound microscope had been invented a generation earlier, it had not yet seen significant use in biology, nor did Harvey use it; thus he failed to discover the capillaries, which complete the chain of anatomical elements involved in the circulation of blood. These vessels were discovered in 1660 by the Italian Marcello Malpighi, shortly after the death of William Harvey. Malpighi first saw capillaries in the lung of a frog. Even today we use this animal to demonstrate capillary circulation in the laboratory, usually using either the web of the foot or a fold of *mesentery,* the very thin tissue that suspends the gut from the dorsal wall.

220. The Coagulation of Blood

Blood may be said to be composed of two parts: a liquid portion called **blood plasma,** or *plasma,* in which are suspended various microscopically visible bodies called **formed elements.** The formed elements include red blood cells, white blood cells, and blood platelets, which will be discussed presently. Whole blood is about 80 percent water and 18 percent proteins plus 2 percent of various other dissolved chemicals.

One of the most important of the properties of blood is its ability to *clot,* or **coagulate,** that is, to turn from a liquid to a firm solid. A few minutes after normal blood is shed from a blood vessel, it clots. Clotting at the site of the wound closes the opening and prevents further loss of blood. Were it not for this property of blood, the slightest wound might result in death. This danger is a very real one for certain rare individuals who suffer from a disease known

as **hemophilia** (Gr. *hemo* = blood + *philos* = loving). The blood of hemophiliacs, though it will clot, clots so slowly that even a tiny cut constitutes a threat to life.

On the other hand, it is equally important that blood not clot while still within a vessel. Under abnormal circumstances, blood may clot, forming a plug, or **thrombus** (Gr. from *trepho* = thicken), locally stopping the flow of blood. The resultant condition is known as **thrombosis** (the Greek suffix *—osis* indicates much, i.e., too much). If a clot is carried around in the blood stream and lodges in a vessel distant from its site of formation, it is called an **embolus** (Gr. plug). The seriousness of thrombosis or **embolism** depends on the vessels plugged. Coronary thrombosis may cause immediate death.

The importance of clotting has stimulated research into the mechanism of the process. The principal and more easily understood facts now known are presented below.

First of all, it is important to realize that the entire blood does not solidify. This can be shown by vigorously stirring some freshly drawn blood with, say, broomstraws. In a few minutes the broomstraws will be covered with a solid, rubbery material. If the stirring is vigorous enough and sufficiently prolonged, all the clottable material will be gathered onto the stirrers. The remainder of the blood, still red, remains fluid indefinitely. The clotted material is called **fibrin** because it appears to be a mass of interwoven fibers; the fluid residue is called **defibrinated** blood.

Fibrin is a protein. It has been shown that this insoluble protein is not present, *as such*, in the blood stream, but rather that there is normally present another protein, only a little different from it chemically, but soluble in blood. Since, under certain circumstances, it gives rise to fibrin, it is called **fibrinogen** (*fibrin* × Gr. *genos* = race, kind, descent; hence, that which gives rise to). So we may write:

$$\text{fibrinogen} \xrightarrow{\text{(under certain circumstances)}} \text{fibrin.} \quad (2)$$

But what makes the fibrinogen turn to fibrin? It does not normally do so, or clots would occur

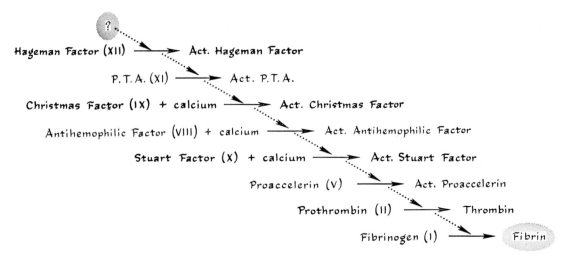

Fig. 27-6. *Tentative scheme of the mechanisms involved in blood clotting. Act. = activated; P.T.A. = plasma thromboplastin antecedent. Clotting factors are sometimes referred to by their Roman numerals, indicated in parentheses. Dotted arrows indicate variable influence, not always well known. (After E. W. Davie and O. D. Ratnoff, Science (1965) 145:1311.)*

in the intact circulatory system at any time. Something must "set off" reaction 2. It has been found that another substance, **thrombin,** acts as a stimulus to set off the reaction. We can amend the above equation as follows:

$$\text{thrombin \& fibrinogen} \longrightarrow \text{fibrin.} \quad (3)$$

The reaction between thrombin and fibrinogen is probably not a simple addition of one to the other in the sense that iron + oxygen $\longrightarrow$ iron oxide. Thrombin modifies fibrinogen in such a way that fibrin is produced; at the end of the reaction, thrombin or some derivative of it may be left over. In other words, Equation 3 is not a complete or exact chemical equation. To indicate this fact, the two reactants are connected by an ampersand (&) rather than by the conventional plus (+).

But where does the thrombin come from? By the argument used before, it cannot be present as such in the blood stream, or the blood would spontaneously coagulate. Experiments have shown that thrombin is indeed normally absent, but that there is present a *precursor* (L. *prae* = before + *curro* = run), called **prothrombin,** from which thrombin is derived. That is:

$$\text{prothrombin} \longrightarrow \text{thrombin.} \quad (4)$$

The pattern of experimental findings begins to emerge: step by step we find an additional link to the reaction chain. A scheme embodying most of the information now known is shown in Figure 27-6. The names "Hageman," "Christmas," and "Stuart" are the surnames of patients in whom the particular clotting defects were first found, i.e., Mr. Christmas lacked the Christmas factor. The exact role played by the product at one level in bringing about the reaction at the next lower level varies and is not always well known; this variable relationship is indicated by the dotted arrows.

It will be noted that calcium takes part in several reactions. A most important source of this is **blood platelets,** tiny bodies present in the blood; these disintegrate following **hemorrhage** (loss of blood from blood vessels) releasing calcium, and perhaps other clotting factors. But why do they disintegrate? That's another problem! The scheme shown in Figure 27-6 surely cannot be part of an indefinite regress, but we do not yet know the entire chain of factors and reactions. However, even our partial knowledge has helped somewhat in the control of hemorrhage in abnormal conditions.

For example, we know that the fat-soluble substance **vitamin K** is required for the synthesis of prothrombin by the body. When the bile duct is obstructed by gallstones, bile does not get into the intestine; hence, fats are incompletely digested; hence, vitamin K is not released from the food to be absorbed by the body. As a result, the patient's blood does not coagulate readily, and an operation performed to remove the offending gallstones is doubly dangerous. The danger can be decreased by giving the patient extra vitamin K before the operation.

In recent years the technique of blood transfusion has been developed to such a high degree that it is now possible to store human blood in "blood banks" for use in transfusions as needed. Even under the best conditions of storage, blood can be kept for only a few weeks. Fortunately, over-age blood need not be wasted, for from it can be separated many medically useful materials. Thrombin extracted from blood is widely used in surgery to bring about the clotting of blood at cut surfaces. The thrombin is frequently applied by means of a sponge made of blood fibrin. Such a sponge, composed entirely of natural materials, can safely be left in the body at the conclusion of an operation, for it will eventually be dissolved and absorbed into the patient's system.

221. The Role of Erythrocytes

One of the principal functions of the blood is the transport of oxygen to all parts of the body. Oxygen is soluble in water and watery solutions like blood. However, it can be shown that a given volume of arterial blood contains many times as much oxygen as can be dissolved in a corresponding volume of water. The great oxygen-carrying capacity of blood is due to the presence of the chemical substance **hemoglobin**, which is contained in the **red blood cells**, or **erythrocytes** (Gr. *erythros* = red). Hemoglobin gives blood its red color. Hemoglobin is a protein that has a remarkable ability to form a loose combination with oxygen. If we symbolize the substance hemoglobin by Hb, we may

indicate the formation of *oxyhemoglobin* thus:

$$Hb + O_2 \longrightarrow HbO_2. \tag{5}$$

But the oxyhemoglobin thus formed can easily decompose into the separate constituents again, thus:

$$Hb + O_2 \longleftarrow HbO_2. \tag{6}$$

In other words, we are dealing here with a **reversible reaction**—a fact that we can indicate by combining Equations 5 and 6 in writing:

$$Hb + O_2 \rightleftharpoons HbO_2. \tag{7}$$

In any reversible reaction, *both reactions are taking place all the time.* Which one takes place to the greater extent? This depends on circumstances. If O_2 is being supplied from outside the reaction system, the rate at which HbO_2 is being formed will exceed the rate at which it is being broken down—a fact that we can indicate by modifying the relative length of the arrows, thus:

$$Hb + O_2 \rightleftharpoons HbO_2. \tag{8}$$

On the other hand, if oxygen is being removed from the reaction system, oxyhemoglobin will be broken up faster than it will be formed:

$$Hb + O_2 \rightleftharpoons HbO_2. \tag{9}$$

With these basic facts in mind, we are in a position to understand how the hemoglobin-containing erythrocytes transport oxygen from the lungs to the respiring tissues of the body. In the first part of the process, the alveoli of the lungs give up oxygen to the blood stream flowing in the surrounding capillaries. As an aid in visualizing this process, Figure 27-7 is presented. Since the blood being brought to the lung capillaries is relatively poor in oxygen, the net movement of oxygen molecules is from alveolar space to capillary blood. The transfer of oxygen would come to an end much sooner were it not for the fact that reaction 10,

$$Hb + O_2 \rightleftharpoons HbO_2, \tag{10}$$

takes place continuously as oxygen is supplied. This reaction occurs inside the erythrocyte, for that is where the hemoglobin is. As it occurs, more oxygen diffuses from the blood plasma in-

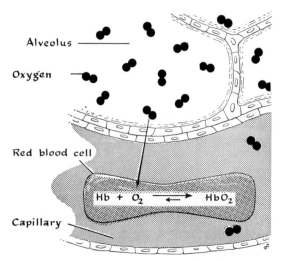

Fig. 27-7. *How oxygen gets from the outside to the erythrocytic hemoglobin, with which it combines chemically.*

to the erythrocyte, thus lowering the concentration of oxygen molecules in the plasma, thus permitting more transfer of oxygen from alveolus to blood capillary. This process continues until the hemoglobin of the red blood cells is saturated with O_2, or until the flow of blood carries the red blood cells beyond the capillaries (into which diffusion from alveoli can take place) into the first small veins (where it cannot). It should be noted that most of the oxygen carried by the blood is carried in chemical combination with hemoglobin rather than in simple solution in the plasma. It has been calculated that if it were not for this chemical transport, the human body would require about 75 times as much blood.

The oxygenated blood in pulmonary veins ultimately reaches the left auricle of the heart, from where it goes to the left ventricle and out by way of the aorta into various arteries of the systemic circulation. In none of these vessels is there any loss of oxygen; not until the blood reaches the capillaries are the vessel walls thin enough to permit diffusion between blood and the surrounding tissues. In the region of the systemic capillaries, the processes previously described in the lung capillaries again take place, *but in the reverse direction.* Recall that the

process of respiration takes place in all cells; this process will lower the concentration of O_2 molecules within the cells. Using Figure 27-8 as a visual aid, picture the resulting net movement of O_2 molecules into the cells from the fluid that surrounds them—a fluid called *lymph,* which will be discussed further in §224. The lowering of the concentration of O_2 molecules in the lymph brings about a transfer, by diffusion, of such molecules from the blood plasma through the capillary walls into the lymph. As O_2 molecules are removed from the plasma, they diffuse from red blood cells to plasma, and within the erythrocytes, reaction 11 takes place:

$$Hb + O_2 \rightleftarrows HbO_2. \qquad (11)$$

Respiration produces CO_2, which must be removed from the tissues. The sequence of events involved in the movement of CO_2 from systemic tissues to alveoli is approximately the same as that just described for O_2 though the direction of transfer is reversed. There is, in addition, a quantitative difference in the mechanisms: although CO_2 is capable of forming a loose chemical compound with hemoglobin, only about 10 percent of the CO_2 carried by the blood is in the form of this compound; the remainder of the CO_2 is carried in the blood plasma.

Fig. 27-8. *How the red blood cells give up their oxygen to the metabolizing cells of the body.*

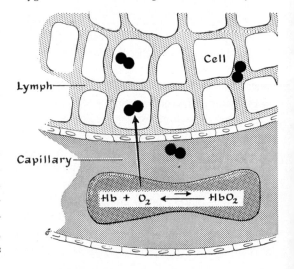

Of great importance is the chemical combination of hemoglobin with **carbon monoxide** (CO). This substance is a normal product of the incomplete oxidation of organic material. Unlike O_2 and CO_2, carbon monoxide forms an irreversible combination with hemoglobin, thus preventing it from functioning as an oxygen carrier. Asphyxiation by inhalation of the exhaust fumes of an automobile in a closed garage is not uncommon. Less well known is the fact that the CO content of cigarette smoke may, in a heavy smoker, combine with as much as 5 percent of his hemoglobin.

222. The Manufacture of Erythrocytes

For convenience in discussion, we have separated the body into "systems"; but such separation is artificial, for the systems interact and interpenetrate in various ways. A good example of such an interrelationship is found in the origin of the erythrocytes. These characteristic blood cells are formed in the marrow of the long bones of the body. Bone marrow of freshly killed animals, especially young animals, is decidedly red because of the great stores of erythrocytes in all stages of formation. The red bone marrow is the only place in the body where red blood cells are formed; hence anything that injures the bone marrow affects the blood system. Salts of the "heavy metals," for example, lead, mercury, and radium, when taken into the body, accumulate in the bone marrow and seriously interfere with the formation of erythrocytes. Heavy metals are easily deposited in the bone marrow but can be removed only with difficulty. As a consequence, continual exposure to nonlethal concentrations of these substances may result in their accumulation in the bone marrow until they reach lethal concentration; heavy metals are **cumulative poisons.** An environmental concentration of a substance that may be harmless for a month or year may kill a man after 10 or 20 (or more) years' exposure. One can readily appreciate the difficulty of defining "safe working conditions"

in an industry in which the use of such substances is unavoidable.

Mature erythrocytes in humans and other mammals—as opposed to those in frogs and other amphibia—have no nuclei. They are incapable of reproduction. Because they are therefore not typical cells, many workers prefer to call them red blood *corpuscles*. Within the bone marrow, however, may be found similar bodies that *do* possess nuclei, and research leaves no reasonable doubt that erythrocytes are derived from these nucleated cells, which are called **erythroblasts** (Gr. *blastos* = a germ, bud; immature cells, from which mature ones are derived, are frequently identified by the suffix –*blast*). Erythroblasts are capable of dividing; some of the daughter cells perpetuate the erythroblast line, while others lose their nuclei by degeneration and become erythrocytes. Normally, only the latter are released into the blood stream.

Human erythrocytes vary little from a diameter of 7.6 microns—a fact worth remembering as a means of estimating the size of other cells seen in the same field under a microscope. (Ellipsoidal frog erythrocytes have a greatest diameter of about 20μ.) The number of red blood corpuscles per cubic millimeter is about 5 million in men, about 10 percent less in women. This number is fairly constant. New corpuscles are being continuously formed in the bone marrow, while old ones are continually being removed. How long does an erythrocyte last? Various means have been developed for attacking this problem, the most accurate of which is probably the tagged-atom method (§31). When humans are fed the amino acid glycine, containing labeled nitrogen, the erythrocytes subsequently formed contain these labeled atoms. The rate of disappearance of the labeled erythrocytes indicates that the *average* life span of a red blood corpuscle is about 120 days.

Aged erythrocytes are engulfed and destroyed by special cells called **macrophages** that are found in great abundance in the **spleen,** an organ near the stomach. This organ thus acts as an "erythrocyte wrecking-yard."

223. The Response to Low Oxygen

The breathing system readily makes adjustments to an increase in carbon dioxide in the blood stream, and somewhat less readily and less reliably to a decrease in oxygen. The responses are slowly made and do not much ameliorate a condition of **acute hypoxia** (i.e., a suddenly developing condition of low oxygen supply), but are of appreciable aid in **chronic hypoxia*** (i.e., hypoxia that endures for a considerable time).

Following a hemorrhage, the spleen, which is a highly distensible organ, contracts to release its store of blood. (In the cat, as much as one-sixth of the blood may be stored in the spleen.) If this maneuver fails to raise the O_2 concentration sufficiently, another, and slower reaction may set in: the red bone marrow is stimulated to release erythrocytes at a faster than normal rate; even some nucleated cells, the erythroblasts, may be released, resulting in a condition known as **erythroblastosis.** This condition is easily determined by a microscopic examination of the blood; appearance of nucleated red cells in a blood preparation is, in fact, evidence of present or recent hypoxic conditions. Such a response may be occasioned by a low oxygen concentration in the surrounding atmosphere, as at high altitudes; or by **anemia,** a lack of sufficient hemoglobin, due either to a low concentration of normal red blood cells or to low concentration of hemoglobin within the erythrocytes; or by hemorrhage. Erythroblastosis is an adaptive response that may, if not too long continued, enable the organism to survive abnormal conditions.

The mechanisms involved in the permanent and useful adjustment of humans to the low oxygen conditions of high elevations are still incompletely known. Many who can survive at high altitudes cannot, apparently, achieve a life of normal vigor under these conditions. Great individual differences exist. Studies made of some South American Indians who, for generations, have performed hard work in mines at an elevation of more than 5,000 meters, indicate that they habitually breathe more deeply than do sea-level men, and that they have 38 percent more erythrocytes per unit volume of blood and 30 percent greater volume of blood, thus increasing the total amount of hemoglobin in the body by 80 percent.

224. Lymph

All the cells of the body are bathed by a fluid called **lymph.** Exchanges between blood and cells, as described in §221, always take place via this fluid. It is the true environment of the cells. We may accurately call it the *internal environment* of the body, to use the inspired combination of contradictory terms coined by the French physiologist Claude Bernard (1813–1878).

Lymph is derived from blood. Blood, under pressure, constantly loses some of its fluid through the walls of the capillaries. This fluid has substantially the composition of plasma but is called lymph. The principal difference between the two is in the protein content; lymph has only about half as much protein.

What is the ultimate fate of lymph? Surprisingly enough, it has a sort of circulation of its own. It has not a completely closed system like the blood, but it includes definite vessels of its own, though many of them are hard to find. The general path of lymph is this: The substances that make up lymph are filtered through the walls of the capillaries into the intercellular spaces where the lymph moves somewhat at random among the cells, ultimately coming to flow in tiny channels called **lymphatic vessels,** or simply **lymphatics.** Lymphatics unite with one another, and ultimately with blood vessels (veins), thus returning their materials to the general circulatory system. There is no heart to move the lymph; its movements are principally due to the squeezing action of the adjacent muscular tissues. Lymphatic circulation is, consequently, slow and uncertain; exercise increases it.

---

* 27-3. The Greek *hypo* means under, and is hence used to indicate the subnormal; *oxia* here refers to oxygen. An older term for hypoxia is "anoxia." Why is this older term less apt?

Lymph is formed by a filtration process in which the pressure involved is blood pressure and the filter is the wall of the capillary. Normally, the rate of formation is equal to the rate of return to the blood stream, but the equilibrium is sometimes upset. When the formation rate exceeds the return rate, the increased volume of fluid around the cells creates a puffiness called "dropsy" or **edema** (Gr. swelling). The immediate cause of the condition may be any of several: increased capillary pressure, increased permeability of the capillary walls, or decreased rate of return of lymph due to increased pressure of blood in the veins. The permeability of capillaries to passage of fluids is especially easily altered. For instance, the bacteria in an infected wound apparently release chemicals that increase the permeability of the capillaries in that region, resulting in local swelling. Even a noninfected, but injured, tissue may somehow affect capillary permeability; anyone who has "caught" a baseball on the end of his finger can

Fig. 27-9. *The products of fat digestion enter the body by way of lymph vessels called lacteals. The lymph ultimately joins the blood stream via the thoracic duct. The products of carbohydrate and protein digestion enter the blood stream directly, going into blood vessels which enter the liver via the hepatic portal vein.*

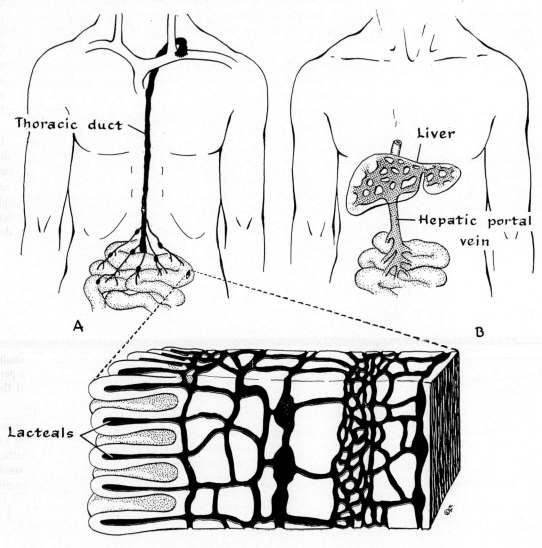

vouch for this. These are both examples of local alteration of capillary permeability. A general alteration may also occur, for instance in "starvation edema," or "prison-camp edema," in which the underfed victim develops a deceptively bloated appearance, the exact cause of which is not known, although it is clearly the result of inadequate cellular nutrition.

225. The Transport of Food and Wastes

Recall that food absorbed through the intestinal wall passes into two different circulatory systems: the products of fat digestion go into lacteals (part of the lymphatic system); the products of protein and carbohydrate digestion pass into the blood system.

The lacteals from the intestine come together to form larger vessels, the ultimate vessel being a large lymphatic called the **thoracic duct,** which pours its products into one of the large veins near the heart (Fig. 27-9A). Fats are carried in the blood stream principally as microscopic globules suspended in the blood.

The route followed by the products of protein and carbohydrate digestion is different. These products are absorbed directly into blood vessels. These blood vessels unite (Fig. 27-9B)

to form the **hepatic portal vein,** which subdivides into capillaries in the liver. The chemical composition of blood from the intestine is considerably altered in the liver. A large fraction of the carbohydrates is stored as glycogen ("animal starch") by the liver. Various natural but toxic (poisonous) products of protein digestion are changed by the liver into nontoxic substances. This detoxifying action is one of the important functions of the liver.

The exchange of molecules of foodstuffs between blood and tissues is brought about by the same processes of random molecular motion, governed by the same principles of probability (Chap. 3) that govern exchanges of O_2 and CO_2 between blood plasma and cells. The utilization of foodstuffs by cells in the process of respiration decreases the concentration of food molecules in the cells relative to that in the blood, thus causing a diffusion of molecules of foodstuff from blood plasma to lymph to body cells.

In cellular metabolism there are produced, in addition to the H_2O and CO_2 indicated in the conventional equation of respiration, a number of other waste products, for example, various organic nitrogen wastes. These diffuse through the lymph to the blood plasma, from which they are later removed by means that are described in Chapter 31.

Questions and Problems

27-4. Make a list of the **boldface** terms in this chapter and write a brief description or definition of each. Compare your work with the text.

27-5. Write out a brief description of the work of the following men, with the approximate dates: Bernard, Harvey, Malpighi.

27-6. Trace the course of blood through the mammalian heart.

‡27-7. During prenatal life, the human heart has an opening between the two auricles. Oc-

casionally, this opening persists into adulthood. What effect would you expect this persistence to have on the athletic abilities of the individual? Explain in detail.

27-8. Blood flow, like all flow of liquids in pipes, has to work against resistance. Drawing on common knowledge, can you predict whether the resistance would be greater in the small vessels or in the large? When the capillaries are partially constricted, does the heart have to work harder, or not as hard, in order to force blood around the system at the same rate?

27-9. The right side of the heart is not as large and muscular as the left side. Assuming that each side is as powerful as it needs to be, can you suggest a reason for this difference?

27-10. By definition, venous blood is blood poor in oxygen. Name an artery that carries venous blood and a vein that carries arterial blood.

‡27-11. The volume of blood in an adult human amounts to about 5 liters. From this fact and others mentioned in the text, it is possible to calculate the approximate number of erythrocytes destroyed per day. How many are destroyed per second? Where are they destroyed?

27-12. How many red blood cells are formed per second? Where are they formed?

27-13. If blood contained no hemoglobin, how great would the volume of blood have to be, in an adult man, in order to carry as much oxygen as the present volume of normal blood carries? Would this volume suffice for the transport of CO_2?

‡27-14. The coach catches one of his runners puffing furiously on a cigarette just before a race, and rebukes him. "Oh, it's all right," the runner replies: "These cigarettes won't hurt me—they've been de-nicotinized." Should the coach be concerned?

27-15. In the Antarctic Ocean there are several species of fish 2 feet in length or less which do not have erythrocytes, hemoglobin, or any other blood pigment. The oxygen-carrying capacity of their blood is only about 12 percent that of the blood of comparable fish with erythrocytes. What rational connection do you see between their size, their geographic location, and their physiology?

†27-16. Leonardo da Vinci "saw" the tiny pores in the septum of the heart that Harvey denied —saw them and sketched them. How could so excellent an artist and observer do this? What relevance does this have to your own experiences in the biology laboratory?

27-17. The citrate ion of sodium citrate has the ability to combine with calcium ions so that they are not available for other reactions. Sodium citrate is routinely added to the blood that is being transferred from one person to another. Why?

27-18. When sweet clover spoils, it sometimes produces a substance known as *dicumarol*. If cattle eat this, they develop a disease known as "spoiled sweet clover disease." Dicumarol apparently prevents the synthesis of prothrombin. What are the consequences of this action?

27-19. Laws regarded as sacred by orthodox Jews dictate that all male children shall be circumcised on the eighth day after birth. We now know that the level of prothrombin in the blood is much higher at 8 days than at birth. (a) Is the Hebrew practice defensible on scientific grounds? (b) Do you think scientific facts account for the religious practice? Justify your conclusions.

27-20. For many years, hemophilia was known only in humans. In recent years, this hereditary disease has also been found in dogs. How should this recent discovery aid in elucidating the physiological cause of hemophilia? Would this discovery be of any value in a society that forbade experimentation with nonhuman animals?

27-21. The rise of science in the past three centuries has been attended by some opposition to the scientific attitude. Wordsworth, for instance, ridiculed the investigative spirit thus, in "A Poet's Epitaph":

> *Physician art thou? one, all eyes,*
> *Philosopher! a fingering slave,*
> *One that would peep and botanize*
> *Upon his mother's grave?*

Opposition to certain modes of study has sometimes cropped up even in the ranks of scientists. For instance, the biologist who coined the term "tissue," M. F. X. Bichat (1771–1802), remarked that it is permissible to calculate the return of a comet, the resistance of a fluid moving in a tube, the velocity of a projectile, etc.; but to calculate (with Borelli) the force of a muscle, or (with Keil) the velocity of blood, or (with Jurine, Lavoisier, and others) the quantity of air entering the lungs is to build on quicksand. Intrinsically solid though the edifice may be, it soon tumbles for want of a solid foundation.

In the light of a particular example presented in this chapter, what general criticism may be made of Bichat's position?

Readings

Few classical reports of scientific discoveries reveal the methods of science as well as Harvey's *De Motu Cordis*. Fortunately, there is available an excellent translation from the original Latin, from which the passages in this chapter were quoted with the permission of the translator, Dr. Leake, and the publisher, Charles C. Thomas. Brief selec-tions from Harvey may also be found in Moulton and Schifferes, Boynton, and Fulton. In Chapters 2 and 3 of the latter book may be found also reprints of other original reports in the field of circulation, including works by Malpighi, van Leeuwenhoek, and Stephen Hales.

28 The Endocrine Organs

226. Limitations of Analysis and Exposition

Proficiency in any skill can never reach the highest level until the performer comes to understand the limitations of the tools he uses. Learning is a skill. One of the limitations of the learning process is that it occurs seriatim, whereas the world on which it is focused is generally arranged otherwise. Learning takes time, and so we learn a-b-c-d . . . which may produce misconceptions, if the facts are really part of a complex in three or more dimensions. A-b-c-d . . . that's one dimension. A graph or a diagram has two dimensions. A plaster model has three dimensions. Three dimensions may be called to mind by a two-dimensional picture addressed to a viewer who accepts the *conventions* of perspective drawing. But the realities of physiology involve usually a minimum of four dimensions, the fourth being time. Seriatim exposition, graphs, and perspective drawing are not enough; the student must also have a memory! That is, he must have a memory that is *productive,* one that has a "scanner" which never ceases to go over old material, so that while reading Chapter X he suddenly recalls and sees the significance of something he read in Chapter X-minus-2, which he then retrieves and fits into the jigsaw puzzle being created by Chapter X.

Nowhere are the above remarks more rele- vant than in the consideration of the activities of the **endocrine glands** (the organs that produce hormones), the *glands of internal secretion.* Hormones are secreted into the blood stream and go to all parts of a three-dimensional body; their effects are spread over the fourth dimension, time. Frequently they set in train another series of reactions of some completely different system, say, the nervous system, which will in turn affect still another. In fact, the system of the body is similar to the ecological system subsumed in the concept of the "Web of Life" (§102); the interrelationships of parts are so complex that when we interfere with it we find we can never do merely one thing—which presents serious, though not insurmountable, barriers to intelligent action.

227. The Integration of Functions

The integration of the activities of the various parts of the animal body is brought about by two systems: the nervous system and the endocrine system (operating through the circulatory system, usually*). Of these the endocrine system is probably the more primitive. Certainly it is if we apply the name hormone to any substance produced by one part of an organism that

---

* 28-1. Why "usually"? What would characterize endocrine action in an organism without a circulatory system?

affects the metabolism of another. In this broad sense, one might say that the nucleus has an endocrine function: it produces RNA which passes out into the cytoplasm (which is another part of the organism we call a cell). However, this unconventional view is not particularly useful. We are more interested in those multicellular organs that are specialized to produce hormones, or internal secretions, that is, substances that are liberated into the body (blood stream) rather than to the exterior. (There is, however, nothing to forbid an organ—for example, the pancreas—to be a gland of both internal and external † secretion.)

One of the remarkable things about hormones is their evolutionary stability. The insulins secreted by man, horse, and cow are chemically distinguishable, but their differences are less remarkable than their similarities. Experimentally, they are almost completely interchangeable—which is fortunate for man. Thousands of diabetics are kept alive by the pancreas extracts of hundreds of thousands of cows.

"Endocrine evolution," P. B. Medawar has said, "is not an evolution of hormones but an evolution of the uses to which they are put; an evolution not, to put it crudely, of chemical formulae but of reactivities, reaction patterns and tissue competencies." The thyroid hormone of the frog is, chemically at least, approximately the same as that of man. But the frog tadpole has evolved a sensitivity that causes the tadpole gills and tail to be resorbed in the presence of large amounts of this hormone—a reaction system that would hardly be appropriate to *Homo sapiens*.

The principal endocrine glands of vertebrates are shown in Figure 28-1, with the human body as a backdrop. Some of these organs and their functions have been known since antiquity. The **gonads,** for example, have been known for thousands of years as great influencers of behavior. The castration (removal of the testicles, the male gonads) of male farm animals as a

† 28-2. The internal secretion of the pancreas is insulin; what are the substances externally secreted? Justify your answer.

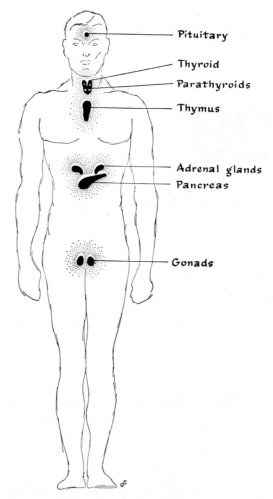

Fig. 28-1. *The principal endocrine glands of the human body.*

means of gentling and fattening them is perhaps the oldest surgical operation practiced by man. By contrast, the existence and significance of the **adrenals** were harder to discover: it is noteworthy that Vesalius' remarkably accurate figures of the human body do not include these inconspicuous organs.

Roughly, we may say that a hormone may act in one of two ways. *First,* it may stimulate another organ, performing the sort of action one would expect of the nervous system, though in not quite so rapid a manner. Secretin acts in this way, stimulating the pancreas to activity. It seems that the epithelium of the duodenum secretes another similar hormone, **cholecysto-**

kinin, which causes the gall bladder to release its stored bile into the intestinal cavity.

A more widespread stimulatory effect is exerted by the *adrenalines,* secretions of the **adrenal medulla,** the central portion of each adrenal gland (L. *medulla* = marrow, pith, hence center). Two kinds of adrenal medulla secretion have been identified: **adrenaline,** in the narrow sense, and a slightly different compound **nor-adrenaline.** Both cause profound changes in all parts of the body. Adrenaline causes a release of glycogen from the liver, expansion of blood vessels in the heart, brain, and limbs, and contraction of vessels in the abdomen. It diminishes fatigue, speeds blood coagulation, and causes the spleen to release its stores of blood. To generalize, it may be said that adrenaline mobilizes the body for an emergency, such as the sudden appearance of an enemy.

Nor-adrenaline has only one important primary effect: it stimulates the contraction of small blood vessels, thus increasing resistance to flow of blood. The two forms of adrenaline occur in various proportions in different species, even in different individuals within a species, and some generalizations can be made about the variations. Nor-adrenaline is relatively high in aggressive animals such as lions, young humans, and paranoid adult humans—that is, individuals who react to threats (real or imaginary) by hating. The secretion of adrenaline, on the other hand, is more characteristic of timid animals such as rabbits, and social animals such as baboons, and "mature" human beings. Humans suffering from depression or anxiety may produce a still higher concentration of adrenaline.

In addition to their role as activators, some hormones may (*second*) furnish substances that play fundamental roles in the metabolic activities of other parts of the body. A hormone may act either as one of the reactants in a metabolic reaction, or (more likely) as an enzyme or a part of an enzyme in the reaction. This type of hormonal function seems to be the more common. It is a matter of common knowledge today that a secretion of the **thyroid gland,** the substance **thyroxin,** increases the metabolic ac-

tivities of all parts of the body. Many other hormones are known to play an important or even vital role in metabolism, in growth, and in reproduction. The effects of such hormones, as contrasted with those of the first group, appear only slowly, typically after several days, and are long sustained.

The action of individual hormones is often difficult to deduce because of the complex interactions of hormones. There are a number of endocrine cybernetic systems that maintain remarkably stable conditions in the body. One such system is shown in Figure 28-2, which follows the type of analysis developed in Chapter 8. As can be seen, stability in thyroid activity is maintained by a negative feedback system that involves the anterior lobe of the pituitary gland which secretes a **thyrotrophic hormone.**

228. The Methods of Studying Hormones

How can one prove the existence of a hormone—how prove that an organ liberates into the blood stream a substance that affects other parts of the body? Or that some substance found in the blood stream is produced by a particular organ? There is no one method that works in all cases, but several different methods of attack are used, either separately or together, in studying the problems of **endocrinology,** the science that deals with hormones and endocrine glands. For convenience, the methods of study may be separated into the following categories:

1. EXTIRPATION STUDIES. If a certain gland produces a particular hormone that causes certain effects, removal of the gland should be followed by a disappearance of the effects. It is obvious that this type of study cannot be carried out if a presumptive endocrine organ is vital for other reasons: The liver, for instance, is suspected of producing one or more hormones, but extirpation of this organ is followed by immediate death. Extirpation experiments may also fail to enlighten if a hormone is, unsuspected by the experimenter, produced by more than one gland.

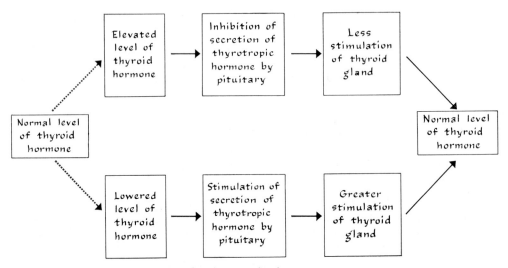

Fig. 28-2. *Cybernetic control of the thyroid gland.*

2. "CHEMICAL SURGERY." A substance called **thiouracil** interferes with the function of the thyroid gland, preventing it from synthesizing thyroxin. Administering thiouracil (or any of a number of chemically related compounds) has the effect of extirpating the gland without surgery. Such a procedure is particularly valuable in thyroid study, because there are often small islands of this tissue scattered throughout the chest region, in addition to the standard glands placed properly according to the diagram.

3. REPLACEMENT STUDIES. An experiment involving extirpation alone is subject to the criticism that it includes no adequate control. It might always be objected that it was not the disappearance of the gland that caused the subsequent effects but that it was the operation itself. An adequate control to an extirpation experiment may be had by putting the gland back into some of the animals from whom it was removed, though not necessarily in the same anatomical site. If the gland is truly one of internal secretion, it will still be able to exert its effect from an abnormal site, provided it establishes adequate connections with the blood system.

4. INJECTION OF EXTRACTS. One need not necessarily replace the old endocrine gland—in

fact, to make the proof more complete, it is desirable that there be extracted from the gland something that produces the same effect as the whole gland, when this portion is injected into experimental animals. This something is best a pure chemical substance, but to bring the proof to this stage of completion requires a considerable development of the related science of biochemistry. This stage is usually achieved only after much study of a hormone. In most extract studies, the extract must be injected directly into the blood stream, for seldom will the active chemical survive the action of the digestive juices. Thyroid extract, which may be taken by mouth, is a remarkable exception to the general rule.

5. PARABIOSIS STUDIES. That lactation—the secretion of milk—is under hormonal control was demonstrated a long time ago by the experience of two Bohemian sisters, Rosa and Josepha Blazek. These girls were Siamese twins; that is, they were born with their bodies partially fused. One of them, Rosa, became pregnant and bore a child. Following this, both Rosa and Josepha produced milk. Since there was no indication of any nervous connection between the two, hormonal influence was indicated.* A very nice "natural experiment," but

---

* 28-3. What hormone? Consult Table 28-1.

of course Siamese twins do not happen along every day, nor do they always behave properly (from the investigator's point of view). Conjoined twins can, however, be created in experimental animals, by surgical means using very young animals or even embryos, thus producing **parabiotic twins,** as they are called. Paul Bert, in Claude Bernard's laboratory, was the first one to use this procedure, in 1862.

6. ADDITIVE STUDIES. If the organ studied is a vital one, it is sometimes possible to show, with a considerable degree of probability, that the organ has endocrine functions, either by transplanting an *extra* such organ into an animal or by injecting extracts of the organ and looking for an augmentation of the effect suspected.

7. IDENTIFICATION OF HORMONE IN BLOOD. If there really is a hormone involved, it should be possible to demonstrate its presence in the blood. Usually such a demonstration is first made by a biological assay, or **bio-assay,** that is, by showing the hormonal effect of donor blood upon a recipient animal deprived of the endocrine organ in question. Chemical methods of assay, more desirable from several points of view, are seldom available in the early stages of hormone investigation. It is desirable to have an assay method that is quantitative; with such a method the experimenter should be able to show quantitative differences in the hormone content of the blood in animals whose glands are variously stimulated, or which contain various quantities of glandular tissue.

8. "WINDOW STUDIES." How could we continuously observe the effect of hormones (or anything else in the blood) on a tissue without removing the organ of which it is part? By putting a window in the organ, of course. Unfortunately, the body fluids soon cloud any window we insert. There is, however, another method of achieving the same end. A tiny bit of the tissue can be transplanted to the rear of the eye where it will *implant* and become *vascular-*

ized (i.e., develop blood-vessel connections with the body). Then the experimenter, using an oculist's instruments, can look into the eye and see the condition of the tissue. Much that we know about menstruation has been learned by watching the response to hormones of uterine tissue transplanted to the eye of a monkey. Such an experiment interferes with the vision of the experimental eye, but probably* produces no pain after the implant has healed.

9. STUDY OF SPONTANEOUS DEFECTS. Nature sometimes sets up experiments for us, so to speak, as she does in producing the spontaneous parabiotic twins we call Siamese. More commonly, disease may cause destruction or increased growth of an organ or portion thereof, with concomitant changes in physiology. Where a given, well-defined **pathology** (abnormal physiology) is suspected to be due to a particular organ derangement, in post-mortem examination one looks for parallel anatomical abnormalities. Such correlations have frequently given the first clue to endocrine functions.

229. A Synopsis of the More Important Hormones

By combination of the various methods of study described above, the endocrine nature of many of the organs of the body has been established. Most of the more important and better established hormones are listed in Table 28-1, together with their origins and actions. Since hormones have such a wide variety of actions, for the sake of unity, discussion of individual hormones will be relegated to the sections where the functions in question are discussed. Moreover, since a particular function may be subject to both hormonal and nervous control, it is desirable to discuss the nervous system before discussing such functions.

---

* 28-4. Why the cautious "probably"? How can the experimenter tell?

TABLE 28-1 *The Principal Endocrine Organs of the Body, Some Secretions, and Their Effects.*

ORGAN	HORMONE	PRINCIPAL EFFECTS
Duodenum, mucous epithelium	Secretin	Stimulates secretion of digestive juices by pancreas.
	Cholecystokinin	Causes gall bladder to release bile into gut.
Thyroid	Thyroxin	Stimulates metabolism.
Pancreas (Islands of Langerhans)	Insulin	Affects metabolism, particularly of carbohydrates and fats.
Parathyroid	Parathormone	Affects metabolism of calcium and phosphorus.
Anterior lobe of pituitary	Growth	Stimulates growth.
	Gonadotrophic	Stimulates gonads.
	Thyrotrophic	Stimulates thyroid.
	Corticotrophic (ACTH)	Stimulates adrenal cortex.
	Prolactin	Stimulates secretion of mammary glands.
	Diabetogenic	Antagonizes pancreatic Islands of Langerhans.
Posterior lobe of pituitary	Pitocin	Increases contractility of uterine muscle.
	Pitressin	Contraction of blood vessels; prevention of diuresis.
Adrenal medulla	Adrenalines	Various; mimic stimulation by sympathetic nerves.
Adrenal cortex	Cortisones	Affect metabolism, kidney function, and inflammation.
Testis	Testosterone	Influences secondary sexual characteristics and behavior.
Ovarian follicle	Estrogen	Influences secondary sexual characteristics and behavior.
Corpus luteum	Progesterone	Cooperates with estrogen.
Placenta	Estrogen, and others	Involved variously in pregnancy.

Questions and Problems

24-5. Make a list of the **boldface** terms in this chapter and write a brief description or definition of each. Compare your work with the text.

‡28-6. The presentation of ideas may be in various numbers of dimensions. Try to give a dimensional analysis of the following works: (a) a painting by Mondrian, (b) a painting by Rubens, (c) plain song, (d) Mozart's *Jupiter Symphony,* (e) a fable by Aesop, (f) an article in the *Atlantic,* (g) James Joyce's *Ulysses,* (h) a textbook on embryology.

28-7. How do you suppose prehistoric man discovered the useful effects (useful to man, that is) of the castration of animals?

‡28-8. The element iodine is an essential part of the thyroxin molecule. If an animal is fed a radioactive isotope of iodine, 80 percent of the element accumulates in the gland; in large enough doses, it will destroy the gland. There is one form of cancer of the thyroid that can be destroyed in this way. For this form, why is this treatment superior to surgery?

28-9. If the above treatment succeeds, what therapy must be used for the rest of the person's life?

‡28-10. The following should be discussed as an example of scientific method: "Monday, I drank whisky and ginger ale, and got drunk. Tuesday, I drank rum and ginger ale, and got drunk. Wednesday, I drank gin and ginger ale, and got drunk. Since the ginger ale is the common factor in all these experiences, it follows that ginger ale causes drunkenness. From now on, I'm swearing off ginger ale."

Readings

Two classical endocrinology reports are included in Chapter 8 of Fulton. For a survey of the effects of hormones on a wide variety of vertebrates, see Beach's *Hormones and Behavior*.

Scientific American Offprints

138. Sir Macfarlane Burnet. *The Thymus Gland*

188. Raphael H. Levey. *The Thymus Hormone*

29 Disease Control Mechanisms

230. What Is Disease?

Hippocrates (460?–?377 B.C.), the legendary father of medicine, said that disease has two aspects: suffering **(pathos)** and toil **(ponos).** As we interpret this, by *pathos* we mean primarily the direct effects of the injurious agent (bacteria, etc.) on the body, whereas the *ponos* refers primarily to the attempts of the body to restore itself to normal (if we may speak teleologically). A fair share of the discomfort (*disease*) is often due to the body's toil; in some abnormal conditions, *ponos* makes up almost all of the disease, and medical treatment must be focused on the problem of "teaching" the body the right thing to do.

231. Cellular Defenses

Among the best-understood causes of disease are the pathogenic microorganisms. Let us begin with a consideration of the defenses against these agents. The primary defense against them is that external barrier we call the skin. This barrier varies in thickness in different parts of the body: contrast the lips with the soles of the feet. Under most circumstances, bacteria are unable to penetrate either skin or mucous epithelium. When such a penetration is made, the invaders may succeed in establishing themselves in the host tissues, setting up an **infection.**

In most cases, infection is localized. The invading organisms (usually bacteria), in the course of their metabolism and multiplication, exude various chemical substances which evoke defensive measures by the circulatory system. Nearby capillaries expand, thus permitting more rapid flow of blood to the region, causing a local rise in temperature. At the same time, *white blood cells,* or **leucocytes** (Gr. *leukos* = white), migrate through the walls of the adjacent capillaries and, chemically attracted by the invaders, move toward the colony of invading organisms. These white blood cells resemble amoebae in their ability to surround and ingest foreign organisms or foreign particles. They are called **phagocytes** (Gr. *phago* = to eat). They are, therefore, an important agent in controlling infections by disease organisms. Not all leucocytes are phagocytic, but for our present purposes we need make no distinction. Unlike erythrocytes, leucocytes possess nuclei and have the ability to multiply by cell division. They are much less abundant in the blood stream than are the red blood cells: normally, there are only 5,000–9,000 white blood cells per cubic millimeter of blood. When examination of the blood reveals an excess (15,000–60,000 per cubic millimeter), an infection is indicated. (Numbers much above this range indicate a different

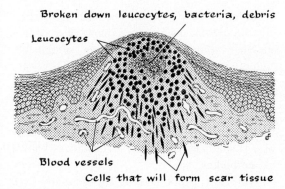

Broken down leucocytes, bacteria, debris

Leucocytes

Blood vessels

Cells that will form scar tissue

Fig. 29-1. *The structure of a pimple.*

condition—namely, **leukemia.** In this condition, which is a kind of cancer, the number of leucocytes per cubic millimeter may rise as high as a million.)

If the infection is localized, and if the defenses of the body are in good condition, there is produced a localized **inflammation,** the signs of which are five: redness, swelling, heat, pain, and interference with function. If very small and localized, the area may be called a pimple; if somewhat larger, a boil or carbuncle. Within the inflamed area (Fig. 29-1) a warlike competition is waged between the invaders and the defensive cells of the host. In the struggle, many phagocytes are themselves killed. The accumulation of dead bacteria and phagocytes and body fluids produces a swelling, the pressure of which, perhaps augmented by unusual chemicals produced by the competing cells, stimulates local nerve endings, producing pain. Most often the local contest ends in victory for "the home team" (otherwise our species would not exist). In the last stages of the life history of a pimple, some of the host cells lay down a wall of scar tissue beneath the pimple; and the millions of dead leucocytes, bacteria, and other debris form a yellow **pus,** making a "head" to the pimple which may break or be deliberately opened by the host. Until the head stage is reached, it cannot be assumed that there is an adequate wall of scar tissue beneath the pimple; opening it before this stage is likely to disrupt the partially formed protective wall, thus aiding further migration of the invaders.

If invading bacteria are not taken care of by local defenses, what happens to them? In the typical case they find themselves first in the lymphatic system (§224), in which they are slowly moved in the general direction of the heart. At strategic points in this ramifying system of vessels there are **lymph nodes.** The locations of the more important of these are shown in Figure 29-*A*. Each node is a sort of elaborate filter (Fig. 29-2*B*) in which fixed (i.e., noncirculating) phagocytic cells remove bacteria and other foreign particles from the lymph passing through. The efficiency of the phagocytes, both *fixed* and *circulating,* is astonishing. In one experiment, a rabbit was injected with enough bacteria to produce a concentration of 1 million bacterial cells per cubic millimeter of

Fig. 29-2. *The location and structure of lymph nodes.*

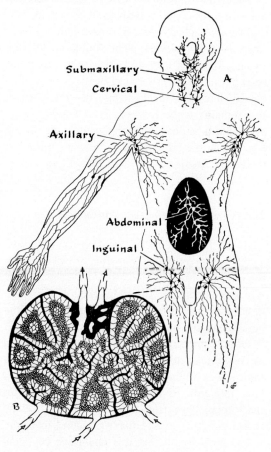

Submaxillary

Cervical

A

Axillary

Abdominal

Inguinal

B

blood; in 30 minutes the concentration in the circulating blood was zero. Post-mortem examination showed great numbers of bacteria in the spleen, liver, and lungs.

As a result of its "toil," a lymph node becomes swollen and sometimes somewhat painful. The **tonsils,** located in the pharynx, are aggregations of lymph nodes that are active in combating infections of the breathing passages. Sometimes the tonsils come out second best in the struggle and themselves become seriously infected. It is often deemed wise to remove tonsils that are habitual losers. The large number of lymph nodes in the middle abdominal region should also be noted. The intestinal epithelium admits not only food but also, at times, some bacteria, the vast majority of which are removed from the system by the abdominal lymph nodes.

When the invasion of disease organisms extends into the blood system itself, we speak of a **septicemia** (Gr. *septos* = putrefying + *aem* from *haima* = blood). The outcome of the struggle between host and invader at this point becomes more uncertain and depends on a variety of defensive mechanisms, of which much still remains to be learned. It is known, however, that a multitude of phagocytic cells in the liver aid in the removal of foreign organisms in the blood circulating through that organ.

232. Chemical Defenses: Antibodies

Thus far we have been speaking of defensive agents and defensive actions that are visible with the ordinary microscope. There are other defensive agents that are invisible; they are, in fact, molecules that are capable of influencing the outcome of the battle between host and invader.

Often a particular species of disease organism evokes almost no local defenses the first time it infects a mammalian body, but will do so in a later infection. Evidently, the first invasion of the foreign organism may change the host so that it is better able to resist a second invasion. It has been found that this change is chemical in nature. A host so changed has in his tissues,

including the blood stream, chemical bodies that are—in various instances—capable of causing a sticking together, or **agglutination,** of the foreign organisms; or of dissolving them (a process called **lysis;** lysis of erythrocytes is called **hemoloysis**); or of otherwise altering the invaders so that they are more easily phagocytized. All these various reactions are the result of actions of a single class of chemical substances known as **antibodies**.

What are antibodies? *Every antibody is a protein belonging to the class of* **gamma globulins.** There is a hereditary abnormality known as **agammaglobulinemia,** in which the blood contains no gamma globulins at all, hence no antibodies, hence no adequate defense against pathogens. However, this condition is exceedingly rare.*

Each specific kind of antibody is typically a particular variety of protein that is not present in the host organism until it has been evoked by the stimulation of a specific foreign substance called an **antigen.** It is essential to realize that an antibody is not active against, nor is its production caused by, the entire organism of an invader. Any invasive organism is made up of many hundreds of different kinds of proteins, and *some* of these proteins are capable of causing the production of antibodies. Each such *antigenic protein* causes the production of, and is affected by, an antibody that is *specific* for it. When a specific antibody combines with its antigen (present in the cell of the invading organism), there is a resultant alteration of the invading cell itself that makes it more liable to agglutination, lysis, or phagocytic destruction. Since, however, the primary phenomena involved in the combination of antigen and antibody are chemical in nature and do not, in essence, involve whole organisms, we can study the phenomena best by using pure proteins as antigens to provoke the production of, or to

---

* 29-1. Why?

29-2. This condition was not discovered until after the sulfa drugs, penicillin, and other antibiotics were discovered. Why not?

29-3. What danger is posed to mankind by his new arsenal of antibiotics?

combine with, specific antibodies. We will now consider some experiments of this type.

233. The Production and Identification of Antibodies

Antibodies can be conveniently obtained by letting a sample of blood coagulate. If clotted blood is stored for an hour or two, the clot will contract, squeezing out a yellowish fluid: this is **serum.** *Serum is blood without the fibrin and without the formed elements* (which are trapped in the clot). Antibodies may be found in serum; since this fluid is the most common source of antibodies for experimental study, the study of antibodies and their reactions is often called the science of **serology.**

The protein **albumin,** extractable from hen's eggs, is capable of stimulating the production of antibodies against it; that is, albumin is an antigen. The means whereby we demonstrate this fact are shown in Figure 29-3. (For clarity, certain of the technical details, including the controls, are not indicated in the diagram.) "Normal" rabbit serum does not have antibodies specific for egg albumin. But if some albumin is injected into the rabbit, in a few days the rabbit serum will contain an antibody specific for albumin. When this specific antibody, which we may call "antialbumin," combines with its antigen (albumin), a visible precipitate is formed. So we may write:

albumin + antialbumin $\longrightarrow$
  [albumin-antialbumin complex] *(1)*
  $\downarrow$
  precipitate.

Not all reactions between antigen and specific antibody result in a precipitate. But various lines of evidence indicate that there is always a combination of antigen and antibody, whatever the visible effect. We may, then, indicate the *general* reaction thus:

antigen + antibody $\longrightarrow$
  [antigen-antibody complex]. *(2)*

Only in the living body can antibodies be

manufactured. Only certain sorts of large molecules, including particularly proteins, are capable of inducing the formation of antibodies. Different proteins induce different antibodies. A protein is a very large molecule made up of a hundred or more amino acid portions, variously combined. The number of conceivable kinds of proteins is almost beyond imagining. Serological studies furnish evidence that the number of kinds of naturally occurring proteins is, indeed, very great.

Suppose a rabbit is "immunized" against the albumin from a hen's egg; that is, the rabbit is induced to form anti-hen albumin. If we now test this antibody against albumin from a duck's egg, a precipitate will be formed, but to a lesser extent; a similar test with albumin from a robin's egg will show still less precipitate; with snake's egg albumin, still less. How can we explain such facts? The most reasonable explanation is this: The proteins we call "albumin" in these various instances are not identical, and the differences in extent of reaction with a single antibody indicate the extent of their chemical differences; for example, duck albumin is chemically more similar to hen albumin than is snake albumin. The study of antigenicity is a most sensitive means of differentiating proteins—substances which are, by ordinary chemical means, difficult to distinguish. A living body is, then, a sort of test tube for the protein chemist.

234. How Is an Antibody Formed?

It is often several days after the initial injection of an antigen before any antibody can be demonstrated in the blood stream. How is the antibody manufactured? And where? At present we do not know. The antibody is probably not formed in the blood stream but somewhere else in the body.

It is possible to measure the concentration of antibody in the blood serum. When an antigen is injected into the body for the first time, the concentration of antibody in the serum rises slowly (Fig. 29-4*A*). Ultimately, the concentration reaches a limit and gradually declines. If,

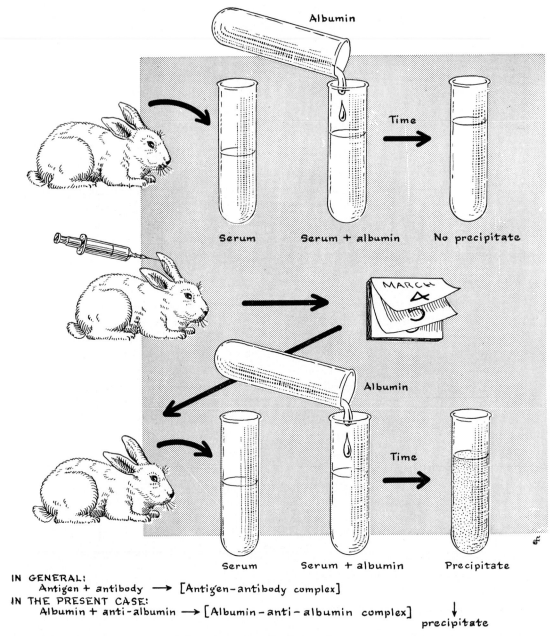

IN GENERAL:
    Antigen + antibody ⟶ [Antigen-antibody complex]
IN THE PRESENT CASE:
    Albumin + anti-albumin ⟶ [Albumin-anti-albumin complex]
                                                              ↓
                                                        precipitate

Fig. 29-3. *The manufacture and detection of antibodies.*

after it has declined nearly to the initial level again, one makes a second injection of the same antigen, the amount of antibody in the blood stream increases very rapidly and may reach a higher level than before (Fig. 29-4B). The rate of increase of antibody is almost independent of the amount of antigen injected. To indulge in a figure of speech, it looks *as if* the first injection of antigen had a slow effect because it took time for the antibody-producing cells (wherever they are) to "learn" how to produce this new antibody. Once they have "learned how," a subsequent injection merely "reminds" these cells to get busy.

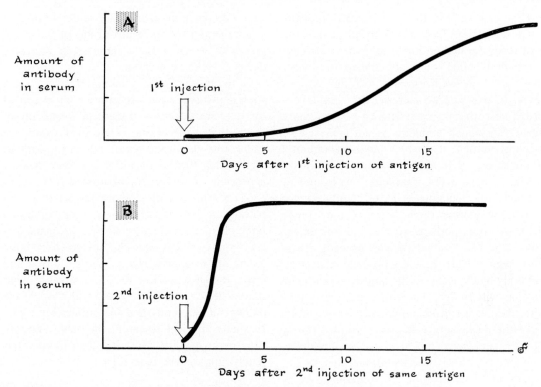

Fig. 29-4. *The slow production of antibody (A) after a first injection of antigen is followed by a prolonged decline in quantity of antibody (not shown). If, after this decline, a second injection of the same antigen (a "booster shot") is given, the rise in antibody level is rapid (B).*

235. Antibodies and Immunology

The science of **immunology,** broadly defined, is concerned with all the reactions of a body that enable it to combat disease organisms, by giving it, to a greater or lesser extent, *immunity* to the attacks of such invaders. Thus defined, immunology includes not only those parts of serology that are concerned with reactions to invading organisms, but also the study of the phagocytic cells of blood, lymph, and liver.

Every invading organism is composed of many proteins that are different from those of the host—**foreign proteins** we call them. Some foreign proteins are antigenic. When antibodies specific for these proteins are present, reactions between antigens and specific antibodies can cause the invading cells to agglutinate, lyse, or become more susceptible to phagocytic attack by cells of the host. Thus the invaders may be weakened and the host more easily enabled to throw off the infection. Antigen-antibody reactions increase the immunity of the host.

Some disease organisms cause their bad effects on the host organism by means of soluble toxins that are exuded from the cells of the invaders. To exhibit some practical applications of immunology, we may consider some phenomena connected with the bacterial species *Clostridium tetani,* the toxin of which produces an uncontrollable contraction of the muscles called **tetanus;** because the effect is often most noticeable in the jaw muscles, tetanus is popularly known as "lockjaw." The bacterial cells themselves, washed free of the proteinaceous toxin, seem to be nearly harmless. The toxin is antigenic, and induces the production of an **antitoxin** by the host, which, if produced soon enough and in large enough quantities, may save the life of the host.

How can we help the host infected with the tetanus bacteria? One way is to inject into the host ready-formed antitoxin, obtained from experimental animals (usually horses or goats) that have survived exposure to the tetanus toxin. In this way we increase the "immunity" of the host, that is, his resistance to the disease agent. Since such immunity is not achieved by the host himself, it is called **passive immunity.** (The animal that *manufactures* the antitoxin is said to have **active immunity.**) Molecules of antibody injected into an animal body do not increase in number; on the contrary, they slowly decrease (due, perhaps, to metabolism? or excretion?). The antibody-producing cells of the host cannot learn how to produce a specific antibody by exposure to the antibody—only the antigen will suffice. Therefore, passive immunity, though it can be supplied quickly, suffers from the disadvantage that it is also lost fairly quickly, and lost completely. Active immunity, though more slowly developed, lasts longer and is subject to reactivation by subsequent exposure to a "booster shot" (recall Fig. 29-4) of the same antigen.

There is another way to combat tetanus. We must distinguish between two properties of the tetanus toxin: its **toxicity** and its **antigenicity.** Presumably, each of these properties is due to certain significant groupings of the atoms that make up this chemical molecule. Fortunately, it appears that the two properties are due to different significant parts of the whole molecule. It is therefore possible to subject the tetanus toxin molecule to mild chemical treatment and thus diminish the toxicity while changing the antigenicity little or not at all. This altered protein molecule is called a tetanus **toxoid** (G. suffix *-oid* = like). An injection of tetanus toxoid causes only mild suffering, but the antibody-producing cells are stimulated to produce an antibody that can combine not only with the tox*oid,* but with the tox*in.*

Every infectious disease is a sort of race between the invader and the host, the former multiplying as fast as possible (and sometimes producing toxins), the latter increasing its defenses (antibodies, and so forth) as rapidly as it

can. The outcome of this race is determined to a large extent by the relative rates of these two processes. Even a slight increase in one may determine the final result.

In the production of tetanus toxoid, we see a special instance of a procedure that is sought for in every infectious disease: a weakening of the **pathogenicity** (illness-inducing) properties of the foreign substances or organisms without diminishing their antigenicity. In some cases it is possible to produce an **attenuated** (i.e., weakened) strain of a disease organism that is still pathogenic but unable to withstand the host's immune reactions. Every disease presents special problems that must be solved, to a large extent, by **empirical** means, that is, by trial and error. It is not possible to tell in advance what treatment, chemical or other, will modify the pathogenicity greatly and the antigenicity little. In such empirical research, the value of using experimental animals (rather than humans) is readily apparent to most men.

236. Allergic Reactions

The reaction (Equation 2, p. 527) between antigen and antibody to form an antigen-antibody complex does not necessarily benefit the animal body in which it occurs. It is possible, for example, to make an animal severely or even fatally ill by properly spaced injections of sufficient quantities of an originally harmless protein. When an animal is so affected, we say that it has become *sensitive* to the foreign protein. If the individual has acquired his sensitivity as the result of natural, rather than experimental, exposure to the foreign substance, we say that he exhibits an **allergy.** The individual who has an allergy to a particular substance shows *allergic reactions* when a tiny amount of the **allergen** (allergy-inducing) substance gets inside his body. Allergic reactions include hives, itchiness, difficulty in breathing, lowering of blood pressure, and many others.

In some diseases, allergy is an important part of the picture. In pulmonary tuberculosis, the disease organisms are confined to lung tissue, but the pathological effects occurring in all parts of the body are usually attributed to allergic reactions. It is likely that allergies play an important role in other diseases; as a working hypothesis, we may assume that allergic reactions are of some importance, great or small, in all chronic (i.e., long-lasting) diseases.

Allergic reactions can be induced by many foreign substances, only some of which are derived from disease organisms. A man may be unable to eat a particular food—say, eggs or strawberries—without suffering allergic reactions. Many dietary allergens are proteins. How can a protein, taken by mouth, cause allergic reactions? According to the scheme of digestion developed in Chapter 26, proteinaceous materials in the gut are outside the body and cannot get into the body without being broken down to amino acids, which are nonallergenic. But the existence of protein food allergies indicates that, in some people, particles more complex than amino acids can get through the intestinal wall; these particles are either proteins or complex allergenic substances derived from proteins. Food allergies occur in some people, not in others. Different people are allergic to different things, but a person who is allergic to one thing is almost certain to be allergic to a number.

There are also many air-borne allergens. "Hay fever" is an allergy to pollen grains of plants, with "ragweed" a common offender in the United States. Many industrial dusts are allergenic for some people, and thus act to limit individual freedom in the choice of occupation.

An individual's allergies may change during the course of his life. Many of the food allergies of a baby are "outgrown" in time. There are clear indications that a tendency to be allergic is inheritable.

237. Stress and Its Consequences

Inflammation is an adaptive response, and like most adaptations it involves a nice balancing of opposing action. It is known that the cortex of the adrenal gland produces both pro-inflammatory hormones (*aldosterone* and *desoxycorti-*

sterone) and anti-inflammatory hormones (*cortisone* and *cortisol*); very likely other endocrine organs are involved also. In recent years much attention has been focused on the hormone cortisone (and its chemical derivatives) by Hans Selye, an Austrian emigrant to Canada.

Selye has called our attention to the fact that the inflammatory process is one that—however helpful it may be—also damages the host in which it occurs. It is to the host's interest to control it, to confine the **stress** it involves to the smallest area compatible with dealing with the **stressor** that causes it. The stressor may be bacteria, a wound, sudden exposure to cold, or any of a large number of other agents. The stressor, in addition to mobilizing the body's defenses in such a reaction as inflammation also mobilizes some counteracting forces, in the manner shown in Figure 29-5. "Knowledge" of the stressor is conveyed to the pituitary gland either by nerves or by chemicals produced by the action of the stressor. The anterior lobe of the pituitary is thereby stimulated to secrete larger quantities of **adrenocorticotrophic hormone** which, mercifully, is usually just called **ACTH.*** Subjected to the stimulus of ACTH, the adrenal cortex then secretes another hormone into the blood stream—namely, **cortisone.** Cortisone has many effects, of which the four most conspicuous are: (1) it causes the stomach to develop small ulcerations, in which action it may be aided by direct effects of the stressor; (2) it causes a shrinking of the lymph nodes and thymus; (3) it causes a rise in blood pressure; and (4) it causes a lowering of the white blood cell count (**leucopenia**).

A constellation of associated symptoms like this is called a **syndrome** (Gr. *syn* = together + *dramein* = to run). The symptoms listed above are part of the first stage of what is called the **general adaptation syndrome,** or **GAS,** a complex of reactions by which the organism adapts to the threat of stress.

Obviously, the reactions evoked by cortisone (and related compounds) are not the ones

---

* 29-4. What does the full name mean?

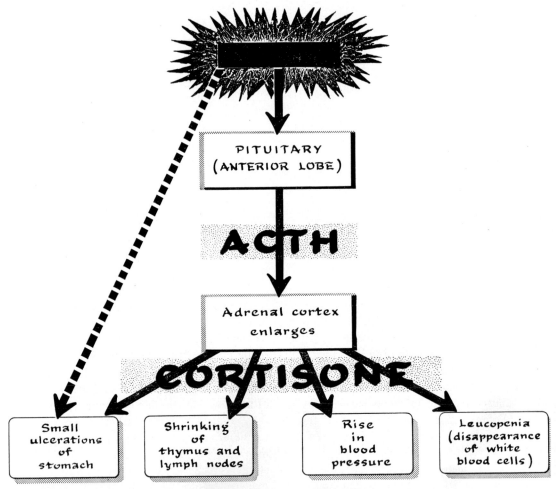

Fig. 29-5. *The principal factors involved in the "stress reaction."*

needed to combat pathogens, but they do serve to control and limit the body's reactions to noxious stimuli. As we have seen in the preceding section, some of the body's defense reactions are sometimes mobilized beyond all need. Plant pollens can never cause an *infection* in a human, but the mammalian body sometimes puts up an all-too-spirited defense against these intrinsically harmless objects—and the defense can cause great distress. Allergy is a "disease of adaptation," a disease of almost pure *ponos*, unaugmented by *pathos*, to use the Hippocratic terms as they were defined in §230. Allergies can, therefore, often be ameliorated by cortisone treatments.

Other diseases of adaptation are rheumatic fever, rheumatism, and arthritis. Cortisone is often a useful drug in treating them, but it is clear that the treatment must be cautiously used with a sharp eye open for damage by the unwanted *side-effects*—namely, the production or aggravation of peptic ulcers, the raising of the blood pressure, or the lowering of the body's defenses against bacterial disease as the white blood cell count is lowered.

238. Blood Transfusions

Some attempts were made to transfuse blood from one person to another as far back as the seventeenth century. The motivation was undoubtedly serious, but the diarist Samuel Pepys, commenting on a report made to the Royal Society in 1666, recorded that "this did give occasion to many pretty wishes, as of the blood of a Quaker to be let into an Archbishop." The proposed experiment was not performed: nor were many others, for the experimenters soon ran into trouble. Every so often, and for no reason that they could see, the recipients of blood were made seriously ill, even killed. The practice was soon outlawed in many countries.

We know now what probably had happened. Donor red blood cells were agglutinated by the recipient's blood plasma. The agglutinated cells later hemolysed, or (more serious) formed thrombi (§220) which plugged capillaries. When these capillaries were in such vital regions as the kidneys or brain, death quickly followed. Why all this happened we did not know until the beginning of the twentieth century. In 1900, the Austrian immunologist Karl Landsteiner (1868–1943) showed that some bloods are naturally incompatible with each other because of antigen-antibody reactions that are remarkable in this regard: *The antibodies involved are naturally present in blood serum without previous exposure to the foreign antigens against which they react.*

The antigens most important in blood transfusion are known as **antigen A** and **antigen B.** These antigens are present in quantity in the red blood cells. The corresponding antibodies are called **anti-A** and **anti-B.** Every person falls in one of the following four classes:

Type A —has A red blood cells—has anti-B in plasma.

Type B —has B red blood cells—has anti-A in plasma.

Type AB—has A and B red blood cells—has neither anti-A nor anti-B in plasma.

Type O —has neither A nor B in red blood cells—has both anti-A and anti-B in plasma.

The facts above may be summarized by saying that each man naturally has all the antibodies he can "afford" to have. (This statement should be regarded merely as a convenient way to remember the facts.)

How do we determine blood types? To do this we use two types of serums: one from persons known to be of type A—such serum contains anti-B; the other, from type B individuals, contains anti-A. A drop of the blood to be classified is put on a microscope slide with a drop of anti-A; another drop of the blood is mixed separately with anti-B. From the behavior of the red blood cells in the presence of the test antibodies, we deduce the blood type of the unknown, as shown in Figure 29-6.

Fig. 29-6. *Typing blood for the A and B antigens by the agglutination method.*

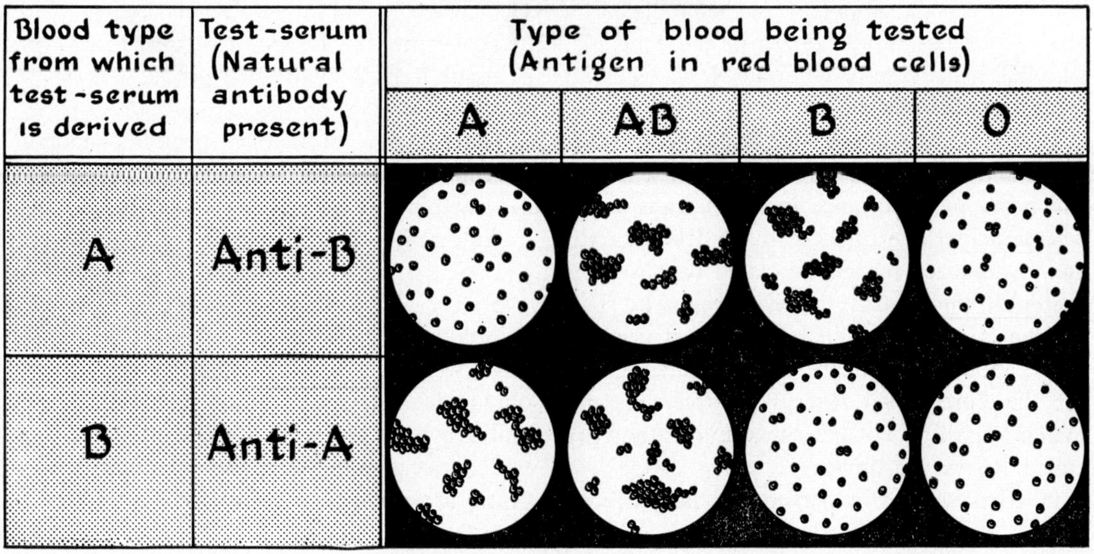

Blood type from which test-serum is derived	Test-serum (Natural antibody present)	Type of blood being tested (Antigen in red blood cells)			
		A	AB	B	O
A	Anti-B				
B	Anti-A				

In blood transfusion, the ideal is to have the **donor** and the **recipient** of exactly the same blood groups. However, experience has shown that it is safe to deviate somewhat from this ideal. As a general rule, we do not need to be greatly concerned with the antibodies present in the donor's blood plasma. The antibodies present in this small quantity of blood are speedily inactivated in the recipient's body by harmlessly combining with dissolved antigens present in the recipient's plasma. The antigens present in the donor's red blood cells are, however, a matter of concern: red blood cells can be agglutinated even when greatly diluted. On occasions when it is not possible to match donor and recipient's bloods exactly, we must ask this question: *Will the donor's red blood cells be agglutinated by the recipient's plasma?* Only a negative answer justifies the transfusion. Since a person with type O blood has red blood cells that have neither antigen A nor antigen B, he is sometimes called a **universal donor.**

The inactivation of antibodies in donor plasma has another fortunate practical consequence. The greater part of the valuable effects of blood transfusion may be obtained by transfusing blood plasma only. Since blood plasma keeps better than whole blood and contains no A or B antigens, it is a much more useful fluid, especially under war and emergency conditions, than is whole blood. The concentration of antibodies in plasma supplies is further reduced by mixing plasmas from a dozen or more people, who will usually be of different blood types, to form a **pooled plasma.**

In addition to the A and B antigens, other blood antigens have been found, only a few of which are of importance in blood transfusion. The principal one of these is the **Rhesus antigen,** symbolized by Rh, so called because it is present in the blood of the rhesus monkey. This antigen is also found in some human erythrocytes; about 5 Americans out of 6 have it, and are therefore called *Rhesus positive.* The remaining sixth do not have this antigen and are called *Rhesus negative.*

A Rhesus-negative person has no antibody against Rhesus unless he has been exposed to Rhesus-positive red blood cells at some time. When an Rh− person who has anti-Rh in his blood plasma receives a transfusion of Rh+ blood, agglutination of the donor's erythrocytes occurs, with potentially serious results to the recipient. There is no such untoward reaction the *first* time Rh+ red blood cells get into the blood stream of the Rh− person. Since, however, in our civilization, it is likely that an individual will receive more than one transfusion during his lifetime, it is of value to type everyone routinely for the Rhesus factor as well as for the A and B antigens.

The Rhesus factor is, as almost everyone now knows, of importance in connection with problems of the newborn. This subject, as well as others associated with blood types, is discussed in Part Five.

239. The Principles of Grafting

No sooner had the principles of blood transfusion been worked out than medical men began to contemplate the replacement of other tissues by tissue donors. Skin transplantations are particularly often needed, as for instance, after serious burns. Can skin be successfully transplanted from one person to another? Unfortunately, it cannot, with rare exceptions (which we will discuss presently).

To begin with, let us distinguish three types of tissue transplantations or grafts:

Heterografts—from one species to another.
Homografts—from one individual to another, within the same species.
Autografts—from one part to another part of the same individual.

Heterografts, fortunately for horticulturists, often work in the plant kingdom (§142); but only under exceptional circumstances in the animal kingdom. Even homografts succeed only under special conditions among animals. Autografts are usually successful, given sufficiently careful surgical technique (aseptic conditions, and so on); though as the individual ages, the probability of success decreases somewhat.

Why are homografts rejected by animals? Breeding experiments give the clue. Some strains of laboratory animals have been closely inbred, generation after generation, producing animals that are genetically almost identical. *Within* such an inbred strain, homografts "take." (*Between* inbred strains, they do not.) The rejection of a graft is evidently the rejection of a foreign gene-produced antigen. In strains of animals that are not inbred, homografts are possible only between identical twins. In fact, a skin-graft test is the most conclusive test we have for identical twins.

There are, however, a number of homografts that are made for medical reasons, and these deserve comment. A segment of artery may be grafted from one individual to another, with successful results. What happens is this: The donated segment is eventually entirely replaced by connective tissue of the recipient, the donor tissue being completely destroyed by the host's phagocytes. The donor vessel serves as a *mold* which determines the pattern of the host's tissues that replace it. The same sort of thing happens with homografts of bone, nerve, and skin (homograft skin being sometimes used in the case of very extensive burns).

In a different category is the grafting of the cornea of the eye, the transparent window at the front of the eye. In the condition known as **cataract** the cornea becomes opaque and useless for vision. It is possible to remove such an opaque cornea and replace it by a fresh one from some other human being (from a living donor or a freshly dead one). Such a homograft is *not* rejected, for the following reason: The immune reaction involved in the rejection of a graft depends on the contact of recipient blood with donor tissue. But the cornea has no blood supply, receiving its food by slow diffusion from adjacent tissues and from the tears. Therefore, a corneal graft is not rejected.

For medical reasons it would be highly desirable to be able to graft tissues from one individual human to another, and a great deal of research is being done in this field. The key problem is apparently one of somehow frustrating the immune mechanism. Limited success has been achieved. For example, mice that are heavily treated with cortisone are more tolerant of homografts, because the immune system is adversely affected by this hormone. The same treatment works well with rabbits, but not so well with guinea pigs and men. Another way of knocking out the immune system is by heavy doses of X-rays. Since the dosages needed are lethal to the blood-forming cells of the bone marrow (and rather damaging generally), the X-radiation must be followed by transplantation of new bone marrow—from the same individual who is going to be used as a donor for whatever other tissue is to be transplanted. In effect, the patient takes on a new antigenic personality, after his own antigenic personality has been destroyed. The whole treatment is of the sort that medical men, with a keen sense of the poetic, call "heroic"—which means, it takes a hero to prefer the treatment to letting nature take its course. It is hoped that experiments along this line will eventually lead to modified procedures that produce more success with less suffering.

Questions and Problems

29-5. Make a list of the **boldface** terms in this chapter and write a brief description or definition of each. Compare your work with the text.

29-6. What has each of the following men contributed to the subjects discussed in this chapter: Hippocrates, Landsteiner, and Selye? Give the approximate dates.

‡29-7. You are given two test tubes: one is labeled "Protein X"; the other, "Protein Y." How could you tell if these tubes really contain different proteins? Describe the procedure.

29-8. A man who cuts his left thumb on Tuesday notices a pealike swelling, tender to the touch, in his left armpit on Friday. What is the cause of this swelling?

‡29-9. There is evidence that antibodies are usually present in most of the cells and cell secretions of the body. Why is only the serum usually used as a source of antibodies in experimental studies?

29-10. In the seventeenth century a French physician named Denys transfused sheep blood into the blood stream of a man. According to his report, the first transfusion did no harm to the man. After the second transfusion of sheep blood into this man, "his arm became hot, the pulse rose, sweat burst out over his forehead, he complained of pain in the kidneys, and was nauseated. The next day the urine was very dark, in fact black," due (as we now know) to the appearance in it of chemical substances derived from the breakdown of erythrocytes. After receiving a third transfusion of sheep's blood, the patient died. Give a reasonable explanation of these historical facts.

‡29-11. Although the *injection* of sheep's blood leads to results like those described in the problem above, the repeated *ingestion* of sheep's blood has no untoward consequences. How do you account for the difference?

29-12. Many an infant has food allergies that he "outgrows" as he matures. We do not know the explanation of these facts. Can you, however, *suggest* a reasonable explanation?

‡29-13. In the Second World War, the per capita number of days spent in the infirmary was much greater among the healthy-looking Scots coming from sparsely settled country districts than it was among the sickly appearing young men from the crowded East End of London. Neglecting possible hereditary differences, can you suggest an explanation for the observation?

29-14. In earlier days medical men often referred to the "laudable pus" that developed

following surgery. Attack and defend the adjective.

‡29-15. The ability to make antibodies is largely lacking during embryonic life. Yet a newborn human baby is immune to many diseases for several months. How come?

29-16. Consider two young mothers coming from the two environments mentioned in question 29-13. Both now live, with their newborn babies, in the same crowded environment. Other things being equal, which baby would you expect to have fewer diseases during the first six months of life?

‡29-17. Yellow-fever virus cannot grow in an adult chicken, which has "natural immunity" to the disease. But the virus can be cultured on chick eggs ("embryonic culture"). How come?

29-18. Suppose an agammaglobulinemic person needed a skin graft. Would it be easier or harder to make it on him than on a normal person? Explain.

‡29-19. A patient with arthritis is given heavy doses of cortisone, following which he develops an active case of tuberculosis. Checking back over his records, the doctor discovers that he had suffered from tuberculosis earlier in his life. Give a plausible explanation of the results.

29-20. A man with an active ulcer and arthritis presents himself to the doctor. What course should the doctor follow?

‡29-21. Many close chemical derivatives of cortisone are being synthesized and tested. In terms of the information contained in Figure 29-5, can you guess what the researchers are looking for?

29-22. A psychological experience can act as a stressor. Can you give a naturalistic explanation of the successes of a faith-healing cult that believes that disease is just an error of the mind—that if we "hold the right thoughts," we won't get sick?

‡29-23. Would this naturalistic explanation be acceptable to members of the cult?

29-24. What is implied by Pepys' remark (§238)?

‡29-25. During the 1930's a "Doctor" Brinkley established a thriving practice in the transplanting of goat testicles (delicately called "goat glands") into old men with young ideas, so as to give them a new supply of testosterone (see Table 28-1, p. 522). Account for the following facts: (a) Many of the patients publicly reported that the operation was a success. (b) All medical men were sure it was an ultimate failure. (c) "Doctor" Brinkley made a fortune.

‡29-26. Consider the art of diagnosis in medicine, as it will be affected in two hypothetical, mutually exclusive situations:

a. Medicine develops in such a way that each illness must be treated by one or more specific drugs. Each of these drugs is of help only in one particular illness, and may even have deleterious effects if used wrongly in the treatment of disease.

b. A half dozen *"boad spectrum antibiotics"* are developed, each of which is useful in the treatment of many diseases, and is almost harmless when wrongly used.

In which situation would you expect the art of diagnosis to become more highly developed? Explain.

29-27. In the situation above in which the art of diagnosis declines, does it matter?

‡29-28. In which situation (Prob. 29-26) will the medical man be more necessary?

29-29. At the present time there is considerable interest in our country in helping the less prosperous countries of the world. To improve such populations medically, how should we most economically go about the job?

‡29-30. In which situation (Prob. 29-26) will the specific disease *morbidity* statistics be more reliable?

29-31. To your knowledge, is medicine in the world today coming to resemble either of the situations described in Prob. 29-26? Which? Explain.

Readings

Lady Mary Montagu's letter on inoculation against smallpox and Jenner's report on vaccination may be read in either Boynton or Moulton and Schifferes. Irrefutable evidence of the utility of smallpox vaccination is presented in Chapter 18 of Cohen. Cohen's Chapter 10 also should be read for its illuminating account of the development of the art and theory of blood transfusion. For further technical (but by no means dull) details in this field of science and medicine, see Wiener's *Blood Groups and Transfusion*. For an excellent general treatment of immunology with emphasis on evolutionary aspects, see Cushing and Campbell. For a discussion of stress, see Hans Selye's *The Stress of Life*, which has some good accounts of the problems that face a scientist who has a heterodox idea.

Scientific American Offprints

78. Sir Macfarlane Burnet. *The Mechanism of Immunity*

148. Rupert E. Billingham & Willys K. Silvers. *Skin Transplants and the Hamster*

160. Choh Hao Li. *The ACTH Molecule*

The Nervous System

30

240. Communication by Nerves

It is a matter of common knowledge that conscious decisions are made in the brain. Suppose I decide to wiggle my toe; instantly, my toe wiggles. The toe-wiggling muscles are found in the lower leg; the decision-making organ is in the cranium, more than a meter and a half away. How does my toe know what my brain wants? How is news of the decision transmitted over nearly two meters of space in so short a time?

The problem seems even more difficult when we recall that the entire body is composed of microscopic cells, packed one against the other for the length and breadth of the body. A "typical" cell—a nearly meaningless term, since there are so many types—is perhaps 50 microns in diameter. Within a distance of a meter and a half, there are about 30,000 cells. Does the message from brain to toe have to pass from cell to cell through 30,000 cells? That would be a very inefficient communication system and, one would suspect, a slow one. By way of analogy, suppose a message from Smith, at the north end of a large city, had to be relayed to Jones, at the south edge, by being passed through 30,000 sets of mouths and ears. This would certainly be a cumbersome method of communication, not to mention an inaccurate one. How fortunate it is that there are telephone

and telegraph wires, slender elements that pierce, as it were, the mass of seething humans and carry the message directly from Smith to Jones, past other intervening and unknowing thousands of individuals.

The brain and the toe are similarly connected by message-carrying cables called **nerves,** the largest of which are easily seen with the naked eye as shiny, tough, white cords that interpenetrate all parts of the body. Nerves carry messages from one part to another, by-passing intervening body cells. They are the telephone cables of the body. But what are these nerves? What are they made of?

The basic morphological unit of nervous action is called a **neuron,** or *nerve cell* (Fig. 30-1*B, F*). Notice that each neuron has one long **nerve fiber** (*C* and *G* in the figure) which, as a matter of fact, may be a meter long or longer—which would be rather difficult to show in its full length on the scale of the drawings given here. These long nerve fibers are gathered together into a bundle; it is such a bundle that we call a "nerve" (Fig. 30-2).

The speed of conduction of an impulse ("message") by nerves varies. The diameter of the individual nerve fiber is one important factor (the greater the diameter, the greater the speed). An increase in temperature increases the speed. Fibers covered by a myelin sheath (*medullated* fibers) conduct more rapidly than

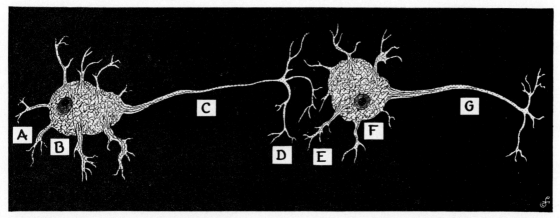

Fig. 30-1. *At the synapse* (D-E) *between two neurons, the message can travel in only one direction, from neuron* B *to neuron* F. *Processes* A *and* E *are afferent fibers;* C *and* G *are efferent fibers.*

"naked" fibers. And the speed of conduction varies from phylum to phylum. Representative values are recorded in Table 30-1.

How "loud" is the "message" a nerve conveys? Using a *nerve-muscle preparation,* that is, an excised muscle with its attached nerve in living condition, we can easily show that, within wide limits, the greater the stimulus given the nerve (e.g., by an electric shock), the greater the response of the muscle. This is hardly surprising. However, if we carry the analysis to the finest level, down to the ultimate nerve fibers, we find something that may surprise us: *A single nerve fiber transmits a single ungraduated impulse, or none at all.* This is called the **All-or-None Law** of nerve action. The graduated response of such an effector organ as a

muscle is produced by the stimulation of a variable number of the nerve fibers affecting it. As a greater stimulus is applied to the nerve, more nerve fibers are excited (perhaps because they have different sensitivities), and hence more muscle fibers are stimulated. Since nerve fibers usually number in the hundreds, the curve of response plotted against stimulus looks perfectly smooth.*

241. The Synapse

The path from brain to toe involves more than one neuron; how many we do not know, but certainly several. We have accepted without question the fact of communication within a cell. What about communication between cells? Clearly, this must occur, too.

Communication between cells is not a general phenomenon; only some cells exhibit it, most notably nerve cells. Every nerve cell connects with at least one other nerve cell to which it gives, or from which it receives, messages. The nature of this connection can be understood by the diagram in Figure 30-1. The junction (region *D–E*) of the processes of two neurons is

TABLE 30-1 *Typical Speeds of Conduction of Nerve Impulses.*

KIND OF NERVE, CONDITIONS	SPEED, METERS PER SECOND
Mammal, medullated nerve, 37°C	120
Mammal, nonmedullated nerve, 37°C	1
Frog, medullated nerve, 20°C	30
Dogfish, medullated nerve, 20°C	35
Pike, nonmedullated nerve, 20°C	0.2
Portuguese man-of-war, fishing filament, 26°C	0.12
Velocity of sound in air, 0°C	331

* 30-1. The *cutaneous dorsi* muscle of the frog is supplied by a nerve that contains only 8 or 9 nerve fibers. Sketch the response curve of this nerve-muscle preparation.

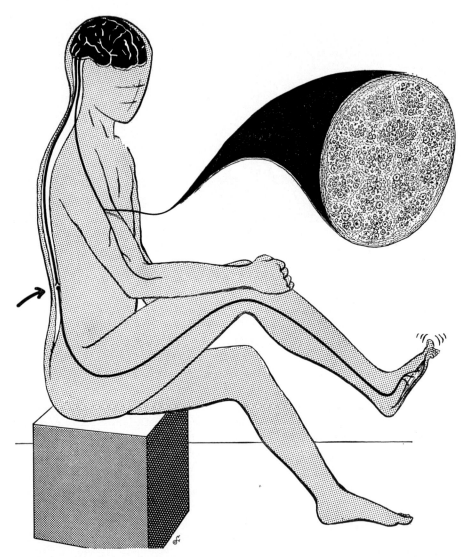

Fig. 30-2. *The nerve fiber that delivers a stimulus to a toe is an extension of a cell whose nucleus is located in the mid-region of the body (see arrow). Thousands of nerve fibers—shown in magnified cross-section above, right—are bound together into a macroscopic nerve (in color).*

called a **synapse** (Gr. *syn* = together + *apsis* = mesh). Experiments have shown that at a synapse a message can travel from one neuron to the next but *in one direction only*. For example, in the figure, a message (detectable by electrical instruments) might travel from *C* to *E* but not from *E* to *C*. Within a single neuron, a message can go in either direction; for instance, from *A* to *C* or from *C* to *A*. In other words, *the synapse acts as a one-way valve* in

the communication system. Messages from head to toe travel over one system of neurons, and from toe to head over another system.

Nerve fibers are identified according to the direction in which they ordinarily carry messages. A fiber that carries a message *to* the main body of the cell (*B* in Fig. 30-1) is called an **afferent** fiber (*A* in the figure). One that carries the message *away* from the cell body is called an **efferent** fiber (*C*). A synapse consists of the junction of the efferent fiber of one neuron with an afferent fiber of another.

242. The Nature of the "Message"

So far, we have been speaking glibly of the "message" that travels along a nerve. What is this message? Elucidation of the nature of this message is a basic problem of modern physiology—a problem not yet completely solved. The partial solution attained at present makes a rather complex story, which we shall simplify.

Whenever a neuron is stimulated at one end, an electrical impulse travels rapidly to the other end. This electrical impulse is not the same as that which travels along an electric wire when a telegraph key is closed. For one thing, the speed of this impulse is much slower—only about 400 kilometers per hour (at the fastest) in a nerve, as compared with nearly 300,000

kilometers *per second* in an ordinary copper wire. This difference in speed stems from a fundamental difference in the source of the current. The impulse in an electric wire can be spoken of as a "simple" electric current; that of a nerve fiber is a by-product of a complex of chemical reactions which produce, first, a modification of the electric charge on the surface of the nerve fiber, and then, second, a restoration of the initial charge. The site of these two successive events moves from one point to another, just as the site of the chemical reactions involved in an ignited powder fuse moves along the fuse.

Figure 30-3 should help to clarify the picture. The breakdown chemical reaction taking place at region *A* causes two things: (1) a loss of charge in the internal membrane of the nerve fiber at *A*, and (2) an initiation of the same chemical reaction at region *B*. The reaction at *B* in turn causes a similar reaction to occur at

Fig. 30-3. *The resting nerve fiber is polarized; i.e., the outside is positively charged relative to the inside. A stimulus causes a wave of depolarization to pass along the nerve fiber, indicated by color. Recovery, which takes place about 0.001 second later, involves repolarization.*

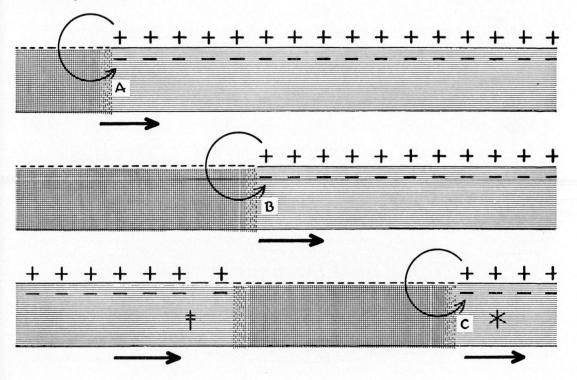

C, and so on from one region to the next. Thus, the impulse travels from region to region at a velocity of about 100 meters per second.

If this chemical reaction, indicated by * in Figure 30-3, were the only one to occur, a given neuron could carry only one impulse and then no more. There is, however, a recovery reaction, indicated by ‡ in the figure, which takes place soon after the breakdown reaction. As soon as the recovery reaction is complete, the nerve is ready for a second impulse, or "message," to pass along it. The time between the breakdown reaction (*) and the recovery reaction (‡) is about $\frac{1}{1000}$ second. The chain reactions diagrammed can pass along the neuron, ‡ behind *, in either direction. If we deliberately stimulate the nerve fiber at the middle of its length, the impulse will travel in both directions until it comes to the extremities, where it will either stop or will go across the synapse, depending on which way the "valve" is oriented. Normally, of course, stimulation at the middle of a nerve fiber does not occur.

The chemical reactions referred to as "breakdown" and "recovery" reactions are not well understood. We do know, however, that they occur only in living neurons, so they may be spoken of as metabolic reactions. Recent biochemical studies show similarities between nerve action and muscle contraction. Both involve the anaerobic breakdown of ATP; and in both, oxygen is required for continuous activity.

The last problem of nerve action is this: What is the message that is delivered by one nerve fiber to another, or by a nerve fiber to one or more muscle fibers? There is considerable, though not conclusive, evidence for the following view. A nerve fiber terminates in close contact with a muscle **endplate** (Fig. 30-4). When an impulse comes down the fiber, it causes the liberation of a chemical called **acetylcholine,** which affects the endplate, causing the muscle fiber to contract. Each nerve impulse causes only a single burst of muscular activity, the ending of which is brought about by **cholinesterase,** an enzyme that destroys acetylcholine. After this has happened, a second nerve impulse causes a second release of acetylcholine, a second contraction, and a second destruction of acetylcholine by cholinesterase. A muscle that

Fig. 30-4. *The fine structure of the juncture of nerve and muscle. (After Bourne,* The Structure and Function of Muscle, *Vol. 1, Academic Press, New York, 1960.)*

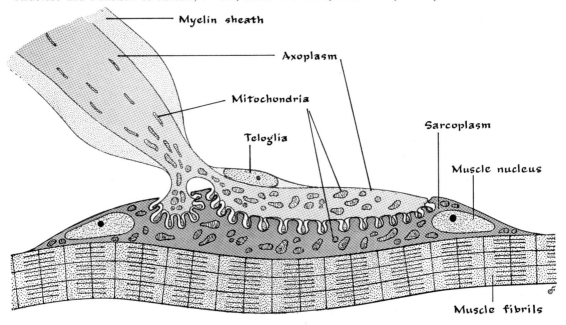

Myelin sheath

Axoplasm

Mitochondria

Teloglia

Sarcoplasm

Muscle nucleus

Muscle fibrils

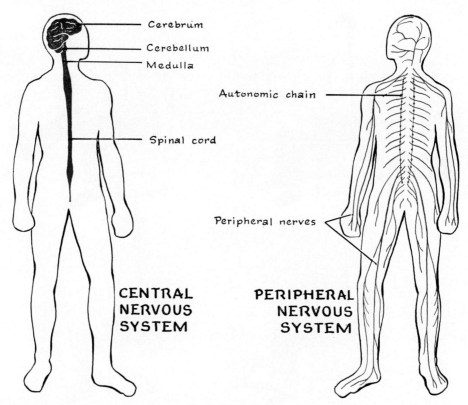

Cerebrum
Cerebellum
Medulla

Autonomic chain

Spinal cord

Peripheral nerves

CENTRAL
NERVOUS
SYSTEM

PERIPHERAL
NERVOUS
SYSTEM

Fig. 30-5. *The principal divisions of the nervous system.*

remains contracted for some time does so only by virtue of a continuous volley of nervous impulses.

243. Consciousness and Animal Experimentation

All of man's reactions to his environment involve his nervous system. Every movement, every thought, is possible only because of his possession of this remarkable integrating system. A skilled pianist runs through a *presto* passage faultlessly; every individual movement of his fingers and arms involves a multitude of nervous impulses. An ice skater performs the "school figures" to perfection; again, his movements are brought about by thousands of the most perfectly timed nervous impulses. Not only are the skilled movements of all sports and physical arts made possible by the extremely intricate organization of the nervous system, but

all thinking as well is carried out by this remarkable system. What structure and functioning can explain the skill of the musical performer and the athlete? What parts and what organization can explain the frightening inventiveness of man's mind? Can we—using the mind itself—understand our own mind and nervous system?

At present, only in part. Of the simpler actions, we have a fair comprehension. The more complex activities we understand at best only vaguely, "intuitively," and uncertainly. This is, however, no reason for surrendering to a mystical feeling of helplessness, however delicious such a feeling may be. When one considers that it is only a little more than a hundred years since the first great advance was made* in the understanding of the nervous system, subsidence into the sensuality of mysticism seems a bit premature.

---

* By Bell and Magendie, in the elucidation of the "reflex arc," to be described in §244.

Fig. 30-6. *When a "hot foot" is given to a normal man* (A), *he not only reacts but feels* (B). *By accident, part of the spinal cord may be cut* (C). *Following this, stimulation of the foot may lead to reflex withdrawal* (D), *but the victim reports no feeling from the affected part.*

Before discussing the organization of the nervous system, it is necessary to formulate some definitions. These definitions can best be made clear by reference to Figure 30-5. The **central nervous system** consists of those parts of the nervous system that are entirely surrounded by the bone of the vertebrae and skull. The **peripheral nervous system** consists of the nerves that connect the central nervous system with the periphery of the body—legs, arms, viscera, and so on.

We shall consider first a simple experiment and a simple question. A man is sitting in a chair. We apply a hot object to his foot (Fig. 30-6*A*, *B*). His foot moves suddenly away from the hot object. *Why does his foot move away from the stimulus?*

"Because," someone volunteers, "he feels the heat and moves his foot to get away from the

objectionable stimulus." This reply raises two questions, one of which we will consider immediately.

Does he move his foot "*because* he feels the heat"? If we say so, we imply that consciousness of the sensation is the cause of the movement or, at least, that there must be consciousness before movement will be initiated. *This is not so.* We can make this denial with confidence as a result of the observation of the reactions of certain, fortunately rare, types of injured individuals. It occasionally happens, owing to war or accidental injuries, that the spinal cord is more or less completely cut across. When the cord is injured in a certain region, the results diagrammed in Figure 30-6*C* and *D* can be obtained. When the injured man's leg is stimulated, it may be withdrawn, just as would be the leg of a normal man, but the injured man maintains that *he doesn't feel a thing.* We may, of course, doubt his statement. (Consciousness is such a thing that *I* can never really know what anyone but *I* feels.) But those who work with such individuals for long always come to the conclusion that the subject really does not have any sensations coming from the region in question. Putting together the results of many such "spontaneous experiments," physiologists have found that a man is conscious of stimuli applied to a certain part of the body only if that part is connected by intact nerve fibers with the uppermost part of the central nervous system, the *brain,* or **cerebrum.** From this, it is concluded that "consciousness"—whatever we mean by that word—is centered in the cerebrum.

From this analysis, there follow two conclusions of importance:

First, when we ask, "Why does an animal's limb move thus and so in response to a stimulus?" we must *not* reply, "Because the animal feels." We do not *know* that the animal feels, and, more important, human data show us that feeling is not a necessary antecedent of a response.

Second, because in humans the cerebrum is the seat of consciousness, and because so many similarities have been found between humans and other animals, we do not hesitate to say that an animal with its cerebrum missing or not functioning has no sensations of pain or any other stimuli. This means that we can, with a clear conscience, experiment with animals that are either *decerebrated* or *under the influence of an anesthetic* such as ether or chloroform, substances that, as human data tell us, stop the functioning of the pain-perceiving centers. Experiments with such animals cause no more pain than operations on humans—pain to which humans willingly subject themselves. In cases in which the experimental animal is destroyed after the experiment without being brought back to consciousness, the experimental animal suffers far less pain than an operated-upon human, for the animal is not subjected to postoperative pains, which are the only ones worth considering.

244. Reflex Action

Complex phenomena are best attacked bit by bit, reduced, if possible, to easily understood elements. With regard to the nervous system and its functioning, the simplest functional unit is what is called a *reflex action,* or **reflex.** We are now in a position to understand this unit.

A reflex action consists of a simple response (e.g., the contraction of the leg muscle) following a simple stimulus (e.g., the application of heat to the sole of the foot). How much of the central nervous system is required for such a simple reflex? Experiments carried out with various animals show that only a small part of the central nervous system is required for such a reflex. Not only is the cerebrum unnecessary, but most of the spinal cord may also be destroyed without destroying a given reflex. Reflex withdrawal of a leg requires the presence of only a small part of the spinal cord at the level where the nerve from the leg joins the cord. Close observation shows that the nerve is divided into two parts: the **ventral root,** which is attached to the ventral part of the spinal cord; and the **dorsal root,** which is attached to the dorsal side. The function of these two "roots" is made clear by the following experiments, the description of which should be read while studying Figure 30-7 closely.

When the main nerve trunk is cut in front of the fork or bifurcation (Fig. 30-7*A*), stimulation of the *distal* cut end (*1*) with an electric current causes the leg muscles to contract. Stimulation of the *proximal* cut end (*2*) causes no visible effect.

If, however, the cut is made instead through the dorsal root only of the bifurcated nerve (Fig. 30-7*B*), the results are different. Stimulation of the distal end (*3*) causes no visible effect; stimulation of the proximal end (*4*) causes the leg muscles to contract.

In another experimental animal (Fig. 30-7*C*), the ventral root of the nerve is cut. In this case, stimulation at point *5* causes no effect; stimulation at point *6* causes the muscles to contract.

From these and other experiments and ob-

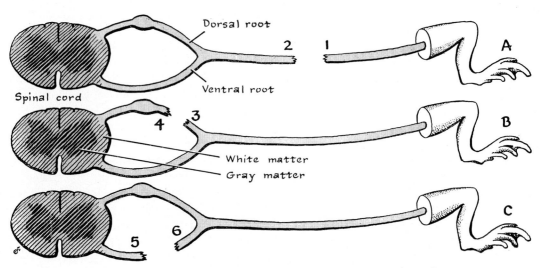

Fig. 30-7. *Experiments that produce the evidence for the concept of the reflex arc.*

servations, it has been deduced that **the dorsal root contains only "sensory" fibers,** nerve fibers that normally carry impulses from sensory areas (in the skin, for instance) to the spinal cord; and that **the ventral root contains only motor fibers,** nerve fibers that normally carry impulses only from the spinal cord to a muscle or gland.

Within the cord, there is evidently some connection between a "sensory" fiber and a motor fiber. Typically, the connection is not a direct one but involves at least one other neuron called a **connector neuron.** The mechanism involved in a reflex action is called a **reflex arc,** the elements of which, diagrammed in Figure 30-8, are **receptor** (sensitive area), "sensory" neuron,

connector neuron, motor neuron, and **effector** (usually a muscle).

It must be emphasized that the diagram greatly simplifies the actual situation. One "sensory" neuron has contact with many connector neurons. Some of these connect with other levels of the spinal cord, ultimately with the brain itself. The impulse carried by a "sensory" neuron is, in part, transmitted to a nearby motor neuron and, in part, shunted to the sensory area of the brain. Only if this latter impulse can get through to the appropriate region of the brain, is any sensation experienced. It is for this reason that we have repeatedly enclosed the adjective *sensory* in quotation marks. The message carried by a "sensory" neuron results in a sen-

Fig. 30-8. *The reflex arc, the simplest unit of nervous response. The arrows show the direction of normal impulses. For experimental evidence, read the text discussion of Figure 30-7.*

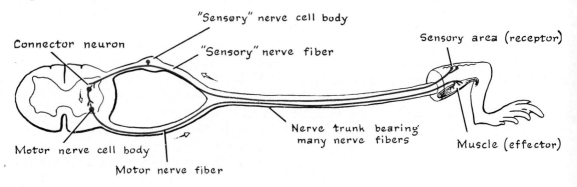

sation only if many other neurons are also present and their connections intact.

245. Teleological versus Mechanistic Explanations

We are now ready to return to the question asked in §243: *Why* does an animal move his foot away from a hot object? An answer suggested there was: ". . . to get away from the objectionable stimulus." Is this a satisfactory answer? It depends on what we mean by "why."

By "why," we may imply, "What purpose does the action serve?" or "What is the goal of the action?" This kind of *why* we may call the **teleological why** (Gr. *teleos* = end, goal). When we answer that the animal moves his foot *to get away from* the stimulus, we are giving a *teleological explanation.* Such an explanation, though satisfactory to many people, is seldom acceptable to scientists. To understand why not, let us consider a different example.

"Why do the wheels of a car turn around?" Suppose, in reply to this, someone said, "The wheels of a car turn around in order to take the passengers somewhere." Teleologically, this might be a correct answer, yet everyone will grant that there is a sense in which it is a false answer. "The wheels of a car turn around because the combustion of gas in the cylinders moves the pistons, thus moving the connecting rods which cause the crank and driving shafts to revolve, thus causing the wheels to turn." This is a better answer; it gives us an idea of the *mechanism* behind the movement of the wheels. It is a *mechanistic explanation.*

Generally, when a scientist asks *why,* he implies a **mechanistic why.** Why does an animal move his foot away from a hot stimulus? "Because the stimulus causes an impulse to pass along sensory neurons into the spinal cord and then through connecting neurons to motor neurons which stimulate muscles which contract, thus causing the leg to move." This is a mechanistic answer. It is usually a better answer. The

mechanism must be there if the action is to take place. The existence of the goal alone will not cause the action. The mechanism may subserve an end, but *the action is brought about by the mechanism, not by the goal.*

246. Innate Reflexes

A simple reflex action of the type just discussed does not have to be learned. It is either present from birth or develops later without learning. It is an **innate reflex.** A specific example of such a reflex is the well-known "knee-jerk" reflex. The stimulus in this case is the sudden stretching of a tendon by a sharp blow; this stretching affects specific sorts of nerve endings that are buried deep in the muscle. The message from these receptors, passing through a reflex arc, causes the contraction of certain muscles. We do not have to learn this reflex. (See Figure 30-9*A.*)

But there are other innate reflexes that are not so simple as this. The **crossed extensor reflex** is an example of a slightly more complicated innate reflex. Under certain conditions, when one leg of, say, a frog is strongly stimulated, not only does this leg *flex* (draw up), but, more slowly, the opposite leg may *extend.* The mechanism of a crossed extensor reflex is diagrammed in Figure 30-9*B.* The crossed extensor reflex is more complicated than the simple reflex, in that it involves synaptic connections between neurons on opposite sides of the spinal cord.

Another stage of complexity is made possible by connections between neurons *at different levels* of the spinal cord. If, using a frog that has been deprived of its brain, we apply dilute acid to the skin of the belly, a very remarkable thing happens. The hind legs of the frog rise and scratch at the belly *as if* the frog were trying to remove the noxious stimulus (Fig. 30-9*D, E*). Since all evidence points to the conclusion that the debrained frog has no consciousness or conscious aims, the apparent pur-

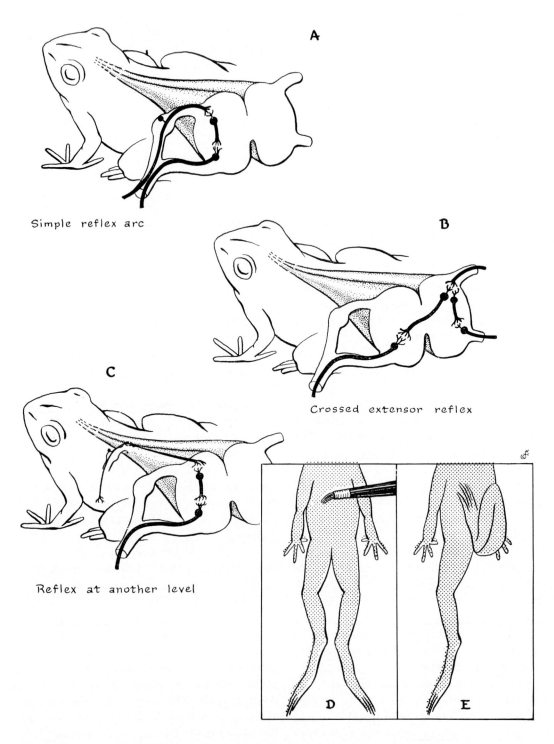

Fig. 30-9. *Minimal neurons needed for various reflexes. (A) For simple reflex. (B) For crossed extensor reflex. The stimulus given in D produces reflex shown in E, which can be explained by the neural connections shown in C.*

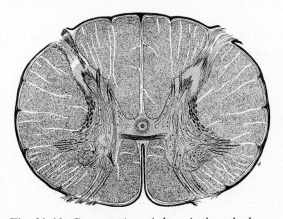

Fig. 30-10. *Cross-section of the spinal cord, showing "gray matter" in color, and "white matter" in black and white. Note the complexity. Because connecting nerve fibers do not, except by chance, lie in the plane of a single cross-section, no complex reflex arcs of the sort diagrammed in Figure 30-9 are to be seen here.*

posiveness of the action is most striking. This action is but another of the many innate reflexes. The teleology is obvious. The anatomical elements involved are indicated in Figure 30-9C.

The nervous pathways indicated are probable paths. The precise course followed by an impulse and the exact neurons involved are seldom entirely certain. The postulated pathways exist; but so do too many others. How can we be sure which pathway is the one actually taken? The trouble is not that we cannot see enough pathways, but that we can see too many (Fig. 30-10). W. S. McCulloch estimates that there are 10^{10} neurons in the human nervous system. Each neuron connects with one *or more* other neurons, so that the number of synapses is greater than 10^{10}. *Directly or indirectly, every neuron of the central nervous system is connected with every other neuron.** In each reflex act, however, only a few of the many possible connections are utilized. The central problem of neurology is to ascertain what determines which few of the many possible connections are made use of in a given action, and why.

---

* 30-2. If there were a neuron not connected with other neurons, how could you discover it?

247. The Autonomic Nervous System

In the discussion of the simple reflex arc, the impression may have been given that the effector is always a muscle. This is not true. Glands also may be effectors. However, the chain of nerves involved in the stimulation of a gland is slightly more complicated. Take the salivary gland, as an example. Although it can be consciously stimulated—we can *will* to increase its flow—the gland is normally controlled unconsciously. We will subsequently examine a complete arc involving both sensory and motor nerves, but for the moment we should focus our attention on only the motor end of the arc. In Figure 30-11 are diagrammed two different systems of central control of an organ: one, of a voluntary muscle; the other, of a salivary gland. Notice that the muscle is stimulated directly by a neuron the greater part of which lies within the central nervous system (Fig. 30-11*A*), whereas stimulation of the salivary gland involves a chain of *two* neurons—one within the central nervous system, connected with a second outside that, in turn, transmits the stimulus to the gland (Fig. 30-11*B*).

All glands, in so far as they are subject to nervous control, are governed by mechanisms like this—mechanisms that involve *at least* one motor neuron lying wholly outside the central nervous system. Innervated in this way are the salivary glands and the pancreas; also many muscles, including those of the viscera, of the walls of the blood vessels, and of the iris of the eye. The members of this heterogeneous assemblage of organs have one thing in common: they are only slightly, or not at all, subject to conscious control. To a willful human, they may seem to be independent, or autonomic, in their actions. For this reason, the part of the nervous system that is concerned with their activity is called the **autonomic nervous system.** Notice that the adjective "autonomic" refers to a (superficial) aspect of the things controlled rather than to the system exercising the regulation, for the autonomic system is definitely guided by impulses from the central nervous system.

The autonomic nervous system is, in part,

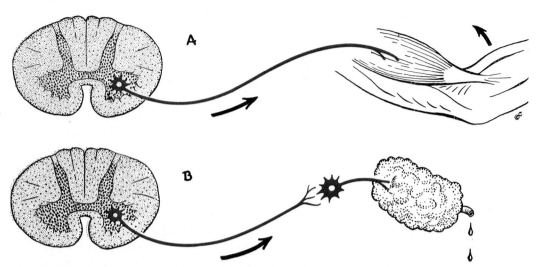

Fig. 30-11. *Innervation of a voluntary organ* (A) *compared with the innervation of an organ controlled by the autonomic system* (B). *In* B, *note the extra motor neuron lying outside the central nervous system.*

identifiable in gross structures visible to the naked eye. Along either side of the spinal cord,

Fig. 30-12. *The autonomic ganglia, which lie outside the central nervous system.*

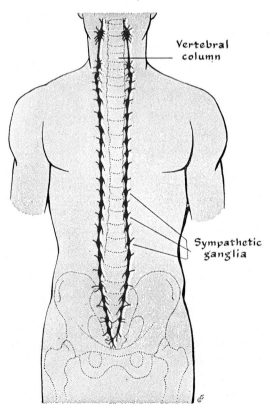

Vertebral column

Sympathetic ganglia

outside the vertebral column, there is a knotted cord of nervous tissue (Fig. 30-12). The knots of this cord are composed of thousands of neurons. Each of these neurons is the second neuron of the chain diagrammed in Figure 30-11*B*. When many nerve cell bodies are massed in bunches like these, each bunch is called a **ganglion** (Gr. a swelling; pl. *ganglia*). These ganglia are autonomic ganglia. Not all the autonomic ganglia occur in macroscopic groups. Many of them, particularly those of the extreme upper and extreme lower part of the system, are dispersed, each ganglion being found close to, or imbedded within, the organ it controls. All these dispersed ganglia (with their associated fibers) are referred to as the **parasympathetic system,** in contrast to the more centrally located system, the **sympathetic system,** the ganglia of which are visible in Figure 30-12.

The separation of the autonomic nervous system into two subsystems mirrors real differences in physiology. Figure 30-13 shows the contrasting effects of these two systems on various organs. Notice that, whereas the parasympathetic system constricts the pupil of the eye, increases the flow of saliva, increases the lumen of the small intestine and decreases that of the large intestine, the sympathetic has the opposite effect in each case. The student cannot predict the

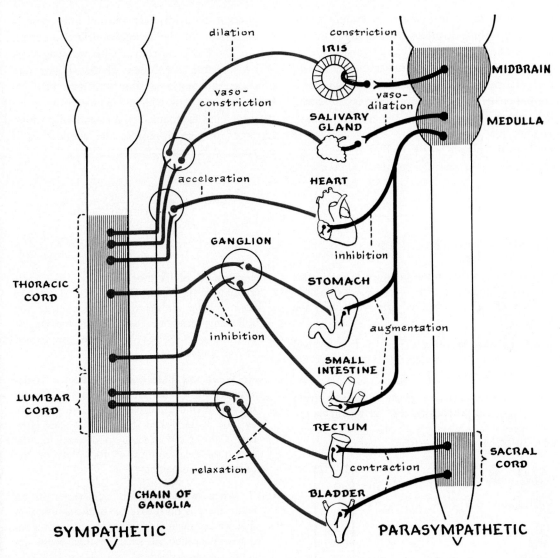

Fig. 30-13. *The two divisions of the autonomic nervous system, the sympathetic in color, the parasympathetic in black. Note their antagonistic actions.*

effect of one of these two systems on a particular organ, but, knowing the action of one system, he can usually predict the action of the other. The sympathetic system and the parasympathetic system are mutually antagonistic.

Antagonism of the sympathetic and parasympathetic systems results in some cases from the fact that they innervate antagonistic muscles, for instance, the circular and radial muscles of the iris of the eye. However, in other cases, the antagonism is due to *different effects on the same effector*. This is something new.

Skeletal muscle is either stimulated by the nerves to contract, or, lacking stimulation, it relaxes. There are no nerves that stimulate skeletal muscle to relax. But smooth muscle and cardiac muscle both have a certain amount of intrinsic activity and can be stimulated either to contract more than usual (by nerves of one division of the autonomic nervous system) or to relax more than usual (by nerves of the other division of the autonomic nervous system).

Besides motor neurons, the autonomic system includes some sensory fibers. The reports of these to the central nervous system seem, however, to be censored. Most of the time we do not know what our viscera are doing: the "reports" are dealt with at levels below that of the cerebral cortex. The heart, for example, is continuously governed by reflexes mediated through the lower levels of the central nervous system; few reports of the action taken are made to the higher levels. Under some circumstances, however, one can become acutely aware of visceral behavior; this unusual awareness is characteristic of the **hypochondriac,** a person who is morbidly concerned with his symptoms and his health. Awareness of the viscera may produce an emotional state which in turn affects the viscera—which then send in more reports. Thus is established a system of positive feedback that may require the services of a psychiatrist before it can be broken.

Questions and Problems

30-3. Make a list of the **boldface** terms in this chapter and write a brief definition or description of each. Compare your work with the text.

‡30-4. In what sense is a powder fuse a good analogy to a nerve fiber? Where does the analogy break down?

30-5. From information given in the text, from the general proposition that all mammals are constructed pretty much alike, and from examination of Figure 30-14, you should be able to give an approximate answer to the following question: How long is the longest cell in a giraffe's body? Tell how you arrived at your answer.

30-6. When the main body of a neuron is destroyed, all of its processes degenerate. By staining methods, degenerated nerve processes may be distinguished from normal ones. How may these facts be used in determining the structural relationships of the parts of the central nervous system?

‡30-7. When whole neurons degenerate in an adult, there is no recovery. On the assumption that we are dealing with neuron degeneration, the degeneration of what neurons could account for the following?

a. The individual's legs are without feeling. He can move them but he cannot feel anything with them, not even their own movement.

b. The individual's legs are paralyzed. Feeling is present but no movement is possible.

30-8. By definition, distinguish between teleological and mechanistic explanations.

30-9. One of the two types of "why's" mentioned in the text (§245) can frequently be replaced by the word "how." Which one?

30-10. A "why" terminated §246. Do you think this was intended to be a *mechanistic why* or a *teleological why?*

Fig. 30-14. *A problem in size.*

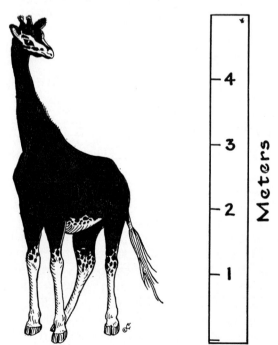

Meters

4

3

2

1

30-11. Science is usually concerned more with which sort of "why"? What other fields of human endeavor are concerned with the other sort?

30-12. Suppose that you ask yourself this question: "How do *I* know that *you* are conscious?" What answer can you give yourself?

30-13. Antivivisectionists frequently cite British statistics which indicate that, over a period of years, some 25 thousand operations were performed on experimental animals under anesthesia, while nearly 600 thousand operations were performed on animals *not* under anesthesia. These figures show, it is asserted, that scientists are cruel. It must be realized, however, that according to British law, any procedure in which the skin is broken is called an "operation"; vaccinations and injections given with hypodermic needles are thus classified as "operations." Of what value are the above statistics, then, in discussing the morality of vivisection?

30-14. Why don't antivivisectionists become upset about the use of the following as experimental subjects: (a) rattlesnakes, (b) frogs, (c) earthworms, (d) protozoa, (e) plants, (f) bacteria?

‡30-15. The drug pilocarpine stimulates the parasympathetic nerve endings. What will be the effect of this drug on (a) the iris, (b) the salivary glands, (c) the rectum?

‡30-16. Atropine causes acceleration of the heartbeat, decrease in the flow of saliva, and dilation of the iris. What part of the nervous system does atropine stimulate?

‡30-17. In extreme fear, men and other animals are likely to defecate and urinate regardless of their surroundings and their training. In addition, the heart beats faster and the mouth becomes dry. Can you give a simple explanation for all these phenomena? What would you predict to be the appearance of the eyes in fear?

30-18. What is blushing? What part of the nervous system controls it? Would you call it a voluntary or an involuntary activity?

‡30-19. An occasional unusual individual can willfully stop the beat of his heart. What part of his nervous system has he learned to control?

30-20. Would you consider the usual lack of willful control of the autonomic nervous system a fortunate or an unfortunate state of affairs? Why?

30-21. Determine the etymology of "hypochondria," and see what sense you can make of the term. It may be necessary to consult a medical dictionary.

Readings

To the Spaniard Ramón y Cajal is due a large share of the credit for establishing the role of neurons in the function of the nervous system. Dorothy Cannon's life of this great scientist not only depicts his personal qualities, but also underscores the extremely difficulty of doing any scientific work in a country lacking the scientific tradition. Another great figure in the field of neurology is the Englishman Sherrington, whose beautifully written *The Integrative Action of the Nervous System* is still, though a half-century old, worth reading. For reprints of still earlier work, see Chapter 7 of Fulton.

For a survey of the role of the autonomic nervous system, Chapters 16 and 17 of Walter B. Cannon's *The Wisdom of the Body* are useful.

The interrelated problems of consciousness and "free will" are perhaps nowhere discussed with greater simplicity and usefulness than in the Epilogue to Schrödinger's *What Is Life?* and Chapter 21 of Rapoport's *Science and the Goals of Man*.

Those interested in exploring the large antivivisectionist literature (most of which was written a half-century or more ago) should first read, for perspective, Helen Hughes' sociological essay, "The Compleat Antivivisectionist." Following this, read Root's "The Case for Animal Experimentation."

Scientific American Offprints

72. R. W. Sperry. *The Growth of Nerve Circuits*

98. Bernhard Katz. *How Cells Communicate*

The Organism as a Whole: Internal Adjustments

31

---

248. The Control of Blood Flow

The cells of a man's body are surrounded by a fluid called *lymph* (§224), which Claude Bernard aptly referred to as the *internal environment* of the body, saying further: "All the vital mechanisms, varied as they are, have only one object, that of preserving constant the conditions of life in the internal environment." Lymph, the internal environment, is remarkably constant in its physical and chemical properties: only within very narrow limits are there variations in the concentrations of salts, in acidity and alkalinity, and in the temperature of this fluid.

Any mechanism that controls the constitution of lymph must also control that of blood, which generally means influencing the flow of blood either locally or generally. To understand the mechanism that controls blood flow, we picture the circulatory system in crude mechanical terms (Fig. 31-1) as a pump and set of pipes, the diameter of which may be varied. Increase in blood flow through the system may be brought about in two ways: (1) by increasing the rate of heartbeat, or (2) by increasing the amount of blood pumped per beat. In our mechanical analogy, the second possibility is represented by an increased length of stroke of the piston. In the animal heart, this effect is achieved by an increase in size of the heart at its maximum volume and a more complete emp-

tying of it. In most normal adjustments to tissue demands for more blood, both means (1 and 2) are used. That the heart beats faster is a matter of common knowledge; that it pumps more blood per beat can be shown experimentally.

The means described above will cause blood to flow faster through all parts of the body. However, one tissue sometimes needs more blood than others. How can the relative volumes flowing through various parts be modified?

The diameter of the "pipes" of the body can be changed. This is particularly true of the smallest arteries of the body. Fluid flows more readily through a large pipe than through a small one; therefore, if the blood vessels in region Y expand (Fig. 31-1B), more blood per second will flow through this region. Alternatively, increase in blood flow through Y can be achieved by *decreasing* the rate of flow through other parts of the body. If the vessels at X are constricted (Fig. 31-1C), more blood per unit time will be forced through region Y.

The rate of flow of blood through the various parts is determined by the rate and extent of heartbeat and by the contraction or expansion of the blood vessels. But what *tells* the heart and blood vessels what to do? This is a complex story, part of which we shall here relate.

The contraction and expansion of the smaller arteries (called **arterioles**) are effected by muscles in their walls (Fig. 31-2). These muscles are smooth muscles, hence not usually under voluntary control. The nerves that innervate them are part of the autonomic system (§247). There are two layers: a layer of circular muscles, and one of longitudinal muscles. Contrac-

tion of the former decreases the diameter of the vessel; of the latter, increases it. Most changes in bore seem to take place, however, largely through the contraction, or absence of contraction, of the circular muscles. In the absence of

Fig. 31-1. *Mechanical analogy, showing three ways of increasing blood flow through region Y: (A) by increasing the activity of the heart; (B) by opening more widely the arterioles in region Y; or (C) by narrowing the arterioles in other regions, represented by X.*

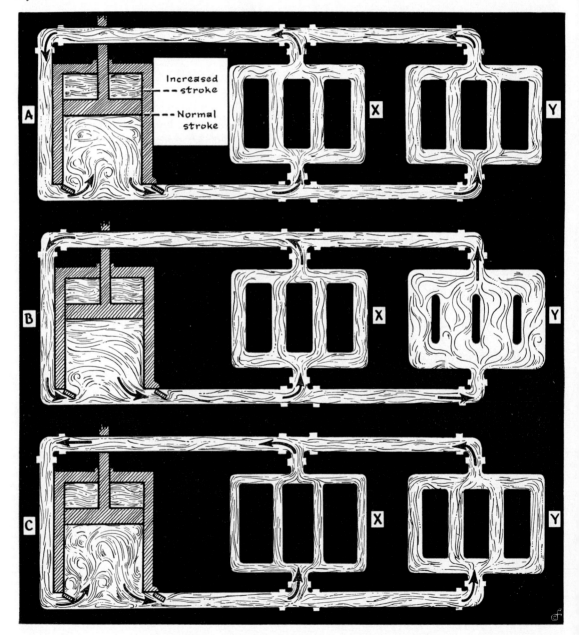

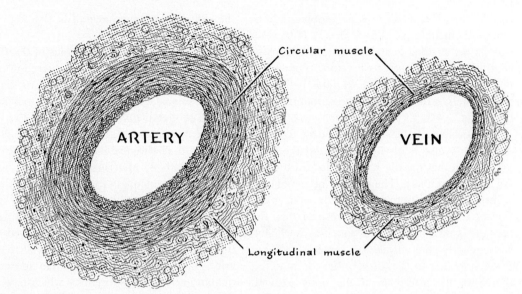

Fig. 31-2. *Small blood vessels in cross-section, showing the muscles that regulate their diameters. Note that the muscular layer of an artery is thicker than that of a vein of the same internal diameter.*

contraction of these muscles, a vessel will automatically enlarge because of the pressure of the blood within.

The autonomic nerves that control the blood vessels are controlled largely by the **medulla** (recall Fig. 30-5). For this reason, the medulla is referred to as the **vasomotor center** of the body (L. *vas, vasculum* = a vessel). The medulla also acts as the breathing and cardiac center of the body.

The musculature of blood vessels can also be directly affected by chemicals. Carbon dioxide causes the circular muscles to relax, thus increasing the flow of blood through vessels. This is undoubtedly important in causing local vasodilatation in response to increased activity of a part of the body. More widespread effects are caused by another chemical, *adrenaline,* a hormone produced by the central portion of the adrenal gland, a portion called the *adrenal medulla.* Adrenaline causes constriction of the arterioles of the viscera and relaxation of the arterioles of the skeletal muscles. This action—a combination of the two diagrammed in Figure 31-1*B* and *C,* with *X* representing the viscera and *Y* representing the skeletal muscles—has the effect of shunting blood from the viscera

to the muscles. Adrenaline is released in increased quantities at times of stress, for example, during fear, anger, or flight. The adaptive value of furnishing more blood to the muscles which need it at those times, at the expense of the viscera whose needs are not urgent, is obvious. The adrenal medulla is innervated by fibers from the autonomic system, and it is evidently through these that the activity of the gland is coordinated with the emotional state of the individual.

It is worthwhile to describe the chain of events that take place whenever the body becomes more active. Increased activity is accomplished by increasing the rate of burning foodstuffs. Increased food-burning produces increased CO_2. Locally, the CO_2 causes dilatation of arteries, as previously explained. Carbon dioxide is carried to the vasomotor center of the medulla, which then sends impulses along the autonomic nerves to the vasoconstrictor muscles of the blood vessels. This action is contrary to the *direct* action of carbon dioxide on these muscles, and the net result is to constrict the vessels in those regions that are not entering into greater activity while allowing the arterioles in the more active region to expand—a useful reaction that is enhanced by the action of adrenaline. As mentioned above, the medulla also acts as the cardiac center. A rise in CO_2 concentration causes this center to stimulate the heart to greater activity, the stimulus being carried by nerves belonging to the autonomic system.

This outline of the nervous control of vasoconstriction also helps us understand the well-known fact that rapidly repeated forced breathing causes dizziness. The greatly increased rate of breathing results in lowering the concentration of CO_2 in the blood; because of this, the medulla is not stimulated as much as normally; consequently, the vasomotor center sends out fewer impulses to the vasoconstrictor muscles; therefore, the arterioles of the body expand. With most of the arterioles dilated, there is a greater volume available to the blood, and, consequently, the blood pressure falls everywhere. The fall in blood pressure results in slower movement of blood; slower-moving blood brings less O_2 to the brain than it needs; hence the individual develops a feeling of dizziness and may even faint.*

249. Temperature Regulation: Adjustment to Heat

The ability of mammals to adjust to high temperature was dramatically demonstrated in 1775 by Charles Blagden, then secretary of the Royal Society. Blagden took some trusting friends into a room where the air temperature was 126° Celsius, where they remained for three-quarters of an hour unharmed, though a steak they took with them was thoroughly cooked during that time. A pot of water covered with oil boiled vigorously, while another pot of water without oil did not, though the water became quite hot. Evaporation of water from the free surface kept the temperature down. Evaporation from

---

* 31-1. Is the reaction that has just been described a homeostatic mechanism?

31-2. Is this reaction of any importance in the life of musicians?

the skin of the experimentalists also kept their temperature from rising.

Water is brought to the surface of the skin in the form of sweat, an external secretion of the **sweat glands,** which lie embedded in the skin near the surface (Fig. 31-3). In passing, it should be noted that mammals have two kinds of sweat glands: the **eccrine sweat glands,** which are distributed over man's whole body surface; and the **apocrine sweat glands,** which, in man, are principally found in the armpits and around the nipples of both sexes, and in the pubic area of females. Both kinds of glands secrete a water-and-salt filtrate derived from the blood plasma, but the secretion of the apocrine glands contains in addition an appreciable quantity of organic substances which have little or no odor when freshly secreted but which can be degraded by bacteria on the skin to substances with characteristic odors. The apocrine glands do not begin to secrete until the time of puberty (sexual maturation). Their general biological significance among mammals generally (whether including man or not) is probably in connection with problems of individual recognition and sexual attraction. They are of limited importance in temperature regulation.

The eccrine sweat glands are largely responsible for our adjustment to heat. As a result of their activity, the skin becomes covered with millions of molecules of water. For simplicity, only a few of these molecules are indicated in Figure 31-3, and their size is much exaggerated. Recall the conceptual scheme of molecules in motion developed in Chapter 3. At any instant, different molecules will be moving at different rates. *What we call the temperature of a substance is a measure of the average speed of its molecules.* If the average molecular speed is great, the temperature is high. Low average speed, low temperature.

Whenever we happen to "look" at the water molecules on the skin, their speeds may be as indicated by the figures written inside each diagrammed molecule. Their average speed is, say, 100. (Never mind what the units are.) An instant later, every molecule is somewhere else, and, because of collisions, the speeds are dif-

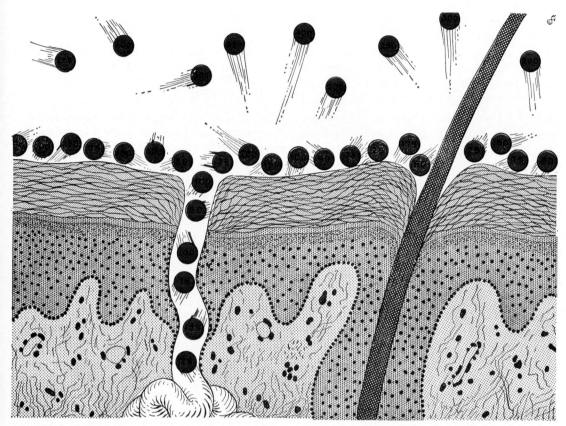

Fig. 31-3. *When some of the water molecules of sweat reach a high enough speed to "take off" the surface of the skin, the average speed of the molecules left behind is necessarily reduced somewhat. That is why sweating cools us.*

ferent; but, in the absence of outside influence, the *average* speed of the molecules remains the same.

The molecules of a gas have a greater average speed than those of a liquid at the same temperature. If we have liquid molecules of a certain kind (water) in contact with gaseous molecules of the same kind (water vapor), every now and then one of the molecules in the water layer will have a speed great enough to jump off and become one of the gaseous molecules. Referring to our diagram, suppose 200 is the speed needed for a molecule to move out of the water layer into the gas above. There are a few molecules of water on the surface of the skin that have this necessary speed. These fast molecules have a high probability of leaving the water layer. When they do, *the average speed of the molecules remaining in the liquid layer will necessarily be decreased. Since the average molecular speed determines what we call temperature, the temperature of the remaining liquid will drop.* The escape of molecules from a liquid into a gas is called **evaporation.** We see why evaporation has a cooling effect.

Sweat contains sodium chloride, or common salt. Sweat is secreted continuously at all temperatures, but its rate of secretion is greatly stepped up under conditions of heat and physical exertion. In one experiment in which a man worked very hard in a hot, dry atmosphere, measurements showed that the loss of water by evaporation amounted to approximately 1.5 liters per hour.

That sweat is not pure water is a matter of considerable practical importance. The concentration of various salts in the body is of great importance; if their concentration falls too low, prostration and even death may occur. Since sweating removes salts from the body, profuse sweating may de-salt the body to a dangerous extent. This is the principal cause of the "heat prostration" and "sunstroke" that afflict workers in hot places such as deserts, deep mines, boiler rooms, and steel mills. It would be more accurate to refer to it as "saltstroke" or "low-salt prostration." Such prostration may be avoided by increasing the intake of salts, particularly of sodium chloride. It is now standard practice in many industries to place salt tablets alongside the water tap with instructions for their use. In this connection, it is interesting to note that desert burros secrete a sweat that is almost pure water, much purer than the sweat of man. These animals are very tolerant of heat. One wonders to what extent differences in human susceptibility to heat are attributable to differences in composition of sweat.

Besides evaporation from the skin, there is also evaporation ("insensible sweating") from the surface of the lungs, and this, too, tends to cool the blood. In dogs, this is the principal method of cooling. Recall the panting of a heated dog. Among humans, an inheritable absence of sweat glands is known, though it is rare. For such humans, hot weather presents a serious problem.

Sweat glands are controlled by the central nervous system. A small region known as the **hypothalamus,** which lies below the cerebrum (Fig. 31-4), is the temperature-regulating cen-

Fig. 31-4. *The temperature-regulating center.*

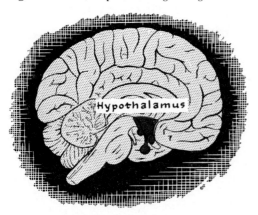

ter of the body. Impulses are sent from this center to the sweat glands via nerves that are part of the autonomic nervous system. Control of the sweat glands may be exerted either by reflex, as the result of stimulation of sensory nerve endings in the skin, or directly, as the result of the stimulation of the hypothalamus itself by the temperature of the blood flowing through it.

250. Temperature Regulation: Adjustment to Cold

Heat is lost from the body by three means: evaporation of water, convection, and radiation. We shall now consider how the body controls heat loss by these means.

Evaporation can be decreased by lessening the activity of the sweat glands. However, evaporation is never completely zero, for the sweat glands are always slightly active even under the coldest conditions. Tracer experiments with tritium water (water containing H^3 in place of H^1) show that the minimal rate of passage of water through the human skin in "insensible perspiration" is 0.01 to 0.05 mg of water per square centimeter per minute. Furthermore, evaporation of water from the exposed surface of the lungs and breathing passages is always taking place and, for obvious reasons, cannot be stopped.

Convection is a term that refers to the gross movements of unequally heated portions of a liquid or gas. Figure 31-5 will perhaps make the idea clear. Hot water is lighter than cold water; consequently, it will move up and away from the hot object, to be replaced by cooler water, which, when heated, will . . . and so on. The movement is called convection; we speak of convection currents in the fluid. A warm man in a cold room (Fig. 31-5) will similarly cause convection currents in the air, which will cause his body to lose heat.

Convection losses are decreased by dead air spaces next to a hot body; in such spaces air can circulate only with difficulty. Birds achieve this end with feathers, most mammals with hair;

Fig. 31-5. *At the left, a warm object heats up the whole aquarium by the convection currents it produces. Similarly, the man at the right warms the cold room by convection of heat from his body.*

but modern man, poor creature, must resort to clothing. When the weather gets colder, the feathers of birds and the hairs of mammals stand out more from their bodies, thus increasing the amount of dead air space. Man, being a mammal, "tries" to do this, too, but the result is little more than ludicrous "goose pimples," formed by the contraction of tiny muscles at the base of insignificant hairs.

Radiation must be distinguished from evaporation and convection. All bodies send out heat rays in all directions. These heat rays are like light rays: they travel in a straight line and can travel through a vacuum. The filament of a light bulb sends out both light and heat rays, which we can feel or see even when the filament is surrounded by a vacuum.

Objects at different temperatures radiate heat to each other (Fig. 31-6*A*). But a hot object sends out more heat rays than does a cooler one (Fig. 31-6*B*, *C*); consequently, the *net effect* will be that the hot object loses heat and the cooler one gains it. In a shorthand way of speaking, we may say that the hot object radiates heat to the colder one. A man facing a snowbank or a glacier is aware of his loss of heat, by radiation, to the cold object (Fig. 31-6*C*). Convection currents in the air, of course, cool him, but over and above this, he is cooled by his radiation. It *feels as if* the glacier were radiating cold to him—which is physical nonsense.

How is heat loss by radiation controlled? It is apparent that the hotter the surface of a man, the more heat will he radiate. How can the surface temperature be controlled? By controlling the rate of flow of warm blood to it. If the blood flows fast, it will keep the surface warm; if it flows slowly, the surface will become cooler. The control of blood flow is brought about, both directly and reflexly, by the hypothalamus. The sensation of heat, originated either locally in the heat receptors, or centrally, causes the heat-control center to send fewer stimuli through the nerves to the circular muscles of the blood vessels. The blood vessels then expand; more blood flows through the capillaries per unit of time, and more heat is radiated away from the body. The adjustment of the size of the surface capillaries causes a change in appearance that is readily observable to the naked eye: the face of a man on a hot day becomes quite ruddy; on a cold day, he becomes pale.

For mammals and birds that live in very cold climates the problem of the loss of heat from the extremities is a serious one that has led to a special solution. Consider a goose paddling around in the Arctic Ocean with the water below 0°C.* The web of her foot is very thin and must lose heat extremely rapidly. Two problems present themselves: (1) How do the living cells withstand so low a temperature? (2) How are the heat losses for the whole bird

---

* 31-3. How can that be? Isn't 0°C the freezing point of water?

Fig. 31-6. *All bodies radiate heat rays in all directions, but since an electric heater sends more heat rays to a man than the man does to the heater* (A), *the net effect is one of radiation from heater to man* (B). *A man standing near a glacier* (C) *loses heat to the glacier by radiation.*

minimized? To the first question, we have no good answer. We can say only that the cells *can* withstand the low temperature. As to the second question, we know a bit more. There is present, high up in the leg and more protected than the terminus, a structure known as the **rete mirabile** (the "wonderful net"). This is a complex bundle of intermixed arteries and veins, in close apposition to one another. The warm blood in the arteries going down is cooled by the cold blood in the veins coming up; correspondingly, the venous blood is warmed before it re-enters the body. The whole system constitutes what an engineer would call a "countercurrent heat exchanger," which helps minimize heat losses.†　Such a system is found in whales, seals, and a number of the birds of cold regions.

---

† 31-4. Does it also help minimize problem 1 above?

251. Variations in Heat Production

So far we have been considering how the body's temperature may be controlled by controlling methods of heat exchange. Body temperature is also affected by variations in the rate of heat production. All living tissue respires, and respiration produces heat. Muscle fibers not only respire; they also contract, an action that involves an increased rate of respiration. Studies made by H. Rohracher beginning in 1940 have shown that muscle fibers are undergoing insensible contractions at all times, producing **microvibrations** of the muscles that can be detected with suitable electronic amplifiers. In adult humans, the average frequency is 7 to 13 per second; in a newborn baby it is 5 to 9 per second. In small mammals and birds the frequency may be as high as 34/sec.

These microvibrations continue throughout life, and even for several hours after death. In sleep and narcosis, their amplitude changes; in fever, the frequency changes. When a person moves from a warm room to a cold one, the frequency changes.

It has been calculated that to produce the amount of heat needed to maintain the normal body temperature of 37°C in a room at 20°C, about 3 percent of the muscle fibers need to be contracting at any one time. When one moves to a cold room either more muscles must contract or muscles must contract harder. Both things happen. In an uncomfortably cold environment, **shivering** occurs; this is the result of the massive contraction of opposing muscles, which produces functionless motion and greatly increased amounts of heat.

Variations in heat production are paid for by variations in food consumption. People in cold countries eat more food than do people in the tropics. This may be partly a matter of custom, but experiments have shown that, when allowed to eat freely, both men and other animals eat more in a cold environment than in a warm one.

The kind of food also influences the rate of heat production. Proteins, for some reason, stimulate respiration. Intake of 500 Calories of proteins causes a greater *immediate* increase in the rate of heat production by the body than does intake of 500 Calories of carbohydrates. Correlated with this is the natural tendency of people in cold climates to eat heavily of meat when given free choice.

The influence of hormones on respiration and heat production is easy to establish but hard to explain. Hormones affect not only respiration, but also many other of the chemical processes that we lump, with respiration, under the term metabolism. The hormone of the thyroid gland, called **thyroxin,** has a marked effect. Patients with a thyroid gland that is not secreting enough hormone into the blood stream have a lower metabolic rate than normal, as much as 40 percent lower. Such individuals, who suffer abnormally in a cold environment, are said to be suffering from **hypothyroidism,** or hypofunc-

tioning of the thyroid. On the other hand, individuals suffering from *hyper*thyroidism produce much more heat than normal and, therefore, may suffer in the summer.

It is of interest to note that one form of *hypo*thyroidism is caused by a diet too low in the chemical element iodine. When not enough iodine is available, the thyroid gland enlarges (*as if* it were trying to make up for the deficiency by harder work), producing the characteristic lump seen in Figure 31-7. The development of his **goiter** (L. *guttur* = throat), as it is called, can be prevented by adding iodine to the diet. In most regions of the world, there is enough iodine in the soil to furnish plants with the iodine man and other animals need for their thyroids to function properly. In some regions, however, the soil is deficient in iodine. In Derbyshire, England, for instance, this is true; as a result, the term "Derbyshire neck" was early applied to this sort of goiter. There are similar regions in Switzerland; and considerable areas in the middle part of the United States, especially around the Great Lakes, have low-iodine soils.

Since diet can induce a goiter and, hence, can affect metabolism, one might regard this as but another example of the effect of diet on heat production. However, it should be pointed out

Fig. 31-7. *Simple goiter. (From Hertzler,* Diseases of the Thyroid Gland, *Paul B. Hoeber, Inc., New York, 1937.)*

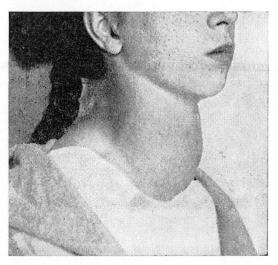

that there is no one "cause" of "simple goiter," as this kind of goiter is called. In the "Goiter Belt" of the middle United States, only a small proportion of the population ever suffer from goiter. There seems to be a hereditary predisposition to simple goiter. There is also a sex difference: women are far more liable to the disease than are men.

Other glands also affect the rates of metabolism and heat production, for poorly understood reasons. In general (adrenaline is an exception), any effect of a hormone on heat production will be a slow one, several days being required for an injection of thyroxin to take effect. The abnormal functioning of *any* gland will probably cause, directly or indirectly, some disturbance of metabolism and heat production.

252. What Is a Pleasant Temperature?

Mammals and birds in general are able to survive in a wide range of temperatures. However, the range that is regarded as *pleasant* by any species (in so far as it can report its feelings) is much less wide. As is well known, relative humidity must be considered along with temperature. At a relative humidity of 100 percent, all cooling by evaporation stops, and the maximum external temperature at which man can live is about 32°C (a bit less than 90°F). On the other hand, the same temperature with only 20 percent R.H. will be generally reported as stimulating, and even enjoyable by some people. Undoubtedly, the degree of fatness, hormonal balance, and previous experience all help to determine a person's reaction to various temperature-humidity conditions. Figure 31-8 gives reactions that are typical of most residents of temperate climes. This figure gives the temperature in degrees Fahrenheit, a quaint system used by only 9 percent of the world's population at the time of the writing of this book. The Fahrenheit system is in the process of being abandoned in the United Kingdom, which will reduce the minority to 7 percent, supposing no further differential in the ratio of reproductive rates of the various parts of the world.

253. The Role of the Kidneys

The gross structures involved in the secretion and passage of **urine** are diagrammed in Figure 31-9*A*. Urine is formed by the **kidneys,** large, bean-shaped organs that lie just back of the posterior wall of the body cavity. Urine is secreted by the solid part of the kidney into the **kidney pelvis** (or *renal pelvis;* L. *ren* = kidney + *pelvis* = basin); thence, it passes down a **ureter.** The right and left ureters empty into the **urinary bladder,** where urine is stored, to be released from time to time into the **urethra,** which carries the fluid to the exterior.

What is the structure of the solid part of the kidney, and what relation does the structure bear to the secretion of urine? If we take a thin slice of kidney and examine it under the microscope, what we see is puzzling: we see various irregular "doughnuts" (Fig. 31-9*B*). Each doughnut, it turns out, is a cross section of a long and tortuous tube. By careful study of many such slices, it has been learned that a kidney is made up of many units like those idealized in Figure 31-9*C*. Notice the **renal tubules** ("little tubes"). A swelling called a **renal corpuscle** (L. *corpusculum,* diminutive of *corpus* = body) is located at one end of each tubule. Inside the corpuscle, we find an aggregation of even smaller doughnuts, which again suggest the existence of tubules. These tubules are filled with blood; they are, in fact, blood capillaries. The whole tuft of tubules is called a **glomerulus** (diminutive of L. *glomeris* = a ball, or ball of yarn); it lies within a capsule called the **renal capsule.** The fluid within this capsule and its connecting tubule is not blood but a watery fluid which resembles very dilute urine. This fluid, which has been filtered from the glomerulus, is called **glomerular filtrate.**

The working unit of the kidney consists of the renal capsule (including the glomerulus) and the attached renal tubule. A *single human kidney is made up of about one million such working units.* How does each renal unit function? The answer to this question was furnished by a technical *tour de force* of A. N. Richards. Although the renal unit is microscopic, Rich-

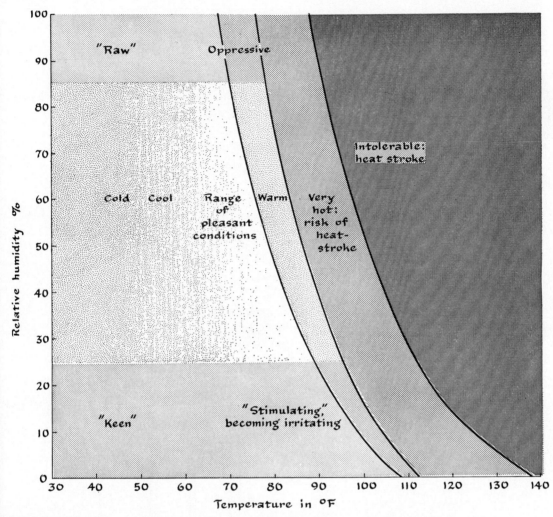

Fig. 31-8. *A graph from which you can predict how pleasant a given temperature and humidity will feel.*

ards and his co-workers, by inserting a tiny glass tube into the space of a renal capsule of a living frog kidney, succeeded in withdrawing a sample of the fluid, which they then chemically analyzed. The results of many such analyses revealed that the capsule fluid has almost the same constitution as blood plasma, except that proteins are lacking. Fluid collected at the far end of the renal unit—that is, urine—shows a composition that differs considerably from that of blood plasma, as Table 31-1 reveals. This table shows that many substances (for instance, chloride ion, urea, and creatinine) are considerably more concentrated in the urine than

they are in the blood plasma or in the glomerular filtrate. How come? Only two possibilities present themselves: either the walls of the renal tubule secrete these substances into the glomerular filtrate; or they remove water from the glomerular filtrate, leaving behind increased concentrations of urea and other substances.

The latter proves to be the case. The volume of glomerular filtrate has been calculated to amount to 75–100 liters a day, but the urine excreted amounts to only about 1–1½ liters per day. This means that the renal tubules return to the blood vessels that surround them up to 99 percent of the water present in the filtrate.

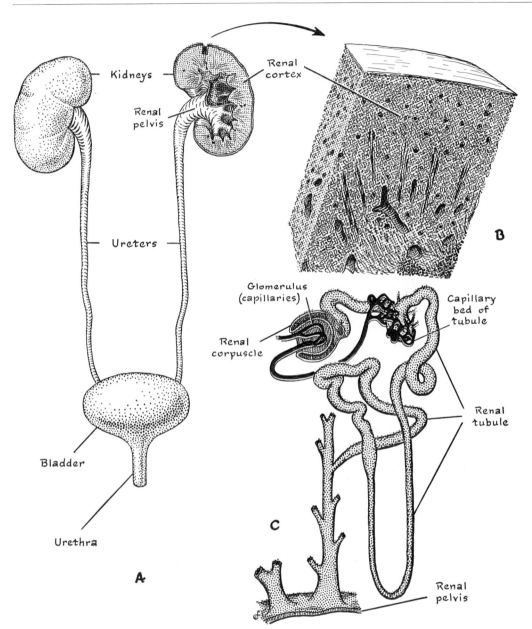

Fig. 31-9. *The excretory apparatus. A human kidney is composed of about a million working units such as that shown in* (C). *Urine begins as a secretion from the glomerulus into the cavity of the renal corpuscle and travels down the renal tubule, ending in the renal pelvis. With no further change in composition, urine traverses the ureters and the bladder, going out via the urethra.*

They also return other substances to the blood, but not in strict proportion to their concentrations in the filtrate. As a result, the concentrations of these other substances are changed as the fluid in the renal tubules is changed to urine. In other words, *the wall of a renal tubule is a secretory tissue;* it is a rather unusual secretory organ in that it secretes material that is almost outside the body back into the body. But it is, nonetheless, a secretory tissue.

TABLE 31-1 *Concentrations of Various Substances in Blood Plasma and in Urine.*

(COL. A)	(COL. B)	(COL. C)	(COL. D)
	PARTS PER HUNDRED		CONCENTRATION
SUBSTANCE			FACTOR
	IN BLOOD		(APPROX.)
	PLASMA	IN URINE	(COL. C/COL. B)
Water	90–93	95	
Proteins	7	0	
Glucose			
(sugar)	0.1	0	
Sodium	0.3	0.35	1
Chloride	0.4	0.6	1.5
Urea	0.03	2	60
Uric acid	0.004	0.05	12
Creatinine	0.001	0.075	75
NH_4 ion	0.001	0.04	40

It is worthwhile now to look again at the functioning of the kidney unit from the point of view of the *work* done. The first stage of the process, the formation of glomerular filtrate by the glomerulus, is a process of simple filtration, as the name implies. To carry out any filtration, force is necessary. In the common filtration process of the chemical laboratory, the *force* is furnished by gravity. The *work* of filtration is performed when the material to be filtered is lifted to the height of the filter papr (Fig. 31-10*A*). The work of glomerular filtration similarly involves a force and work. The force is that of blood pressure pushing against the walls of the glomerular capillaries. The work is the work required to develop the force of the pressure of blood—in other words, the work of the heart (Fig. 31-10*B*). *The work of glomerular filtration is performed by the heart.* As one would deduce from this principle, when blood pressure falls, the amount of glomerular filtrate (also of urine) formed also diminishes. As blood pressure rises, the amount of glomerular filtrate increases.

Increase in blood pressure has another consequence. In the common filtration process, if a thin filter paper is covered by too deep a layer of fluid, the weight of the fluid may partially rupture the filter paper, letting through some of the material. In other words, when the pressure is too great, the filter breaks down. The glomerulus—the filter of the kidney—is similarly subject to overloading. If the blood pressure rises too high, proteins, which are normally

Fig. 31-10. *How the work of glomerular filtration is accomplished.*

A

The work of filtration is carried out when the material is lifted up to the filter, where the fluid can exert pressure against the filter.

B

The work of glomerular filtration is performed by the heart creating blood pressure.

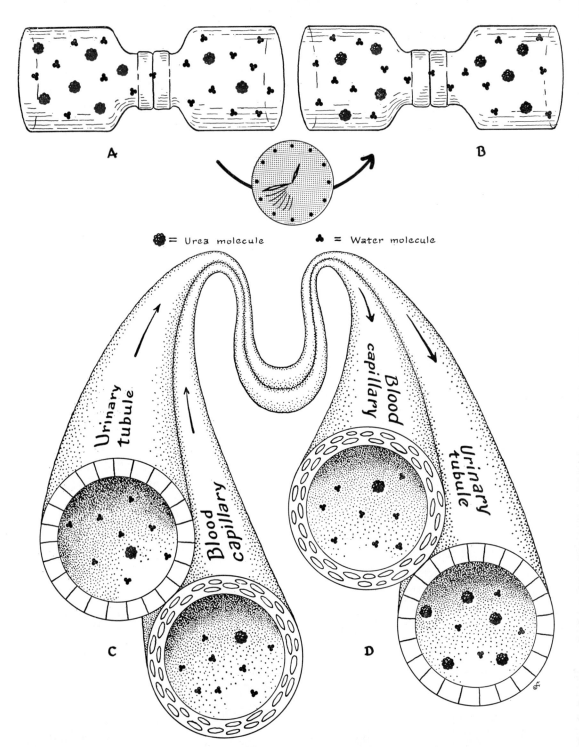

= Urea molecule   ♣ = Water molecule

Fig. 31-11. *By the laws of probability an unequal distribution of molecules in connecting vessels (A) cannot long be maintained (B). But in the kidney, an initially equal distribution of water and urea molecules in the renal tubule and blood capillary at the site of the renal capsule (C) is changed to an unequal distribution as the renal fluid approaches the end of the urinary tubule (D). To achieve an improbable result like this, work must be done. This work is performed by the metabolizing cells of the wall of the urinary tubule.*

held back, may push through the walls of the glomerular capillaries and appear in the urine. Improper functioning of the kidneys is but one of many undesirable consequences of high blood pressure.

Let us now proceed to the other phase of kidney function: the secretion, or reabsorption, of substances—a process carried out by the walls of the tubules. What sort of process is involved here? Is work done? How?

It is necessary to recall our fundamental concepts of molecular activity (Chap. 3). If we have, in intercommunicating "rooms," two species of molecules (Fig. 31-11*A*), the concentration of each of these species will ultimately be the same in both rooms (Fig. 31-11*B*) and will thenceforth remain the same. The molecules move at random. If, at any time, there were more of one species of molecule in the left room than in the right, then the probability of a left-room molecule moving into the right-hand room would be greater than the probability of right-room molecules moving to the left. Consequently, any inequality of distribution would be automatically erased.

But what happens in the renal tubules? This situation is diagrammed in Figure 31-11*C, D,* in which, for simplicity, only two species of molecules are shown: urea and water. In the first part of the tubule (Fig. 31-11*C*), the concentration of each of these substances inside the tubule and in the blood of the capillaries around the tubule is very nearly the same. Later (Fig. 31-11*D*) the urea is much more concentrated inside the tubule. The change is brought about by the activity of the cells of the tubule wall, which push water into the blood while holding back the urea molecules. By simple molecular movements, such a situation would never develop; or, to put it more exactly, it is an extremely improbable situation. *The development of an improbable situation always requires work.* This is the fundamental nature of the work performed by the walls of the renal tubules.

How is this work accomplished? Here, we must admit, we do not know the whole answer. However, this much can be said: The function-

ing of the tubules depends on the metabolism of the cells that line their walls. Dead cells cannot reabsorb materials; anesthetized cells can do so poorly or not at all. It takes living, actively metabolizing cells to develop and maintain an improbable situation.

As we would expect, the functioning of the renal tubule cells depends on an adequate supply of oxygen and foodstuffs. It also depends on a hormone secreted by the small tab of tissue that hangs down from the brain, the pituitary gland (Fig. 31-12). The pituitary is composed of two distinct parts, or *lobes.* The **posterior lobe** secretes a hormone called **pitressin,** which is required by the kidney cells. When adequate pitressin is lacking, as may be the case when the pituitary gland is diseased, the renal tubule cells are unable to secrete much water back into the blood stream; consequently, a large volume of watery urine is excreted. This condition is known as **diabetes insipidus** and can be controlled by periodic injections of pituitary extract. Without such treatment, the afflicted one must sometimes drink many liters of water in a single day to make up his water losses.

254. The Fate of Sugar in the Body

Everyone has heard of **diabetes mellitus,** or "sugar diabetes" (L. *mellis* = honey), a condition in which sugar appears in the urine. What is the cause of this condition?

It will help to describe first the normal movements and transformations of sugar in the body. All sugar is ultimately derived from the food consumed. Digestion of carbohydrates produces the simple sugar glucose, which is absorbed through the intestinal wall into the blood stream. Glucose is transported to all parts of the body, and part of it is used immediately in the metabolism of the cells. However, immediately after a meal, more glucose is taken into the blood stream than is needed at the time for respiration. The excess must be either stored or excreted. It is normally stored, principally in the muscles and in the liver, in the form of a less soluble carbohydrate called glycogen, or

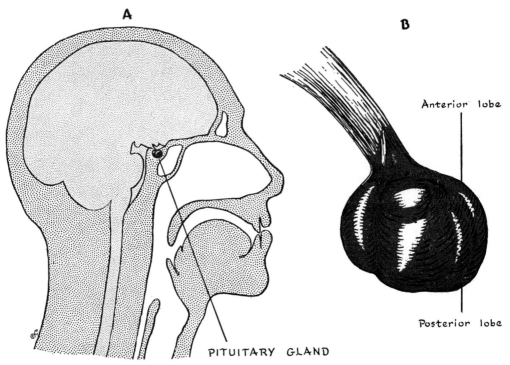

Fig. 31-12. *The pituitary gland, the posterior lobe of which secretes pitressin, which is required for normal functioning of the renal tubule cells.*

"animal starch." That carbohydrates can be so stored is most fortunate or, one might say, necessary. Were it not so, an active man would have to eat continuously.

Glycogen is stored when there is a surplus of glucose in the blood, and released when there is a metabolic drain on the blood sugar. Studies have shown that several hormones are involved in the storage and release of carbohydrates from liver and muscles. Among these hormones are adrenaline, from the adrenal gland, and insulin, a secretion of the pancreas. The latter is an organ of both internal and external secretion. Its external secretions are the digestive enzymes, and its internal secretion is insulin, which it pours into the blood stream. Insulin aids in the process of storing carbohydrates. Adrenaline helps change the glycogen back into sugar, which can be released into the blood stream. Studies made with carbohydrate molecules containing tagged atoms show that both processes go on at the same time. In the period immediately after a large meal, the storage process is

in the ascendancy; during vigorous exercise, the release process is dominant. The rates of these processes are directly determined by the secretion of insulin and adrenaline, as well as by some other hormones.

The renal tubules secrete sugar back into the blood stream again. However, their ability to do so is limited. When the sugar level of the blood is very high, the sugar level of the glomerular filtrate is correspondingly high, and the renal tubules are unable to restore all the sugar to the blood. As a consequence, the urine contains some sugar, as it often normally does after a meal rich in carbohydrates. The chronic presence of sugar in the urine suggests abnormal physiology. If the level of sugar in the blood is also chronically abnormally high, diabetes mellitus is indicated. As a result of inadequate secretion of pancreatic insulin, the metabolism of carbohydrates is interfered with, resulting in an accumulation in the blood of sugar, acetone (which may be smelled on the breath), and other substances. Notice that the appearance of sugar in the urine in diabetes is not due to "kidney trouble" but to "pancreas trouble."

Clinically, severe forms of diabetes are controlled by diet and administration of insulin.

Some mild cases of diabetes that develop usually only after the age of forty may not require insulin, but can be successfully treated with "hypoglycemic sulfonamides," which stimulate the sluggish pancreas to secrete more insulin.

Questions and Problems

31-5. Make a list of the **boldface** terms in this chapter. Write a brief description or definition of each. Compare your work with the text.

31-6. On a hot day, would a man keep cooler by sitting still or moving around? Argue both sides of the case. What factor other than temperature is involved?

‡31-7. In Blagden's experiments (§249), it was found that sprinkling the floor of the room (a) made the floor cooler, and (b) made the room unbearably hot for the people. Explain both phenomena.

‡31-8. Chloroform is immiscible with water and has a boiling point of 61.2°C. Suppose Blagden had used this substance to cover the pot of water instead of oil. What would have happened?

31-9. People who live in tropical regions with heavy rainfall seldom wear raincoats in the rain. Why?

‡31-10. Experience indicates that a man immersed in icy seas (temperature near 0°C) will die in 30–90 minutes if he remains motionless (e.g., clinging to a life raft). If however, he swims actively, he may be able to keep alive for half a day or more. Explain the difference.

31-11. Albacores and mackerels, which are large and active "game fish," have a body temperature several degrees above that of the surrounding water. The body temperature of sardines is not detectably greater than that of the environment. Account for the difference.

31-12. Clothing may act as a protection against the heat of the air as well as against the radiant energy of the sun. In completely dry air,

the highest tolerable air temperature is 138°F in the shade, if the human subject is clothed, but only 113°F in the shade, if nude. Are the traditional practices of primitive peoples in harmony with these facts?

‡31-13. The temperature of mines increases with the depth. It has been found that the highest temperature at which miners can live and work is about 88°F. Why is the limit not closer to 98.6°F?

31-14. In brief form, but as comprehensively as possible, state:

a. the argument for retaining the Fahrenheit scale;

b. the argument for replacing the Fahrenheit scale with the Celsius scale.

31-15. If you lived in a nation that already used only the Celsius scale, what arguments could you give for changing over to the Fahrenheit scale?

31-16. Is the analysis of Prob. 31-15 relevant to Prob. 31-14? Explain.

‡31-17. During the "chills" of malaria, the surface temperature of the body decreases; this leads to decreased heat loss by radiation. The heat loss by convection should also decrease— but it does not. It increases. How can this anomaly be explained?

‡31-18. John and Paul live in apartments that are identical in every respect. Neither has an air-conditioner; each has a large, standard electric refrigerator in the kitchen. On a very hot day, John phones Paul and says, "This is simply unbearable. I'm going to leave my refrigerator door open to cool the apartment."

Paul replies: "I'm not sure it will work, but let's watch our thermometers. Call me back in a couple of hours and tell me what the temperature is in your apartment."

Assuming that their thermometers are identical, accurate, and sufficiently sensitive, what will be the comparative temperatures two hours later? Explain.

31-19. If John were a good enough mechanic (Prob. 31-18), how might he alter his refrigerator so as to get the desired effect? Explain.

‡31-20. What is the net effect of refrigerative air-conditioners on the climate of a city in the summer time? Explain.

31-21. The answer to the preceding problem has what relevance to the problem of the maximum population supportable on the earth?

‡31-22. A tight ring can sometimes be removed from a finger if the hand is first immersed in soapy ice water. Explain.

31-23. "He died of renal failure accompanied by hepatic insufficiency, cardiac complications, and pulmonary edema." What does that mean?

‡31-24. Which food will have the greater immediate effect on heat production—500 Calories of protein or 500 Calories of carbohydrates? What about the total effect, over whatever period of time the food is respired?

31-25. How should the summer diet differ from the winter?

31-26. What is iodized salt? For what is it used?

‡31-27. During sleep the amount of urine secreted per hour is less than that secreted in the waking hours. Suggest an explanation.

31-28. Is the glomerular filtrate outside the body, or inside? Explain.

31-29. When proteins appear in the urine, what may be the trouble?

‡31-30. What effect will the following have on the amount and composition of urine: (a) a meal rich in carbohydrates; (b) large quantities of water; (c) a hot, dry day; (d) high blood pressure; (e) low blood pressure; (f) ruptured renal capsules; (g) hypoinsulinism; (h) death of tubule cells; (i) destruction of the posterior lobe of the pituitary gland?

31-31. Etymologically, what does the word "insulin" suggest? What is the rationale of its derivation? (Answering this may involve recourse to an unabridged dictionary, a medical dictionary, a physiology text, or a histology text.)

Readings

A most pleasing introduction to the principles of regulation in the organism as a whole is Cannon's *The Wisdom of the Body*; for a brief résumé of Cannon's studies see Chapter 8 of Garrett's *Great Experiments in Psychology*. Problems of regulation are approached in a more general way by Norbert Wiener in his *Cybernetics*; although many passages in this work are much too mathematical for most biologists, the book has the virtue of yielding many stimulating insights to the browser.

For more technical information on heat regulation, see Winslow and Herrington's *Temperature and Human Life* or Newburgh's *Physiology of Heat Regulation*. The first essay (by F. R. Wilson) in the latter book throws interesting light on clothing customs and adaptation to climate among various peoples. Schmidt-Nielsen's *Desert Animals* has a wealth of information about problems of heat adaptation.

32

The Senses

255. "Touch"

Traditionally, there are said to be five senses: touch, smell, taste, sight, and hearing. How inadequate this analysis is becomes apparent when we analyze the so-called sense of touch. A simple experiment, which the reader can perform on himself (or better, have someone else perform on him), will demonstrate the multiple nature of this sense. With a little care, rule a grid of squares on the back of your hand, with the lines 2 millimeters apart (Fig. 32-1). Then, with a stylus (a metal instrument with a tip a bit smaller than a pin's head), explore the area systematically for sensitive spots. A stylus that is at "room temperature" is colder than the skin and can be used as a test for cold-sensitive spots. On crosshatched paper, make a record of the distribution of "cold spots," that is, those spots where the coolness can be felt.

A similar record can be made of warm-sensitive spots, using a stylus gently warmed in a flame. When this record is compared with the preceding one, it is discovered that the "cold spots" and the "warm spots" sometimes coincide and sometimes do not. In other words, the

Fig. 32-1. *How to demonstrate that "touch" is more than one sense. See text.*

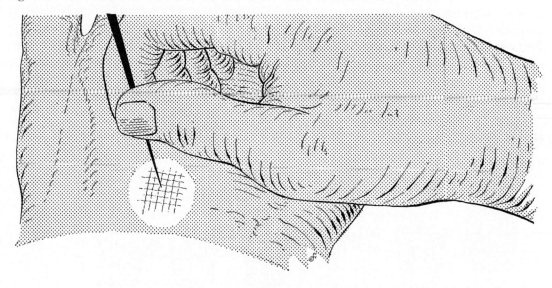

sense of cold and the sense of warmth are two different senses.

This fact is a matter of considerable interest as concerns the methodology of science. We have repeatedly emphasized the importance of analysis, of analyzing complex phenomena in terms of their simplest components, their *elements*. (Here we use the word in its broadest sense—not in its narrow chemical sense.) But what are the elements of any phenomenon or problem? Unfortunately, there is no philosopher's key to open the correct door to analysis. The raw material of all science is sense impressions. It is natural that we should use these as clues to the "elements." Yet, in dealing with problems of heat and temperature, sense impressions led men astray for centuries, causing them to think in terms of two "elements": *heat* and *cold*. It was only when physicists tried a different analysis, in terms of a single "element," *heat*, that facts fell into place. Physics is now based on this single "element," on a single scale of temperature, beginning at −273.18° Celsius, and going upward indefinitely. To the physicist, everything is hot: it's just a question of how hot. There is no such entity as "cold."

There is some truth in T. H. Huxley's statement that science is organized common sense, but we must not push this attitude too far, for the end product of scientific analysis is often contrary to common sense. Most psychological experiences lead to the common sense view of two temperature elements: heat and cold. Yet there was one experience, known for centuries, that could have led men to doubt the two-ele-

ment view of temperature. This experiment is recorded in Figure 32-2. Three buckets are filled with water: one with warm, one with medium, and one with cold water. The experimenter immerses his right hand in the warm, his left in the cold and leaves them there for perhaps a minute, at the end of which time the sensations of hot and cold have almost disappeared. Then he places both hands in the bucket containing water at room temperature (R.T. in the figure). Although both hands are subjected to the same temperature, the left hand reports that the water is warm, and the right hand that it is cold. From this we learn that the cold spots and warm spots are not sensitive to cold and warmth as such, but to changes. Sensitivity to *change* rather than to *absolute state* is a characteristic we shall find in other senses as well. As regards the temperature senses, the receptors are extraordinarily sensitive to change. A rise in temperature—at the level of the sensitive nerve endings under the skin—of only 0.001°C per second, continued for 3 seconds, will produce a sensation of warmth. Sensitivity to a lowering of temperature is only about a fourth as great.

Sensitivity to cold and warmth are part of what is popularly called the sense of touch. There is also sensitivity to touch in the strict sense. To test this, use a single bristle mounted in a holder. A bristle of a given diameter can exert no more than a fixed amount of pressure before it bends; consequently, it can be used for administering a standard stimulus. With such a bristle, you can map the touch-sensitive

Fig. 32-2. *A sense reports change rather than an absolute state.*

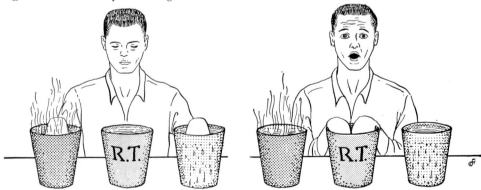

spots, which are found to be distributed independently of the warm and cold spots.

Yet a fourth sense constitutes a part of the sense of touch: the sense of pain. This sense can be tested with a needle-sharp instrument. Pain-sensitive spots are distributed independently of the other spots and are more closely spaced and more widely distributed over the body—a fact that no doubt contributes to the survival of the individual in a dangerous world.

What is the structural basis for the different touch sensations? Microscopic study of sections of skin shows a number of recognizably different nerve endings (Fig. 32-3). It is natural to guess that the different kinds of nerve endings subserve different sensations. It is difficult to prove this, for the phenomena we wish to in-vestigate are **subjective**—phenomena known only by the subject himself, and not identifiable in external objects, as are **objective** phenomena. Sensations of warmth and cold can be reported only by a human, so animal experimentation is ruled out. The curious experimentalist must use himself as the experimental animal, and this a few courageous men have done, first mapping the distribution of various spots on the skin and then having the section of skin sliced off and examined microscopically for the distribution of the various types of end organs and trying thus to correlate specific sensitivities with specific end organs. Unfortunately, the results of such experiments have not always been consistent. The most widely held theories are indicated in the legend of Figure 32-3.

Fig. 32-3. *Distinguishable nerve elements in or near the skin. Names and probable functions: (A) Free nerve endings (pain); (B) Merkel's discs (touch); (C) Meissner's corpuscles (touch); (D) Krause's end bulbs (cold); (E) Ruffini's end organs (warmth); (F) follicle nerve plexus (touch of hair); (G) endings of Ruffini (pressure); (H) Pacinian corpuscles (pressure).*

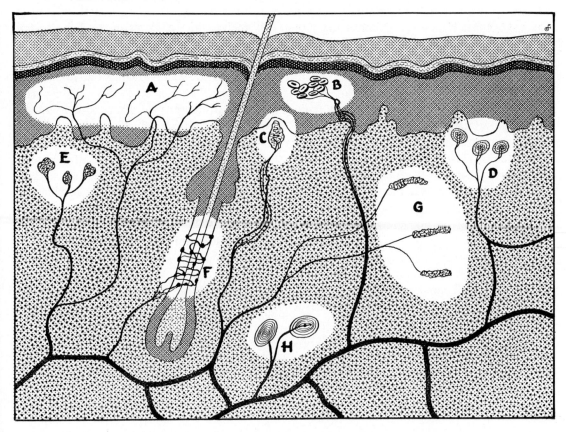

The nature of touch sensations has been somewhat simplified. For one thing, many investigators believe that there is another skin sense, one of pressure, distinct from touch in the strict sense. Moreover, we experience many sensations that are not easily identifiable as any of these simple sensations, for example, stinging, burning, and itching sensations. Consider also the sensations caused by tickling and by an electric shock. It is possible that these sensations are curious mixtures of several of the fundamental sensations.

We must realize also that a sense spot of a named type may be sensitive to more stimuli than its name would indicate, provided the stimulus is great enough. For instance, a very hot object will be *painfully* so, due in part to its affecting spots that we ordinarily regard as pain-receptors rather than heat-receptors. Heat may also affect the cold-receptors, paradoxical as this may seem; recall the shiver that often accompanies sudden immersion in a tub of hot water. The shiver and the sensation of cold come before the sensation of warmth; notice in Figure 32-3 that Krause's end bulbs, the supposed mediators of the sense of cold, are closer to the surface of the skin than are the Ruffini organs, the probable mediators of the sense of warmth.

The various touch senses are among those sometimes referred to as the **exteroceptive senses** (exterior perception)—senses that give us information about the exterior world, as contrasted with other senses, to be discussed subsequently, which give us information about our own interiors. It should be noted that even exteroceptive senses do not really give us information about the external world, but only about our own insides very close to the surface. A warm spot does not tell about external warmth, but only about the temperature changes taking place in the sensitive end organ itself, which is buried under our skin. Subjectively, however, we refer the feeling to the outside and say, "This room is hot," though it would be more accurate (but more pedantic) to say, "My Ruffini end organs report an increase in temperature."

The sense of touch operating through the hair follicles gives a striking example of our false localization of the source of a stimulus. When the hairs of the arm are lightly moved with a pencil, without touching the skin, one gets a distinct impression of feeling the pencil with the hair itself. Yet, all the hair that protrudes from the skin is dead. It can be cut without pain. And if we hold the basal portion of a hair steady with some tweezers, movement of the distal portion gives rise to no sensation. The hair itself is not sensitive. Sensation arises when the shaft of the hair, moving in its **follicle** (sheath), touches the nerve net that surrounds it (Fig. 32-3). This mechanism is a convenient way of extending the sense of touch beyond the limits of the living body by means of nonliving tissue. An exaggerated instance of such a mechanism is seen in the long "whiskers" of a cat, which enable it to get around in tight, dark places.

256. Pain: Puzzles and Implications

The analysis of the senses of touch just given is the traditional one. Underlying it is the desire to analyze psychological phenomena in a simple, mechanistic way—to find a one-to-one correspondence between subjective qualities and objective structures. We want to find end organs the stimulation of which will invariably produce predictable sensations. The simple picture we have given fits many of the facts of experience, but by no means all. Pain is particularly difficult to fit into this mechanistic view. By way of illustration, a number of findings will first be recorded with a minimum of comment; following this, some of their implications will be discussed.

1. How effective is morphine in relieving pain? Studies were made of three kinds of pain: postoperative pain, the pain of chronic cancer, and experimentally induced pain using volunteers. Each "sufferer" was given morphine, and whether or not he reported relief was recorded. Each person was used as a control also, being given a placebo some of the time. A **placebo** (L. I please) is a substance that is known from

other experiments to be without value. A typical placebo is distilled water to which are added sugar, quinine, or whatever innocuous substances may be needed to give it approximately the same taste as the drug (if the drug is taken by mouth). If the drug is colored, the placebo is colored to match.

It is important in carrying out such an experiment that the patient not know when he's receiving the placebo and when the test drug. To make sure that his expectations do not influence the results, one uses **double-blind tests:** the administering nurse does not herself know what she is administering, except by code number. Thus the nurse's possible expectations are prevented from influencing the patient's feelings.

The results of such experiments are shown in Table 32-1. In both types of "natural" pain,

TABLE 32-1 *Pain and Its Relief by Morphine or Placebo. (After Henry K. Beecher, 1959, Science **130**: 267–288.*

EXPERIMENTAL GROUP	PERCENTAGE RELIEVED BY MORPHINE	PERCENTAGE RELIEVED BY PLACEBO
Postoperative pain (122 subjects)	67	39
Pain of chronic cancer (57 subjects)	65	42
Experimentally induced pain	(variable and nonreproducible)	

about 66 percent found relief in morphine; *but about 40 percent reported relief from a placebo.* Plainly, there is more to pain than simple nerve endings. It is also noteworthy that attempts to test substances against experimentally induced pain gave variable and nonreproducible results. The attitude and expectations of a man voluntarily subjecting himself to painful stimuli are certainly different from those of a man who feels fate descending on him.

2. In the Second World War the reactions of soldiers seriously injured at the front was noticed. Only 1 out of 4 expressed a need for pain-killing drugs. In civilian practice, 4 out of 5 patients with comparable wounds ask for drugs.

Is it relevant that to the first group the injury is a harbinger of better times (relief from battle), while to the second it presages worse?

3. As a small child walks past his father, he is swatted on the rear. He looks up at his father with what we can only call a metamorphic expression—one that will turn into a laugh if his father's face is friendly, or will exhibit signs of intense pain if his father looks angry.

4. Hebb, Scott, and Melzack of McGill University raised some dogs in such a way that they were shielded from harmful stimulation. As adults the dogs seemed almost insensitive to pain. In a room with low water pipes, one dog was observed to bump his head on the pipes more than 30 times in an hour without giving any sign of pain.

5. Experiments with 97 pugilists showed that only 10 of them responded significantly to experimentally induced pain.

6. We speak of "painful muscles" being produced by unusual exercise. Yet many people report that "the pain feels good."

7. In the condition known as *hysteria,* the individual may appear utterly indifferent to the most harmful mutilations of his body. A hysteric is indeed a thing to wonder at. During the witch hunts of the Middle Ages, indifference to pain was (following the ideas of Tertullian) regarded as evidence of diabolic possession, and Inquisitors traveling from village to village were accompanied by "prickers," whose function it was to prick suspected people to see if they reacted to pain. Unlucky was he who felt no pain.

8. Hypnotism can destroy perception of pain. The explanation of hypnotism is still not in a satisfactory state, but of the reality of the phenomenon there is no longer any question. It is hard for us to believe facts that do not fit into accepted conceptual schemes of science. For the most part this attitude is productive of good; but, for long, it impeded the use of hypnotism in operations. In the middle of the nineteenth century, a Dr. Ward performed an amputation at the thigh on a hypnotized patient who later reported that he had felt no pain. When this was reported to a medical society, one of the members said that obviously the patient was an

impostor!* Another member asked that the report not be recorded in the minutes, saying: "If the history of the man experiencing no agony during the operation were true, still the fact is unworthy of consideration, because pain is a wise provision of nature, and patients ought to suffer pain while their surgeons are operating; they are all the better for it and recover better."

9. Consider this famous child's trick. Pull a hair out of someone else's head. But as you do it, hit him sharply on the back. If this is forcefully done, he doesn't feel the hair being pulled out.

10. W. S. Gardner and J. C. R. Licklider have shown that sound is a good **analgesic** (Gr. *a, an* = not + *algesis* = pain) for dental work. The patient is fitted with earphones which give him a steady background of music against which he can interpose a variable amount of "white noise." Of 1,000 patients undergoing drilling or extraction of teeth 65 percent found the pain was completely suppressed, 25 percent experienced some pain but asked for no other analgesic, leaving only 10 percent for whom sound was not a sufficient analgesic. An important aspect of the procedure is that the patient himself controls the knobs regulating noise level.

It is clear that we cannot, at the present time, fit all of these data into any simple mechanistic explanation of pain. We need investigations of another sort, which we vaguely refer to as "psychological." Out of such investigations several generalizations have come, which we present not as ultimate, universal "laws" but as tentative "working hypotheses," useful for the guidance of daily affairs.

A. "Pain is a matter of opinion," as one Oriental mystic said. Occidentals find it hard to believe this is wholly true, but there's something in it.

B. We are taught to feel pain. Again, we feel that this is not wholly true; but if we watch carefully the interactions of a mother and her child, we see surprisingly many instances of the

teaching of pain of which both teacher and pupil are unaware.

C. Pain is a form of communication. The expression of pain may be used as a weapon for controlling others. A frequent consequence of the communicatory use of pain is revealed in an aphorism of MacFie Campbell's: "A family is an autocracy ruled by its sickest member."

257. Taste

Much of what we call taste is actually smell, as we learn when a severe cold completely plugs the nasal passages. When so afflicted, we discover that we can still taste a few things: *sweet, salt, sour,* and *bitter*. There are also a few other things we can taste, for example, copper sulfate (though we find it difficult to characterize its taste, except to say that it is harsh and unpleasant). But most of our taste sensations we can categorize under the four italicized words given above. Most of the delights of eating depend on the nose. Deprived of our sense of smell, we have difficulty telling an onion from an apple.

The four taste sensitivities are differently distributed over the surface of the tongue. Using the least strong solution (of sugar, salt, citric acid, or quinine) that will elicit taste sensations, it has been found that the areas sensitive to the various substances are as shown in Figure 32-4A. This does not mean that the substances cannot be tasted everywhere on the tongue—they can—but that the specific sensitivities vary. The sensitivity to quinine, for instance, is six times as great at the back of the tongue as it is at the tip. This fact partly explains the frequent experience of noticing a bitterness in some food or drink only as an "aftertaste," that is, after swallowing. The end organ responsible for the ability to taste is the **taste bud,** a cluster of cells sunk in the surface of the tongue (Fig. 32-4B). The differences in sensitivities of the various parts of the tongue imply differences in end organs, though these have not yet been demonstrated.

Much remains to be learned about the physi-

---

* 32-1. The other side of the coin: One person will often say to another, "Oh, your pain is just imaginary." What about it?

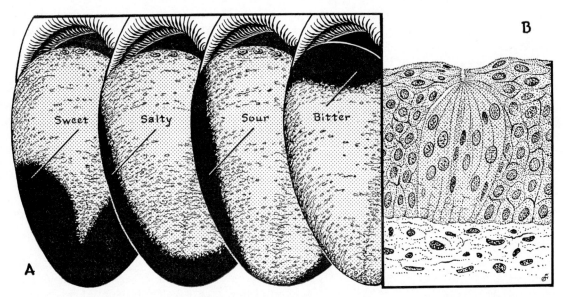

Fig. 32-4. (A) *The areas most sensitive to the different taste qualities are indicated as black areas on the surface of the tongue.* (B) *A magnified section of a taste bud.*

ology of taste, particularly about the results of combining substances with different tastes. Some substances are notorious for their ability to "cover up" unwanted tastes (using "taste" in the broad sense to include both tastes and odors). Ginger and chocolate are such. In the days before strict food laws, moldy wheat was "saved" by making it into gingerbread. Ice-cream makers have found that a mistake in mixing flavoring ingredients need not result in the loss of a "mix"—it can almost always be turned into a satisfactory chocolate ice cream.

Other substances have an unexplained facility of intensifying tastes. Most remarkable of these is the organic substance glutamic acid, or its derivative *monosodium glutamate,* called **MSG** for short. For centuries, Chinese and Japanese cooks used certain seaweeds to intensify the taste of their food. A Japanese chemist, K. Ikeda, found that the active ingredient in seaweeds was glutamic acid. This substance, or MSG, can now be extracted from many other plant materials, including the wastes from sugar-beet factories. Pure MSG produces all four taste sensations in a mild degree. Mixed with other organic substances, it seems only to intensify the taste of the other materials.

Research has disclosed considerable differ-ences between individuals in taste sensitivity. These differences are not merely of a *quantitative* sort, but are also sometimes *qualitative.* The chemical substance *phenylthiocarbamide* (**PTC** for short) tastes bitter to about 7 persons out of 10; to most of the remainder, it has no taste at all, though a few report it as sweet or salty. The uncommon sugar *mannose* tastes sweet to only about 1 person in 5; 10 percent find it bitter; and 55 percent experience a sweet taste followed by a bitter taste. The remainder say it is tasteless.

With the use of pure chemicals, a number of other taste differences have been found. Undoubtedly, differences in taste reactions to pure chemicals are among the factors contributing to differences in judgments of the palatability of various foodstuffs and dishes. The old saying, "There's no disputing tastes," has been given new support.

258. Olfaction

The nose is sensitive to a multitude of volatile substances. The sense of smell, or **olfaction,** is unquestionably more important than taste to most animals. Food, sexual mates, or enemies can often be detected at a great distance and in terrain that makes vision difficult. The amount of substance required for olfactory detection seems sometimes very small. The human nose (by no means the best) reacts to as little as 2.2 × 10^{-12} gram of methyl mercaptan ($CH_3 \cdot SH$), the odor of garlic. However, it is worth pointing out that even this weight, which seems small by everyday standards, contains about 2.8 × 10^{10} molecules.

The nose is sensitive to many more different qualities than is the tongue. There is unquestionably some correlation between chemical structure and odor, though the relations are not simple enough to permit predicting the one from the other with complete accuracy. A good organic chemist, however, finds his nose invaluable in analytical work.

The end organs of the sense of smell are nerve endings modified as shown in Figure 32-5*A*. The placing of the **olfactory tissue** is remarkable. There are only about 2.5 square centimeters of sensitive tissue in each nostril, placed high up in the breathing passages, so that an ordinary, gentle breath causes very little air to go past the sensory cells (Fig. 32-5*B*). A vigorous breath (Fig. 32-5*C*), however, produces a turbulence that carries some air past the olfactory tissue. Hence the importance of *sniffing* when we suspect there is something smellable in the air.

259. The Fatigue of a Sense

In discussing the sensitivity of the temperature receptors of the skin, it was pointed out that the receptors are really sensitive only to *changes* in temperature—that when an area is long exposed to a constant temperature, it ceases to be

Fig. 32-5. *The olfactory nerve endings* (A), *indicated in color, are placed high in the nasal passages* (B). *The nerve endings are scarcely stimulated by a gentle inspiration* (B), *but a vigorous sniff* (C) *brings a good sample of air to the sense organs.*

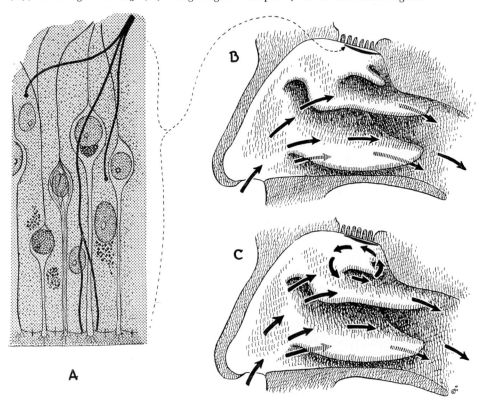

"aware" of that temperature. Another way of verbalizing the same phenomenon is to say that the sense of temperature becomes *fatigued*. The development of fatigue is characteristic of all the senses, to a greater or less degree. The phenomenon of fatigue of the olfactory sense is both conspicuous and practically important.

When we first step into a bakery shop, the olfactory experience is, for most people, one of pure delight. But, if we stay there long, our perception of the odors diminishes almost to the vanishing point. This fatigue of the olfactory sense, it can be shown by experiments, is not a general fatigue. Subjection to the bakery odor does not dull the nose to other, fresh odors. Though there are exceptions, olfactory fatigue is usually specific for each odor. This fact, together with the fact that most of what we call "taste" is actually smell, explains many of the practices of the gourmet, for example, the preference given to the multicourse banquet over the one-dish meal.

Fatigue to *un*pleasant odors is probably a fact of greater importance. It is common practice for domestic gas companies to add malodorous substances to the gas supply. These substances are detectable in very small quantities and serve to warn the home-owner when a leak has developed in his gas lines. However, if the leak develops slowly and steadily while he remains at home, the fatigue of his olfactory sense may keep pace, so to speak, with the increase in concentration of gas in the room, and as a result he may be asphyxiated without his nose ever warning him.

The fatigability of the olfactory sense may even have international consequences. Some white Occidentals speak disparagingly of the odors of humans of other racial groups, the implication being, "Of course, *we* don't smell." However, white people who have spent much time in China sometimes learn to their horror that the Chinese consider them distinctly odorous in an objectionable way. This is a fact that a man can never discover about himself because of the phenomenon of olfactory fatigue. How can one smell the body he has lived with all of his life? There is probably nothing white

people can do about their affliction—though frequent baths may help minimize the offense—but it is a fact they should always keep in mind in their dealings with other peoples. Satisfactory relations with others require more than good will; self-awareness is also necessary.

260. Hearing

That which is the primary function of the ear we shall ignore for the present—namely, its function as an organ of equilibrium. In primitive vertebrates, the ear was only an organ of equilibrium; the auditory function was assumed much later in evolutionary development. In man, the ear serves both functions.

For convenience, the ear is considered as consisting of three portions: the outer, middle, and inner ears. The **outer ear** (Fig. 32-6) consists of the decorative flap on the outside of the head, called the **pinna** (Gr. a kind of mussel, evidently because of its resemblance to a mussel half-shell), and the **external auditory passage** leading inward. In so-called lower animals, the pinna serves as an admirable trumpet to collect and concentrate the sound waves; it can be moved or turned so as to be most favorably oriented toward the source of the sound. Recall, for instance, the mobile pinnae of horses and mules. Among men, only a few virtuosi can move their ears at all, and then to little or no acoustic advantage. To achieve the sound-gathering effect of a large pinna, a man may cup his hand behind his ear and aim the concavity at the source of a sound. This act is especially useful to the hard-of-hearing.

The problem of hearing is one of concentrating and transmitting vibrations. What we call *sound waves* consist of alternate regions of condensation and rarefaction of air molecules. These waves move at a speed of about one-fifth mile per second (though the individual molecules move very little—just as the particles of water in a pond move very little as waves pass over the pond). The pinna concentrates the waves somewhat and directs them down the external auditory passage, at the end of which

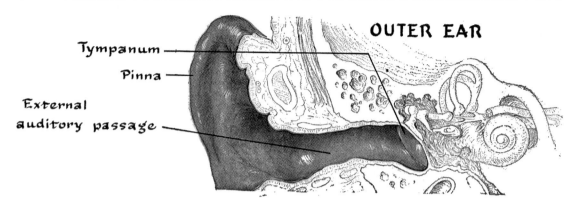

Tympanum

Pinna

External
auditory passage

Fig. 32-6. *The parts of the outer ear.*

they strike the **tympanum,** or *eardrum.* In this way, wave motion in the air is translated into vibratory motion of the eardrum.

Following the route of this vibration, we go next to the middle-ear cavity (Fig. 32-7), an air-filled space in which repose three bones hinged together: the **malleus,** the **incus,** and the **stapes** (i.e., the hammer, the anvil, and the stirrup, from their resemblance to these objects). The first bone, the malleus, is attached to the tympanum; the last bone, the stapes, is attached to a similar membrane at the other side of the middle-ear cavity, the so-called **oval window.** The path of the vibration so far is this: Air waves striking the tympanum move it; the tympanum moves the malleus, which moves the incus, which moves the stapes, which moves the membrane of the oval window. What does the oval window move?

The oval window forms the boundary of the inner ear (Fig. 32-8). The inner ear is the ac-

tual organ of hearing; it is here that mechanical vibrations are converted into nerve impulses. All the rest of the machinery of the outer and middle ear is merely for the purpose of conveying the vibrations to this region. *The inner ear is filled with fluid.* When one recalls that fluids cannot be compressed, it will be realized that the pressure exerted by the stapes against the oval window must somehow be relieved. The relief mechanism is the membrane called the **round window.** Vibration of the oval window causes the fluid within to vibrate, which in turn vibrates the round window.

The part of the inner ear concerned with hearing is called the **cochlea** (L. snail). How does the vibration of the fluid in the cochlea give rise to sensations? We can understand the mechanism better if, in imagination, we straighten out the cochlea (Fig. 32-9*B*), and then slice across it and examine the slice under the microscope(Fig. 32-9*C*). A section of the

Fig. 32-7. *The parts of the middle ear.*

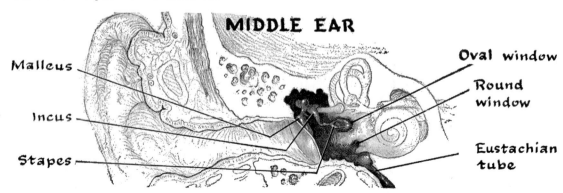

Malleus

Incus

Stapes

Oval window

Round window

Eustachian tube

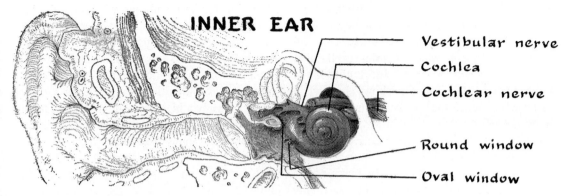

INNER EAR

Vestibular nerve
Cochlea
Cochlear nerve

Round window
Oval window

Fig. 32-8. *The inner ear structures that are concerned with hearing.*

Fig. 32-9. (A) *The cochlea of the ear. Imagine the cochlea to be much enlarged and uncoiled* (B); *a cross-section of it reveals the structures shown in* C.

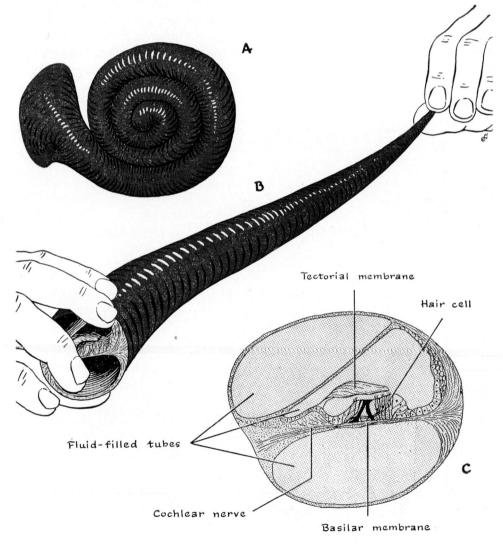

A

B

Tectorial membrane

Hair cell

Fluid-filled tubes

Cochlear nerve

Basilar membrane

C

cochlea shows more details than we need as-similate at first. In the center there is a flexible ledge called the **tectorial membrane** (L. *tectorium* = a cover) which overhangs hairlike processes attached to nerve cells. Studies made with experimental animals show that when sound waves reach the ear, nerve impulses pass along the nerves that come from the hair cells below the tectorial membrane. How can a sound stimulate these cells?

At this point, we must enter the realm of hypotheses. Experimentation presents so many difficulties that the true mechanism of hearing is not yet firmly established. The picture presented below is supported by considerable indirect evidence.

The **basilar membrane,** on which the **hair cells** rest, is flexible. It seems reasonable to suppose that vibration of the fluid of the cochlea will cause vibration of the basilar membrane.

Vibration of the membrane will move the hair cells up and down; this movement of the hair cells will press them against the tectorial membrane, thus stimulating the hair cells and causing a nervous impulse to travel along the nerve. (Notice that if this theory is true, the sense of hearing is only a highly modified sense of touch, evoked by touching the cochlear hair cells).

There are many phenomena an adequate theory of hearing must account for. For one thing, man can discriminate approximately 340,000 different tones. Moreover, when two or more pure tones are sounded simultaneously, our ear can detect this fact and, with training, can analyze the mixture into separate components. Most people can do this by a matching procedure, but a minority of individuals gifted with "absolute pitch" can *name* the component notes without recourse to matching.

The approximate range of the human ear is

Fig. 32-10. *Sensitivity of the human ear to various audio frequencies.*

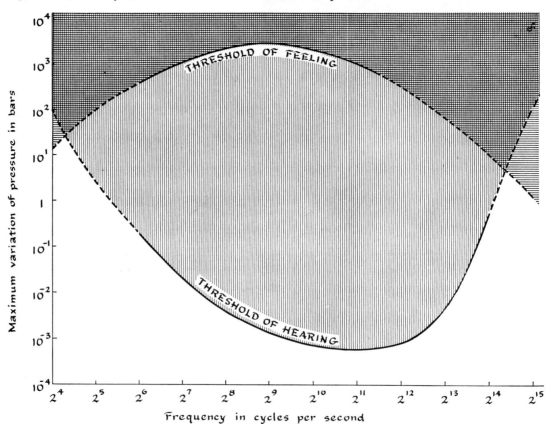

Fig. 32-11. *Stroboscopic photograph of a bat approaching (right to left) a mealworm thrown into the air (bottom to top). The bat finds the food by echo location. (Courtesy Frederic A. Webster.)*

shown in Figure 32-10. The lower curve gives the **threshold** of hearing,* that is, the lowest energy level of the sound waves that will produce a perceptible sound. It will be noted that the maximum sensitivity of the ear is at about three octaves above middle C. The hearing curve is dotted at each end to indicate considerable individual variability. The merging of hearing into feeling at the lower end is noticed by anyone who listens to the lowest notes of a fine pipe organ. At the other extreme, the feeling of high-pitched notes soon becomes painful. Loss of hearing in the upper register is a normal accompaniment of age; a man of fifty hears about an octave less than a boy of ten, the best age for hearing.

It is, of course, well known that the hearing range of animals varies. The hearing of dogs, for example, extends farther into the upper register than does man's. This fact is the basis for Francis Galton's "silent" or "supersonic" dog whistle. In recent years, the hearing of bats has been very thoroughly investigated by Donald Griffin of Harvard, who has found that, whereas the hearing of man stops at about 2^{14} cycles per second, that of some species of bats extends up to around 2^{17} cps. This is a matter of great practical importance to the bat, for it has made possible the evolution of an echo location system that is far superior to that of most animals. Locating objects by echoes is possible to any animal with two ears; the differences in the echoes of an object as they are heard by the two ears can be interpreted in terms of the size, distance, and direction of the object. Man, being primarily a sight-oriented animal, usually does not pay much attention to echoes. A blind man may, however, become pretty proficient at the art of navigation by "sonar." However, the efficiency of echo location is directly related to the number of cycles per second of the sound. The greater the number of cps (the shorter the

* 32-2. Explain this architectural metaphor.

wave length), the finer the discrimination possible. The noises emitted and heard by bats are of such a short wave length that a bat can fly through a pitch-black room strung with wires without hitting a one. Insectivorous bats locate their food by echo location. Figure 32-11 shows the maneuver of a bat approaching its food. These bats usually feed on very small insects (even as small as fruitflies), taken on the wing; but these are hard to photograph. Therefore, to make photography easy, a quite unnatural food was used, a "mealworm" (larva of a beetle), which was thrown into the air. The photograph shows two superimposed pictures of the same bat and worm, taken at an interval of one-twelfth second. The lower image of both bat and worm was taken with the first flash of the stroboscope, the upper with the second. The accuracy of the bat's aim is obvious.

261. Vision

For man, and many other diurnal animals, vision is perhaps the most important sense by which knowledge of distant things is gained. Visible light is only a very tiny portion of the "electromagnetic spectrum," as Figure 32-12 emphasizes. With his physical instruments, man can easily study radiations ranging in wave length from 10^5 meters to 10^{-20} meters, but with his eye he can see only from about $10^{-6.4}$ to $10^{-6.2}$ meters. But this small portion of the spectrum is so subdivided (so to speak) by his visual apparatus that he can distinguish some 7,500,000 different colors.

The structure of man's light-perceiving organ, his eye, can best be studied by comparing it to a camera (Fig. 32-13). The camera consists of a system of lenses whose net effect is that of a convex lens; a dark chamber filled with air; and a sensitive screen, called the film, at focal distance from the lens system. There is also a diaphragm between the lenses for modifying the amount of light that reaches the film. Also present, but not indicated in the diagram, is a shutter, which is usually closed.

The eye is strikingly similar to the camera.

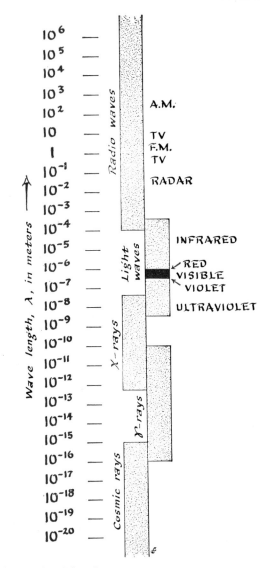

Fig. 32-12. *The electromagnetic spectrum.*

Again, there is a system of lenses—two lenses in this case—one of which is called the **cornea** (L. *corneus* = horny, tough) the other being called the **lens;** a dark chamber filled with fluid; and a sensitive screen called the **retina** (derived, for reasons we will soon appreciate better, from the Latin *rete* = net). Between the lenses is a diaphragm called the **iris.**

There are three conspicuous differences in construction between camera and eye. In the first place, the eye has no shutter like the camera—unless one wishes to regard the eyelid as

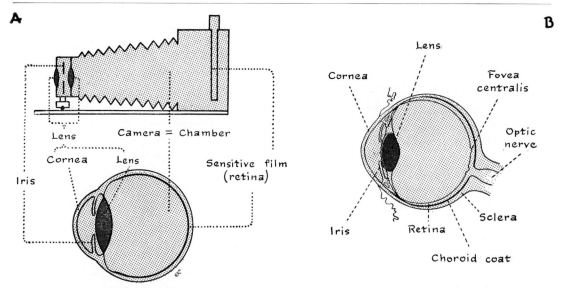

Fig. 32-13. (A) *The basic similarities of the eye and a camera.* (B) *A larger view of the eye with the more important structures labeled.*

Fig. 32-14. *Accomodation to near objects can be made* (A) *by moving the lens farther from the retina or film; this method is employed in the camera and in the eyes of squids and some fish. Man and many other animals achieve the same end by altering the curvature of the lens* (B).

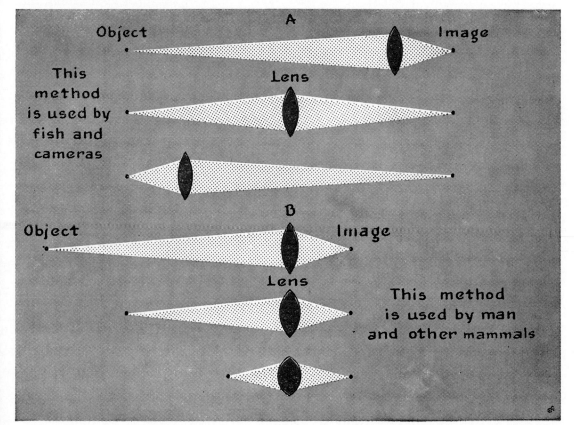

a shutter. The eye can remain open continuously because—second difference—the sensitive screen (retina) can be used over and over again for "taking pictures" in the eye; whereas, in the camera, the screen (film) can be used for only one picture (unless one doesn't object to double exposures).

The third conspicuous difference lies in the method of focusing. With a fixed convex lens and a movable object, experiments show that, as the object approaches the lens, the position of the image on the other side moves in the same direction, that is, away from the lens (Fig. 32-14A). Obviously, there is no one focal distance at which all objects, however far from the lens, can be focused. If a picture-taking system is to work for both near and far objects, one of two modifications of the system must be possible. Either it must be possible to change the lens-to-screen distance (Fig. 32-14A), or it must be possible to change the curvature of the lens (Fig. 32-14B). In the camera, the first adjustment is made; in the human eye, the second. Interestingly enough, the eyes of many fish adjust after the fashion of the camera.

The greater part of the lens action of the eye is carried out by the cornea. The "lens" is merely an *auxiliary lens* to permit accommodation. In one form of a disease called **cataract,** the lens becomes opaque. Vision can be restored by removal of the lens, and substitution of a corresponding glass spectacle lens outside the eye—a lens that cannot accommodate to various distances, of course. In another form of cataract, the cornea becomes opaque. The only remedy for this abnormality is the replacement of the defective cornea with a healthy, living cornea from a living, or recently living, donor. There is a slowly growing tradition of making provision for this laudable use of part of one's body after death.

The retina is the sensitive screen on which the image formed by the lens system is projected. This screen is made up—as we shall see presently—of thousands of nerve endings, tightly packed together. How can light affect a nerve or a nerve ending? Ordinary nerves are not stimulated by this agent. By what means are retinal nerves stimulated by light?

Research has shown that the perception of light involves a cycle of chemical reactions, briefly diagrammed in Figure 32-15. In the retina there is a red-colored chemical compound called **visual purple.** It is made up of two parts: a protein, and a simpler compound, **retinene,** which gives it its color. Visual purple is unstable in the presence of light: it breaks down to protein and retinene. Retinene further decomposes to form a substance already familiar to us, vitamin A. In the presence of living, actively metabolizing cells, vitamin A plus protein can be used to make visual purple once more.

The light-induced decomposition of visual purple to form retinene plus protein is called the "primary light reaction." Some substance or substances (perhaps the retinene) produced by this reaction stimulate the nearby nerve endings, thus producing (when the impulse gets to the brain) a sensation of light. In other words, the basic reaction of vision is a chemical one and, as such, falls into the same class as the reactions responsible for taste and smell.

The function of vitamin A should be noticed. Undoubtedly every vitamin is required because it plays a definite role in the metabolism of the body. Determining the functions of the various vitamins has been a long and difficult job, which is still not finished. Vitamin A was the first vitamin to be firmly tied to body chemistry. It is required for the synthesis of visual purple. One of the clinical signs of vitamin A deficiency is "night blindness," in which the eyes of the sufferer fail to respond to weak light. As a result, such a person can see well only in strong light, such as daylight.

The chemical reactions involved in vision take place among the cells of the retina. The retina is an exceedingly complex structure, as Figure 32-16 makes evident. It is composed of many different kinds of cells, only some of which are identified in the figure. The sensitive cells are called **rods** and **cones.**

How fine a line one can see is determined by many factors, which fall into two main classes: the quality of the optical system (lens, cornea,

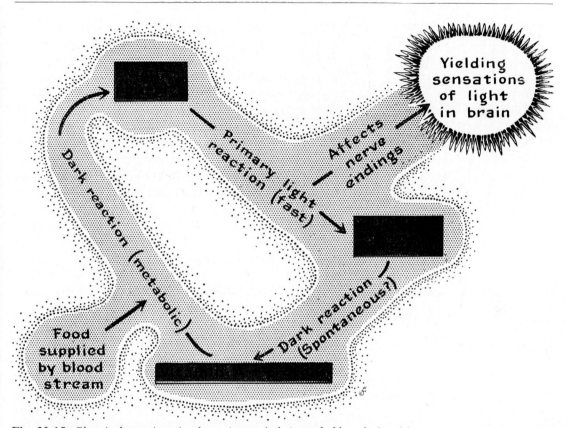

Fig. 32-15. *Chemical reactions in the retina and their probable role in vision.*

and so on), and the fineness of the retinal mosaic. The first varies enormously, as the abundance and variety of spectacles in our society bear witness; the extent of the variation of the second has not been studied, but it probably varies greatly also. It should be pointed out that in the eye of each individual there is considerable variation from one region of the retina to another. In the central region, the **fovea centralis** (L. a small pit) (Fig. 32-13*B*), which contains only cones—a point we shall return to later—the cones are only a third as wide as they are elsewhere in the retina, and there are about six times as many cones per unit area as there are cones and rods in other regions. This is the region we use whenever we give our closest attention; we focus the object on this area of "finest grain." Another factor that contributes to the relatively greater acuity of vision in this region is the relation of rods and cones to nerve cells. In the central region, there is one nerve cell for each sensitive cell, as depicted in Figure

32-16. Elsewhere, there are more sensitive cells than nerve cells; and the more distant the region from the fovea centralis, the greater this ratio. At the edge of the retina, there are as many as 250 sensitive cells to each nerve cell, and all 250 sensitive cells act as a unit in the visual mosaic.

What are the functions of rods and cones? What are their differences? The answers to these questions have been found by correlating the distribution of rods and cones over the retinal area with observed differences in capabilities of different parts of the retina.

With respect to structure:

1. The centermost part of the fovea centralis contains only cones; and there are very few rods in any part of the fovea.

2. In regions other than the fovea, both rods and cones are present; the greater the distance from the fovea, the more rods and the fewer cones.

With regard to function:

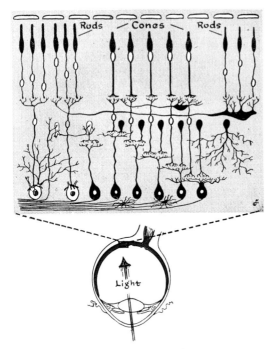

Fig. 32-16. *The construction of the retina. Notice the many structures the light must pass through before it strikes the light-sensitive elements, the rods and cones.*

1. Perception of color is excellent in the fovea and declines gradually with distance from the fovea. (With your eye fixed on a point straight ahead, have someone else bring a colored object slowly into your field of vision, moving it from periphery to center. Notice that you can *see* the object before you can tell its color.)

2. Perception of dim light is most acute outside the fovea. (In looking for stars at night, notice that you can see the dimmest of them only "when you don't look at them," that is, when you don't focus them on the fovea.)

From these observations, we deduce that perception of color is a function of the cones; and that, though both rods and cones are sensitive to light, the rods are the more sensitive.

An important characteristic of our vision is that known as **persistence of vision.** If a light is alternately turned on and off with increasing frequency, at a certain frequency (called the **critical fusion frequency**) the observer reports that the light is continuously on. At this (and

higher) frequencies the image seen during the light phase persists during the dark. The critical fusion frequency is different for different individuals and for the same individual under different physiological conditions. Typically it ranges from 15 to 30 alternations per second. Motion pictures depend on the persistence of vision for their success in creating an illusion of continuous motion. Images are flashed on the screen 48 times per second, and after every flash the screen is completely dark, but we are unable to perceive this fact.

262. Are There Other Senses?

The traditional view is that there are five senses. We have seen how inadequate this view is—how, for instance, "touch" is a complex of several different senses. Yet it may be maintained that the traditional number of five is still correct, in a sense—that analysis has merely resulted in showing that what were thought to be unitary senses are actually classes of senses. Are there any other senses—senses that detect physical events other than sound waves, light waves, chemical reactions, or the impingement of one body on another? Is there a "sixth sense"?

From time to time some investigator has reported evidence for the transmission of information from one human to another without the intermediation of sound, light, electric impulses, or any other known physical means of communication. One of the most recent of these claimants speaks of "extrasensory perception," or ESP. Reports tell of the occasional passage of ideas or images from one human to another in a distant room, without the use of any detectible means of transmission. Can a human send out some sort of "thought waves" that are not light waves, radio waves, sound waves, or any other known physical phenomenon? Can some humans receive and interpret them?

There is a great contrast between the attitude of the nonscientific press and that of scientists. Although the lay press gives much space and serious consideration to the possibility of a sixth sense, scientists (by and large) give scant credence and little attention to it. Why is this? At least two factors contribute to the attitude of scientists; they are worth stating here for the light they throw on the way scientists work.

First, and most important, the results reported have not proven to be repeatable by other scientists, and thus the facts fail to satisfy the scientific criterion of repeatability (§3). For every investigator who has reported positive evidence of "extrasensory perception" or "sixth sense," dozens of at least equally competent and careful workers have obtained only negative evidence.

Second, the reported phenomena do not fit in with any conceptual scheme known to scientists. How is one to visualize a message which is not transmitted by light, sound, electricity, magnetism, radio waves, or any other known means? Since a fact may be a fact even though it is mysterious, this second objection has less logical force than the first, but *psychologically* it contributes greatly to the attitude of scientists toward the spasmodic reports of a "sixth sense." By itself, this reason would not be enough; coupled with the first it is sufficient to justify refusal to devote further attention to this subject unless and until repeatable evidence is produced.

Questions and Problems

32-3. Make a list of the **boldface** terms in this chapter. Write a brief description of each. Compare your work with the text.

‡32-4. Some fishes, some insects, some birds, and most primates have color vision; most other tested animals seem to have only monochromatic vision. What kind of evolution is this called?

32-5. A government agency criticized a dogfood manufacturer for labeling different boxes of its dogfood as being "chicken flavor," "beef flavor," "milk flavor," etc., when investigation disclosed that only minute quantities of the substances named had been added to the basic formula in manufacturing. The company's lawyer defended the practice in these words: "Until we can get a dog who speaks the English language, we can't tell whether these biscuits really have a meat or a chicken flavor. Since you cannot prove that they don't, you have no grounds for objection."

Identify and discuss the issues involved.

32-6. Generally, does a sense organ tell us about the absolute value of a stimulating condition or about its rate of change? Evidence?

32-7. What justification could one give for lumping the sense of hearing with the senses of touch? Or the sense of sight with the senses of smell and taste?

32-8. Mr. Smithers, who had run hard for four blocks, noticed the odor of some flowers in Jones' room the minute he stepped in. Mr. Van Alstyne, who was driven to Jones' door by a chauffeur, did not notice the odor until it was called to his attention. Assuming that the men are equally sensitive to odors, and equally observant, can you explain the difference in their reactions?

‡32-9. Three families live among the glue factories (Fig. 32-17). Mrs. Dyer, Mrs. Freeman, and Mrs. Hardin have never been known to leave their houses. The town's two glue factories are distinguishable by name but not by odor. From midnight to noon, the wind blows continuously from north to south, and from noon to midnight from south to north. The wind never blows in any other direction and there are never any lulls. One of the housewives never complains of the odor. Which one? Why?

32-10. At one time, it was believed that infantile paralysis could be prevented in children by frequently spraying the upper nasal chambers with a chemical that hardened the epithelium and temporarily destroyed the nerve endings.

Fig. 32-17. *The impingement of physiology on real estate values.*

While undergoing this treatment, the children complained that they did not enjoy eating as much as usual. Can you explain this reaction?

‡32-11. Compare the following sentences:
a. The sun is 93 million miles away.
b. Man is an animal.
c. This rose is red.
d. This fruit is sweet.
e. This fruit is good.

Does the word "is" have the same meaning in all these sentences? If not, explain.

32-12. Cite instances in which failure to recognize the multiple meanings of the word "is" might lead to difficulties in human relationships.

32-13. A manufacturer develops a new model refrigerator that produces very little noise, most of which is high-pitched. After several thousand of these have been placed in homes, a number of the customers complain of the noise of the machine. When these reports are followed up, it is noticed that most of the complaints come from families with children, a few from families without, and none at all from households composed only of retired couples. Suggest a simple, possible explanation for these facts.

How could the company carry out research designed to get rid of the offending noise?

‡32-14. *Backsonia herbivora*, the spotted whangdoodle of the Western plains, has a critical fusion frequency of 60 cps. As is well known, in their mentality and tastes, whangdoodles are indistinguishable from men. Do whangdoodles like to go to the movies?

‡32-15. About 1900, a German physician named Stenger discovered an important fact about hearing and pointed out its usefulness in forensic medicine. If, using earphones, the same sound is brought to both ears, but more strongly in one than the other, the normal person will identify the sound as coming solely from the ear receiving the stronger stimulus. Explain carefully how this phenomenon can be used to detect malingering.

32-16. An individual is outfitted with earphones so that his own speech is fed back to his ears through an apparatus with a variable delay. When there is a delay of about one-quarter of a second, he loses the ability to speak normally: his speech becomes slow, arrhythmic, and even disorganized. Give a cybernetic explanation.

32-17. What forensic use might be made of the phenomenon described above?

‡32-18. Completely deaf, but not mute, people have to be retrained to speak every few years by special teachers. Why does their ability to

speak deteriorate slowly in the intervals between training sessions?

32-19. Describe two kinds of cataract. Describe the remedial treatments.

32-20. What is the evidence that the retinal cones are concerned with color vision? That both rods and cones are sensitive to light but that the rods are more sensitive?

32-21. Where in the body is sensation located? Discuss this problem.

‡32-22. The English philosopher Bertrand Russell has remarked: "If one person sees red where another sees green, and green where another sees red, the fact will be undiscoverable and harmless." True or false? Explain.

32-23. Positive evidence of extrasensory perception is reported by *A*. *B* repeats the experiments and confirms *A*'s report. *C, D, E, F, G, H, I,* and *J* repeat the experiments and report only negative findings. From these facts, should we conclude that ESP truly exists or not?

32-24. What is the proper criterion of a "scientific truth"—that it shall be based on findings that *have been repeated* or on findings that *are repeatable?* Justify your answer.

‡32-25. Does a fish at the bottom of the sea know what "wetness" is?

32-26. We speak of a feeling of "wetness"; does this mean another primary sense must be added to those listed in §255? Explain.

32-27. A dog that is trained to find the owner of a glove presented to it will be confused if it is handed a glove belonging to one member of a pair of identical twins. What is the significance of this observation?

‡32-28. The retinas of mice and dogs are deficient in cones. What would you predict about their vision?

32-39. Would you expect cone-free retinas to be commoner among diurnal or nocturnal animals?

‡32-30. The following passage occurs in Herodotus (fifth century B.C.):

The water of this stream is lukewarm at early dawn. At the time when the market fills it is much cooler; by noon it has grown quite cold; at this time therefore they water their gardens. As the afternoon advances, the coldness goes off, till, about sunset the water is once more lukewarm.

What is the most likely explanation of the report?

Readings

For original papers in the field of sensory perception, see Dennis' *Readings in the History of Psychology.* On the "central" aspects of perception, Adrian's little book is excellent. The question of ESP is a splendid one for probing the nature of scientific method. See especially an article by George R. Price in *Science,* **122**:359–367 (1955), and various rejoinders in *Science,* **123**:7–19 (1956). Also see Brown's *Probability and Scientific Inference.*

The exciting story of echo location by bats may be found in Griffin's *Listening in the Dark.*

Scientific American Offprints

133. E. G. F. Sauer. *Celestial Navigation by Birds*

145. W. H. Thorpe. *The Language of Birds*

173. C. G. Johnson. *The Aerial Migration of Insects*

179. W. R. A. Muntz. *Vision in Frogs*

184. A. C. Crombie. *Early Concepts of the Senses and the Mind*

411. Arthur D. Hasler and James A. Larsen. *The Homing Salmon*

458. Donald S. Blough. *Experiments in Animal Psychophysics*

459. Robert L. Fantz. *The Origin of Form Perception*

The Organism as a Whole: External Adjustments

33

263. Where Do We Feel?

Consider our sensations of feeling, tasting, smelling, hearing, and seeing. Where do we have these sensations? The natural response is that we feel at our skin, taste in our mouth, and so on. But do we? In a sense, yes; but we know enough of physiology now to bring forward evidence not compatible with this simple view.

Occasionally, as a result of accident, war injury, or required surgery, a portion of the principal part of the brain, the cerebrum, is exposed. Although the membranes surrounding the cerebrum are very sensitive to touch, it has been found that the brain-stuff itself shows no sensitivity and can be painlessly touched or cut without an anesthetic. When certain spots in the mid-region of the cerebrum are touched, the patient reports a sensation of touch in distant parts of his body. When the brain is touched at one spot, he may report a feeling in his hand; at another, a feeling in his leg. More striking, he may sometimes report that he feels his leg is moving, even though he can see it is not. *Where* is the feeling in this case? In his leg, where he says he feels it, or in his cerebrum, which the experimenter knows is being touched?

Whatever the answer to the vexing question, "Where is the sensation located?" * sensation normally involves the following three elements:

* Some say this is a meaningless question, that is, one that cannot be answered.

a receptor, "sensory" and other nerve fibers, and the sensory area of the brain. Normally, when the receptor is stimulated, it sends a stimulus along a chain of nerve fibers that terminate in the sensory areas of the cerebrum. We know this, for we can, with electrical instruments, detect currents traveling along the nerves coming from the receptor to the brain. Sensation can be elicited in any of three ways:

1. By stimulation of the receptor—the normal way.

2. By stimulation of the nerves. Everyone has experienced the "natural experiment" of striking his funny bone, which is really an exposed nerve trunk in the elbow. Besides the local pain, due to local receptors in the elbow, the blow often leads to a tingling sensation in the finger tips because of the direct stimulation of the sensory nerves coming from the fingers.

3. By stimulation of the "sensory area" of the brain. Here again, common experience presents us with an example: A blow in the back of the head produces images of stars, rockets, and other pyrotechnics when none are visible to bystanders.

If the sense-receptor is destroyed, there will normally be no more sensation. If the sensory nerve is destroyed, no more sensations occur, even though receptor and brain are intact. If the sensory area of the brain is destroyed, sensation ceases. Where, then, is the sensation located?

Interestingly enough, it is not always true

that destruction of receptors leads to loss of sensation in the part affected. Frequently, a man who has had a leg or an arm amputated, later has recurrent feeling in the nonexistent limb. He is said to possess a "phantom limb." In this case, the receptors are gone; only the sensory nerves and the sensory areas of the brain are still intact. Probably, some abnormality of the remaining nerve stump stimulates sensory nerve fibers. The stimulus is interpreted as coming from the regions that used to be in contact with the nerve, the fingers and hand of a once-existent arm, for instance. Sometimes the pain is quite intense and precisely localized, and the patient reports the localization even though he *knows* that the pain cannot be where he says it is. In severe cases, it may be necessary to put the nerve into a long sleep by injecting alcohol or other anesthetic directly into the nerve.

There are regions of the body in which the supposed *locus* of the sensation cannot be accurately determined. The abdominal cavity is one —a fact of some inconvenience when it is necessary for a physician to diagnose an ailment from a pain vaguely located "somewhere" in the mid-region. In some cases pain may be pre-

cisely, but wrongly, located. Some of these mistaken localizations are consistent (which isn't so bad); for instance, stimulation of the central region of the diaphragm causes pain that is positively identified as coming from the shoulders (Fig. 33-1). The same nerve trunk supplies nerves to both regions, and apparently, one might say, we never learn which fibers go to which region. Another and more common example of referred pain is that which follows the ill-advised swallowing of a too-large piece of food. For some time thereafter, we may feel a lump "in our throat." An X-ray examination, using a lump opaque to X-rays, shows that the mass is really lodged down against the cardiac sphincter of the stomach several inches lower than we "feel" it.

In the preceding paragraph, it was implied that we *learn* to associate the sensations coming from certain nerves with stimulation of a certain part of the body. This is unquestionably true for most sensory functions. As an example of a learned association, consider the way we orient the visual field. A convex lens, such as we have in our eyes, inverts the image. Why, then, does not the world appear upside down, like this? The answer is, there is no reason why

Fig. 33-1. *Stimulation of the diaphragm, as indicated by arrows, produces pains in the shoulder regions.*

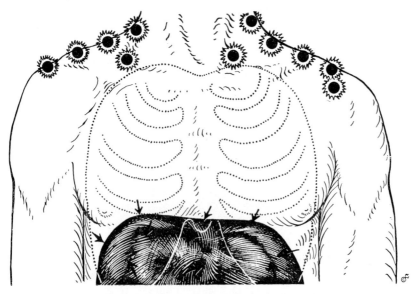

it should. We have sensations *from* the retina, but no sensations *of* it; it has no "right-side-upness." Conclusive proof of the correctness of this viewpoint is furnished by the experiments in 1896 of the American psychologist G. M. Stratton, who donned inverting prisms to see how the world would look. As expected, the world looked upside down—at first. He was scrupulous to look at the world only through his peculiar spectacles, doffing them only at night in a completely dark room. In one week's time the world came to appear right-side-up and the subject could perform all his accustomed movements with their accustomed delicacy.

After this period of learning, Stratton removed his inverting spectacles and the world once more looked upside down, though the position of the image was what would ordinarily be regarded as normal. It appeared upside down until the subject once more learned how to interpret the visual stimuli in terms of the world of space outside himself. This experiment, and observation of the learning process in infants, make it very probable that we have no a priori knowledge of how to interpret the messages that come from the retina. We learn.

Before closing this discussion of sensation, it may be of interest to mention an unproved, and perhaps unprovable, hypothesis of the nature of sensation. Consider the question: What is the objective difference between qualitatively different kinds of sensations? A well-trained philosopher may say that this question does not make sense. But what we mean is this: What that we know of, objectively, determines the reported differences between sensations? Take the sensations of seeing and hearing: Why are they different? We know that it is not because of the difference in end organs—in receptors—because:

1. If the receptors are destroyed, direct stimulation of the nerves, as by a blow or an electric shock, will still yield the "proper" sensations; for example, stimulation of the auditory nerve gives rise to a sensation of sound, of the optic (visual) nerve to a sensation of sight, though the stimulus is precisely the same.

2. The messages that normally come along the optic and auditory nerves show no significant differences when studied with electrical instruments.

If the qualitative character of the sensation is not determined by either the end organ or the nerve, it must be determined by what we call the "sensory area" of the brain. From this deduction, Emil DuBois-Reymond (1818–1896) predicted that if we could cut the optic nerve and the auditory nerve, and then join the cut stumps so that the eye now sent impulses to the auditory region and the ear to the visual region of the brain, we would then be able to *see* thunder and *hear* lightning. This seems a reasonable hypothesis in the light of the facts. No one has carried out the experiment. The speculation is nonetheless a fascinating one.

264. What Do We Mean by the Word "External"?

The remainder of this chapter is devoted to a discussion of various mechanisms by which we adjust to the demands and opportunities of the external world. Yet, by this time, it should be apparent to the student that it may be difficult to define what is external to the body and what is internal to it. Is the orientation of the visual scene present in the world outside us, or is it in ourselves? Where is the pain felt by a phantom limb? Is this room really hot, or are my Ruffini end organs acting up? What do I know of an outside world—is there *really* one, or is there only *me*?

Such questions are much too deep for analysis here. It is clear, however, that any statement about occurrences in a world outside my body is an inference based on assumptions that are difficult to justify. Rather than attempt a rigorous presentation, we will here adopt a pragmatic, "common-sense" viewpoint and assume, without further question, the customary distinction between the external world and the internal world. If there is no absolutely clear-cut distinction between the two, perhaps this fact need cause us no more procedural embarrassment than our inability to differentiate sharply between the verbal categories of "plants" and "animals," or of "living" and "nonliving." Provided we keep in the backs of our minds a remembrance of the existence of a difficulty, there may not be any serious danger in proceeding on a basis of common-sense assumptions.

265. Control of Movement: Proprioceptive Senses

How do we move our bodies about in the external world? How do we make them move as we wish? How does a man know what his body is doing? One may first think of the eyes: Each of us can see what he is doing. This is part of the answer, but only a part. We can control our movements accurately even in the dark: How do we do it?

We tend to think of movement as a simple thing. I wish to move my arm: I move it—*presto!* But observe the difficulty an infant experiences in performing even the "simplest" act, such as grabbing a rattle. Maybe the "simple" is not simple after all. It takes a child weeks to learn to grab and months to learn to walk. What is so difficult about these movements? What is it that has to be learned?

Recall the basic structure of a limb. Two bones, connected by a flexible joint, can have their relationships to each other altered by contraction either of an extensor muscle, thus increasing the inner angle made by the bones, or of a flexor muscle, thus decreasing this angle. This, simply stated, is the mechanism of movement of bones. But it is too simply stated. No bone is moved by only two muscles. It takes six muscles to give the forearm its various movements, and many more to carry out the multiple movements of the hands and fingers. One anatomist has estimated that no less than 54 muscles are involved in a "simple" forward movement of one leg, as in walking. The complexity of the muscular system is clearly evident in Figure 33-2. It seems not unreasonable to con-

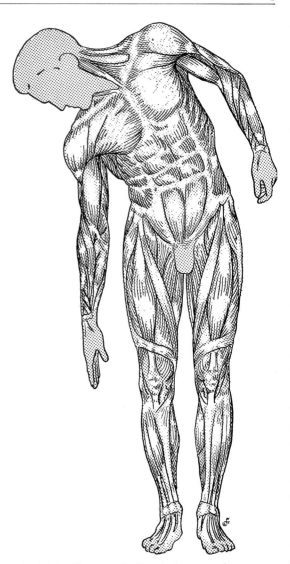

Fig. 33-2. *The complexity of the muscular system of man.*

jecture that a rather complex system of control is required for managing all these muscles.

Every motion of the skeletal system involves the simultaneous contraction of antagonistic muscles; change in position of the part occurs because one of the antagonists contracts more strongly than the other. To make a successful movement—say, reaching out and grasping a bottle of ink on the desk before you—you must not only (1) be able to cause the muscles to contract in the right amount, but you must, at every moment, (2) know just where your arm is and what it is doing. *Vision is not necessary for this knowledge.* Close your eyes and reach for the bottle; you can still reach it with almost complete accuracy and efficiency. Your knowledge of where your limbs are and what your muscles are doing does not depend on vision. You can "feel" where they are and what is going on.

What sort of feeling is this? Touch, warmth, cold? It is none of these. This sort of feeling tells each of us about the position of his own body in the world; such senses are called **proprioceptive senses** (L. *proprius* = one's own), in contrast to the exteroceptive senses, which (supposedly!) tell us about the external world itself. The existence of proprioceptive senses was not suspected until about a century ago.

One of the proprioceptive senses is **muscle sense.** Embedded in every muscle are numerous nerve endings that are stimulated by the changing pressure of the surrounding muscle fibrils. When these receptors are stimulated, they send messages to the central nervous system, thus keeping it continuously informed of what the muscle is doing. We think of a muscle as an effector, which it is primarily, but the great English physiologist Charles Sherrington estimated that 40 percent of the nerve fibers attached to a muscle are *sensory* fibers. One might call a muscle a sense organ, though it is a rather self-centered one, reporting information only of its own affairs.

Another of the proprioceptive senses is **tendon sense.** Every muscle is connected to bones by some sort of connective tissue, which, when in the form of a long strip, is called a tendon. Embedded in the tendons are nerve end organs that inform us when the tendon is on a stretch, thus adding to our knowledge of our body. Tendons cannot expand or contract, but are moved passively. They are, therefore, not effectors but receptors only.

Continuous knowledge of the position of our muscles and the tension of the muscles and tendons permits us to know where our muscle-moved parts are, in what direction they are moving and how fast, and what opposition they are encountering, that is, how hard the muscles

are having to work to effect movement. For instance, we make our estimates of the weight of objects using these proprioceptive senses. If, for instance, we are asked to say which of two melons is the heavier, we "heft" them in our hands, noting, however unconsciously, how much stretch the muscles and tendons of our arms are put to, and on this basis deliver a judgment. The more nearly equal two weights are, the more difficult it is to distinguish them. One can easily distinguish between 2 pounds and 3 pounds, but not between 2 pounds even and 2 pounds 1 ounce. However, one can distinguish between a 1-ounce letter and a 2-ounce one. How does it happen that a 1-ounce difference can be detected in the latter case but not in the former? Obviously, because the *relative* difference in weights of the two objects is great only in the latter case. Two ounces are twice as heavy as 1 ounce, but 2 pounds 1 ounce is only 3.1 percent greater than 2 pounds. Numerous experiments show that it is the *relative difference* that is important in evaluating quantities. For what we might call the "hefting sense," an ability to distinguish a relative difference of about 1 part in 30 is normal.

The doctrine that it is relative differences that are perceived holds not only for stimuli arising from the proprioceptive sense, but also for those from most of the other senses. For each sense, there is a smallest relative difference that is perceptible. The law holds only over the middle region of perceptibility, however. When stimuli are very slight, or very great, we are less able to distinguish small relative differences. Moreover, the magnitude of this "smallest perceptible relative difference" varies widely among humans, and such differences undoubtedly help determine individual aptitudes for various vocations.

266. Control of Movement: The Semicircular Canals

When the structure and function of the inner ear were first discussed, an important portion of this organ was deliberately ignored: the

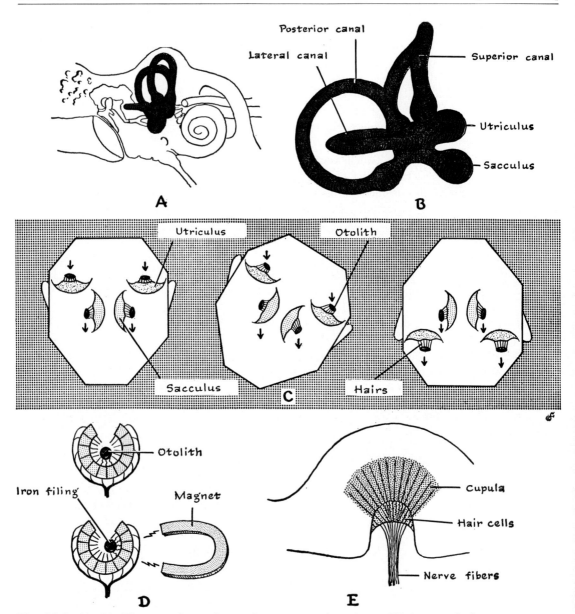

Fig. 33-3. (A, B) *The utriculus and sacculus, organs of static equilibrium, and the semicircular canals, organs of dynamic equilibrium.* (C) *The effect of body position upon position of the otoliths.* (D) *Otolith of a shrimp, in which function can be experimentally demonstrated.* (E) *Sense organs within the semicircular canals.*

fluid-filled portions that are illustrated in Figure 33-3*A*, *B*. The time has come to remedy this omission.

Occasionally, the inner ear is completely destroyed by disease. If both ears are so affected, the individual becomes stone-deaf, of course, and, in addition, his sense of equilibrium is seriously affected. In a completely dark room he is unable to move or stand upright because he has lost all sense of "down-and-upness." He still has the proprioceptive senses from his tendons and muscles and sense of touch and pressure in his skin, and these help him slightly in perceiving his relations to his surroundings (he can feel the pressure of his body on the floor through the soles of his feet, for instance), but this aid is not enough to enable him safely to move around in the dark. In the light his eyesight makes safe locomotion possible.

Most of our orientation to our surroundings is brought about through three kinds of senses: the proprioceptive senses of muscles and tendons, vision, and the inner-ear senses. The inner-ear senses are of two sorts: static and dynamic. The static sense tells us the position of the head with respect to gravity, and the dynamic sense tells us of change in rate of movement or change in direction of movement of the head.

Experiments with animals and observation of natural anomalies in man have shown that the organs of static sense are the swollen bulbs, the **sacculus** (L. little sack) and **utriculus** (L. little bag), seen in Figure 33-3*B*. Inside these bulbs are the structures diagrammed in Figure 33-3*C*, sensitive cells with flexible hairs supporting an **otolith** (Gr. *otos* = ear + *lithos* = stone), a tiny pebble of calcium carbonate. Since the otoliths are not rigidly fixed in position, different positions of the head will result in unequal stimulation of the sensitive hair cells. Perception of this inequality is believed to be the means by which we know the position of the head with respect to gravity.

This theory of the mechanism of static equilibrium in humans has not been proved, but it receives strong, though indirect, support from experiments performed on shrimp by the Viennese physiologist A. Kreidl. A shrimp has a similar equilibrium organ (Fig. 33-3*D*), which, at certain stages in its life history, is easily accessible from the outside. The ingenious experimenter made use of this convenient situation by replacing the stony otoliths with iron filings. Then, when he brought a strong magnet close to the shrimp, the animal oriented itself to the face of the magnet instead of to the gravity of the world, thus proving, in the case of the shrimp at any rate, the correctness of the theory of otolith function. In mammals, the minute otoliths are almost inaccessible to operative procedure, so it is doubtful if the theory will be critically tested in them.

Knowledge of movement of the body is derived from the **semicircular canals.** Notice (Fig. 33-3*B*) that these canals are oriented at right angles to each other, corresponding to the three planes of space. Inside the semicircular canals are sense organs of the sort shown in Figure 33-3*E*. The canals are filled with fluid; movement of fluid past these sense organs, occurring during acceleration, causes sensations of movement.

Our perception of movement at times leads to unpleasant consequences. Repetitive motion of certain sorts can lead to **motion sickness** (called also, with less generality, "seasickness" or "airsickness"). The phenomenon, though humorous to the bystander or in retrospect, is totally lacking in gaiety for the subject at the time. Anacharsis (ca. 600 B.C.), a Scythian philosopher, remarked that "People may be divided into three classes: those who are alive, those who are dead, and those who are at sea." Some animals, for example, cats, canaries, rabbits, guinea pigs, and monkeys, are almost totally immune to the ailment. Horses, dogs, cows, and sheep are about as susceptible as man. Dogs become immune when the semicircular canals are destroyed. In man at least, factors other than messages from the inner ear may contribute to the condition: vision, possibly the kind of food in the stomach, remembrance of past experiences, and other factors that may be vaguely described as "psychological." There are great individual differences in susceptibility; it is doubtful if any human above the age of two years is completely immune. Of those who are markedly susceptible, at least 95 percent can become adjusted to a nauseating motion. In recent years some drugs, among them Dramamine, have been found to lessen susceptibility in most people.

267. Control of Movement: The Cerebellum

It was mentioned earlier that over fifty muscles are used in making a simple forward movement of a leg in walking. It will be readily appreciated that the sequence and strength of the contractions of these various muscles must be

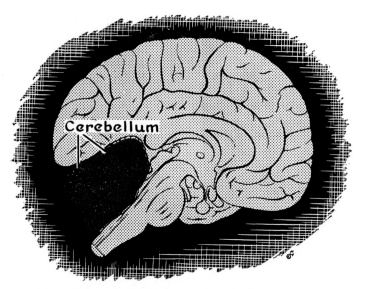

Fig. 33-4. *The cerebellum, often called the brain's executive secretary.*

finely and intricately organized if the foot is to go where and when we want it to. When we recall that a walking movement is not the only foot movement possible—that we may run, hop, skip, or jump at will; that all these movements entail different patterns of muscle contractions; and that while we are moving, we may be carrying on a conversation or thinking about something else—then do we appreciate how marvelous is the unconscious control of our complicated movements. Where is this control exercised? What is the *central* organ involved?

Extirpation experiments show that the **cerebellum** (Fig. 33-4) is the organ essential to the fine control of movements. When it is removed, the animal becomes, for a time, completely incapacitated. After some weeks, it manages to move about slowly and awkwardly. It sways and falls frequently; when it tries to extend a limb to a certain place, it is very likely to overshoot the mark. Tremors of the muscles are frequent. Voluntary movements are achieved with difficulty, and the gait of such an animal is said to resemble that of a drunken man. Humans suffering natural damage to the cerebellum exhibit a similar "drunken" gait. This fact suggests that some of the effects of alcohol may be

explained by its anesthetic effect on the cerebellum.

In humans, the growth of a tumor in the cerebellum may lead to loss of accurate movements in some part of the body. Frequently, the affected part is flabby: the muscles are completely relaxed. This raises a point we have not made before: *In the normal animal, the skeletal muscles are never completely relaxed, even in sleep.* At all times, the muscles are under some tension; we say they possess **tone.** All the muscles of the body are continuously receiving slight nerve impulses—recall the microvibrations of the muscles (§251)—which keep them contracted just enough to be firm and ready for action, but not enough to cause movement. When the nerves to a muscle are cut, the muscle immediately assumes a flabbiness never observed in a normal animal except, possibly, in a very deep sleep or drunken stupor.

It is important to realize that, in the absence of the cerebellum, voluntary movements are still possible; but such movements lack smoothness and accuracy. As we shall see presently, the ability to initiate voluntary movements lies in the *cerebrum* of the central nervous system. The decisions made by this part are communicated to the cerebellum and thence to the spinal cord and out to the proper muscles. The movement of a limb involves a continuous stream of motor impulses passing out to the muscles and another stream of sensory impulses going from the proprioceptive sense organs in muscles and tendons back to the spinal cord and cerebellum. By means of such a feedback system, the "instructions" to the muscles are continually modified to conform to the latest information available regarding their exact position. In assimilating and acting on this information, the cerebellum plays the central role. It is, to use a figure of speech from the business world, the "executive secretary" of a system in which the cerebrum is the "executive."

268. Functions of the Cerebrum

The **cerebrum** is the large portion of the central nervous system that is ordinarily designated by the term "brain." The association of the anatomical entity *brain* with the functional entity *mind* was postulated as far back as the sixth century B.C. by Alcmaion of Croton. Curiously, two centuries later Aristotle (384–322 B.C.) denied this connection, assigning intelligence to the heart and regarding the brain as a gland for the secretion of "phlegm" to cool the heart.* The correct view was not re-established until after Aristotle's death, by the Alexandrian anatomist Herophilos.

The size of the brain in various mammals is given in Table 33-1. Figures stated in cubic centimeters were determined by measuring the capacity of the skull; those given in grams were determined by weighing the brain itself. The specific gravity of brain tissue is only slightly greater than one, so the two methods of measurement are approximately equivalent. The figures are average or mean values and so conceal the variation, which is considerable. Five skulls of the Australopithecines, presumed ancestors

TABLE 33-1   *Brain Size of Various Mammals Including Man. Numbers in Parentheses Represent Size of Sample, When Known To Be Small. (Anthropoid Data from H. V. Vallois, 1954. C. R. Acad. Sci. (Paris)* **238:** 1349.)

ANIMAL	AVERAGE SIZE (CC OR G)
Gibbon (*Hylobates*)	89 cc
Chimpanzee	394 cc
Orangoutang	411 cc
Gorilla	498 cc
Australopithecines (5)	576 cc
Pithecanthropes (3)	871 cc
Sinanthropes (4)	1,046 cc
Ngandong man (6)	1,100 cc
Pre-Neanderthal man (2)	1,175 cc
Neanderthal man (6)	1,438 cc
Homo sapiens	1,450 g
Dolphin (Tursiops truncatus)	1,650 g
Elephant	6,075 g
Whale (Physeter catodon)	9,200 g

of modern man, had capacities of 450, 480, 500, 700, and 750 cc, a considerable variation. Undoubtedly, when more skulls are found the range of variation will be extended.* In *Homo sapiens,* where the sample is large, the brain size of "normal" people ranges from about 1,000 g to 1,600 g. Above 1,000 g there is no necessary connection between brain size and intelligence. The Russian novelist Turgenev had a brain weighing 2,012 grams; Anatole France's weighed only 1,138 grams, after making an adjustment for his advanced age at death (81 years). During the last fifty years of life, the brain shrinks some 10 percent in weight. At birth, the brain weighs about 380 grams, which is one-eighth of the body weight.

The cerebrum is divided by a longitudinal indentation, or *fissure,* into two equal halves called **cerebral hemispheres.** The side-view in Figure 33-5 shows one hemisphere, together with the names of the various lobes, and an indication of some of the localization of func-

---

* 33-1. You laugh? In imagination, put yourself back into Aristotle's time and try to assemble the evidence that would be needed to convince him of the modern view.

---

* 33-2. What is the statistical justification for this statement?

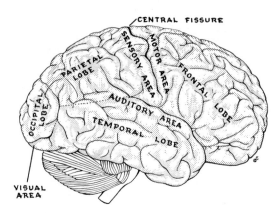

Fig. 33-5. *The principal external divisions of the cerebrum, and the functions of some of the regions.*

tions. The nerve cell bodies—several billion of them—are found almost entirely in a thin surface layer of the brain called the **cerebral cortex,** which is gray in color. The nerve processes that connect these neurons with one another make up the white inner part of the brain.

Localization of function in the brain is established by various means. Disease may destroy part of the cortex; and from the functions that are impaired, we deduce a connection between area and function. Experimentally, with lower animals, a portion of the cerebrum may be injured. Other useful information has been accumulated from the study of human brains that have been exposed to permit surgery. It is possible to stimulate painlessly regions of the brain and observe the effects in other parts of the body. It is also possible to stimulate peripheral receptors and, with sensitive electrical instruments, to observe the reception of signals in various parts of the brain. Indeed, some information is obtainable in this way even when the brain is not exposed: an **electroencephalograph** charts "brain waves" when the electrodes are applied to the outside of the skull. The interpretation of these waves is still a matter of difficulty.

A striking fact of brain function is the inverse relationship of the two cerebral hemispheres to the two sides of the body. The left side of the brain exchanges messages with the right side of the body; the right cerebral hemisphere, with

the left side of the body. The distribution of sensory fibers from the eyes is somewhat exceptional, and deserves comment here. As shown in Figure 33-6, at the **optic chiasma** (Gr. cross) there is only a partial crossing over of sensory fibers going from the eyes to the occipital lobes of the brain. The fibers from the left side of each retina go to the left occipital lobe, from the right to the right. As a result, the separation of sensations is not in terms of left and right sense organs (eyes), but in terms of left and right portions of the visual field. The left side of the brain receives the images from the right

Fig. 33-6. *The distribution of visual fields to the occipital lobes.*

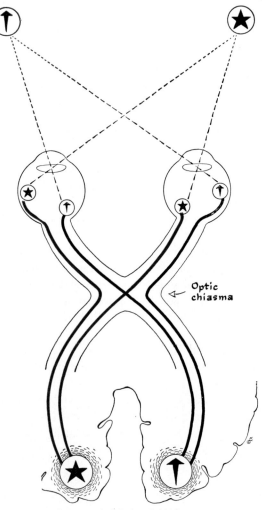

Occipital lobes of brain

half of the visual field; this same hemisphere of the brain also exchanges messages with the right hand, foot, and so forth. It seems reasonable to suspect, as the English physiologist E. D. Adrian has pointed out, that hand-eye cooperation is facilitated by this fact.

The apparent final destination of most of the impulses coming from most of the sense-receptors of the body is a region just posterior to the **central fissure** (see again Fig. 33-5) of each cerebral hemisphere. Imagine a transverse cut made through the "sensory" area of a hemisphere. If we indicate on a map of such a section the region in which feelings from the various regions of the body are localized, the result will be that shown in Figure 33-7, *left.* The body is curiously inverted, with sensations from the lower parts of the body delivered to the top of the cerebrum. The strange "sensory homunculus" indicated here is so drawn that the area of each part of the homunculus is proportionate

to the area of cerebral cortex devoted to sensations from that region of the body. Notice that the hand is larger than the trunk of the body; this relationship makes sense in terms of the relative importance of sensations from these parts of the body in determining our daily adjustments to the external world. The size of the lips, however, seems out of line with man's way of living; it has been suggested that this relationship is a leftover from earlier stages in our evolution when the face (together with its sensory bristles) was relatively more important than it is now in exploring the environment.

There are also regions of the brain the stimulation of which results in movement of one or another part of the body; these are called "motor" areas. One lies anterior to each central fissure. Figure 33-7, *right,* shows the distribution of motor areas in this region, together with a "motor homunculus" constructed according to the principles previously described. Careful

Fig. 33-7. *Localization of sensory and motor regions in the cerebrum. "Homunculi" are so constructed that the size of each part of a homunculus is proportional to the brain area devoted to that function. (From Penfield and Rasmussen,* The Cerebral Cortex of Man, *copyright 1950, with the permission of the Macmillan Company, New York.)*

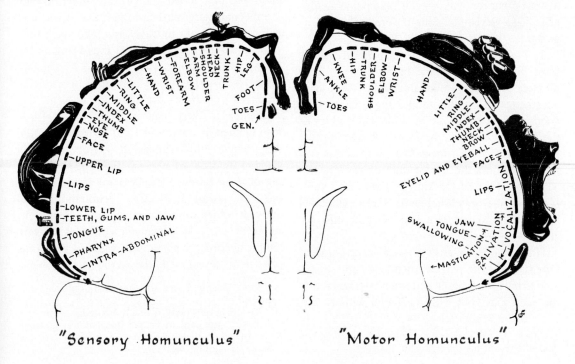

"Sensory Homunculus"   "Motor Homunculus"

study and comparison of these two homunculi yield considerable insight into the relation of a human body to its environment.

269. Anesthesia as an Ethical Problem

In addition to its localized functions, the cerebrum as a whole is somehow connected with the general phenomenon we call "consciousness." If the flow of blood to the brain is diminished slightly, the person becomes unconscious. Lowering the oxygen content of the blood has the same effect, as do chemicals that appreciably slow the metabolism of the brain cells. During the nineteenth century the first two of the great general * anesthetics, ether and chloroform, were discovered, and the attempt to introduce them into medical practice provoked a storm of opposition. Many courageous doctors fought the good fight for anesthesia, none of them more ably than the Scotsman James Young Simpson (1811–1870). The battle has now been won, but it is worth going over it again because the arguments that were used against anesthesia are, from time to time, used against other innovations. The campaign against anesthesia developed four different tactical arguments.

1. *Factual issue.* It may be hard to believe now, but many reputable medical men of the nineteenth century maintained that the use of anesthetics in operations did more harm than good. For example, a Dr. John Hall, chief of the Medical Staff of the British Expeditionary Army during the Crimean War, warned his colleagues against the use of chloroform, saying: "The smart use of the knife is a powerful stimulant and it is much better to hear a man bawl lustily than to see him sink silently into the grave."

How is one to answer such an argument? One suspects the perpetrator of sadism—a suspicion that is strengthened when we learn that the same Dr. Hall was associated with an un-

savory case in which a private died after receiving 150 lashes. But such an *argumentum ad hominem*† is not enough. One must resort to facts. This, James Simpson did in gathering together hospital data on the outcome of amputations of the leg at the thigh. In 1,745 operations performed without anesthesia, the mortality was 42 percent; in 145 performed with anesthesia, it was 25 percent.* Anesthetics were clearly vindicated.

2. *"Unnatural" issue.* James Simpson fought his hardest battle to get anesthetics used in childbirth. One of his fellow-doctors maintained that pain during parturition was a "desirable, salutary and conservative manifestation of the life-force." An Irish lady protested that it was "unnatural for you doctors in Edinburgh to take away the pains of your patients." To which Dr. Simpson retorted: "How unnatural it is for you to have swum over from Ireland to Scotland against wind and tide in a steamboat." In subsequent statements he pointed out how the identification of the unnatural with the immoral had been made before, in arguing that vaccination was unnatural (immoral); that emancipation of slaves was unnatural (immoral)†; that it was unnatural (immoral) to use mechanical grain-harvesters; that it was unnatural (immoral) to travel in a mailcoach that went all of 10 miles an hour, thus bringing on (it was said) apoplexy in many of its passengers. The argument that unnatural or artificial practices or devices are immoral goes all the way back to Tertullian in the third century, who defined as unnatural (and hence immoral) the practice of circumcision, acting in plays, shaving the face, using cosmetics, and the wearing of *dyed* fabrics. The last proscription gives the show away. Evidently, Tertullian thought undyed fabrics were natural. Perhaps they grew on trees. . . . In seventeen centuries of polemics against the unnatural, there is only one consistent thread: it is the *recent* technological

---

* 33-3. As opposed to local anesthetics such as Novocain. Explain the difference in meaning.

† 33-4. Meaning? And why are such arguments disapproved of?

* 33-5. The mortality is much less today. Why?

† Slaves were said to be the lineal descendants of Ham, of whom the Bible said "a servant of servants shall he be unto his brethren."

advance that is identified as unnatural and immoral.

3. *Religious issue.* "In sorrow shall she [woman] bring forth children," said Simpson's opponents, quoting Scripture. And what was sorrow if not pain? How did he dare go against the Bible? Such an argument is not rationally answerable (since it stands, by its nature, outside rationality), but Simpson was fortunately a bit of a Bible scholar himself. He pointed out that, according to the second chapter of Genesis, when the Lord God was ready to make Eve out of one of Adam's ribs, he first "caused a deep sleep to fall upon Adam." What was this deep sleep if not anesthesia? Need we mortals hesitate to use the means *He* has sanctified?

4. *Social issue.* The final tactic employed to prevent the use of anesthesia is one that is seldom explicitly argued, but always lies beneath the verbal barrage—namely, the social issue. That which is new should not be done because *it just isn't done.* In a few years Simpson countered this with the most effective of all arguments: he was instrumental in getting Queen Victoria to use anesthesia in her accouchement. That did it. From then on, it was chic to use an anesthetic.

270. Conditioned Reflexes

When we can be unemotional about it, looking back at such a battle as that waged over anesthesia, we can see that, in the most general sense, the whole process was one of *learning:* a whole community had to learn how to accept an invention that a few of its most gifted members had learned how to make. Now all this is learning at a very complex level—far too complex to yield, as yet, to scientific analysis. We are still laboring only in the lower floors of the structure-in-progress we call **psychology** (Gr. *psyche* = breath, soul, mind), the science of the mind. We can do no more here than sketch the merest rudiments of this field, taking up first the idea of conditioned reflexes as developed by the Russian physiologist Ivan Pavlov (1849–1936).

If food is placed in the mouth of a dog, the dog salivates. Salivation under these conditions is an innate reflex. Though we can never know, we do not hesitate to assume that the dog also has some consciousness of the taste of the food, a consciousness centered in the cerebrum. A simple way to indicate these events is by a sort of "wiring-diagram," as shown in Figure 33-8*A*, in which *M* represents a part of the cerebrum concerned with sensations from the mouth.

If a bell is rung, the auditory region (*E* in Fig. 33-8*B*) registers sensations of hearing, but there is no salivation. If, however, we present food to the dog at the same time that we ring a bell, the dog salivates because of the innate reflex previously mentioned. If we repeat this act many times: sound of bell—food; sound—food; sound—food: then some modification takes place inside the brain of the dog. It is as though some association area (*A* in Fig. 33-8*C*) noticed the concurrence of the two events and—to continue the story—ultimately caused the dog to react to the sound alone by salivating. By such means a new reflex is set up, which may be diagrammed as shown in Figure 33-8*D*—a reflex in which the proper sensory impulses coming from the ear result in motor impulses being sent out to the salivary gland. Such a learned reflex is called a **conditioned reflex.**

How is a conditioned reflex established? What change takes place in the central nervous system? We know that the presence of the cerebrum is essential; but beyond that, there is not much certain knowledge. In discussing the conditioned reflex, we have used what might be called a "telephone-switchboard analogy" of the functioning of the brain, but whether the complete explanation of the cerebral events involved fits this analogy accurately is not certain. The picture presented is, however, a useful one for at least a first orientation in this field.

The ringing of the bell need not be simultaneous with the presentation of food; the sound can precede the food. The longer the period between the **unconditioned stimulus** (the sound) and the **innate stimulus** (the taste), the more repetitions will be required to set up the **conditioned response.** This is as we would expect.

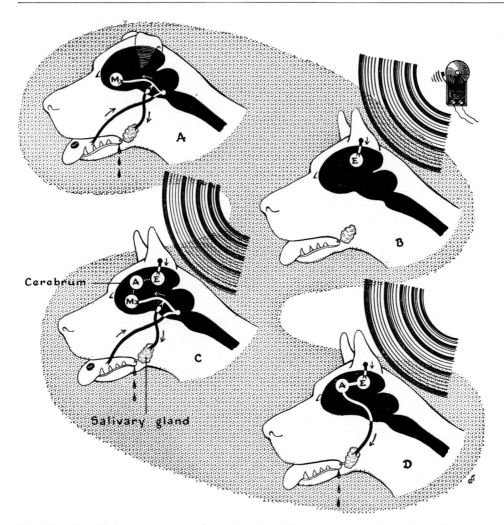

Fig. 33-8. *Establishment of a conditioned reflex. The taste of food evokes salivation* (A). *The sound of a bell does not* (B). *When taste and sound are simultaneously present* (C), *somehow an association is made in the cerebrum between sensations from ear and mouth. Once this association exists, sound alone will evoke salivation* (D).

We easily associate two events that happen simultaneously, but not so easily do we "see" the connection of events that are separated in time.

It will be readily appreciated that the sound of a bell is not the only stimulus that can be developed into a conditioned stimulus. An animal can be conditioned to a sight, a sound, a touch, or any other perceptible stimulus. As a matter of fact, the mechanism of the conditioned stimulus permits us to determine what stimuli an animal can perceive. Can a dog see ultraviolet light? We cannot ask him, but we can see if ultraviolet light can be established as

a conditioned stimulus. It cannot; therefore, we conclude that a dog cannot see ultraviolet light. (Neither can we.) Similar experiments tried with bees show that they *can* perceive ultraviolet.

Since we have learned how to establish conditioned reflexes in other animals, a door hitherto closed to us has opened. It is hard for us to penetrate the mind of an animal that does not speak. But, with the mechanism of the conditioned reflex, we can pry into the minds of other animals—the more "intelligent" ones, at any rate. Can a dog tell the difference between red and green? We cannot ask him. But we can condition him to salivate when a red light is flashed on. After he is conditioned, we can then condition him not to salivate when a green light is shown. When we have succeeded in doing this, we can try different intensities of colored lights, and if we can find a particular intensity of red that he cannot distinguish from a particular intensity of green, we must say then that he cannot distinguish red and green; which is indeed the case. Studies of this sort indicate that dogs cannot distinguish any colors; they can merely distinguish intensities.

Even a noxious stimulus can be made into a conditioned stimulus. Pavlov found that he could condition dogs to salivate on being given an electric shock. By first using mild shocks and gradually increasing their strength, he found it possible to train dogs to react to strong, and probably painful, shocks by salivating, instead of fighting or running away. One can easily think of similar instances among humans. Consider, for instance, the punishment the stooge of a slapstick comedian may take, all for a bit of money, that is, for the wherewithal to stimulate his salivary glands. This striking example is not fundamentally different from a sort of learning to which all of us are exposed. For the sake of anticipated pleasures, we daily put up with unpleasant experiences and abjure present delights. In his ability to act in the light of distant and subtle goals, rather than responding thoughtlessly to momentary pain or pleasure, man is without peer among living things.

271. Imprinting

In 1935 Konrad Lorentz described another type of learning which he called **imprinting.** The meaning of this term can most easily be made clear by describing some typical experiments.

Young ducklings follow their mother. Why? Do they instinctively recognize her as "mother"? Or are they conditioned to do so because she finds them food? Lorentz showed

that the answer to both questions was *No.* If duck eggs are allowed to hatch where there is no mother duck in sight, and if a larger duck is not introduced into the field of view until two days after hatching, the ducklings do *not* follow it. In other words, there is a **critical period** during which ducklings can be imprinted with the image of "mother" (to use a term that is perhaps too anthropocentric, too rich in meaning). The critical period in ducklings is from 0 to 36 hours after hatching, with the peak in susceptibility at 13 to 16 hours.

The imprinting process does not require a genuine duck for its model—almost any moving object will do. A wooden, motor-driven duck does quite well. Lorentz found that he himself could be a perfectly good "mother" in this sense; ducklings exposed to him as the first moving object during the critical period thereafter followed him around as faithfully as they would have followed any duck, had the duck been seen first. One is reminded of the scene in Shakespeare's *A Midsummer Night's Dream* in which we learn of Oberon's threat toward Titania:

> *The next thing that she waking looks upon,*
> *Be it lion, bear, or wolf, or bull,*
> *On meddling monkey, or on busy ape,*
> *She shall pursue it with the soul of love.*

The ability to be imprinted has been found in a number of species. Imprinting differs from conditioning in a number of significant respects:

1. The *earliest* experience is most important in imprinting.
2. Imprinting can be blocked by the "tranquilizer" meprobamate; conditioning cannot. It is the act of imprinting only that is blocked; retention of imprinting is unaffected.
3. Pain and fear *reinforce* imprinting; they interfere with conditioning.
4. A massing of experiences in time favors imprinting. Spacing favors learning by conditioning. The more effort the subject has to make during imprinting (as by being forced to climb up an inclined plane to reach "mother") the stronger is the imprinting.

5. A critical period is characteristic of imprinting, not so of conditioning.

One cannot but wonder about the possible applications of the idea of imprinting to the human situation. There is some evidence to suggest the existence of critical periods for learning to react to authority-figures. The critical periods (if they exist) may not be so sharply defined in humans, nor the experiential changes so irrevocable. We are loathe to experiment with human babies in the ways that would be required to get definitive answers to these questions. We should probably be guided by our inhibitions in this matter, yet there is great need for sounder information. We become increasingly more aware of the crucial importance of the earliest years of life in the educative process; ignorance of what goes on here produces economic and human losses we can ill afford.

272. Brain, Mind, and Intelligence

The great majority of the known, precise localizations of functions in the brain have been indicated in Figures 33-5, 33-6, and 33-7. Attempts to localize the processes of learning and thinking have been almost completely unsuccessful. Destruction or removal of the parts of the parietal lobes (see again Fig. 33-5) result in some loss of memory and some impairment of learning ability, but the exact results of a particular extirpation are not predictable. It is interesting to note that the two cerebral hemispheres are not equal in importance: instances of injury to only one side of the brain show that the left cerebral hemisphere is more important to a right-handed person than is the right hemisphere. For a left-handed person, the reverse is true. Apparently, most of a man's thinking takes place in that hemisphere that is dominant in the control of his bodily activities.

One of the strangest facts of brain physiology is the apparent lack of specific function of the anterior part of the frontal lobes, the **prefrontal areas.** A considerable mass of the prefrontal lobes can be severely damaged or removed without causing obvious damage to the individual's behavior. Memories are not lost, and intelligence (as measured by ordinary tests) is unimpaired. Close observation, however, reveals subtle but important changes in the personality: there is a lack of "drive," or of persistence, often coupled with a striking disregard of the social amenities and the interests of others. The changes that accompany injury to this region are undeniable, but difficult to describe. The functions of the prefrontal areas seem to be general rather than specific.

In speaking of learning, so far we have discussed only phenomena involved in conditioning an animal. It must not be supposed, however, that learning is nothing more than the accumulation of conditioned reflexes. A rat taught to run a maze that is dry, will swim, without error, through the same maze flooded with water. The muscular movements are quite different in the second case; hence the rat is not simply using a set of conditioned reflexes. There must be, in the rat's mind, some perception of the pattern of the maze. A dog taught to distinguish between a triangle and a square will make the distinction no matter what the size of the triangle or the thickness of the lines. We say that the animal has performed an act of **abstraction:** it has abstracted the *concept* of triangularity from the particularities of the instances presented it.

The various abilities to learn, to recall, to abstract, and to perceive relevancies of concepts constitute part of what we call **intelligence.** We have available various means of measuring intelligence, one of the oldest of which is the Stanford-Binet test, which measures what is called the Intelligence Quotient, or I.Q. But what do such tests measure? Is a person with a high I.Q. one who necessarily acts "intelligently" in all real-life situations? Psychologists agree that there is not a perfect correlation between the two. There are many critical comments that can be made about any intelligence test, but perhaps the most important is this: "Intelligence" itself is not a clearly defined concept. The history of human intellectual endeavor shows that hazy concepts often lead to confusion. Progress in chemistry was impeded for nearly a century by adherence to the ill-conceived idea of phlogiston. In physics, the concepts of heat and temperature were confusedly muddled together for centuries; progress in the study of energy was held up until the two concepts were unscrambled. In psychology, the concept of intelligence is undoubtedly a confused mixture of concepts. The word "intelligence" might be compared to the word "strength" as applied to materials. "Strength" is a complex of many different concepts: hardness, ductility, resistance to compression, resistance to shear, and so on. The word "intelligence" will probably eventually disappear from exact scientific writing, to be replaced by several other concepts. (One contemporary psychologist analyzes it into four separate components, another into seven.) The word may always, however, have a certain value in inexact exposition, just as we still find the word "strength" useful.

273. The Experimental Study of Neuroses

Although conditioned reflexes do not constitute the whole of the psyche, the detailed study of such reflexes has yielded many, and sometimes surprising, insights into psychic problems. Some illuminating experimental findings are recorded below.

Conditioned stimuli can be "unconditioned." A simple way to do this is to present the conditioned stimulus, for example, the sound of a bell, many times without the "reward" of the innate stimulus, for example, the taste of food. If, to use the example suggested, the bell is rung a number of times and food is *not* presented, the dog no longer salivates on hearing the bell. Does this mean that the dog has *forgotten* the connection between the two? It does not seem likely. If the ringing of the bell is once more followed by the presentation of food, the conditioned reflex is re-established almost immediately. The second time it takes only one or two sound-food presentations to establish the association, instead of the dozen or so originally required. Extinguishing a conditioned reflex is

itself a conditioning process. In this connection, it is not without interest to learn that there is abundant psychological evidence to prove that a great part (perhaps all?) of what we call "forgetting" in humans is an active, positive process. *We forget because we want to.* This seems to be frequently true—a fact which every student should remember.

Related to the phenomenon of "unconditioning," or extinction of conditioning, is the phenomenon of **differential inhibition.** This may be illustrated by the following example:

A tone of a fixed pitch is set up as a conditioned stimulus. Then a note *one-half tone lower* is sounded, and no food is given. This routine is repeated a number of times until the animal has been conditioned to salivate for the higher note but not for the lower. Then a normal rate of secretion of saliva for the higher note is determined and is found to be, say, 12 drops.

Now:

Sound lower tone once. Result: 0 drops.
Sound higher tone once. Result: 12 drops.
Sound lower tone four times. Results: 0, 0, 0, and 0 drops.
Sound higher tone once. Result: 1 drop.

The dog "should" have produced 12 drops in response to the last stimulus but produced only one drop, apparently because the repeated presentation of the "negative" stimulus (the lower tone) had resulted in a "spreading," so to speak, of the negative response. Or, we might say that repeated stimulation by the negative stimulus *inhibited* the action of the positive stimulus.

Out of such studies of inhibition has come another discovery. Under some conditions, the "spread" of inhibition is greater, extending, for instance, to conditioned tones that are more distant than a semi-tone from the negative stimulus, or even to conditioned stimuli of different qualities, such as sight stimuli. In extreme instances, dogs subjected to inhibition *go to sleep.* This observation led Pavlov to postulate that sleep is essentially a widely spread inhibitory state, and that every inhibition may be regarded as a partial, localized sleep. That sleep may vary in its *extension* is known to everyone who has been faced with the problem of attending to something while he sleeps. The mother of a sick child or the soldier who must be on the lookout for certain warning sounds may sleep and yet respond to the slightest stimulus of a significant sort. With experience, such partial sleep can give fairly satisfactory rest.

Using the mechanism of the conditioned reflex to explore the discriminatory capacities of dogs, Pavlov made other observations that throw light on human problems. A dog was conditioned to salivate at the sight of an ellipse, but not at the sight of a circle. Then, it was presented with ellipses that were more and more nearly like circles. When the ratio of the two axes of the ellipse was about 9:8, the limit of canine discriminatory ability was reached. At this stage, a dog would give one of two reactions: either it would bark and yelp meaninglessly, straining wildly at its harness; or it would go into a sort of trance, refusing to attend to anything for a long period of time. Pavlov pointed out that these reactions resemble two well-known types of **neuroses** in humans: **hysteria** (the former), and **neurasthenia** (the latter). Which reaction was produced seemed to be less a function of the particular experimental set-up than it was of the temperament of the dog. After the upsetting experience, the dog had to be given a long rest from the experiments before it could be used again. Its retraining period was prolonged and necessarily involved much exposure to easily solvable problems.

This is only one of the ways in which neuroses can be caused in experimental animals. Many other procedures have been followed, but whatever the details, the experiments boil down to this: The experimenter in some sense "double-crosses" the subject, either by demanding too much in the way of discriminatory ability or by deliberately changing the conditions of reward or punishment in a manner that is unpredictable from the subject's viewpoint. When the subject must make a choice, and it has no certain guide to action, it frequently, and in a sense, logically, retreats into neurotic behavior.

274. Some Human Implications

Probably every discerning reader of the preceding two paragraphs will recognize therein experiences of a sort that he himself has had and reactions that he himself has exhibited. All of us are subjected to frustrating experiences in life, and our reactions are not always the completely logical ones we demand of others. It is perhaps not too much to say that everyone exhibits some neurotic behavior, however mild, at some time during his life. Nevertheless, such behavior is not, on principle, to be encouraged. There is ample evidence that, in the final balance, neuroses are costly in whatever terms one makes a reckoning.

In addition to the neuroses, there are **psychoses;** these are the more aggravated forms of abnormality. Psychotic people cannot make a satisfactory adjustment to the ordinary world and are best confined to institutions. At present, psychoses are seldom cured.

Throughout this chapter we have tacitly adhered to a philosophical position deriving from the French philosopher and mathematician René Descartes (1596–1650), who held that the mind and the body were distinct entities. This doctrine is called the **mind-body dichotomy** (Gr. *dicheres* = dividing in twain). The idea is so embedded in the structure of our language that it is difficult to speak in other terms, and yet we know many instances in which the distinction breaks down. An abnormal psychological state often results in the appearance of paralysis of a part—a paralysis that is said to be **functional** (rather than **organic**—as would be paralysis due to degeneration of nerves). The causes of functional diseases are (by definition) not visible, and can be cured without making visible changes in the structure of the patient. As a generalization, it may be said that *there is a functional equivalent of every known organic* *disease.* Equally important, the medical profession now recognizes that every organic disease has its psychic component. Medical practice that emphasizes this fact (thus departing from the traditional Cartesian position) is referred to as **psychosomatic medicine** (Gr. *psyche* = mind + *soma* = body).

The direct, specifiable costs of mental illness in the United States is about two billion dollars a year. The indirect costs are more arguable, but they are probably several times greater; they include, for example, the loss of approximately two-thirds of a million man-years of work per year.* The noneconomic costs of mental illness, though impossible to quantify, are probably more important. How can we diminish all these costs? We are working toward this desirable end by several means.

BY VERBAL MEANS. Neuroses can frequently be cured by getting the patient to "talk out" his troubles, thus revealing the underlying causes to him. Success in such endeavor requires a high degree of skill, developed professionally among the **psychiatrists** (who must be M.D.'s) and the **psychoanalysts** (who need not be M.D.'s). Such treatment is very expensive in both time and money. It can scarcely be said to be available to either the poor or the middle class, without outside subsidy.

BY SURGICAL MEANS. In some instances epilepsy has as its immediate cause a brain tumor, the removal of which cures or ameliorates the disease. Other instances of abnormalities modifiable by surgery are known. An operation called **frontal lobotomy** has been much used to help certain states. The early development of this operation as a treatment of psychological disorders was due largely to the Portuguese surgeon Egas Moniz. It has been particularly useful in relieving conditions of great anxiety and depression. While not as extreme in

* 33-6. In 1963, the per capita income in the U.S. was $2,449. Using this figure, can you calculate the monetary loss of the man-years of work given above? Explain.

its effects as a frontal lobectomy, it may have undesirable side-effects. The patient so treated becomes indifferent to the needs of others, even the closest of kin; by some, he would be said to lack a conscience. There is a very real question as to whether a frontal lobotomized individual should be considered thoroughly *competent* in the legal sense, for example, whether he should be adjudged competent to make a last will and testament.

BY CHEMICAL MEANS. The criticism of the Cartesian mind-body dichotomy can be sharpened by a consideration of data from the field of endocrinology. Artificial administration of hormones frequently has psychic effects that are sometimes too subtle to be easily described, but at other times are obvious. A previously normal adult who begins to suffer from severe hypothyroidism becomes mentally depressed and sluggish in his reactions; administration of thyroxin relieves the "mental" as well as the "physical" symptoms. When hypothyroidism prevails from birth, the effect is different. "Physically," the person is a midget; "mentally," he is an imbecile, an individual of very little intelligence, but so amiably tractable as to have earned the name **cretin,** a corruption of the French *chrétien,* or Christian. In addition to the hormones, there are many artificial drugs, particularly the **tranquilizers,** that have notable effects on behavior. The tranquilizing drugs developed in the second half of the twentieth century have had an important effect on the population of mental hospitals. In 1954, the number of resident patients in public psychiatric hospitals was at an all-time high of 381 per 100,000 population. By 1963, the figure had fallen steadily to 320 per 10^5. The rate of admissions actually rose somewhat during that period, but this rise was more than compensated for by the shortening of the period of hospitalization made possible by the use of drugs. Early return to the home environment not only lessens expenses but also improves therapy; *in general,* the home is a better place for the tractable ill person than is the hospital.

(It should be noted that the figures given above do not include senile patients, who are increasing in numbers as a result of improvements in physical medicine which are creating a problem that society is reluctant to face.)

BY HEREDITARY MEANS. Heredity contributes to the development of amaurotic idiocy, Huntington's chorea, epilepsy, and various types of subnormal mentality. In at least one disease, it is known that the hereditary effect is produced by means of an alteration of the body chemistry: In the hereditary disease **phenylketonuria,** idiocy is due to an abnormal metabolism that results in the appearance in the body of phenylketones, a class of chemical compounds not normally found in the body. While we still have much to learn of the relation of heredity to mental functioning, it is clear that the frequency of many mental abnormalities could even now be decreased by societal control of matings, were we willing to submit to such control.

BY SOCIAL MEANS. That environment (as distinguished from heredity) contributes to mental abnormality is attested to by a large body of humane literature. This conclusion is supported by the implications of such experiments as those of Pavlov. There are, in addition, many reports in the field of anthropology that illuminate the connection of social organization and individual mental health. In her *Patterns of Culture,* Ruth Benedict shows how the social customs of the Kwakiutl Indians of the Pacific Northwest encourage psychotic tendencies; in contrast, the folkways of the Zuni Indians of the Southwest are such as to develop emotional stability among the members of the tribe.

In discussing the causative factors involved in ulcers, it was pointed out that these abnormalities are in part a by-product of the social order. Change the social order and you change the psychiatric picture of the community. Peptic ulcer, which was a disease of women in the nineteenth century, has become a disease of men in the twentieth—though it would be diffi-

cult to say (without provoking an argument) what is the significant social change responsible for this change.

But what we want is not merely to shift a neurotic symptom (like ulcers) from one sex to another, but to eradicate both it and its cause from the whole population; or, more accurately, to reduce its incidence to the lowest level commensurate with the attainment of other ends that are worth pursuing. To most people the word "normal" is almost a synonym for "average" or "typical" or "common," but he who looks at the members of our society with a keen psychiatric eye cannot agree. Consider a few statistics. A total of 10,762,853 pounds of aspirin were manufactured in the year 1948—enough, at 10 grains per dose, for 7.5 billion headaches; 374,113 pounds of barbiturates were produced—enough for a billion sleepless nights. During the Second World War, 12 percent of all men examined for service were rejected for psychiatric reasons; 49 percent of all service discharges for mental or physical reasons were for mental. A careful study of the students of London colleges (1954) revealed that 5 percent of the students were near-psychotics. An exhaustive survey of a "normal" American town of 3,000 inhabitants showed that 48 percent of the population had records of such psychiatrically significant symptoms as "nervous breakdown," ulcers, asthma, and hypertension.

To the student of psychology or comparative anthropology, all is not well with our society. How it should be altered to make it mesh with human nature no man has yet the authority to say. It may take another century's study to make clear what we must do. Whatever we learn, we can confidently predict that it will imply far-reaching changes in the organization of society—changes so extreme that the threat of them will evoke once again defensive measures of the sort encountered by James Young Simpson in his struggle to get mankind to give up the "blessings" of "natural" pain. The struggle will be severe; but the goal worth it. As one of the leading psychiatrists of our day, Lawrence S. Kubie, has said:

The ultimate prevention of the neutrotic process can bring humanity to its first true maturity. We are emerging from an era of human history which spans all recorded time, an era in which it has been assumed naively that it is easy to be psychologically well. Slowly we have learned that this is not so, and that to be a human being is so complex a task that the human race is not yet up to it. We have learned that wisdom about the world around us, scholarly erudition, high purpose and even religious faith have not alone or together been able to prevent neurotic distortions of human life. We must also admit humbly that we still know so little about the processes of normal development that the adult who is truly normal is still a happy accident.*

* *Practical and Theoretical Aspects of Psychoanalysis.* New York: International Universities Press, Inc. (1950), p. 11. By permission of publisher and author.

Questions and Problems

33-7. Make a list of the **boldface** terms in this chapter. Write a brief description or definition of each. Compare your work with the text.

‡33-8. Which of the following occupations could be successfully followed by a man with poor proprioceptive senses: architect, mathematician, violinist, public speaker, sculptor, wrestler, gymnast, accountant, physicist? Justify your answers, briefly.

33-9. In the meat market, the butcher picks up a roast. The customer says, "That will weigh 10¼ pounds." The butcher hefts it and says, "No—I'd say 10½ pounds." Assuming that the butcher has normal sensitivity, is he justified in making a correction of this order of magnitude in the estimate?

33-10. What kind of nerves, motor or sensory, innervate the following: (a) muscle; (b) tendon; (c) skin, exclusive of hair follicles and sweat glands; (d) hair follicles and surrounding area; (e) sweat glands?

‡33-11. An inmate of an institution for the totally blind suffers an infection that completely destroys his inner ears. What sort of life will he lead thereafter?

‡33-12. There are three deaf men: *A*, *B*, and *C*. *A*'s deafness can be alleviated by hearing aids, and he can move about safely in a completely dark room. *B*'s deafness is not helped by hearing aids, but he too can move about safely in a dark room. *C*'s deafness also cannot be helped by hearing aids, and he falls frequently when he tries to move in the dark. Assuming that the defects in each man are confined to the ears, what are the most probable defects in these cases?

33-13. The German mathematician and philosopher Leibniz, in 1714, wrote:

Memory provides the soul with a kind of consecutiveness which resembles reason, but which is to be distinguished from it. Thus we see that when animals have a perception of something which strikes them, and of which they have formerly had a similar perception, they are led by means of representations in their memory to expect what was combined with the thing in the previous perception, and they come to have feelings similar to those they had on the previous occasion. For instance, when a stick is shown to dogs, they remember the pain it has caused them and howl and run away.

In modern terminology, what is Leibniz talking about?

33-14. Many red-green color-blind men have no difficulty in distinguishing between red and green traffic lights. How do you explain this fact?

‡33-15. If a man cannot distinguish between reds and greens, what color does he see them as? All as shades of red? Or of green? Can one use the mechanism of the conditioned reflex to answer this question? If this is possible, describe the experimental procedure.

33-16. Pasteur, in his forty-sixth year, suffered a "stroke," resulting in paralysis of the left side of his body, owing probably, to a broken blood vessel in one cerebral hemisphere. Which hemisphere—left or right?

‡33-17. The word "tone" (as in muscle tone) is derived from the Greek word *teino*, meaning stretch. Can you account for the application of this word to music?

33-18. A little boy had his appendix removed. Telling of his experiences afterwards, he said: "They put me on a white bed on wheels and then they stuck a needle in my arm and I disappeared." Could you prove to him that he is wrong? If so, how?

33-19. Review your life during the last 24 hours. Make a list of the differences there would have been in it if you had conscientiously refused to use any unnatural thing or perform any unnatural act.

33-20. We locate thinking in the head. But some Pueblo Indians of North America locate it in the heart; some Negro tribes of Africa, in the belly. How could you disprove these views?

Readings

A recounting of classical experiments may be found in Garrett's *Great Experiments in Psychology*. Halstead's *Brain and Intelligence* discusses the data from surgical interference with the frontal lobes, particularly with respect to the question, "What is intelligence?"

Deutsch's *The Mentally Ill in America* is a fascinating history of the care of the insane and the changing attitudes toward them. See also Chapters 15 and 16 of White's *A History of the Warfare of Science with Theology in Christendom* for the struggle to get insanity considered a natural rather than a religious phenomenon.

The relation of social organization and mental health is, explicitly or otherwise, the subject of a great mass of anthropological literature. Benedict's *Patterns of Culture* should certainly be read. Margaret Mead's trilogy *From the South Seas* is also rich in insights; her *And Keep Your Powder Dry* sums up her viewpoints in the form of advice to a society living in a state of war or under the threat of war. But perhaps the briefest and best summary of all of the relationship of individual to society is to be found in Walt Whitman's poem, "There was a Child Went Forth."

Scientific American Offprints

402. Eleanor J. Gibson & Richard D. Walk. *The "Visual Cliff"*

412. Konrad Z. Lorenz. *The Evolution of Behavior*

416. Eckhard H. Hess *"Imprinting" in Animals*

418. Howard S. Liddell. *Conditioning and Emotions*

429. Harry F. Harlow. *Love in Infant Monkeys*

473. Harry F. & Margaret Kuenne Harlow. *Social Deprivation in Monkeys*

478. Victor H. Denenberg. *Early Experience and Emotional Development*

481. Leonard Berkowitz. *The Effects of Observing Violence*

34

Human
Reproduction

275. Historical Perspective

Anyone who has read the history of Darwin's *Origin of Species* and its reception by the public, cannot but have been impressed by the courage of T. H. Huxley in championing this heretical work at a time when, to do so, was to risk ostracism. Huxley was an intellectual in the best sense: brilliant, honest, and a breaker of taboos. Yet there was one taboo that even he did not break: the Victorian taboo against the discussion of sex. Huxley wrote a textbook entitled *Elementary Physiology*, first published in 1866, which he revised repeatedly throughout his life. But to the day of his death, in 1895, this much-used textbook included not a word about the human reproductive system. This fact is all the more remarkable when viewed against the background of Huxley's famous statement, quoted in §1 of the present text, beginning with the words, "Suppose it were perfectly certain . . . ."

The Victorian age was an amazing, an exceptional age; it was a time when bulls were called "he-cows"; when the legs of pianos were modestly covered with pantaloons; and when Lady Gough, in her book *Etiquette* (1863), advised, without a trace of irony: "The perfect hostess will see to it that the works of male and female authors be properly separated on her book shelves. Their proximity, unless they happen to be married, should not be tolerated."

Who regrets the passing of such an era? Certainly not a biologist, to whom sex is a part of life, every bit as deserving of study and contemplation as the processes of nutrition and metabolism. Of all the characteristics of life, reproduction is the most peculiarly biological: a species that cannot reproduce soon ceases to be an object of study.

The general characteristics of reproduction we have studied earlier. What we here take up is the study of human reproduction. Many important human problems revolve around the act of sexual union or **copulation,** but some of the most important aspects of these problems are not biological at all, in the narrow sense; rather, they are ethical, legal, or religious. These latter aspects are perhaps the most important but they are ignored here because a biologist, *qua* biologist, has no competence to discuss them. What will now be studied are certain basic biological facts that underlie the more important human problems. A knowledge of biology is a prerequisite to ethical study.

276. The Production of Male Gametes

That the male is essential for reproduction must have been one of the earliest discoveries in pure biological theory made by prehistoric man. When we stop to think of it, we marvel that the discovery was ever made, involving as it does

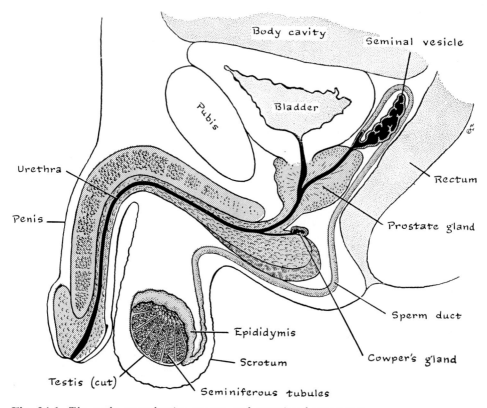

Fig. 34-1. *The male reproductive organs and associated structures.*

the perception of a cause-and-effect relationship in which the effect is separated from the cause by some 10 lunar months.* However this discovery was made, man has known for thousands of years that the fluid injected into the female by the male, the **semen** (L. *sero* = to sow), has something to do with reproduction. For rather less than two centuries we have known that the essential component of the semen is the multitude of male gametes or spermatozoa. Each human spermatozoon consists of a compact "head," about 2μ wide by 4μ long, to which is attached a "tail" that is $30\text{--}50\mu$ in length. Although a sperm cell is tiny, it may be seen with only moderate magnification if suitably illuminated, for it moves with great agitation, progressing at a speed of about 50 microns per second. Leeuwenhoek, who first described sper-

matozoa in 1679, saw them with a lens that probably magnified no more than 200 diameters. Though spermatozoa were seen comparatively early in the period of modern science, their significance was a matter of dispute for about 200 years.

The male structures associated with the production and emission of sperm cells are shown in Figure 34-1. The male gametes are produced by the two **testes.*** Within each testis are found many greatly convoluted tubules called **seminiferous tubules,** within which are produced the sperm cells. The process of sperm formation, called **spermatogenesis,** takes about 2 days; the time taken for passage of spermatozoa through the male reproductive tract is about 12 days.

---

* 34-1. As a speculation, try to imagine the circumstances under which a primitive man might have made this discovery. How easy do you suppose it was for the discoverer to convince others?

---

* Singular *testis*. The diminutive form *testicle* is an exact synonym which, for some obscure reason, is the more commonly used word in popular literature referring to human testes. In scientific literature, "testis" is almost always the term used, whether referring to the organ of humans or other animals.

The number of sperm cells produced in a man's lifetime is almost astronomical. Each copulation results in the release of from 300 million to 500 million spermatozoa. On a conservative assumption of one copulation per week for 30 years, this would amount to at least 500 billion spermatozoa produced and released by one man. The population of the entire world is only about 2 billion humans at the present time, so it would appear to be theoretically possible, if certain practical difficulties could be surmounted, for one man to father the entire next generation of humans. Put another way, the spermatozoa required to father the next generation of human beings have a total volume approximately equal to that of one-third of a stick of chewing gum.

The organs that produce the sex cells (sperms or eggs) are called **gonads** (Gr. *gonos* = seed). The testis is the male gonad; the ovary is the female gonad. Although the female gonads are hidden within the body, the male gonads are evident from the outside. For many years, speculative men were puzzled about the significance of this difference in position. It was not until 1922 that the teleological "cause" was independently discovered by biologists in three different countries.

The first clue in the solution of this problem came from natural abnormalities. During early development of the human male, the gonads start out as organs lying *within* the body. As development proceeds, the testes pass out of the body proper and come to lie within a pendant bag, the **scrotum.** Occasionally, however, testes fail to make this descent, remaining within the body, a condition known as **cryptorchidism.** Individuals suffering from this defect are *sterile;* that is, they do not produce living spermatozoa. However, if by a surgical operation the testes are caused to descend into the scrotum, the individual may soon become fertile.

Knowledge of this fact and a realization that testes in the scrotum would not be as warm as testes inside the body led some biologists to guess that testes might function correctly only at a temperature lower than that of the rest of the body. With this hypothesis in mind, the testes of experimental animals were kept at body temperature by various means, for instance by being bound close to the body by well-insulating cloth. When the testicular temperature was thus raised to that of the interior of the body, the testes soon ceased to produce living sperm.

Most male mammals carry their testes outside the body. This position of the testes exposes these organs not only to accidental damage but also to deliberate injury. Among rodents (rats, mice, squirrels, and others), males, when fighting, instinctively attack the testes. Fortunately for the attacked rodent, there is a muscle attached to each testis by which the gonad can be temporarily pulled back inside the body. That this mechanism is not always used soon enough has been revealed by surveys that show that a considerable percentage of wild male squirrels have been emasculated in combat.

277. The Production of Female Gametes

The female gonads, the **ovaries,** lie completely within the body cavity (Fig. 34-2). In cross sections of an ovary there is occasionally seen a clear area, or **ovarian follicle** (diminutive of L. *follis* = wind bag), first observed in 1672 by a fellow-townsman of Leeuwenhoek, R. van de Graaf. Such an ovarian follicle, or *Graafian follicle,* was mistakenly believed, by its discoverer, to be an egg. It was not until 1827 that the facts were revealed, at which time the German biologist K. E. von Baer showed that the egg is but a single cell lying within the multicellular follicle. In humans, such an egg, or **ovum,** is barely visible to the naked eye, being about 130μ in diameter. The mass of a human egg is about 75 thousand times as great as that of a single spermatozoon.

In the production of gametes, the female is not so extravagant as the male. In the male, spermatogenesis continues throughout the lifetime of the adult. In the female, **oogenesis** (the production of eggs, or ova) has a quite different time schedule. Meiosis begins before birth, in many cells of the ovary, and stops in prophase

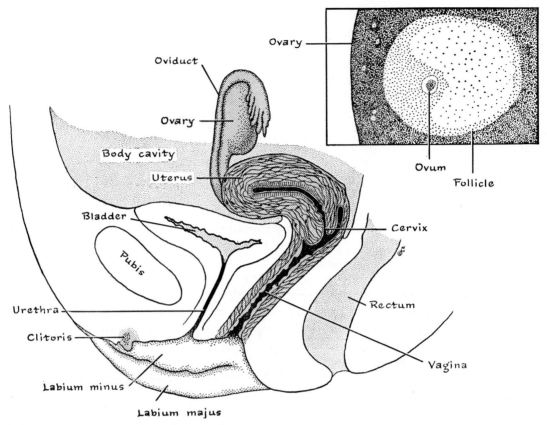

Fig. 34-2. *The female reproductive organs and associated structures.* Upper right: *A magnified view of a portion of an ovary.*

(§58). The female child is born with about 2×10^6 cells in this immature state. Throughout her life this number is diminished by normal degeneration of these cells; only about 400 complete their meiosis and are released in the process of **ovulation.** The completion of meiosis takes place just before ovulation, for each ovum that is released; from this it follows that the meiotic process, for some of the cells in the ovary, takes nearly 50 years to run to completion.

Both ovaries produce eggs, but normally, it is believed, only one is released at a time, that is, only one during any one month, in humans. As a result, most human births are of a single child. About 1 birth out of every 90 is a multiple birth, that is, a birth of more than one child. Two sorts of processes account for multiple births. In some cases, a fertilized egg di-

vides to form two separate, complete zygotes, each of which develops into a normal human. Such humans resemble each other very closely and are called **identical twins,** or *one-egg twins.* Another sort of unusual occurrence that accounts for multiple births appears to be the release of more than one ovum at a time. If two such ova are fertilized, the result will be the production of **fraternal twins,** or *two-egg twins,* which resemble each other no more than ordinary brothers and sisters. They just happen to be born at the same time.

Family pedigrees show that the tendency to produce twins is inherited; this perhaps means that what is inherited is a tendency of the ovaries to release more than one egg at a time. Racial groups differ in their tendency to produce multiple births. The highest recorded rate is among the Belgians, with 1 multiple birth per

56 births. Low rates occur among the Japanese, 1 per 145; the Chinese, 1 per 294; and among the Annamese of Cochin China, said to have a rate of only 1 per 10,000. Among animals of the same species, large strains usually have more offspring than small strains. Among humans, the same tendency is noticeable and, presumably, accounts in part for the racial differences just recorded.*

278. Factors Involved in the Ejection of Male Gametes

For many animals that live in the water and produce young that can take care of themselves, the bringing-together of the gametes is simply done. The sperm and eggs are shed into the surrounding water; the sperm swims to and enters the egg, and the resultant zygote starts to develop into some sort of self-sufficient youngster. The probability of a meeting of egg and sperm is sometimes increased by the secretion of sperm-attracting chemicals by the egg.

In animals, *fertilization always takes place in liquid surroundings.* This necessity, for such it is, requires that land animals, surrounded by dry air, must somehow surround their uniting gametes by fluids. Furthermore, in higher animals (e.g., mammals), the zygote and the embryo into which it develops are helpless for a long period and must be thoroughly protected and nourished by the mother. Logically connected with these two necessities are the organs and structures we are accustomed to think of as specifically sexual, for example, the uterus and the breasts.

The spermatozoa ejected by a human male are surrounded by semen. Only a small fraction of the semen consists of sperm cells. Most of it is fluid contributed by various portions of the male genital system. The path of sperm cells going from the testis to the opening of the penis can be seen in Figure 34-1. During their journey through the epididymis and past the prostate and Cowper's glands, the sperm cells are mixed with various secretions that apparently furnish nourishment and chemical protection to the spermatozoa after they are deposited in the vagina of the female.

The discharge of semen (**ejaculation**) occurs in the culmination (the **orgasm**) of copulation. Preliminary to copulation, the penis changes from a flaccid organ to a firm one, a process known as **erection.** Erection is brought about by a constriction of small blood vessels, thereby slowing the exit of blood from the penis while leaving the entering blood flow unimpeded. As a result, the spongy tissue of the penis becomes filled with blood under pressure, and the penis erects. When the penis is in this condition, entrance into the vagina can be effected and semen deposited therein.

Copulatory activity in the male is determined principally by the amount of the hormone **testosterone** secreted into the blood stream by the testes, though psychological factors also play an important role among humans. The behavior of domesticated animals can be greatly modified by **castration,** that is, by removal of the gonads. If a male is castrated while still young, he not only is made sterile, but also fails to develop into a typical male. Males are frequently distinguished by **secondary sexual characteristics,** such things as a large comb in roosters, a male-type feather pattern in many birds, and facial hair in man. A castrated male does not develop secondary sexual characteristics. Moreover, the copulatory activity of the adult fails to develop in castrates; castrated males, with few exceptions, show no interest in females as females. Their interest in males also tends to be impersonal, so to speak. Normal adult males of many species instinctively fight each other. Such fighting, which may result in serious or fatal injuries, is almost completely lacking in castrated animals. Besides this, if castration is performed early, the male develops a body

---

* The critical reader will detect a lack of scientific exactness in the use of the word "tendency." To say there is a *tendency* explains nothing. In the present case, one would like to know *why* large animals (within one species) have more offspring than small, that is, *what chain of events* accounts for this fact.

conformation closer to that of the female, often putting on considerable fat. For these reasons, a castrated animal is more valuable to the animal husbandman than the normal one, and we find that castration of most of the males (some must be saved for breeding) has been carried on by livestock raisers for thousands of years.

Until only a few hundred years ago, castration of humans was extensively practiced in what we now regard as the civilized world, and even now is performed in remote regions. The custom has been justified variously: as a means of creating reliable haremkeepers (*eunuchs*) in the Moslem world, or of producing permanent male sopranos—the pitch of the voice is partly a secondary sexual characteristic—for church choirs in the Western world.

Castration is no longer extensively practiced in any country we would cheerfully called civilized. However, another operation, called **sterilization,** is frequently performed. Because castration and sterilization are often confused in the public mind, it is important that we carefully distinguish between the two here.

The sterilization of a male is accomplished by severing the sperm duct from each testis. (See Fig. 34-1.) Since each sperm duct is also called a **vas deferens,** this operation is referred to as a **vasotomy.** As a result of such an operation, spermatozoa can no longer reach the exterior. Semen, however, is still formed. The testes, still in place and unharmed, continue to secrete testosterone into the blood stream. The desire of the individual toward the opposite sex is unchanged, as is his ability to copulate. Indeed, if the operation—which is a minor one— were skillfully performed without the individual's knowledge, he would never know of it unless his lack of children made him suspicious. Sterilization makes an individual sterile, that is, incapable of producing children; but nothing else.

Sterilization is frequently used to prevent the breeding of mental defectives. The morality of its use is still a matter of debate. It is not expected that all persons will view the matter in the same light. It is important, however, that everyone understands precisely what sterilization is and what it does.

279. Ovulation, Fertilization, and Implantation

Typically, in a human female, only one Graafian follicle ripens each month and discharges its egg to the exterior. Although there are two ovaries, only one such discharge occurs in a month's time, which suggests that there is some means, at present unknown, whereby the activities of the two ovaries are coordinated. The process of ovulation is indicated diagrammatically at the top of Figure 34-3. The released egg travels down an oviduct (see again Fig. 34-2), toward the **uterus.** Although occasionally aided by peristaltic-like contractions of the muscular walls of the oviduct, this short journey of the egg takes 3 days or a bit more, which suggests that its passage is actively delayed. Certain it is that the union of egg and sperm normally occurs only in the oviduct. An egg that has reached the uterus without encountering a spermatozoon is incapable of being fertilized. Following fertilization, mitotic cell divisions take place, producing the earliest stages of the multicellular embryo even before the individual gets out of the oviduct.

The delay of the egg in the oviduct gives the uterine wall time to undergo certain changes that must take place before the uterus is ready for **implantation,** that is, attachment of the embryo. During the time that an egg is maturing in the follicle, the wall of the uterus is becoming thicker and more fully *vascularized,* that is, more richly supplied with blood. This change in the uterine wall is brought about by the hormone **estrogen,** secreted by the ovary, and perhaps by other hormones. At the time of ovulation, the uterine wall is still not completely ready for implantation. Its further maturation is aided by a hormone from a rather surprising source. After the discharge of an egg, the ruptured follicle changes in appearance, developing into a structure known as a **corpus luteum.**

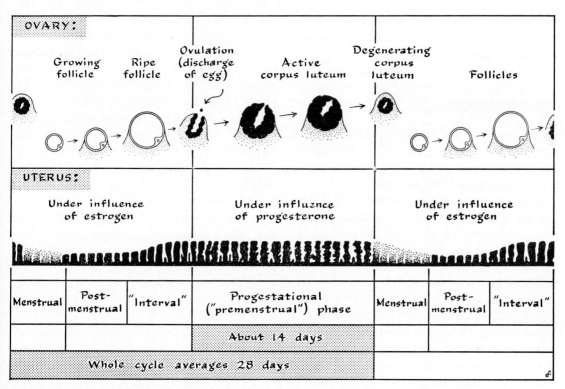

Fig. 34-3. *Factors associated with the sexual cycle in women.* (*From Corner,* The Hormones in Human Reproduction, *1947, courtesy Princeton University Press, Princeton.*)

The name, which is Latin for "yellow body," is apt in cattle, but not so in humans, where the corpus luteum is pink. The corpus luteum (Fig. 34-3) secretes a hormone that brings about the final maturation of the uterine wall during the three days that the egg is in the oviduct. At the end of this period, the uterus is ready for the implantation of the fertilized egg, ready for the act of "carrying" the embryo, an act called **gestation.** Because it prepares the uterus for gestation, the hormone produced by the corpus luteum is called **progesterone.** The corpus luteum is essential to the continuation of pregnancy in mice, rabbits, and cows, but is not required in the later stages in mares, monkeys, guinea pigs, and humans.

Estrogen, the hormone produced by the ovaries, has a number of effects. It is the female counterpart of testosterone, bringing about the development of such secondary sexual charac-

teristics as the well-developed breasts of the female and the feminine pattern of body fat deposition. The removal of both ovaries causes not only sterility, but also modifications of sexual behavior and of secondary sexual characteristics. As in the case of males, a distinction should be made between castration—the operation just described—and sterilization, which may be accomplished by tying and cutting the oviducts. From the fancied resemblance of an oviduct to an ancient war horn (Gr. *salpinx*), this operation is called a **salpingotomy.** Since, to carry it out, the abdominal cavity must be entered, this operation is a bit more serious than vasotomy. However, for a few days immediately after childbirth, the oviducts are exceptionally easy to reach by operative procedure. When performed at this time, the operation is such a minor one that it does not necessitate hospitalization of the mother beyond the normal post-delivery period. The moral questions involved in such an operation are, of course, the same as in male sterilization.

280. Menstruation

In the preceding discussion it has been assumed that the ovum, after its release from the follicle, becomes fertilized. But most of the time this is not the case. What happens then?

The events that follow ovulation are tied to the fate of the corpus luteum. The final preparation of the uterine wall for implantation is brought about by the hormone progesterone, secreted by the corpus luteum. If the egg is not fertilized and consequently does not implant, the corpus luteum degenerates. With the lowering of the concentration of progesterone in the blood coming to it, the uterine wall is unable to remain in its thickened, progestational state. The surface of the wall sloughs off, carrying with it tiny blood vessels and their contained blood. The blood and cellular debris pass from the uterus through the vagina to the exterior. This material constitutes the *menstrual flow,* and the phenomenon just described is called **menstruation** (L. *mensis* = month, because the flow occurs, on the average, about once a month in mature human females).

Even before menstruation is completed, another Graafian follicle is maturing. At the conclusion of menstruation—the process typically takes from 5 to 7 days—the uterine wall begins to thicken again, first under the influence of estrogen from the ovary, later under the influence of progesterone from the corpus luteum, until it is again in a condition suitable for implantation of an embryo. If fertilization does not occur, menstruation again takes place. The principal events of the menstrual cycle are diagrammatically summarized in Figure 34-3.

There is much that we do not know about menstruation—about the exact role of all the hormones involved and about the causes of menstrual disorders. Menstruation occurs only in a few species of animals, in man and in some of the "higher" monkeys and apes. The needed

experimental animals are, therefore, expensive and not plentiful; much of our knowledge of menstruation has to be gained from the incomplete data of human clinics. As a result, knowledge is gained but slowly. Consideration of the causes of the slow progress in this field makes more evident the importance of animal experimentation in studying human biological problems, most of which can be attacked by using cheap and plentiful kinds of nonhuman animals.

281. The Control of Conception

In all human societies, there have been two acute problems concerned with reproduction: how to prevent conception when children are not wanted, and how to encourage it when they are. The former, the problem of **contraception** ("against conception"), will be taken up first.

To prevent, or to diminish, the probability of conception, various means have been employed, among which the following are the more important: sexual abstinence, restriction of intercourse to the "safe period," use of mechanical barriers to the migration of spermatozoa in the female reproductive tract, and the use of spermicides.

During the second quarter of the twentieth century there was considerable propaganda in favor of the **rhythm method** of birth control. This method is rather interesting in terms of the biology involved. It requires sexual abstinence during a certain portion of the sexual cycle. In Figure 34-3 note that ovulation occurs at about 14 days after the beginning of the preceding menstrual period. The egg can be fertilized during a period of not more than 3 days, and perhaps during less than 1. Spermatozoa are capable of uniting with an egg for only a very short period after ejaculation, perhaps for only a day or less. It follows, therefore, that only during a very small part of the menstrual cycle can copulation induce conception. Other parts of the cycle are so-called safe periods. In the rhythm method of birth control, sexual intercourse is restricted to the safe periods. It must be observed, however, that the determination of safe periods is subject to considerable error. There are differences in the length of the menstrual cycle in different women, unpredictable variations in its length in the same woman; and the time of ovulation undoubtedly also varies, perhaps sometimes in response to psychological influences. Among women at the beginning and near the end of their child-bearing periods the menstrual cycle is least regular; these are the times when various sociological factors make pregnancy most undesirable.

In recent years two very promising methods of birth control have been discovered: "the pill" and the IUCD. The **contraceptive pill** is a steroid compound which has an effect like that of progesterone—it inhibits ovulation. Taken between normal menstrual periods it creates a permanent safe period. The failure rate seems to be about 2 pregnancies per 100 woman-years of exposure to the risk of pregnancy. This should be compared with the failure rate of the rhythm method which is about 14 per hundred woman-years for the five-sixths of the female population with regular enough periods to use it (for the other one-sixth, the rhythm method is useless). There is reason to hope that future research will improve the performance of oral contraceptives.

The **IUCD**—intra-uterine contraceptive device, also called the IUD—is a plastic filament formed into a variety of shapes among which the coil is favored. It can be inserted into the uterus by a physician or even by properly instructed *paramedical* personnel (midwives, interns, practical nurses, etc.). In place in the uterus, the IUCD prevents conception or attachment of the embryo by means that are not understood. About 10 percent of the patients spontaneously expel the devices; even *in situ* they occasionally fail. Their future in prosperous populations is a matter of debate, but they hold great promise for the majority of women among the impoverished, illiterate peoples of the world, giving their women much-wanted freedom from the consequences of unwanted fecundity.

In our society and in our time, we have been made more aware of the problem of preventing conception than we have of the opposite problem of encouraging it. Nevertheless, involuntary sterility has been known for thousands of years, as is apparent from reference to the Bible (see, for instance, *Genesis,* Chapters 16–21). The causes are many and only partly understood. Most primitive peoples, especially in male-dominated societies, tend to lay the "blame" for sterility on the wife. It is now clear that the source of the sterility can at least as often be properly ascribed to the husband. Physicians who specialize in sterility problems have noticed that the numbers and kinds of spermatozoa in semen show individual variations. Figure 34-4 shows a few of the many types that have been found; it is believed that only the type of sperm cell shown near the center of the figure is normal and capable of fertilizing an egg. This type is usually present in the greatest numbers. When the proportion of abnormal types is as great as 25 percent, the male is usually sterile.

Furthermore, it has been found that when the number of spermatozoa per cubic centimeter of semen is less than 60 million, conception is unlikely. An overwhelming amount of evidence, including direct observation, indicates that in *all* plants and animals only one male cell is required to fertilize each egg. There is no question but that this is true for humans, too. Why, then, do millions of spermatozoa appear to be required in copulation when fertilization requires but one cell?

We can give a probable answer to this question. The answer lies partly in the geography involved. Referring to Figure 34-5, notice that the place where semen is deposited, the upper end of the vagina, is at a considerable distance from the place where fertilization must occur, the oviduct. The distance is at least 7,000 times as great as the length of the head of the sperm. It is hardly to be wondered at if a great many of the sperm never get near their goal. Translating the problem into everyday terms, imagine a crowd of men released about 13 kilometers from their goal (that is, a distance about 7,000 times the length of one man). It is easy to

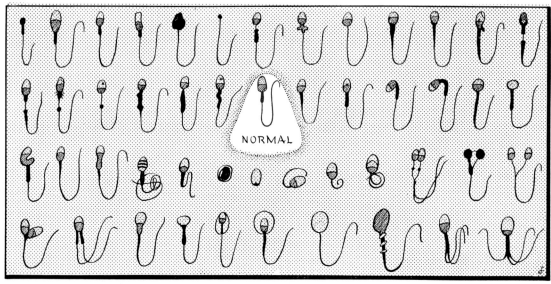

Fig. 34-4. *Some of the variety observed among human spermatozoa. The normal type is in the center. When abnormal types constitute more than 25 percent of the spermatozoan population, the man is usually sterile.*

Fig. 34-5. *The cervix of the uterus (left) is occluded by a plug of mucus. The penetration of the mucus by spermatozoa may be aided by a mucus-dissolving enzyme that is demonstrable in spermatozoa.*

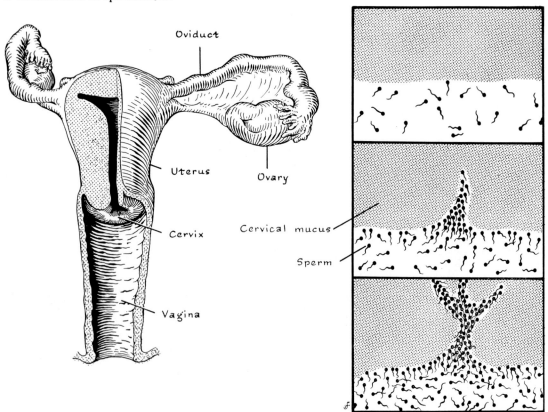

imagine that a great many of the men, for want of strength, motivation, sense of direction, or whatnot, might never reach the goal. A minimum number of men might have to be released to make reasonably certain that one completed the trip in the allotted time. For similar reasons, a minimum number of sperm may be needed to give a reasonable probability of one arriving at the ovum soon enough.

There is probably another reason why so many sperm seem to be required. The **cervix,** or neck of the uterus, is normally filled with a mucus. It has been found that sperm cells contain a specific enzyme that digests the cervical mucus. The thickness of mucus is probably greater than any one sperm cell can digest its way through; the spermatozoa that get through appear to be the ones that move in a crowd, each individual contributing its bit to the process of digestion (Fig. 34-5). This fact may help explain the need for the tremendous number of sperm.

282. Maternal Care of the Child

The implantation of the young embryo in the wall of the uterus soon results in the development of a special structure adapted to the exchange of dissolved materials between mother and child. This structure, the **placenta,** consists of closely adjoining tissues of both mother and child (Fig. 34-6). On one side of this double wall of tissue, flows the blood of the child; on the other, flows the mother's blood. That the two blood streams are not normally commingled is apparent from the fact that mother and child may belong to two different blood groups. By molecular diffusion, molecules of foodstuffs and oxygen move from the capillaries of the mother's blood stream, through the placental barrier, and into the blood capillaries of the child. The placental blood vessels of the child fuse to form the **umbilical vein,** in which blood is transported from the placenta to the child's body via the **umbilical cord,** which connects the two. In the child's body the blood gives up its charge of food and oxygen and picks up carbon dioxide

and other waste materials, which it carries back, via umbilical arteries, to the placental blood vessels from which the waste materials will diffuse to the blood in maternal capillaries. During pregnancy, then, the mother's lungs furnish the child with O_2, her digestive system furnishes it with food; and her lungs dispose of the child's CO_2, while her kidneys get rid of its other waste products. The agency for the exchange of these materials is the placenta. There are no nervous connections between mother and child.

During the earliest stages of implantation, the uterus is inhibited from taking any action that might expel the embryo by the progesterone secreted by the corpus luteum. Although this endocrine body persists to the end of pregnancy, it is not essential to the continuance of implantation in humans, as it is in many other animals. Removal of the ovaries during pregnancy causes **abortion** (premature expulsion of the embryo) in many animals, but not in humans. There is evidence that the human placenta itself secretes a hormone that inhibits any expulsive tendencies of the uterus.

Finally there comes a time (after about 9 calendar months in humans) when the offspring *is* expelled from the uterus. What factor or factors cause pregnancy to terminate and birth **(parturition)** to begin are not known. Does the embryo or placenta "keep its own time," so to speak, or is there a change in the mother's hormonal balance that causes parturition to take place? Presumably, nervous influences are not required to start the process, but they can have an influence, as is shown by the fact that a severe emotional or nervous upset to the mother can cause a premature birth.

The process of birth begins with rhythmic contractions of the smooth muscles of the wall of the uterus. Later, these muscular movements are aided by contractions of the muscles of the abdominal wall. At the same time, the exit of air from the trachea may be periodically prevented, increasing the pressure in the entire abdominal cavity, thus aiding in the expulsion of the child. It is clear that a highly muscular torso is an aid to easy birth. This one factor is probably the principal one accounting for the easier

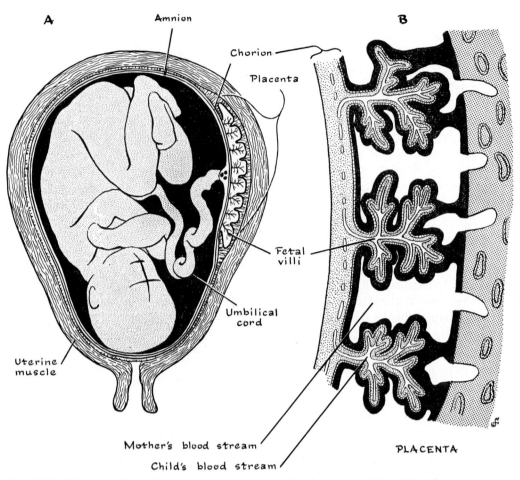

Fig. 34-6. *The normal position of the mature fetus in the uterus* (A). (B) *Placenta magnified and simplified. Fetal tissues are indicated in color, maternal tissues in black. Note that, normally, there is no mixing of maternal and fetal bloods.*

birth among primitive, that is, hard-working, women, as compared to "civilized" ones. However, with the present increase in the fashionableness of vigorous sports the differential is lessening.

The vagina, normally a passage much too small for so large an object to pass through, enlarges sufficiently during the latter stages of pregnancy to permit the child to be squeezed through it. Also, the pubic bones that surround the vagina and meet in front of it have their suture, evidently under the influence of hormones, loosened to the point where the bones can be partly sprung apart at birth. Normally, a child is born head first; when any other part of its body is presented first, the delivery is

more difficult and may necessitate the use of instruments. Shortly after the child is born, the placenta is expelled; for this reason, the placenta is called the "afterbirth."

For the child, being born brings about the most sudden and radical revolution of its entire life. In its mother's uterus, it does not need to breathe, feed, or maintain its own temperature, nor is it required to move around (though it does move, as any mother can tell). The most radical change at birth is that involved in breathing for itself—a change that involves both the breathing and the circulatory systems.

The lungs of an unborn child are in a completely unexpanded condition and contain no gas whatever. As soon as the child is born, he must do his own breathing and *do it right*. He has no time to learn; there are no second chances for first failures. Breathing, as we know, means much more than merely filling the lungs with air. The chemical mechanism of breathing has already been described. The child is born with this mechanism. As soon as the concentration of CO_2 in his blood rises, his medulla is stimulated to send messages to the breathing muscles, causing the appropriate motions. Be-sides the chemical mechanism, there is another factor involved in normal breathing: an inherent tendency in the medulla to send impulses at regular intervals. This inherent rhythm is often almost lacking in the newborn child; as a result, its breathing tends to occur in alternating periods of activity, in response to high CO_2 content, and in periods of complete inactivity following the lowering of CO_2 content of blood by heavy breathing. This sort of breathing

Fig. 34-7. *The fetal heart has two short circuits between the two pump systems:* (1) *an opening between the two auricles (the* foramen ovale), *and* (2) *a special vessel (the* ductus arteriosus) *between the pulmonary artery and the aorta.*

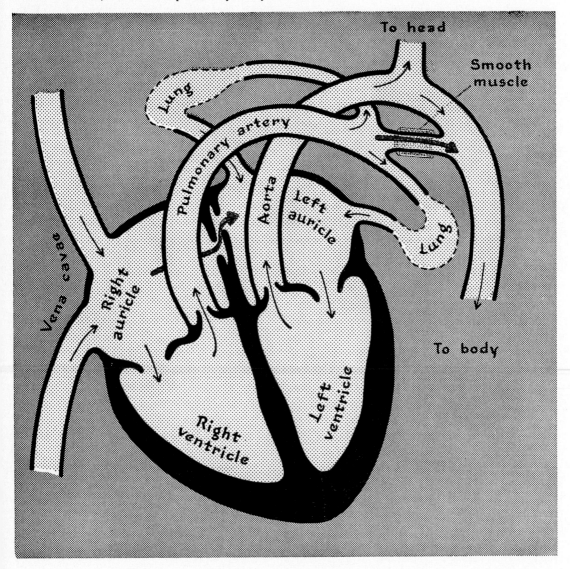

(called Cheyne-Stokes breathing) is frequently observed during infancy. Usually, the medulla develops its inherent rhythm long before adulthood, though there are exceptions. It is noteworthy that even the normal adult may show Cheyne-Stokes breathing in extremely deep sleep.

Recall the double nature of the circulatory system and the reasons therefor. The need for both a pulmonary and a systemic circulation in the adult does not exist in the unborn child; yet, the child must have such a system all ready to go at the time of birth. The means by which the embryo compromises the conflicting needs is extremely neat. The adult-type system of separated circulatory systems is first developed with "by-passes" in the vascular network that allow blood to go from the pulmonary system to the systemic system without passing through the lungs. One of these by-passes (Fig. 34-7) is an opening between the two auricles. It is guarded by flaps of tissue that, during embryonic life, do not interfere with the passage of blood from the right auricle to the left auricle. After birth, because of pressure relationships too complicated to discuss here, the flaps close and remain closed. Ultimately, new tissue grows across the opening, and the two auricles are thenceforth completely separated—in 4 out of 5 persons. The remaining 20 percent of the population have a tiny opening between the right and left auricles.

The other short circuit is a blood vessel that connects the pulmonary artery with the aorta. This vessel remains open until birth. It is surrounded by a muscle (Fig. 34-7) that, in response to some unknown stimulus connected with being born, contracts at the time of birth, completely closing the vessel, and thus causing all the blood in the pulmonary artery to go through the capillaries of the lungs before getting out into the systemic circulation. Once the muscle of the by-pass blood vessel contracts, it never relaxes and, in a few weeks, growth of new tissue occludes the vessel. The muscle degenerates and disappears. A muscle that is destined to contract but once in an individual's life, then to perish! It would be difficult to find

a more striking instance of the adaptation of structure to function.

After birth, the young mammal is ready to do his own breathing and feeding. He is not, however, ready for an adult diet. The digestive tract of newborn mammals has only limited digestive and assimilatory capacities and must be furnished a special and easily assimilable diet. In a state of nature (to ignore, for the present, modern human practices) the diet of the newborn consists wholly of milk secreted by the **mammary glands** of the mother. The final stages of the maturation of these glands is brought about during pregnancy by **prolactin,** a hormone secreted by the anterior lobe of the pituitary. During pregnancy the actual flow of milk is prevented by a hormone secreted by the placenta. After the expulsion of child and afterbirth, the secretion of the pituitary gland exerts its full effect.

283. Development: Growth and Differentiation

The development of an adult from a zygote involves **growth,** that is, increase in size. Growth is made possible by the multiplication of cells by repeated mitotic divisions, each of which is followed by increase in size of the daughter cells. But development involves more than growth: it also involves **differentiation** of cells. The new individual initially consists of but one cell: the zygote. This divides to form two similar cells; these divide to form four; then to eight—and so on. There soon comes a time when not all of the cells derived from cell divisions are alike; they have become different— they have *differentiated.* By the time the child is born, there are dozens of different kinds of cells—liver cells, nerve cells, smooth muscle cells, striated muscle cells, and others—all derived by differentiation from a single cell, the zygote.

The study of growth and differentiation constitutes the science of **embryology.** Because human embryos are not easily obtainable for study and experimentation, the greater part of our

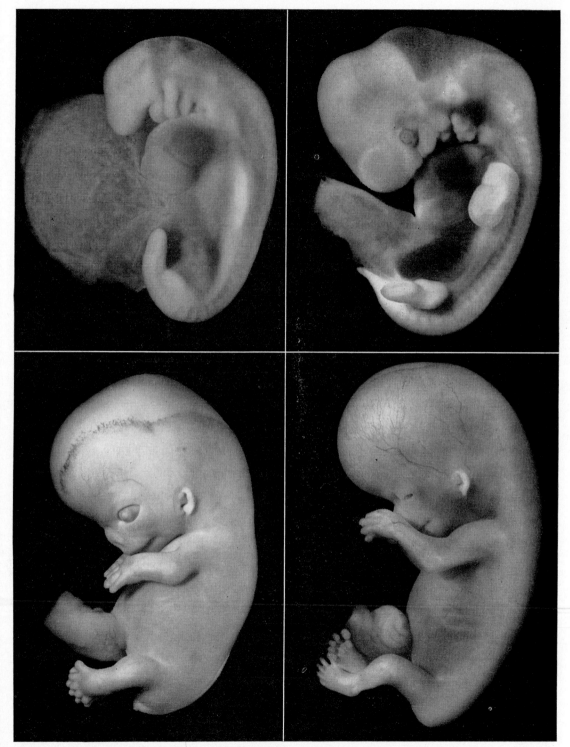

Fig. 34-8. *Human embryos.* Top left, *27 days after ovulation* (× *11*); top right, *34 days* (× *5*); lower left, *43 days* (× *3*); lower right, *56 days* (× *2*). (*Courtesy* **G. W.** *Corner and the Carnegie Institution of Washington.*)

knowledge in this field has been obtained by study of other animals. This study of the early embryological stages has particularly benefited from the availability of "lower" forms of life.

Differentiation to the stage in which the embryo is recognizably human takes place in a surprisingly short period of time. Notice, in Figure 34-8, the essentially human form of an embryo recovered after only 43 days of pregnancy (only 15 percent of the full term). By this time, most of the differentiation of cell types has already occurred. Changes in appearance after this time are due largely to **differential growth,** which changes the proportions between the various parts. At 43 days of true (embryonic) age, the length of the head is more than a third the total distance from head to toe; in an adult, the fraction is about one-seventh. Many other instances of differential growth can easily be seen by comparing the picture of the 43-day-old embryo with any convenient adult.

The process of development does not stop at birth. The bodily proportions of the infant are gradually changed to adult proportions. In addition, other important changes occur, particularly in the sexual organs and those parts of the body that exhibit the secondary sexual characteristics. Sexual maturity is reached during the second decade of life. Among the events that mark this period in both sexes is the appearance of coarse, curly hair in the lower abdominal region. This region is called the *pubes,* and the time during which this, and other, maturing processes occur is called **puberty** (L. *puber* = of ripe age). The denseness of the general body hair also increases in both sexes at this time, though the change is typically greater in the male. Heavy facial hair (beard and moustache) also develop in the males of some racial groups (not including many Mongolians and their derivatives, the American Indians). In females, the mammary glands enlarge and develop, and the feminine body contours develop. In each sex the gonads and sexual organs enlarge and become functional. All of these changes are due to the increased secretion, by the gonads, of sex hormones, principally testosterone in the male and estrogen in the female. The increased activity of the gonads seems to be caused principally by the increase in secretion of **gonadotrophic hormones** (gonad-stimulating) by the anterior lobe of the pituitary gland. What causes the change in activity of the pituitary gland as the age of puberty approaches is yet to be determined.

Puberty is also a time of greatly accelerated general bodily growth. The principal endocrine organ causing growth at this (or any other) time is also the anterior lobe of the pituitary. Some of its effects are exerted directly by means of a growth hormone that it secretes; other effects are exerted indirectly through its hormonal stimulation of other glands, for example, the thyroid gland and the gonads. Because of its many hormones and their numerous important effects, the pituitary is often called the "master gland" of the body. The fact that it secretes many different hormones makes difficult the experimental determination of the various functions of this gland. That many of the pituitary hormones are proteins adds further to the difficulty of isolating, identifying, and administering them medically.

Development does not cease with the attainment of sexual maturity. The process of aging continues; some functions of the body may, for a time, improve, but for the most part there is a gradual deterioration of physiological abilities after puberty. With respect to sexual functions, a decided change takes place during the fifth decade in females. Over a period of a few years the activity of the ovaries rapidly decreases. The menstrual periods become at first irregular and then cease altogether as ovulation stops. Secretion of hormones by the ovaries falls to a low level, and associated with this are psychic changes that are extremely variable. This period is called the "change of life," or the **menopause.**

As the final stage in the development of multicellular organisms comes death itself. The data from tissue-culture studies indicate unambiguously that single cells or colonies of similar, undifferentiated cells are potentially immortal. Why death should come to a complex, highly differentiated body is most unclear, but there is a widespread suspicion that it is perhaps an inevitable outcome of the very processes of differentiation and growth that, in their early stages, make possible the attainment of that felicitous state we call maturity. Whether such a suspicion is well founded is for future research to tell. Whatever the case, death is, for

the individual multicellular organism, inevitable. For the species, it is not. By reproduction, a tiny bit of "protoplasm"—the zygote—is started on a fresh journey of growth and differentiation, repeating, in a general way, the experience of its parents.

Questions and Problems

34-2. Make a list of the **boldface** terms in this chapter. Write a brief definition or description of each. Compare your work with the text.

‡34-3. In cryptorchidism, the sperm-producing cells of the testes do not function, but the hormone-producing cells do. Which does this condition resemble more closely—castration or sterilization?

34-4. What is the etymology of "cryptorchidism"? Do you know of common words using the same roots?

‡34-5. Some people have speculated as to whether the prolonged hot baths of the Japanese may not have a tendency to lower their reproductive rate. What physiological facts led to this speculation?

34-6. Why is an expectant mother urged to walk a mile a day?

‡34-7. Some people believe that a mother can influence the character of her unborn child "thinking the right thoughts." If such prenatal influence exists, what is the route of the "message"—nervous or hormonal? Do you think it likely that it could be directional and specific, for example, a mother could produce a musical child by much listening to symphonies?

34-8. From Charles Darwin's *Variation of Animals and Plants under Domestication* (1868), Vol. 2, p. 264:

Dr. William Hunter, in the last century, told my father that during many years every woman in a large London Lying-in Hospital was asked before her confinement whether anything had specially affected her mind, and the answer was written down; and it

so happened that in no one instance could a coincidence be detected between the woman's answer and any abnormal structure; but when she knew the nature of the structure, she frequently suggested some fresh cause.

a. What important principle of scientific investigation is illustrated here?

b. What bearing does this principle have on a type of evidence commonly put forward in support of ESP?

‡34-9. A French naturalist, F. A. Pouchet, claimed (1847) to have seen an alimentary tract in human spermatozoa. He bolstered his claim with this argument: "If there is growth there must be nutrition, and if there is nutrition there must be an alimentary tract."

Comment on the argument.

34-10. G. W. Bartholomew (*Eug. Rev.*, **49**:187–195, 1958) estimated that by 1955 some 50,000 children had been produced in the United States by transemination ("artificial insemination"). All this is an outgrowth of a technical accomplishment first achieved by the Catholic priest Lazaro Spallanzani, who, in 1786, successfully inseminated a dog artificially. A contemporary French biologist, Charles Bonnet, commenting on this feat in a letter to the *abbé*, said:

Je ne sais même si ce que vous venez de découvrir, n'aura pas quelque jour dans l'espèce humaine des applications auxquelles nous ne songeons point et dont les suites ne seront pas légères.

Do you think the suspicions of Bonnet have yet been realized? What about the future?

‡34-11. "Blue babies" are babies whose blood (both arterial and venous) appears blue under

the skin, instead of rosy. They sometimes grow into adults who are incapable of much exertion.

a. What is the significance of the blue color?

b. What abnormalities of development could account for the babies' condition?

c. Could these abnormalities be remedied surgically and, if so, how?

34-12. In rabbits it has been found that ovulation normally occurs only after copulation has taken place. It has been shown that it is the act of copulation that is the stimulating factor rather than any chemical stimulus from semen or spermatozoa. Describe what must be the experimental evidence for this last statement.

34-13. Have we completely escaped the taboos that restricted T. H. Huxley in writing a biology textbook?

34-14. One mutant type of mouse produces embryos that fail to develop a placenta; nevertheless they manage to survive to the limb-bud stage. If they can survive that long, why not longer?

‡34-15. In cybernetic terms, how would you characterize Cheyne-Stokes breathing?

Readings

For a general orientation, read N. J. Berrill's *Sex and the Nature of Things.* For a discussion of human aspects, see Corner's two excellent books, *Ourselves Unborn* and *The Hormones in Human Reproduction.* For the historical development of knowledge in this field, see Meyer's *The Rise of Embryology.*

Interference with the normal reproductive processes has raised a number of legal problems that are as yet unresolved. For example, consider the child produced by artificial insemination using semen from a man who is not the legal husband of the mother. Is such a child legitimate, in the legal sense? And what about vasotomy and salpingotomy operations, when performed at the request of the patient. Do they fall under the legal heading of mayhem, and render the doctor liable to later prosecution? Levinson's *Symposium on Medicolegal Problems* contains lively verbatim reports of conferences of doctors and lawyers on such problems. These reports clearly highlight the differences in attitude between these professions, one of which represents the spirit of innovation (and progress?), while the other is professionally concerned primarily with the conservation of traditions.

More extensive discussion of the ethical implications of scientific and technological discoveries in this field will be found in Fletcher's *Morals and Medicine* and Williams' *The Sanctity of Life and the Criminal Law.* For the historical background of our ideas on sex, see Taylor's *Sex in History.* The controversy that developed over the propriety of various methods of birth control is treated in the third part of my *Population, Evolution, and Birth Control.*

Scientific American Offprints

163. Arpad Csapo. *Progesterone*

414. N. Tinbergen. *The Curious Behavior of the Stickleback*

488. Daniel S. Lehrman. *The Reproductive Behavior of Ring Doves*

V | Heredity

My time will come.
GREGOR MENDEL

35

The Particulate Theory of Inheritance

284. The Mendelian Level of Analysis

History is not a chain of discrete events laid out like beads in a chain. There is a tremendous amount of temporal overlap of different processes in the development of both ideas and institutions. The total reality of history is so rich in detail that we cannot gain a complete knowledge of the past without sacrificing our own lives. Therefore we simplify the subject called "history," rather than entirely give up our effort to understand our origins.

Table 35-1 exhibits a greatly simplified history of the development of man's ideas of heredity. It would be easy to find fault with this listing, but it will serve to develop the motivation of the present chapter. In fact, the story can be simplified still further. We may divide the history of genetics into three phases, and arbitrarily ignore their overlaps in dating them:

Prehistory to 1900   Blending theory
1900 to 1953   Mendelian genetics
1953 to ?   Molecular genetics

With little need for qualification, we can say that the difference between the first two periods is the difference between error and truth. By contrast, the difference between the second and third periods is a difference in levels of analysis. Molecular genetics does not contradict Mendelian genetics; rather it analyzes genetic problems on a much finer scale. One approach is

not right and the other wrong; nor is one intrinsically better. It depends on what we want to accomplish. If an analogy will help, consider

TABLE 35-1 *A Simplified History of Genetics.*

TIME	DEVELOPMENT
Prehistory to 1908	Reign of the blending theory of inheritance; largely at subconscious level.
1866	Publication of Mendel's theory of particulate theory of inheritance; unnoticed by scientific world.
1900	Rediscovery of Mendel's paper, and independent discovery of Mendelian genetics by De Vries, Correns, and Tschermak.
1908	Groundwork of population genetics laid independently by Hardy and Weinberg.
1900–ca. 1950	Thorough development of Mendelian genetics and cytogenetics; beginnings of biochemical genetics.
1930	Implications of particulate theory made clear by Fisher.
1928–1953	Beginning with Griffith's work, groundwork laid for molecular genetics.
1953	With the publication of Watson and Crick's model of DNA, molecular genetics begins explosive phase of development.

a situation in the physical sciences. When we try to predict the path of a satellite around the earth we do so on the assumption that it is a rigid, unitary body, although we know perfectly well that the satellite is made up of myriads of much tinier bodies—molecules, atoms, or protons and electrons—each with its own proper motions. One carries the analysis only as far as is convenient for the purpose at hand.

In Part I of this book, the elements of molecular genetics were outlined, together with some applications of the ideas of base-pair substitutions. Now we shall largely ignore this fine scale analysis and instead treat of larger unanalyzed units called genes. We may think of each gene as a segment of DNA that is about 450 nucleotide pairs long. This particular length is not a necessary assumption—it merely gives the order of magnitude. In the discussions that follow, the gene will be manipulated as an intellectual unit, ignoring its fine scale structure, which is still largely unknown.

285. Blending Theory versus Particulate Theory

In the study of heredity at the gene level *Drosophila melanogaster* has played a very important role. This little fly is variously called a fruit fly, a vinegar fly, a pomace fly, and a garbage fly. It is a harmless creature less than 2 millimeters long that breeds rapidly under laboratory conditions, producing large numbers of offspring. To illustrate the principles of heredity, we shall consider first the inheritance of eye color, using two contrasting stocks; one with normal red-colored eyes, the other with brown eyes. To obtain uniform results that are easy to analyze, it is advisable to begin with "pure stocks," that is, with a stock of red-eyed flies that, when bred among its own kind, produces only red-eyed offspring, generation after generation; and a similar stock of brown-eyed flies.

What happens when we breed a pure "red" fly with a pure "brown" fly? When we carry out the experiment, we find that all the offspring

("hybrids") from this cross are red-eyed. What has happened? Has "redness" somehow overpowered "brownness," perhaps destroying it? Or is it that we merely cannot detect "brownness" when the two characteristics are mixed together?

We find the answer when we breed two of the red-brown hybrids together. Such matings produce mostly red-eyed flies, but in addition some brown flies are produced. These browns, if mated only among themselves, will produce only brown-eyed offspring, generation after generation.

What do these facts signify? Briefly, they disprove one ancient concept of heredity, and lend support to a modern scheme. For centuries it had been commonly supposed that heredity involves some sort of a blending process in which the hereditary material from one parent is blended with that from another, much as one might mix two different batches of paint. According to such a scheme, the red-eyed hybrids from red and brown parents would be incapable of producing any brown-eyed offspring —for how could one *unmix* mixed paints? But since the hybrids can, in fact, produce brown flies, it follows that the *blending theory* is not tenable.

We must, instead, use a *particulate theory* to explain the facts. Evidently, the hybrids from a red-brown cross contain not only particles "for redness" but also particles "for brownness," as is shown by their breeding behavior. When the two kinds of particles are present in the same fly, we can, by visual inspection, detect only the "red particles." But the "brown particles," though visually indetectable, are unchanged by their association with the "red particles," as is shown by the fact that there can be obtained from the hybrids a stock of brown-eyed flies that produces only brown-eyed offspring generation after generation.

Evidently, the appearance of an individual is affected by some sort of particles that are inheritable; these particles we call *genes*. A large body of evidence indicates that genes are constituents of the chromosomes of the cells. How the distribution of the chromosomes in meiotic division affects the distribution of genes will become apparent by a close study of Figures 35-1 and 35-2.

In Figure 35-1 are shown two flies: one with dark eyes (red eyes) and the other with shaded eyes (to represent brown eyes). Somatic *Dro-* *sophila* cells have four pairs of chromosomes. These are represented diagrammatically in the figure. It is known that the gene "for redness" is present on a certain chromosome called chromosome II. Each of the two chromosome II's of a somatic cell has one such gene. Although

Fig. 35-1. *A mating of a red-eyed male (♂) fruit fly (dark eyes) with a brown-eyed female (♀) fruit fly (striped eyes). The chromosomes present in the somatic and germinal cells are indicated diagrammatically. The gene for red eyes, B, is indicated by a dark bar, its allele, b, by a clear bar. The heterozygous offspring, Bb, has red eyes, showing that B is dominant to b. A reciprocal mating, brown ♂ × red ♀, would yield the same results.*

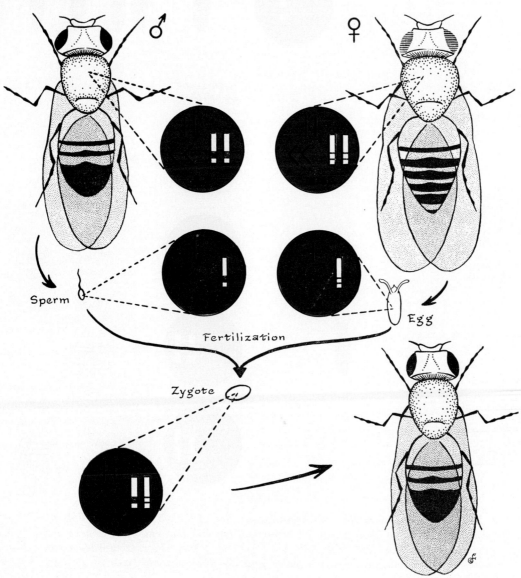

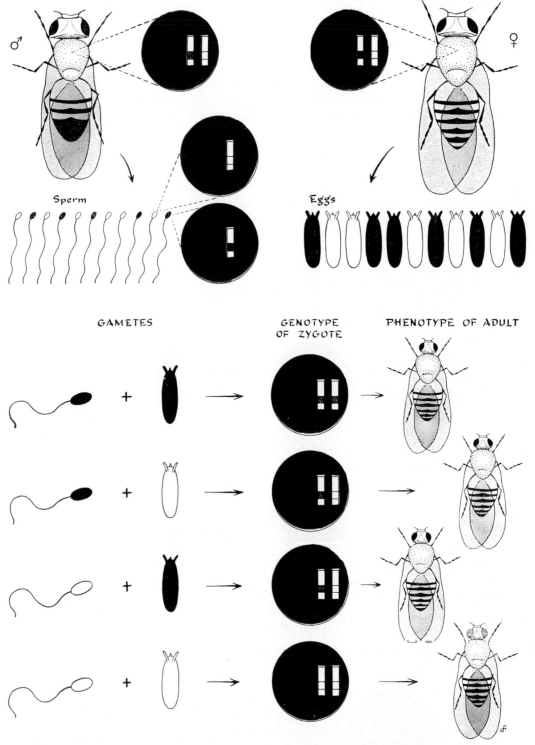

GAMETES   GENOTYPE   PHENOTYPE OF ADULT
OF ZYGOTE

Fig. 35-2. *The results of mating two heterozygous flies. Although it is not possible to determine the genotype of a gamete by inspection, gametes that carry the B gene are represented here in black ink, those with the b gene by white. The four possible kinds of fertilization are indicated below, together with the three possible kinds of zygotes.*

it is questionable whether anyone has ever seen a gene, we have boldly represented the genes in the diagram, as an aid in following their behavior during reproduction. The gene that causes red eyes to develop we have represented by a solid bar; the gene that may bring about the development of brown eyes we have represented by a clear bar.

A gamete contains a haploid set of chromosomes, one of each distinguishable kind. Correlated with this, a gamete contains only one of each type of gene. Of the genes we are now interested in, each gamete contains either the gene for redness or the gene for brownness, *but not both* (see diagram). If two genes affect the same characteristic of an organism in contrasting ways, and if a gamete can contain only one (either one) but not both of the genes, then the genes are said to be **alleles** of each other. The red gene is an allele of the brown gene; the brown gene is an allele of the red. Genes that are alleles of each other occupy the same position **(locus)** of the same type of chromosome. Each locus of a single chromosome can be occupied by only one allele.

When a gamete containing a red gene unites with a gamete containing a brown gene, there is formed a zygote that contains both. By mitotic divisions there is formed a multicellular organism—a fly—in every one of whose somatic cells both alleles are present. Although these genes may produce effects in all parts of the body, the effects are too subtle to be easily detectable in most parts. In the eyes, however, they influence the color. But since, in the hybrid, only the red allele has a detectable effect, we say that it is **dominant** to the brown allele; or that the latter is **recessive** to the former.

At this point it would be well to introduce other elements of genetic practice. The names of genes are commonly abbreviated; by convention, the use of a capital letter indicates a dominant allele; of a small letter, a recessive one. Officially, the symbol for brown is *bw,* but for simplicity we shall here write it as *b;* its allele, which causes red color to appear, we shall write as *B.* Because we cannot always tell from the appearance what genes are present,

we distinguish between the **phenotype** of an organism—its appearance—and its **genotype**—the genes it carries. Thus the phenotype red is associated with two genotypes, *BB* and *Bb;* the genotype *bb* has the phenotype brown. If both genes of a pair are the same allele (e.g., *BB* or *bb*), we say the organism is **homozygous;** if they are different (e.g., *Bb*), the organism is **heterozygous.**

What happens when two red-eyed flies heterozygous for brown mate? Figure 35-2 is designed to help us visualize this process. Both parents are *Bb.* As a result of meiosis, each parent produces both *B* gametes and *b* gametes. Whenever one (or both) of the gametes uniting to form a zygote contains the dominant gene, the fly developing from the zygote will have red eyes. When both gametes are *b* gametes, the zygote (*bb*) will develop into a brown-eyed fly; this will happen, on the average, about one-fourth of the time. But before attempting to understand the reason for this particular fraction, we need to understand the basis for making quantitative predictions in genetics.

286. Revealing Gametes by a Test-Mating

A heterozygous individual produces two kinds of gametes. What proportion of each does it produce? How can we determine it? Given a fruit fly of genotype *Bb,* how can we determine the relative numbers of *B* gametes and *b* gametes it produces? The gene in question has no effect (so far as we know) on the appearance of the gametes themselves. We can tell the difference between the alleles only on the basis of their effect on the adult. To tell whether a particular gamete contains *B* or *b,* we must permit it to unite with another gamete of the opposite sex, forming a diploid zygote. What sort of gametes of the opposite sex should we use? Plainly ones that will not, of themselves, confuse the results by influencing the eye color of the offspring: that is, they should be *b* gametes only, which will be produced exclusively only by a *bb* fly.

In summary, to determine the gametes produced by a *Bb* fly, we mate it with a homozygous recessive fly, *bb*. The ratio of *B* gametes to *b* gametes produced by the heterozygous fly will determine the ratio of *Bb* zygotes to *bb* zygotes produced by this mating. When this experiment is performed, it is found that *about half* of the offspring produced are red-eyed, the remainder being brown-eyed. Therefore we know that the ratio of *B* gametes to *b* gametes is about ½:½, or 1:1. Because a mating with a homozygous recessive individual reveals the kinds and relative numbers of gametes produced (and hence the genetic constitution of the parent), such a mating is called a **test-mating, or test-cross.**

Is this what we would expect on the basis of the conceptual relation of genes to chromosomes? A little thought shows that it is. During meiosis, unlike alleles should be distributed to gametes in exactly equal numbers. But why do we *not* find the two kinds of zygotes in *exactly* equal numbers? To answer this, we need only visualize the situation thoroughly, in which effort Figure 35-3 may help. Chance plays a part in sexual reproduction. Even though a male *Bb* fly might produce *B* sperm and *b* sperm in exactly equal numbers, "luck" determines whether a particular sperm succeeds in uniting with an egg or not; therefore, the frequency of *Bb* and *bb* zygotes will be only approximately equal, just as a tossed coin will turn heads and tails with only approximately equal frequency. "Chance," we say, "determines" whether a particular egg is fertilized by a *B* sperm or a *b* sperm, and whether a particular toss of the coin yields heads or tails.

In the genetic example, chance enters also in places other than at the fusion of gametes. It enters in earlier, in the mortality of cells produced by meiosis: Not all of the haploid nuclei produced by reduction division become nuclei of functional gametes. In the female, we expect only one-fourth of the haploid nuclei to be egg nuclei, the remainder being nuclei of polar cells. In both sexes, there is "accidental" loss of gametes. The end result of random loss of haploid nuclei is that what might otherwise have been

an exact equality of types becomes only an approximate equality. Though approximate, it is not unpredictable; the variations follow the same "laws of chance" that "govern" the falling of a coin. Slight deviations from the expected numbers are common; great deviations are very infrequent. A hundred coins flipped at once will frequently yield a heads:tails ratio of, say, 45:55 (instead of the expected 50:50), but a ratio of, say, 30:70 will be very rare indeed. Similar remarks apply, with necessary changes, to the ratios of the two types of offspring produced from a mating of a heterozygous fly with a homozygous recessive fly.

The deviation of a ratio observed in a sample from the ideal ratio expected on theoretical grounds is said to be due to **sampling error.** It will be useful to point out some of the characteristics of sampling errors, and their importance in the study of human genetics.

It is easy to see that *the smaller the sample, the greater the sampling error.* With a perfectly balanced coin, we should not be surprised if, in flipping it 10 times, we obtained 2 heads and 8 tails; but we should be greatly surprised (or more likely, suspicious) if, in 1,000 tosses, the coin yielded 200 heads and 800 tails. The sampling error, stated in relative terms, should decrease as the size of the sample increases. In genetic studies it is difficult to determine the "true" ratio when only a small number of offspring are available. Because human families are always small (from a geneticist's point of view), a genetic ratio cannot be determined with confidence on the basis of one family. It is a practice, therefore, to lump the results of many similar matings of humans to determine the most probable true ratio.

It follows from the argument above that *with only a small number of offspring, there is a fair probability that an expected class will be completely missing.* To illustrate, albinism (deficiency in pigmentation of hair, eyes, skin) is due to a recessive gene. A heterozygous individual, *Cc*, mated to an albino, *cc,* should produce about half and half albinos and normals. Yet, among families of only four children (from such parents) not infrequently (about one time

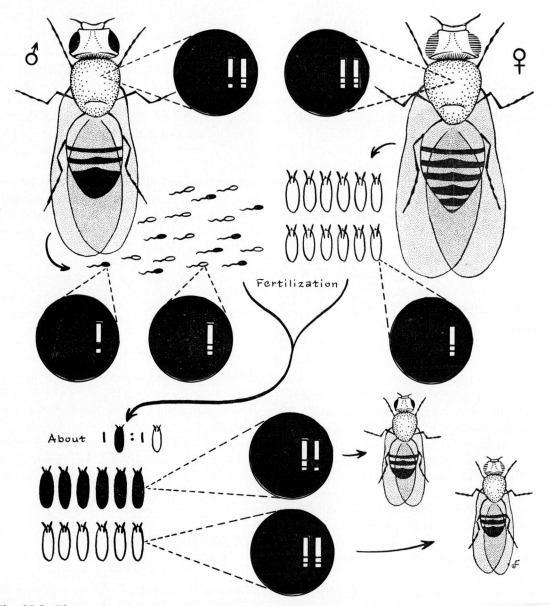

Fig. 35-3. *The results of mating a heterozygous fly with a homozygous recessive fly. The homozygous fly produces only one kind of gamete. The heterozygous fly produces two sorts of gametes, as indicated by the difference in shade of the sperm cells. The two kinds of gametes occur in approximately equal numbers. A reciprocal mating, heterozygous ♀ × homozygous recessive ♂, would yield the same results.*

out of eight) all of the children will be alike, either all albino or all normal. As a consequence of this principle, when the characteristics of the children are used to infer the genotypes of the parents, the certainty of the inference is proportional to the size of the family.

287. Result of Mating Hybrids

A commendable conceptual scheme not only subsumes the facts it is devised to deal with, but also can be used to make verifiable predictions. In dealing with the results of a test-cross, we have seen that they can be accounted for by a genetic scheme that postulates the existence of submicroscopic agents called genes, which are parts of visible chromosomes and which are distributed to gametes by a meiotic process, subject to random loss. Can this scheme predict correctly the results of other matings? We shall see that it can.

Suppose two heterozygotes (*Bb* and *Bb*) mate. What will the results be? Each individual will produce *B* and *b* gametes in approximately equal numbers. What unions will take place? Plainly, there are only four types of mating that can occur:

1. *B* sperm with *B* egg, yielding *BB* zygote
2. *B* sperm with *b* egg, yielding *Bb* zygote
3. *b* sperm with *B* egg, yielding *Bb* zygote
4. *b* sperm with *b* egg, yielding *bb* zygote

What will be the relative frequency of these four types of mating? Since approximately one-half of the sperm are *B*, approximately one-half of the zygotes obtained will have a sperm-derived dominant gene (types 1 and 2 above). If the union of gametes is a chance affair—the simplest assumption, which there is no reason to doubt—on the average, half of the eggs encountered by sperms will be *B* eggs (type 1), the other half being *b* eggs (type 2). In other words, of all zygotes formed, approximately one-fourth (one-half *of* one-half) will be *BB* zygotes, produced by the union of *B* sperm with *B* egg (type 1). By similar reasoning, approximately one-fourth of the zygotes will be *bb* zygotes (type 4).

Finally, what fraction of the zygotes will be *Bb*? Here we must distinguish two cases: in one, the dominant gene comes from the sperm (type 2); in the other, from the egg (type 3). By the line of reasoning already used, the frequency with which each of these cases occurs is one-fourth; therefore, the fraction of the zygotes that will be *Bb* zygotes—without regard to the gametic origin of the different alleles—will be the sum of the two cases, or $\frac{1}{4} + \frac{1}{4} = \frac{1}{2}$. In summary, mating *Bb* with *Bb*, yields approximately $\frac{1}{4} BB + \frac{1}{2} Bb + \frac{1}{4} bb$. Phenotypically, the ratio is about $\frac{3}{4}$ red:$\frac{1}{4}$ brown.

In genetic studies the hybrids formed from the mating of two pure stocks are commonly mated among themselves to produce another generation. To distinguish these various generations, the following terms and abbreviations are conventionally used: The original parents are called the **parental (P)** generation; their hybrid offspring are called the **first filial (F₁)** generation (L. *filialis* = pertaining to son or daughter); and the offspring of these hybrids are called the **second filial (F₂)** generation. In general, in any mating in which the parents differ by one gene-allele (say, *A* and *a*), the results of producing F₁ and F₂ generations can be expressed as follows:

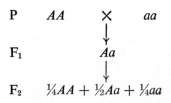

In the above symbolization we have, for brevity, omitted the "approximately's" in the F₂ generation, but it must not be forgotten that they exist. The F₂ genotypic ratio of $\frac{1}{4} : \frac{2}{4} : \frac{1}{4}$ is only an approximate one, subject to sampling errors. The phenotypic ratio, $\frac{3}{4} A-:\frac{1}{4} aa$ (assuming *A* is dominant to *a*) is also only an approximate one.

288. Alternative Ways of Predicting Offspring

Given the genotypes of any two parents of opposite sexes, how can we predict the offspring? In any such problem, we can work out the solution step by step, as was done in the preceding section. Or we can get the same result more briefly by one of the following two methods.

PUNNETT SQUARE METHOD. In this method, proposed early in the twentieth century by the English geneticist R. C. Punnett, the gametes formed by one parent are listed in a column at the left of a square or rectangle, and those formed by the other parent are entered in a row along the top. The union of the various types of gametes are shown in the boxes in the square. When some of the boxes contain repetitions of zygote types, it is desirable to gather together the similar zygotes in making a summary statement. To illustrate the method, we show the result of crossing $Aa \times Aa$; the expected frequencies of gametes and zygotes are indicated by the parenthetical fractions.

♀ gametes	(½)	(½)
♂ gametes	*A*	*a*
(½) *A*	(¼)*AA*	(¼)*Aa*
(½) *a*	(¼)*aA*	(¼)*aa*

Summary: ¼*AA* + ¾*Aa* + ¼*aa*

As another example, suppose the mating is of $AA \times Aa$. In this case, our Punnett square will be as follows:

♀ gametes	(1)
♂ gametes	*A*
(½) *A*	(½)*AA*
(½) *a*	(½)*Aa*

Summary: ½*AA* + ½*Aa*

ALGEBRAIC METHOD. The same results can be obtained more rapidly by simple algebraic representation of the genetic facts. In a cross of $Aa \times Aa$, we can represent the gametes of one parent by writing (½*A* + ½*a*); and of the other similarly. The act of fertilization we represent by algebraic multiplication of these two expressions, thus:

$$(\tfrac{1}{2}A + \tfrac{1}{2}a)^2 = \tfrac{1}{4}AA + \tfrac{2}{4}Aa + \tfrac{1}{4}aa.$$

The mating of $AA \times Aa$ is represented thus:

$$(1A)(\tfrac{1}{2}A + \tfrac{1}{2}a) = \tfrac{1}{2}AA + \tfrac{1}{2}Aa.$$

Notice that we indicate the probability that a gamete produced by AA will be A by the numeral 1, which is the probability value of absolute certainty.

Although, to the eye, the Punnett square and the algebraic methods may seem to be different, the logical form of the two is identical. Which method one prefers is a matter of taste.

289. The Work of Mendel

Although men had been interested in heredity for centuries, it was not until 1866 that any considerable light was thrown on the problems of inheritance. In that year, Gregor Mendel, an Augustinian monk in central Europe (in what was later to become Czechoslovakia), published an account of his researches with peas, together with an explanation in terms of a particulate scheme. The chromosomes, and their behavior during cell division, had not yet been discovered, so it is not surprising that Mendel's scheme included no reference to these bodies. Indeed, his scheme had no explicit reference to any material structures within the cells, but one can recognize in Mendel's writings a clear conception of those particles that were later to be called genes. Mendel's work showed clearly that each gamete must contain one of each kind of gene, and each (somatic cell of the) adult must contain two.

Some appreciation of the thoroughness of Mendel's work may be gained from an examination of Table 35-2, which summarizes part of his data. A comparison of the data given in columns 4 and 5 furnishes us with an illustration of the principle mentioned earlier: that (in general) the larger the size of the sample, the smaller the sampling error, and consequently the more closely does an actual ratio approximate the expected ratio. The importance of obtaining large samples by repetition of experiments becomes obvious when we learn that, from one of the plants that constituted a part of his experiment No. 1, Mendel obtained 43 round seeds and only 2 wrinkled seeds in the F_2. Had he possessed only these data, Mendel would surely never have arrived at the correct solution to his problem.

TABLE 35-2   *Summary of Some Genetics Experiments of Mendel: The F_2 Generation.*

(1) MENDEL'S EXPERIMENT NUMBER	(2) DOMINANT CHARACTER	(3) RECESSIVE CHARACTER	(4) NUMBER OF F_2 PLANTS EXAMINED	(5) RATIO, DOMINANT TYPES TO RECESSIVE TYPES
5	Green pod	Yellow pod	580	2.82:1
6	Axial flowers	Terminal flowers	858	3.14:1
3	Violet-red flowers	White flowers	929	3.15:1
7	Long stem	Short stem	1,064	2.84:1
4	Inflated pods	Constricted pods	1,181	2.95:1
1	Round seeds	Wrinkled seeds	7,324	2.96:1
2	Yellow seeds	Green seeds	8,023	3.01:1

290. The Neglect of Mendel, and Its Significance

The publication of Mendel's work in 1866 was met by a deafening silence in the scientific world. At the time Mendel died, in 1884, there was probably not a single eminent scientist who realized the importance of his work. Not until three other men had independently discovered the same facts and published their findings in 1900 did the name of Mendel become known. Why was this? It was not because his work was published obscurely, for the journal in which it appeared had a reasonably wide circulation (for a scientific journal) in Europe and the United States. Furthermore, Mendel was furnished (as was, and still is the custom) "reprints" of his article—forty of them—which he distributed to friends and influential scientists working in the same general field. Evidently none of these otherwise competent men appreciated the implications of his work. In science, few instances are known in which an important work was so long neglected. How can we account for the neglect of Mendel's work?

Any statement as to why something did *not* happen in history is subject to error to a peculiarly large degree; yet (with this qualification) we may be able to account reasonably well for the nonrecognition of Mendel by his contemporaries. In part, this neglect may be attributable to inattention: Darwin's *Origin of Species,* published only seven years earlier, had excited the scientific world and turned so many biologists' attention to problems of evolution that these scientists failed to give critical attention to discoveries made in the related field of heredity. (An element of fashion operates even in the field of scientific research.) Perhaps more important in causing the neglect of Mendel than mere fashion was the intellectual training and turn of mind of the biologists of the period. If we read at random in the journals of botany and zoology of the period and then read Mendel's paper, we are struck most forcibly by the contrast. With exceedingly rare exceptions, botanists and zoologists of that time were engaged only in *descriptive* work—in describing new species, naming them, telling where they were found, what they ate, and so forth. Mendel's work, by contrast, is *analytical:* using quantitative data and analytical insight, he succeeded in deducing the existence and behavior of those invisible entities we now call genes. Perhaps the mere fact that Mendel made use of algebra kept many good biologists of his day from seriously examining his paper.

Between the time of its publication (1866) and the time of its rediscovery (1900), many events in biological science prepared the way for an appreciation of Mendel's paper. For one thing, there was during these years the development of the science of **biometry,** the science that deals with the application of statistical methods to biological problems. The early development of this science was brought about largely by the Englishman Francis Galton and his students. As it happened, Galton himself opposed Mendel's ideas when they were rediscovered, but his influence in establishing a corps of biologists capable of appreciating an analytical argument undoubtedly helped to bring about an acceptance of the new work.

During the same period another line of development in biological science paved the way for the science of genetics. Chromosomes were discovered, and their behavior during mitosis and meiosis unraveled. During the 1880's it occurred to a number of investigators, notably to the Germans Wilhelm Roux and August Weismann, that the regular behavior of the chromosomes exactly fitted them to be the carriers of hereditary qualities. Late in the following decade three different investigators—the Dutchman Hugo de Vries, the German Carl Correns, and the Austrian Erich von Tschermak—independently of one another established the basic principles of heredity, only to make the bitter discovery that their work had been anticipated more than a generation earlier. When de Vries, Correns, and Tschermak exhumed Mendel's paper, the recognition of its importance was immediate. *The time was then ripe* for the reception of the new idea, as it was not in 1866. Immediately, a host of scientific workers entered the new field, confirmed the basic findings with other organisms, and presently showed, by many lines of evidence, that the chromosomes were the material bearers of the hereditary particles.

291. On the "Scientific Method"

In the light of Mendel's experiments we can, with profit, re-examine the question of the "scientific method," first discussed in §3. We shall first take up the question of the meaning of evidence, and what meaning is to be attached to the word "proof."

Consider the data presented in Table 35-2. Do these *prove* that Mendel's particulate hereditary scheme is true? In popular usage, the word "prove" has a strong aura of absolutism about it; if we employ the word "prove" with such a connotation, we must certainly deny that Men-

del's data *prove* his point. According to his scheme, the F_2 phenotypic ratio should be 3:1. In not a single one of his seven experiments is that ratio exactly realized.

But, it might be suggested, is not a 3:1 ratio the unique ratio that fits the diverse data best? Even this is not true. If all Mendel's data are lumped, it turns out that the observed ratio is 2.98:1. This means that a 3:1 ratio does not fit his data as well as does a ratio of 2.98:1 or 2.99:1 or 2.97:1 or 2.98546:1 or—literally an infinity of other possible ratios. Plainly, in a summary analysis of such observational data, we do not choose that ratio which fits better than all others, but rather we choose a ratio *which has meaning in the light of a conceptual scheme and which agrees reasonably well with the observations.* In spite of their superior agreement with the observational data, the ratios of 2.98:1, 2.99:1, and so on, are rejected because they are not part of any conceptual scheme.

". . . *agrees reasonably well* . . ." What constitutes reasonable agreement? And how does one determine it? Here we enter the realm of statistical theory, which is rich in technical details. Fortunately, the sense of the conclusions of statistics can be conveyed without getting bogged down in the details of the procedure. We may illustrate the principles by giving an analysis of Mendel's experiment No. 5. In this experiment (see Table 35-3), the number of yellow pods observed exceeded the number expected (out of a total of 580) by 7; correspondingly, 7 fewer green pods were found than were expected on the assumption of a 3:1 ratio.

TABLE 35-3 *Mendel's Experiment No. 5: Characteristics of F_2 Plants.*

CHARACTER	NUMBER OBSERVED	NUMBER EXPECTED, ON THE MENDELIAN SCHEME	DEVIATION OF OBSERVED FROM EXPECTED
Green pods	428	435	−7
Yellow pods	152	145	+7
Total	580	580	

Is this a reasonable agreement between observation and theory, or is it not? To determine this, we must convert our question into another, which includes the word "probability." This other question can be stated in various ways, of which we will use a relatively simple form, unencumbered by rigorous qualifications. We ask: *"If the hypothesis is indeed true, what is the probability—if chance alone causes deviations —of obtaining deviations as great or greater than those observed?"*

That is, if the heredity of green and yellow pods is indeed governed by the Mendelian scheme, and if we set up many experiments, each yielding 580 F_2 plants, how often would we expect the deviation from the expected ratio of 435:145 (3:1) to be 7 or more? Statistical analysis shows that out of 100 such experiments, we would expect about 85 of them to yield a deviation equal to or greater than that observed. Therefore, most reasonable men would agree that the deviation observed is not excessive. The data do not cast doubt on the Mendelian conceptual scheme. Therefore we are justified in retaining it.

Have we *proved* the truth of the scheme? Somehow, "prove" seems too strong a word. We have merely shown that the data agree with it reasonably well. Even if the experiment had yielded exactly 435 greens:145 yellows, we should not use the word "proof." Such a perfect agreement we should, as a matter of fact, regard as accidental, if we encountered it in our own experiments; and in the reports of others, we might even regard it with suspicion. This point should be clear: No conceivable data could *prove* the truth of a hypothesis, if we use the word "prove" in its common sense.

The data of genetics are exceptionally well suited to numerical analysis, but they are not different in their nature from all the rest of biology, and, indeed, all science. In the nineteenth century many men spoke of the absolute certainty of science; the words "law" and "proof" were popular. Today we realize that considerations of probability enter into all phases of science, and we prefer the less forceful words "principle" and "demonstration." We no longer think in terms of absolutely certain or proved laws; rather, we speak of "principles" from which we can make predictions that agree reasonably well with our observations. The intellectual difference between these two points of view is profound.

In retrospect, what is the method of science, as illustrated by the history of the Mendelian conceptual scheme? Without doing too great violence to the complexity of that very human endeavor we call science, we may say it proceeds in three stages:

1. From observations and analysis, a hypothesis is evolved.

2. With this hypothesis, predictions are made.

3. New data are gathered, and comparisons are made between predictions and observations.

If the observations do not agree reasonably well with the predictions, doubt is cast on the hypothesis. It will then be re-examined, perhaps cast away entirely, or amended somewhat. If there is reasonable agreement between predictions and observations, the hypothesis is retained. If predictions made from it continue to be verified, and if the implications of the hypothesis are continually seen to be more and more far-reaching, we may come to speak of it as a "conceptual scheme." Or the word "theory" may be preferred. Or even—though this is not without danger—the word "law" may be used.

If this that has just been outlined is the scientific method, where can one learn to practice it? Can it be taught in a course? Are there books on the subject? Yes, there are some. The second phase listed above—making predictions from given hypotheses—is the province of logic and mathematics. To make predictions, we think; if the situation is complicated, we may get a "mechanical brain" to do this job for us. The third phase—the testing of hypotheses—is also treated in books. The titles of some of these indicate that they are about science, or the scientific method; some of the best of them are in the fields of biometry, statistics, and the design of experiments.

But what of the first phase—the invention of

a hypothesis? Are there no books that will teach us how to discover fruitful hypotheses? Alas, there are not. The world is so full of happenings that it will not do to try to observe *all* that happens, in even the tiniest field, in the hope that the underlying pattern will necessarily be seen. The totality of unselected experiences is simply confusing. At some point in the process of observing, an investigator gets a "hunch," which guides him in making further observations. How did Mendel first arrive at his hypothesis? He does not say; we do not know. Perhaps he did not know, either. The process of arriving at fruitful scientific hypotheses is as mysterious as the process of creating a work of art. Indeed, most great scientists who have tried, by introspection, to figure out how they work have concluded that inventing or discovering scientific concepts is indeed an art.

In popular writings on science the role of chance is commonly emphasized, with such stories as that of Roentgen's discovery of X-rays, of Oersted's discovery of electromagnetism, or of Fleming's discovery of penicillin. The popularity of such emphasis perhaps has its source in the well of wishful thinking that impels even rational men to play slot machines. Scientists, and historians of science, are not inclined to give so much weight to the importance of chance observations in furthering science. Opportunities to make such "chance" observations occur frequently, but only seldom is there a properly thoughtful spectator to observe and interpret the events. In the words of Pasteur, "Chance favors the prepared mind." The works of Charles Darwin, the originator of the modern theory of evolution, furnish us a striking example of how even a great scientist can miss seeing the obvious ("obvious" to us, blessed with hindsight). In his *Variation of Animals and Plants Under Domestication,* published in 1868, Darwin tells of some breeding experiments with snapdragon flowers, involving a strain with peloric (abnormal) flowers. (The following passage has been somewhat abbreviated.)

I crossed the peloric snapdragon with pollen of the common form; and the latter, reciprocally, with peloric pollen. I thus raised two great beds of seedlings, and not one was peloric. The crossed plants, which perfectly resembled the common snapdragon, were allowed to sow themselves, and out of a hundred and twenty-seven seedlings, eighty-eight proved to be common snapdragons, two were in an intermediate condition between the peloric and normal state, and thirty-seven were perfectly peloric, having reverted to the structure of their one grandparent.

Here, if we neglect the exceptional two intermediate and unclassifiable plants, we have a close approach to a 3:1 ratio in the F_2 generation. From this observation Darwin *might* have developed the genetic scheme published (unknown to Darwin) two years earlier. That he did not we can only attribute to a lack of proper "preparation" of his mind, though that is scarcely more than a verbal answer. How *can* a mind be prepared to evaluate observations and invent fruitful hypotheses?

Mysterious though the process of scientific discovery may be, there are at least two generalizations that can be made about it. First, though successful scientists can rarely reconstruct the train of thought that preceded the final illumination, it is clear that inspiration seldom comes except after a long period of hard work and intense preoccupation with a problem. The inventing of fruitful hypotheses is not a spare-time occupation.

Second, though there are no books or courses that can inculcate this aspect of the method of science, it can, nevertheless, be somehow transmitted from one man to another. Scientists are trained by scientists, mostly by example, rather than by precept. Nearly every scientific laboratory plays two roles: in it, knowledge is advanced; and, at the same time, a new generation of scientists is trained in the art of scientific procedure. As a rough generalization, the greater scientists are ones who have themselves served their apprenticeship in the laboratories of great scientists. There are exceptions to this, of course—Mendel is certainly one. But the general truth of this statement reveals one of the reasons for the marked centralization of scientific activity. In only a few countries of the world is there any scientific activity at all; and in these, activity is markedly centralized. It is clear that communication, in a broad sense, is essential to the vigorous pursuit of science. Science is a social activity.

Questions and Problems

35-1. Make a list of the **boldface** terms in this chapter. Write a brief definition or description of each. Compare your work with the text.

35-2. Consider an organism that has two pairs of chromosomes in its diploid cells. Let us represent the state of a diploid cell by writing $AABB$, in which A stands for one kind of chromosome, B for the other. Using this notation, how would you represent the haploid cells?

‡35-3. Suppose that the members of one "homologous pair" of chromosomes (i.e., the A's or the B's) in the organism described in the preceding question can be distinguished microscopically—a fact that we can indicate by writing the chromosomal constitution of a diploid cell as A_1A_2BB. As a result of meiosis, such a diploid cell could produce how many distinguishable kinds of haploid cells? Diagram the course of meiosis in such an organism, labeling the chromosomes and showing what the meiotic products will be.

35-4. Suppose we can distinguish the members of both pairs of chromosomes of the organism described in question 35-3. In this case, we indicate the chromosomal constitution of a diploid cell by writing $A_1A_2B_1B_2$. In meiosis, how the members of one pair of chromosomes are distributed to the haploid cells has no influence on the distribution of the members of other chromosome pairs. In this organism, how many different kinds of haploid cells can be produced?

‡35-5. In terms of the symbols used, what are the four kinds of haploid cells referred to in question 35-4?

35-6. Express the result obtained in question 35-4 as a power of 2.

‡35-7. Suppose an organism has three pairs of chromosomes, in which the members of each pair are somehow distinguishable. Indicate its chromosomal constitution by $A_1A_2B_1B_2C_1C_2$. How many distinguishable kinds of haploid cells can be produced, and what are they?

‡35-8. Express the numerical answer obtained in question 35-7 as a power of 2.

35-9. Consider an organism in which the members of each of four pairs of chromosomes can be distinguished. Symbolize a diploid cell thus: $A_1A_2B_1B_2C_1C_2D_1D_2$. How many distinguishable kinds of haploid cells could be produced by the meiotic process? Give the answer both as an ordinary numeral and as a power of 2.

‡35-10. *Generalize* the results obtained in questions 35-4 to 35-9 by stating how many different kinds of haploid cells may conceivably be produced by an organism that contains x pairs of chromosomes, in which the members of each pair are somehow distinguishable.

‡35-11. In humans there are 23 pairs of chromosomes. Suppose, in one individual, that the two members of each homologous pair of chromosomes differ in some respect. How many different gametes could such an individual conceivably produce?

35-12. Hereditary characteristics are transmitted from parent to child via the chromosomes. How does the answer obtained in question 35-11 help explain the diversity of children that may be produced by a single pair of parents?

35-13. It is a question of the "honesty" of three coins—whether each coin is so made that, when flipped, heads is as likely to turn up as tails. Coin A is flipped 5 times, turning up heads once. Coin *B* turns heads 4 out of 5 times. Coin *C* turns heads 400 out of 500 times. State your conclusions clearly and explicitly.

35-14. It is reported that a particular coin is "dishonest" or biased, because "when properly flipped, it turned heads upward 80 percent of the time." No other data are given in the report. What criticism can be made of such a report?

35-15. You wish to know whether a particular coin is biased or not. If it turns heads 47 times out of 100, what do you conclude? State your conclusion fully.

35-16. You wish to know whether a particular coin is biased. If it turns heads 87 times out of 100, what do you conclude? State your conclusion fully.

35-17. A man says: "I want to know whether this coin is properly made or not—whether it has a bias or not. I want a *Yes* or *No* answer, without qualifications." Is his request a reasonable one? Explain.

‡35-18. Using a coin that you have repeatedly found to be without bias, *you* find that, in one particular "run," the coin turns heads 98 times out of 100. What do you conclude? State all the possibilities.

‡35-19. You read in a scientific journal a report by Dr. Alexis C. Ananias, in which he states that, using a coin that had repeatedly behaved as though it were without bias, in one particular run he observed the coin turn heads 98 times out of 100. What do you conclude? Is your conclusion in this instance in any way different from the conclusion reached in question 35-18?

‡35-20. You are given two unbiased coins: a nickel and a penny. If you flip them both at once, how many different results are possible? List them.

35-21. You are given two unbiased coins, both pennies. If you flip them both at once, what are the possible results? List them. What are the expected relative frequencies of the possible results?

35-22. You are given two unbiased pennies. Either you are unable to distinguish between these two coins, or you are not interested in doing so. With this restriction, how many distinguishably different results are possible? List them. What are their expected relative frequencies?

‡35-23. "If two pennies are flipped at once, they may both fall heads; both tails; or one may be heads and the other tails. Since there are three possibilities, and the last-named possibility is 1 out of 3, it follows that the probability of the coins' showing unlike faces is ⅓." Discuss this statement critically.

35-24. In humans, boys and girls are born almost equally frequently. Whether a particular conception will be of a male or a female seems to be a matter of chance. Consider all births of fraternal twins. What are the possibilities (with respect to sex) and their expected frequencies?

‡35-25. Consider all births of one-egg twins. Are the expectations here the same as found in question 35-24? Explain.

35-26. Birth records of twins give the sexes of the siblings. How could one sometimes tell, from the birth records alone, whether an appreciable proportion of twin births were of one-egg twins, or whether (on the contrary) most were of two-egg twins?

(*Note:* Problems 35-27 to 35-35 all refer to albinism, *c* representing the gene for albinism, and *C* its normal allele.)

‡35-27. If, in humans, *CC* mates with *cc*, what would be the expected genotypes and phenotypes, and their relative frequencies (if more than one type appears), on the assumption that many children are produced?

35-28. Suppose (see 35-27) only a few children are produced. Need the above answer be modified?

‡35-29. *Cc* mates with *cc*, producing many children. Possible results? Expected results?

35-30. Suppose, from the mating of *Cc* with *cc*, only two children are produced. Possible results? Expected results? If this answer differs in any way from the answer to 35-29, explain.

35-31. On the basis of genealogical study it is known that an individual is either *CC* or *Cc*.

What sort of mating would be most likely to reveal which of the two possibilities is true? Explain.

35-32. Given the uncertainty as to whether an individual is *CC* or *Cc,* would it be easier to resolve the uncertainty in humans or in rabbits? Why?

35-33. From his genealogy it is known that Mr. X is either *CC* or *Cc.* If he marries and has children, are there any possible results that would permit us to say, with complete certainty, that Mr. X is *Cc*? Explain.

‡35-34. Are there any results that would permit us to say, with complete certainty, that Mr. X (see 35-33) is *CC*? Explain; compare this answer with the answer to 35-33.

‡35-35. Albinia and Smudgia are neighboring kingdoms. The ratio of albinos to nonalbinos is about the same in both kingdoms. The inhabitants of Albinia, influenced by race propaganda, decide that the only true Albinian is one who is an albino, and set out, by drastic decrees governing matings, to produce a pure albino population. The nationalists of Smudgia, on the other hand, favor only nonalbinos and enact similar decrees aimed at producing a 100 percent pure nonalbino population. Which kingdom will arrive at its goal first? Explain.

35-36. A fancier of colored rabbits occasionally encounters albinos among the offspring of his colored breeding stock. How could the fancier, in the least time (though not necessarily with the least trouble), eliminate albinism from his stock? Explain in complete detail.

35-37. Have you ever heard of any Tahitian, Siamese, Cambodian, Nigerian, or Abyssinian scientists? If not, why not, do you suppose?

35-38. In Darwin's autobiography, written in 1876, there occurs the following passage:

During the three years which I spent at Cambridge my time was wasted, as far as the academical studies were concerned, as completely as at Edinburgh and at school. I attempted mathematics, and even went during the summer of 1828 with a private tutor (a very dull man) to Barmouth, but I got on very slowly. The work was repugnant to me, chiefly from my not being able to see any meaning in the early steps in algebra. This impatience was very foolish, and in after years I have deeply regretted that I did not proceed far enough at least to understand something of the great leading principles of mathematics, for men thus endowed seem to have an extra sense.

What historic failure of Darwin's does this passage help to explain?

35-39. From a thoughtful consideration of question 35-38, and any other relevant material, what can you say of the utility and importance of mathematics in the training of scientists? Are there fields of knowledge outside the sciences to which your remarks may apply? (The answer to this question will be at least a brief essay.)

Readings

Interesting data and comments on the conditions of scientific discovery and the role of chance are to be found in Chapters 2 and 3 of Cohen. As yet, not much illumination has been cast on the difficult problem of inventing fruitful hypotheses. It appears that the most important writings on the science of heuristics—a science that does not yet exist—have been contributed by the mathematicians. Poincaré's famous essay on mathematical creation is reprinted in Moulton and Schifferes. The relation—the conflict, one might almost say —between the rigorous attitude and the spirit of discovery is beautifully treated in the concluding chapter of Kasner and Newman's *Mathematics and the Imagination.* Pólya's *How to Solve It* is a notable effort to convey the attitude of the intellectual pioneer as exemplified in mathematical situations. Peters' excellent collection, *Classic Papers in Genetics,* includes Mendel's paper, which is strongly recommended to the serious student.

Excellent accounts of Mendelian genetics will be found in Srb, Owen, and Edgar's *General Ge-netics* and Stern's *Human Genetics.* For an amusing account of the pitfalls of statistical interpretation see Huff's *How to Lie with Statistics*—amusing, but educational.

36

Genetic Aspects of Some Human Problems

292. The Analysis of Human Data

From the outset it should be clear that the study of heredity in man presents difficulties. As compared with peas and fruit flies, people have distressingly few children per mating (from the geneticist's point of view). The time from one generation to another is much too long from the point of view of the observer—who is also a human. And—in our society at least—matings are determined by the desires of those who mate, rather than by the scientific needs of geneticists. All of these factors make it more difficult to obtain the large numbers of cases needed for accurate deductions. They do not, however, make the study of human genetics impossible. Some ingenious statistical techniques have been devised for the analysis of human data. With these, the existence of many gene-controlled characteristics has been demonstrated. Some of the better-known human genes will be discussed in this and succeeding chapters.

The ability to taste a specific chemical substance called "PTC" is determined by inheritance. How is it inherited? Suppose we examine a few family pedigrees (Fig. 36-1). In diagrams like those shown, a square indicates a male (♂), a circle a female (♀). In the present instance, a colored symbol denotes a "taster" (i.e., one who can taste PTC), and a gray symbol a nontaster. The meaning of the lines join-

ing the symbols can be deduced from the following statement: Figure 36-1E states, in symbolic form, that a man who can taste marries a woman who cannot, and they have four children: a boy who is a taster, a girl who is a taster; then a boy who is a nontaster, and a girl who is a nontaster.

Think how confusing data such as those shown in the figure must have been in pre-Mendelian days! From matings of two tasters come, in different instances, all three conceivable kinds of families (A, B, and C). Similarly, from matings of unlike parents come all three kinds of families. Only when two nontasters mate are the results consistent: all children of nontasters are nontasters. To one ignorant of genetic theory the data might seem so confusing and self-contradictory as to raise doubts about the importance of heredity in determining tasting ability. To the geneticist, however, pedigree G immediately suggests that the ability to taste PTC is determined by a dominant gene, say, T, the lack of this ability being found in tt individuals. Various statistical analyses confirm this hypothesis.

Can we deduce the genetic constitution of the individuals shown in the pedigrees given? Working from the bottom upwards, we deduce the following: In G, all individuals are tt. In E and F, all tasters are Tt, all nontasters tt (of course). In D, the mother is TT or Tt, and the children are Tt. In C, both tasters must be het-

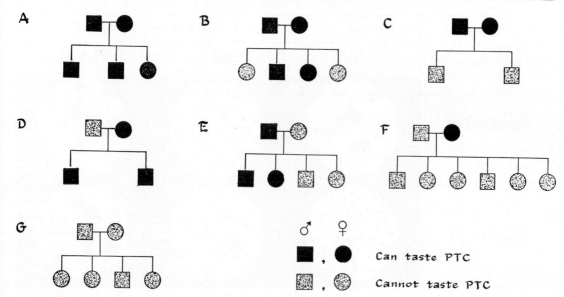

Fig. 36-1. *What is the genetic explanation of the ability to taste PTC?*

erozygous; in *B*, both parents must be heterozygous, but the taster children may be either *TT* or *Tt*. In *A*, we know that every individual shown must have at least one dominant gene; but more than that we cannot say with certainty.

(*The student should carefully consider each of the pedigrees shown in the light of the above remarks. If he does not see the justification for the statements, he is not prepared to read farther, but should first review Chapter 35.*)

293. The M-N Antigens: Inheritance Without Dominance

Although the genes that were first discovered were ones that exhibited dominance or recessiveness, these characteristics are not found in all sets of alleles. As an example of a gene in which neither allele exhibits dominance over the other we may consider the genes determining the M and N blood-group system in man.

M and N are symbols for particular proteins that may be present in the red blood cells of man. A person may have only one type, in which case he is said to belong to either blood group M or blood group N, as the case may be; or both, in which case he belongs to group MN.

These proteins are not antigenic for humans, but can be demonstrated by evoking specific antibodies against them in rabbits, by the method outlined in §233. With such antibodies available, it is easily possible to determine the blood group of an unknown human blood, as indicated in Figure 36-2.

It has been found that M-N blood groups are determined by a single pair of alleles, which we may represent by the italic letters *M* and *N*. Each allele exerts its effect independently of the other. Consequently, a person of *MM* genotype has phenotype M; genotype *NN* produces phenotype N; and genotype *MN* produces phenotype MN. If both parents are MN, all three types of offspring may be produced. If the parents are M and MN, only M and MN offspring may be produced. If one parent is M, and the other is N, the children will be like neither parent—MN.

(*Again, the student should verify the correctness of the statements just made before he reads on.*)

294. Multiple Alleles: A-B-O

Each of the examples presented so far has been concerned with the hereditary distribution of

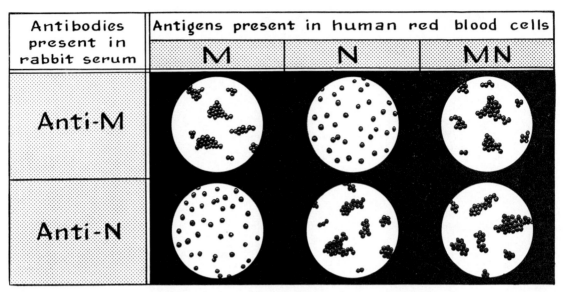

Antibodies present in rabbit serum	Antigens present in human red blood cells		
	M	N	MN
Anti-M			
Anti-N			

Fig. 36-2. *Typing blood for M and N antigens by the agglutination method.*

only two alleles. The difference between alternative alleles is undoubtedly a difference in nucleotide sequence, no doubt often a difference in only a single nucleotide pair, as was pointed out in the analysis of the difference between the alleles for sickle-cell hemoglobin and normal hemoglobin (Chap. 6).

A gene consists of a linear sequence of many nucleotide pairs—typically 450. Several different substitutions are possible at each nucleotide locus; deletions are possible; additions are possible; inversions are possible. All these add up to literally thousands of possible alleles for each gene locus. What fraction of the theoretical possibilities is realized is quite unknown. Some of the possibilities may be incapable of replication; others may kill the cell they are in. Some mutations at different nucleotide loci may produce phenotypes that are indistinguishable from each other. But, however important these limiting restrictions may be, there should certainly be more than two alleles for each 450 nucleotide-pair genetic locus.

The traditional emphasis on two-allele systems has its origins partly in practice, partly in pedagogy. We first *discover* a gene when we find a single mutant allele; mutant plus wild type makes a two-allele system. It is only later that we find other alleles at the same gene

locus; in general, the longer we study a gene locus the more alleles we discover. Pedagogically, the behavior of multiple alleles in heredity is a bit more difficult to explain, so we postpone discussing them until the two-allele system is understood. The time has come.

Hereditary differences in the chemistry of the blood include the A-B-O system. Actually, quite a few alleles are known for this system, but we will consider only three alleles, which we shall designate by the italic letters *A*, *B*, and *O*. Since a human is diploid, he can have not more than two of these alleles, for example, *AA*, *AB*, *BO*, and so forth. With respect to dominance, both *A* and *B* are dominant to *O*, but *A* and *B* show no dominance with respect to one another. It follows that a person of blood type (phenotype) A may be either of two genotypes: *AA* or *AO*. Phenotype AB = genotype *AB*. Phenotype O = genotype *OO*. As a few examples of possible genetic results: Blood type A mated with blood type B may produce A or AB or B or O children; A mated with A may produce A or O children; A mated with O may produce A or O; AB with O can produce only A or B.

(Again, the student should verify the correctness of the statements just made before he reads on.)

A and B represent substances in human red blood cells that are antigenic to humans who do not possess these substances. The importance of these blood groups in blood transfusions has already been considered (§238).

295. The Logic of Paternity Tests

It occasionally happens that a suspicion arises that infants belonging to different families have been accidentally exchanged; or that a child reputed to be legitimate is not. For hundreds of years men have made rough attempts to solve such cases on the basis of superficial resemblances between parents and children. It has long been recognized that a large subjective element enters into such judgments, which have, therefore, been accorded only limited confidence in courts of law. With the discovery of the blood antigens and their inheritance, there have been opened up new possibilities of settling such cases. The presence, or absence, of a given antigen can be determined with the greatest certainty by an impartial expert. The hereditary nature of these antigens is now beyond reasonable doubt. The sorts of judgment that may be rendered will be evident from the following cases.

Problem: A man of type AB, married to a woman of type O, questions the legitimacy of her child, type O. What should the judgment be? *Answer:* The child *cannot* be his, since he can produce only two types of sperm cells (*A*-sperm and *B*-sperm), and consequently cannot father any *OO* zygotes. . . . In making such a positive answer, we ignore the possibility that there has been a change in his genes during the process of gamete formation. Such changes, or *mutations,* will be discussed in Chapter 35. Suffice it to say here that mutation is a very rare event; the frequency of a mutation in a given gene is of the order of one mutation per million gametes. In law, as a practical matter, we ignore the possibility of such an unlikely event.

Problem: A woman of blood type O has a child of type B; the mother accuses Mr. X, who

is type AB, of being the father of her child. What should the judgment be? *Answer:* The data permit no judgment. Mr. X *could* be the father of the child; but so could literally millions of other men, of types B and AB. The data must clearly be regarded as inconclusive and should not affect the judgment of the court, which must be made on other grounds.

Problem: In a paternity suit, the man is types O and MN; the mother is A and N; and the child is B and N. The jury decides on the basis of all the evidence presented that the man is the father, and the court rules that he must support the child. After the trial is over, the foreman of the jury is questioned on this curious decision. He replied: "Well, the jury just didn't think much of the scientific evidence. According to the A-B test, the man couldn't be the father. According to the M-N test, he could. It can't be very good science when two different tests don't give the same answer." Is his attitude justified?

The jury's attitude shows a gross misconception of the meaning of the tests. The only result that should be influential in determining a decision is a test that *excludes* paternity. In any case, there are many features that would not permit such exclusion, for example, the fact that the child is white, and the putative father is white, or that both have blue eyes, or that both have ten fingers. But if a single test excludes the man as a possible father, he is positively excluded, regardless of the number of tests that fail to exclude him.

The use of blood tests as an aid in determining parentage (or more exactly, in *excluding* it), though still regarded with disfavor in some regions, is gaining year by year. To be sufficiently accurate for legal purposes, such tests must be carried out by specialists in the technique, for, as with all scientific tests, it is possible to get the wrong answer if the technique is faulty. An essential part of the court testimony is, therefore, evidence of the competence of the experts, who must, of course, be disinterested.

It must not be supposed that heredity tests are limited to the blood groups mentioned in the examples above. A total of eight different systems of blood groups are now known. Most of these are not, for technical reasons, suitable at the present time for extensive use in legal matters. But we may expect that the number seeing legal use will increase, and with this growth, the chance of proving nonparentage will also increase. Nor is there any reason for limiting legal heredity tests to blood tests. Other features may, on occasion, be used. That they are not more often used is due to a number of factors. For one thing, many of the external factors (color of skin, color of hair, shape of nose, and so forth) are determined by several pairs of alleles, and the way in which they interact is not known with sufficient certainty. For another, some external features are readily modifiable by environmental means (e.g., color of hair). Yet other externally visible characteristics are seldom part of court evidence precisely because they are so strongly determined by heredity, and are so obvious: for example, it would not often happen that a twelve-fingered man (**hyperdactyly**—too many fingers—is due to a dominant gene) would deny the parentage of a twelve-fingered child. It is therefore probable that the legal determination of parentage will continue to rest largely on the determination of chemical substances in the blood, substances whose hereditary nature is clear and for which there exist accurate, reproducible assays.

296. The Rhesus Factor in Childbirth

The existence of a blood antigen called the Rhesus antigen, or Rhesus factor, was briefly mentioned in §238. The presence of this antigen in the red blood cells is determined by a dominant gene symbolized by *Rh*. Rhesus-negative persons (Rh−) are *rh rh*. Rhesus-positive persons (Rh+) are either *Rh Rh* or *Rh rh*. The inheritance of these alleles follows the ordinary Mendelian rules.

Particular interest in the Rhesus gene is occasioned by its role in causing some of the natural abortions and miscarriages of human embryos. If a woman of genotype *rh rh* mates with a man of *Rh rh* or *Rh Rh* constitution, her child may

be *Rh rh*. Difficulties in gestation sometimes occur when the mother is Rhesus negative and the child is Rhesus positive. If any of the child's red blood cells—which contain the Rhesus antigen—get through the placenta and into the mother's blood system, the foreign protein will stimulate the production of an antibody (anti-Rhesus). This antibody is a soluble material that can go through an intact placenta. When it gets into the blood stream of the infant, it combines with the child's red blood cells, causing their destruction. The sequence of events is diagrammed in Figure 36-3. The damage may be so extensive as to cause the death and abortion of the child. If the damage is less severe, the child is born with a serious case of jaundice, the yellow skin color of jaundice being due to the presence of erythrocyte breakdown products in the blood stream. In such jaundice there is a "compensatory" increase in the rate of release of red blood cells from the bone marrow, which may even release erythroblasts (the immature erythrocytes—see §222); hence the name of the ailment, **erythroblastosis fetalis** (L. *foetus* = an offspring).

One of the interesting points about the Rhesus story is that it casts doubt on our picture of a placental barrier (§282) that is impermeable to all particles larger than molecules. If the Rhesus antigen occurs only in the red blood cells of the fetus, then the development of anti-Rhesus in the *rh rh* mother implies that these cells have gotten through a break in the barrier. On the other hand, it is possible that the Rhesus antigen may be detached from cells and move through the placenta by molecular diffusion. There is not, at present, any means of proving the correctness of one view or the other. It is next to impossible to demonstrate the existence of a break in the placenta just large enough to permit the postulated amount of whole blood to pass through, for quantitative studies show that only a drop or two of the child's blood would be sufficient to produce the effects observed.

Instances in which the mother is Rhesus negative and the child is Rhesus positive do not all result in complications. The first child of a

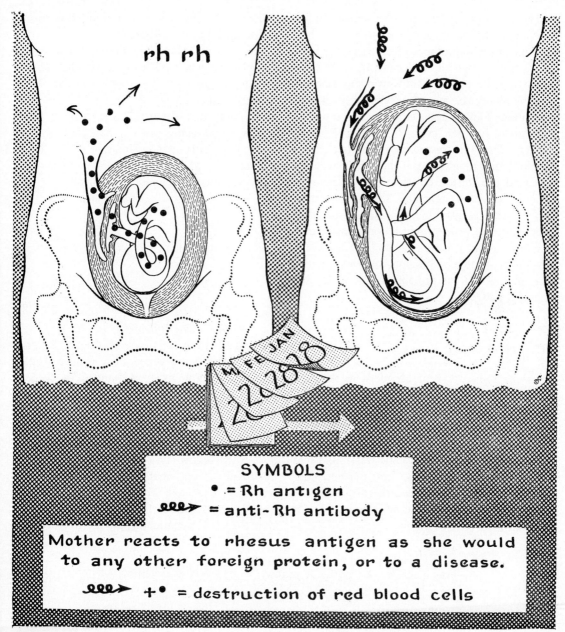

rh rh

SYMBOLS
• = Rh antigen
ℓℓℓℓ➤ = anti-Rh antibody

Mother reacts to rhesus antigen as she would to any other foreign protein, or to a disease.

ℓℓℓℓ➤ + • = destruction of red blood cells

Fig. 36-3. *The Rhesus factor and its possible effects.*

union of a Rh− ♀ with a Rh+ ♂ is seldom affected. Whether subsequent children will be affected is unpredictable. If the mother is exposed to Rhesus antigen and if she develops the antibody, she may still be able to have several children if their births are spaced sufficiently widely to allow the concentration of antibody in her blood to fall to a low level before each new conception occurs. Even if a jaundiced child is born, it may be saved by prompt and frequent blood transfusions during the first few months of its life. A Rhesus-negative mother married to a man heterozygous for the Rhesus gene would, of course, produce children half of whom would be expected to be Rhesus negative and, hence, not liable to infantile jaundice.

The discovery of the possible effects of incompatible Rhesus types in mother and child has shown the importance of an early typing of the blood of female children. If a Rhesus-negative girl receives a transfusion of Rhesus-positive blood, she may develop so great a concentration of anti-Rhesus antibody that it will be impossible for her ever to bear a Rhesus-positive child, thus restricting her in her choice of a husband. In addition, if she herself receives a second transfusion of Rh+ blood, she may suffer a dangerous reaction. This second danger, of course, also faces a Rhesus-negative male who receives repeated blood transfusions. For this reason, it is now becoming routine for hospitals to type blood donors and blood recipients for the Rhesus protein as well as for the A and B antigens.

297. Lethal Genes

After the rediscovery of Mendel's work, various characteristics in many animals and plants were subjected to genetic analysis. Investigations proved that the majority of the traits were but additional examples of simple Mendelian characters, but occasionally one was found that did not, at first, seem to fit into the new conceptual scheme. One of the earliest of these was yellowness in mice. The basic genetic data for this trait are recorded below.

yellow mice that yielded nothing but yellow offspring, litter after litter.

After some initial flounderings in a sea of hypotheses, geneticists came up with a simple explanation that fitted perfectly into the Mendelian scheme. To explain the facts, it was necessary only to assume that the "yellow gene" was a **lethal gene,** that is, one that brought about the death of individuals in whom it was homozygous. Matings of two yellow mice could be represented in genetic terms thus:

$$Yy \times Yy$$
$$\downarrow$$
$$\tfrac{1}{4}yy \text{ (gray)} + \tfrac{2}{4}Yy \text{ (yellow)} + \tfrac{1}{4}YY$$
$$\downarrow$$
$$\text{(die before birth)}$$

The ratios of living offspring fit this hypothesis, for, *of the living offspring* ($\tfrac{1}{4} + \tfrac{2}{4} = \tfrac{3}{4}$), one-third ($\tfrac{1}{4}$ out of $\tfrac{3}{4}$) are gray and two-thirds ($\tfrac{2}{4}$ out of $\tfrac{3}{4}$) are yellow. The results of mating these yellows is as demanded by theory: they do not breed true, again producing $\tfrac{1}{3}$ gray and $\tfrac{2}{3}$ yellow among their living offspring.

Other data were soon found to corroborate the theory. Counts revealed that matings of yellow with yellow produced litters that were about 25 percent smaller than the normal—as would be expected. Post-mortem examination of mothers killed early in pregnancy showed that their uteri contained, on the average, the

	A	B	C
	gray × gray	gray × yellow	yellow × yellow
	↓	↓	↓
	all gray	½ gray + ½ yellow	⅓ gray + ⅔ yellow

The results listed under *B* indicate that yellow is dominant to gray. The mating under *C* is evidently one involving heterozygotes. But the ratio ($\tfrac{1}{3} : \tfrac{2}{3}$) is not quite what we would expect ($\tfrac{1}{4} : \tfrac{3}{4}$); and large enough numbers have been obtained to show that the difference between the observed and expected ratios is significant. More important is the additional genetic fact that no one has ever found a pair of

normal number of embryos. The implication was clear: about one-fourth of the embryos in *Yy* mothers mated with *Yy* fathers die before parturition. Since this is the same as the expected number of homozygous yellows (which never occur among the living offspring), it is probable that the *YY* embryos die before birth.

How are we to refer to a gene like this? Is it dominant or recessive? If we call it a "yellow gene," we may say it is dominant; if we call it a "lethal gene," we may refer to it as a recessive. The matter is purely one of terminology, and may be judged according to individual taste. Some call such genes "semidominant." The important things to remember are the facts.

Many lethal genes have been found in species that have been much studied genetically. Many of these genes have no known dominant effects —merely their recessive lethal effects. Such genes are not easy to discover; but, once suspected, their existence can be proved by various techniques.

In man, a number of lethal genes have been demonstrated, all of which are "semidominant." No doubt there are other lethals that produce no obvious phenotypic effects in the heterozygous condition. Such genes will be difficult to demonstrate in a species in which controlled matings cannot be carried out. Undoubtedly, some of the spontaneous abortions that occur in humans are due to the expulsion of embryos that have died as the result of being homozygous for recessive lethal genes. What fraction of the spontaneous abortions fall in this category cannot be stated at the present time.

Questions and Problems

36-1. Make a list of the **boldface** terms in this chapter. Write a brief definition or description of each. Compare your work with the text.

36-2. Four pedigrees are given in verbal form below. Convert each of these pedigrees into a diagram of the sort shown in Figure 36-1.

a. An albino man marries an albino woman. They have three children: an albino boy, then an albino girl, and finally an albino boy.

b. An albino woman, the daughter of normal parents and the sister of four normal brothers, marries a normal man. They produce eight boys and five girls, all normal.

c. An albino man marries a normal woman. They produce, in order: a normal girl, an albino girl, a normal boy.

d. A normal man whose parents and grandparents were normal marries a normal woman whose parents and grandparents were normal. From this union come one albino girl, one normal girl, and one normal boy.

‡36-3. Are all the data presented in question 36-2 consistent with the theory that albinism is due to a recessive gene? If not, point out the inconsistencies.

36-4. On the basis of the conclusion reached in 36-3, and after defining the meaning of your

gene symbols, write the genotype of each individual in the pedigrees in 36-2. When either of two genotypes is possible, write both, connected by the word "or."

‡36-5. One authority on blood groups has repeatedly urged that laws be established making compulsory the typing of every female child for the Rhesus factor, and that the results be engraved on a bracelet perpetually worn on the wrist of each typed female. Explain the reasoning behind this proposal.

‡36-6. A man of blood types M and AB marries a woman of types N and O. What types of offspring might they produce?

36-7. Some marriages in which both partners are of blood type A produce only one type of offspring, whereas other such marriages produce two types of off-spring, with respect to this blood group. Ignoring the possibility of illegitimacy, what possible explanation(s) can you suggest?

‡36-8. A man of blood types MN and A marries a woman of types MN and B. How many and what types of offspring might they produce?

‡36-9. Wiener, in his *Blood Groups and Transfusions*, tells the following case:

After eight years of married life, during which time she had frequent intercourse with her husband, but had failed to become pregnant, Mrs. X met and fell in love with Mr. Y. During the ensuing five years, three children were born. In the meantime, the persons involved had tried to come to an understanding and wished to determine which of the two men was the father of each child. The bloods of those involved were examined with the following results:

Blood of	Group	Type
Husband	O	MN
Lover	A	N
Wife	O	MN
First child	O	MN
Second child	O	M
Third child	A	N

What do you conclude as to the paternity of each child? Give your reasoning.

36-10. After a whirlwind courtship a college girl marries a wealthy boy in her biology class. He is the beneficiary of a trust fund that is to be turned over to him at the age of 30. Should he die before reaching that age, the money is to be held in trust for his children, if any. Should he die before the age of 30 without children, the estate passes to his relatives.

A year after the marriage a boy is born. Two years later, the husband is killed in an accident. At this point, the executors of the trust question the legitimacy of the child. As determined by a professional testing laboratory, the blood types of the mother are B and M; of the child, A and MN. There is no record of the husband's blood type except that found in his biology laboratory notebook, which shows that he determined his blood to be of type O. What influence should this record have in deciding the case?

‡36-11. Having more than the normal number of fingers is most commonly spoken of as *polydactyly*. The American geneticist C. H. Danforth first pointed out that the correct name for this condition is *hyperdactyly*—the term adopted in the present text. What is the etymological issue involved?

‡36-12. Mrs. Jones becomes pregnant once a year. Her first three children are normal and are born without mishap. The fourth child is definitely jaundiced, but survives. The fifth child dies of jaundice shortly after birth. The sixth, seventh, and eighth conceptions end in abortion. The ninth child is carried to term, and is completely normal. Assume that the Rhesus gene is involved in these events. Give the genotype of Mr and Mrs. Jones and all the children conceived, indicating any uncertainties and the reasons therefor.

‡36-13. In solving problems similar to that posed in 36-12, *as a matter of method* one should not postulate illegitimacy except as a last resort. Why not? What important methodological principle is involved?

Readings

For further details of the inheritance of many human genes, including those of blood antigens, see Stern. Wiener's monograph, *Blood Groups and Transfusions,* gives many fascinating case histories in the field of paternity tests, including the one quoted in question 36-9, by permission of the publisher and author.

37

Sex and Cytogenetics

298. How Many Chromosomes?

An important subdivision of genetics is **cytogenetics,** which may be defined as the branch of cytology focused on the genetic apparatus of the cell, particularly the chromosomes. Each species has a characteristic number of chromosomes, some of which are recorded in Appendix 9. The number of chromosomes is easier to determine in a species with a small number, such as *Drosophila melanogaster,* with its diploid number of 8, than it is in a species with a large number, such as man, with his 46. A statement like the preceding one has, as an unexpressed addendum, the phrase "other things being equal." As a matter of fact, other things aren't equal. The chromosomes of mammals and birds are particularly difficult to study. Typically, they are short and relatively featureless, and inclined to stick together, making it difficult to count them. As a result, many of the chromosome numbers recorded for members of these classes, particularly in the older research literature, are not very reliable. With respect to the chromosome number in man, a review of the literature is enlightening. As Table 37-1 shows, the reports have by no means been consistent. For a generation after Painter's work in 1923, the diploid number 48 was accepted as correct. Then in 1956 two cytologists, Joe Hin Tjio and Albert Levan, published a short paper that brought about a complete change of opinion.

By this time there were available cytological techniques that were greatly improved over those used by earlier workers; and with these, Tjio and Levan could consistently find only 46

TABLE 37-1   *Number of Chromosomes Reported for Man.*

YEAR	AUTHORITY	DIPLOID NUMBER
1891	Hansemann	18, 24, or 40
1912	de Winiwarter	47 in males
1918	Evans	48
1921	Painter	45–48 (46 most probable)
1923	Painter	48
1956	Tjio and Levan	46
1957–1958	Kodani	46, 47, and 48
1956 *et seq.*	(Many, independently)	46

chromosomes in human somatic cells. An **idiogram,** that is, a formal arrangement, of these is shown in Figure 37-1. Shortly after Tjio and Levan's work, another worker reported various numbers of chromosomes—46, 47, and 48—in different human beings. But many other researchers, examining human cells in the light of the controversy, have all confirmed Tjio and Levan's work. By 1959, cells from more than 200 different individuals had been critically examined, with consistent results. We may, therefore, accept 46 as the correct diploid number for *Homo sapiens.*

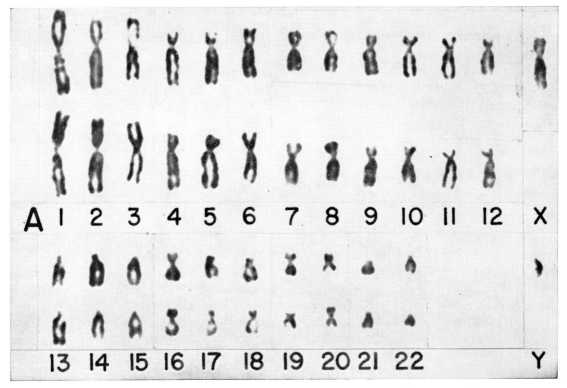

Fig. 37-1. *Photomicrographs of human chromosomes arranged and numbered according to the "Denver System."*

299. Heterosomes and Sex Determination

A careful examination of the diagrammatic diploid cells of the flies in Figure 35-1 or 35-3 discloses that in the male there is one pair of chromosomes that is not quite a well-matched pair. This is not true of the female. The corresponding chromosomes of the female, the uppermost pair in each figure, are called the **X-chromosomes.** The male has only one X-chromosome, and its odd mate is called a **Y-chromosome.** The X and the Y behave in meiosis as if they were good mates, though microscopic evidence reveals differences between them. The X- and Y-chromosomes are called **heterosomes,** to distinguish them from all the other chromosomes, which are called **autosomes.**

Since the male contains two different heterosomes, and since heterosomes behave like members of a pair in meiosis, it is apparent that the male will produce two different kinds of gam-etes: one an X-sperm, and the other a Y-sperm —as indicated in Figure 37-2. The male is therefore called the **heterogametic sex.** The two kinds of gametes appear in approximately equal numbers, which we have indicated in the diagram by writing *ca.* ½ below each type of gamete. The female is the **homogametic sex** and produces only X-eggs.

When an X-egg joins with an X-sperm, the XX-zygote develops into a female.

When an X-egg unites with a Y-sperm, the XY-zygote develops into a male.

Since males must mate only with females (and vice versa), a little thought will show that this mechanism insures the appearance of males and females in approximately equal numbers, generation after generation. Sex is determined by chromosomal make-up.

One naturally suspects that maleness is produced by the Y-chromosome, and facts bear out this suspicion in men and mice. Rarely, by accident, a mouse will be produced that has only one X-chromosome and no Y-chromosome. Such an **XO** individual, if it is a mouse, is a female* and may be fertile; but if it is a human, an XO female is always sterile. People suffering from **Turner's syndrome,** incompletely developed females, are XO individuals.

Another abnormality that occasionally turns up is an **XXY** individual. In man, such a chromosome complement produces a male, but with feminine characteristics (e.g., some development of the breasts, accompanied by no sperm production); the complex of symptoms is called **Klinefelter's syndrome.** From these results, it seems fair to say that the Y-chromosome is necessary to produce a male, but that the quan-

* 37-1. Mated with a normal male, what ratio of males to females would it produce? (Assume, as it probably true, that at least one X-chromosome is needed for viability.)

titative relation between X's and Y's is also important.

There is considerable variation among animals with respect to sex-determining mechanisms. In *Drosophila,* an XO individual is a male, and an XXY individual is female, from which it appears that it is the *ratio* of X-chromosomes to autosomes that determines sex. (This difference between mechanisms in fly and man would never be guessed so long as only normal cytological situations were known.) Among the Hymenoptera, as we learned when studying the bees (§173), a quite different mechanism is found: two kinds of eggs are laid by the queen, the haploid eggs turning into males and the diploid eggs into females.* An-

* 37-2. What about meiosis in gametogenesis in drone bees?

Fig. 37-2. *A method of sex determination. The male produces two sorts of gametes in equal numbers, Y-gametes (left) and X-gametes (middle). The female produces only X-gametes. The XY-zygotes develop into ♂ ♂; the XX-zygotes develop into ♀ ♀. This mechanism insures the approximate equality in numbers of the two sexes.*

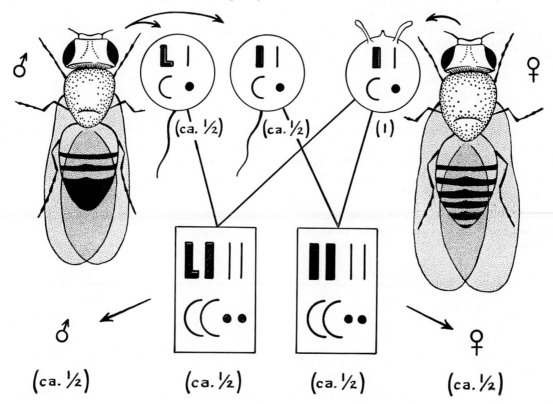

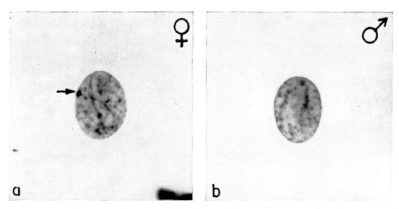

Fig. 37-3. *The "sex chromatin," indicated by arrow, usually shows in cells taken from human females (left) and seldom in male cells (right). (Courtesy Grumbach and Barr; from Curt Stern,* Principles of Human Genetics, *2nd ed., W. H. Freeman and Company, San Francisco and London, 1960.)*

other system of sex determination occurs among birds and moths, which is a sort of mirror-image of the mammalian system: the hetero-gametic sex is the female. The female in such species is called ZW, the male ZZ.

Intersexuality and imperfect sexuality, though uncommon among human beings, present serious personal problems for the individuals afflicted. Undoubtedly, many causes contribute to these conditions, including endocrine imbalance and psychological influences. It is now clear that cytogenetics is sometimes involved. For unknown reasons, more or less complete sex reversal sometimes occurs in embryogeny, but without any change in cytology. In general, we should suspect that being genetically one sex and morphologically another is likely to lead to difficulties. The possibility of testing this suspicion has been greatly improved by the recent development of the **Barr test.** M. L. Barr and E. G. Bertram, in 1949, found that ordinary somatic cells (e.g., leucocytes) of females show a certain chromosomal structure (Fig. 37-3) which is almost invariably absent in male cells. This darkly staining spot is called **sex chromatin.** It is found not only in the primates but also in many other mammals (not, however, in rodents and rabbits). With the Barr test it is now possible easily to verify the genetic sex of human beings. A summary of the normal and some of the more common aberrations is given in Table 37-2. None of the abnormal types are very common, fortunately. A large survey showed that about 0.03 percent of all newborn female babies are XO; about 0.3 percent of the male babies are chromatin-positive and hence presumably XXY.

TABLE 37-2   *Some Genetic Correlates of Sexuality in Humans.*

NAME	PHENOTYPE	SEX CHROMATIN	GENETIC CONSTITUTION	OTHER CHARACTERISTICS ( ) = VARIABLE
Male	♂	−	XY	
Female	♀	+	XX	
Klinefelter's syndrome	♂	+	XXY	Small testes; (gynaecomasty)
Turner's syndrome	♀	−	XO	No ovaries; (webbed neck)
Metafemale	♀	+	XXX	Subnormal sexuality; subnormal mentality
Testicular feminization	♀	−	XY & gene *Tr*	Undescended testes; (small) vagina; externally ♀

300. X-linked Inheritance

In all of the matings recorded in the preceding chapter, it makes no difference whether the genotypes of the two sexes are as stated, or whether the sexes and genotypes are interchanged. That is, a mating of $Aa \, \male \times aa \, \female$ produces the same results as the **reciprocal mating** $aa \, \male \times Aa \, \female$. The great majority of the genes in all organisms behave in this way. There are, however, some genes that do not behave identically in reciprocal matings. Among these are the so-called sex-linked genes, that is, the genes carried in the X-chromosomes. The X-chromosome, like the autosomes, is made up of hundreds of genes. The Y-chromosome, how-

ever, appears to be almost devoid of genes. We shall, for simplicity, here regard it as a genetic blank.

Among the X-borne genes in *Drosophila* is one called "miniature," because it causes the wings to be smaller than normal. Miniature (*m*) is recessive to normal (*M*). Females must have two "doses" of *m* to be miniature, but males need have only one dose of *m* to be miniature, since the Y-chromosomes have no counteracting gene.

In Figure 37-4 is diagrammed the result of the cross of a miniature male with a normal female. In the F_1 generation, only the females can have the *m* gene, because every male necessarily gets its X-chromosomes from its mother,

Fig. 37-4. *Inheritance of a "sex-linked character" indicated in two ways. (A) The uncommon allele is represented as a colored band on the X-chromosome, the wild-type allele as a black band. The Y-chromosome may be considered a genetic blank. (B) Symbolization is simplified by ignoring the X-chromosome and writing the uncommon allele in colored ink, the wild-type allele being in black. The Y-chromosome is retained to avoid errors in thinking of meiosis, but it is written in parentheses in order that the chromosome will not be mistaken for a gene.*

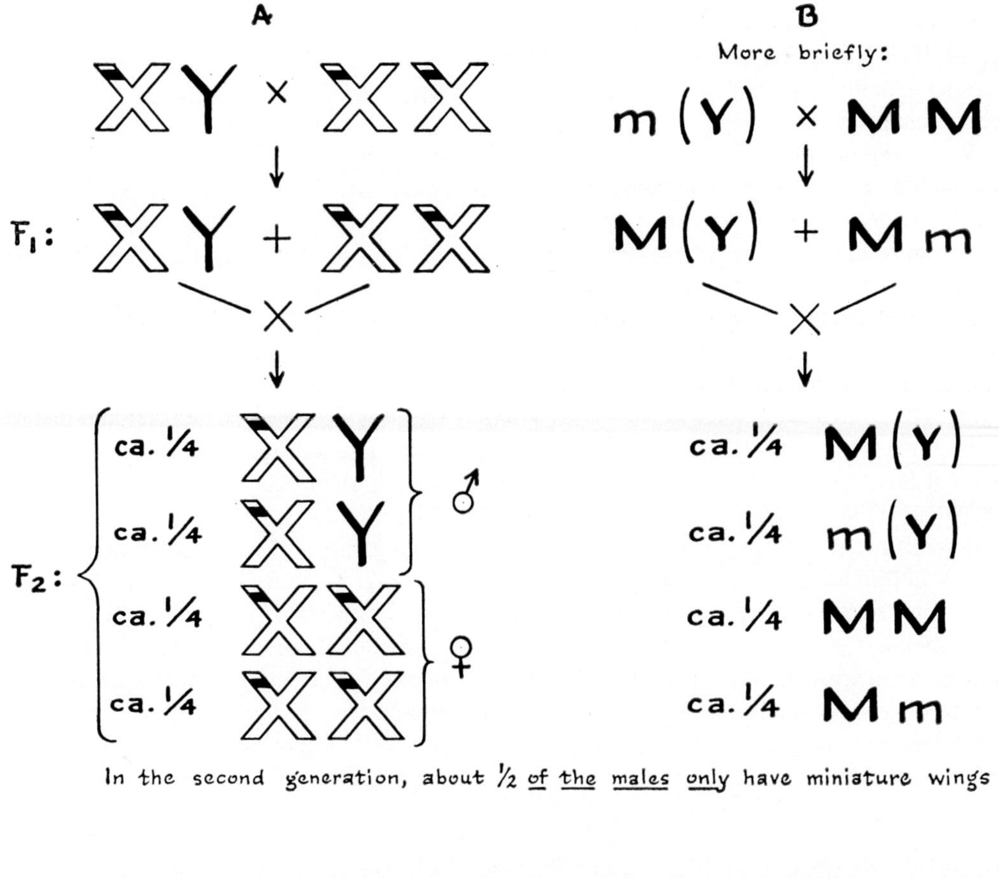

In the second generation, about ½ of the males only have miniature wings

who has only normal genes (*M*) to contribute. If we now make a brother-sister mating in the F_1, in the F_2 there will once more appear the miniature character, and it will be in the male sex again, as it was in the grandfather. It was this apparent tendency of a mutant character to stay linked to one sex that led people to call this sort of inheritance "sex-linked inheritance."

However, the sex linkage is, in a sense, spurious. Miniature females can be produced by the following mating:

$$Mm \times m(\mathrm{Y})$$
$$\downarrow$$
$$Mm + mm + M(\mathrm{Y}) + m(\mathrm{Y})$$

About one-half of the female offspring will have miniature wings, since they have no dominant *M* to produce normal wings.

Red-green color blindness in humans is a recessive sex-linked gene. A father can transmit it to his daughters, who will be only "carriers" if they are heterozygous. He cannot transmit it to his sons, who get an X-chromosome only from their mother. In the United States, the frequency of red-green color-blind men is about 1 in 12. This means that, out of all the X-chromosomes in the United States, only about $\frac{1}{12}$ bear such a gene.

What will be the frequency of color-blind women? For a woman to be color-blind, she must, to speak loosely, have *two* "color-blind" X-chromosomes. In very general terms we may say that it is a matter of chance whether she gets these chromosomes. In the whole "population" of X-chromosomes, 1 out of 12 chromosomes carries the gene for color blindness. One out of every 12 women will, then, have at least one such X-chromosome. *Of these women,* 1 out of 12 will have the other X-chromosome bearing this gene. That is, *of all women,* one-twelfth of one-twelfth $(\frac{1}{12} \times \frac{1}{12})$, or $\frac{1}{144}$, will have two X-chromosomes bearing the gene for color blindness, and will consequently be red-green color-blind. Color blindness is much rarer in women than in men. This difference has nothing to do with sexuality as such, but is merely a consequence of the fact that the responsible gene is on a heterosome.

Another X-link gene known in man is the gene for hemophilia, a disease in which the blood coagulates unusually slowly. Because a clot may take from a half-hour to several hours to form, the tiniest cut is a serious threat to life. The responsible gene is recessive and is carried on the X-chromosome. Its mode of inheritance does not differ from that of color blindness.

On the physiological side, hemophilia is undoubtedly caused by some derangement in the blood-clotting mechanism described in §185. Perhaps if we knew what the trouble is, we could help the victims of the hereditary disease. Little progress has been made as yet in probing this physiological puzzle. It is easy to see the reason for the slow progress. Where can one get hemophilic blood for study except from a hemophiliac, who endangers his life in furnishing samples? However, a strain of spaniels has been found in which occurs what appears to be the identical ailment. With this source of non-human experimental material available, we can reasonably hope to make progress in alleviating the sufferings of human hemophiliacs.

301. The Lyon Hypothesis

Recall the fundamental idea that the chromosomes are bearers of information. The DNA in the chromosomes is a complex of coded instructions for making the great variety of polypeptides, proteins, and enzymes required for the machinery of the cell. The omission of any portion of these instructions causes serious defects, as we see in Turner's syndrome; often such an omission is fatal. Redundance in part of the instructions is generally serious, too: note the characterization of the "metafemale" in Table 37-2.

Of course, there is a bit of a puzzle in the fact that a quantitatively exact duplication of all the information is normal to all diploid organisms; but if we accept (as we must) the normality of this redundance, we can dimly understand why a *partial* further redundance or a partial deficiency in the coded instructions might well be serious for the organism. An extra blueprint slipped into the complete set required to make a jet bomber would cause trouble, too.

What, then, about the sex chromosomes? A male has only one X (and a nearly information-free Y), but a female has 2 X's: of the information carried on the X-chromosome the female has twice as much as the male. Most of this information has nothing to do with sexual differences; how, then, is the difference in dosage of information compensated for? This is called the problem of **dosage compensation.**

In 1962, Mary F. Lyon proposed an interesting solution to this problem. The chromosomal material of a cell in interphase is so extended that it does not show up when subjected to nuclear staining. As the cell gets ready to divide the chromatin *condenses* to make much shorted segments; in the condensed condition it is easily revealed by nuclear stains (§14). The existence of the Barr body in a cell in interphase indicates that a small part of the chromatin must be in the condensed phase. The Lyon hypothesis holds that this chromatin is one of the two X-chromosomes. There are many reasons for thinking that only the DNA in chromatin that is in the extended state is capable of being transcribed to RNA; condensed chromatin is informationally dumb. Lyon has proposed that the dosage compensation problem is solved in man and many other mammals by having one of the X-chromosomes in every somatic cell of a female in the condensed state; in this way the functional informational content of male and female cells is quantitatively the same.

In a female (with her two X-chromosomes), which X is condensed? A priori, one can see no reason why one should be preferred to the other. It should be a matter of chance. We should be able to verify this prediction if we can find a gene that produces a visible effect restricted to the cell in which the gene occurs (rather than producing a hormone that circulates to all cells). An individual heterozygous for contrasting, locally effective alleles should be a **mosaic** of cells or tissues, depending on which gene is in the developmentally effective state of chromatin extension, and which in the ineffective,

condensed state. Not many genes are suitable for this test, but one that is is the X-linked gene for **anhidrosis** (lack of sweat glands).

Males with this abnormal allele lack sweat glands entirely, and suffer greatly. Many die in infancy; others live to a precarious adulthood, kept alive in hot weather by cold baths, air conditioning and the like. Heterozygous females

Fig. 37-5. *Anhidrosis: the mosaic resulting from "Lyonization" of X-chromosomes.*

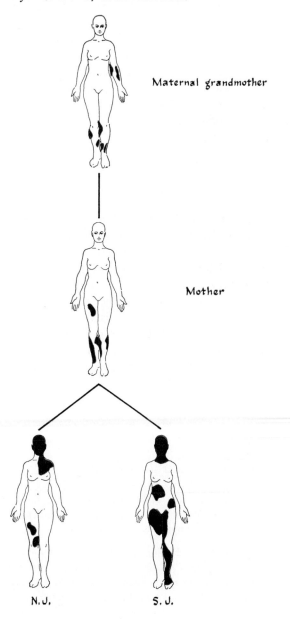

exhibit the defect in a very variable way. Figure 37-5 shows the condition of three generations of women in an anhidrotic family. The distribution of skin lacking in sweat glands is indicated by the colored areas in the figure. It will be noted that mother and grandmother were almost normal; correlated with this, they did not suffer in hot weather. The identical twin daughters, however, were less fortunate, particularly the one labeled "S.J.," who suffered considerably from heat. This gene also causes abnormal dentition, found in both twins, but not in mother or grandmother. The twins were unquestionably one-egg twins. The difference in patterning of the skin indicates that it is a matter of chance which X-chromosome becomes condensed. As a result of her greater area of abnormal tissue, S.J.'s health was much poorer than her sister's, and her growth was comparatively stunted.

302. X-linked Lethals

In §297 it was stated that a recessive lethal may be detectable in experimental animals even when the gene causes no known phenotypic manifestation in heterozygotes. It might be wondered how such a gene could be detected. One class of genes for which the method of detection is fairly easy to understand is that of the sex-linked lethal genes. If we represent a normal male as $L(Y)$, completely normal females will be LL, and normal female "carriers" of the

lethal gene will be Ll. Males of genotype $l(Y)$ and females of ll (if produced) die before birth. The only possible matings involving both alleles will be:

$$Ll \times L(Y)$$
$$\downarrow$$
$$\tfrac{1}{4}LL + \tfrac{1}{4}Ll + \tfrac{1}{4}L(Y) + \tfrac{1}{4}l(Y) \text{ (which die)}$$

Notice that the sex ratio, at birth, instead of approximating the normal 1:1 is here 2 ♀ ♀ :1 ♂ ($\tfrac{2}{4}:\tfrac{1}{4}$). Whenever this ratio occurs in the offspring of a single pair of parents, we are justified in suspecting the presence of a recessive lethal borne on a heterosome (assuming that there are enough offspring to justify confidence in the ratio). As further tests of the hypothesis, we can carry out breeding tests on the offspring. The males should, of course, produce the normal sex ratio if mated to females from other stocks that do not carry the lethal gene. The females, however, differ. Half of the females produced from a mating which produced a deficiency of males should themselves produce such 2 ♀ ♀ :1 ♂ families, regardless of the genetic constitution of their mates. The other females should produce normal families.

Many sex-linked recessive lethals have been found in *Drosophila,* where the large families (100 or more offspring) permit us to recognize an unusual sex ratio. We suspect that such lethals occur also in man; but human families are so small as to make the gathering of statistically significant data almost impossible.

Questions and Problems

37-3. Make a list of the **boldface** terms in this chapter. Write a brief definition or description of each. Compare your work with the text.

‡37-4. J. C. F. Poole, in 1953, reported on two hemophiliacs. Coagulation time was very long with the blood of each, observed separately; but a mixture of their bloods coagulated in the

normal time. What does such an observation imply about the *entity* "hemophilia"? Couch your answer in terms of the information included in Figure 27-6.

37-5. A red-green color-blind man marries a normal woman. From this union one color-blind daughter is born. Give the genotypes of these three people. List the genotypes of all possible offspring from this marriage.

‡37-6. A normal male marries a normal female whose father was normal. They produce a color-blind boy. From which of his four grandparents did this child derive his gene for color blindness?

37-7. A color-blind man marries a woman who is not color-blind. Assuming there is no information regarding the woman's ancestry, what will most probably be the genotype and phenotype of her daughters?

‡37-8. A normal woman married to a normal man produces two color-blind sons, two normal sons, and four normal daughters. After the death of this husband, she marries a color-blind man. How would the offspring expected from this second union compare with those realized from the first?

37-9. If a normal woman marries a normal man and two of her three sons are hemophilic, what is her genotype?

‡37-10. If a normal woman marries a normal man and one of her eleven sons is hemophilic, what is her genotype?

‡37-11. There are three children in a family: Henry is hemophilic, and George and Mary are not. The latter two, knowing that hemophilia is a "hereditary disease" and not desiring to bring more hemophiliacs into the world, consult a genetic adviser. In full detail, what should be his advice to each?

‡37-12. In a certain population, 1 out of 20 of the men has hereditary red-green color blindness. What proportion of the women in this population are red-green color-blind?

37-13. In a certain population, 4 percent of the men suffer from hereditary red-green color blindness. What percentage of the women in this population are red-green color-blind?

37-14. In a certain population, approximately 1 out of every 81 women has hereditary red-green color blindness. What proportion of the men of this population would be expected to be color-blind?

‡37-15. According to the chromosomal theory of sex determination developed in this chapter, it would be expected that male and female babies would be born with equal frequency. Yet records of millions of human births show that for every 100 girls born there are about 106 boys. The departure from an expected 1:1 ratio is not due to sampling error. Could the discrepancy be attributed to the effects of sex-linked recessive lethal genes present in the population? Explain.

37-16. By refined statistical analysis, E. Novitski in 1953 showed that there is a change in the sex ratio of children conceived that is attributable solely to the age of the father, the age of the mother being without influence. The male: female ratio is higher for younger fathers; in older fathers it approaches closely to 1:1. Suggest an explanation.

‡37-17. I. M. Nilsson, 1959, reported a family in which a normal father and mother produced four hemophilic boys and one hemophilic girl. The girl gave a negative Barr test. Give the most plausible genetic explanation of these facts.

37-18. In cats there is an X-linked gene that functions in the following way. Among males, $B(Y)$ is black, $b(Y)$ is yellow. Among females, BB is black, bb is yellow, and the heterozygote is a mosaic of black and yellow patches. Such a cat is called "calico" or "tortoiseshell." Calico males are very rare, and the few that have been reliably studied have proved to be sterile.

What is the most reasonable explanation of these facts?

37-19. C. A. Joel, 1955, reported the case of a man whose first and second wives spontaneously aborted all their babies. When the second wife was artificially inseminated from another donor, she successfully bore a child. What is the most probable explanation of these facts?

‡37-20. Garn and Rohmann, 1962, comparing the time of ossification of bones in siblings of three classes, namely sister-sister, brother-brother, and brother-sister, found that there was the highest correlation in the sister-sister pairs. The authors pointed out that this is just what we should expect from our knowledge of heredity. Reconstruct their argument in explicit detail.

‡37-21. Experimenters at the U.S.D.A. Research Center at Beltsville, Md., have succeeded in producing parthenogenetic turkeys. During 1960, 15 were produced. All were diploid. All were males. Is this what you would expect? Try to explain both expected and unexpected aspects of the results.

37-22. One of the parthenogenetic males described in the above problem became a father, by a normal female. Predict the sex of the offspring. What would be the particular advantage of such a bird in genetic experiments?

37-23. An enterprising business administration student who flunked his genetics course sets himself up in business. By mail, for a $10 fee, he offers to predict the sex of unborn offspring: "your money back if not satisfied," he advertises.

To maximize his earnings, how should he make his predictions?

37-24. Leeuwenhoek stated that there are two different kinds of sperm cells, but he failed to give his evidence. We have good evidence for this belief now, but we still are unable to tell them apart. Suppose that some day we learn to distinguish and to separate the X-bearing sperm from the Y-bearing sperm. What will be the likely social consequences of this advance in knowledge? Would you regard this development as desirable or not? If undesirable, is it preventable? (An essay of some length is in order.)

Readings

Stern's *Human Genetics* is the standard work to consult for further details on the genetics of sexuality. Boyer's collection of *Papers on Human Genetics* has reprints of classic contributions to human cytogenetics, including Lyon's paper on sex chromatin and gene action. Any attempt to discern the social implications of human genetics inevitably leads to controversy; before adding needlessly to this disorder it would be well to read L. C. Dunn's "Cross currents in the history of human genetics," in Boyer's volume.

38 Populations of Genes

303. Probability Theory

Before studying examples of inheritance involving more than one set of different alleles in the same cross, it will be well to make explicit some basic principles of probability that have been used more or less implicitly in preceding sections.

Probability is measured on a scale that runs from 0 (impossibility) to 1 (absolute certainty). The probability of a coin turning heads is $\frac{1}{2}$; that is, we expect about half of a large number of throws to result in heads. The probability of a die (sing. of dice) turning four is $\frac{1}{6}$ (there are six sides to a die). In the long run, we expect the four on a die to turn up about one-sixth of the time, that is, in about 1 out of every 6 throws.

Suppose we throw the coin and the die at the same time. What is the probability of a particular double event—say, of heads on the coin and four on the die—*in the same throw?* The probability of four on the die is $\frac{1}{6}$. In a large number of throws, there will be many instances in which the die turns four; *in these particular instances,* the coin (thrown simultaneously) will turn heads $\frac{1}{2}$ of the time. Therefore, *of all throws* of die and coin simultaneously, the result will be heads on coin *with* four on die $\frac{1}{2}$ of $\frac{1}{6}$ of the time, or $\frac{1}{2} \times \frac{1}{6} = \frac{1}{12}$ of all double throws. We can generalize this instance and express the rule in words, as the **Product**

Rule of Probability: *If a particular double event is composed of two independent single events both of which must occur in the same instance, then the probability of the double event is the product of the separate probabilities of the single events.*

A different problem faces us when we wish to know the probability of the occurrence of *any one* of several events. Suppose we toss a nickel and a penny simultaneously. What is the probability that exactly one—either one—of the coins will turn heads (the other turning tails)? The probability of heads-on-nickel with tails-on-penny is $\frac{1}{2} \times \frac{1}{2} = \frac{1}{4}$ (Product Rule). The probability of tails-on-nickel with heads-on-penny is $\frac{1}{2} \times \frac{1}{2} = \frac{1}{4}$. Of all the equally probable double events—nickel^Heads^ penny^Heads^; nickel^Heads^ penny^Tails^; nickel^Tails^ penny^Heads^; nickel^Tails^ penny^Tails^—the *type* of double event we are interested in—namely, heads on only one coin—constitutes two out of four $= \frac{2}{4} = \frac{1}{2}$. From this instance, we may verbalize the general rule, as the **Sum Rule of Probability:** *If a type of event may occur in several mutually exclusive ways, the probability of the type is the sum of the probabilities of the different ways.*

An examination of the material in the preceding chapters will show that both of these rules were used, though not explicitly. The rules will see further use in the present chapter. It is easy to know which rule to use if one remembers the following advice: If the question is "What is the probability of *both* . . . ?"—the Product Rule applies. If the question is "What is the probability of *either* . . . or . . . ?"—the Sum Rule applies.

304. The Independence of Genes

Important among the evidences Mendel marshaled for the particulate nature of inheritance was the demonstration of independent assortment of two or more sets of genes. In one of his experiments he crossed a pure stock that had round seeds that were yellow in color, with another that had wrinkled seeds that were green, producing a **dihybrid** generation, that is, organisms hybrid for two different sets of genes. The F_1 seeds were all round and yellow. In symbols:

$$P \qquad RRYY \times rryy$$
$$\downarrow$$
$$F_1 \qquad RrYy$$

What sorts of gametes should the F_1 form, and in what proportions? Half of the gametes should contain *R,* half *r*; half should contain *Y,* half *y*. If the alleles affecting shape are distributed *independently* of those affecting color, there should be four types of gametes (*RY, Ry, rY, ry*) in equal proportions. How can we tell if this happens? By a test-cross (§286) with *rryy*. When Mendel carried out this test, he obtained the results shown in Table 38-1. It is apparent that the agreement between the observed frequencies and the expected frequencies is extremely close. The genes behave as parti-

TABLE 38-1 *Results of Test-Cross of* RrYy *Peas with* rryy *Peas (Mendel's data).*

CLASS	FRACTION EXPECTED	NUMBER OBSERVED	NUMBER EXPECTED
Round, yellow	$\frac{1}{4}$	31	27.5
Round, green	$\frac{1}{4}$	26	27.5
Wrinkled, yellow	$\frac{1}{4}$	27	27.5
Wrinkled, green	$\frac{1}{4}$	26	27.5
Total	1	110	110

cles, which, during meiosis, are distributed to the gametes independently of each other.

What, then, would be an F_2 generation derived from an original cross of *RRYY* with *rryy*? That is, what will be the offspring of F_1 pea plants, *RrYy,* if they are allowed to fertilize themselves (as peas can)? Since, as we have seen, the R set of alleles and the Y set behave independently, we can calculate the expected frequencies with the aid of the Product Rule. In the F_2, $\frac{3}{4}$ should have at least one *R* gene, which we indicate by *R*—; $\frac{1}{4}$ should be *rr*. And, independently of these, $\frac{3}{4}$ should be *Y*—; and $\frac{1}{4}$ should be *yy*.

Combining:

The probability of round, yellow (*R–Y–*) is $\frac{3}{4} \times \frac{3}{4} = \frac{9}{16}$.

The probability of round, green (*R–yy*) is $\frac{3}{4} \times \frac{1}{4} = \frac{3}{16}$.

The probability of wrinkled, yellow (*rrY–*) is $\frac{1}{4} \times \frac{3}{4} = \frac{3}{16}$.

The probability of wrinkled, green (*rryy*) is $\frac{1}{4} \times \frac{1}{4} = \frac{1}{16}$.

In the F_2 from such a dihybrid cross, Mendel obtained 315 round, yellow seeds; 108 round, green seeds; 101 wrinkled, yellow seeds; and 32 wrinkled, green seeds. If the student will carry out calculations analogous to those exhibited in Table 38-1, he will see that the agreement between observed and expected is reasonably close, thus furnishing additional evidence in favor of the Mendelian scheme. The student may also wish to verify that the same results may be derived from a Punnett square, constructed with four different gametes (*RY, Ry, rY, ry*) from each parent.

305. The Linkage of Genes

All of the genetic characters that Mendel reported studying behaved independently of one another in the manner just described. After the rediscovery of Mendel's work, instances were found in which such complete independence was not observed. As an example, we may consider some experimental data collected by the American geneticist C. B. Bridges, a member of the laboratory of the Nobel prize winner T. H. Morgan. A fruit fly with purple eyes and vestigial wings (*pr pr vg vg*) was crossed with a normal red-eyed, long-winged fly (*Pr Pr Vg Vg*). All the F_1's (*Pr pr Vg vg*) had red eyes and long wings. When Bridges crossed F_1 females with *pr pr vg vg* males, he obtained the results shown in Table 38-2. Had the genes for

TABLE 38-2   *Results of Test-Cross of F_1 Obtained from Cross of Purple Vestigial with Normal* Drosophila (*Bridges' data*).

CLASS	NUMBERS
Red eyes, long wings	1,339
Red eyes, vestigial wings	151
Purple eyes, long wings	154
Purple eyes, vestigial wings	1,195
Total	2,839

these two characters been distributed independently of each other, there would have been about 709¾ of each class (¼ × 2,839). Plainly, the numbers found depart widely from the numbers expected on an assumption of complete independence. There are too many red-eyed, long-winged flies, and too many purple-eyed, short-winged flies, with corresponding reductions in the other two classes.

Does this mean that there is some sort of affinity, say, between the *Pr* and *Vg* alleles, and between the *pr* and *vg* alleles? This hypothesis is immediately disproved by the following data. A cross was made between *Pr Pr vg vg* and *pr pr Vg Vg*. F_1 females, heterozygous for both pairs of genes, were test-crossed, as before. The results are shown in Table 38-3. In this cross the *Pr* and *vg* alleles seem to have stayed together more than they should, as did the *pr* and *Vg* alleles—a rather different result from the preceding. How can we explain these apparently contradictory findings? Can they be fitted into one conceptual scheme?

The data can be easily explained on the assumption that the gene for eye color (purple or

TABLE 38-3   *Results of Test-Cross of F_1 Obtained from Cross of Purple, Long with Red, Vestigial* (*Bridges' data*).

CLASS	NUMBERS
Red eyes, long wings	157
Red eyes, vestigial wings	965
Purple eyes, long wings	1,067
Purple eyes, vestigial wings	146
Total	2,335

normal) and the gene for wing length (vestigial or normal) occur in the same chromosome. We say that such genes are *linked,* or show **linkage.** We may indicate this fact by enclosing within parentheses alleles that are part of a single chromosome; the mating described in the paragraph above we symbolize thus: (*Pr vg*) (*Pr vg*) × (*pr Vg*) (*pr Vg*). The hybrid produced from these would be (*Pr vg*) (*pr Vg*). We see now the implication of the experimental results. As shown by the test-mating (Table 38-3), the gametes (*Pr vg*) and (*pr Vg*) are the commonest; the gametes (*Pr Vg*) and (*pr vg*) can, on our hypothesis, be produced only if there is an exchange of material between the two homologous chromosomes. We can picture this as a **crossover** in the region between the two genes. There is good evidence that crossovers occur during the stage in meiosis when each kind of chromosome is represented by four strands. As an aid in visualizing the process, Figure 38-1 is presented. In *A* is shown a meiosis without a crossover; in *B,* one with. The cytological details have been greatly simplified.

In the two experiments described above, the average percentage of crossover types is about 12 percent. Experiments with other linked genes give crossover percentages ranging all the way from very close to zero to nearly 50 percent. How can we explain such variation? The simplest assumption is that the probability of a crossover is proportional to the distance between genes on a chromosome. Various lines of evidence indicate that this is substantially true. By carefully determining the crossover values between the various genes, a "chromo-

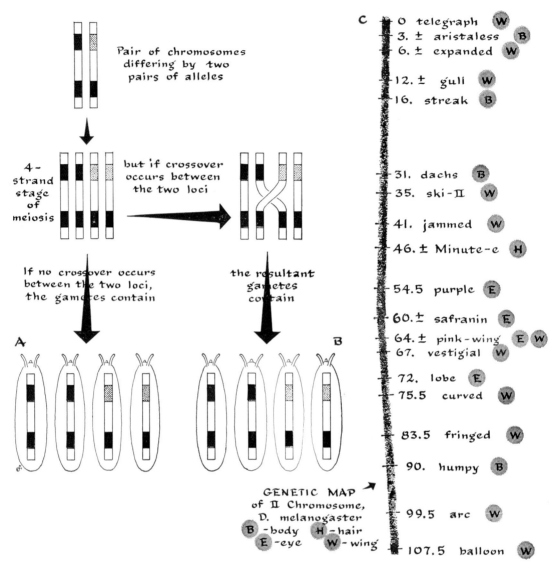

Fig. 38-1. *In the formation of gametes, genes that are in the same chromosome are sometimes assorted independently* (B), *at other times not* (A). *The closer together the genes are, the more frequently they stay together in meiosis. The distances between genes can be deduced from the frequencies of cross-overs. In this way chromosome maps, such as that shown in* C, *are constructed.*

some map" can be constructed; Figure 38-1C shows such a map for chromosome II of *Drosophila melanogaster,* the chromosome that has the genes purple and vestigial. Note that the genes are arranged in single file. All the genes shown constitute a **linkage group,** that is, a group of genes which do not behave with complete independence in meiosis. In *Drosophila* *melanogaster* there are four linkage groups and four pairs of chromosomes; in *Drosophila virilis* there are six linkage groups and six pairs of chromosomes; in peas there are seven of each; in corn, ten. The fact that the number of linkage groups in a species equals the number of *pairs* of chromosomes is additional evidence that genes are parts of chromosomes.

306. The Significance of Sex

There are many organisms that do not reproduce sexually, but only by asexual means involving cell division by mitosis. What is the essential difference between the two types of reproduction in the light of genetics?

Mitosis results in the production of new cells with the exact genotype of the parental cells. Sexual reproduction, involving as it does both meiosis and fusion of gametes, is capable of producing new genotypes. That is, from a cross of *AABB* and *aabb* there will come not only descendants that are like these progenitors, but also the new genotypes *aaBB* and *AAbb*. Of course, sexual reproduction is capable of producing new types only if there is genetic diversity in the progenitors. Sexual reproduction occurring among members of a *really* pure stock (*AABBccDDeeffgg* . . .) has no such effect.

Linkage of genes has only a transient effect in modifying the effect of sexual reproduction. If parental types (*ABC*)(*ABC*) and (*abc*) (*abc*) are crossed, most of the offspring in the F$_2$ will be of one parental type or the other. But there will be a few new types, and these will increase, as the result of additional crossovers, as one generation succeeds another. *In the long run,* even linked genes are distributed independently among the offspring. Linkage merely acts as a sort of friction in the distributing system.

307. Quantitative Variation

Among the problems that did not yield readily to a Mendelian analysis in the early days of genetics were those involving quantitative variation, as seen in such characteristics as weight, length, intelligence, and color. For the most part, the variations in size within a species present us with a continuous series: crosses between individuals of different sizes seldom, either in the first or the second generation, produce a ratio of sizes that is easily recognizable as Mendelian. Nevertheless, inheritance in such quantitative traits may be brought within the conceptual scheme of genetics, as was first

shown by the Swedish geneticist H. Nilsson-Ehle in 1909.

Nilsson-Ehle had two strains of wheat: one with dark-red kernels, the other with white kernels. When these two were crossed, they gave an F$_1$ that was very uniform and of an intermediate shade. The F$_2$ kernels could be sorted out into five color classes, ranging from the dark red of one parental strain to the white of the other. About $\frac{1}{16}$ of the F$_2$ were white, and $\frac{1}{16}$ were dark red. Such results can be easily explained on the assumption that two pairs of alleles are involved, say *A* and *a,* and *B* and *b*; each capital-letter allele gives 1 unit of color to the wheat kernels, and *A* and *B* are indistinguishable phenotypically. The genotypes *AAbb, aaBB,* and *AaBb* all look alike. On such a hypothesis we may work out the expected F$_2$, as shown in Table 38-4. The frequencies expected in each color class (see bottom row) were verified by Nilsson-Ehle. Furthermore, predictions of the results of various breeding tests of the F$_2$

TABLE 38-4 *Quantitative Inheritance with Two Pairs of Cumulative Genes.*

F$_2$ GENOTYPE	COLOR CLASS, AND FREQUENCY EXPECTED IN F$_2$ (1 "CAPITAL-LETTER GENE" = 1 UNIT OF COLOR)				
	4	3	2	1	0
AABB	1/16				
AABb		2/16			
AAbb			1/16		
AaBB		2/16			
AaBb			4/16		
Aabb				2/16	
aaBB			1/16		
aaBb				2/16	
aabb					1/16
Totals, as fraction of F$_2$ population	1/16	4/16	6/16	4/16	1/16

classes were also verified: for example, the white F_2's bred pure, as did also the dark red; when self-fertilized, plants from each of the lightest red grains in F_2 produced $\frac{1}{4}$ white + $\frac{2}{4}$ light red + $\frac{1}{4}$ medium red—and so on. The explanation met all the tests applied to it.

Inheritance in quantitative character may involve more than two pairs of cumulative alleles.

Fig. 38-2. *How variation that is continuous, or nearly so, may be explained in genetic terms. (See text.)*

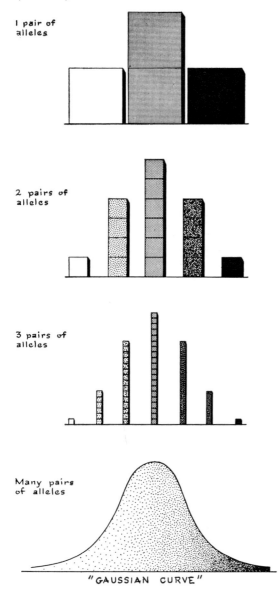

I pair of alleles

2 pairs of alleles

3 pairs of alleles

Many pairs of alleles

"GAUSSIAN CURVE"

In one strain of wheat there have been found three such pairs. In this strain, the frequencies of the seven color classes, as the student may verify by constructing a table similar to Table 38-4, are $\frac{1}{64}$, $\frac{6}{64}$, $\frac{15}{64}$, $\frac{20}{64}$, $\frac{15}{64}$, $\frac{6}{64}$, and $\frac{1}{64}$.

Suppose that many more genes were involved. What would the distribution of classes then look like? In Figure 38-2 are shown the block diagrams **(histograms)** for one pair of alleles, two pairs, and three pairs. According to statistical theory, as the number of pairs of genes becomes large, the histogram approaches a particular smooth, bell-shaped curve shown at the bottom of the figure, a curve known as a **Gaussian curve**—after the German mathematician K. F. Gauss (1777–1855), who first pointed out many of its scientific applications.

It has been found that the theory discussed above has many applications among both plants and animals. It can readily be appreciated that the ease of demonstrating cumulative quantitative genes is inversely related to the number of genes involved. In most cases, environmental factors also affect such characteristics as size and color. If the number of genes affecting one of these characteristics is large, the number of genetic classes is large, and the differences between the classes are small and consequently likely to be confounded by variations brought about by environmental differences. As a result, when a preliminary genetic analysis indicates that three or more genes are responsible for quantitative differences, the geneticist seldom considers it worth the effort to prove completely the Mendelian nature of the genetic factors. In fact, agricultural geneticists working with such quantitative characteristics as weight, height, and fertility, plan their research mostly on the basis of theory that would serve equally well for the idea of blending inheritance (§285). They do not for a moment believe in the outmoded blending theory, but mathematical methods based on the idea of continuous variation are quite useful when many pairs of genes affect a single characteristic, and when the effects of these genes are further confounded by subtle environmental variations.

308. Beyond the F₂

Why, it may be asked, in approaching genetic problems by the Mendelian path, do we speak of the F_1 and F_2 generations, but seldom of the F_3? To answer this question let us work through a particular example.

Suppose we take the gene called "miniature" in fruit flies. The symbol for this allele is *m*. The wild-type fly, with long wings, is of the genotype *MM*. *M* is dominant to *m*. Without determining the facts we will assume that all three genotypes are equally competent to survive and breed in the environment at hand. This is an important assumption, essential to our theoretical approach. Obviously a lethal gene would be progressively reduced in frequency in the population, as one generation succeeded another. A semilethal would also be progressively reduced in frequency, though at a slower rate. More generally, any disadvantageous al-

1,250 *MM* flies produce 2,500 *M* gametes and   0 *m* gametes
2,500 *Mm* flies produce 2,500 *M* gametes and 2,500 *m* gametes
1,250 *mm* flies produce   0 *M* gametes and 2,500 *m* gametes
            TOTALS   5,000 *M* gametes and 5,000 *m* gametes

lele is subject to the force of natural selection. In developing the theory of **population genetics** we will first ask about the hereditary behavior of a pair of alleles that are, by hypothesis, of equal selective value. We will assume that *M* and *m* are such.

Suppose we cross one wild-type fly to a miniature fly and save all the offspring, while keeping the generations separate. We would expect results like these:

Parents   1 *MM*   1 *mm*
F_1 100 *Mm*   (mated among themselves)
F_2 1,250 *MM*   2,500 *Mm*   1,250 *mm*
F_3 ?

What will the F_3 be like? Plainly, we are up against a more difficult problem, because there are three different genotypes in the F_2, and we don't know which will mate with which. However, we do not need to know. By our assumption of no forces operating on the population, we assume that there is no preference of one kind of fly for another. Preference would

amount to a force. If there is no preference, **mating is at random.**

Our initial abstraction of no forces operating on the population implies a further assumption: all flies produce the same number of gametes, that is, all genotypes are equally fertile. If all flies produce the same number of gametes, and all matings are at random, then, we may say that the coming together of gametes is also at random, with the restriction that a sperm can unite only with an egg and vice versa. Therefore, to know the probability of two specified types of gametes coming together, we need only know their relative frequency. That is now to be determined.

Since, by hypothesis, all flies produce the same number of gametes, we shall assume, for simplicity, that each fly produces exactly two gametes. Every gamete is either *M* or *m*. What is the relative frequency of the two types? We count them up:

In other words, one-half of the gametes are *M* and one-half are *m*.

What will happen if these gametes, in these relative frequencies, mate at random? We may, for convenience in visualizing the situation, imagine that we have two gene pools, one of male gametes, half of which are *M*, the other half being *m*; and the other are female gametes, half *M*, half *m*. A zygote is formed when we draw one gamete from each pool.

What is the probability of drawing gametes that will produce an *MM* zygote? This is the probability of drawing an *M* gamete from one pool ($=\frac{1}{2}$); *multiplied by* (recall the Product Rule, §303) the probability of drawing an *M* from the other pool ($=\frac{1}{2}$); that is, $\frac{1}{2} \times \frac{1}{2} = \frac{1}{4}$. Therefore, $\frac{1}{4}$ of the offspring in the next generation will be *MM*.

By similar reasoning, ¼ will be *mm*.

What of the heterozygotes, *Mm*? Here we must consider two different cases:

a. probability of *M* sperm (½) multiplied by probability of *m* egg (½); or ½ × ½ = ¼
b. probability of *m* sperm (½) multiplied by probability of *M* egg (½); or ½ × ½ = ¼

Since either event will result in *Mm* zygote, we *add* their probabilities, getting ¼ + ¼ = ½.

The constitution of the F₃ generation will, therefore, be:

$$¼MM + ½Mm + ¼mm$$

Notice that *the constitution of the F₃ generation is the same as that of the F₂*. Obviously, the F₄ will again be the same, and so on indefinitely. In each generation, one-half of the genes will be *M* and one-half will be *m*. In other words, **in the absence of selective forces, the gene frequency will remain the same indefinitely.** This principle is called the **Hardy-Weinberg Law.** It is named for the English mathematician G. H. Hardy and the German physician W. Weinberg; in 1908 these men independently discovered the principle.

309. Calculating Gene Frequencies

The method used above for calculating the frequency of genotypes was rather extended. The calculations can be put in more compact form.

$$\underbrace{(½M + ½m)}_{\text{♂ gametes}} \times \underbrace{(½M + ½m)}_{\text{♀ gametes}}$$

$$= \underbrace{¼MM + ½Mm + ¼mm}_{\text{zygotes}} \quad (1)$$

Or, since both "gene pools" are the same:

$$(½M + ½m)^2 = (½)(½)MM + (2)(½)(½)Mm$$
$$+ (½)(½)mm$$
$$= ¼MM + ½Mm + ¼mm \quad (2)$$

With this simpler way of setting up the problem, we are on the road to finding an attack that will solve more general problems. Suppose

we have a large population of equally fertile flies that show no mating preferences, etc., etc., a population in which the relative frequency of *A* genes is .1 and of *a* genes is .9. What will be the relative frequencies of the various genotypes in the next generation? Reasoning as before, we write:

$$(.1A + .9a)^2$$
$$= (.1)(.1)AA + (2)(.1)(.9)Aa + (.9)(.9)aa$$
$$= .01AA + .18Aa + .81aa \quad (3)$$

This is straightforward enough. Now let us generalize the method of attack by asking: What will be the frequency of the various genotypes if the relative frequency of *A* is *p* and of *a* is *q*, where p + q = 1? (The digit 1 represents totality.) By the same method, we get:

$$(pA + qa)^2 = p^2AA + 2pqAa + q^2aa \quad (4)$$

This is the Hardy-Weinberg Law stated in general mathematical terms. It may seem a colorless and uninteresting generalization, but with it we can do some useful things. Suppose *A* is dominant to *a*. We cannot tell *AA* individuals from *Aa* individuals phenotypically. Phenotypically, the population is divided into two different groups: the group of *aa* organisms and another group that we may symbolize by writing *A—*, where the dash stands for an unknown gene.

Suppose, in a particular case, that the frequency of *A—* is .19 and of *aa* is .81. What are the frequencies of the two genes? We cannot readily calculate them from the frequency (.19) of *A—*, because this is a mixed group, being composed of both *AA* and *Aa* individuals. But we can easily calculate the frequency of *a* from the frequency (.81) of *aa*. By equation (4), the frequency of *aa* is q^2. The frequency of *a* is *q* $(= \sqrt{q^2})$. In our particular case, q = $\sqrt{q^2}$ = $\sqrt{.81}$ = .9. By way of a check, we know this is right because this is what we started with in equation (3).

As a concrete example of the application of the Hardy-Weinberg Law, let us consider the distribution of the alleles for tasting (*T*) or not tasting (*t*) the substance PTC (§292). In a particular sample of some 3,600 U.S. citizens,

seventy percent could taste PTC and thirty percent could not. That is, the observed frequency of $T-$ was .70, of tt was .30. What is the frequency of the two genes in that population? It should be clear that we must make our calculation from the second of the two figures, thus:

$$\text{Frequency of } t = \sqrt{\text{Freq. of } tt}$$
$$= \sqrt{.30} \cong .55 \qquad (5)$$
$$p + q = 1 \text{ (definition)} \qquad (6)$$

Hence, by difference,

$$\text{frequency of } T = 1 - .55 = .45 \qquad (7)$$

With this result, we are now in a position to calculate the relative frequencies of the three genotypes in our population, using the Hardy-Weinberg Law, equation (4).

$$(.45T + .55t)^2 \cong .2TT + .5Tt + .3tt \qquad (8)$$

With this result, we could answer a question such as the following: A woman is a nontaster. Assuming that the ability to taste does not influence her choice of a mate, what is the probability that at least some of her children will be like their mother?

The children will be like their mother only if her husband is either: Tt or tt. The probability of her mate being the former is .5; of being the latter is .3. Since *either* will result in some children like their mother, the probability that some of the children will be like their mother is $.5 + .3 = .8$.

Notice that, in solving this problem, we have assumed a large number of children. If the woman has only a small number of children, in a mating with a Tt man, *by chance* it might happen that none of the children would be like their mother. This chance can be calculated, but doing so would take us too far into the realm of mathematics for our present purposes.

Questions and Problems

38-1. Make a list of the **boldface** terms in this chapter. Write a brief definition or description of each. Compare your work with the text.

(*Note:* In the following problems assume that coins and dice are without bias and are properly thrown; and that the probability of male births is exactly equal to the probability of female births.)

38-2. A man flips a coin 10 times, obtaining 5 heads and 5 tails. What is the probability that the eleventh flip will produce heads?

38-3. A man flips a coin ten times, obtaining 10 heads. What is the probability that the eleventh flip will produce tails?

‡38-4. Those who would answer questions 38-3 by saying that the probability of a change in results is greater than ½ are victims of the "gambler's fallacy." Explain the fallacy involved in such an answer.

38-5. A married couple with one child are expecting to have a second. What is the probability that it will be a boy? Will knowledge of the sex of the first child influence us in answering the question?

‡38-6. The ten children in a family are all boys. What is the probability that the eleventh will be a girl?

38-7. Student R says that the answer to question 38-6 is some number greater than ½. In the light of the facts of meiosis and of those associated with fertilization, write a brief rebuttal of R, showing him the implications of his answer.

‡38-8. Two dice are thrown at once. What is the probability that both will turn up a 6?

38-9. One die is blue, the other is red. The two dice are thrown at once. What is the probability that the blue die will turn 6, while the red die will turn 5?

‡38-10. Two indistinguishable dice are thrown at once. What is the probability that one of the dice will turn 6 and the other 5?

‡38-11. In a certain city the frequency of albinos is 1 in 1,000. Albinism is due to a recessive autosomal gene. A name is picked at random from the city directory. What is the probability that it will be the name of (a) an albino female, (b) an albino male, (c) a non-albino male?

38-12. Some individuals whose only known ancestors are Norwegian have hair that resembles tightly curled sheep's wool. Such "woolly hair" is due to an autosomal dominant gene that is not on the same chromosome as the albino gene.

A woolly-haired albino, only one of whose parents was woolly-haired, marries a straight-haired woman who is heterozygous for albinism. What is the probability that a child of theirs will be (a) woolly-haired, (b) albino, (c) woolly-haired and albino, (d) a woolly-haired albino girl?

‡38-13. Both a man and his wife are heterozygous for both the albino gene and the woolly-haired gene. What is the probability that a child of theirs will be (a) woolly-haired, (b) albino, (c) woolly-haired and albino, (d) a woolly-haired albino girl?

38-14. How many small squares are there in the Punnett square that shows the results of mating Aa with Aa?

‡38-15. How many small squares are there in the Punnett square that shows the results of mating:
a. $GgHh$ with $GgHh$?
b. $GgHhIi$ with $GgHhIi$?
c. $GgHhIiKk$ with $GgHhIiKk$?
d. Two individuals both of whom are heterozygous for n pairs of genes?

38-16. What are the relative advantages and disadvantages of predicting offspring by Punnett square and algebraic methods? Discuss critically.

38-17. How many different kinds of gametes can be produced by individuals of each of the following genotypes:
a. GG?
b. Gg?
c. $GgHh$?
d. $GgHhIi$?
e. $GgHhIiKKLLMMNNooppQQ$?

f. An individual heterozygous for n pairs of genes?
g. An individual heterozygous for n pairs of genes, and homozygous for m pairs of genes?

‡38-18. What do we mean when we say, "The genotype of this individual is Gg"?

38-19. Consider the following two questions:
Question A: How many different kinds of gametes may be produced by an individual of genotype $GgHhIi$?
Question B: What are the relative frequencies of the different kinds of gametes produced by an individual of genotype $GgHhIi$?
In answering either of these questions does one need to know if the genes in question are linked? If so, which question? Make the reasons for your answer clear.

‡38-20. In *Drosophila melanogaster,* chromosome II bears the genes black, purple, vestigial, and speck. Chromosome III includes the genes roughoid, sepia, hairy, and scarlet. Suppose that a female heterozygous for two gene pairs is mated with a male homozygous for the recessive alleles of both pairs. From which of the following females would you expect the offspring to be nearly equally divided among the four possible genotypes? Explain.

The female is heterozygous for (a) black and purple, (b) black and hairy, (c) speck and scarlet, (d) hairy and scarlet, (e) sepia and vestigial.

38-21. In many fruit trees it is possible for the nurseryman to bring about reproduction or propagation either sexually (by seeds) or asexually (by grafts of somatic tissues onto other tree stocks). In which type of propagation is (a) meiosis necessarily involved, (b) mitosis involved, (c) fertilization involved?

‡38-22. A nurseryman, after sexually crossing many different strains of apple trees, obtains one tree that produces superlative apples. He wishes to sell trees of this new type. To increase his supply of this type, should he propagate it sexually or asexually? Explain.

38-23. An experiment station has loquat trees of many different pure strains, none of which is deemed to be of much commercial value. In

an attempt to find a superior loquat, should the staff members propagate the trees sexually or asexually? Explain.

‡38-24. There are two pure lines of plants: one tall (60 cm) and one short (40 cm). When these are crossed, the F_1 plants are rather uniformly 50 cm in height. Of the F_2, about ¼ are 40 cm high, ½ are 50 cm high, and the remainder are 60 cm in height. Give a genetic explanation of these facts.

38-25. There are two pure lines of plants: one tall and one short. In the F_2 of a cross of these two lines, about ¹⁄₁₆ of the plants are as tall as the tall parental type. Suggest a simple genetic explanation.

‡38-26. On the basis of the answer given to question 38-25, how many height classes would you expect in the F_2?

38-27. There are two pure lines of plants: one tall and one short. In the F_2 of a cross of these two lines, approximately 7 percent of the plants are as tall as the tall parental type. Suggest a simple genetic explanation. How many pairs of genes seem to be involved?

‡38-28. There are two pure lines of plants: one tall and one short. In the F_2 of a cross of these two lines, slightly less than 2 percent of the offspring are as tall as the tall parent. Assuming a genetic explanation of the sort worked out by Nilsson-Ehle, how many pairs of genes are involved?

38-29. In question 38-28, how many height classes would you expect in the F_2?

38-30. Many geneticists believe that instances of quantitative variation often have a genetic basis like that proposed by Nilsson-Ehle for wheat, but perhaps involving more than two pairs of genes. But, to date, few instances involving more than two pairs of genes have been successfully demonstrated. *Assuming* that often many pairs of genes are so operating, can you suggest reasons for our failure to demonstrate ("prove") the existence of the genes?

‡38-31. In a certain city the frequency of red-green color blindness among men is 1 in 11. A name is picked at random from the city directory. What is the probability that it will be:

a. A male?
b. A male who is color-blind?
c. A female?
d. A female who is color-blind?

‡38-32. Suppose student Q answers question 38-31d as follows: "The probability of color blindness is ¹⁄₁₁; the probability of a female is ½; therefore, the probability of a female who is color-blind is ¹⁄₁₁ × ½ = ¹⁄₂₂." Explain Q's error.

38-33. Suppose, in Prob. 38-31, that the telephone directory had been consulted instead of the city directory: would this have made any difference in the answers? Explain.

38-34. Brachydactyly (abnormally short fingers) is a dominant trait. In the early days of genetics, a distinguished statistician remarked that, because brachydactyly was dominant, "in the course of time one would expect, in the absence of counteracting factors, to get three brachydactylous persons to one normal." Criticize this statement.

‡38-35. Suppose that, in a given population, 64 percent of the people are "tasters" and 36 percent are nontasters. Which gene is the more common, the gene for tasting or its allele?

38-36. An island is newly populated with 1,000 individuals of genotype AA and 1,000 of genotype aa. Assume that each group consists of equal numbers of males and females. Assume that mating is at random. Assume that there are no selective differences among the genotypes. When equilibrium has been achieved, what will be: (a) the frequencies of the genotypes? (b) the gene frequencies?

‡38-37. Assume all conditions are the same as given in the preceding problem, except that the initial population consists of 1,000 individuals of genotype AA and only 100 of genotype aa. When equilibrium has been achieved, what will be: (a) the frequencies of the genotypes? (b) the gene frequencies?

‡38-38. Assume all conditions the same as in the preceding problem, except that the initial population consists of 1,000 of genotype AA, *all female*; plus 100 of genotype aa, *all male*. When equilibrium has been achieved, what will be: (a) the frequencies of the genotypes? (b) the gene frequencies?

38-39. Animal breeders traditionally have paid more attention to the selection of the males of the breeding stock than they have to the females. Is there a rational defense for this attitude? Explain.

38-40. Whatever may have been recent practice, in older days it was the rule of warfare that "to the victor belonged the spoils." Men of the conquered group were often nearly exterminated, and the women were appropriated to the uses of the victorious men. What would be the probable genetic consequences of this type of warfare?

‡38-41. If the Amazons really existed, and if they behaved in warfare in about the same way as other ancient peoples (correcting for their sex), what were the genetic consequences of war for them and their defeated foes?

38-42. If Plato had had H. G. Wells' "Time Machine," and using this had become acquainted with Darwin's and Norbert Wiener's ideas, he no doubt would have said, "Now I understand why Amazons, be they ever so powerful, never can conquer the world permanently." Explain the meaning of this remark in cybernetic terms.

Readings

The classic paper of Hardy may be found in Peters; that of Weinberg, in Boyer. Chapters 11 and 12 of Cohen recount the story of the development of hybrid corn in such a way as to throw important light on the relationships of pure and applied science, and on the social and intellectual factors involved in the advancement of knowledge.

For a further introduction to the study of probability, Chapter 7 of Kasner and Newman is recommended: it describes many surprising applications of this field of study.

The application of population genetics to human problems is well treated in Stern. In addition, the following books are valuable references for this field: Burdette's *Methodology in Human Genetics,* Li's *Human Genetics,* and Neel and Schull's *Human Heredity.*

39

Development as a Genetic Problem

310. The Circuitousness of Development

An organism is not merely its final, adult form: it is all the stages that lead to it. We usually name genes from some final effect; but we know that each gene causes a great complex of effects at various levels of analysis and stages of development. The goal of genetic explanation will not be complete until we succeed in showing the role of genes at every stage of development. At present, we have made scarcely a dent in this problem. This chapter is inserted here not so much to show what we know about the interrelationships of genetics and embryology as to exhibit the magnitude of our ignorance. The embryological facts here described are almost wholly without genetic explanation—yet. Therein lies a great opportunity for future scientists.

The development of an organism is not a straight-line process. What it is to become is by no means obvious from the start. Indeed, an organism may develop first into a self-sufficient being of quite a different sort from its final form. Everyone knows the story of the tadpole and the frog (Fig. 39-1A). For an organism that "intends" (!) to become a frog, becoming first a tadpole seems a strange procedure.

Development, in whatever organism we study, seems to take a circuitous route. To get a quick view of a not unusual example of development, notice (Fig. 39-1B) the development of a frog, which we select because its development takes place in a pond (or a laboratory dish) where we can watch it easily.

We begin with the fertilized egg or zygote. Within four hours after fertilization, the zygote has taken the first step toward adulthood: it has become divided into two cells by a plane passing vertically through its middle. In another hour, another vertical plane, at right angles to the first, has divided the two into four cells. An hour later, division in a third plane, at right angles to the first two, produces eight cells. After a few more divisions, there are too many cells to be readily counted, and we speak of the egg as being in the **late cleavage** stage. At this point we interrupt our survey of the external view of development to look inside the developing ball of cells (Fig. 39-2). After many cell divisions a cavity develops inside the ball of cells. At this stage the embryo is called a **blastula** (Gr. *blastos* = germ, bud), the cavity being the **blastocoele** (Gr. *koilos* = hollow). Somewhat later, there develops an **invagination** (a pushing in) of cells from the outside layer (Fig. 39-2B) to form a cavity called the **archenteron** ("primitive gut"). The opening of this cavity to the exterior is called the **blastopore.** At this stage, the embryo is spoken of as a **gastrula.**

If a late gastrula stage is sliced in the proper plane, there will be seen three layers of cells (Fig. 39-2D), named (from the outside inward) ectoderm, mesoderm, and endoderm. By following the history of these **embryonic germ layers** carefully, embryologists have learned that each gives rise to specific structures in the adult body. The embryonic **ectoderm** (Gr. *ectos* = outside + *derma* = skin) gives rise to these (and other) adult structures: the epidermal layer of the skin; the hair; the nails; the sweat glands; the lens of the eye; and, perhaps rather surprisingly, the entire nervous system. Embryonic **endoderm** (Gr. *endon* = within) produces the lining of the entire digestive tract, and of the breathing passages; the liver, and the pancreas. The embryonic **mesoderm** (Gr. *mesos* = middle) produces bones and other

Fig. 39-1. *The circuitous way a multicellular organism has of developing from an egg to an adult. Amphibia are taken as particular examples.*

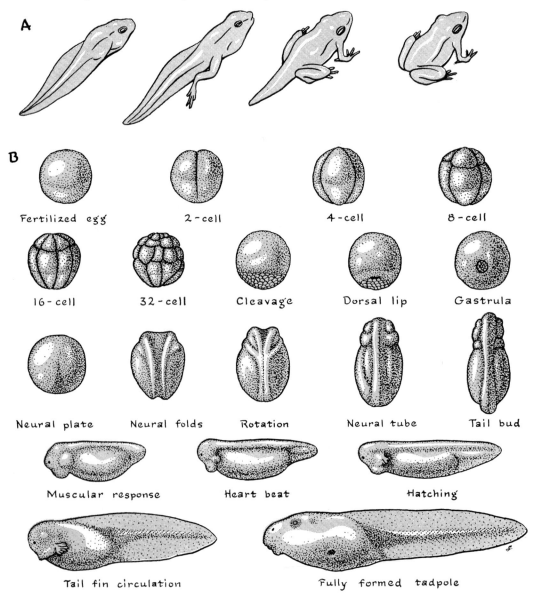

RANA PIPIENS

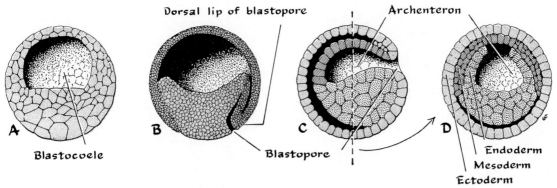

Fig. 39-2. *Some early stages of amphibian embryology.*

connective tissues; muscles; the dermal layer of the skin (lying beneath the epidermal layer); blood vessels; and the gonads.

To return to the developmental stages shown in Figure 39-1, shortly after the gastrula stage, ridges called **neural folds** appear in the epidermis. These ridges move toward each other and fuse to form a hollow tube. This hollow tube, made of ectoderm, is the **neural tube,** which later differentiates to become the nervous system. During the same period, other changes take place, producing a being that definitely resembles a tadpole. During these stages, the developing embryo is surrounded by a transparent coat of jelly (not shown in the figures). Presently, the animal breaks through the jelly and starts to swim around, though even at the time of hatching it is not a completely formed tadpole. It is blind because its cornea is not yet transparent, and the circulation in its tail is still to be established. These and other deficiencies are remedied within a few days after hatching.

311. The Mechanical Factors in Development

Development includes both growth and differentiation. From a single cell—the zygote—arise many different kinds of cells and different kinds of structures. What are the forces that bring about differentiation in the embryo? This question may be regarded as the subject matter of analytical embryology. Hardly more than a beginning has been made in answering it.

As has been made clear in the discussion of the embryonic germ layers, we can, with considerable precision, predict the fate of various parts of an embryo. How early in development is certain prediction possible? Are the parts of an embryo subject to a sort of predestination? We shall illustrate some of the difficulties met in attacking this general problem by considering first an embryo in the two-cell stage. Each of these cells normally gives rise to one side of the embryo, as indicated in Figure 39-3A, B. Does this mean that each of these two cells is capable of producing only one-half of an embryo?

The first experiment designed to answer this question seemed to give an affirmative answer. The experimenter killed the left of the two cells with a hot needle (Fig. 39-3C). The right cell then developed into an embryonic right half only. (Ultimately, this half also died, probably because of toxic substances coming from the dead "protoplasm" in the left; but this is a matter of secondary importance.)

The correct interpretation of these observations was given by the German embryologist Hans Spemann. With a fine hair, he constricted the egg, jelly and all, in the plane of the separation between the two cells (Fig. 39-3E), causing them to separate. Each cell developed into a completely normal, though half-sized tadpole.

How can we reconcile the difference in re-

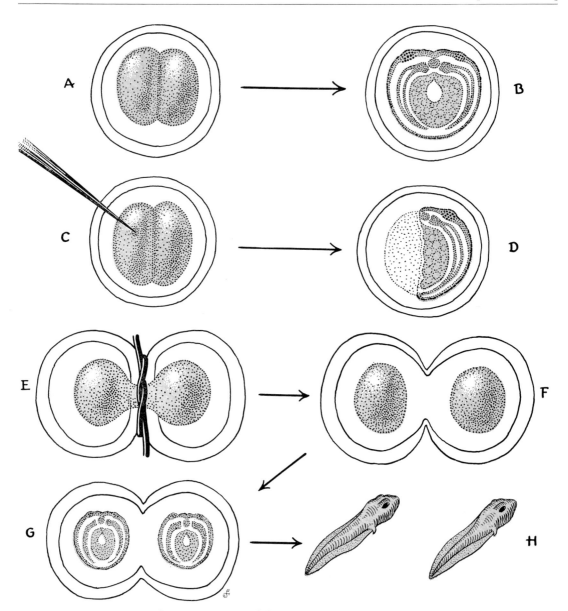

Fig. 39-3. (A) *The two-cell stage of an amphibian.* (B) *Cross-section of a later stage; each cell has developed into a half embryo. If one cell at the two-cell stage is killed with a needle* (C), *the other cell develops into only half an embryo* (D). *But if two living cells are completely separated* (E, F) *so that neither interferes with the development of the other, two normal, though diminutive, tadpoles result* (G, H). *These tadpoles are identical twins and have the same genes.*

sults of the two experiments? From Spemann's experiment, we can only conclude that each of the first two cells is capable of forming a complete embryo. We must, then, account for the earlier results. The simplest explanation would seem to be this: The unkilled cell is perfectly capable of developing into a complete embryo, but the dead material (Fig. 39-3D) is in its way. It is prevented by the dead "protoplasm" from developing into the left half of an embryo, just as it is normally prevented from doing so by the living left half-embryo abutting it.

From experiments like these comes the general principle: *What any cell or tissue does at any moment in embryological development is determined by two factors: its own capabilities, and the influence of the tissues around it.* The influence of the surrounding tissues in the present example seems to be merely a mechanical one.

Before going on, some sidelights may be pointed out. Since both of the tadpoles produced by the constriction experiment (Fig. 39-3E–H) come from the same zygote, they must have the same genes; hence—if their environment is the same—they should develop into indistinguishable adults. They do. This experiment gives a clue to the origin of identical twins in humans. Because of the inaccessibility of human embryos, we well may never *know* what happens

to produce identical twins. But, it is very reasonable to assume that, in the early stages of embryonic development, perhaps in the two-cell stage, the embryo, for unknown reasons, separates into two cells, or two halves, each of which then develops into a normal child, both with the same genotype.

312. The Chemical Factors in Development

Differentiation of a tissue depends on its intrinsic ability and its environment. We have seen an example in which the environment exerts an effect that is probably only mechanical. Now we shall give an example of a chemical action of the environment.

The eye, marvelous organ that it is, has a lowly beginning (Fig. 39-4). The first sign of it in the embryo is a thickened tissue lying

Fig. 39-4. (A) *Eye of an adult amphibian.* (B-G) *Induction of lens by the developing eye-cup during embryogeny.*

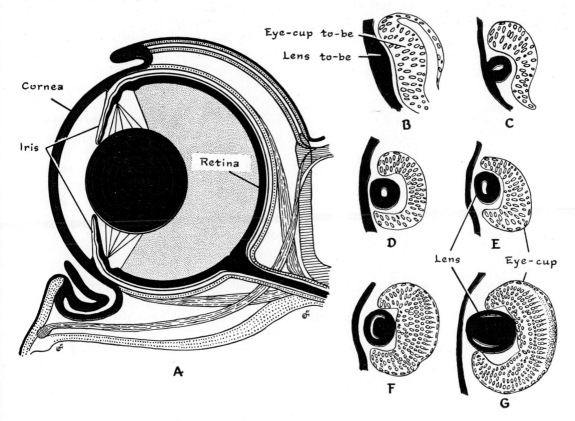

under the epidermis in the head region of the developing animal (Fig. 39-4*B*). This thickened tissue bends inward in the middle, as it grows, to form an eyecup (Fig. 39-4*G*), which, in the adult, will include the retina and underlying structures. As this process is going on, the epidermis just outside the developing eyecup thickens and pinches off a ball of cells that moves inward and forms the lens of the eye. What makes the epidermis behave so? There appear to be no mechanical forces in the embryo causing this effect. In the early stages, there is no contact between the eyecup and the epidermis. The simplest hypothesis is a chemical one: The eyecup produces a stimulating substance that passes to the overlying epidermis. Though no such substance has yet been isolated, all the evidence fits this hypothesis.

If the eyecup produces a chemical that can cause epidermis to form a lens, it should be possible to use a detached eyecup to induce lens formation from epidermis that ordinarily would not form a lens. A simple, though delicate, operation proves this to be so. If the eyecup-to-be is detached from its moorings in the head region of the developing tadpole and moved back to the trunk region, as the eyecup develops in the new location, the overlying epidermis thickens and forms a typical lens. This lens will never serve a useful function because the eye, being in the wrong part of the body, will never be properly innervated. Nevertheless, in response to some subtle message from the eyecup, the epidermis is induced to form a lens. Such **induction,** as the process is called, of one structure by a nearby structure or tissue strengthens the hypothesis that a chemical substance is involved.

313. Competence, Induction, and Aging

The detached eyecup need not be transplanted to another part of the same animal; we may transplant it to a different animal. Thus we may bring about the formation of several eyes, though only the original two will be functional. However, it has been found that a transplanted developing eyecup will not always cause the development of a lens. Induction is successful only if the **host** animal (the one receiving the transplant) is of the right age. If it is too old, the **donor** tissue is unable to induce lens formation. We say that the old host tissue is *incompetent* to form a lens—that it has lost its **competence.** What competence consists of we do not know, but, as defined by this sort of experiment, it can be shown to be a characteristic that may be at first absent in a tissue, then present for a period, and then lost for good.

The idea of competence has helped explain, in an embryological way, many abnormalities, or *anomalies,* as well as structural differences between closely related species. We give an example. In every large cave, there may be found blind animals of several different species. These blind cave-forms include crayfish, insects, fishes, lizards, and salamanders. Their blindness is hereditary. What is the reason for it? We could give a glib teleological answer: They don't need to be able to see in the dark. But what is the embryological course of events that leads to their blindness?

Study has shown that different species are blind for different embryological reasons. In some of the fishes and salamanders, blindness results because the epidermis overlying the eyecup is not competent to form a lens at the time the eyecup is formed. Since no lens is formed, no cornea is formed, and the epidermis in this region becomes opaque, as it does in other regions, thus causing blindness. Whether the epidermis is competent earlier and loses its competence, or whether it is never competent, is not known. This sort of situation suggests that normal development involves a nicely integrated complex of *timings*. Merely a slight change in the rate of development of one tissue may throw it out of phase with the rest, with striking consequences in the adult. We see, vaguely at least, why almost any new mutation is harmful to the species, unless, at about the same time, it finds itself in a new environment.

We too often think of development as a process that takes place only before birth or hatching. Actually, of course, development continues after birth, though at a slower rate and with less spectacular results. The same principles could be expected to apply to development on both sides of the arbitrary date line we call the birth date. As an example of how the idea of competence may be used to include postembryonic events, consider the effect of the pituitary gland on growth. The anterior lobe of the pituitary secretes many hormones, at least one of which stimulates the growth of bones and cartilage. If this growth hormone is produced in unusually large amounts during the period of growth, a human of gigantic stature is produced (Fig. 39-5), some **pituitary giants** being fully 9 feet tall.

At the end of the normal period of growth, the long bones lose their ability to grow. Normally at this time, the rate of production of pituitary growth hormone also diminishes. We may say that the tissue (bone) loses its competence at the same time that the inductor (pituitary) nearly stops producing this inductive agent. But a few islands of tissue retain their competence after puberty, for example, the bone-forming tissues of the jaw, hands, and feet, and the cartilage-forming tissue of the nose and ears. Normally, these tissues grow slowly throughout most of the adult life, particularly the nose and ears. If there is a postpubertal flare-up of activity of the inductor (pituitary), all these competent tissues react in a normal way, producing abnormally large jaw, hands, feet, nose, and ears. (Fig. 39-6).

Our first reaction, when we learn about the loss of competence or of inductive capacity, may be: "Too bad; old age is setting in. Something has been lost." But, from the above example, we see how necessary such losses are to normal development. If tissues did not lose their competences and their inductive capacities, growth would be one continuous runaway process leading to the early death of the whole disorganized mass of repetitive and hypertrophied organs and tissues. Only if competences and capacities are lost in a fixed, orderly fashion is a final, definite form possible. Specific morphogenesis is made possible by

Fig. 39-5. *Overactivity of the anterior lobe of the pituitary gland during childhood leads to giants such as this teen-age boy shown with his father, a man of normal size.*

the continuous loss of capacities and competences—by aging, if you will. Since most of these abilities are lost long before birth, it may be said that the process of growing old is nearly completed by the time the law takes cognizance of our existence. The continuous loss of capacities and competences in the years after birth is but a continuation of a process begun long before the natal day. It is not unlikely that old age and death are the inevitable con-

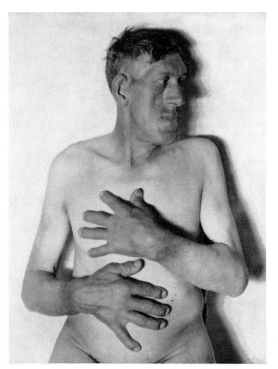

Fig. 39-6. *Acromegaly, a condition due to the production of growth hormone by the pituitary after most of the bones of the body have lost their competence to respond to it. Note the characteristic overlarge hands, jaw, nose, and ears. (From Major,* Physical Diagnosis, *W. B. Saunders Co., Philadelphia.)*

sequences of the development of a complicated morphology.

Before leaving this subject, we want to point out that we have not explained, in physical and chemical terms, what is involved in the possession and loss of "competence." We have merely given a unifying name to a group of phenomena, a name that will be useful only as it focuses our attention on the underlying problems. What, for instance, is the genetic explanation of the loss of competence? Are genes lost during cell division? It seems unlikely, since the somatic cells of an individual have the same chromosomes. It is hard to imagine the chromosomes regularly multiplying and dividing without their constituent genes also doing so. Yet many cells of the body have particular abilities that are not general. How can

genetically identical cells differ in their abilities? This is a major problem of embryological genetics.

314. Sidelight: Cancer

In the nine months before birth, the human body increases two billionfold in mass. In the years after birth, it increases only about twentyfold. By the time we are old enough to vote, most of our tissues have ceased growing (though the adipose connective tissue retains its growing capacity to a sometimes embarrassing degree). Occasionally, however, some other tissue will suddenly reassume its youthful character and start growing at the embryonic rate again. Such a rejuvenated tissue we call a **neoplasm** (Gr. *neos* = new, recent + *plasma* = image, or substance formed). If it is relatively harmless, it is popularly called a **tumor;** if it is harmful, or *malignant,* it is generally called a **cancer.**

The potential seriousness of a neoplasm lies in the fact that it has regained the ability to grow at a juvenile rate. It is precisely because some cells are not "acting their age" that they become potentially dangerous. The more "sedate" cells around them, which have settled down to an almost nonreproductive old age, are at a competitive disadvantage with these indecently rejuvenated cells. The growth of a neoplasm may completely disrupt the activity of the organ it is in. If the organ is a vital one, death may follow. This is the first threat of a neoplasm. Its second threat lies in the danger of **metastasis** (Gr. *meta,* signifying change + *stasis* = placing). After a period of growth in one place, the neoplasm may abruptly release some of its abnormal cells into the circulatory system, to be carried to all parts of the body, lodging in various places and starting new cancerous growths in a dozen or more places. Once a malignant growth has started to metastasize, the prognosis is unfavorable. At least one of the many new loci of growth is almost certain to be in a vital spot.

With respect to growth rate, neoplastic cells

show a reversion to the youthful condition. In other respects, they are something new. They can be recognized microscopically as abnormal cells. Their chromosomes are usually in a state of disrupted confusion—a suggestive point.

What causes cancer? We do not know. Experimentally, we can induce cancers by the application of certain chemical compounds collectively called **carcinogens.*** Among experimental animals, some strains are highly susceptible to the action of carcinogens; others are highly resistant. Strains are also known in which individuals "spontaneously" develop one or another kind of cancer, without known environmental cause. Heredity in such cases has a demonstrable effect, but there are apparently many genes involved, and genetic analysis is difficult. There is now good evidence that at least some animal cancers are caused, or provoked, by particular virus infections. The virus brings with it an abnormal hereditary message that becomes incorporated with the host DNA, thus producing a new, reproducible hereditary message. The practical significance of this new knowledge is not yet clear.

What can the individual do about cancer? *Have it diagnosed early.* A cancer that is not diagnosed until several years have elapsed may

* *Carcinoma* is the technical name for one type of cancer.

already have started metastasizing. Then it is too late. It is important for all people, particularly those past their youth, to have the cause of every persistent pain traced. A *few* persistent pains prove to be due to cancer. It is important to catch these few. An early diagnosis makes possible treatment that has a good probability of eliminating a cancer before metastasis sets in.

In the treatment of cancer, X-rays and high-energy radiations from radioactive elements have proved most useful. Such radiations are dangerous. That they can be used therapeutically is due to the fact that actively multiplying cells are much more susceptible to the lethal action of such radiations than are cells in the interphase stage of mitosis. In an adult, the cells of most of the tissues of the body divide infrequently (some never in the adult, e.g., nerve cells). Neoplastic cells divide rapidly. Therefore, it is frequently possible to destroy a cancerous growth by (1) using a radiation dosage that is carefully calculated to kill the more susceptible cancer cells, while permitting normal cells to survive; and (2) focusing the radiation on the neoplasm, to the exclusion (so far as is possible) of normal tissues. It is easy to see that the adoption of the second measure is out of the question when a cancer has metastasized widely.

Questions and Problems

39-1. Make a list of the **boldface** terms in this chapter. Write a brief definition or description of each. Compare your work with the text.

39-2. Distinguish between *growth* and *differentiation.* What would be the result if a zygote underwent one process and not the other? (Consider both cases.)

‡39-3. In armadillos, four young are produced at a birth: either four males or four females, never a mixture. Suggest a reasonable hypothesis to account for these facts.

39-4. Explain how the *fact* of competence presents biologists with a puzzle.

39-5. Why are most new mutants deleterious to the species? Point out both embryological and genetic factors involved.

39-6. In a very large biology class each student measures the length of his ears as well as that of his parent of the same sex. Although there are variations, statistically speaking the ears of the parents are larger than the ears of the children. From this fact, student J concludes that external ears are in the process of evolving to smaller size. Give another reasonable hypothesis to account for the facts. What observations could be made to critically test your hypothesis?

‡39-7. Examine Figure 39-5 closely. What signs of an overactive pituitary do you see in addition to the over-all size?

‡39-8. Cancer is a rarity among infants and young children, whereas it is not uncommon among the aged. Among forms of cancer in which heredity plays an important part, why would you expect the incidence at various ages to be as described in the preceding sentence?

39-9. How is it possible to kill cancer cells by X-radiation without seriously harming the normal cells that surround them?

39-10. In individuals suffering from *hereditary phenylketonuria,* the following syndrome is found: excretion of chemicals called phenylketones in the urine; intelligence of idiot or imbecile grade; jerky, exaggerated movements; hair lighter than in normal siblings. Are these various characteristics due to (a) linked genes; (b) one gene with one primary effect; (c) one gene with several primary effects? Discuss these possibilities critically, telling how one might make further observations to reach a firm conclusion.

Readings

For many and diverse sidelights on the phenomena of growth, see Chapter 3 of Thompson's *On Growth and Form.* The bearing of the facts of comparative embryology on the theory of evolution is pointed out in de Beer's little book, *Embryos and Ancestors.* Interrelationships of genetic and embryological problems are presented, from a general embryological standpoint in Waddington's *Organisers and Genes;* with a medical perspective in Grüneberg's *Animal Genetics and Medicine.*

Scientific American Offprints

45. C. H. Waddington. *How Do Cells Differentiate?*

94. Michail Fischberg & Antonie W. Blackler. *How Cells Specialize*

95. A. A. Moscona. *How Cells Associate*

103. George W. Gray. *The Organizer*

105. Marcus Singer. *The Regeneration of Body Parts*

Interactions of Heredity and Environment

40

315. Heredity or Environment?

"Which is more important—heredity or environment?" Perhaps no question is more commonly asked of the geneticist by the layman. It looks like a good question: it is couched in proper grammatical form, the meaning of all the words is well known. So there is a widespread belief that the question should be answerable. Before discussing the question further, we shall examine some data bearing on the problem.

In corn (maize) there are many genes that affect the color of the kernels. Some strains of corn are white under all known environmental conditions. Other strains are yellow, purple, red, or some other color. Among the various kinds of red corn there is one that is called "sun-red." Kernels of this variety are white ordinarily, but if the corn-shucks are peeled back exposing the kernels to light for a while, they turn red. Suppose we were asked, "Is redness due to heredity or environment?" How would we answer this question? If we were observing a population of mixed "normal" white and sun-red corn all of the ears of which were exposed to the light, we could conclude that heredity was the determining factor, for (under these conditions) all of the expectations based on the Mendelian scheme would be verified. On the other hand, if we were observing a population of corn plants all of which were homozygous for sun-red, but which grew under varying conditions of exposure, we could conclude that the environment was the determining factor. The only way we can resolve such contradictory conclusions is by stating the generalization that *in the development of any phenotype, both hereditary and environmental factors are involved.* In some cases, we can experimentally demonstrate the importance of both kinds of factors; in others, we can *demonstrate* only one clearly. But, as a procedural matter, it is well to assume this generalization in all cases.

In man and other animals there are a number of instances known in which variations in the expression of a gene are brought about by normal variations in the environment. Many of these, like sun-red in corn, have to do with variations in exposure to light. Various genes are involved in freckling in man, but the extent of the freckling is determined by light. We may say that genes determine whether a person *can* freckle; the environment determines whether susceptible people *will* freckle. Whether one's skin is white, tan, or red is also influenced by both heredity and environment (exposure to sunlight).

In mice it has been found that some strains are subject to "audiogenic seizures"—epileptic-like fits evoked by exposure to the sound of jingling keys, whistles, or bells. Susceptibility to such seizures is clearly gene-determined, though how many genes are involved is not yet known. In one strain of mice, the seizures are so severe that exposure to two minutes' bell-ringing causes death in 90 percent of the mice. Should we say that fits in these mice are due to heredity or environment?

Many pathological conditions in humans clearly show both environmental and hereditary elements. Human epilepsy is sometimes caused by nonhereditary tumors; in other cases there is no apparent structural abnormality of the central nervous system. In these latter, it is possible to detect abnormalities in the electrical rhythms of the brain. Such "irregular brain waves" are found in about 10 percent of the general population. The inheritance of the waves seems to be determined by a simple dominant gene. But of those people who possess the gene, not more than 1 in 20 ever develops epilepsy. Evidently, factors other than this gene are involved—perhaps other genes, certainly environmental factors. Diabetes mellitus shows a similar relationship of heredity and environment—with the environment being largely a matter of diet. Diabetes often fails to develop in genetically diabetic people who eat a diet low in sugars and fats. In populations living on a near-starvation diet, diabetes is almost unknown.

316. The Genetic Environment: The Use of Words

We have previously seen (Chap. 33) that a rigid distinction between organism and environment is not possible. We shall now see that, in genetic matters, it is not possible to distinguish rigidly between genes and *their* environment.

In rabbits there is a gene *B* that produces black-colored rabbits. Rabbits of genotype *bb* are chocolate color. There is another set of alleles, *C* and *c*, that distinguishes beween colored rabbits and albinos: *cc* are albinos. Rabbits of genotypes *B–C–* are black; of *bbC–* are chocolate; and of *BBcc, Bbcc, bbcc* are all albino. Plainly, whether gene *B* will have an effect or not is determined by the presence or absence of another gene, gene *C*. In other words, there is a sense in which one may speak

of the *genetic environment* of a gene. This instance is not exceptional, but on the contrary, is undoubtedly typical. No gene acts alone; every gene acts in concert and in opposition to other genes.

How shall we name gene *B*? Is it a gene "for" blackness? Only if it is in the proper environment. This environment includes both genetic factors (present within the organism) and environmental factors in the ordinary sense (e.g., sunlight in the case of freckling). The use of the preposition "for" is certainly open to objections. It might be taken to imply teleology (recall §245) or at the least a too-simple equivalence of gene name and action. Yet it is difficult to avoid this way of speaking of genes without incurring equal dangers associated with excessive circumlocution. Therefore we will continue to speak of genes as being "genes for" —but the student should not forget the warning.

The word "lethal," as used in genetics, is also subject to qualification. Consider the genes that bring about audiogenic seizures in mice. Under experimental conditions in which the noise level is high, these genes may cause all or nearly all of a given stock to die of fits; the genes might then be said to be lethal genes. Yet, under quiet conditions, the same strain of mice may live as well as other strains that do not have these genes. Plainly, the adjective "lethal" in general implies a particular environment (which may, however, be inescapable). A somewhat different example is furnished by the albino gene in humans. Human albinos are handicapped only slightly (principally by poor vision) as compared with "normal" people. However, among the Lolos of South Africa, according to the anthropologist Lévy-Bruhl, albino children are put to death. In this *social* environment, one might say that the gene for albinism is a lethal gene.

The lethality of a gene is conditioned also by the genetic environment. When St. Bernard dogs are bred with dogs of other breeds, a large proportion of the offspring are born dead, and all of them show signs of an abnormally active pituitary gland. Evidently, the St. Bernard owes its characteristic appearance (huge head, huge paws) to a gene or genes that cause overactivity of the pituitary glands. In the St. Bernard there are other genes ("modifiers") that keep this gene from showing the lethal effects it shows when present in other genetic environments.

317. Twin Studies

"Which is more important—heredity or environment?" It should, by this time, be obvious that this is an unanswerable question. Our inability to answer it is not caused by the imperfection of our knowledge, but rather by the nature of the question itself. Heredity and environment interact in many and devious ways to produce the final phenotypic result. No answer to the *general* question is possible.

Nevertheless, there are *particular* instances in which we may assign more weight to one class of factors or to the other. Whether a child is born an albino or not seems to be purely a matter of heredity; which is to say, the trait is not influenced by the small range of environmental differences present in the human uterus. On the other hand, a man's probability of being struck by lightning is probably independent of heredity. In between these two extremes is a vast array of human characteristics that are determinably affected by both hereditary and environmental factors. For these, one wants some way of evaluating the relative role of the two kinds of influence.

One of the neatest ways of determining the relative importance of heredity and environment is by means of twin studies. Many of the features of human variation in which we are most interested—intelligence, resistance to disease, temperament—are most difficult to study. There are, first of all, difficulties in defining what we wish to study in such a way that it can be measured. Second, there is the undeniable fact that the environment can modify these characteristics greatly, and the environment operates in many and subtle ways. One cannot, for instance, assume that the environment is the same for all the children in a single family; the

first-born, for example, lives in a quite different environment from the last-born. One cannot even assume that twins of the same sex live in precisely the same environment. However, it does seem reasonable to assume that the *differences* in the environment of *fraternal* twins of the same sex must be very nearly the same as the differences in the environment of *identical* twins (of the same sex). Therefore, if, with respect to the trait being studied, fraternal twins of the same sex differ more than do identical twins, it can reasonably be assumed that the larger part of the discrepancy of the two is due to the fact that fraternal twins do not have identical genotypes, whereas identical twins do. In other words, if fraternal twins differ from one another more than identical twins differ from one another, hereditary influences are indicated.

In Table 40-1 are summarized many com-

TABLE 40-1 *Comparison of Differences between Fraternal (Two-Egg) Twins and Identical (One-Egg) Twins. (Data summarized from many authors, as reported in Stern, 1949.)*

CHARACTERISTICS	FRATERNAL TWINS		IDENTICAL TWINS	
	NO. OF PAIRS	PERCENTAGE OF PAIRS IN WHICH TWINS DIFFER	NO. OF PAIRS	PERCENTAGE OF PAIRS IN WHICH TWINS DIFFER
Feeble-mindedness	237	50	202	6
Manic-depressive insanity	84	86	56	16
Schizophrenia	90	89	62	32
"Criminality"	111	66	111	28

parative studies of twins. The material for these studies was gathered by following up the record of each twin who showed the trait in question, determining whether the other twin exhibited the trait, and whether the twins were identical or fraternal. It will be noted that in every instance the difference between fraternal twins is greater than the difference between identical twins. Therefore, heredity is indicated as contributing significantly to the development of feeble-mindedness, manic-depressive insanity, schizophrenia, and "criminality." The fact that identical twins sometimes differ indicates either a difference in the environment of identical twins or inaccuracies in our methods of measurement. Notice that, save in 6 percent of the cases, when one identical twin is classified as feeble-minded, the other is likewise so classified. In "criminality" the agreement is less complete: 28 percent of the twin-pairs differ. This is not surprising if we consider the complex of factors that enter into determining such a classification: temperament, ability, temptation, opportunity, and luck (in being caught and classified, or not).

The literature on twin studies is large. Some of the most significant studies have been made of twins, of both kinds, that have been separated shortly after birth and raised in different environments. In all such cases the resemblance between identicals reared apart is greater than that between fraternals reared apart; for many traits, identicals reared apart resemble each other more closely than do fraternals reared together.

318. Down's Syndrome

One of the more perdurable of the scientific controversies of the first half of the twentieth century was that waged over **mongolism.** This name had been given to a syndrome that includes a Mongolian fold of the eyelids (hence the name), a characteristic texture of the tongue, and (most importantly) idiocy. In the seventh decade of this century, a group of geneticists issued a public statement urging that the name of this abnormality be changed. Their argument was quite simple, and may be paraphrased as follows. Suppose a Japanese geneticist discovered a new hereditary idiocy in which the individual did *not* have a Mongolian fold of the eyelids. Suppose this Japanese scientist, struck by the facial resemblance of these babies to some of his American friends, decided

to name the deformity "americanism": how would we feel about *that?* It is difficult to imagine that we would feel honored. Following the Golden Rule we surely should be willing to abandon the name "mongolism."

It has been proposed that the name **Down's syndrome** be substituted for the affliction, making use of the surname of one of the first men to recognize it as a clinical entity. Whether this new coinage will replace the century-old term remains to be seen. It will be used here. Unfortunately, "Down's syndrome" has no recognized adjectival form (as has "mongolism" in "mongoloid"). To remedy this deficiency, *downic* will here be used when there is need for an adjective.

About 1 child in every 600 is born a downic. Why? For generations, two different answers were given: "environment" and "heredity." The first answer was favored by most medical men, who pointed out that the probability of an affected child increases markedly with increase in the age of the mother (Fig. 40-1). The age of the father is without effect. From these facts it was argued that the abnormality was somehow caused by deficiencies of the aging uterus —an environmental effect.

Geneticists argued for a genetic cause (which perhaps should not surprise us). Ordinary family-pedigree analysis gave little support to this position, but twin studies were quite enlightening. When one member of a pair of fraternal (two-egg) twins is a downic, the other twin is *not.* But identical or one-egg twins are either

Fig. 40-1. *The frequency of Down's syndrome as a function of the age of the mother.*

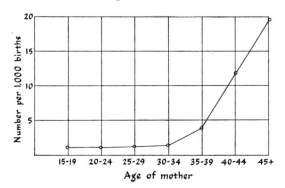

both normal or both downic. Some twins share the same uterus, environment seemed ruled out and a genetic cause indicated.

The situation was so confusing that no less than 39 distinguishable hypotheses were evolved to explain "mongolism." All this Babel of explanations was gratifyingly silenced by the development of human cytogenetics. In 1959 three French scientists, J. Lejeune, R. Turpin, and M. Gautier, reported that downics exhibit a condition known as **trisomy;** that is, one of the kinds of chromosomes is present in a triple dose in the somatic cells, instead of the usual double dose (diploidy). This finding has been amply confirmed by other workers.

How does trisomy come into being? The most probable mechanism is one long known in the genetics of other organisms, an anomaly of meiosis called **nondisjunction.** Normally, in reduction division, each gamete receives only one member of each pair of chromosomes. Sometimes this segregation of homologous chromosomes fails to take place, resulting in one gamete getting two members of one pair, and some other gamete getting none. The union of the first type of gamete with a normal gamete of the opposite sex results in a **trisomic** individual —that is, an individual with three members of one chromosome-type, the other types of chromosomes being present in only the diploid condition. When the second type of abnormal gamete mentioned above (the gamete lacking one chromosome) unites with a normal gamete there is produced a **monosomic** individual.*

Trisomics are abnormal because they have an unbalanced set of genetic instructions. We have previously encountered an example in Klinefelter's syndrome (§299), a case of trisomy of the X-chromosome. The complementary instance of X-monosomy produces the abnormality called Turner's syndrome. The trisomy involved in Down's syndrome is a trisomy of one of the smallest of the human chromosomes, either No. 21 or No. 22 (Fig. 37-1),

usually assumed (for convenience) to be No. 21. Some geneticists avoid the undesirable term "mongoloid" by using the term **21-trisomic;** or more simply, *trisomic,* when the context makes clear what is meant. The complementary monosomic is not known, perhaps because the gamete cannot survive in the complete absence of the information carried in chromosome No. 21. The increase in frequency of nondisjunction with increasing age is a well known genetic phenomenon throughout the living world. The lack of influence of the father's age on the frequency of Down's syndrome is probably attributable to the nonviability of the abnormal sperm produced; the conditions required for the survival and functioning of a tiny, active male gamete may be more severe than those required by the larger, immobile female gamete.

Sufferers from Down's syndrome have notably poor health. Almost half of them die in the first year of their life, some of them from leukemia. The survivors are unusually susceptible to infectious diseases. In the days before antibiotics, most downics died before reaching sexual maturity. Now many survive to adulthood, and a few have even produced children. As of 1961, there were records of 11 downic mothers producing 12 children, by fathers who were genetically, if not ethically, normal. Of these children, 5 were downic and 7 normal.*

That the number of chromosomes is not, *per se,* the important factor in the production of Down's syndrome is shown by another cytological situation found in some affected families. Among the cytological accidents that can occur is the **translocation** of part or all of one chromosome to a nonhomologous chromosome to which it becomes attached. Once the attachment is made, the new chromosome-complex acts like an ordinary chromosome in mitosis and meiosis. Human beings are known in whom

---

* 40-1. After reviewing §58 if need be, draw a series of diagrams illustrating the process of nondisjunction, and fertilization of the products. This should be done before reading further.

---

* 40-2. Diagrammatically indicate the cytology of these matings, giving the mathematical expectations of the various types.

40-3. Is the normal child of a downic mother a poor risk for parenthood? Explain.

40-4. Suppose (Heaven forbid!) two downics should mate and produce many children: what would you expect among the offspring?

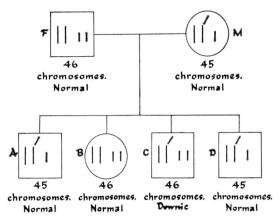

Fig. 40-2. *The genetic constitution of a family in which there is translocation of a No. 21 chromosome. Each individual has another 21 normal pairs of chromosomes, not indicated.*

a No. 21 chromosome has become translocated to a No. 13 chromosome. In Figure 40-2 we see the genetic results in one family in which this translocation occurs. The father is completely normal, with 23 pairs of chromosomes, of which only two pairs are indicated: No. 13 (in black) and No. 21 (in color). The mother's cells have only 45 chromosomes each, but careful cytological examination shows that one of her No. 13 chromosomes has a No. 21 attached to it. The other No. 21 is free in her cells. The marriage of this pair produced the children shown: two normal children with only 45 chromosomes; and two children with the normal number of 46 chromosomes, of whom one suffered from Down's syndrome because he had the information contained in No. 21 chromosome present in the triploid condition. From these results it is clear that it is not the actual number of chromosomes that produces the abnormality, but the extra increase in genetic information, which amounts to about 0.5 percent.

Instances have been found in which other, larger autosomes are present in the trisomic condition, but they are much rarer, and their deleterious effects even worse than those of Down's syndrome. Nondisjunction and translocation may be about equally common for all chromosomes, but the cell is probably not able to tolerate large doses of redundancy (beyond that furnished by ordinary diploidy).

319. Inheritance Not Dependent on Expression

If a strain of corn homozygous for sun-red were grown generation after generation, during which time all the kernels were carefully shielded from the sun, would the ability to turn red on exposure to light be lost in the course of time? The simple answer is *No.* Suppose a strain of rabbits, all of genotype *BBcc* (albino but homozygous for black gene) is maintained for many generations, will the black gene be lost? Again the answer is *No,* as can be shown by crossing such rabbits with a strain homozygous for *C.* Genes (for sun-red, black, or whatever) are passed on from generation to generation by means of mitosis, meiosis, and fertilization without regard to the ultimate action of the hereditary particles. We might say that, from the gene's point of view, how it reveals itself in the phenotype is an accident determined by its interactions with other genes and with environmental factors. Inheritance does not depend on phenotypic expression.

The foregoing point may seem painfully obvious; but its human implications are frequently missed. Although we have not yet succeeded in analyzing the various discrete genetic particles involved, there is no doubt that heredity is a contributing factor in determining resistance to disease. Susceptibility to tuberculosis, tumors, epilepsy, diabetes, and many other human ailments show a tendency to "run in families." How, then, are we to look upon the practice of medicine? The goal of medicine is to eliminate human disease—*by treatment of the phenotype.* It is as though we were to eliminate redness in corn by protecting sun-red strains from light. All practical plant breeders know that the only stable solution to such a problem is to control the breeding of the stock, preventing or discarding offspring of the unwanted types. There are many weighty reasons for hesitating to employ similar measures with humans. As our success with medical measures for the treatment of the phenotype increases from year to year, these reasons gain weight. Yet it must not be forgotten that the solution we achieve by medical means is an unstable one, easily upset by a partial collapse of the civilization on which medicine depends. What practical conclusion should follow from this fact is a matter of debate.

320. Are Acquired Characteristics Inherited?

If a man, by exercise, develops his muscles to an unusual degree, will this development be passed on, even in small part, to his sons? If a man becomes a great scholar, will that fact somehow affect the genetic constitution of his children in such a way that they will be, by nature, more intelligent because of his activities? Are acquired characteristics inherited?

Belief in the inheritance of acquired characteristics is centuries old, and is widespread even today. Yet, to summarize a large body of evidence, the belief is without scientific support. There have been reports—in fact, not a few—of experimental confirmation of the belief. But, without exception, none of these reports has survived critical examination. Repetition of the experiments by independent, competent scientists has always yielded negative evidence. Since the criterion of repeatability (§3) has not been met, the doctrine of the inheritance of acquired characteristics is not scientifically tenable.

In passing, it should be pointed out also that the idea of such inheritance comes in conflict with the broad conceptual scheme of genetics. Look again at Figure 7-1 (p. 000). Note the essential separation of the two streams of tissue: somatic and germinal. *If* there is any inheritance of acquired characteristics, then some sort of influence must bridge the gap between somatic tissues (which are subject to modification by environment and experience) and germ tissues. A hormone, perhaps? But think of the great precision in hormonal action demanded by this unproved hypothesis!

How real the gap is between somatic and germinal tissues in animals has been shown by many experiments in which ovaries have been transplanted from one mother to another of a different genotype. If ovaries from a yellow mouse (recall §297) are transplanted to a normal female (whose own ovaries are removed), and if this mouse is then bred to a normal mouse, half of the offspring are yellow, though neither "parent" has this dominant gene. The ovary, it is clear, breeds true to its genotype, without regard to the genotype of the surrounding tissue. Similar experiments carried out with other animals involving many different genes have, without exception, yielded similar results. The genetic separation of somatic cells and germ cells is real.

321. Mutations and Their Production

Natural mutation is a rare event. Undoubtedly, every gene is capable of mutating, but the rate at which it does so is generally slow. A mutation rate of one per million may be taken as typical. The following explanation illustrates what is meant by the preceding statement. A male rabbit of genotype BB (black) produces millions of sperm. Most of his sperm are B-containing sperm. But an occasional sperm—about one out of a million—will have an allele of B— say, b. Other genes also mutate during the process of sperm formation, independently of the B gene.

Consider the experimental difficulties of finding mutations. In the first place, they are rare. Second, experience has shown that most new mutations are recessive. And how can a geneticist find a recessive mutation if he doesn't know what he is looking for? Finding it will depend on the lucky chance of a mating of two heterozygotes (say, Bb and Bb), which may occur many generations after the initial mutation.

The development of genetics was accelerated when a means was found of speeding up the rate of mutation. In 1927, the American geneticist H. J. Muller (later a Nobel laureate) showed that exposure of fruit flies to X-rays increased mutation rates. A short time later, another American geneticist, L. J. Stadler, found the same effect in corn. The **mutagenic** effect of X-rays has since then been shown to be general. Other **mutagens** have also been found—for example, ultraviolet light and various chemicals including nitrogen mustard—but X-rays remain the most powerful and most useful agent discovered to date.

What sort of mutations are produced by X-rays? In much-studied organisms like *Drosophila* a great variety of mutations, both natural and radiation-induced, have been studied, and it is clear (if we ignore certain minor qualifications) that artificially produced mutations are like the naturally occurring ones. They differ only in that the rate of their appearance is greater.

Of the greatest practical importance is this fact: *Most new mutations are recessive.*

Almost without exception, *new mutations are deleterious to the organism, or at best neutral.* This also is an observational fact. Yet it may seem a strange, even a diabolical, quirk of fate that it should be so. Can we account for it? We can, and by rather simple logic.

Consider *Drosophila melanogaster:* This species has probably been in existence a million years, maybe many millions. Each year millions of millions of flies are produced in the wild. In the millions of millions of gametes that join to produce these flies there must be many new mutant genes. For millions of years this has been so. On the basis of present experience we can only assume that the great majority of the mutations that occurred in the past were "bad." But occasionally, during that time, the mutation process may have produced a new allele that was better for the organism than the old allele of the same gene. Individuals possessing this new allele would have a slight advantage over the other flies in the struggle for existence. They would, consequently, multiply more rapidly than their fellows; as a result, the frequency of the new allele in the population would increase, and presently it would become the more abundant allele of that gene. Such a process of natural selection must have been occurring during all the millennia that *Drosophila melanogaster*

has been in existence. The fruit flies we see today represent the end result of millions of mutational events and selections. They "fit" the environment well. The process of mutation continues to occur, but, since the best of the alleles have already been selected for, we are very unlikely, in a short human lifetime, to find a new allele that is a better one for the fruit flies. Only if the environment of the organism is changed sufficiently to make some new type more "fit" is there an appreciable probability of a "good" mutation. The remarks that have here been applied to *Drosophila* apply to all organisms.

322. Genetic Counseling

An important application of genetic knowledge begins when a married couple has doubts about the wisdom of producing a child. Perhaps they have learned of defective ancestors on one side of the family; or perhaps they have just had the harrowing experience of producing a defective child, and wonder if heredity or environment was at fault. Whatever the reason, they present the problem to their family physician who (it is to be hoped) refers them to a specialist in genetic counseling. What can a genetic counselor tell them?

To begin with, nothing—nothing until he has looked thoroughly into the problem. If the mother has just borne a defective child—and this is the more common reason for seeking counsel—there is the very real possibility that some environmental factor was at the root of the trouble. Some drug that the mother took during the early stages of pregnancy may have damaged the sensitive fetus, producing a **phenocopy** of a known genetic disorder. In the early 1960's in western Europe a sedative called "thalidomide" produced literally thousands of babies with defective limbs before its danger to pregnant mothers was realized. When such an environmental agent is unmasked, the advice to the prospective mother is obvious: don't take the drug during pregnancy.

German measles **(rubella)** is also a great

maimer of children. At least 10 percent of the women who contract rubella during the first three months of pregnancy produce a child that is defective in one way or another—blind, deaf, mentally defective, with a defective heart—the list of possibilities is long and heart-rending. Just what damage is done is dependent on precisely when the virus gets through the placenta and into the embryo. It is the **organ primordium** —the very earliest stage of development of each organ—that is most sensitive to damage by virus or drug.

Since the thalidomide scandal we realize that few of the "safe" drugs have been adequately checked out against the rigorous demands of early pregnancy. Physicians are now much more conservative in prescribing drugs during the first trimester. The widespread and routine use of tranquilizers, sedatives, and other drugs in our prosperous society makes the unplanned pregnancy especially dangerous, since damage may be done before the woman is sure she is pregnant. To the biologist, this is a strong argument for planned parenthood.

Assuming that all known environmental factors have been ruled out, what does the genetic counselor advise a mother who has borne one defective child? The answer depends on the analysis of the particular case, but some of the patterns of counseling can be pointed out in general terms, using what we already know about Down's syndrome for illustrations.

A woman of 30 who has just borne a downic child asks the counselor if it will be safe for her to bear another child. A cytological examination should be made first. If the woman proves to have a chromosomal translocation, then the counselor can tell her that the risk for each child is 50 percent, which is certainly high. If she is not a translocation type, then the probable cause is nondisjunction during oögenesis. The risk of this is a function of age. Looking at Figure 40-1 we see that the risk at age 30 is about 0.1 percent. We should not assume that the risk for a woman who has had a downic child is significantly different from that for a woman who has not; each meiotic accident is, in general, an independent event.

Notice that in discussing this case no explicitly *directive* advice was mentioned. Most counselors will not say, "You should not have another child," but rather (to use the translocation-mother as an example) "If you have any more children, the chance of affliction *for each of them* is 50 percent." A factual statement of this sort is believed by most (but not all) counselors to be the proper one to make, leaving the decision to the parents.

TABLE 40-2 *Approximate Incidence of Selected Congenital Malformations, Showing Increase in Risk for Later Children in a Given Family Once It Is Known That One Child in the Family Has the Defect. (Source: R. C. Anderson & S. C. Reed, 1954.* Journal-Lancet (*Minneapolis*) **74**:175–176.)

MALFORMATION	INCIDENCE IN POPULATION	RISK FIGURE FOR LATER SIBLINGS
All malformations	1 in 65	1 in 20
Central nervous system malformations (35%)		
Anencephalus	1 in 450	1 in 50
Spina bifida	1 in 375	1 in 25
Hydrocephalus	1 in 550	1 in 60
Muscular-skeletal malformations (25%)		
Harelip with or without cleft palate	1 in 1000	1 in 7
Cleft palate alone	1 in 2500	1 in 7
Hyperdactyly	1 in 1200	1 in 2
Syndactyly	1 in 2000	1 in 2
Clubfoot	1 in 1000	1 in 30
Congenital hip dislocation	1 in 1500	1 in 20
Cardiovascular malformations (20%)		
Patent ductus arteriosus	1 in 2500	1 in 50
Genitourinary malformations (6%)		
Hypospadias	1 in 1000	1 in 50 (?)
Gastrointestinal malformations (3%)		
Tracheo-esophageal fistula	1 in 6000	less than 1 in 100
Atresia ani	1 in 5000	less than 1 in 100
Multiple malformations (11%)		

Unlike Down's syndrome, most genetic defects require an inquiry into both sides of the family. Sometimes the inquiry uncovers a well known genetic situation and the counselor can give his answer in terms of a precise probability based on good theory. Unfortunately, in our present stage of ignorance, the underlying genetics is often obscure, and then counsel must be given in terms of crude experience, unilluminated by theory.

Table 40-2 shows the **empiric risk** of various of the commoner congenital abnormalities. The data were gathered from the United States, and the risks deduced might not apply to other populations. The data certainly confound hereditary and environmental influences. The figures in black give the risk of each particular anomaly for any child yet to be born, in the absence of all knowledge about the family. The figures in color give the revised estimate of the risk once it is known that a particular couple has produced one child of the specified type. To take an example: the general risk of a child's being born with a congenital hip dislocation is only 1 in 1500 (black figures), a risk that does not inhibit any woman from breeding. Once a couple has produced one such child, however, the counselor can tell them that the risk *for them* has now increased to 1 in 20 (colored figures) for each birth. This knowledge will influence the decisions of some couples; in any event, they should think about it.

323. Eugenics: A Controversial Possibility

Each human gamete contains a hereditary message composed of some 10^{10} nucleotide pairs. Assuming—and what a gratuitous assumption it is!—that the parent who produced the gamete was without genetic flaw, what is the probability that his gamete, with its 10^{10} nucleotide loci, will be flawless?

For perspective, an analogy may help. This book contains approximately 2×10^6 printed letters in it. These letters were arranged by linotypers who copied the manuscript of the author. Assuming that the author's manuscript was without error—gratuitous assumption!—what is the probability that the copy has no error? If you are a careful reader you know the answer long before you get to this, the last chapter. The probability is, for all practical purposes, zero.

Error in copying the hereditary message is inevitable. Because of the degeneracy of the genetic code (§51), some errors may not matter. There's no profit in talking about errors of this sort, so we will talk only about errors that have translatable differences in developmental meaning. What the frequency of these errors is we don't know, but it is hardly conceivable that even once in a million times would a message 10^{10} units long be replicated without at least one significant error.

Probably most mutational errors are lethal at the very earliest stages. There may be a tremendous wastage of genetic material at the early stages—*but this is a matter of little importance*. A man in his prime produces about 10^8 spermatozoa a day. If we could observe the early stages of the duplication of DNA in his germinal tissue we would probably find that, each day, millions of spermatozoa are never formed because of spoilage in the genetic replication process. But who would weep over the loss of a few million spermatozoa?

Even the DNA messages that are incorporated into viable spermatozoa are far from error-free. From 10 to 25 percent of a man's sperm cells are visibly, obviously defective. Some of the defects may have environmental explanations, but surely not all. Furthermore, it seems a priori reasonable that some important DNA defects may produce no visible change in the spermatozoa. Ova, of course, are subject to similar losses.

Losses continue after the union of sperm and egg. A study made by A. T. Hertig, J. Rock, and E. Adams in 1956 indicated that at least a third of all children conceived are defective and die in the first month or two of prenatal life, most of them so early that the death and expulsion (or resorption) of the embryo occurs before the woman knows that she is pregnant. Of the embryos surviving this early period, another 10 percent are spontaneously aborted at some later time in pregnancy. It is generally held that at least half of these abortuses are genetically defective.

For a complex of reasons that is not easy to specify, it is clear that the later in development the wastage occurs, the more seriously we regard it. Loss of DNA destined for gametes— loss of gametes—loss of zygotes—loss of early embryos—loss of late embryos: this is a series of progressively more important (and less frequent) losses. By the time a child is born, genetic defects have reached the level of emotional importance.

It will be noted in Table 40-2 that the frequency of all congenital defects is given as 1 in 65—that is, 1.5 percent. Other studies give values as high as 4 percent. There are three easily recognizable sources of variation in these figures: (1) How serious must a defect be to be worth listing? (2) At what age is the child classified? (Some inherent defects do not show up until years after birth.) and (3) What population is being studied? (There are statistically significant differences between different racial and ethnic groups.) Whatever the over-all figure, it is usually estimated that about half the defects have genetic causes. That means that between one and two percent of all children born are genetically defective.

Genetic defects are not, strictly speaking, self-eliminating. Elimination is by selection, natural or other. In any nonhuman population the cybernetics of the system is easy to see: natural selection acts as an ever-present negative feedback, correcting for the deviations from the genetic set point produced by mutation. Were it not for the corrective feedback of natural selection, the errors made in replicating DNA generation after generation would accumulate indefinitely.

When subjected to sufficiently sensitive genetic tests, all natural populations prove to have a supply of mutant genes in them. The level of the "mutational load" remains approximately constant from generation to generation. The factors involved in maintaining this constancy are illustrated in *A* of Figure 40-3. The rate of elimination of mutants equals their rate of production by the natural background of cosmic radiation and the natural instability of genes. There is a certain minimum rate of mutation. Corresponding to this, there is at all times a minimum supply of mutant types in the population. Equilibrium exists.

As is well known, man is now embarked on a program of increasing the amount of high-energy radiation impinging on his germ tissue, through increased medical use of X-rays, through the explosion of atomic bombs and the resultant production of "fallout" (radioactive substances coming down from the atmosphere), and through similar effects produced by the peaceful release of atomic energy. The result of all this activity is to increase the mutation rate, thus increasing the supply of mutant types at equilibrium (yet to be reached), as shown in *B* of Figure 40-3.

Man has developed another interesting way of altering the natural equilibrium. By somatic medicine he has learned to restrict the rate of elimination of mutants (*C* of Fig. 40-3). The result again is to increase the supply of mutant types in the population (more people suffering from hemophilia, agammaglobulinemia, diabetes, epileptiform seizures, and so on). If the mutants saved do not breed, the added cost to society is less than if they breed and produce more of their own kind in subsequent generations.

Can man do nothing to improve his genetic condition? Theoretically he can. The elimination of genes by natural selection is only a probability matter. Even in a state of nature, there is an equilibrium supply of deleterious genes. Man could, if he wished, decrease this supply in his own species, by two general means: (1) by restricting further the breeding of homozygous deleterious types, and (2) by identification—by genealogical and sometimes

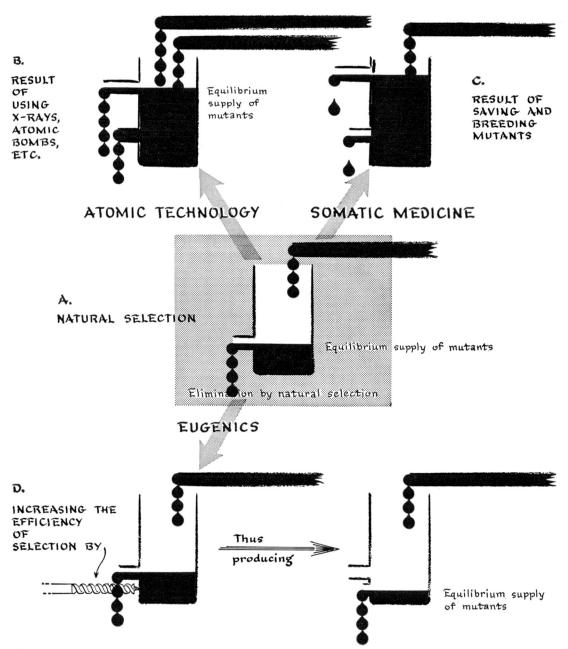

Fig. 40-3. *The effects of man's actions on the genetic burden of* Homo sapiens.

biochemical means—of heterozygotes, followed by restriction of their breeding. The result of such **eugenic** measures would be to lower the supply of mutant types at equilibrium (*D* of Fig. 40-3).

Should man resort to eugenics? The question clearly involves more than biology, since eu-

genic measures (of which there is a wide variety) involve some sort of interference with personal freedom. The interference may be as obvious as a fiat by the state, or as subtle as an appeal to conscience. What means of persuasion or coercion is best employed is a psychological and sociological question of great difficulty. Some may feel that where knowledge is so difficult and action so perilous we should simply do nothing. If this path is open to us, we should certainly take it. Unfortunately, it is not. Let us note here the human implications of the fundamental ecological principle enunciated earlier: *We can never do merely one thing.* When we use medicine to extend the life of the genetically defective of this generation, unless we introduce some control of breeding, we inevitably increase the load of suffering in subsequent generations. If the practices we have unthinkingly drifted into are solidified into unchangeable dogma, then it becomes certain that the suffering of each succeeding generation will be greater, without discernible limit.

On the other hand, if we decide to change our ways, the change itself will bring suffering of another sort. Change in the things that matter is never welcomed with enthusiasm. In ignorance—the ignorance of a child, the ignorance that absorbs the message of the "western" movie as gospel—in ignorance, the ethical choice seems to be between good and evil. With knowledge and wisdom we see that the significant choice is always between one evil and another. Having upset the primeval balance of nature by producing Pasteur and all that his name symbolizes, mankind must now invent new corrective feedbacks to restore the equanimity of life.

Questions and Problems

40-5. Should a genetics counselor give only nondirective advice? Develop as completely as you can both the affirmative and the negative arguments. Compare your analyses with another student's.

‡40-6. At what level of risk of a defective child do you think a couple should refrain from procreating? Explain.

‡40-7. In converting a manuscript to a book, who or what plays the role of natural selection in maintaining the set point of perfect copy?

40-8. Is it essential to the nature of *Homo sapiens* that a man have 46 chromosomes? Explain.

40-9. In the Chinese primrose there is a gene that in the homozygous condition (*ww*) produces redness in the flowers, providing they are grown at 20°C. The allelic dominant gene (*W*) produces white flowers at the same temperature. When the flowers develop at 30°C, they are white, regardless of the genotype. Which is more important—heredity or environment?

40-10. Suppose that you are a nurseryman with a large supply of Chinese primrose seeds in which there are nearly equal numbers of the three genotypes *WW*, *Ww*, and *ww*. Suppose that white flowers bring a very high price, and red flowers are valueless. What can you do to make the maximum amount of money in one year from the product of your mixed batch of seed?

‡40-11. Suppose that you intend to sell white Chinese primrose flowers (see preceding question) for many years. Assume that the fashion in primroses remains constant. Take into account the fact that it costs money to heat the greenhouse in which you raise your flowers. What plan of action should you pursue to make the maximum profit in the long run? Give complete operational details.

‡40-12. How many gene loci are involved in audiogenic seizures in mice is not known, but it is certain that heredity is involved. Suppose that you have a large colony of mice of mixed heredity with respect to audiogenic seizures. You propose to keep the colony for one generation only. You are kind to animals, and wish to spare your charges unnecessary pain and inconvenience. How should you maintain your colony to keep pain and unhealthy reactions at a minimum?

‡40-13. Suppose that, given the initial colony described in the preceding problem, you intend to keep a colony of mice indefinitely. Suppose, further, that the only quarters available to you are fairly noisy, occasionally very much so, and that it is impracticable to diminish the amount of noise. If you wish to have your animals suffer the least *in the long run,* what should be your plan of action? Give full operational details.

40-14. Consider the implications of your answers to the preceding four problems. Would you wish to extend the implications to human affairs? If not, why not? Explain fully.

40-15. Diabetes is a very rare disease among the inhabitants of China. Without assuming the existence of innate differences between Chinese and Occidentals (though, of course, there may be such), can you suggest an explanation for the observed difference in incidence of diabetes in these two populations?

40-16. Human embryos that are spontaneously aborted are almost always dead before they are expelled. The underlying causes of aborted embryos are various. Among experimental animals it is possible to show that genetic factors play a role. Presumably, the same is true in humans. On the *assumption* that the spontaneous abortions in the following instances have a genetic explanation, give a possible explanation of all the facts.

Kate, married to George, has 10 pregnancies, of which 6 end in spontaneous abortions. After having 4 children, Kate and George are divorced. Subsequently, Kate marries Henry, and has 5 pregnancies, producing 5 live children. George remarries, and his new wife, Jane, subsequently has 6 pregnancies, producing 6 live children.

40-17. The surgical removal of some birthmarks is facilitated by X-radiation given in a dosage that is nearly harmless to the individual. Suppose two women, both twenty years of age, have birthmarks of identical size: on the arm of one woman, on the abdomen just below the navel of the other. From a genetic point of view, is X-ray therapy as advisable for one woman as for the other? Explain.

‡40-18. Which came first—the chicken or the egg?

Readings

Chapters 25–27 of Stern give an excellent summary of the heredity and environment problem as it affects humans. In Newman, Freeman, and Holzinger's classic work, *Twins: A Study of Heredity and Environment,* may be found detailed comparisons of human twins reared together versus those reared separately. For a summary of the known and probable genetic effects of high-energy radiations, including those produced by atomic disintegration, consult Schubert and Lapp. S. C. Reed's *Parenthood and Heredity* is a fascinating collection of actual cases in genetic counseling.

Scientific American Offprints

29. H. J. Muller. *Radiation and Human Mutation*

55. James F. Crow. *Ionizing Radiation and Evolution*

BIBLIOGRAPHY

ADRIAN, E. D. 1947. *The Physical Background of Perception.* London: Oxford University Press.

ALLEE, W. C. 1951. *Cooperation Among Animals.* New York: Schuman.

ANDREWS, HENRY N., JR. 1947. *Ancient Plants and the World They Lived In.* Ithaca, N.Y.: Comstock.

ARMSTRONG, EDWARD A. 1947. *Bird Display and Bird Behavior.* New York: Oxford University Press.

BAKER, HERBERT G. 1965. *Plants and Civilization.* Belmont, California: Wadsworth.

BAKER, JOHN R. 1948–1953. "The Cell Theory: A Restatement, History and Critique." *Quarterly J. Micro. Sci.,* **89:**103–125; **90:**87–108; **93:**167–190; **94:**407–440.

BATES, MARSTON. 1949. *The Natural History of Mosquitoes.* New York: Macmillan.

BEACH, FRANK A. 1947. *Hormones and Behavior.* New York: Paul B. Hoeber.

DE BEER, G. R. 1940. *Embryos and Ancestors.* London: Oxford University Press.

———. 1964. *Charles Darwin.* Garden City, N.Y.: Doubleday.

BENEDICT, RUTH. 1934. *Patterns of Culture.* Boston: Houghton Mifflin.

BERRILL, N. J. 1953. *Sex and the Nature of Things.* New York: Dodd, Mead.

BEST, CHARLES HERBERT, and NORMAN BURKE TAYLOR. 1944. *The Living Body.* New York: Holt.

BONNER, JAMES, and ARTHUR W. GALSTON. 1952. *Principles of Plant Physiology.* San Francisco and London: W. H. Freeman and Company.

BOREK, ERNEST. 1961. *The Atoms Within Us.* New York: Columbia University Press.

BOYER, SAMUEL H., IV, ed. 1963. *Papers on Human Genetics.* Englewood Cliffs, N.J.: Prentice-Hall.

BOYNTON, HOLMES. 1948. *The Beginnings of Modern Science.* New York: Walter J. Black (Classics Club).

BRONOWSKI, JACOB. 1951. *The Common Sense of Science.* London: Heinemann.

BROWN, G. SPENCER. 1957. *Probability and Scientific Inference.* London: Longmans, Green.

BUCHHEIM, ROBERT W. 1958. *Space Handbook.* N.Y.: Modern Library Paperback.

BUCHSBAUM, RALPH. 1948. *Animals Without Backbones.* 2nd ed.; Chicago: University of Chicago Press.

———, and LORUS J. MILNE. 1960. *The Lower Animals.* Garden City, N.Y.: Doubleday.

BULLOCH, WILLIAM. 1938. *The History of Bacteriology.* London: Oxford University Press.

BURDETTE, WALTER J., ed. 1962. *Methodology in Human Genetics.* San Francisco: Holden-Day.

CAMERON, A. G. W., ed. 1963. *Interstellar Communication.* N.Y.: W. A. Benjamin.

CANNON, DOROTHY F. 1949. *Explorer of the Human Brain: The Life of Santiago Ramón y Cajal.* New York: Schuman.

CANNON, WALTER B. 1932. *The Wisdom of the Body.* New York: Norton.

CARLSON, ANTON J., and VICTOR JOHNSON. 1948. *The Machinery of the Body.* 3rd. ed.; Chicago: University of Chicago Press.

CARSON, RACHEL L. 1951. *The Sea Around Us.* New York: Oxford University Press.

———. 1962. *Silent Spring.* Boston: Houghton Mifflin.

CHRISTENSEN, CLYDE M. 1951. *The Molds and*

Man. Minneapolis: University of Minnesota Press.

COCHRAN, DORIS. 1964. *Living Amphibians of the World.* Garden City, N.Y.: Doubleday.

COHEN, I. BERNARD. 1948. *Science, Servant of Man.* Boston: Little, Brown.

CONANT, JAMES B. 1951. *Science and Common Sense.* New Haven, Conn.: Yale University Press.

CORNER, GEORGE W. 1942. *The Hormones in Human Reproduction.* Princeton, N.J.: Princeton University Press.

————. 1944. *Ourselves Unborn.* New Haven, Conn.: Yale University Press.

CURTIS, OTIS F., and DANIEL G. CLARK. 1950. *An Introduction to Plant Physiology.* New York: McGraw-Hill.

CUSHING, JOHN E., and DAN H. CAMPBELL. 1957. *Principles of Immunology.* New York: McGraw-Hill.

DARWIN, CHARLES. 1881. *Formation of Vegetable Mould Through the Action of Worms.* (Many editions available.)

————. (1950). *Charles Darwin's Autobiography.* Ed. by Sir Francis Darwin. New York: Schuman.

————. 1859. *The Origin of Species by Means of Natural Selection or the Preservation of Favored Races in the Struggle for Life.* (Many editions available.)

DASMANN, RAYMOND F. 1963. *The Last Horizon.* New York: Macmillan.

DENNIS, WAYNE. 1948. *Readings in the History of Psychology.* New York: Appleton-Century-Crofts.

DEUTSCH, ALBERT. 1949. *The Mentally Ill in America.* New York: Columbia University Press.

DOBELL, CLIFFORD. 1932. *Antony van Leeuwenhoek and His "Little Animals."* London: John Bale Medical Pub.

DOBZHANSKY, THEODOSIUS. 1951. *Genetics and the Origin of Species.* 3rd. ed.; New York: Columbia University Press.

DOETSCH, RAYMOND N. 1960. *Microbiology.* New Brunswick, N.J.: Rutgers University Press.

DOLE, STEPHEN H. 1964. *Habitable Planets for Man.* New York: Blaisdell.

DUBOS, RENÉ J. 1950. *Louis Pasteur: Free Lance of Science.* Boston: Little, Brown.

EISELEY, LOREN. 1959. Charles Darwin, Edward Blyth, and the theory of natural selection. *Proc. Amer. Philos. Soc.,* **103:**94–108.

ELIAS, HANS. 1950. "Discovery by Illustration." *Sci. Monthly.* **70:**229–232.

ELTON, CHARLES. 1927. *Animal Ecology.* New York: Macmillan.

————. 1958. *The Ecology of Invasions by Plants and Animals.* London: Methuen.

FLETCHER, JOSEPH. 1954. *Morals and Medicine.* Princeton, N.J.: Princeton University Press.

FRISCH, KARL VON. 1950. *Bees: Their Vision, Chemical Senses, and Language.* Ithaca, N.Y.: Cornell University Press.

FROMM, ERICH. 1956. *The Art of Loving.* New York: Harper.

FULTON, JOHN FARQUHAR. 1930. *Selected Readings in the History of Physiology.* Springfield, Ill.: Thomas.

GARDNER, MARTIN. 1957. *Fads and Fallacies in the Name of Science.* New York: Dover.

GARRETT, HENRY E. 1951. *Great Experiments in Psychology.* 3rd. ed.; New York: Appleton-Century-Crofts.

GILLIARD, E. THOMAS. 1958. *Living Birds of the World.* Garden City, N.Y.: Doubleday.

GOIN, COLEMAN J., and OLIVE B. GOIN. 1962. *Introduction to Herpetology.* San Francisco and London: W. H. Freeman and Company.

GRANT, MADELEINE PARKER. 1953. *Microbiology and Human Progress.* New York: Rinehart.

GRANT, VERNE. 1963. *The Origin of Adaptations.* New York and London: Columbia University Press.

GRAY, ANNIE P. 1954. *Mammalian Hybrids. A Check-List with Bibliography.* Farnham Royal, Bucks, England: Commonwealth Agric. Bureaux.

GRAY, JAMES. 1953. *How Animals Move.* Cambridge: Cambridge University Press.

GRIFFIN, DONALD R. 1958. *Listening in the Dark.* New Haven, Conn.: Yale University Press.

GRÜNEBERG, HANS. 1947. *Animal Genetics and Medicine.* New York: Paul B. Hoeber.

GUETZKOW, H. S., and P. H. BOWMAN. 1946. *Men and Hunger.* Elgin, Ill.: Brethren Pub. House.

HAGGARD, HOWARD W. 1929. *Devils, Drugs, and Doctors.* New York: Harper.

HALDANE, J. B. S. 1940. *Possible Worlds.* London: Heinemann.

HALL, THOMAS S. 1951. *A Source Book in Animal Biology.* New York: McGraw-Hill.

HALSTEAD, WARD C. 1947. *Brain and Intelligence.* Chicago: University of Chicago Press.

HARDIN, GARRETT. 1956. "Meaninglessness of the Word Protoplasm." *Sci. Monthly,* **82:**112–120.

———. 1959. *Nature and Man's Fate.* New York: Rinehart.

———. 1963. "The Cybernetics of Competition: A Biologist's View of Society." *Persp. Biol. and Med.,* **7:**58–84.

———. 1964. *Population, Evolution, and Birth Control.* San Francisco and London: W. H. Freeman and Company.

HARDY, ALISTAIR. 1956. *The Open Sea.* Part I, *The World of Plankton.* London: Collins.

HARTMAN, PHILIP E., and SIGMUND R. SUSKIND. 1965. *Gene Action.* Englewood Cliffs, N.J.: Prentice-Hall.

HARVEY, WILLIAM. 1931. *Anatomical Studies on the Motion of the Heart and Blood.* Springfield, Ill.: Thomas.

HENDERSON, L. G. 1913. *The Fitness of the Environment.* New York: Macmillan.

HERALD, EARL S. 1962. *Living Fishes of the World.* Garden City, N.Y.: Doubleday.

HERBER, LEWIS. 1962. *Our Synthetic Environment.* New York: Knopf.

HERMS, WILLIAM B. 1950. *Medical Entomology.* 4th ed.; New York: Macmillan.

HUFF, DARRELL. 1954. *How to Lie with Statistics.* New York: Norton.

HUGHES, HELEN MACGILL. 1947. "The Compleat Antivivisectionist." *Sci. Monthly,* **65:**503–507.

HURLEY, PATRICK M. 1959. *How Old Is the Earth?* New York: Doubleday (Anchor Books).

HUTCHINSON, JOSEPH, ed. 1965. *Essays on Crop Plant Evolution.* Cambridge: University Press.

HUXLEY, JULIAN. 1953. *Evolution in Action.* London: Chatto & Windus.

———, and H. B. D. KETTLEWELL. 1965. *Charles Darwin and His World.* London: Thames & Hudson.

HUXLEY, T. H. 1900. *Life and Letters of Thomas Henry Huxley.* 2 vols. New York: Appleton.

IMMS, A. D. 1947. *Social Behavior in Insects.* London: Methuen.

KASNER, EDWARD, and JAMES NEWMAN. 1940. *Mathematics and the Imagination.* New York: Simon and Schuster.

KEYS, ANCEL, *et al.* 1950. *The Biology of Human Starvation.* 2 vols. Minneapolis: University of Minnesota Press.

KLOTS, ALEXANDER B. and ELSIE B. KLOTS. 1960. *Living Insects of the World.* Garden City, N.Y.: Doubleday.

KRAUT, H. A., and E. A. MULLER. 1946. "Calorie Intake and Industrial Output." *Science,* **104:** 495–497.

LARGE, E. C. 1940. *The Advance of the Fungi.* New York: Holt.

LEHNINGER, ALBERT L. 1965. *Bioenergetics.* New York: Benjamin.

LEVINSON, SAMUEL A. (ed.). 1948. *Symposium on Medicolegal Problems.* Philadelphia: Lippincott.

LI, C. C. 1961. *Human Genetics.* New York: McGraw-Hill.

LOTKA, ALFRED J. 1925. *Elements of Physical Biology.* Baltimore: Williams & Wilkins.

MACGINITIE, G. E., and NETTIE. 1949. *Natural History of Marine Animals.* New York: McGraw-Hill.

MCLEISH, JOHN, and BRIAN SNOAD. 1958. *Looking at Chromosomes.* London: Macmillan.

MAUROIS, ANDRÉ. 1959. *The Life of Sir Alexander Fleming.* New York: E. P. Dutton.

MEYER, ARTHUR WILLIAM. 1939. *The Rise of Embryology.* Stanford, Calif.: Stanford University Press.

MOORE, RUTH. 1961. *The Coil of Life.* New York: Knopf.

MOTTRAM, V. H. 1948. *Human Nutrition.* Baltimore: Williams & Wilkins.

MOULTON, FOREST RAY, and JUSTUS J. SCHIFFERES (eds.). 1945. *The Autobiography of Science.* New York: Doubleday, Doran.

NEEL, JAMES V., and WILLIAM J. SCHULL. 1954. *Human Heredity.* Chicago: University of Chicago Press.

NEWBURGH, L. H. (ed.). 1949. *Physiology of Heat Regulation.* Philadelphia: Saunders.

NEWMAN, HORATIO H., F. N. FREEMAN, and K. J. HOLZINGER. 1937. *Twins: A Study of Heredity and Environment.* Chicago: University of Chicago Press.

NOBLE, ELMER A. and GLENN A. NOBLE. 1964. *Parasitology*. Philadelphia: Lea & Febiger.

ODUM, EUGENE P. 1959. *Fundamentals of Ecology*. 2nd. ed.; Philadelphia: Saunders.

OPARIN, A. I. 1960. *Life: Its Nature, Origin and Development*. Edinburgh and London: Oliver and Boyd.

OSBORN, FAIRFIELD. 1948. *Our Plundered Planet*. New York: Macmillan.

PAULING, LINUS. 1964. *College Chemistry*. 3rd. ed.; San Francisco and London: W. H. Freeman and Company.

PETERS, JAMES A., ed. 1959. *Classic Papers in Genetics*. Englewood Cliffs, N.J.: Prentice-Hall.

PLATT, JOHN RADER. 1962. *The Excitement of Science*. Boston: Houghton & Mifflin.

POLANYI, MICHAEL. 1946. *Science, Faith and Society*. London: Oxford University Press.

PÖLYA, GYÖRGY. 1948. *How to Solve It*. Princeton, N.J.: Princeton University Press.

RAPOPORT, ANATOL. 1950. *Science and the Goals of Man*. New York: Harper.

READ, JOHN. 1948. *A Direct Entry to Organic Chemistry*. London: Methuen.

REED, SHELDON C. 1963. *Parenthood and Heredity*. New York: Wiley.

ROE, ANNE, and GEORGE GAYLORD SIMPSON. 1958. *Behavior and Evolution*. New Haven, Conn.: Yale University Press.

ROOT, WALTER S. 1957. "The Case for Animal Experimentation." *Trans. N.Y. Acad. Sci. Ser. II*, **19**:204–214.

ROUECHÉ, BERTON. 1954. *Eleven Blue Men*. Boston: Little, Brown.

RUDD, ROBERT L. 1964. *Pesticides and the Living Landscape*. Madison, Wisc.: University of Wisconsin Press.

RUSSELL, BERTRAND. 1917. *Logic and Mysticism*. London: Allen and Unwin.

SANDERSON, IVAN T. 1955. *Living Mammals of the World*. Garden City, N.Y.: Doubleday.

SCHMIDT, KARL P., and ROBERT F. INGER. 1957. *Living Reptiles of the World*. Garden City, N.Y.: Doubleday.

SCHMIDT-NIELSEN, KNUT. 1964. *Desert Animals*. Oxford: Clarendon Press.

SCHRÖDINGER, ERWIN. 1947. *What Is Life?* New York: Macmillan.

SCHUBERT, JACK, and RALPH E. LAPP. 1957. *Radiation, What It Is and How It Affects You*. New York: Viking Press.

SCOTT, JOHN PAUL. 1958. *Animal Behavior*. Chicago: University of Chicago Press.

SEARS, PAUL B. 1935. *Deserts on the March*. Norman, Okla.: University of Oklahoma Press.

SELYE, HANS. 1956. *The Stress of Life*. New York: McGraw-Hill.

SHAPLEY, HARLOW, SAMUEL RAPPORT, and HELEN WRIGHT. 1946. *A Treasury of Science*. New York: Harper.

SHERRINGTON, CHARLES S. 1906. *The Integrative Action of the Nervous System*. New Haven, Conn.: Yale University Press.

SIMPSON, GEORGE GAYLORD. 1949. *The Meaning of Evolution*. New Haven, Conn.: Yale University Press.

SMITH, GEDDES. 1941. *Plague on Us*. New York: The Commonwealth Fund.

SRB, ADRIAN M., RAY D. OWEN and ROBERT S. EDGAR. 1965. *General Genetics*. 2nd. ed.; San Francisco and London: W. H. Freeman and Company.

STANIER, ROGER Y., MICHAEL DOUDOROFF, and EDWARD A. ADELBERG. 1957. *The Microbial World*. Englewood Cliffs, N.J.: Prentice-Hall.

STANLEY, WENDELL, and EVANS G. VALENS. 1961. *Viruses and the Nature of Life*. New York: E. P. Dutton.

STENT, GUNTHER S. 1963. *Molecular Biology of Bacterial Viruses*. San Francisco and London: W. H. Freeman and Company.

STERN, CURT. 1960. *Principles of Human Genetics*. 2nd. ed.; San Francisco and London: W. H. Freeman and Company.

SVERDRUP, H. F., M. W. JOHNSON, and R. H. FLEMING. 1942. *The Oceans*. New York: Prentice-Hall.

TAYLOR, G. RATTRAY. 1953. *Sex in History*. London: Thames and Hudson.

THIRRING, HANS. 1958. *Energy for Man*. Bloomington: Indiana University Press.

THOMPSON, D'ARCY W. 1944. *On Growth and Form*. New York: Macmillan.

TIFFANY, LEWIS H. 1939. *Algae: The Grass of Many Waters*. Springfield, Ill.: Thomas.

VALLERY-RADOT, R. 1928. *Life of Pasteur*. New York: Doubleday, Doran.

VOGT, WILLIAM. 1948. *Road to Survival*. New York: Sloane.

WADDINGTON, C. H. 1940. *Organisers and Genes*. Cambridge: Cambridge University Press.

WALKER, ERNEST P. 1964. *Mammals of the World*. Baltimore: Johns Hopkins Press.

WELTY, JOEL CARL. 1963. *The Life of Birds*. New York: Knopf.

WHEELER, WILLIAM MORTON. 1939. *Essays in Philosophical Biology*. Cambridge, Mass.: Harvard University Press.

———. 1923. *Social Life Among the Insects*. New York: Harcourt, Brace.

WHITE, ANDREW DICKSON. 1896. *A History of the Warfare of Science with Theology in Christendom*. 2 vols. New York: Appleton.

WHITE, PHILIP R. 1954. *The Cultivation of Animal and Plant Cells*. New York: Ronald Press.

WHITEHEAD, ALFRED NORTH. 1925. *Science and the Modern World*. New York: Macmillan.

WIENER, ALEXANDER S. 1943. *Blood Groups and Transfusions*. 3rd ed.; Springfield, Ill.: Thomas.

WIENER, NORBERT. 1948. *Cybernetics*. New York: Wiley.

———. 1950. *The Human Use of Human Beings*. Boston: Houghton, Mifflin.

WILLIAMS, GLANVILLE. 1957. *The Sanctity of Life and the Criminal Law*. New York: Knopf.

WILSON, CHARLES MORROW. 1943. *Trees and Test Tubes: The Story of Rubber*. New York: Holt.

WINSLOW, C. E. A., and L. P. HERRINGTON. 1949. *Temperature and Human Life*. Princeton, N.J.: Princeton University Press.

ZIRKLE, CONWAY. 1949. *Death of a Science in Russia*. Philadelphia: University of Pennsylvania Press.

GLOSSARY

Given below are brief definitions of some of the commoner and more important terms of the biological sciences. The principal omissions fall into two classes: (1) names of simple morphological structures (e.g., basidium, pancreas), which are best learned by reference (through the Index) to the relevant figure or description; and (2) the really "big" words like *life, biology, probability,* and *evolution,* an understanding of which is best sought through study of the exposition in the text, rather than in neat but rather empty definitions.

If you find the term you want neither in the Glossary nor in the Index, consult a dictionary (not a bad habit to develop, anyway!).

achondroplastic synonym for chondrodystrophic; pertaining to dwarf with short "long bones" in legs and arms, normal torso.

acoelomate animal without coelom (body cavity).

acromegaly condition characterized by skeletal overgrowths (feet, hands) caused by excess pituitary hormone.

ACTH adrenocorticothrophic hormone.

activated sludge a flocculent suspension of aerobic microorganisms capable of effecting removal of polluting matter when aerated with sewage or similar liquids.

adiabatic without loss or gain of heat.

adipose fat; fatty tissue.

ADP adenosine diphosphate nucleotide.

adrenergic fibers nerve fibers that release adrenalinelike substances.

adventitious appearing not in usual place (e.g., adventitious root sprouting from plant stem).

aerobe organism that requires molecular oxygen (O_2) to live.

aerosol a mist or cloud of foreign matter dispersed in the atmosphere.

albino organism markedly lacking in pigment; hereditary, recessive.

allantois extraembryonic membrane in reptiles, birds, mammals; functions as embryonic urinary bladder, or as support for blood vessels to and from placenta.

alleles different forms of "same" gene; undoubtedly, chemical differences in DNA at given locus of given chromosome producing demonstrably different hereditary effects.

allosteric protein a protein whose properties are changed by the binding of specific small molecules (allosteric effectors) at a site other than the active site for the normal substrate.

alpha particle a helium nucleus emitted in radioactive decay.

alpha ray a stream of alpha particles.

amnion one of extraembryonic membranes.

anaerobe organism that can live in absence of O_2.

anaesthetic causing loss of sensations, consciousness.

analgesic dulling sense of pain while leaving other senses operative.

anhydrase enzyme catalyzing removal of one H_2O unit from substrate molecule.

anode the electrode which is at a positive potential with respect to the cathode.

anorexia lack or loss of appetite for food.

antheridium male gamete-producing organ of plant.

anthocyanins accessory pigments in plants.

antibiotic substance produced by one organism having adverse effect on other species.

antiseptic substance that kills pathogenic microbes.

apogamy direct production of sporophyte by gametophyte generations, without intervention of gametes.

apospory direct production of gametophyte by sporophyte generation, without intervention of spores.

archegonium egg-producing organ (e.g., of fern).

archenteron central cavity of gastrula, lined by endoderm, representing future digestive cavity of adult.

assimilation taking of food molecules into body.

ATP adenosine triphosphate nucleotide.

autograft tissue graft from one part of individual to another part of same individual.

autoradiography record of the distribution of radioactivity in a thin section (e.g., of tissue), using the effect of the beta or gamma rays.

autosomes all chromosomes except heterosomes.

autotroph organism that can use CO_2 as sole carbon source.

avogadro's number the number of atoms (or molecules) in 1 gram atomic (or molecular) weight of any substance. It is equal to 6.02×10^{23} for all substances.

back-cross synonym for test-cross.

bacteriophage virus that parasitizes and destroys bacteria.

base analogs purines and pyrimidines that differ slightly from the normal nitrogenous bases.

base pairing rule the requirement that adenine must always pair with thymine (or

uracil), and guanine with cytosine, in a nucleic acid double helix.

benthonic living on bottoms of oceans and lakes.

Bergmann's Rule principle that homothermal animals living in cold climate are larger than their close relatives with similar way of life in warmer climates.

beta particle a high-velocity electron emitted in radioactive decay.

beta ray a stream of beta particles.

bio-assay chemical analysis using reactions of living organisms for assay.

Biogenetic Law "ontogeny recapitulates phylogeny."

biological half-life the time taken for an organ to eliminate through biological processes one-half of the quantity of a specified element that has been introduced into it.

bioluminescence visible light produced as by-product of metabolism (as by fireflies).

biosphere total living matter of world; an abstraction.

biotin one of B vitamins.

breeder reactor a reactor which contains fertile material in the core, so arranged that it is converted to fissile material by neutron irradiation. In this way the reactor produces more fuel than it consumes.

Brownian movement irregular movement of microscopic particle, caused by bombardment of molecules.

budding modified mitotic cell division in which one daughter cell is larger than the other (as in yeasts).

buffer substance which minimizes changes in *pH* (acidity, alkalinity) as acid or base is added.

caecum cavity open at one end; blind pouch in intestine.

cambium meristematic tissue that produces xylem and phloem.

carapace hard case or shield (e.g., covering of lobster, turtle).

carboxyl group acid group of organic molecules: —COOH.

carcinogen agent that produces cancer (carcinoma).

carcinoma one class of cancer.

cardiac pertaining to heart.

carnivore eater of animals.

carotenoids carrot-colored organic substances, from some of which vitamin A can be produced.

carrier individual who carries infectious pathogenic organisms without being much hurt by them.

catalase enzyme that decomposes hydrogen peroxide (H_2O_2) to water and oxygen.

cathode the electrode which is at a negative potential with respect to the anode. The cathode is usually at earth potential.

cercaria larval stage in life cycle of flukes.

chemosynthesis synthesis (by organism) of organic carbon from CO_2, using energy released from some other chemical reaction.

chemotropism growth of plant oriented by chemicals.

chitin nitrogenous organic "plastic," characteristic of exoskeleton of arthropods.

chloroplast plastid containing chlorophyll.

cholinergic fibers nerve fibers that release acetylcholine.

chondrodystrophic pertaining to dwarf with short "long bones" in legs and arms, normal torso.

chorion one of extraembryonic

membranes in reptiles, birds, mammals; part of placenta.

chromosome threadlike body inside nucleus; rich in DNA, and bearer of genes.

climacteric synonym for menopause; change of life in women.

cline smooth transition of forms within species, changing systematically with geographical position.

clone organisms that have descended from common ancestor by asexual propagation only.

coelom body cavity, in which lie viscera.

coenocytic tissue tissue in which nuclei are not separated from each other by cell membranes.

coenzyme substance, usually organic, that is required to make enzyme active.

colchicine organic substance (derived from plant *Colchicum*) which suppress spindle formation and consequently arrests cell division at metaphase. Properly used, it may induce polyploidy.

colloid system of dispersing medium and dispersed substance, particles of latter consisting of either (a) many molecules each, or (b) single giant molecules; but in either case forming stable suspension.

colostrum first, lymphlike secretion of mammary glands of pregnant or just-delivered mammals.

commensal organism living symbiotically with host; host neither benefits nor suffers from association.

companion cell living cell adjacent to sieve tube of plant phloem.

compensation point depth in water at which photosynthesis exactly equals respiration.

conjugation adherence of two cells (e.g., protozoa) prior to sexual fusion.

constitutive enzyme an enzyme that is synthesized in fixed amounts, irrespective of growth conditions.

coronary pertaining to heart.

cps cycles per second; said of sound or other harmonic function.

cyclosis streaming around of living material inside of cell.

curie unit of radioactivity equal to 3.7×10^{10} disintegrations per second.

cyst thick-walled resting stage, as in some protozoa.

cytochrome hydrogen-carrying molecule in cellular respiration.

cytology study of cells.

cytolysis dissolution or disintegration of cell.

dalton a unit of weight equal to that of a single hydrogen atom.

deamination removal of amino group from organic molecule.

decarboxylation removal of carboxyl group (—COOH) from organic molecule.

deciduous said of tree that sheds all its leaves seasonally.

definitive host host in which sexual phase of parasite's life cycle occurs.

dehydrogenation removal of hydrogen from molecule.

demography study of populations.

denaturation alteration of architecture of protein molecule, thus altering some of its characteristics (e.g., solubility).

dephosphorylation removal of phosphate group from molecule.

deuterium heavy hydrogen (H^2).

diffusion random spreading of population of molecules, due to molecular motion.

digestion conversion of large molecules of food to smaller molecules.

dimorphism state of having two distinct adult forms; as in sexual dimorphism.

dioecious having the male reproductive organs in one individual, the female in another.

diploblastic having two primary germ layers: ectoderm and endoderm (e.g., coelenterates).

diploid number number of chromosomes in cell that has two of each distinguishable kind of chromosome; the normal number for somatic cells of most "higher" plants and animals.

distal farther from midline of body (antonym of proximal).

DNA polymerase enzyme that catalyzes formation of DNA from deoxyribonucleoside triphosphates, using DNA as a template.

dose-rate the rate at which energy is absorbed per unit mass of a specified material.

dosimeter an instrument which measures the dose of radiation over a given time.

double-blind test test in which drug and placebo are code-numbered so that neither patients nor nurse knows which is which.

ecdysis emergence of imago (adult) from pupa; or any shedding of exoskeleton of one stage permitting emergence of next stage.

ecological niche not place, but way of life of organism—food it eats, its temperature requirements, etc.

ectoparasite parasite attached to outside of host (e.g., flea).

effective half-life the time taken for the amount of a radioelement, which has been introduced into a specified organ, to diminish to half its initial value by the combined processes of radioactive decay and biological elimination.

electron a fundamental particle with mass 0.00055 atomic mass unit and a single negative charge equal to 4.802×10^{10} electrostatic unit.

electron volt a unit of energy equal to the energy acquired by an electron accelerated through a potential difference of 1 volt. 1 eV = 1.60209×10^{12} erg.

empirical determined by experience only, without theoretical explanation or foundation.

emulsion colloidal system in which both dispersed and continuous phase are liquids (e.g., milk).

endergonic energy-requiring, as in chemical reaction.

endocrine pertaining to hormones or hormone-producing glands.

endoplasmic reticulum cytoplasmic structures acting as depot of enzymes.

endoradiosonde miniature radio transmitter (less than 2 cc in volume) which can be swallowed and thereafter radio out information (temperature, acidity, pressure, etc.) of its surroundings.

enucleated cell cell from which nucleus has been removed.

epigenesis embryological doctrine that final form of organism is not explicitly present in earlier forms, but develops from earlier states step by step.

episome a genetic element that can exist either free or as part of the normal cellular chromosome. Examples of episomes are the sex factor and lysogenic phage DNA.

erg the work done by a force of 1 dyne acting through a distance of 1 centimeter.

ESP extrasensory perception, i.e., supposed sensory perception by means other than senses.

estivation summer dormancy; similar to hibernation.

estrogen female sex hormone.

eugenics genetic knowledge applied to human problems.

euphotic zone zone in body of water in which net photosynthetic increase occurs.

exergonic energy-yielding, said of chemical reaction.

exocrine applied to gland which releases secretion through duct.

fauna animals collectively.

fermentation metabolic utilization of carbohydrates without O_2.

fibroblast connective tissue cell, giving rise to fibrous parts of tendons, etc.

fission synonym for cell division.

fission chain reaction a chain reaction is one in which one or more of the products of the reaction are instrumental in perpetuating that reaction. In a fission chain reaction a neutron reacts with a fissile nuclide to produce fission products and further neutrons which, under suitable conditions, are capable of causing the fission of further fissile nuclei.

fixation (cytology) killing of cells preparatory to staining.

flavoprotein hydrogen carrier in cellular respiration.

flora plants collectively; may be restricted, as in bacterial flora.

fluoroscope a machine in which penetrating radiation, such as X-radiation, after passage through a system falls upon a fluorescent screen, thus enabling the internal structure of that system to be visualized.

gametangium structure that produces gametes.

gametes reproductive cells that unite to form zygote: male gamete is sperm cell; female gamete, egg; normally haploid.

gametophyte individual plant-stage that produces gametes.

gamma radiation electromagnetic radiation of short wavelength emitted in radioactive decay.

ganglion collection of nerve cell bodies lying outside brain and spinal cord.

GAS general adaptation syndrome.

gel colloid in quasi-solid state (e.g., Jell-o).

genome entire haploid set of genes.

genotype genetic constitution of organism.

geotropism growth of plant oriented by gravity.

geriatrics medical study of diseases of old age.

gerontology study of the processes of aging.

germ layers ectoderm, mesoderm, and endoderm.

gestation process or period of carrying young in uterus.

gibberellins plant hormones that stimulate elongation of plant.

globulins class of proteins; the

gamma globulins include the antibodies.

glucose $C_6H_{12}O_6$ (grape sugar).

greenhouse effect heating of closed space by trapped energy.

half-life time required for half the atoms of unstable isotope to decompose.

halophyte organism living in salty environment.

heavy water water in which the hydrogen component is present as deuterium; that is, deuterium oxide.

helix spiral in three dimensions.

hepatic pertaining to liver.

herbivore eater of plants.

hermaphroditic producing both kinds of gametes from same individual.

heteroecious pertaining to parasite that requires two hosts for completion of its life cycle.

heterogamous having uniting gametes unequal in size.

heterograft graft of tissue from one species to another.

heterosomes chromosomes concerned with sex determination.

heterosporous producing two kinds of spores that develop into two kinds of gametophytes (plants).

heterotroph organism that requires organic carbon for its nutrition.

holophytic synonym for autotrophic; used by some protozoologists.

holozoic synonym for heterotrophic; used by some protozoologists.

homeostasis condition in which relative constancy is maintained within organism despite environmental fluctuations.

hominoid manlike; applied to various fossil ancestors of man.

homogenate uniform mixture (e.g., slurry of killed, ground-up cells).

homograft graft of tissue from one individual to another individual of same species.

homosporous producing only one kind of spore which grows into single kind of gametophyte (plants).

humoral pertaining to the body fluids.

humus organic portion of soil.

hydrolysis splitting of large molecule of H_2O.

hydrophyte organism living in damp or watery places.

hydroponics culture of plants without soil.

hyperparasitism infection of parasite by other parasites.

hypertonic having osmotic potential greater than that of standard (cell).

hypha single fungal filament.

hypotonic having osmotic potential less than that of standard (cell).

idiopathic adjective, applied to disease, meaning cause unknown.

imago adult (of insects with metamorphosis).

imperfect flower flower that includes sexual parts of one sex only.

inductor embryonic tissue (or substance) that causes differentiation of another tissue.

ingestion taking in of food.

instar any stage in species with sequence of developmental forms.

integument covering, skin.

intercellular between (or among) cells.

intermediary metabolism the chemical reactions in a cell that transform food molecules into molecules needed for the structure and growth of the cell.

intermediate host host in which asexual phase of parasite's life cycle occurs.

internode section of plant stem between two successive nodes (e.g., as in bamboo).

intracellular within cell.

invagination local infolding of layer of tissue, leading to formation of pouch or sac.

invertase enzyme that splits sucrose into glucose and fructose.

in vitro "in glass," e.g., maintenance of living cells in test tubes.

in vivo "in life," e.g., inside living organism (antonym of in vitro).

ion exchange the property possessed by certain materials of exchanging the cations or anions, with which these are charged, for other ions when a solution containing them is brought into contact with the material.

isogamous having uniting gametes equal in size.

isosmotic of equal osmotic potential on both sides (of membrane).

isotopes two (or more) forms of same element with same atomic number but different atomic weight.

kelp popular name for large seaweed.

ketogenic fatty-acid producing (e.g., certain amino acids after deamination).

kinetochore synonym for centromere.

labile easily destructible.

larva immature form of species; often wormlike in arthropods.

leaky protein a protein coded by a mutant gene which shows less than complete loss of normal ability.

leukemia cancerous condition of blood; characterized by overproduction of leucocytes.

leukopenia condition in which blood has deficiency of leucocytes.

lignin complex organic compounds; second to cellulose in abundance in wood.

linkage group group of genes that are members of same chromosome.

littoral sea floor from shore to edge of continental shelf.

luciferase enzyme which, acting on substrate luciferin, produces light (bioluminescence).

lycopodium a type of spore having a diameter of about 32 microns.

lymph fluid derived by filtration of blood through wall of capillary; almost the same as plasma.

lysis "dissolving" (destruction) of cells.

lysogenic bacterium a bacterium that contains a prophage.

macromolecule a molecule with a molecular weight ranging from a few thousand daltons to millions.

macroscopic larger than microscopic.

maize corn in United States.

maximum permissible body burden the total body content of a radioisotope which if maintained, will not deliver to any critical organ a dose greater than the maximum permissible.

maximum permissible concentration the concentration of a radioisotope in air, water, milk, etc., which will deliver not more than the maximum permissible dose to a critical organ when breathed or consumed at a normal rate.

maximum permissible dose the dose of ionizing radiation accumulated in a specified time, of such magnitude that no bodily injury may be expected to result in the lifetime of the person exposed and no intolerable burden is likely to accrue to society through genetic damage to his descendants.

mean free path the average distance that a particle (such as an electron) moves between successive encounters with other particles (such as the atoms of a medium).

medullated fibers nerve fibers that are covered by myelin sheath.

medusa floating form of coelenterate.

meiosis reductional division of cells.

melanic dark, perhaps nearly black, variant of species.

menopause change of life in women; synonym for climacteric.

meristem embryonic tissue in adult plants capable of giving rise to adult tissues.

mesophyte terrestrial organism living in moderately moist region.

metamorphosis change of form, as from larva to adult in insects.

metastasis fragmentation of cancer; transport of fragments to new sites in body, where fragments may grow new cancers.

microbe any microscopic form of life; most commonly including bacteria, fungi, protozoa, unicellular algae, and possibly viruses.

mimicry superficial resemblance of certain animals, particularly insects, to other and better-protected species, resulting in some protection to mimics.

mitosis equational division of cells.

monoecious having both male and female reproductive organs in the same individual.

monolayer a layer of molecules that is uniformly one molecule thick.

monomer basic subunit from which, by repetition of a single reaction, a polymer can be made. For example, amino acids (monomers) condense to yield polypeptides (polymers).

monophyletic developed from single ancestral type (antonym of polyphyletic).

monosomy diploid set of chromosomes minus one chromosome.

morphogenesis process (e.g., embryogeny) of developing the form of an organism.

mucosa mucus-secreting membrane (e.g., lining of intestine).

mutant changed form of gene; i.e., either recently mutated gene, or allelic form different from "wild-type" ("natural" type).

mutation process which results in gene changing from one heritable allele to another heritable allele.

mycelium collective term for many fungal hyphae (filaments).

mycorrhiza fungal mycelia growing symbiotically with plant roots.

myelin fatty material that surrounds axons of neurons.

myosin protein found in muscle.

nekton actively swimming organisms of ocean.

neoplasm (abnormal) new growing tissue (e.g., tumor, cancer).

nephric pertaining to nephron, hence to kidney.

neritic near shore and above littoral zone.

nuclear fission the splitting of the nucleus of a heavy atom into two fragments of approximately equal mass, generally by neutron bombardment.

nuclear fusion the joining of light nuclei to form a heavier one.

occupational exposure exposure to ionizing radiation incurred in work with sources of such radiation, as distinct from exposure incurred by the general public from natural sources of radiation or contamination of the environment.

oceanic of open ocean (antonym of neritic).

olfactory pertaining to odor and its perception.

omnivorous eating both plants and animals.

oögonium egg-producing organ (plant).

organelle equivalent of organ, in unicellular organism.

osmosis process in which water migrates through differentially permeable membrane because of different concentration of solutes on the two sides.

osmotic pressure same as osmotic potential (see Index).

oviparous pertaining to reproduction in which eggs are released from female, development of offspring taking place outside mother's body.

ovoviviparous pertaining to reproduction in which eggs are retained inside mother's body during development, but without nourishment passing from mother to offspring.

paleontology study of past or fossil life; usually of animals only, paleobotany being study of fossil plants.

parabiotic twins separate individuals artificially joined so that diffusible substances can pass from one to the other; artificial Siamese twins.

parenchyma tissue of pith and cortex, in plant stems and roots.

parthenogenesis development of egg without fertilization.

pasteurization heating of foods to temperature that kills pathogens but not necessarily other microbes.

pathogen disease- or sickness-producing microbe.

pathology abnormal physiology.

pelagic pertaining to open water of ocean.

pentadactyl limb five-digited limb, characteristic of higher vertebrates.

perfect flower flower that includes both male and female sexual parts.

pH symbol denoting relative concentration of hydrogen ions in solution: Neutral point is pH 7.0; below that is progressively more acid; above it, progressively more alkaline.

phagocyte leucocyte that ingests particles (bacteria) in ameboid fashion.

phenotype type of organism with respect to its appearance.

phloem plant vascular tissue through which fluids pass from shoot to root.

phosphorylation addition of phosphate group to compound; important in transfer of energy.

photolysis destruction of compound by light.

phototropism growth of plant oriented by light.

phycocyanin blue pigment of blue-green algae.

phycoerythrin accessory red pigment of red algae.

phytoplankton collective term for plants found in plankton.

placebo dummy drug used for control part of experiment, or to placate patient who demands, but does not need, medication.

placenta double membrane with great surface for diffusional exchange of food and wastes between mother and child.

plankton organisms floating at surface of water.

plasma blood minus formed elements (blood cells).

plasma membrane cell membrane.

plasmodesmata strands of material (living?) connecting cells.

plastid cytoplasmic bodies of definite form (in given species); possibly self-reproducing, in this environment.

plexus network, especially of nerves or blood vessels.

pluripotent said of cell that can differentiate into any one of several different types of cells.

pollination transfer of pollen (male gametophyte) to female flower or female part of flower.

polymerase enzyme that polymerizes mononucleotides thus producing DNA.

polymorphism state of having more than two adult forms in same species, as in ants with many different castes.

polyp sessile stage in life cycle of coelenterates.

polyphyletic derived from more

than one ancestral type, as by hydridization (antonym of monophyletic).

polyploidy state of having more than a diploid set of chromosomes.

polytene chromosomes same as giant chromosomes.

preformation embryological doctrine that adult features already exist in miniature in zygote (antonym of epigenesis).

progesterone hormone secreted by corpus luteum and placenta; prepares uterus for implantation of zygote.

proprioceptive sense sense that gives information of position of one's own body.

prothallus gametophyte of fern.

provirus state of a virus in which it is integrated into a host cell chromosome and is thus transmitted from one cell generation to another.

proximal closer to midline of body (antonym of distal).

pseudocopulation copulation of male insect with flower that resembles female insect; producing pollination of flower, not an interkingdom hybrid.

pulmonary pertaining to lungs.

pupa stage during which arthropod larva metamorphoses into imago (adult).

pyloris opening from stomach to intestine.

rad the unit of absorbed radiation dose: a dose which results in the absorption of 100 ergs per gram of specified material.

radioactive half-life the time required for the number of atoms of a radioactive species to decay to one-half its present value.

radioautograph photograph of biological tissue impregnated

with radioactive material made directly by radioactivity itself.

radio pill miniature radio transmitter (less than 2 cc in volume) which can be swallowed and thereafter radio out information (temperature, acidity, pressure, etc.) of its surroundings.

relative biological effectiveness the ratio of the dose (in rads) of gamma radiation from cobalt-60 to the dose (in rads) of any type of ionizing radiation which produces the same, specified, biological effect.

rem the quantity of ionizing radiation which has the same specified biological effect as one rad of gamma radiation from cobalt-60.

renal pertaining to the kidneys.

replicate more than one duplicate.

resolving power ability of lens system to distinguish two points as two.

R.H. relative humidity; amount of moisture in air expressed as percentage of total that can be held in air at that temperature.

rhizoid rootlike structure.

RNA ribosenucleic acid; class of chemical compounds related to DNA, but usually more characteristic of cytoplasm than of nucleus.

roentgen the quantity of X- or gamma radiation such that the associated corpuscular emission per 0.001293 gram of air produces, in air, ions carrying one electrostatic unit of charge of either sign. 1 roentgen corresponds to an absorbed dose of from 0.92 to 0.97 rad when delivered to muscular tissue.

saprophyte organism that lives

on dissolved organic matter.

saprozoic synonym for saprophytic; used by some protozoologists.

scale insects members of family Coccidae; suck plant juices.

scion shoot portion of grafted pair of plants.

semipermeable membrane same as differentially permeable membrane (see Index).

septicemia infection in which infectious agents appear in blood stream.

serology literally, study of serum; in practice, study of antibodies particularly.

serum blood minus fibrin (clot) and formed elements (blood cells).

sex chromosomes synonym for heterosomes.

sieve tubes one kind of phloem element (plants).

simian pertaining to monkeys.

sinus cavity, recess, or depression, especially in bone.

sol quasi-liquid state of colloidal system.

solute that which is dissolved in solvent.

solvent liquid phase of solution.

somatic cells all cells of multicellular organism exclusive of reproductive cells.

somatic mutation mutation in genetic material of cells not destined to produce gametes; not verifiable by breeding tests.

somites longitudinally arranged segments of segmented animals.

sphincter ring-shaped muscle capable of closing tubular opening by constriction (e.g., pyloric sphincter, which closes opening between stomach and intestine).

sporangiophore filament that

bears sporangium (which contains spores).

sporangium spore-containing receptacle.

spore resistant stage, usually single cell.

sporophyte plant stage that produces spores.

steric (stereochemical) pertaining to the arrangement in space of the atoms in a molecule.

sterile incapable of reproduction; or (microbiology) free of living organisms.

steroids class of fatty organic compounds that includes cholesterol, vitamin D, sex hormones, adrenocortical hormones, and carcinogens.

stock root portion of grafted pair of plants.

suppressor gene a gene that can reverse the phenotypic effect of a variety of mutations in other genes.

symbiosis intimate living together of two species.

synapse point of contact of two communicating nerve fibers.

syncytial synonym for coenocytic; pertaining to multinucleate tissue.

syndrome set of associated symptoms.

synergistic cooperative in action (e.g., hormones which work together to produce effect).

tagged atom isotope of element that can be detected by physical means, in presence of population of other elements not so distinguished.

tautology logically circular statement ("A is A").

taxis directed movement, in response to environmental stimulus.

taxonomy science of classifying species.

teleology doctrine that natural events are goal-directed, occurring according to preordained purposes.

template pattern or mold that guides formation of replicates; concept is often used in gene theory and immunology.

test-cross mating with homozygous recessive type, to reveal hidden recessive gene (if present).

thigmotropism growth of plant oriented by physical contact with something.

threshold lowest value of stimulus that will produce response.

thrombus blood clot within circulatory system.

topology study of geometrical properties that are independent of measure; "rubber-sheet geometry."

torus three-dimensional geometrical figure, of which doughnut is example.

tracer experiment experiment in which movement of element in organism is followed by use of unusual isotope of the element that can be detected by physical means.

transducer (physics) device that changes message from one sensory class to another (e.g., telephone receiver, which changes sound waves to electrical impulses).

transduction transfer of genetic material from one bacterium to another through agency of virus.

transpiration evaporation of water from leaves and other exposed surfaces of plant.

transuranium elements elements with atomic number greater than 92.

trisomy diploid set of chromosomes plus one extra chromosome.

tritium radioactive hydrogen isotope of mass 3.

trophallaxis exchange of food between different organisms, as between parents and offspring in social insects.

trophic pertaining to feeding.

tropic pertaining to growth; not to be confused with tactic (taxis).

tropism differential growth, directed by environmental stimulus.

turgor state of being swollen by internal pressure; said of cell in hypotonic solution.

turnover number number of molecules of substrate acted on per minute by enzyme which "has" the turnover number.

tyndallization synonym for sterilization by intermittent heating (see Index).

ultracentrifuge a high-speed centrifuge that can attain speeds up to 60,000 rpm, producing centrifugal fields up to 500,000 times gravity, thus sedimenting macromolecules.

vacuole fluid-filled balloon in cytoplasm.

variegated leaf leaf containing its chlorophyll in patches, which may be either randomly or regularly distributed.

vascular pertaining to system for transporting fluids.

vascular bundle bundle of xylem and phloem elements, for conduction of fluids in plant.

vasectomy popular name for vasotomy (cutting of vas deferens, thus producing sterility in male).

vector organism that aids dissemination of disease organism.

viscera collective term for entrails, or contents of abdominal and thoracic cavities.

vitreous glasslike.

viviparous pertaining to reproduction in which developing embryo is surrounded by and nourished by mother for considerable time.

xanthophylls accessory plant pigments.

xerophyte organism living in very dry environment.

xylem plant vascular tissue through which fluids pass from root to shoot.

zooplankton collective term for animals found in plankton.

zygote single (normally diploid) cell resulting from fusion of egg and sperm.

ANSWERS TO PROBLEMS

At the end of each chapter some problems have a double dagger (‡) in front of the number; answers to these problems are given below. The student is warned that the answer here given is often more telegraphic in style than is acceptable on an assignment written by him. The answers given below are intended to serve as a check on his thinking after he has struggled with the problems.

1-7. In psychoanalytic thought, the suckling period is a time when the child is master of his world; he has only to cry, to get the world to serve him; weaning and toilet-training show him that he is not master.

1-10. Motion. He must avoid letting his prey see him move.

1-14. Assimilation usually produces an organism largely independent of type of food. Perhaps difference here is connected with the fat (storage product), which is not so constant in composition as is muscle; fat is more influenced by food from which it is made.

1-17. By definition, perfect murders cannot be identified or counted. (However, a limit could be set: their number could not be greater than the total number of deaths annually.)

1-21. The *plis cachetés* were a bit of a dirty trick: if the scientist learned that someone else had confirmed his claims, he could have the letter opened and assert priority. If his finding proved false, he could just quietly let the letter die. Such a practice would encourage premature and careless claims, and yet discourage hard work; for the scientist, like other men, may be egotistical and want credit for what he does.

1-23. To call attention to the double meaning: (a) simple, easily understood; (b) made up of the smallest particles or ideas of analysis. Both

the physicist's proton and the biologist's "life" may be elementary in the second sense, but not in the first.

2-14. No metabolism within vacuole; different chemical concentration there; delimited from cytoplasm by a membrane that is like the cell membrane.

2-15. In mixed culture, the ratio of fibroblasts to epithelial cells constantly increases. With periodic discarding of a large fraction of the culture, sooner or later only fibroblasts will be found in the fraction used.

2-18. Pinocytosis discovered in same year (1931) as electron microscope; but since E.M. not very useful until 1950's one would guess it was not used in this discovery. Text states that pinocytosis was first seen in *living* amoebas; this rules out E.M.

2-22. Five pairs.

2-24. 175 microns by 40 microns.

2-25. Section 11 gives power of electron microscope as 2.5 orders of magnitude greater than light microscope. Volume observed will be magnified by $(2.5)^3$ or 15.6 orders of magnitude; which is about 10^{16}. One hour $\times 10^{16}$ divided by 10^4 hrs (per year) $= 10^{12}$ years $=$ a million million years.

3-9. Molecules in ice farther apart.

3-10. Procedure determines true temperature of water plus the thermometer, which entered at different temperature. Error can be corrected by knowing mass and specific heat of thermometer. Important point: Method of measuring may influence results obtained.

3-12. Algae in intertidal zone carry on more exchange with swirling waters, can grow faster, larger.

3-14. (a) Indefinite rise in liquid level in thistle tube, until stopped by gravity. (b) First a rise in level in thistle tube, followed by a fall until, ultimately, fluid same level inside and out.

3-16. By doing work.

3-19. Liquid; "supercooled," if you wish.

3-21. (a) $(300/18) \times 6 \times 10^{23} = 10^{25}$ molecules per glassful. (b) Volume of ocean $= 10^{25} \div 10^2 = 10^{23}$ glassfuls of water.

3-23. A mechanist, surely.

3-24. Physicists' calorie is 0.001 as large as nutritionists' Calorie which is also called a kilocalorie.

4-10. $\quad$ $E = 0.55 = (T_2 - 293°)/T_2$
$(0.45)T_2 = 293°$
$\quad T_2 = 651°$ Celsius

Temperature, Fahrenheit
$\quad = (C° \times 9/5) + 32°$ (Appendix 3)
$\quad = (650° \times 9/5) + 32°$
$\quad = 1172° + 32°$
$\quad = 1204°$ Fahrenheit

4-12. The blood flows because the heart pumps it; it is respiration that makes it possible for the heart to pump. Therefore the energy lost in this way has already been measured by respiration.

4-14. Label worm with a pellet of radioactive material, follow wanderings with Geiger counter.

4-18. It could be used for energy. As for rebuilding Kitty's "protoplasm," you can argue either way: *No,* because the amino acids of Looking-glass proteins are all *dextro,* and hence won't fit into a normal, laevo-cat. *Yes,* because the

only way Kitty can get at the Looking-glass milk is by passing through the mirror and being converted to a *dextro*-Kitty.

4-20. That the catalyst is indeed involved in the chemical reaction. Evidently the atoms of Pt are combined with the substrate *and moved slightly in position* each time this happens, in a random way. When the catalyst-substrate combination is broken up, metal is redeposited. (Gravimetric analysis is analysis by weighing.)

4-23. Amino acids: a, e; carbohydrates: b, c, f; fatty substances: d, g.

4-25. A trisaccharide. By two condensations, that is, removal of two molecules of water per molecule of raffinose formed.

4-26. a. $20 \times 20 = 400.$ b. $20^3 = 8,000.$

4-27. The number is 20^{150}. $20^{150} = (10^{150}) \times (2^{150})$. To evaluate 2^{150}: $2^{150} = (2^{10})^{15} \cong (10^3)^{15} \cong 10^{45}$. Putting the two portions together: $(10^{45}) \times (10^{150}) = 10^{195}$. That's 1 followed by 195 zeros!

4-30. $3 \times 10^4 \times 60 \times 24 = 4.32 \times 10^7.$

4-32. Mercury alters enzymes, which are proteins.

4-34. A 3-carbon sugar. You should be able to figure this out from the *implicit* definition at the beginning of Sec. 39.

4-36. All but vacuolar contents and cell wall.

5-21. (a) The manuscript of a book copyrighted in 1952 was probably finished in 1951, so Hershey and Chase's work was not available. However, there was already a great deal of work (Feulgen; Avery, MacLeod, and McCarty) to indicate the importance of nucleic acids in heredity and in chromosomes. Even in 1951 the substance of chromosomes was commonly referred to as "nucleo-proteins," meaning nucleic acids plus proteins. As for (b), the proteins in chromosomes should no longer be emphasized —though we need to know more of their role there.

5-25. In terms of mechanism, each helix acts as a negative template. In terms of final result, since a double helix produces two double helixes, one might say that DNA acts as a positive template. But language seems somehow at fault here. The phrase "semi-conservative" is beating around the same bush.

5-27. $(6 \times 10^{-12}$ gm$) \times (7.7 \times 10^{10}$ people$) \div (60 \times 10^{-3}$ gm$) = 7.7$ postage stamps' weight. In round numbers, 8 ordinary postage stamps.

5-28. $(6 \times 10^{-12}$ gm$) \times 10^{14} = 6 \times 10^2$ gm $= 600$ grams. (From Appendix 3): 0.6 kg $\times 2.205 = 1.3$ lbs.

6-13. a. One possibility: GUU-CAU-UUA-ACU-CCU-GAA.   b. CAA-GTA-AAT-TGA-GGA-CTT.

6-14. No. of possibilities for the different amino acids: Val-2, His-2, Leu-6, Thr-4, Pro-4, Glu-2; multiplying these numbers together we get 768.

6-15. One.

6-16. Spacing, for convenience: CGG-UCC-CCC-UAC-AUA-AGU.

6-17. Arg-Ser-Pro-Tyr-Met-Ser.

6-18. Arg-Pro-Pro-Thr-Nonsense-?

6-20. Use Table 6-3. Must be sure to use *diploid E. coli* so it is comparable to others; for this, 8×10^7. Divide all numbers by this figure, yielding:

E. coli	1
chicken	62.5
mouse	162.5
guinea pig	212.5
human	262.5

6-22. Five.

6-26. The Spanish language has very nearly a one-to-one relation between sound and spelling. English, by contrast, has considerable degeneracy in the sound-spelling code; hence the necessity of memorization of many specific codings as well as the degenerate coding system. A spelling bee is rather pointless for Spanish children who have only the nondegenerate coding system to learn.

7-5. Nasturtium, because it is a higher plant, so most of the organism is diploid. In the alga, only

the zygote is diploid; it is unlikely to show much in the welter of characters influenced by dominance.

7-9. AB.

7-10. Two: A_1B and A_2B.

7-11. Four: A_1B_1, A_1B_2, A_2B_1 and A_2B_2.

7-12. Life doesn't begin; it is merely passed on from one cell to another, as life cycle diagrams show.

7-13. $3.5 \times 10^9 \times 10^{14} = 3.5 \times 10^{23}$.

7-15. Given the general fact of dominance of normal alleles, the diploid is less vulnerable to adverse mutational changes.

8-9. No. There is no negative feedback to correct for errors. It is a rigidly determinative system.

8-11. As a mono-heterotherm.

8-14. Scale effect. Even by violent exertion one small bee cannot make up for the heat loss at his surface.

8-15. A hummingbird weighs 28.35 g $\div 8 = 3.5$ g. It requires 7.6 Cal $\div 3.5$ g $= 2.17$ Cal/g. A similar man would require $(7 \times 10^4$ g$) \times (2.17$ Cal/g$) = 1.5$ Cal $\times 10^5 = 150,000$ Calories per day. Since the actual daily requirement is only about 3,000 Cal, such a man would require 50 times as much.

8-19. One eighty-ninth $(7.6 \div .085)$.

8-20. Set up a proportion and solve. $(.085)/(3.5) = x/(7 \cdot 10^4)$. $x = 1,700$ Calories. This is 57% of 3,000 Calories, the normal daily energy requirement.

8-21. The direct answer: he hasn't evolved this ability. Teleological explanation: the torpor of hibernation makes an animal vulnerable to its enemies. This disadvantage must be offset by some advantage. A hummingbird that did *not* hibernate would require 36% more Calories. Warming up from hibernation requires only a little more than 1% increase (1/89) in Calorie intake. A man who hibernated would save *less* than 36% because of the scale effect on cooling; but warming up would require in the neighborhood of 57% increase. (Approximate analysis.) Therefore daily hibernation is uneconomical for a large animal with its relatively low metabolic rate.

8-23. In general, the larger the animal, the lower the critical temperature (scale effect again).

8-25. (a) No basis for predicting the norm, except that we would be surprised if it lay outside the range defined by elephants and goats —36–40°C. (b) On the assumption that this early man had not yet invented clothing, he would still be hairy and we would expect the critical lower temperature to be in the region of −40°C, as it is for dogs and cows, animals of roughly the same size.

9-4. In a static society, interest must have as negative feedback inflation, repudiation of debts, etc. We have for some time been able to allow money at interest because the total income of the population has increased at the same or greater rate. When we reach the end of the present technological revolution we must give up interest in order to achieve stability in the economic system without painful negative feedbacks.

9-7. $\dfrac{\log N - \log N_o}{\log (1 + i)} = t.$

9-8. $\dfrac{.30103}{\log (1 + i)} = t_2.$

9-9. $\text{antilog} \left(\dfrac{\log N - \log N_o}{t} \right) - 1 = i.$

9-11. $(148.847 \times 10^{16} \text{ cm}^2) \div (18 \times 10^2 \text{ cm}^2)$ $= 8.269 \times 10^{14}.$

9-12. Use equation from (9-7).

$t = \dfrac{14.917453 - 9.544068}{.008600} \text{ yrs} = 625 \text{ years}$

9-22. If the death rate falls, the population of people living at any one time necessarily rises. Since, by hypothesis, the number of births per woman per lifetime does not increase, the number of births per population (per year) must necessarily decrease.

9-24. (a) 114,800 years. (b) 25,000 mph—easy to remember, for 25,000 mi = circumference of earth.

9-25. To circle the earth in less than an hour it would have to exceed the escape velocity—which would take it out of orbit.

10-4. Like all set points, the phenostatic set point can only be determined by observation. The meaning of the phrase is embedded in Fig. 10-2.

10-6. A short-run experiment is closer to the natural situation where there are no walls and a predator seldom has more than one chance with a given prey.

10-9. Because of the scale effect, metabolic rate will be, in part, inversely related to size and controlled by the same factors. Insofar as the metabolic rate can vary independently of size, a high metabolic rate will be selected against in times of starvation, a low rate in most other times by all forms of competition.

10-14. No. To exert its centripetal effect it is only necessary that selection take *proportionately* more of the more extreme values. That it does so is evident from Columns 4 and 5 of the table.

10-16. A brood of 3. More fertile as well as less fertile swifts contribute fewer offspring to the next generation, so selection operates against both increases and decreases in fertility.

10-20. No. First, some of the 10 percent are undoubtedly caused by environmental factors (disease, malnutrition, etc.). This would tend to reduce the figure. Acting in the other direction, Hertig, Rock, and Evans' observations indicate that genetic error must be much greater—undoubtedly above 38 percent (38 percent + some invisibly damaged early embryos + some of the 10 percent known aborted + about 1 percent congenitally defective).

11-9. DDT-resistant flies are "fittest" only in a DDT-environment; remove the DDT and they are less fit than non-resistant flies.

11-13. *A,* Arizona; *B,* Oregon; *C,* Minnesota; *D,* Arctic. The warmer the region, the greater the cooling surface (ears) needed.

11-15. All members of a clone are genetically identical. Among vertebrates, identical twins are genetically identical; unfortunately, there are not many of them.

11-16. Certainly not. Notice how different their eating habits are.

11-17. Less expensive to have type shipped; but greater possibility of loss. Many museums will not ship out types.

12-9. False. If we fill in a missing link between A and F, thus: A-C-F, we thereby replace one missing link (A-F) with two (A-C and C-F). Of course, the *extent* of each missing link will now be less.

12-11. 22,651,200 years.

12-13. $7,000 \div 86,400 = 0.081$ days.

12-14. 10 December.

12-16. The prefix *a-* means not; *zoic,* animal, hence life: Period before there was life on earth.

13-11. "Atom" means nonsplittable. But it is by splitting atoms that we get the energy out. (Fusion will also yield energy.)

13-13. Yes. Grain fed directly to humans supported ten times as many lives as grain circulated through chickens to humans.

13-15. Model *A*. Model *G,* because of greenhouse effect, heats up in summer; air conditioner runs off motor. (Heater in winter uses spare heat from water cooling system and does not influence gas mileage.)

13-17. Increase temperature, because with less photosynthesis, more CO_2, more greenhouse effect.

13-19. Meat of carnivores only about 10 percent as abundant as meat of herbivores.

13-21. Ideas on outbreaks of no application to their situation because of great stability of complex tropical webs of life.

13-23. During the winter, photosynthesis is diminished and so CO_2 content of air rises, as compared with summer when photosynthesis is at maximum rate.

14-5. The deep water would become heated and rise to the surface, bringing with it its dissolved nitrates and phosphates which would cause an increase in plankton, and ultimately in fish and whales that are food for men.

14-8. *Cyano-* (Gr. *kyanos* = a dark-blue substance).

14-9. Psilophyta, because the smallest number; and because the fact that all other figures end in zero suggests that they have been rounded off —which they have.

14-12. "Is" would imply consciousness of purpose.

14-16. The euphotic zone extends downward only about 80 meters: how could coral, which depends on photosynthesis of algae grow below that? It can't. Probably there was a slow submergence of a rock that was initially near the surface, the growth upward of coral matching the rate of submergence (Darwin's theory).

14-18. $75 \times 10^{21} = 75 \times (10^3)^7$
$\cong 75 \times (2^{10})^7 \cong 64 \times (2^{10})^7 \cong 2^6 \times 2^{70}$
$\cong 2^{76}$. So: only a bit more than 76 days required.

15-8. Only cave guano can be protected from water and consequent loss of nitrogen from microbial action.

15-9. He tries to avoid making surface injuries on which *Saprolegnia* could grow.

15-11. Shielding from air—wax on jelly; thick skin left on ham. Addition of fungicides (leather) or fungistats (bread).

15-14. Aerobic. More energy available for growth, so more yeast cells result.

15-15. The difference in energy between Equation 1 and Equation 2 is $(674 - 22)$ Cal = 652 Cal. If 2 gram-moles of alcohol are respired, they will yield 652 Calories (Principle: Conservation of Energy). *One* gram-mole of ethanol will yield one-half as much, or 326 Calories.

15-17. Scale effect allows more rapid dissipation of heat.

15-19. Hagelstein was called a curator of Myxomycetes (plants) because he was employed by a botanical institution; but he himself apparently felt these organisms should be regarded as animals (Mycetozoa).

15-21. Would have to have available strains of known type to test it with. Unknown is opposisite of type it will mate with.

16-8. Boil it for, say, 5 minutes. Then incubate it at room temperature. Spores survive, germinate.

16-10. Instead of heating every day, you would have to use longer periods, say, 2 or 3 days, to allow for germination at slower speed.

16-12. Competitive Exclusion Principle. House mouse is selective culture medium for *E. muriseptica,* field mouse for streptococci. Practical use: by serial transfer, one can purify either species. (Inoculation into other species is check on purity.)

16-14. "Money!"

16-17. The beef. It is possible to make a beef pie without thoroughly heating the beef. Peaches and tomatoes are ruled out because acid; beans because boiled every day.

16-19. How could one taste it without getting a lethal dose?

16-21. The latter. Otherwise tyndallization wouldn't work.

16-23. Respiration of microbes produces the heat. If sedimentation were slower, there would be more complete use of organic matter in mud, consequently, less heat produced and accumulated in sediment.

17-6. Basically, such an argument implies that environments compete for the attention of organisms, which is not true. The pioneer organism is not competing with the organisms it left behind, but only with the organisms (if any) in the new environment. Its survival (and further evolution) will be determined only by its reaction to the new environment.

17-8. Of the amphibia (frogs, etc.). Both groups live on land, for the most part moist, but have to have water available for their gametes to get together.

17-13. A catapult.

17-15. Will practically prevent self-fertilizing, inbreeding.

18-13. Flowering plants. Members of same clone have identical heredity. Only identical twins (rare, and few) in mammals have same advantage.

18-15. As a result of successive mutations, it will become more heterozygous. It will be unable to change rapidly genetically, hence will be able to survive only those environmental changes for which it has sufficient individual adaptability.

18-16. Usually we reckon age as beginning at zero with the seed. On this basis, every garlic plant is probably thousands of years old.

18-18. Certainly apocryphal. Improved apples are very heterozygous; their seedlings would be almost all worthless.

18-20. Heat coagulates proteins; thus plasmodesmata might be coagulated, plugging sieve-plate holes.

18-22. Dating by cross-comparison of trees and timbers. Drought from narrowness of growth rings.

18-24. To cut down transpiration so it is not too much for the undoubtedly now diminished number of undamaged root hairs.

19-5. Sticky pollen sticks best to insects. Sticky pollen is poor for dispersal by air because several grains stuck together could not float as far through air.

19-7. No. Such would be poorly suited to dissemination of the seed.

19-8. Tribe *B.* Because tribe *A* will presumably be planting the same fields every year. Always some of their grain will be "volunteer," coming from self-shattering heads. The nomadic habit of *B* selects for nonshattering heads.

19-9. A head that shatters scatters its progeny more widely than does a nonshattering head.

19-10. All agricultural practices aim at creating single-species fields, rather than complex, ecologically balanced communities. A single-species field is ideal for the explosive multiplication of a pest.

20-10. Many people are carriers; that is, for them the protozoan is parasitic but not pathogenic.

20-12. The "Great Depression." General social disorganization and poverty slowed up the draining and treatment of swamps and drove many people to live in poorer areas; also they could not afford medication.

20-15. Mutation and natural selection (with a new set point) have produced the new strains. A possible solution: rapid alternation of insecticides.

20-17. Fresh water is more variable, less dependable. Freshwater organisms have had to evolve greater individual adaptability.

20-19. The result may not be satisfactory over the long term, but as a temporary expedient at least it has the virtue of keeping alive the feeling of puzzlement.

20-21. (This anticipates a point to be made later.) The vacuolar membrane is like the cell membrane; things inside the vacuole are really outside the organism. They enter the organism when either (a) they cross the vacuolar membrane, or (b) the vacuolar membrane breaks down.

21-9. In general, fresh water is more variable from place to place and time to time, and so species have had to evolve greater adaptability.

21-11. Among animals, support for large moving form on land becomes impossibly difficult. With plants, large static form can live better on land; it would be difficult for it to remain attached in moving water, especially near shore; and photosynthesis is out of the question in water at 200 feet.

21-13. (a) Radial; (b) bilateral; (c) bilateral. (a) and (b) are perfect; (c) is imperfect—e.g., steering wheel not centered.

21-15. The surface film of water.

21-17. Not really. As Butler said, "A hen is only an egg's way of making another egg." The worms serve their "purpose" in producing the next generation. Natural selection does not select for senility.

21-19. From the name and the language one can assume that the implicit scale is Fahrenheit. If so, $-10°F$ for two weeks is enough (unless the roast is huge) for it takes only 10 days at $-10°F$ to kill the trichina, as you can calculate. Of course, if Mrs. M. will just cook the roast *done,* the question need not arise.

21-21. Most parasitic diseases (e.g., malaria, shistosomiasis) require work to eliminate them—work in draining swamps, spreading insecticides, etc. Because parasitized people are little fit to do work, positive feedback insures that no progress will be made. If outsiders help, this is because the knowledge of the need acts as a negative feedback with the outsider as the agent. A nonparasitized party, with knowledge and will, must be included in the system to get this corrective action.

21-23. Traces of hirudin from the leech inhibit blood clotting.

21-25. Serve to disperse the species.

22-9. Gr. *ephemeros* = daily, lasting but a day. Consider English adjective "ephemeral." Pteron = wing.

22-13. It never will. Final size of fly determined at time it metamorphoses from pupa.

22-15. The lowest note the human ear can hear is about 20 cps; the hummingbird wings complete 50 cps, which produces an audible low hum. Seagull wings beating at 5 cps produce a note below the range of human hearing.

22-18. Note that the number of bees is constant, so the total amount of metabolism is approximately constant. Given a constant total metabolism it is better, at a lower temperature, to diminish the amount of surface by contracting, even though the surface:volume ratio goes up.

22-20. The one that smells like the female, for it would be difficult for the species to evolve males that were indifferent to females, whereas it would be not so serious if the animals evolved indifference to one of their foodstuffs.

22-22. If genes for polygamy (polyandry) appeared, they would be selected for, thus eventually negating this method of control.

22-24. It would be duller. Bright flowers are used to attract insects and birds. Wind-pollinated flowers are inconspicuous.

22-26. Yes, in a sense. Worker bees inherit their potentiality for sterility (given certain food); the species "gets away with it" because the whole hive is the unit of selection.

22-30. Probably not. Economically the nectar would be a waste, though this is probably a small matter. More important, the nectar might act as a "releaser" for insect reactions inappropriate to effecting pollination—unless another mutation relocated the pollen.

22-32. Neglecting any interest in the animals as such, there are two questions we have some interest in: "How do you talk to a Martian?" and "How do you talk to an idiot?" If we ever encounter intelligent beings from another planet, their language will undoubtedly be so different from ours that we will have to have the most profound understanding of the meaning of language to communicate with them at all. The same sort of problem is involved in communication with schizophrenics and other "abnormal" types in our own species. (Note that idiot etymologically means *a private person;* the root implies private, proper, peculiar—rather than shared, common, general.)

23-7. Rise produces expansion of bladder which makes fish have less specific gravity which causes greater rise—positive feedback—leading to, sometimes, ultimate explosion of fish.

23-13. Fairly recently evolved from land forms.

23-15. Whales in *order* Cetacea. Any subdivision thereof must be a *suborder* or *superfamily*—not a phylum.

23-17. In cold countries, cold-blooded animals are inactive much of the time, during which time they can't grow. In inactive state must remain hidden—harder, for large forms.

23-19. Scale effect: heat loss from small endotherm is very high and must be compensated for by great intake of Calories.

23-21. An example: when man finds an unusually meaty pig he does not immediately kill it and eat it, but he eats the poorer animals before they breed, saving the desired form for breeding. In general, the animal husbandman eats the best last. Similarly, with respect to tameness, the most difficult to catch are eaten first.

23-23. Because of the Pyramid of Protoplasm, a carnivore must draw its food from at least 10 times as great an area; it must become a wanderer.

24-7. Being buoyed up by the water, whale skeleton need not be so big (strong).

24-9. By X-ray photos or fluoroscope.

24-11. Direction of movement determined by mode of attachment of muscle tendons.

24-13. It takes muscles to breathe (diaphragm, intercostal muscles) so they die as soon as they need to breathe. Before birth, the placental circulation furnished them with oxygen.

24-18. Female.

25-5. No. Both lungs would collapse.

25-7. He puts a snippet of the child's lung in water. If it floats, it shows that the child once took a breath. (Not stillborn.)

25-9. Figure shows a section through alveoli; some of the alveoli were missed by the plane of cutting.

25-11. Area of idealized cylindrical man (neglecting his ends) is $2\pi rh = (2)(\pi)(0.2)(2)$ m^2 = 2.5 m^2. Divide 40 to 80 by 2.5, yielding 16 to 32—the number of revolutions the man must make.

25-13. If on top, would be kept cooler by circulation of outside air through nearby pharynx into mouth.

25-15. Less serious. No N_2 to cause "bends."

25-17. Mass of atmosphere is 5.2×10^{15} metric tons. If we take population to be 3.5×10^9, then dividing first figure by the second gives 1.5×10^6 metric tons.

25-19. Unlikely. Once he becomes unconscious (no "will power"), medulla takes over.

25-21. On such a standard, O_2 should be banned, since it is lethal in 100 percent concentration. Not scientifically defensible.

25-25. He does not breathe pure tobacco smoke, so the effective concentration is less. However, *heavy* smokers do suffer from some pulmonary edema.

25-27. Largely for "aesthetic" reasons, that is, to persuade people to use this method which might otherwise be unacceptable.

25-29. When going up, extra middle-ear pressure tends to blow Eustachian tube open, relieve pressure. When going down, excess pressure in pharynx tends to close the tube. See Fig. 25-9.

26-6. Part of system for closing opening to esophagus (see Fig. 22-3).

26-8. Because topologically the inside of G-I tract is outside body.

26-10. Pepsin would not work; ptyalin is active longer.

26-12. Gr. *pan* = all + and *creas* = flesh. Probably in reference to its lack of bone. But apt also in that the juices attack all three kinds of flesh, or food.

26-14. Vitamin A—present in many natural oils.

26-16. Scientifically wrong, because UV of the sun causes chemical reaction in skin which makes the vitamin; there is no *substance* in light. But from practical point of view, this misconception may lead to correct practice.

26-18. Certainly not. Fluoride is a food, since it cures nothing, but is required for normal growth. Chlorine is a medicine, since it kills disease germs, but is not required for normal growth.

26-20. The 1900–1930 change is part of the already noted shift: with increasing independence (irresponsibility?), women have fewer ulcers. The reversal beginning in 1932 may be connected with the Depression—unemployed men being home and relatively irresponsible. Speculative.

26-22. Probably there will be an increase in ulcers among them; freedom, responsibility, and ulcers tend to be associated.

26-24. Referring to §130, one finds that this toxin is a protein. Most of the protein molecules are digested by the gut. Only 10^{-5} of them escape digestion.

26-26. $3 \times (1{,}600 + 2{,}000) = 10{,}800$.

26-28. Food is not a limiting factor. Therefore team *C*, with 4 men, will do 33 percent more work than team *D*, with 3 men.

26-29. Food now limiting. M.C. (maintenance Calories) for team *D* is $3 \times 1{,}600 = 4{,}800$, leaving $(8{,}000) - (4{,}800) = 3{,}200$ W.C. (work Calories). For team *C*: M.C. $= 4 \times 1{,}600 = 6{,}400$, leaving $(8{,}000) - (6{,}400) = 1{,}600$ W.C. Therefore team *D* (3 men) will do 100 percent more work than team *C* (4 men).

26-32. Should have the minimum number of horses needed for getting the work done, so as to minimize maintenance Calories.

26-36. 182.5 kg; 2.6 (if he weighs 70 kg).

27-7. Greatly diminish them, because of lower concentration of O_2 in blood.

27-11. Blood volume = 5,000 cc = 5×10^6 mm^3. No. RBC = $5 \times 10^6 \times 5 \times 10^6 = 25 \times 10^{12}$. Fraction of RBC destroyed per day = $\frac{1}{120}$. No. destroyed per day = $(250 \times 10^{11}) \times \frac{1}{120} \cong 2 \times 10^{11}$. No. seconds in a day = $(60) \times (60) \times (24) = 86{,}400 = 8.64 \times 10^4$. No. RBC destroyed per second = $(2 \times 10^{11}) \div 8.64 \times 10^4 \cong 2.3 \times 10^6$. Destroyed in spleen.

27-14. Certainly. Setting aside the nicotine question, the carbon monoxide will diminish the capacity of the blood to hold oxygen, and so diminish the runner's speed.

27-16. It is very easy to see what "authorities" say there is to see. For Leonardo, Galen was the source of error; for the biology student, it is . . . ?

28-6. Obviously controversial. It may make some people mad. But here goes! (a) Certainly 2-dimensional. (b) Also 2-dimensional, but illusion of 3 dimensions. (c) Any sound is in 1 dimension + time = 2 dimensions. (d) Just like c, but one could argue for the illusion of more (counterpoint), analogous to perspective in painting. (e) One dimension only—time, with the ideas (nondimensional) lined up in time.

(f) Seldom more than 1-dimensional. (g) Joyce, like a good poet, strives for more than 1 dimension and may achieve it. (h) There is a striving to present the ideas in 4 dimensions— 3 + time. There is, I think, an important point here: that literary writing appears rather impoverished to scientists because it has so few dimensions to it. (Literary quarterlies would be aghast at the thought of presenting a graph!)

28-8. The radio-iodine will destroy all patches of thyroid no matter where they are; whereas a surgeon may have trouble finding some of the thyroid.

28-10. Plainly, more field studies are required.

29-7. Inoculate X into a rabbit. Wait for a couple of weeks for the rabbit to develop anti-X. Then test anti-X against X and against Y. It should give the same amount of reaction against both if X and Y are the same. Reciprocal experiment desirable.

29-9. Chemical reactions easier to see and study when solutions are used. With whole cells some of the reactants might be adsorbed on the cells.

29-11. Proteins in gut digested to amino acids before absorption. Amino acids universal; not antigenic.

29-13. East Enders had already been exposed to many diseases and developed antibodies against them that Scots lads did not have.

29-15. Passive immunity. Antibodies passed into it from mother.

29-17. Not only acquired but natural immunity is developed after embryonic stages are passed.

29-19. Tuberculosis germs are notorious for surviving as relatively inactive, but living patches in the lung, walled off by the inflammation process. Decrease inflammation by cortisone, and the bacteria may break loose.

29-21. Drugs that will separate the various effects, each one having, preferably, only one effect, with no side-effects.

29-23. No. The decision to seek and accept (or to reject) naturalistic explanations is a commitment made outside of science. For a good discussion of this point, see Michael Polanyi's *Science, Faith and Society*.

29-25. First (b): the heterographs must have ultimately been completely resorbed. But before this (a), it might yield a few days' (or weeks', possibly) supply of usable hormone. However, psychological factors—wishful thinking—probably more important. After all, much of what we call "sex" is in the head. And as for (c), "there's no fool like an old fool," of which the supply may even be increasing.

29-26. Diagnosis would become better developed in situation *a* because unskillful physician would have less success than skillful one, and so would be selected against.

29-28. In *a*.

29-30. "Morbidity" means state of being diseased —not to be confused with "mortality"! Certainly in *a*.

30-4. Chain-reaction transmission of a chemical reaction along one dimension. But powder fuse does not reconstitute itself.

30-7. Case a: sensory neurons gone. Case b: motor neurons gone.

30-15. It will constrict iris, cause increased saliva, and contraction of rectum.

30-16. Sympathetic.

30-17. Sympathetic nervous system is stimulated. Irises will dilate—hence "wide eyes" of fear.

30-19. Autonomic, especially parasympathetic.

31-7. Evaporation of water from the hot floor (a) cooled the floor and (b) increased the relative humidity of the room so that evaporation cooling of people was less effective.

31-8. First the chloroform would have boiled off; then the water; and, if the concentration of chloroform in the room was sufficiently high, the men would have been anesthetized.

31-10. Temperature kept up by increased metabolism.

31-13. 100 percent R.H. in deep mines. At 88°F, 100 percent R.H. body can keep only as cool as

98.6° because of constant production of heat. Raise external temperature, body temperature goes up.

31-17. In the "chills" there is vigorous shivering, which increases the movement of air at the surface of the body, hence also convection losses.

31-18. John's apartment will be hotter for, by the Second Law of Thermodynamics, the coils of the refrigerator can be cooled only by the expenditure of work and the *over-all* production of heat. In effect, he is converting electrical energy into heat, just as effectively as if he tried to cool his apartment with an electric heater.

31-20. All the heat pumped out of rooms heats up the outside still further.

31-22. Soap furnishes lubrication. Cold water causes contraction of blood vessels, hence of flesh. (Effect on metal of ring is less.)

31-24. Immediate: protein. Ultimate: both the same, by definition of Calories.

31-27. Sleep produces lowered blood pressure, which produces less urine.

31-30. (a) more sugar; (b) more urine; (c) less urine; (d) more urine; possibly with protein in it; (e) less urine; (f) proteins in urine; (g) sugar in urine; (h) proteins in urine; (i) copious, watery urine.

32-4. Convergent evolution.

32-9. Mrs. Freeman has no complaints because her nose is continuously fatigued.

32-11. No. (a) The "is" of simple predication. (b) The "is" of definition. (c) This is predication of a quality that some might not be able to perceive. (d) Like the preceding. (e) A value judgment.

32-14. Nope. Movies flicker for them. Most annoying.

32-15. If a man asserts that he is deaf in the right ear, feed sound to both ears, but more strongly to the right. Hearing it only in the right, the malingerer will claim to hear nothing, thus revealing the function of his right ear.

32-18. Without unconscious self-criticism made possible by auditory feedback, the speech of the deaf person gradually deviates from the pattern taught him.

32-22. True. *A* and *B* can verify that they use the same symbols for a color, not that the color looks the same to both.

32-25. Certainly not.

32-28. They are completely color-blind.

32-30. Water probably same temperature all day long. It was the difference between it and variable air temperature that led to erroneous interpretation.

33-8. Mathematician, public speaker, accountant; possibly architect and physicist.

33-11. Contact with external world limited to touch. Balancing difficult—dependent entirely on proprioceptive sense.

33-12. (a) Inner ear is okay; probably middle-ear trouble. (b) Probably cochlea damaged, but not rest of inner ear. (c) Inner ear completely destroyed.

33-15. Not possible to find out how they look *to him*. Conditioned reflex tests discrimination, not sensory quality.

33-17. Probably refers to the stretching of a string, say, of a lute.

34-3. Sterilization.

34-5. Prolonged heat in testes prevents spermatogenesis. (No indication that Japanese baths are long enough.)

34-7. Route must be hormonal.

34-9. The facts are that *micro*organisms do not have alimentary tracts because (theory) of the scale effect.

34-11. (a) Imperfect separation of systemic and pulmonary circulations. (b) Either the ductus arteriosus is still present, or the opening between the two auricles. (c) Both can be remedied, but operation on the living heart is very difficult.

34-15. The set point seems to be the same; but there seems to be "stickiness" in the error-actuated feedback. The corrective feedback seems to have a threshold.

35-3. 2 kinds—namely, A_1B and A_2B.

35-5. A_1B_1, A_1B_2, A_2B_1, and A_2B_2.

35-7. 8. $A_1B_1C_1$, $A_1B_1C_2$, $A_1B_2C_1$, $A_1B_2C_2$, $A_2B_1C_1$, $A_2B_1C_2$, $A_2B_2C_1$, $A_2B_2C_2$.

35-8. 2^3.

35-10. 2^x.

35-11. 2^{23} ($\cong 8,000,000$ = exactly 8,388,608).

35-18. It is difficult to doubt the evidence of one's own eyes, so "you" would probably conclude a "miracle" had happened (if "you" retained faith in lack of bias). The unusual had been witnessed.

35-19. Controversial. Probably conclude Dr. Ananias deserved his name (see Acts, Chap. 5).

35-20. 4, namely Nh-Ph, Nh-Pt, Nt-Ph, Nt-Pt.

35-23. The error: assuming that all possibilities are equally probable. (Tomorrow, I will be either dead, or alive. It does not follow that the probability that I will be dead is one-half.)

35-25. Both boys—½; both girls—½. Identical twins have same genes, hence are of same sex.

35-27. All *Cc;* phenotype normal.

35-29. Expected: half *Cc* (normal), half *cc* (albino). Possible: any proportions of the two types.

35-34. No. Even if all his children were normal, he might be *Cc*.

35-35. Albinia. No albino carries a hidden "dark" gene; whereas many Smudgians carry hidden albino genes.

36-3. Consistent.

36-5. To prevent a Rhesus-negative girl from being transfused Rh + blood, which would prevent her ever bearing an Rh+ child.

36-6. MN and A; MN and B.

36-8. A total of 12, namely: M-A, M-B, M-O, M-AB; N-A, N-B, N-O, N-AB; MN-A, MN-B, MN-O, MN-AB.

36-9. First child could have been produced by either. Second child could not be lover's because it has no N-gene; therefore it is presumed to be husband's (could be). Third child: A-gene rules out husband, but could be lover's.

36-11. Everybody is polydactylous—which means having many fingers. Hyperdactyly means too many fingers.

36-12. Evidently, Mr. Jones is heterozygous, Mrs. Jones is homozygous Rh negative. Heterozygous children: #4, 5, 6, 7, 8. Homozygous Rh negative: #9. Unknown: #1, 2, 3; antibody not yet built up.

36-13. "Illegitimacy" is a panchreston, an "explain-all," that works too well to be an acceptable scientific hypothesis.

37-4. The two types of blood have complementary properties, each having the factor the other lacks. To take an example known to be true: a person suffering from "Christmas disease" lacks Factor IX but possesses Factor VIII; a hemophiliac of the classic type lacks Factor VIII, but possesses Factor IX. Mixed together, these bloods coagulate.

37-6. Maternal grandmother.

37-8. Sons will be the same. Half her new daughters expected to be colorblind, *cc*.

37-10. *Hh*.

37-11. George is safe. But Mary has ½ chance of being a carrier, ⅛ chance of producing hemophiliac.

37-12. $(\frac{1}{20})^2 = \frac{1}{400}$.

37-15. No. Sex-linked lethals would decrease proportion of males.

37-17. Mother must be *Hh,* father is *HY*. Sons are *hY*. Since daughter is chromatin negative, she is probably a genetic male (*hY*) who has undergone a reversal of sex.

37-20. Brother-sister differ most, since one is XY and the other XX; the secondary effects of developing sexuality will exaggerate the primary genetic differences. Brother-brother pairs will be least like because the two X's will, about half the time, be different X's (from the mother). Sister-sister pairs necessarily share one X (from the father) which, by the general effects of gene-dominance will tend to mask whatever differences there may be between the remaining X's.

37-21. Because of the ZW system in birds, these males must have started out life as haploid Z eggs which then (surprisingly) became diploid; this made them ZZ and they (unsurprisingly) became males.

38-4. As Borel said: "A coin has neither conscience nor memory."

38-6. $\frac{1}{2}$.

38-8. $(\frac{1}{6}) \times (\frac{1}{6}) = \frac{1}{36}$.

38-10. $(2) \times (\frac{1}{6}) \times (\frac{1}{6}) = \frac{2}{36} = \frac{1}{18}$.

38-11. (a) $(\frac{1}{1000}) \times (\frac{1}{2}) = \frac{1}{2000}$. (b) $(\frac{1}{1000}) \times (\frac{1}{2}) = \frac{1}{2000}$. (c) $(\frac{999}{1000}) \times \frac{1}{2} = \frac{999}{2000}$.

38-13. (a) $\frac{3}{4}$. (b) $\frac{1}{4}$. (c) $(\frac{3}{4}) \times (\frac{1}{4}) = \frac{3}{16}$. (d) $(\frac{3}{4}) \times (\frac{1}{4}) \times (\frac{1}{2}) = \frac{3}{32}$.

38-15. (a) 16. (b) 64. (c) 256. (d) $(2^n)^2$.

38-18. We mean that he is known to be heterozygous for the gene G, which is the only one we are interested in (or know about) at the moment. He has many other genes that we're not considering.

38-20. (b) (c) and (e) involve genes that are *not* on the same chromosome; they will be distributed independently, consequently the four kinds of gametes will occur in equal numbers. (a) and (d) involve linked genes.

38-22. Asexually, so as not to break up his good (heterozygous) combinations of genes.

38-24. Call genes A and a. One unit of A adds 10 cm to basic 40 cm. Two units add 20 cm.

38-26. 5. (4 capital letter genes, 3 capital letter genes . . . down to 0 capital letter gene.)

38-28. $\frac{1}{4} \times \frac{1}{4} \times \frac{1}{4} = \frac{1}{64}$, which is about 2 percent. So, 3 genes.

38-31. (a) $\frac{1}{2}$. (b) $(\frac{1}{2}) \times (\frac{1}{11}) = \frac{1}{22}$. (c) $\frac{1}{2}$. (d) $(\frac{1}{2}) \times (\frac{1}{11}) \times (\frac{1}{11}) = \frac{1}{242}$.

38-32. Color blindness is *not* independent of sex.

38-35. $q = \sqrt{.36} = .6 = $ freq. of gene for nontasting. Freq. of "tasting gene" $= 1 - .6 = .4$. So gene for nontasting is the more common, though nontasters are less common than tasters.

38-37. (a) $(\frac{10}{11}A + \frac{1}{11}a)^2 = .826AA + .165Aa + .008aa$. (b) $(\frac{10}{11}A + \frac{1}{11}a) = .909A + .091a$.

38-38. The *aa* males are equal in genetic weight to the entire population of *AA* females, because females (*AA*) can mate only with males (*aa*) in producing the F_1. Therefore the answer is the same as for Prob. 38-36.

38-41. By killing all the conquered females the Amazons eliminated the vanquished population as a separate entity. By breeding themselves to the vanquished males, they downgraded their children in the direction of the defeated group.

39-3. Embryo separates at 4-cell stage into 4 separate cells.

39-7. Very large hands. (The feet of this boy, Robert Wadlow, were very large, but not obvious perhaps in figure.)

39-8. Natural selection acts against juvenile cancer, scarcely at all against cancer of the aged.

40-6. Most important point: expectation of loss = (probability of loss) × (magnitude of loss). For a minor defeat, we are willing to run greater risks. It is hard to see on what basis we might agree on a conventional limit for "acceptable" expectation of loss.

40-7. The proofreader, whoever he may be.

40-11. Purify stock by keeping at 20°C and weeding out red flowers. Remainder will not require so much heat.

40-12. Keep it quiet.

40-13. Make it noisy and let natural selection get rid of unwanted mice.

40-18. The egg. Arbitrary element involved in calling organism *Gallus domesticus*. Egg will reach that arbitrary set of genes before chicken will.

APPENDIXES

APPENDIX 1. THE PERIODIC SYSTEM

ELEMENTS INCORPORATED INTO LIVING MATTER

▓ Certainly and invariably

░ Dubiously or variably

1

HYDROGEN 1 H 1.008	HELIUM 2 He 4.003

	Ia	IIa	IIIa	IV	V	VIb	VIIb	VIII			Ib	IIb	IIIb	IV	Va	VIa	VIIa	O

2

I	II	III	IV	V	VI	VII	O
LITHIUM 3 Li 6.940	BERYLLIUM 4 Be 9.013	BORON 5 B 10.82	CARBON 6 C 12.01	NITROGEN 7 N 14.008	OXYGEN 8 O 16.000	FLUORINE 9 F 19.00	NEON 10 Ne 20.183

3

SODIUM 11 Na 22.991	MAGNESIUM 12 Mg 24.32	ALUMINUM 13 Al 26.98	SILICON 14 Si 28.09	PHOSPHORUS 15 P 30.975	SULFUR 16 S 32.066	CHLORINE 17 Cl 35.475	ARGON 18 Ar 39.944

	Ia	IIa	IIIa	IV	V	VIb	VIIb	VIII			Ib	IIb	IIIb	IV	Va	VIa	VIIa	O

4

POTASSIUM 19 K 39.100	CALCIUM 20 Ca 40.08	SCANDIUM 21 Sc 44.96	TITANIUM 22 Ti 47.90	VANADIUM 23 V 50.95	CHROMIUM 24 Cr 52.01	MANGANESE 25 Mn 54.94	IRON 26 Fe 55.85	COBALT 27 Co 58.94	NICKEL 28 Ni 58.71	COPPER 29 Cu 63.54	ZINC 30 Zn 65.38	GALLIUM 31 Ga 69.72	GERMANIUM 32 Ge 72.60	ARSENIC 33 As 74.91	SELENIUM 34 Se 78.96	BROMINE 35 Br 79.916	KRYPTON 36 Kr 83.80

5

RUBIDIUM 37 Rb 85.48	STRONTIUM 38 Sr 87.63	YTTRIUM 39 Y 88.92	ZIRCONIUM 40 Zr 91.22	NIOBIUM 41 Nb 92.91	MOLYBDENUM 42 Mo 95.95	TECHNETIUM 43 Tc [99]	RUTHENIUM 44 Ru 101.1	RHODIUM 45 Rh 102.91	PALLADIUM 46 Pd 106.4	SILVER 47 Ag 107.880	CADMIUM 48 Cd 112.41	INDIUM 49 In 114.82	TIN 50 Sn 118.70	ANTIMONY 51 Sb 121.76	TELLURIUM 52 Te 127.61	IODINE 53 I 126.91	XENON 54 Xe 131.30

6

CESIUM 55 Cs 132.91	BARIUM 56 Ba 137.36	LANTHANIDE SERIES 57-71	HAFNIUM 72 Hf 178.50	TANTALUM 73 Ta 180.95	TUNGSTEN 74 W 183.86	RHENIUM 75 Re 186.22	OSMIUM 76 Os 190.2	IRIDIUM 77 Ir 192.2	PLATINUM 78 Pt 195.09	GOLD 79 Au 197.0	MERCURY 80 Hg 200.61	THALLIUM 81 Tl 204.39	LEAD 82 Pb 207.21	BISMUTH 83 Bi 209.00	POLONIUM 84 Po 210	ASTATINE 85 At [210]	RADON 86 Rn 222

7

FRANCIUM 87 Fr [223]	RADIUM 88 Ra 226.05	ACTINIDE SERIES 89-103

LANTHANUM 57 La 138.92	CERIUM 58 Ce 140.13	PRASEODYMIUM 59 Pr 140.92	NEODYMIUM 60 Nd 144.27	PROMETHIUM 61 Pm [145]	SAMARIUM 62 Sm 150.43	EUROPIUM 63 Eu 152.35	GADOLINIUM 64 Gd 157.26	TERBIUM 65 Tb 158.93	DYSPROSIUM 66 Dy 162.51	HOLMIUM 67 Ho 164.94	ERBIUM 68 Er 167.2	THULIUM 69 Tm 168.94	YTTERBIUM 70 Yb 173.04	LUTETIUM 71 Lu 174.99
ACTINIUM 89 Ac 227	THORIUM 90 Th 232.05	PROTACTINIUM 91 Pa 231	URANIUM 92 U 238.07	NEPTUNIUM 93 Np [237]	PLUTONIUM 94 Pu [242]	AMERICIUM 95 Am [243]	CURIUM 96 Cm [245]	BERKELIUM 97 Bk [249]	CALIFORNIUM 98 Cf [249]	EINSTEINIUM 99 Es [254]	FERMIUM 100 Fm [255]	MENDELEVIUM 101 Md [256]	NOBELIUM 102 No [253]	LAWRENCIUM 103 Lw [257]

APPENDIX 2. RADIOACTIVE ISOTOPES

Half-life and significant radiations of a selection of radioactive isotopes.

Isotope	Half-life	Significant Radiation		
		alpha	beta	gamma
radium-226	1,620 years	+		+
radon-222	3.8 days	+		
radon-217	0.001 second	+		
uranium-238	4.5 billion years	+		+
uranium-235	710 million years	+		+
cerium-144	285 days		+	+
cesium-137	30 years		+	+
iodine-131	8 days		+	+
gold-198	2.7 days		+	+
phosphorus-30	2.5 minutes		+	
strontium-90	28 years		+	
cobalt-60	5.2 years		+	+
carbon-14	5,730 years		+	
tritium (H³)	12.3 years		+	

For further reference:
Lange's Handbook of Chemistry, latest edition. Sandusky, Ohio: Handbook Publishers, Inc.
Handbook of Chemistry and Physics ("the rubber handbook"), latest edition. Cleveland, Ohio: Chemical Rubber Publishing Co.

APPENDIX 3. THE METRIC SYSTEM

General System of Multiples

Multiple	Prefix	Symbol
10^{12}	tera	T
10^9	giga	G
10^6	mega	M
10^3	kilo	k
10^2	hecto	h
10	deka	da
10^{-1}	deci	d
10^{-2}	centi	c
10^{-3}	milli	m
10^{-6}	micro	μ
10^{-9}	nano	n
10^{-12}	pico	p
10^{-15}	femto	f
10^{-18}	atto	a

LENGTH

Metric to English

1 Ångstrom = 1Å = 10^{-8} cm (centimeter).
1 micron = 10^{-3} mm (millimeter) = 10^{-6} m (meter).
1 cm = 0.3937 in. (inch).
1 m = 3.281 ft. (foot).
1 km (kilometer) = 0.62140 mi. (mile).
1 light-year = 9.461×10^{12} km = 5.88×10^{12} mi.

English to Metric

1 in. = 2.540 cm.
1 ft. = 30.48 cm.
1 yd. (yard) = 0.9144 m.
1 mi. = 1.609 km.

VOLUME

Metric to English

1 cm³ = 0.0610 cu. in.
1 liter = 0.2643 U.S. gal. (gallon).
1 liter = 0.220 Imperial gal.

English to Metric

1 cu. in. = 16.387 cm³.
1 U.S. gal. = 3.785 liters.
1 Imp. gal. = 4.546 liters.

WEIGHT

Metric to English (Avoirdupois)

1 g (gram) = 0.03527 oz. (ounce).
1 kg = 2.205 lb. (pound).
1 metric ton = 1,000 kg = 0.9842 long tons = 1.1032 short tons.

English (Avoirdupois) to Metric

1 oz. = 28.35 g.
1 lb. = 16 oz. = 0.4536 kg.
1 long ton = 1.016 metric tons.

TEMPERATURE

Metric to English: Degrees Fahrenheit = °F = (°C × ⁹⁄₅) + 32. (⁹⁄₅ = 1.8.)
English to Metric: Degrees Celsius = °C = (°F − 32) × ⁵⁄₉. (⁵⁄₉ = 0.5556.)
Celsius to Kelvin (Celsius Absolute): °K = °C + 273.2.
[Absolute zero, the temperature at which all molecular thermal motion ceases, is −273.18°C = −459.72°F.]

APPENDIX 4. PHYSICAL AND ASTRONOMICAL VALUES

Miscellaneous Constants

Avogadro's number $= 6.023 \times 10^{23}$ molecules per gram-molecular weight.

Volume of gram-molecular weight of ideal gas at standard conditions $= 22.4$ liters.

Velocity of light $= c = 2.99793 \times 10^{10}$ cm per second.

1 year $= 365$ days, 5 hours, 48 minutes, 45.51 seconds $= 3.1557 \times 10^7$ seconds.

1 Astronomical Unit (A.U.) $=$ mean distance, earth to sun $= 149.5 \times 10^6$ km.

Mass of atmosphere $= 5.2 \times 10^{21}$ g.

Highest mountain, Mt. Everest $= 8,840$ m.

Greatest ocean depth, Mariana Trench $= 11,035$ m.

Solar energy falling on 1 cm², at normal incidence $= 1.92$ calories per minute.

Thermal gradient near surface $\cong 30°C$ per km.

Daily additions of meteoritic dust to earth $\cong 10^{10}$ g.

Escape velocity $= 11.2$ km per second.

Solar System

BODY	MASS (EARTH = 1)	DIAMETER (KM × 10³)	SURFACE GRAVITY (EARTH = 1)	DISTANCE FROM SUN (KM × 10⁶)	SOLAR IRRADIANCE (EARTH = 1)
Sun	334,400	1,391			
Mercury	0.0463(?)	5.14	0.30(?)	58	6.69
Venus	0.816	12.6	0.91	108	1.93
Earth	1.00	12.756	1.00	150	1.00
Moon	0.0123	3.476	0.165		1.00
Mars	0.1077	6.86	0.38	228	0.43
Jupiter	317	143.6	2.68	778	0.037
Saturn	95	120.6	1.15	1,428	0.011
Uranus	15	53.4	0.99	2,872	0.0027
Neptune	18	49.7	1.28	4,498	0.0011
Pluto	0.8(?)			5,910	0.00064

1 light-year $= 9.46 \times 10^{17}$ cm $= 6.33 \times 10^4$ A.U.

1 parsec $= 3.26$ light-years.

Earth

Equatorial radius $= 6,378.388$ km.

Polar radius $= 6,356.912$ km.

Mass $= 5.983 \times 10^{27}$ g.

Land area $= 148.847 \times 10^6$ km².

Ocean area $= 361.254 \times 10^6$ km².

Ocean volume $= 1,370 \times 10^6$ km³.

Universe

Density of matter in intergalactic space $= 10^{-29}$ g per cc.

Amount of matter in intergalactic space $\cong$ amount of matter bound in stars.

Radiation from our entire galaxy $= 9 \times 10^8$ times radiation of our sun.

Size of known universe $= 10^{12}$ times size of our galaxy; includes 10^8 systems comparable to ours.

Number of stars now observable $= 10^{20}$.

APPENDIX 5. EXPONENTIALS

Expressing Numbers as Exponentials

Scientists so frequently express numbers as exponentials—for example, 6.06×10^{23}—that it is well for all of us to know what such numbers mean, how they are used, and why they are used. The last question is the easiest to answer (at least in part): we use exponentials because they are brief, and immediately meaningful, once the system is understood. We can make these points clear by taking a simple example and developing its meaning.

A scientist might say: "The population of the United States is about 1.9×10^8 people." What does this mean? The expression "10^8" tells us to multiply eight 10's together. If you carry out this operation, you find that:

$$10^8 = 100,000,000.$$

Notice that there are 8 zeros in the expression on the right-hand side. This is just exactly the same as the exponent of 10 on the left—8. This is why exponential powers of 10 are so immediately meaningful. This relationship is true only if the "base"—the number that carries the exponent—is 10. Powers of 9, 8, or 13, for example, cannot be so immediately comprehended.

To return to our example: Our number is 1.9×10^8, or $1.9 \times 100,000,000$. Which equals 190,000,000. There is another way of looking at the problem. When we say 1.9×10^8, the "10^8" gives us directions for moving the decimal point *to the right* 8 places. Thus:

$$1\!\!\smile\!\!9\ 0\ 0\ 0\ 0\ 0\ 0\ 0\!\!\smile\!\!0\ 0,$$

which is 190,000,000.0

Suppose you are given the inverse of the problem above—suppose, for example, that you are told that the population of Gibraltar is

20,402, and you are asked to express this as an exponential number accurate to two decimal places. How do you do it? Simply move the decimal point over *to the left* (until there is only one digit on the left of the decimal), *counting the number of places you move it.* This number is the exponent of 10. Thus:

$$2\!\!\smile\!\!0\ 4\ 0\ 2\!\!\smile$$

So we may say:

$$20,402 = 2.04 \times 10^4.$$

Multiplying Exponential Numbers

a. *Problem:* multiply $10^3 \times 10^4$. Without thinking about the matter, we would probably guess that the answer can be stated as 10^x—but what is x? Do we add the exponents or multiply them? Is the answer 10^7 or 10^{12}? Let's see.

$$10^3 = 1,000,$$
$$10^4 = 10,000,$$
$$1,000 \times 10,000 = 10,000,000,$$

which is 10^7. So evidently we add the exponents when we multiply the numbers. We can express this in more general form:

LAW $10^a \times 10^b = 10^{a+b}.$

b. *Problem:* multiply $10^3 \times 7^4$. There is no simple way to do this because the "base" of one exponential number is 10, and of the other is 7. The base need not always be 10: $7^3 \times 7^5 = 7^8$, for example. But the base of the two numbers multiplied must always be the same. So we can generalize our law of exponents still further:

LAW $y^a \times y^b = y^{a+b}.$

c. *Problem:* multiply $(2 \times 10^3) \times (6 \times 10^4).$

To do this, we make use of a law called the Associative Law, which says that if we have several quantities that are to be multiplied together, we may carry out the multiplications in any order that we please. So we may write:

$$(2 \times 10^3) \times (6 \times 10^4) = (2 \times 6) \times (10^3 \times 10^4).$$

Now, $2 \times 6 = 12$.

And (by the rules of exponents) $10^3 \times 10^4 = 10^7$. So:

$$(2 \times 10^3) \times (6 \times 10^4) = 12 \times 10^7, \text{ or } 1.2 \times 10^8.$$

Meaning of Negative Exponents

Suppose someone says that there are 1×10^{-2} grams of salt in a certain vessel. What does this mean? The directions previously given for interpreting exponents as a shift in the place of the decimal point suffice for this case, only the negative sign means we shift the decimal the opposite direction. The comparison given below should help:

Review problem:

$$1 \times 10^2 = 1.0000 \times 10^2.$$

Move the decimal 2 places to the right:

$$1.0\;0\!\!\underbrace{\;0\;0}$$

making: $1\,0\,0.\,0\,0$

New problem:

$$1 \times 10^{-2} = 1.0000 \times 10^{-2}.$$

Move the decimal 2 places to the left:

$$0\!\!\underbrace{\,0\;1}.\,0\,0\,0\,0$$

making $0.\,0\,1$

Remembering Which Way to Move the Decimal Point

If a student has not thought about exponentials for several days, he may say, "I know that the expression 10^{-3} tells us to move the decimal 3 places. But to the left or to the right? I can't remember. How do you remember which way to move it?"

The answer is quite simple: *Don't remember —think.* (As a matter of fact, this is a good general rule.)

10^3 is greater than 10; therefore, move the decimal point in such a direction as to get a number greater than 10. The answer, of course, is 1,000.

10^{-3} is less than 10; so move the decimal point in such a direction as to get a number less than 10. The answer is 0.001.

Dividing Exponential Numbers

Suppose we are told that there are 5,000 oranges distributed among 100 baskets, and are asked how many oranges there are per basket? Using exponentials, we write:

$$\frac{\text{No. oranges}}{\text{No. baskets}} = \frac{5 \times 10^3}{10^2} = 5 \times 10^1 = 50$$

$$\text{oranges per basket.}$$

We can look at our operations in two different ways:

1. We can make the rule $y^a \div y^b = y^{a-b}$, thus generalizing our rule for multiplication (given earlier).

Or,

2. We can note that

$$\frac{1}{10^2} = \frac{1}{100} = 0.01 = 10^{-2}.$$

Operationally, whenever we move an exponential member from "upstairs" in a fraction to "downstairs," or in the reverse direction, we change the sign of the exponent. Thus:

$$\frac{1}{10^3} = \frac{10^{-3}}{1} = 10^{-3}$$

$$\frac{1}{10^{-5}} = \frac{10^5}{1} = 10^5$$

And, in our example:

$$\frac{5 \times 10^3}{10^2} = \frac{5 \times 10^3 \times 10^{-2}}{1} = 5 \times 10^{3-2}$$

$$= 5 \times 10^1 = 5 \times 10 = 50.$$

Meaning of Zero as an Exponent

What is the value of 10^0? Of 100^0? Perhaps the easiest way to approach the problem is to study examples in which such an exponent would occur. Suppose we have 500 oranges distributed in 100 baskets. What is the average number of oranges per basket?

$$\frac{\text{No. oranges}}{\text{No. baskets}} = \frac{5 \times 10^2}{1 \times 10^2} = 5 \times 10^2 \times 10^{-2}$$
$$= 5 \times 10^{2-2} = 5 \times 10^0.$$

Analysis shows us that 10^0 must equal 1, if the answer is to be correct. So:

$$10^0 = 1.$$

In fact,

$$100^0 = 1.$$
$$1{,}000{,}000{,}000^0 = 1.$$

In fact, any positive number to the "zeroth" power equals 1.

Surprising? Yes. But a little thought will show that any other answer will lead to inconsistent arithmetic and algebra.

Dealing with Exponents of 2

In biological problems we frequently encounter exponential powers of 2, because doubling is a common process. For example, if a cell divides once every hour, how many cells will there be 30 hours or 40 hours later? 2^{30}, or 2^{40}, of course. But how big is 2^{30} or 2^{40}? It is not immediately apparent.

Fortunately, we can easily calculate the approximate value of any power of 2 by making use of an approximate identity, as will be shown below.

It happens that $2^{10} = 1{,}024$.

Now, $10^3 = 1{,}000$.

So we may say:

$2^{10} \cong 10^3$. (The symbol $\cong$ is read as "is approximately equal to.")

To convert any power of 2 to a power of 10, first express the power of 2 in units of 2^{10}.

As examples:

$$2^{10} = 1{,}024.$$
$$2^{20} = 2^{10} \times 2^{10} = 2^{10+10} = 2^{2 \times 10} = (2^{10})^2.$$
$$2^{30} = 2^{10} \times 2^{10} \times 2^{10} = 2^{10+10+10} = 2^{10 \times 3}$$
$$= (2^{10})^3.$$

Notice that we have, in working out these examples, discovered a new rule, namely:

$$2^{10 \times a} = (2^{10})^a;$$

or, more generally:

$$y^{a \times b} = (y^a)^b.$$

Now for a few more examples:

$$2^{24} = 2^4 \times (2^{10})^2.$$
$$2^{47} = 2^7 \times (2^{10})^4.$$
$$2^{83} = 2^3 \times (2^{10})^8.$$

And so on. Once you have gotten the exponential decomposed so that part of it is in the form $(2^{10})^b$, you can then replace the expression inside the parentheses by 10^3, making it read $(10^3)^b$.

To conclude the three examples just above:

$$2^{24} = 2^4 \times (2^{10})^2 \cong 2^4 \times (10^3)^2,$$
$$\cong 2^4 \times 10^6,$$
$$\cong 16{,}000{,}000,$$
$$\cong 1.6 \times 10^7.$$

And:

$$2^{47} = 2^7 \times (2^{10})^4,$$
$$\cong 2^7 \times (10^3)^4,$$
$$\cong 128 \times 10^{12},$$
$$\cong 1.28 \times 10^{14}.$$

And:

$$2^{83} = 2^3 \times (2^{10})^8,$$
$$\cong 8 \times 10^{24}.$$

APPENDIX 6. MISCELLANEOUS MATHEMATICAL FORMULAS

Quadratic equation

$$ax^2 + bx + c = 0.$$

$$x = \frac{-b \pm \sqrt{b^2 - 4ac}}{2a}.$$

Sphere

Surface $= 4\pi r^2$,   where $\pi = 3.1416\ldots$
                          and $r =$ radius.

Volume $= \frac{4}{3}\pi r^3$.

Cylinder

If $h =$ altitude of right cylinder, and
$r =$ radius of end plate, then

area of curved surface $= 2\pi rh$;
area of *each* end plate $= \pi r^2$;
volume $= \pi r^2 h$.

Compound interest

$$A = P\left(1 + \frac{i}{q}\right)^{nq},$$

where $A =$ final amount,
  $P =$ initial principal,
  $i =$ interest rate,
  $q =$ times per year compounded,
  $n =$ number of years.

Logarithms

$$\log ab = \log a + \log b.$$

$$\log \frac{a}{b} = \log a - \log b.$$

$$\log a^n = n \log a.$$

$$\log \sqrt[n]{a} = \frac{\log a}{n}.$$

APPENDIX 7. ORGANIC COMPOUNDS OF BIOLOGICAL IMPORTANCE

Amino acids

The chemical formulas of the twenty amino acids that occur in proteins. The common groups involved in peptide bonds are shaded.

Name	Abbreviation	Formula
Alanine	Ala	CH_3—CH—COOH NH$_2$

Arginine	Arg	NH_2—C—NH—$(CH_2)_3$—CH—COOH
		      ‖
		     NH NH$_2$

Asparagine	Asn
	(Asp-NH$_2$)
		H_2N—C—CH_2—CH—COOH
		      ‖
		     O NH$_2$

Aspartic Acid	Asp	HOOC—CH_2—CH—COOH NH$_2$
Cysteine	Cys (Cy-SH)	HS—CH_2—CH—COOH NH$_2$
Glutamic Acid	Glu	HOOC—$(CH_2)_2$—CH—COOH NH$_2$
Glutamine	Gln (Glu-NH$_2$)	H_2N—CO—$(CH_2)_2$—CH—COOH NH$_2$
Glycine	Gly	CH_2—COOH NH$_2$
Histidine	His	⎡‾‾‾‾‾⎤—CH_2—CH—COOH N⇌NH NH$_2$
Isoleucine	Ilu (Ileu)	CH_3—CH_2—CH—CH—COOH CH$_3$ NH$_2$
Leucine	Leu	CH_3—CH—CH_2—CH—COOH CH$_3$ NH$_2$

Name	Abbreviation	Formula
Lysine	Lys	$H_2N-(CH_2)_4-CH-COOH$ $\quad\quad\quad\quad\quad\quad NH_2$
Methionine	Met	$CH_3-S-CH_2-CH_2-CH-COOH$ $\quad\quad\quad\quad\quad\quad\quad\quad NH_2$
Phenylalanine	Phe	$\langle\bigcirc\rangle-CH_2-CH-COOH$ $\quad\quad\quad\quad\quad\quad NH_2$
Proline	Pro	(pyrrolidine ring)$-COOH$ N H
Serine	Ser	$CH_2-CH-COOH$ $OH\quad NH_2$
Threonine	Thr	$CH_3-CH-CH-COOH$ $\quad\quad\, OH\quad NH_2$
Tryptophan	Try	(indole ring)$-CH_2-CH-COOH$ $N\quad\quad\quad\quad\quad NH_2$ H
Tyrosine	Tyr	$HO-\langle\bigcirc\rangle-CH_2-CH-COOH$ $\quad\quad\quad\quad\quad\quad\quad\quad NH_2$
Valine	Val	$CH_3-CH-CH-COOH$ $\quad\quad\, CH_3\quad NH_2$

Composition of Nucleic acids

The bases (or nitrogen-containing ring compounds) are linked to a sugar and a phosphate to form a nucleotide. Nucleotides are linked together to form a nucleic acid or polypeptide chain.

THE BASES

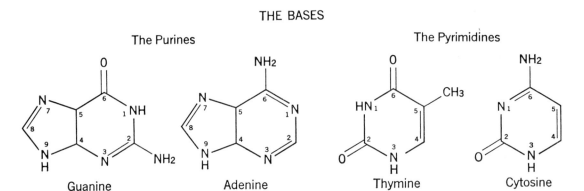

The Purines

Guanine

Adenine

The Pyrimidines

Thymine

Cytosine

THE SUGARS

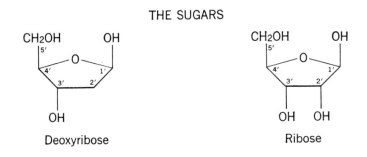

Deoxyribose

Ribose

A NUCLEOTIDE

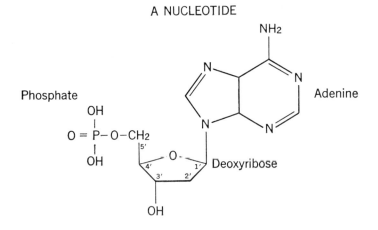

Phosphate

Adenine

Deoxyribose

A NUCLEIC ACID

$$-P - S - P - S - P - S - P - S - P - S -$$

APPENDIX 8. ANTIQUITY OF CULTIVATED PLANTS

Old World Species

A. Cultivated for more than 4,000 years:

almond	cucumber	millet	soybean
apple	date palm	olive	tea
apricot	fig	onion	turnip
banana	flax	peach	watermelon
barley	grape	pear	wheat
broad bean	hemp	rice	
cabbage	mango	sorghum	

B. Cultivated for 2,000–4,000 years:

alfalfa	cotton	oats	rye
beet	garden peas	pepper (black)	sugar cane
carrot	lettuce	plum	taro
celery	mustard	poppy	vetch
cherry	nutmeg	radish	yam

New World Species, Pre-Columbian

avocado	corn (maize)	pineapple	sweet potato
beans	papaya	potato	tobacco
cacao (cocoa)	peanut	pumpkin	tomato
cassava	pepper (red)	squash	

APPENDIX 9. HAPLOID CHROMOSOME NUMBERS

Group	Species	Haploid Number
Fungi	*Achlya bisexualis*	3
	Allomyces javanicus (various strains)	13–28
	Giberella lateritium	6
	Neurospora crassa	7
Angiospermae: Monocots	Bluegrass (*Poa pratensis*)	28–124
	Maize (corn) (*Zea mays*)	10
	Oats (*Avena sativa*)	21
	Rice (*Oryza sativa*)	12
	Rye (*Secale cereale*)	7
	Wheat (*Triticum aestivium*)	21
	Wheat (*T. durum*)	14
	Onion (*Allium cepa*)	8
	Garlic (*A. sativum*)	8
Angiospermae: Dicots	Cabbage (*Brassica oleracea*)	9
	Radish (*Raphanus sativus*)	9
	Kalanchoö	ca. 250
	Broadbean (*Vicia faba*)	6
	Cotton (*Gossypium barbadense*)	26
	Flax (*Linum usitatissimum*)	15
	Tobacco (*Nicotiana tabacum*)	24
Vertebrates: Fish	Siamese fighting fish (*Betta splendens*)	21
	Guppy (*Lebistes reticulatus*)	24
Vertebrates: Amphibians	Frog (*Hyla arborea*)	12
	African toad (*Xenopus laevis*)	18
Vertebrates: Mammals	Opossum (*Didelphys virginiana*)	11
	Mouse (*Mus musculus*)	20
	Rat (*Rattus norvegicus*)	21
	Dog (*Canis familiaris*)	39
	Cat (*Felis catus*)	19
	Cow (*Bos taurus*)	30
	Horse (*Equus caballus*)	33
	Chimpanzee (*Pan troglodytes*)	24
	Mandrill (*Papio sphinx*)	21
	Spider monkey (*Ateles paniscus*)	17
	Man (*Homo sapiens*)	23

For further reference:

William S. Spector (ed.). 1956. *Handbook of Biological Data.* Philadelphia and London: W. B. Saunders. Tables 72–74, pp. 92–96, from which most of the above data was abstracted, with the permission of the publishers and the National Academy of Sciences.

APPENDIX 10. TEMPERATURES OF ENDOTHERMS

In degrees Celsius. When in air whose temperature is outside the *critical air temperatures* listed, the animal either fails to maintain a constant temperature, or equilibrates at a temperature other than the normal.

Animal	Normal Rectal Temperature	Critical Air Temperature	
		Lower	Upper
Man	37.2	17–22	32
Cat	37.2–39		32
Chicken	40–42	−34	33
Cow, dairy	38–39	−40	21–27
Dog	39	−40	29
Echidna			35
Elephant	35.9–36.7		
Goat	40		
Guinea pig	38.5–39.9	−15	30
Hamster	37		
Horse	38		
Monkey	38		30–32
Mouse	35.2–37.8	13	32
Pigeon	42–43		
Platypus	32.5		
Rabbit	39.6	−7	28–30
Rat	35.8–37.6	−7	29
Sheep	38		41–43
Sloth	33–34.4		
Squirrel	35.5–38.4		
Swine	38–39.6		29.5

For further reference:

William S. Spector (ed.). 1956. *Handbook of Biological Data.* Philadelphia and London: W. B. Saunders. Table 365, p. 437, from which the above data were abstracted, with the permission of the publishers and the National Academy of Sciences.

APPENDIX 11. EXTREMES OF WEATHER

Temperature (*Degrees Celsius*)

Lowest recorded temperature in the 48 contiguous states of the U.S.: −54° in Yellowstone Park, Wyoming in 1933.

Lowest temperature in Alaska: −61° at Fort Yukon, in 1934.

Lowest in the world: −74° in Antarctica, in 1958.

Highest recorded temperature in the United States: 57° in Death Valley, California, in 1913.

Highest in the world: 58° in Libya, North Africa, in 1922.

Precipitation (*In Centimeters*)

Annual

Average, for United States (48 states): 74 centimeters.

Wettest state, Louisiana: 140 cm, average.

Wettest region of record, summit of the island of Kauai, Hawaii: 1,585 cm falling in one year ending in July, 1948.

Wettest local average annual rainfall in the 48 contiguous states, at Wynoochee Oxbow, Washington (13 year record): 383 cm.

Driest state, Nevada: 22.38 cm, average.

Driest local record, at Bagdad, California (5 year record): 1.996 cm per year.

24-Hour Period

In the United States, in the lowlands of Kauai, Hawaii: 117 cm, in 1956; an equal record is known for Luzon, Philippines, in 1911; no greater on record.

One Month

Wettest month of record, for Cherrapunji, India, in August, 1841: 612 cm.

Snowfall

Greatest seasonal, in the 48 contiguous states, at Tamarack, California, winter of 1906–7: 2,245 cm.

Heavy snowfall records: at Giant Forest, California, 152 cm in 1 day; at Angola, New York, 107 cm in 2 days; at The Dalles, Oregon, 137 cm in 3 days; at Vanceboro, Maine, 244 cm in 4 days.

Hail

Largest hailstone of record fell at Potter, Nebraska, July, 1928; it weighed 680 grams.

Frequency of hailstorms: in the Denver to New York airway it is estimated that 1 thunderstorm in 800 produces hailstones as large as walnuts; and 1 storm in 5,000, stones as large as baseballs.

Wind

A hurricane (or typhoon) is defined as a windstorm with winds with a velocity of 120 kilometers per hour or greater. Winds with velocity in excess of 300 km per hour have been measured.

APPENDIX 12. MAXIMUM SPEEDS OF ANIMALS

Animal and Conditions	Speed (mph)
Homing pigeon—level flight, no wind	94.3
Golden plover	62
Hummingbird—level flight	23
Hummingbird—power dive	64
Mallard duck—level flight	60
Swift	57
Pheasant	48
Quail	45
Wild turkey	32
Housefinch	22
African elephant	24
African rhinoceros	ca. 30
Cheetah	44
Greyhound	40
California sea lion—underwater	10
Dolphin	20–25
Racehorse	40
Antelope—short distance on Gobi Desert	60
Redracer snake	3.6
Salmon—over short distance	23
Barracuda	27
Flying fish—in air	30
Dragonfly	60
Man—sports record, short distance	22.3
Man—sports record, 1 mile	14.9
Man—stop-watch record of a Masai warrior carrying spear and shield, chased by a rhinoceros	18.4

For further reference:

R. Meinertzhagen. 1955. "The Speed and Altitude of Bird Flight (with notes on other animals)." *Ibis,* **97**:81–118.

W. E. Lanyon. 1962. "A speed trap for birds." *Natural History, 71* (Aug.–Sept.):38–43.

APPENDIX 13. MAMMALIAN REPRODUCTION

Species	Age at Puberty (in months)	Gestation Period (in days)	Days after Birth to Double Birth-Wt.
Man (*Homo sapiens*)	144–180	267	180
Chimpanzee (*Pan troglodytes*)	100	227	
Armadillo (*Dasypus novemcinctus*)	12	120	
Bat (*Rhinolophus ferrumequinum*)	15		
Cat (*Felis catus*)	6–15	63	9
Cattle (*Bos taurus*)	6–14	281	47
Dog (*Canis familiaris*)	6–8	63	8
Ferret (*Mustela furo*)		42	
Fox, red (*Vulpes fulva*)	10	52	
Goat (*Capra hircus*)	8	148	
Guinea pig (*Cavia porcellus*)	2–3	68	
Hamster (*Mesocricetus auratus*)	1.3–2	16	
Horse (*Equus cabballus*)	12	336	60
Mink (*Mustela vison*)	8–9	50	
Monkey, rhesus (*Macaca rhesus*)	36	160	
Mouse (*Mus musculus*)	1.2	19	
Opossum (*Didelphys virginiana*)	8	12.5	
Rabbit (*Oryctolagus cuniculus*)	5.5–8.5	31	6
Rat (*Rattus rattus*)	1.5–3	22	
Sheep (*Ovis aries*)	7–8	151	10
Swine (*Sus scrofa*)	5–8	114	18

For further reference:

William S. Spector (ed.). 1956. *Handbook of Biological Data*. Philadelphia and London: W. B. Saunders. Table 105, p. 128, from which most of the above data was abstracted, with the permission of the publishers and the National Academy of Sciences.

APPENDIX **14.** LONGEVITY

Length of life, typical and maximum reliably recorded. The unit is years, unless otherwise indicated.

Organism		Typical Length of Life	Maximum Length of Life
Plants:	Cypress (Santa Maria del Tule; Oaxaca, Mex.)		1,500
	Sequoia gigantea		3,215
	Bristlecone pine (*Pinus aristata*)		4,600
Coelenterata:	*Actinia mesembryanthemum*		70
Nematoda:	*Wuchereria bancrofti* [elephantiasis]		17
Rotifera:	Various species	2–3 weeks	5 months
Arthropoda:	Lobster	ca. 20	
	Termite	ca. 20	
	Ant (*Formica fusca* ♀)		15
Mollusca:	*Helix spiriplana*		15
	Oyster (*Ostrea edulis*)		12
Vertebrates:	Vasa parrot (*Terathopsius ecaudetus*)		54
	Condor (*Vultur gryphus*)		52
	Domestic pigeon (*Columba livia domestica*)		30
	Marion's tortoise (*Testudo sumeiri*)		152+
	Galapagos tortoise (*T. elephantopus*)		100+
	Bullfrog (*Bufo bufo*)		36
	Pike		40
	Elephant (*Elephas indicus*)		77
	Rhinoceros (*Rhinoceros unicornis*)		49
	Chimpanzee (*Pan troglodytes*)		39
	Cat (*Felis catus*)		31
	Laboratory mouse		39 months
	Horse (*Equus caballus*)		ca. 50
	Dog (*Canis familiaris*)	18	34
	Domestic rabbit		14
	Man (*Homo sapiens*)	70	120

For further reference:
Alex Comfort. 1956. *The Biology of Senescence*. New York: Rinehart.

Index